SCHOLARSHIPS,

FELLOWSHIPS

AND LOANS

ISSN 1058-5699

SCHOLARSHIPS, FELLOWSHIPS AND LOANS

A GUIDE TO EDUCATION-RELATED FINANCIAL AID PROGRAMS FOR STUDENTS AND PROFESSIONALS

Volume One
Sponsors and Their Scholarships: A–H

Thirtieth Edition

GALE
CENGAGE Learning

Detroit • New York • San Francisco • New Haven, Conn • Waterville, Maine • London

GALE
CENGAGE Learning®

Scholarships, Fellowships and Loans, 30th Edition

Product Management: Jerry Moore

Project Editor: Bohdan Romaniuk

Editorial Support Services: Wayne Fong

Composition and Electronic Prepress: Gary Leach

Manufacturing: Rita Wimberley

For product information and technology assistance, contact us at **Gale Customer Support, 1-800-877-4253.**
For permission to use material from this text or product, submit all requests online at **www.cengage.com/permissions.**
Further permissions questions can be emailed to **permissionrequest@cengage.com**

While every effort has been made to ensure the reliability of the information presented in this publication, Gale, a part of Cengage Learning,does not guarantee the accuracy of the data contained herein. Gale accepts no payment for listing; and inclusion in the publication of any organization, agency, institution, publication, service, or individual does not imply endorsement of the editors or publisher. Errors brought to the attention of the publisher, and verified to the satisfaction of the publisher, will be corrected in future editions.

EDITORIAL DATA PRIVACY POLICY: Does this product contain information about you as an individual? If so, for more information about our editorial data privacy policies, please see our Privacy Statement at www.gale.cengage.com.

Gale
27500 Drake Rd.
Farmington Hills, MI, 48331-3535

ISBN-13: 978-1-4144-6916-4 (3 vol. set)
ISBN-10: 1-4144-6916-0 (3 vol. set)
ISBN-13: 978-1-4144-6917-1 (vol. 1)
ISBN-10: 1-4144-6917-9 (vol. 1)
ISBN-13: 978-1-4144-6918-8 (vol. 2)
ISBN-10: 1-4144-6918-7 (vol. 2)
ISBN-13: 978-1-4144-8894-3 (vol. 3)
ISBN-10: 1-4144-8894-7 (vol. 3)

ISSN 1058-5699

This title is also available as an e-book.
ISBN-13: 978-1-4144-7420-5
ISBN-10: 1-4144-7420-2
Contact your Gale sales representative for ordering information.

Printed in the United States of America
1 2 3 4 5   17 16 15 14 13

Contents

This edition of *Scholarships, Fellowships, and Loans (SFL)* provides access to nearly 7,400 sources of education-related financial aid for students and professionals at all levels. *SFL*'s scope ranges from undergraduate and vocational/technical education through post-doctoral and professional studies. Students and others interested in education funding will find comprehensive information on a variety of programs in all educational areas, including:

- Architecture
- Area and Ethnic Studies
- Art
- Business
- Communications
- Computer Science
- Education
- Engineering
- Health Science
- Humanities
- Industrial Arts
- Language
- Law
- Literature
- Liberal Arts
- Library Science
- Life Science
- Medicine
- Mathematics
- Performing Arts
- Philosophy
- Physical Sciences
- Social Sciences
- Theology and Religion

SFL Provides Detailed Information on Awards

SFL provides all the information students need to complete their financial aid search. Entries include: administering organization name and address; purpose of award; qualifications and restrictions; selection criteria; award amount and number of awards granted; application details and deadlines; detailed contact information.

Additionally, look for the section on federal financial aid following the User's Guide for a quick summary of programs sponsored by the U.S. government, as well as information on the AmeriCorps program. There is also a section that lists higher education agencies by state.

Five Indexes Allow Quick and Easy Access to Awards

Whether you are a high school student looking for basic undergraduate financial aid, a scientist investigating research grants, or a professional attempting to finance additional career training, SFL aids your search by providing access to awards through the following indexes:

Field of Study Index categorizes awards by very specific subject fields.

Legal Resident Index targets awards restricted to applicants from specific geographic locations.

Place of Study Index provides a handy guide to awards granted for study within specific states, provinces, or countries.

Special Recipient Index lists awards that are reserved for candidates who qualify by virtue of their gender, organizational affiliation, minority or ethnic background.

Sponsor and Scholarship Index provides a complete alphabetical listing of all awards and their administering organizations.

Catchwords

SFL includes catchwords of the organization on each corresponding page, to aid the user in finding a particular entry.

As we make our way through difficult economic times, there is a growing need for a more highly-trained and educated work force. From political discussions and debates to reports from future-oriented think tanks and other groups, there is agreement that postsecondary education is a key to success. Yet how are students and their families to afford the already high (and constantly rising) cost of higher education? Searching for financial aid can be very tedious and difficult, even though hundreds of millions of dollars in aid reportedly go unclaimed every year.

Scholarships, Fellowships and Loans (SFL), the most comprehensive single directory of education-related financial aid available, can save you time, effort, and money by helping you to focus your search within the largest pool of awards and avoid pursuing aid for which you do not qualify. In most cases, the detailed descriptions contain enough information to allow you to decide if a particular scholarship is right for you to begin the application process. *SFL* lists almost 7,400 major awards available to U.S. and Canadian students for study throughout the world. Included are:

- scholarships, fellowships, and grants, which do not require repayment;

- loans, which require repayment either monetarily or through service;

- scholarship loans, which are scholarships that become loans if the recipient does not comply with the award's terms;

- internships and work study programs, which provide training, work experience, and (usually) monetary compensation; and

- awards and prizes that recognize excellence in a particular field.

Also included are other forms of assistance offered by associations, corporations, religious groups, fraternal organizations, foundations, and other private organizations and companies. *SFL* includes a broad representation of government-funded awards at the national and state levels, as well as a representative sampling of lesser-known and more narrowly focused awards, such as those of a strictly local nature or programs sponsored by small organizations. Financial aid programs administered and funded by individual colleges or universities are not included in *SFL*. Both need- and merit-based awards are included. Competition-based awards and prizes are included when they offer funds that support study or research and are intended to encourage further educational or professional growth.

Students of All Types Can Benefit

Traditional students as well as those returning to school, non-degree learners, those in need of retraining, and established professionals can use the funding sources listed in *SFL* for formal and non-formal programs of study at all levels:

- high school

- vocational

- undergraduate

- graduate

- postgraduate

- doctorate

- postdoctorate

- professional development

Content and Arrangement

Scholarships, Fellowships and Loans is organized into a main section containing descriptive listings of award programs and their administering organizations, and five indexes.

The main section, Sponsors and Their Scholarships, is arranged alphabetically by name of administering organization. Entries for each organization's awards appear immediately following the entry on the organization. Each entry contains detailed contact and descriptive information, often providing users with all the information they need to make a decision about applying.

The indexes provide a variety of specific access points to the information contained within the organization and award listings, allowing users to easily identify awards of interest.

Practical Tips on How to Find Financial Aid

While there are many education-related financial aid programs for students of all types and study levels, the competition for available funds is steadily increasing. You will improve the likelihood of meeting your financial aid goals if you:

- carefully assess your particular needs and preferences;

- consider any special circumstances or conditions that might qualify you for aid; and

- carefully research available aid programs.

The following pages list some general guidelines for making your way through the search and application process.

Start Your Search Early

Any search for financial aid is likely to be more successful if you begin early. If you allow enough time to complete all of the necessary steps, you will be more likely to identify a wide variety of awards for which you qualify with plenty of time to meet their application deadlines. This can increase your chances of obtaining aid.

Some experts recommend that you start this process up to two years before you think you will need financial assistance. While you will probably be able to obtain some support if you allow less time, you might overlook some important opportunities.

Some awards are given on a first-come, first-served basis, and if you do not file your application early enough, the aid will already be distributed. In many cases, if your application is late you will not be considered, even if you have met all of the other criteria.

An early start will also allow you to identify organizations that offer scholarships to members or participants, such as student or professional associations, in time to establish membership or otherwise meet their qualifying criteria.

Assess Your Needs and Goals

The intended recipients for financial aid programs and the purposes for which awards are established can vary greatly. Some programs are open to almost anyone, while others are restricted to very specific categories of recipients. The majority of awards fall somewhere in between. Your first step in seeking financial aid is to establish your basic qualifications as a potential recipient. The following are some general questions to ask yourself to help define your educational and financial needs and goals:

- What kinds of colleges or universities interest me?

- What careers or fields of study interest me?

- Do I plan to earn a degree?

- Am I only interested in financial aid that is a gift, or will I consider a loan or work study?

- In what parts of the country am I willing to live and study?

Leave No Stone Unturned

After you have defined your goals, the next step is to identify any special factors that might make you eligible for aid programs offered only to a restricted group. Examine this area carefully, and remember that even minor or unlikely connections may be worth checking. The most common qualifications and restrictions involve:

- citizenship
- community involvement or volunteer work
- creative or professional accomplishment
- employer
- financial need
- gender
- merit or academic achievement
- military or veteran status
- organization membership (such as a union, association, or fraternal group)
- place of residence
- race or ethnic group
- religious affiliation

With many awards, you may be eligible if your spouse, parents, or guardians meet certain criteria by status or affiliations. You should be aware of your parents' affiliations even if you don't live with one (or both) of them, or if they are deceased. And given enough lead time, it may be possible for you (or your parents) to join a particular organization, or establish necessary residence, in time for you to be eligible for certain funds.

Contact Financial Aid Offices

Most colleges, universities, and other educational institutions offer their own financial aid programs. Their financial aid offices may also have information on privately sponsored awards that are specifically designated for students at those institutions. Contact their respective financial aid offices to request applications and details for all of the aid programs they sponsor and/or administer.

Use *SFL* to Identify Awards Sponsored by Private Organizations and Corporations

Scholarships, Fellowships and Loans (SFL) is the most comprehensive single source of information on major education-related financial aid programs sponsored and administered by private organizations and companies for use by students and professionals. Using *SFL* as a starting point, you can quickly compile a substantial list of financial aid programs for which you may qualify by following these simple steps:

- Compile an initial list of awards offered in your field of study.

- If you have already chosen your field of study, look in the Field of Study Index to find listings of awards grouped by more precise disciplines (such as Accounting or Journalism). If you choose this approach, your initial list is likely to be shorter but more focused. Eliminate awards that cannot be used at your chosen level of study or that do not meet your financial needs. Are you an undergraduate only interested in scholarships? Are you a graduate student willing to participate in an internship or take out a loan? Consult the User's Guide to determine which of the study level categories and award types apply to your particular situation. Both indexes clearly note the study levels at which awards may be used. The Field of Study Index also lists the type of financial aid provided.

- Eliminate awards by citizenship, residence, and other restrictions (minority status, ethnic background, gender, organizational affiliation) that make you ineligible.

- If your list is based on the Field of Study Index, you will need to look under the section for qualifications in each descriptive listing to see what requirements apply.

- Read the descriptive listings for each of the award programs left on your list. The descriptive listings should contain all the information you need to decide if you qualify and should apply for each of the awards on your list.

Expand Your List of Possibilities

If you are willing to take the initiative and do a little extra digging, you should be able to add to your list of institution-related and privately sponsored programs. In most cases, the best possibilities fall into these two areas:

Government Agencies and Programs. The Sponsors and Their Scholarships main section includes a broad representation of award programs sponsored by federal and state governments. Since these listings are not meant to be exhaustive, you should be able to identify additional programs by contacting the government agencies responsible for education-related financial aid programs listed here. On the federal level, contact the U.S. Department of Education at 400 Maryland Ave., SW, Washington, DC 20202, or on their website at http://www.ed.gov, for up-to-date information on U.S. Government award programs. For a broad overview of federal financial aid, consult the Federal Programs section. Similarly, you may contact your state department of education for details on what is offered in your particular state. Please see the State Higher Education Agencies section for state-by-state listings.

Local Sources of Awards. A surprisingly large number of financial aid programs are sponsored by small and/or local organizations. *SFL* contains a representative sampling of such programs to encourage you to seek similar programs in your own geographic area. High school guidance counselors are often aware of local programs as well, and they can usually tell you how to get in touch with the sponsoring or administering organizations. Local newspapers are also rich sources of information on financial aid programs.

Allow Enough Time for the Application Process

The amount of time needed to complete the application process for individual awards will vary, so you should pay close attention to application deadlines. Some awards carry application deadlines that require you to apply a year or more before your studies will begin. In general, allow plenty of time to:

- Write for official applications. You may not be considered for some awards unless you apply with the correct forms.

- Read all instructions carefully.

- Take note of application deadlines.

- Accurately and completely file all required supporting material, such as essays, school transcripts, and financial records. If you fail to answer certain questions, you may be disqualified even if you are a worthy candidate.

- Give references enough time to submit their recommendations. Teachers in particular get many requests for letters of recommendation and should be given as much advance notice as possible.

Make Sure You Qualify

Finally, don't needlessly submerge yourself in paperwork. If you find you don't qualify for a particular award, don't apply for it. Instead, use your time and energy to find and apply for more likely sources of aid.

Available in Electronic Formats

Licensing. *Scholarships, Fellowships and Loans* is available for licensing. The complete database is provided in a fielded format and is deliverable on such media as disk or CD-ROM. For more information, contact Gale's Business Development group at 1-800-877-GALE, or visit our website at http://gale.cengage.com/bizdev/.

The Directory is also available online as part of the Gale Directory Library. For more information, call 1-800-877-GALE.

Comments and Suggestions Welcome

We welcome reader suggestions regarding new and previously unlisted organizations and awards. Please send your suggestions to:

Scholarships, Fellowships and Loans
Gale, Cengage Learning
27500 Drake Rd.
Farmington Hills, MI 48331-3535
Phone: (248) 699-4253
Toll-free: 800-347-4253
Fax: (248) 699-8070
Email: Bob.Romaniuk@cengage.com

Scholarships, Fellowships and Loans is comprised of a main section containing descriptive listings on award programs and their administering organizations, and five indexes that aid users in identifying relevant information. Each of these sections is described in detail below.

Sponsors and Their Scholarships

SFL contains two types of descriptive listings:

- brief entries on the organizations that sponsor or administer specific award programs

- descriptive entries on the award programs themselves

Entries are arranged alphabetically by administering organization; awards administered by each organization follow that organization's listings. Entries contain detailed contact and descriptive information. Users are strongly encouraged to read the descriptions carefully and pay particular attention to the various eligibility requirements before applying for awards.

The following sample organization and award entries illustrate the kind of information that is or might be included in these entries. Each item of information is preceded by a number, and is explained in the paragraph with the same number on the following pages.

Sample Entry

▮1▮ 3445
▮2▮ Microscopy Society of America
▮3▮ 4 Barlows Landing Rd., Ste. 8 Woods Hole, MA 02543
▮4▮ *Ph:* (508) 563-1155
▮5▮ *Fax:* (508) 563-1211
▮6▮ *Free:* 800-538-3672
▮7▮ *E-mail:* businessofficemsa.microscopy.com
▮8▮ *URL:* http://www.msa.microscopy.com
▮9▮ 3446
▮10▮ MSA Presidential Student Awards
▮11▮ *(Graduate, Undergraduate/*
▮12▮ *Award*

▮13▮ Purpose: To recognize outstanding original research by students. ▮14▮ Focus: Biological Clinical Sciences—Microscopy, Physical Sciences—Microscopy. ▮15▮ Qualif.: Candidate may be of any nationality, but must be enrolled at a recognized college or university in the United States at the time of the MSA annual meeting. ▮16▮ Criteria: Selection is done based on the applicant's career objectives, academic record, and financial need. ▮17▮ Funds Avail.: Registration and round-trip travel to the MSA annual meeting, plus a stipend to defray lodging and other expenses. ▮18▮ Number awarded: 5. ▮19▮ To Apply: Write to MSA for application form and guidelines. ▮20▮ Deadline: March 15. ▮21▮ Remarks: Established in 1979. ▮22▮ Contact: Alternate phone number: 800-538-EMSA.

Descriptions of Numbered Elements

▮1▮ **Organization Entry Number.** Administering organizations are listed alphabetically. Each entry is followed by an alphabetical listing of its awards. All entries (organization and award) are numbered in a single sequence. These numbers are used as references in the indexes.

▮2▮ **Organization Name.** The name of the organization administering the awards that follow.

▮3▮ **Mailing Address.** The organization's permanent mailing address is listed when known; in some cases an award address is given.

▮4▮ **Telephone Number.** The general telephone number for the administering organization. Phone numbers pertaining to specific awards are listed under "Contact" in the award description.

▮5▮ **Fax Number.** The facsimile number for the administering organization. Fax numbers pertaining to specific awards are included under "Contact" in the award description.

▮6▮ **Toll-free Number.** The toll-free number for the administering organization. Toll-free numbers pertaining to specific awards are included under "Contact" in the award description.

▮7▮ **E-mail Address.** The electronic mail address for the administering organization. Electronic mail addresses pertaining to specific awards are included under "Contact" in the award description.

▮8▮ **URL.** The web address for the administering organization.

▮9▮ **Award Entry Number.** Awards are listed alphabetically following the entry for their administering organizations. All entries (organization and award) are numbered in a single sequence. These numbers are used as references in the indexes.

▮10▮ **Award Name.** Names of awards are always listed. Organization titles or acronyms have been added to generic award names (for example, MSA Undergraduate Scholarships, Canadian Council Fiction Writing Grant, etc.) to avoid confusion.

▌11▐ Study Level. The level of study for which the award may be used. One or more of the following terms will be listed:

- All: not restricted to a particular level.

- High School: study at the secondary level.

- Vocational: study leading to postsecondary awards, certificates, or diplomas requiring less than two years of study.

- 2 Year: study leading to a bachelor's degree within two years

- 4 Year: study leading to a bachelor's degree within four years

- Undergraduate: study immediately beyond the secondary level, including associate, colleges and universities, junior colleges, technical institutes leading to a bachelor's degree, and vocational technical schools.

- Graduate: study leading to an M.A., M.S., LL.B., LL.M., and other intermediate degrees.

- Master's: study leading specifically to a master's degree, such as a M.A., M.S., or M.B.A.

- Postgraduate: study beyond the graduate level not specifically leading to a degree.

- Doctorate: study leading to a Ph.D., Ed.D., Sc.D., M.D., D.D.S., D.O., J.D., and other terminal degrees.

- Postdoctorate: study beyond the doctorate level; includes awards intended for professional development when candidates must hold a doctoral degree to qualify.

- Professional Development: career development not necessarily restricted by study.

▌12▐ Award Type. The type or category of award. One or more of the following terms will be listed:

- Award: generally includes aid given in recognition and support of excellence, including awards given through music and arts competitions. Non-monetary awards and awards given strictly for recognition are not included.

- Fellowship: awards granted for graduate- or postgraduate-level research or education that do not require repayment.

- Grant: includes support for research, travel, and creative, experimental, or innovative projects.

- Internship: training and work experience programs. Internships that do not include compensation of some type are not included.

- Loan: aid that must be repaid either monetarily or through service. Some loans are interest-free, others are not.

- Prize: funds awarded as the result of a competition or contest. Prizes that are not intended to be used for

study or to support professional development are not included.

- Scholarships: support for formal educational programs that does not require repayment.

- Scholarship Loan: a scholarship that becomes a loan if the recipient does not comply with the terms.

- Work Study: combined study and work program for which payment is received.

- Other: anything that does not fit the other categories, such as a travel award.

▌13▐ Purpose. The purpose for which the award is granted is listed here when known.

▌14▐ Focus. The field(s) of study that the recipient must be pursuing.

▌15▐ Qualif. Information regarding applicant eligibility. Some examples of qualification requirements include the following: academic record, citizenship, financial need, organizational affiliation, minority or ethnic background, residency, and gender.

▌16▐ Criteria Information concerning selection criteria.

▌17▐ Funds Avail. The award dollar amounts are included here along with other relevant funding information, such as the time period covered by the award, a breakdown of expenses covered (e.g., stipends, tuition and fees, travel and living allowances, equipment funds, etc.), the amount awarded to the institution, loan repayment schedules, service-in-return-for-funding agreements, and other obligations.

▌18▐ Number awarded. Typical number of awards distributed.

▌19▐ To Apply. Application guidelines, requirements, and other information.

▌20▐ Deadline. Application due dates, notification dates (the date when the applicant will be notified of receipt or denial of award), disbursement dates, and other relevant dates.

▌21▐ Remarks. Any additional information concerning the award.

▌22▐ Contact. When contact information differs from that given for the administering organization, relevant addresses, telephone and fax numbers, and names of specific contact persons are listed here. When the address is that of the administering organization, the entry number for the organization is provided.

Indexes

Field of Study Index classifies awards by one or more of 450 specific subject categories, allowing users to easily target their search by specific area of study. Citations are arranged alphabetically under all appropriate subject terms. Each citation is followed by the study level and award type, which appear in parentheses and can be used to narrow the search even further.

Legal Residence Index lists awards that are restricted by the applicant's residence of legal record. Award citations are arranged alphabetically by country and subarranged by region, state or province (for U.S. and Canada). Each citation is followed by the study level and award type, which appear in parentheses and can be used to eliminate inappropriate awards.

Place of Study Index lists awards that carry restrictions on where study can take place. Award citations are arranged alphabetically under the following geographic headings:

- United States
- United States—by Region
- United States—by State
- Canada
- Canada—by Province
- International
- International—by Region
- International—by Country

Each citation is followed by the study level and award type, which appear in parentheses.

Special Recipient Index lists awards that carry restrictions or special qualifying factors relating to applicant affiliation. This index allows users to quickly identify awards relating to the following categories:

- African American
- Asian American
- Association Membership
- Disabled
- Employer Affiliation
- Ethnic Group Membership
- Fraternal Organization Membership
- Hispanic American
- Military
- Minority
- Native American
- Religious Affiliation
- Union Affiliation
- Veteran

Awards are listed under all appropriate headings. Each citation includes information on study level and award type, which appear in parentheses and can be used to further narrow the search. Users interested in awards restricted to particular minorities should also look under the general Minorities heading, which lists awards targeted for minorities but not restricted to any particular minority group.

Sponsor and Scholarship Index lists, in a single alphabetic sequence, all of the administering organizations, awards, and acronyms included in *SFL*.

Federal aid for college students is available through a variety of programs administered by the U.S. Department of Education. Most colleges and universities participate in federal programs, but there are exceptions. Contact a school's financial aid office to find out if it is a participating institution. If it participates, the student works with financial aid counselors to determine how much aid can be obtained.

Aid for students comes in three forms: grants (gifts to the student), loans (which must be repaid), and work-study jobs (a job for the student while enrolled in which his/her pay is applied to his school account). These types of aid are further explained below. More information can be found at http://www.ed.gov.

Grants

Pell Grants are intended to provide funds for any undergraduate student (who does not already have a degree) who wishes to attend college regardless of family financial background. They are available through the financial aid office at the school. The maximum Pell Grant award for the 2012-2013 award year (July 1, 2012 to June 30, 2013) is $5,550

Federal Supplemental Educational Opportunity Grants (FSEOG) are intended for students with exceptional financial need, these grants are typically for smaller amounts (between $100 and $4,000) than Pell Grants. They are available on a limited basis.

Loans

Student loans are available a variety of ways. Loans may not be taken out for more than the cost of attendance at the school, which is determined by the financial aid administrator. Grants and other forms of aid are taken into consideration when determining the amount a student will be allowed to borrow. Loan amounts may be reduced if a student receives other forms of aid. Loans are divided into two types, subsidized and unsubsidized:

Subsidized loans: the federal government pays the interest on the loan until after schooling is complete.

Unsubsidized loans: the student incurs the interest charges while in school, but payment of the charges may be deferred until schooling is complete. The advantage of unsubsidized loans is that there are usually fewer restrictions against obtaining them. Amounts available through these programs vary depending on academic level. The total debt a student or a student's parents may accumulate for that student is $31,000 for a dependent undergraduate student, $57,500 for an independent undergraduate student (with a limit of $23,000 in subsidized loans), and $138,500 for a graduate or professional student (with a limit of $65,500 in subsidized loans) or $224,000 for health professionals.

Available Funding Programs Direct Loan Program

These low-interest loans bypass lending institutions such as banks. They are a direct arrangement between the government and the student (administered by the school). There are four repayment options for the Direct Loan program: the Income Contingent Repayment Plan, the Extended Repayment Plan, the Graduated Repayment Plan, and the Standard Repayment Plan.

Direct subsidized loans may be taken out for a maximum of $3,500 by incoming freshmen, while juniors and seniors may borrow up to a maximum of $5,500. The amounts for independent undergraduate students range from $9,500 to $12,500 per year for direct loans. Independent students face some restrictions on the amount of subsidized funds they can receive from the program. At least half of the funds borrowed through the Direct Loan program by independent students must come from unsubsidized loans. Graduate students may borrow up to $20,500 directly, with a maximum of $8,500 in subsidized loans.

Federal Family Education Loans (FFEL)/Stafford

Loans This program provides funds to the lending institution(s) of the student's choice. Before borrowing the funds, the student must complete a Free Application for Federal Student Aid (FAFSA) and a Federal Stafford Loan Application (FSLA). Both forms are available at participating schools' financial aid offices and on the Internet at http://www.ed.gov. There are three repayment options for FFEL/Stafford Loans:

Fixed, Graduated, and Income-Sensitive. Any FFEL/Stafford loan must be paid back within ten years.

This program is also divided into subsidized and unsubsidized loans. However, students may not borrow simultaneously from this program and the Direct Loan program. Students may borrow separately subsidized and unsubsidized funds from either program. The maximum amounts that can be borrowed through this program are the same as through the Direct Loan program.

Direct and FFEL/Stafford Program Loans for Parents (PLUS)

Parents may borrow for their children's education through the aforementioned Federal Loan programs. They are responsible for the repayment of the loans. The maximum amount to be borrowed is the cost of attending the school minus other forms of aid already obtained. For 2012-2013, the fixed rate for a Direct PLUS loan is 7.9% and for a FFEL PLUS loan is 8.5%. Parents who borrow through the FFEL/Stafford program make arrangements with the lender for repayment.

With the Direct PLUS loan, parents fill out a Direct PLUS Loan Application, available at the school's financial aid office. The funds are disbursed to the school. Parents may choose from three repayment plans: Standard, Extended, or Graduated. To obtain funds for their children through the FFEL/Stafford Program, parents make the arrangements with the lending institution. The school is not involved in the application process.

Perkins Loan Program

The Perkins Loan program allows students who have unusual financial need to borrow funds not otherwise available from other loan or grant programs. Up to $5,500 is available to undergraduates each year (up to $8,000 for graduate students). These loans have a fixed interest rate of 5%. Perkins Loans must be repaid within ten years.

Federal Work-Study Program

Work-study is an arrangement that allows students to work on campus while they are enrolled to help pay their expenses. The federal government pays the majority of the student's wages, although the department where the student works also contributes. The employment must be relevant to the student's field of study and only so much time per semester may be devoted to the job. If the student earns the amount of aid prior to the end of the semester, work is terminated for the duration of the award period.

Other Considerations

Application: Applying for federal student aid is free. All federal aid is obtained by first completing a Free Application for Federal Student Aid (FAFSA). After the application is submitted, it will be processed by the Department of Education. The student then receives a Student Aid Report (SAR), which contains a figure for Expected Family Contribution. This is the amount that the student should plan on providing from non-federal sources in order to attend school.

Dependency: If a student is eligible for independent status, more money may be available in the form of loans. The interest rates and the programs for repayment, however, are the same. Independent status provides more financial aid for students who do not have the benefit of parental financial contributions.

Deadline: FAFSA deadlines are set by federal and state agencies, as well as individual schools, and vary widely. Applicants are encouraged to apply as soon as possible after January 1 of the year they plan to enroll, but no earlier.

Special Circumstances: The financial aid counselor at the school will often listen to extenuating circumstances such as unexpected medical expenses, private education expenses for other family members, or recent unemployment when evaluating requests for assistance.

Contact Information for Federal Financial Aid Programs

Call (800)433-3243 to have questions answered or to request the *Student Guide to Financial Aid*; (319) 337-5665 to find out if your application has been processed; (800) 730-8913 (TTY) if you are hearing impaired; (800) 647-8733 to report fraud, waste, or abuse of federal student aid funds; or visit http://www.ed.gov for application forms, guidelines, and general information.

President Clinton launched this volunteer community service program in September 1993 through the *National and Community Service Trust Act*, aimed at helping college-bound young people pay for their education while serving their communities. AmeriCorps volunteers receive minimum wage, health benefits, and a grant toward college for up to two years.

Funds for the program are distributed by the federal government in the form of grants to qualifying organizations and community groups with the goal of achieving direct results in addressing the nation's critical education, human services, public safety, and environmental needs at the community level. The program provides meaningful opportunities for Americans to serve their country in organized efforts, fostering citizen responsibility, building community, and providing educational opportunities for those who make a substantial commitment to service.

The AmeriCorps programs are run by not-for-profit organizations or partnerships, institutions of higher learning, local governments, school or police districts, states, Native American tribes, and federal agencies. Examples of participating programs include Habitat for Humanity, the American Red Cross, Boys and Girls Clubs, and local community centers and places of worship. Volunteers have nearly 1,000 different groups from which to choose. The AmeriCorps Pledge: "I will get things done for America to make our people safer, smarter, and healthier. I will bring Americans together to strengthen our communities. Faced with apathy, I will take action. Faced with conflict, I will seek a common ground. Faced with adversity, I will persevere. I will carry this commitment with me this year and beyond. I am an AmeriCorps Member and I am going to get things done."

Eligibility and Selection for Service in AmeriCorps

Citizens and legal resident aliens who are 17 years of age or older are eligible to serve in AmeriCorps before, during, or after post-secondary education. In general, participants must be high school graduates or agree to achieve their GED prior to receiving education awards. Individual programs select service participants on a nondiscriminatory and nonpolitical basis. There are national and state-wide recruiting information systems and a national pool of potential service volunteers.

Term of Service

One full-time term of service is a minimum of 1,700 hours over the course of one year or less; one part-time term of service is at least 900 hours over two years or less. Short-term service (such as a summer program) provides eligibility for reduced part-time status.

Compensation

You will receive a modest living allowance, health insurance, student loan deferment, and training. After you complete your term of service, you will receive an education award to help pay for your education. Serve part-time and you will receive a portion of the full amount. The amount is tied to the maximum amount of the U.S. Department of Education's Pell Grant. For terms of service that are approved using 2009 funds (or earlier funds) the award continues to be $4,725 for a year of full-time service, and is pro-rated for part-time service based on the full-time amount. For terms of service that are supported with 2010 funds the award value increased to $5,350. For terms of service that are supported with 2011 funds the award value increased to $5,550.

How Can I Use an Award?

These awards may be used to repay qualified existing or future student loans, to pay all or part of the cost of attending a qualified institute of higher education (including some vocational programs), or to pay expenses while participating in an approved school-to-work program. Awards must be used within seven years of completion of service.

Contact

Individuals interested in participating in AmeriCorps national service programs should apply directly. For basic program information, individuals can call the AmeriCorps Information Hotline at 1-800-942-2677 or visit their Web site at http://www.americorps.gov.

State Higher Education Agencies

The following is an alphabetic state-by-state listing of agencies located in the United States. Many of these agencies administer special federal award programs, as well as state-specific awards, such as the Tuition Incentive Program (TIP) offered by the state of Michigan for low-income students to receive free tuition at community colleges. Financial aid seekers should contact the agency in their home state for more information.

ALABAMA

Alabama Comm. on Higher Education
P.O. Box 302000
Montgomery, AL 36130-2000
(334)242-1998
http://www.ache.state.al.us

ALASKA

Alaska Comm. on Postsecondary Education
P.O. Box 110505
Juneau, AK 99811-0505
(907)465-2962
http://www.alaskadvantage.state.ak.us/

ARIZONA

Arizona Comm. for Postsecondary Education
2020 N. Central Ave.,
Ste. 650
Phoenix, AZ 85004-4503
(602)258-2435
http://www.azhighered.org

ARKANSAS

Arkansas Dept. of Higher Education
114 E. Capitol Ave.
Little Rock, AR 72201-3818
(501)371-2000
http://www.adhe.edu

CALIFORNIA

California Student Aid Comm.
PO Box 419026
Rancho Cordova, CA 95741-9026
(916)526-8047
http://www.csac.ca.gov

COLORADO

Colorado Dept. of Higher Education
1560 Broadway, Ste. 1600
Denver, CO 80202
(303)866-2723
http://highered.colorado.gov

CONNECTICUT

Connecticut Dept. of Higher Education
61 Woodland St.
Hartford, CT 06105-2326
(860)947-1800
http://www.ctdhe.org

DELAWARE

Delaware Higher Education Office
The Townsend Building
401 Federal St., Ste. 2
Dover, DE 19901
(302)735-4120
http://www.doe.k12.de.us/infosuites/students_family/dheo/about.shtml

DISTRICT OF COLUMBIA

District of Columbia Dept. of Human Services
Office of Postsecondary Education, Research, and Assistance
810 1st St., NE, 9th Fl.
Washington, DC 20002
(202)727-6436
http://osse.dc.gov/seo/cwp

FLORIDA

Office of Student Financial Assistance
Dept. of Education
325 W. Gaines St.

Turlington Bldg., Ste. 1514
Tallahassee, FL 32399-0400
(800)336-3475
http://www.floridastudentfinancialaid.org

GEORGIA

Georgia Student Finance Comm.
2082 E. Exchange Pl., Ste. 200
Tucker, GA 30084
(770)724-9000
http://www.gsfc.org/gsfcnew/index.cfm

HAWAII

Hawaii State Postsecondary Education Comm.
2444 Dole St., Rm. 209
Honolulu, HI 96822-2302
(808)956-8213

IDAHO

Idaho State Board of Education
PO Box 83720
Boise, ID 83720-0037
(208)334-2270
http://www.boardofed.idaho.gov

ILLINOIS

Illinois Student Assistance Comm.
1755 Lake Cook Rd.
Deerfield, IL 60015-5209
(800)899-4722
http://www.collegezone.com

INDIANA

State Student Assistance Comm. of Indiana
W462 Indiana Government Center South
402 W. Washington St.
Indianapolis, IN 46204

(317)232-2350
www.in.gov/ssaci/

IOWA

Iowa College Student Aid Comm.
603 E. 12th St., 5th Fl.
Des Moines, IA 50319
(877)272-4456
http://www.iowacollegeaid.org

KANSAS

Kansas Board of Regents
1000 SW Jackson St., Ste. 520
Topeka, KS 66612-1368
(785)296-3421
http://www.kansasregents.org

KENTUCKY

Kentucky Higher Education Assistance Authority
PO Box 798
Frankfort, KY 40602-0798
(800)928-8926
http://www.kheaa.com

LOUISIANA

Louisiana Office of Student Financial Assistance
602 N. Fifth St.
Baton Rouge, LA 70802
(225)219-1012
http://www.osfa.state.la.us

MAINE

Maine Education Assistance Division
Finance Authority of Maine (FAME)
5 Community Dr.
P.O. Box 0949
Augusta, ME 04332-0949
(207)623-3263
http://www.famemaine.com

MARYLAND

Maryland Higher Education Comm.
6 N. Liberty St.
Baltimore, MD 21201
(410)767-3301
http://www.mhec.state.md.us

MASSACHUSETTS

Massachusetts Dept. of Higher Education
One Ashburton Pl., Rm. 1401
Boston, MA 02108-1696

(617)994-6950
http://www.mass.edu

MICHIGAN

Michigan Higher Education Student Loan Authority
Student Scholarships and Grants
P.O. Box 30462
Lansing, MI 48909-7962
(888)447-2687
http://www.michigan.gov/mistudentaid

MINNESOTA

Minnesota Office of Higher Education
1450 Energy Park Dr., Ste. 350
St. Paul, MN 55108-5227
(651)642-0567
http://www.ohe.state.mn.us/index.cfm

MISSISSIPPI

Mississippi Institutions of Higher Learning
3825 Ridgewood Rd.
Jackson, MS 39211
(601)432-6198
http://www.ihl.state.ms.us

MISSOURI

Missouri Dept. of Higher Education
205 Jefferson St.
P.O. Box 1469
Jefferson City, MO 65102-1469
(573)751-2361
http://www.dhe.mo.gov/

MONTANA

Montana Board of Regents
Office of Commissioner of Higher Education
Montana University System
2500 Broadway St.
PO Box 203201
Helena, MT 59620-3201
(406)444-6570
http://www.mus.edu

NEBRASKA

Nebraska Coordinating Comm. for Postsecondary Education
P.O. Box 95005
Lincoln, NE 68509-5005
(402)471-2847
http://www.ccpe.state.ne.us/
PublicDoc/CCPE/Default.asp

NEVADA

Nevada Department of Education
700 E. Fifth St.
Carson City, NV 89701
(775)687-9200
http://www.doe.nv.gov

NEW HAMPSHIRE

New Hampshire Higher Education Comm.
101 Pleasant St.
Concord, NH 03301-3494
(603)271-3494
http://www.state.nh.us/postsecondary

NEW JERSEY

Higher Education Student Assistance Authority
P.O. Box 545
Trenton, NJ 08625-0545
(800)792-8670
http://www.hesaa.org

NEW MEXICO

New Mexico Higher Education Dept.
2048 Galisteo St.
Santa Fe, NM 87505-2100
(505)476-8400
http://www.hed.state.nm.us

NEW YORK

New York State Higher Education Svcs. Corp.
99 Washington Ave.
Albany, NY 12255
(888)697-4372
http://www.hesc.com

NORTH CAROLINA

North Carolina State Education Assistance Authority
PO Box 14103
Research Triangle Park, NC 27709
(919)549-8614
http://www.ncseaa.edu

NORTH DAKOTA

North Dakota University System
North Dakota Student Financial Assistance Program

10th Fl., State Capitol
600 E. Boulevard Ave., Dept. 215
Bismarck, ND 58505-0230
(701)328-2960
http://www.ndus.edu

OHIO

Ohio Board of Regents

State Grants and Scholarships Dept.
30 E. Broad St., 36th Fl.
Columbus, OH 43215
(614)466-7420
http://www.ohiohighered.org

OKLAHOMA

Oklahoma State Regents for Higher Education

Oklahoma Guaranteed Loan Program
655 Research Pkwy.
Suite 200
Oklahoma City, OK 73104
(405)225-9100
http://www.okhighered.org

OREGON

Oregon Student Access Comm.

1500 Valley River Dr., Ste. 100
Eugene, OR 97401
(541)687-7400
http://www.osac.state.or.us

PENNSYLVANIA

Pennsylvania Higher Education Assistance Agency

1200 N. 7th St.
Harrisburg, PA 17102-1444
(800)233-0557
http://www.pheaa.org

RHODE ISLAND

Rhode Island Higher Education Assistance Authority

560 Jefferson Blvd., Ste. 100
Warwick, RI 02886-1304
(401)736-1100
http://www.riheaa.org

SOUTH CAROLINA

South Carolina Comm. on Higher Education

1122 Lady St., Ste. 300
Columbia, SC 29201
(803)737-2297
http://www.che400.state.sc.us

SOUTH DAKOTA

South Dakota Education Access Foundation

115-1st Ave., SW
Aberdeen, SD 57401
(888)502-5902
http://www.sdeducationaccess.org/

TENNESSEE

Tennessee Higher Education Comm.

Parkway Towers
404 James Robertson Pkwy., Ste. 1900
Nashville, TN 37243-0830
(615)741-3605
http://www.state.tn.us/thec

TEXAS

Texas Higher Education Coordinating Board

P.O. Box 12788
Austin, TX 78711-2788
(512)427-6101
http://www.thecb.state.tx.us

UTAH

Utah State Board of Regents

Board of Regents Building, The Gateway
60 South 400 West
Salt Lake City, UT 84101-1284
(801)321-7101
http://www.utahsbr.edu

VERMONT

Vermont Student Assistance Corp.

10 E. Allen St.
P.O. Box 2000

Winooski, VT 05404
(802)655-9602
http://www.vsac.org

VIRGINIA

State Council of Higher Education for Virginia

James Monroe Bldg.
101 N. 14th St., 10th Fl.
Richmond, VA 23219
(804)225-2600
http://www.schev.edu

WASHINGTON

Washington State Higher Education Coordinating Board

917 Lakeridge Way
P.O. Box 43430
Olympia, WA 98540-3430
(360)753-7800
http://www.hecb.wa.gov

WEST VIRGINIA

West Virginia Higher Education Policy Comm.

1018 Kanawha Blvd., E., Ste. 700
Charleston, WV 25301-2800
(304)558-2101
http://www.hepc.wvnet.edu

WISCONSIN

Wisconsin Higher Education Aids Board

131 W. Wilson St., Ste. 902
P.O. Box 7885
Madison, WI 53707-7885
(608)267-2206
http://heab.state.wi.us

WYOMING

Wyoming Community College Comm.

2020 Carey Ave., 8th Fl.
Cheyenne, WY 82002
(307)777-7763
http://www.communitycolleges.wy.edu

U.S. State Abbreviations

AK	Alaska
AL	Alabama
AR	Arkansas
AZ	Arizona
CA	California
CO	Colorado
CT	Connecticut
DC	District of Columbia
DE	Delaware
FL	Florida
GA	Georgia
GU	Guam
HI	Hawaii
IA	Iowa
ID	Idaho
IL	Illinois
IN	Indiana
KS	Kansas
KY	Kentucky
LA	Louisiana
MA	Massachusetts
MD	Maryland
ME	Maine
MI	Michigan
MN	Minnesota
MO	Missouri
MS	Mississippi
MT	Montana
NC	North Carolina
ND	North Dakota
NE	Nebraska
NH	New Hampshire
NJ	New Jersey
NM	New Mexico
NV	Nevada
NY	New York
OH	Ohio
OK	Oklahoma
OR	Oregon
PA	Pennsylvania
PR	Puerto Rico
RI	Rhode Island
SC	South Carolina
SD	South Dakota
TN	Tennessee
TX	Texas
UT	Utah
VA	Virginia
VI	Virgin Islands
VT	Vermont
WA	Washington
WI	Wisconsin
WV	West Virginia
WY	Wyoming

Canadian Province Abbreviations

AB	Alberta
BC	British Columbia
MB	Manitoba
NB	New Brunswick
NL	Newfoundland and Labrador
NS	Nova Scotia
NT	Northwest Territories
ON	Ontario
PE	Prince Edward Island
QC	Quebec
SK	Saskatchewan
YT	Yukon Territory

Other Abbreviations

ACT	American College Testing Program
B.A.	Bachelor of Arts
B.Arch.	Bachelor of Architecture
B.F.A.	Bachelor of Fine Arts
B.S.	Bachelor of Science
B.Sc.	Bachelor of Science
CSS	College Scholarship Service
D.D.S.	Doctor of Dental Science/Surgery
D.O.	Doctor of Osteopathy
D.Sc.	Doctor of Science
D.S.W.	Doctor of Social Work
D.V.M.	Doctor of Veterinary Medicine
D.V.M.S.	Doctor of Veterinary Medicine and Surgery
D.V.S.	Doctor of Veterinary Science
FAFSA	Free Application for Federal Student Aid
FWS	Federal Work Study
GED	General Education Development Certificate
GPA	Grade Point Average
GRE	Graduate Record Examination
J.D.	Doctor of Jurisprudence
LL.B.	Bachelor of Law
LL.M.	Master of Law
LSAT	Law School Admission Test
M.A.	Master of Arts
M.Arch.	Master of Architecture
M.B.A.	Master of Business Administration
M.D.	Doctor of Medicine
M.Div.	Master of Divinity
M.F.A.	Master of Fine Arts
MIA	Missing in Action
M.L.S.	Master of Library Science
M.N.	Master of Nursing
M.S.	Master of Science
M.S.W.	Master of Social Work
O.D.	Doctor of Optometry
Pharm.D.	Doctor of Pharmacy
Ph.D.	Doctor of Philosophy
POW	Prisoner of War
PSAT	Preliminary Scholastic Aptitude Test
ROTC	Reserve Officers Training Corps
SAR	Student Aid Report
SAT	Scholastic Aptitude Test
Sc.D.	Doctor of Science
TDD	Telephone Device for the Deaf
Th.d.	Doctor of Theology
U.N.	United Nations
U.S.	United States

1 ■ 101st Airborne Division Association

PO Box 929
Fort Campbell, KY 42223-0929
Ph: (931) 431-0199
Fax: (931) 431-0195
E-mail: assocmemberinfo@comcast.net
URL: www.screamingeagle.org

2 ■ Chappie Hall Scholarship Program *(Graduate, Postgraduate, Undergraduate/Scholarship)*

Purpose: To provide financial assistance to students who have the potential of becoming assets to the nation. **Focus:** General Studies. **Qualif.:** Applicant's parents, grandparents, spouse, living or deceased must be a former or present member of the 101st Airborne Division; must have an overall "C" or better grade average during the past school year; must demonstrate financial need. **Criteria:** Selection is done based on the applicant's career objectives, academic record, financial need and insight gained from the letter requesting consideration, as well as letters of recommendation.

Funds Avail.: Amount not specified. **Number Awarded:** 11. **To Apply:** Applicant must complete and submit the following required documents: a typed personal letter; proof of membership of parent, grandparent, husband, or wife in the 101st Airborne Division Association; a transcript of school records; two letters of recommendation; small photo (head and shoulders) to be used for. publication in "The screaming Eagle" if scholarship grant is awarded; letter of acceptance from a university or college and the address of the department of office at the university or college where a scholarship check could be mailed; and not less than 250-word essay, but not exceeding 300 words on patriotism. **Deadline:** May 4.

3 ■ AACE International

1265 Suncrest Towne Centre Dr.
Morgantown, WV 26505-1876
Ph: (304) 296-8444
Fax: (304) 291-5728
Free: 800-858-2678
E-mail: info@aacei.org
URL: www.aacei.org

4 ■ AACE International Competitive Scholarships *(Undergraduate/Scholarship)*

Purpose: To advance the study of cost engineering and cost management through the integrative process of total cost management. **Focus:** Engineering. **Qualif.:** Applicants must be full-time students pursuing a related degree in engineering and other related courses. **Criteria:** Recipients are selected based on academic performance, extra-curricular activities and an essay on the value of study of cost engineering or total cost management.

Funds Avail.: $2,000-$8,000. **To Apply:** Applicants must fill out the application form. **Deadline:** February 15. **Contact:** Charla Miller at cmiller@aacei.org.

5 ■ AASP - The Palynological Society

University of N Carolina at Pembroke
Geology, Old Main 213
Pembroke, NC 28372
Ph: (910) 521-6478
E-mail: mbfarley@sigmaxi.net
URL: www.palynology.org

6 ■ American Association of Stratigraphic Palynologists Student Scholarships *(Graduate/Scholarship)*

Purpose: To support studies in palynology. **Focus:** Earth Sciences; Geology. **Qualif.:** Applicants must be beginning graduate students or advanced graduate students. **Criteria:** Selection is based on applicant's qualifications and the quality of proposed project.

Funds Avail.: $2,000. **Number Awarded:** 2. **To Apply:** Applicants must submit four copies of completed application form (available at the AASP Awards Committee Chair, or can be downloaded from the website). **Deadline:** March 31. **Contact:** Martin Farley at the above address.

7 ■ Paleontological Society Student Research Grants *(Graduate, Undergraduate/Grant)*

Purpose: To support research in the field or any aspect related to paleontology. **Focus:** Earth Sciences; Geology. **Qualif.:** Applicants must be undergraduate or graduate student members of the Paleontological Society conducting a research on any aspect of paleontology. **Criteria:** Awards are based upon scholastic ability, potential, professional interest, character and financial need.

Funds Avail.: $800. **To Apply:** Applicants must submit a completed application form (available at the website) and a letter of support from research advisor (must be sent to michalk@vt.edu). **Deadline:** February 25. **Contact:** Materials should be submitted to powell@juniata.edu.

8 ■ AAUW

1111 16th St. NW, Ste. Mailrm
Washington, DC 20036-4809

Awards are arranged alphabetically below their administering organizations

Ph: (202) 785-7700
Fax: (202) 872-1425
E-mail: connect@aauw.org
URL: www.aauw.org

9 ■ American Association of University Women American Fellowships *(Doctorate, Postdoctorate/Fellowship)*

Purpose: To support female doctoral candidates and scholars completing dissertations and seeking funds for postdoctoral research leave from accredited institutions. **Focus:** General studies. **Qualif.:** Applicants must be U.S. citizens or permanent residents. **Criteria:** Candidates are evaluated on the basis of scholarly excellence, teaching experience and active commitment to help women through service in their communities, professions, or fields of research.

Funds Avail.: $6,000 up to $30,000. **To Apply:** Applicants must check online for further information about the award. **Contact:** Questions about application must be directed to Iowa office, Dept. 60, 301 ACT Dr., Iowa City, IA 52243-4030; Phone: 319-337-1716; E-mail: aauw@act.org.

10 ■ American Association of University Women Career Development Grants *(Postgraduate/Grant)*

Purpose: To support women who hold bachelor's degree preparing to advance their careers, change careers, or re-enter the work force. **Focus:** General studies. **Qualif.:** Applicants must be U.S. citizens or permanent residents. **Criteria:** Applicants must be AAUW members and women of color who are pursuing their first advanced degree or credentials in non-traditional fields.

Funds Avail.: $2,000 up to $12,000. **To Apply:** Applicants must check online for further information about the award.

11 ■ American Association of University Women International Fellowships *(Graduate, Postgraduate/Fellowship)*

Purpose: To provide fund for full-time study or research in the United States to women who are not United States citizens or permanent residents. **Focus:** General studies. **Qualif.:** Applicant must be a citizen in a country other than the United States, or must hold a non-immigrant visa if residing in the United States. **Criteria:** Candidates are selected based on academic and professional qualifications, need for the specialized knowledge and skills of the country where she came from, commitment to the advancement of women and girls in her home country as demonstrated by her previous work and proposed study or research, documented evidence prior to her community service in the home country particularly activities concerning women and girls lives' improvement.

Funds Avail.: $18,000 up to $30,000. **To Apply:** Applicant must check online for further information about the award. Applicants must submit the following supporting documents in a single packet: official transcript; proof of bachelor's degree; proof of doctorate degree (for Postdoctoral applicants); official report of TOEFL test scores or request for waiver; letter of admission; and acknowledgement postcard. **Contact:** Questions about application must be directed to Iowa office, Dept. 60, 301 ACT Dr., Iowa City, IA 52243-4030; Phone: 319-337-1716; E-mail: aauw@act.org.

12 ■ American Association of University Women Master's and First Professional Awards *(Professional development/Award)*

Purpose: To financially support women intending to pursue a full-time course of study at accredited institutions. **Focus:** Women's studies. **Qualif.:** Applicants must be U.S. citizens or permanent residents; must be full-time women who are enrolled at an accredited U.S. institution. **Criteria:** Selected Professions Fellowships are awarded for the following programs: Architecture (M.Arch, M.S.Arch), Computer/Information Sciences (M.S.), Engineering (M.E., M.S., Ph.D.), Engineering Dissertation Award also awarded Mathematics/Statistics (M.S.), and fellowships in the following degree programs are restricted to women of color, who have been underrepresented in these fields: Business Administration (M.B.A., E.M.B.A.), Law (J.D.), Medicine (M.D., D.O.).

Funds Avail.: $5,000 up $18,000. **To Apply:** Applicants must check online for further information about the award.

13 ■ American Association of University Women Selected Professions Fellowships *(Professional development/Fellowship)*

Purpose: To support women intending to pursue a full-time course of study at an accredited institution during the fellowship year. **Focus:** Architecture; Business administration; Computer and information sciences; Engineering; Law; Medicine. **Qualif.:** Applicants must be U.S. citizens or permanent residents. **Criteria:** Selection of candidates based upon the following programs: Architecture (M.Arch, M.S.Arch), Computer/Information Sciences (M.S.), Engineering (M.E., M.S., Ph.D.), Engineering Dissertation Award also awarded Mathematics/Statistics (M.S.), and fellowships in the following degree programs are restricted to women of color, who have been underrepresented in these fields: Business Administration (M.B.A., E.M.B.A.), Law (J.D.), Medicine (M.D., D.O.).

Funds Avail.: $5,000 to $18,000. **To Apply:** Applicants must check online for further information about the award. **Contact:** For more information, applicants may send mail to AAUW customer service center at Dept. 60, 301 ACT Dr., Iowa City, IA 52243-4030; Phone: 319-337-1716; E-mail: aauw@act.org.

14 ■ AAUW Legal Advocacy Fund (LAF)
1111 16th St. NW
Washington, DC 20036
Ph: (202) 785-7700
Fax: (202) 872-1425
Free: 800-326-AAUW
E-mail: connect@aauw.org
URL: www.aauw.org/act/laf

15 ■ AAUW Legal Advocacy Fund American Fellowships *(Doctorate/Fellowship)*

Purpose: To support women doctoral candidates completing dissertations or scholars seeking funds for postdoctoral research leave from accredited institutions. **Focus:** General studies. **Qualif.:** Applicants for postdoctoral fellowships must be U.S. citizens and must hold a Ph.D., Ed.D., D.B.A., M.F.A., D.M.; Applicants for the summer/short-term must be U.S. citizens and will hold a doctorate or M.F.A. degree; Applicants for dissertation must be U.S. citizens or permanent residents, must be in a program other than an engineering program, must be in or entering the final year

Awards are arranged alphabetically below their administering organizations

of dissertation, must have a dissertation proposal approved by the committee, must have all course work completed and have passed all preliminary exams. **Criteria:** Candidates are evaluated on the basis of scholarly excellence, teaching experience, and active commitment to helping women and girls through service in their communities, professions, or fields of research.

Funds Avail.: Amount not stated. **To Apply:** Candidates may apply for only one of the awards. A complete application must consist of: application with budget information, narrative autobiography, statement of project (description of project, design, research methodology and excepted contribution to knowledge); clear statement of financial need; name(s) of the university, institution, or other location where study will be carried out; and three recommendations. All documents must be postmarked by the deadline in hard copy format: Transcript(s)/Proof of Doctorate; Institution Certification Form; Institution Letter; and Filing Fee. **Deadline:** November 15. **Contact:** AAUW Educational Foundation Dept. 60, 301 ACT Drive, Iowa City, IA 52243-4030.

16 ■ AAUW Legal Advocacy Fund Career Development Grants *(Professional development/ Grant)*

Purpose: To support women who hold a bachelor's degree and are preparing to advance their careers, change careers, or re-enter the work force. **Focus:** General studies. **Qualif.:** Applicants must be US citizens or permanent residents who hold a bachelor's degree or specialized training in technical or professional fields. **Criteria:** Special consideration is given to AAUW members, women of color, and women pursuing their first advanced degree or credentials in nontraditional fields.

Funds Avail.: Amount not specified. **To Apply:** Questions on the application form must be answered. Applicants must submit all the required components: proposed budget and narrative; recommendation to be completed online; and filing fee of $35. **Deadline:** December 15. **Contact:** AAUW Educational Foundation Dept. 60, 301 ACT Drive, Iowa City, IA 52243-4030.

17 ■ AAUW Legal Advocacy Fund International Fellowships *(Doctorate, Graduate/Fellowship)*

Purpose: To award a full-time study or research in the United States to women who are not United States citizens or permanent residents. **Focus:** General studies. **Qualif.:** Applicants must be citizens in a country other than the United States, or must hold a non-immigrant visa if applicants reside in the United States; must complete an academic degree (either in the US or abroad) equivalent to a US bachelor's degree; must intend to devote herself full-time to her proposed academic plan during the fellowship year; must intend to return to her home country to pursue a professional career; and must be proficient in English, unless applicants can verify that their native language is English or that she received her undergraduate degree from or will have completed one semester of full-time study in her discipline at a university in the United States. **Criteria:** Award is given based on academic and professional qualifications; the need of the applicant's country for the specialized knowledge and skills that she plans to acquire; applicant's commitment to the advancement of women and girls in her home country as demonstrated by her previous work and her proposed study or research; documented evidence of prior community or civic service in the home country, particularly activities that contributed to the improvement of the lives of women and girls; quality and

feasibility of the proposed plan of study or research and proposed time schedule; planned confirmed place of work after returning to home country; English proficiency; financial need; and country of residence at the time of application (Preference will be given to women who reside in their home country at the time of application).

Funds Avail.: Amount not specified. **To Apply:** Applications must be submitted online. Applications and supporting documents will not be accepted via fax or e-mail. The following requirements must be submitted before the deadline: application form which includes research program/thesis/ course work proposal, three recommendations and filing fee of $30. **Deadline:** December 1. **Contact:** AAUW Educational Foundation Dept. 60, 301 ACT Drive, Iowa City, IA 52243-4030.

18 ■ AAUW Legal Advocacy Fund Selected Professions Fellowships *(Doctorate, Graduate/ Fellowship)*

Purpose: To award women who intend to pursue a full-time course of study at accredited institutions during the fellowship year. **Focus:** Architecture; Computer and Information Sciences; Engineering; Statistics; Business Administration; Law; Medicine. **Qualif.:** Applicants must be U.S. citizens or permanent residents who are full-time students. **Criteria:** Panel of academic and practicing professionals who work in the respective selected professions fields will review and evaluate all fellowship applications for recommendation to the Program Committee of the AAUW Educational Foundation Board. Final fellowship selections are approved by the Foundation Board of Directors.

Funds Avail.: Amount not specified. **To Apply:** Applicants must accomplish complete application package which consist of: application; budget information for Administrative and Internal Revenue Service Purposes; narrative autobiography; detailed statement of thesis or special project (applicable to engineering and medical students only); statement of applicant's career plans and professional goals; three letters of recommendation; and dean's letter (applicable to medical students). Applicants must also submit supporting documents such as: official transcripts and a bound set of reproductions of a range of the applicant's design projects. 10 to 12 samples may be submitted in the portfolio, no larger than 8" x 10" in size (applicable to architecture students only). **Deadline:** January 10. **Contact:** AAUW Educational Foundation Dept. 60, 301 ACT Drive, Iowa City, IA 52243-4030; Phone: 319-337-1716; Email: aauw@act.org.

19 ■ Aboriginal Nurse Association of Canada (ANAC)

56 Sparks St., Ste. 502
Ottawa, ON, Canada K1P 5A9
Ph: (613) 724-4677
Fax: (613) 724-4718
Free: 866-724-3049
E-mail: info@anac.on.ca
URL: www.anac.on.ca

20 ■ Baxter Corporation - Jean Goodwill Scholarships *(Postgraduate/Scholarship)*

Purpose: To encourage and help nurses of Aboriginal ancestry to obtain the specialized knowledge they require. **Focus:** Nursing. **Qualif.:** Applicants must be students who

Awards are arranged alphabetically below their administering organizations

are graduating from a registered nurse course and are accepted into one of the following specialized training programs: community health nursing, outpost nursing, midwifery; must be or will be enrolled in a bachelor level nursing program; can be graduate nurses already serving in isolated communities and who are accepted into community health nursing, outpost nursing or midwifery program. **Criteria:** Applicants are selected based on the selection board's review of the application materials. Preference will be given to applicants of aboriginal ancestry who intend to serve in the North.

Funds Avail.: $2,500. **Number Awarded:** 2. **Deadline:** July 1. **Remarks:** Candidates may apply for scholarship for each year of study.

21 ■ The Frederick B. Abramson Memorial Foundation

PO Box 7810
Washington, DC 20044
Ph: (202) 470-5425
Fax: (202) 318-2482
E-mail: info@abramsonfoundation.org
URL: www.abramsonfoundation.org

22 ■ The Frederick B. Abramson Memorial Foundation Scholarships *(Undergraduate/ Scholarship)*

Purpose: To help defer college expenses at a four-year accredited institution. **Focus:** General studies. **Qualif.:** Applicants must be graduating from a public senior high school located in the District of Columbia; applicant must be a resident of District of Columbia; applicants must have admitted to and committed to attend an accredited four-year college in the US as a candidate for a degree; applicants must have demonstrated commitment to community service and social change; applicants must have demonstrated financial need; applicants must have at least 2.75 GPA or better; at least 1000 between math and verbal SATs and at least a score of 3 and above in the essay section; must have a family income of less than $70,000. **Criteria:** Recipients are selected based on financial need, academic standing, and upon the decision of the Foundation Board of Directors.

Funds Avail.: $10,000. **To Apply:** Applicants must submit an application form; essay; two letters of recommendation in which one is from the councilor and one is from the teacher; a copy of College Financial Aid Application or Student Aid Report; official transcript through midterm period of second semester of senior year including the SAT scores; budget for preferred college; letter of acceptance from college of choice; and a financial aid award letter from college of choice. Send completed application to Scholarship Committee, The Frederick B. Abramson Memorial Foundation, 2040 S St. NW, Washington, DC 20009. **Deadline:** April.

23 ■ The Frederick B. Abramson Public Interest Fellowships Awards *(All/Fellowship)*

Purpose: To honor and further the ongoing value of educational attainment; to further the importance of community service and mentoring, especially for minorities and women; to further the legal representation for disadvantaged individuals and the public interest. **Focus:** Law. **Qualif.:** Applicants must be graduating law students, judicial law clerks, or practicing attorneys wishing to work in public

interest law. **Criteria:** Recipients are selected based on the determination of the Foundation Board of Directors.

Funds Avail.: $10,000. **To Apply:** Applicants must complete the application form; applicants must submit a resume; two letters of recommendation; confirmation of public interest job; statement of financial responsibilities; statement of interest and career plans. **Deadline:** August 18. **Contact:** Fellowship Committee, The Frederick B. Abramson Memorial Foundation, c/o The Bauman Foundation, 2040 S St. NW, Washington, DC 20009. Phone: 202-683-4816; Fax: 202-328-2003; info@abramsonfoundation.org.

24 ■ Academy of Criminal Justice Sciences (ACJS)

PO Box 960
Greenbelt, MD 20768-0960
Ph: (301) 446-6300
Fax: (301) 446-2819
Free: 800-757-2257
E-mail: info@acjs.org
URL: www.acjs.org

25 ■ Affirmative Action Mini Grants and Student Scholarships *(All/Grant)*

Purpose: To promote the involvement of all minority groups in the academy. **Focus:** Law. **Qualif.:** Applicants must be members of a group who have experienced historical discrimination (i.e., African American, Asian American, Native American, persons of Hispanic descent); enrolled in criminal justice, criminology or related programs; available for undergraduates, masters, and doctoral students. **Criteria:** Recipients are selected based on the AACJS Affirmative Action Committee panel's review of application materials.

Funds Avail.: $600. **Number Awarded:** 2. **To Apply:** Applicants must submit a completed manuscript (not more than 30 pages in length) examining criminal justice/criminological issue; a 10-page, double-spaced, typed proposal discussing: (a) the nature of the research topic, (b) why the research is important, and where relevant, (c) the methods used, (d) the findings of the research, and (e) the theoretical, methodological, and/or policy implications of the results. **Deadline:** November 1. **Contact:** Delores Jones-Brown, 212-237-8390, djonesbr@jjay.cuny.edu.

26 ■ Academy of Medical-Surgical Nurses (AMSN)

PO Box 56
Pitman, NJ 08071
Ph: (856) 256-2422
Fax: (856) 589-7463
Free: 866-877-2676
E-mail: amsn@ajj.com
URL: www.medsurgnurse.org/cgi-bin/WebObjects/ AMSNMain.woa

27 ■ Career Mobility Scholarship Awards *(Doctorate, Undergraduate/Scholarship)*

Purpose: To provide financial assistance for AMSN members who wish to further their education. **Focus:** Nursing; Surgery; Medicine. **Qualif.:** Applicants must be members of AMSN for at least one year. **Criteria:** Ap-

Awards are arranged alphabetically below their administering organizations

plicants will be selected based on the jury's review of application materials and other supporting documents.

Funds Avail.: $1,000. **Number Awarded:** 1. **To Apply:** Applicants must submit a completed application form; a brief description (one page, double-spaced with size 12 font) discussing how additional education will enhance the care of Adult Medical-Surgical patient; and a self-addressed stamped postcard. Electronic submission is preferred; otherwise applicant must submit additional nine blinded photocopies of application and of required documentation. **Deadline:** May 15. **Remarks:** Fax copies will not be considered.

28 ■ Academy of Model Aeronautics (AMA)

5161 E Memorial Dr.
Muncie, IN 47302
Ph: (765) 287-1256
Fax: (765) 289-4248
Free: 800-435-9262
E-mail: davem@modelaircraft.org
URL: www.modelaircraft.org

29 ■ AMA/Charles H. Grant Scholarships
(Undergraduate/Scholarship)

Purpose: To assist students in their educational pursuits. **Focus:** Aeronautics. **Qualif.:** Applicants must be full members of AMA for 36 months prior to applying; must be high school graduates; accepted by a college/university offering a certificate or degree program. **Criteria:** Applicants will be rated based on grade average, test results, modeling activities and citizenship achievement.

Funds Avail.: No specific amount. **To Apply:** Applicants must submit a completed application form. **Deadline:** April 30. **Contact:** Application form and supporting documents must be mailed to AMA office.

30 ■ Sig Memorial Scholarships *(Undergraduate/ Scholarship)*

Purpose: To assist students in their educational pursuits. **Focus:** Aeronautics. **Qualif.:** Applicants must be full members of AMA for 36 months prior to applying; high school graduate; accepted by a college/university offering a degree program; and have demonstrated financial need. **Criteria:** Applications will be evaluated by the AMA Scholarship Committee.

Funds Avail.: No specific amount. **To Apply:** Applicants must submit a completed application form together with a 1-page statement about the need of financial support. **Contact:** Scholarship Committee Chairman, Bob Underwood.

31 ■ Telford Scholarships *(Undergraduate/ Scholarship)*

Purpose: To assist students in their educational pursuits. **Focus:** Aeronautics. **Qualif.:** Applicants must be full members of AMA 36 months prior to applying; high school graduates; accepted by a college/university offering a degree program; and have participated in any of AMA and FAI activities/events. **Criteria:** Applications will be evaluated by the AMA Scholarship Committee. Selection is based on the participation in competition activity by AMA and FAI.

Funds Avail.: No Specific amount. **To Apply:** Applicant must submit a Contest Classification form to list competitions that applicant participated in. **Deadline:** April 30. **Contact:** Scholarship Committee Chairman, Bob Underwood.

32 ■ Academy of Motion Picture Arts & Sciences (AMPAS)

8949 Wilshire Blvd.
Beverly Hills, CA 90211
Ph: (310) 247-3000
Fax: (310) 859-9619
E-mail: publicity@oscars.org
URL: www.oscars.org

33 ■ Academy of Motion Picture Arts and Sciences Student Academy Awards
(Undergraduate/Award)

Purpose: To encourage and reward excellence in filmmaking at the collegiate level. **Focus:** Media arts. **Qualif.:** Filmmaker must be a full-time student in a degree-granting program at an accredited US college or university. The film must have been made in a teacher-student relationship within the curricular structure of that institution. If the filmmaker has graduated or left such a program, the film may be submitted no later than one year from the filmmaker's date of departure. For foreign filmmakers, applicants must be enrolled in CILECT-affiliated colleges and universities outside the borders of the United States and must have previous professional experience. **Criteria:** Submitted entries will be judged on four categories: Animation, Documentary, Narrative and Alternative.

Funds Avail.: $2,000-$5,000. **To Apply:** All entries must be submitted electronically. The maximum running time allowed for entries in all categories is 40 minutes. Domestic applicants must print a hard copy of their entry form and submit it together with their DVD to the appropriate Regional Coordinator. To be officially completed, the hard copy must contain the applicant's signature(s) and the signature of their supervising faculty advisor. For foreign applicants, all entries submitted must be in English, subtitled in English or dubbed in English. Entries will be accepted in the 16mm, 35mm and 70mm format or in the Digital Betacam format. Film prints submitted must be composite, with opticals or magnetic soundtracks. **Deadline:** April 1 Domestic; March 24 - Foreign. **Remarks:** Established in 1972. **Contact:** Richard Miller, rmiller@oscars.org.

34 ■ Academy of Television Arts & Sciences Foundation

5220 Lankershim Blvd.
North Hollywood, CA 91601
Ph: (818) 754-2802
URL: www.emmysfoundation.org

35 ■ Fred Rogers Memorial Scholarships
(Graduate, Undergraduate/Scholarship)

Purpose: To provide financial assistance to students pursuing a degree in a children's media related course. **Focus:** Early childhood education; Child development; Television; Filmmaking; Music; Media arts. **Qualif.:** Applicants must be undergraduates or graduate students of accredited colleges and universities; must demonstrate a commitment, through coursework or experience, to any combination of at least two of the following fields: early childhood education; child development/child psychology; film/television production; music; animation; interactive media (for Pittsburgh based schools only). **Criteria:** Selection will be based on submitted application and materials.

Funds Avail.: $10,000. **Number Awarded:** 4. **To Apply:**

Awards are arranged alphabetically below their administering organizations

Applicants must complete the application form available online; must attach background information about the plan for the use of the scholarship money and a proposed detailed budget on how the scholarship funds will be used; must submit a recommendation letter from two persons, either faculty members or professionals from the children's media industry who have worked with the applicant. **Deadline:** February 28. **Contact:** Michele Fowble.

36 ■ Accredo's Hemophilia Health Services Inc.

201 Great Circle Rd.
Nashville, TN 37228-1701
Ph: (615) 352-2500
Fax: (615) 261-6730
Free: 800-800-6606
E-mail: info@hemophiliahealth.com
URL: www.hemophiliahealth.com

37 ■ HHS Memorial Scholarships *(Graduate, Undergraduate/Scholarship)*

Purpose: To support persons with hemophilia and related bleeding disorders to continue their higher education. **Focus:** General studies. **Qualif.:** Applicant must be a U.S. citizen with hemophilia (factor VIII or IX), von Willebrand disease (type 1, type 2, 2A, 2B, 2M, or 2N or type 3) or other bleeding disorders; must be a high school senior, college freshman, sophomore, junior or college senior planning to attend graduate school or a student already enrolled in a graduate school. **Criteria:** Selection is based on financial need, community involvement, academic achievements and records, and on the essay.

Funds Avail.: At least $1,500. **To Apply:** Applicants must complete the application online. **Deadline:** May 1. **Contact:** Shayne Harris at 615-850-5212 or shayne.harris@ accredo.com.

38 ■ Acoustical Society of America (ASA)

2 Huntington Quadrangle, Ste. 1N01
Melville, NY 11747-4505
Ph: (516) 576-2360
Fax: (516) 576-2377
E-mail: asa@aip.org
URL: asa.aip.org

39 ■ Acoustical Society of America Minority Fellowships *(Graduate/Fellowship)*

Purpose: To support minority students in their pursuit of graduate-level degrees in acoustics. **Focus:** Audiology. **Qualif.:** Applicant must be a permanent resident or citizen of the United States at the time of application; a member of an ethnic minority group (Hispanic, African-American or Native American) that is underrepresented in the sciences; and accepted into, or good academic standing in, a graduate degree program. **Criteria:** Selection is based on academic record, personal statement and letters of recommendation from three instructors or employers.

Funds Avail.: No specific amount. **To Apply:** Applicants must submit a completed application form along with official transcripts of all college and university study; Graduate Record Exam scores; a personal statement; and three letters of recommendation. **Remarks:** Established in 1992. **Contact:** Elaine Moran at the above address.

40 ■ Frederick V. Hunt Postdoctoral Research Fellowships in Acoustics *(Postdoctorate/Fellowship)*

Purpose: To further the science of, and education in acoustics. **Focus:** Audiology. **Qualif.:** Applicant must be conducting a research on a topic in acoustics at a chosen institution. **Criteria:** Selection is based on the submitted application and materials.

Funds Avail.: No specific amount. **Number Awarded:** 1. **To Apply:** Applicants may contact the Society for the application information. **Deadline:** September 4.

41 ■ Raymond H. Stetson Scholarships in Phonetics and Speech Science *(Graduate/Scholarship)*

Purpose: To facilitate the research efforts of promising graduate students. **Focus:** Speech and language pathology/audiology. **Qualif.:** Applicant must be a member of the Acoustical Society of America prior to, or at the time of, the application deadline. Evidence of good academic standing in a graduate degree program is also required. **Criteria:** Selection is based on applicant's academic record, personal statement, letters of recommendation, the research paper and relevance of the research area.

Funds Avail.: No specific amount. **To Apply:** Applicants must submit a completed application form together with official transcripts of university graduate study; a personal statement; a current curriculum vitae; a research paper; and two letters of recommendation. **Remarks:** Established in 1998. **Contact:** Elaine Moran at the above address.

42 ■ Adelante Fund

8415 Datapoint Dr., Ste. 400
San Antonio, TX 78229
Ph: (210) 692-1971
Fax: (210) 692-1951
Free: 877-692-1971
E-mail: info@adelantefund.org
URL: www.adelantefund.org

43 ■ Adelante Fund Hope Scholarships, CPS Energy Dependents *(Undergraduate/Scholarship)*

Purpose: To support Hispanic students in their educational pursuit. **Focus:** General studies. **Qualif.:** Applicant must be an incoming freshman or undergraduate college student; attend an accredited college/university in San Antonio recognized by the U.S. Department of Education; have and maintain a 2.5 GPA or above based on a 4.0 scale; and be involved in community service. **Criteria:** Selection is based on the application materials.

Funds Avail.: $1,500-3,000. **To Apply:** Applicants must submit a completed application together with the required documents. **Deadline:** May 25. **Remarks:** Active or retired CPS Energy guardians or parents must obtain a signature from a HOPE officer on the Scholarship Eligibility Form found on the CPS Energy Intranet.

44 ■ Adelante Fund Hope Scholarships, San Antonio, TX Students *(Undergraduate/Scholarship)*

Purpose: To support Hispanic students in their educational pursuit. **Focus:** General studies. **Qualif.:** Applicant must be an incoming freshman or undergraduate college student; attend an accredited college/university in San Antonio

Awards are arranged alphabetically below their administering organizations

recognized by the U.S. Department of Education; have and maintain a 2.5 GPA or above based on a 4.0 scale; and be involved in community service. **Criteria:** Selection is based on the application materials.

Funds Avail.: $3,000. **To Apply:** Applicants must submit a completed application together with the required documents. **Deadline:** May 25.

45 ■ Adelante Fund UPS Scholarships
(Undergraduate/Scholarship)

Purpose: To support Hispanic students in their educational pursuit. **Focus:** General studies. **Qualif.:** Applicant must be an incoming or current undergraduate student at a 4-year non-profit University in San Antonio, TX; a US citizen or Legal Permanent Resident; and maintain a GPA of 3.0 or above. **Criteria:** Selection is based on the application materials.

Funds Avail.: $3,000. **To Apply:** Applicants must submit a completed application together with the required documents. **Deadline:** January 31.

46 ■ MillerCoors Chicago Scholarships *(Community College, Undergraduate/Scholarship)*

Purpose: To support Hispanic students in their educational pursuit. **Focus:** General studies. **Qualif.:** Applicant must be an incoming freshman or current undergraduate college student; must attend an accredited community college or university in the Chicago Metro area; a US citizen or Legal Permanent Resident; and have and maintain a GPA of 3.0 or above (on a 4.0 scale). **Criteria:** Selection is based on the application materials.

Funds Avail.: $1,500. **To Apply:** Applicants must submit a completed application together with the required documents. **Deadline:** May 25.

47 ■ MillerCoors Engineering and Sciences Scholarships *(Undergraduate/Scholarship)*

Purpose: To support Hispanic students in their educational pursuit. **Focus:** Electrical engineering; Mechanical engineering; Computer and information sciences; Biochemistry. **Qualif.:** Applicant must be eligible for college junior or senior status and pursue a degree in Electrical Engineering, Mechanical Engineering, Computer Science or Biochemistry. Must be a US citizen or Legal Permanent Resident; be of Hispanic descent; maintain a GPA of 3.0 or above (on a 4.0 scale); and must attend a partnering university. **Criteria:** Selection is based on the application materials.

Funds Avail.: $3,000. **To Apply:** Applicants must submit a completed application together with the required documents. **Deadline:** May 25.

48 ■ MillerCoors National Scholarships
(Undergraduate/Scholarship)

Purpose: To support Hispanic students in their educational pursuit. **Focus:** Business; Economics; Accounting; Marketing and distribution; Public relations; Communications; **Qualif.:** Applicant must be eligible for college junior or senior status and pursue a degree in International Business, General Business, Economics, Finance, Accounting, Marketing, Public Relations, General Communications or Sales. Must be a US citizen or Legal Permanent Resident; be of Hispanic descent; maintain a GPA of 3.0 or above (on a 4.0 scale); and must attend a partnering university. **Criteria:** Selection is based on the application materials submitted.

Funds Avail.: $3,000. **To Apply:** Applicants must submit a completed application together with the required documents. **Deadline:** May 25.

49 ■ Adler Pollock & Sheehan, P.C.
One Citizens Plaza, 8th Fl.
Providence, RI 02903-1345
Ph: (401) 274-7200
Fax: (401) 751-0604
URL: www.apslaw.com

50 ■ Adler Pollock & Sheehan Diversity Scholarships *(Undergraduate/Scholarship)*

Purpose: To support and encourage more diverse candidates to enter the practice of law and to diversify and enrich both the firm and profession. **Focus:** Law **Qualif.:** Applicants must: be member of a diverse group; be entering first year of an ABA accredited law school anywhere in the US; have permanent residence in Massachusetts or Rhode Island; have a strong academic achievement; have demonstrated financial need. **Criteria:** Scholarship is given to students who have demonstrated commitment to academic excellence and commitment to the community.

Funds Avail.: $10,000. **To Apply:** Applicants must submit the following: a completed application form; one-page typed essay; a certified copy of college transcript; an acceptance letter from an ABA accredited law school and written notice of intention to attend; a copy of their FAFSA and any other financial aid application, as well as any financial aid they have been offered by the law school they will be attending and by any other source; copies of applicants' and their parents' federal and state tax returns filed in the most recent year; photo ID; proof of Legal Residency in US; two letters of recommendation from persons who are not related to the applicants and who are familiar with the students' academic achievements, character and commitment to the community. **Deadline:** June 1.

51 ■ Administrative Sciences Association of Canada (ASAC)
c/o University of Windsor
Odette School of Business
Odette Bldg., Rm. 446
401 Sunset Ave.
Windsor, ON, Canada N9B 3P4
Ph: (519) 253-3000
Fax: (519) 973-7073
E-mail: templer@uwindsor.ca
URL: www.asac.ca

52 ■ ASAC-CJAS PhD Research Grant Awards
(Doctorate/Grant)

Purpose: To support Canadian PhD students during their doctoral research. **Focus:** Business administration. **Qualif.:** Applicants must be full-time Canadian PhD students at Canadian universities in the areas of administrative sciences and business administration; must have successfully completed their examination and have not yet defended their dissertation. **Criteria:** Applications will be assessed based on the quality and originality of the proposal, research/scholarly achievements of the applicant, and special circumstances or other factors deemed appropriate in a particular instance.

Funds Avail.: $2,500. **Number Awarded:** 1. **To Apply:**

Awards are arranged alphabetically below their administering organizations

Applicants must submit curriculum vitae, two letters of reference, transcript from current program of study, certificate(s) of approval for research involving the use of human subjects from the host university and budget justification. **Deadline:** December 31. **Contact:** Andrew Templer at the above address.

53 ■ Advancing Hispanic Excellence in Technology, Engineering, Math and Science (AHETEMS)

416 Yates St., Box 19019
University of Texas at Arlington
Arlington, TX 76019-0019
Ph: (817) 272-1116
Fax: (817) 272-2548
E-mail: ahetems@shpe.org
URL: www.shpefoundation.org

54 ■ AHETEMS/ExxonMobil Scholarships
(Undergraduate/Scholarship)

Purpose: To enhance and achieve the potential of students pursuing degrees in engineering. **Focus:** Engineering, Civil; Engineering, Electrical; Engineering, Mechanical; Engineering, Petroleum. **Qualif.:** Applicant must be a U.S. citizen; enrolled full-time (12 hrs undergraduate) during the academic year at an accredited university in the U.S. or Puerto Rico; have a minimum GPA of 3.0 on a 4.0 scale; majoring in civil, chemical, electrical, mechanical, or petroleum engineering. **Criteria:** Selection is based on demonstrated significant motivation and aptitude for a career in science, technology, engineering or mathematics.

Funds Avail.: $2,500. **To Apply:** Applicants must complete the application form online. In addition, applicants must submit via mail the Scholarship Certification Form along with the personal statement, official transcript, letter of recommendation, and a resume to AHETEMS. **Deadline:** April.

55 ■ AHETEMS General Scholarships *(Graduate, Undergraduate/Scholarship)*

Purpose: To enhance and achieve the potential of Latino students pursuing degrees in engineering, math and science. **Focus:** Engineering; Mathematics and mathematical sciences; Science; Technology. **Qualif.:** Applicant must be of Hispanic-descent; accepted into or attending an accredited 2-year or 4-year college/university in the U.S. or Puerto Rico; enrolled full-time (12 hrs undergraduate, 9 hrs graduate) during the academic year; or a high school graduating senior graduating from an accredited U.S. high school with a diploma; have a minimum GPA of 3.00 on a 4.0 (high school senior and undergraduate), or 3.25 on a 4.0 scale (graduate student); majoring in science, technology, engineering, mathematics or a related field; and pursuing first bachelors, masters or doctoral degree (students pursuing a second bachelors, etc. are not eligible). **Criteria:** Selection is based on demonstrated significant motivation and aptitude for a career in science, technology, engineering or mathematics.

Funds Avail.: $1,000-$3,000. **To Apply:** Applicants must complete the application form online. In addition, applicants must submit via mail the Scholarship Certification Form along with the personal statement, official transcript, letter of recommendation, and a resume to AHETEMS.

56 ■ AHETEMS Professional Scholarships
(Graduate/Scholarship)

Purpose: To enhance and achieve the potential of Latino students pursuing degrees in engineering, math and sci-

ence. **Focus:** Engineering; Mathematics and mathematical sciences; Science; Technology. **Qualif.:** Applicant must be employed full-time in the U.S. or Puerto Rico in a technical career field; enrolled in a science, technology, engineering, or mathematics graduate degree program at an accredited university in the U.S. or Puerto Rico at least half-time (6 hrs/credits) throughout the academic year; have a minimum 3.25 on a 4.0 GPA; be a SHPE member in good standing both at the time of application and throughout the academic year (non-member may become member at the time of application); pursuing a first masters or doctoral degree. **Criteria:** Selection is based on demonstrated significant motivation and aptitude for a career in science, technology, engineering or mathematics.

Funds Avail.: $2,000. **To Apply:** Applicants must complete the application form online. In addition, applicants must submit via mail the Scholarship Certification Form along with the personal statement, official transcript, letter of recommendation, and a resume to AHETEMS.

57 ■ Advertising Production Club of New York (APC)

Euro RSCG Life, 7th Fl.
200 Madison Ave.
New York, NY 10016
Ph: (212) 251-7295
Fax: (212) 726-5057
E-mail: admin@apc-ny.org
URL: www.apc-nyc.org

58 ■ Advertising Production Club of New York High School Scholarships (APC)
(Undergraduate/Scholarship)

Purpose: To provide financial assistance to those studying graphic arts and communications. **Focus:** Graphic art and design; Communications. **Qualif.:** Applicants must be graduating high school students with graphic arts/communications curriculum; must have "B" average upon graduation; and must have plan to attend an accredited college program in a full-time basis. **Criteria:** Preference will be given to those individuals who have not previously been awarded a scholarship through the APC.

Funds Avail.: $250. Funds are applied to tuition expenses. **Number Awarded:** 2. **To Apply:** Guidelines and application forms are available from the Advertising Production Club office or can be downloaded from the APC website; must submit a completed hard copy of the application form together with the registration receipt for the new semester, college transcript and acceptance letter; and must present an identification and confirmation by the high school principal. **Deadline:** March 1. **Contact:** Application form and all supporting documents should be mailed to Advertising Production Club Scholarship Fund, PO Box 382, New Hyde Park, NY 11040; E-mail: info@apcscholarshipfund.org.

59 ■ Advertising Production Club Scholarship Awards *(Graduate, Undergraduate/Scholarship)*

Purpose: To provide financial assistance to students pursuing a full-time graphic arts/communications degree. **Focus:** Graphic art and design; Communications. **Qualif.:** Applicant must be a resident of New York City metro area attending a graphic arts/communications degree program full-time in any college in the New York City metro area. **Criteria:** Preference will be given to those individuals who have not

Awards are arranged alphabetically below their administering organizations

previously been awarded a scholarship through the APC.

Funds Avail.: $500. Funds are applied to tuition expenses. **Number Awarded:** 4. **To Apply:** Guidelines and application forms are available from the Advertising Production Club office or can be downloaded from the APC website. Applicants must submit a completed hard copy application with the APC office together with registration receipt for the new semester, college transcript and acceptance letter. **Deadline:** October.

60 ■ APC Tuition-Assist Scholarship Awards
(Graduate, Undergraduate/Scholarship)

Purpose: To provide assistance to students with financial need. **Focus:** General studies. **Qualif.:** Applicant must be a resident of New York City metro area enrolled as a full-time student in an accredited degree-granting program in any college in the U.S. **Criteria:** Preference will be given to those individuals who have not previously been awarded a scholarship through the APC.

Funds Avail.: No specific amount. **To Apply:** Guidelines and application forms are available from the Advertising Production Club office or can be downloaded from the APC website. Applicants must submit a completed hard copy application with the APC office together with registration receipt for the new semester, college transcript and acceptance letter. **Deadline:** October.

61 ■ PGSF-GATF Scholarships *(Graduate, Undergraduate/Scholarship)*

Purpose: To provide financial assistance to students pursuing graphic communications careers. **Focus:** Graphic art and design; Communications. **Qualif.:** Applicant must be a resident of New York City metro area attending a graphic arts/communications degree program full-time in an accredited college in the U.S. **Criteria:** Preference will be given to those individuals who have not previously been awarded a scholarship through the APC.

Funds Avail.: Amount not specified. Funds are applied to tuition expenses. **Number Awarded:** 2. **To Apply:** Guidelines and application forms are available from the Advertising Production Club office or can be downloaded from the APC website. Applicants must submit a completed hard copy application with the APC office together with registration receipt for the new semester, college transcript and acceptance letter. **Contact:** Application form and supporting documents must be submitted to Advertising Production Club Scholarship Fund, 276 Bowery, NY 10012; Phone: 212431-4675; Fax: 212431-5786; E-mail: info@apcscholarshipfund.org.

62 ■ Advocates for the American Osteopathic Association (AAOA)
142 E Ontario St.
Chicago, IL 60611-2864
Ph: (312) 202-8192
Fax: (312) 202-8224
Free: 800-621-1773
E-mail: aaoa@osteopathic.org
URL: www.advocates4dos.org

63 ■ AOA Research Grants *(Graduate/Grant)*

Purpose: To improve American healthcare through the promotion of osteopathic medicine. **Focus:** Osteopathic. **Qualif.:** Applicants must be osteopathic physicians, holding a faculty or staff appointment at an AOA-accredited, affili-

ated, or approved osteopathic institution; or a biochemical researcher who demonstrates evidence of professional training and experience as appropriate for his/her individual discipline and who holds a faculty or staff appointment at an AOA accredited, affiliated or approved osteopathic institution; an osteopathic physician, holding a faculty or staff appointment at an academic or healthcare institution having accreditation, affiliation, or approval as appropriate for that institution's activities. **Criteria:** All awards are subject to final approval by the AOA Board of Trustees.

Funds Avail.: Will not exceed $50,000 per year. **To Apply:** Application forms are available at DO Online, under "Research and Grants" in both fillable form and PDF format. Applicants are encouraged to review all materials and instructions, and are invited to contact division staff if there are questions about the meaning of a specific provision in the application prior to submission. **Deadline:** December 1.

64 ■ Advocates' Society
1700-480 University Ave.
Toronto, ON, Canada M5G 1V2
Ph: (416) 597-0243
Fax: (416) 597-1588
E-mail: mail@advocates.ca
URL: www.advocates.ca

65 ■ Catzman Awards for Professionalism and Civility *(Professional development/Award)*

Purpose: To recognize individuals who have demonstrated a high degree of professionalism and civility in the practice of law. **Focus:** Law. **Qualif.:** Candidates must show professionalism and civility, and have made contributions to legal education. **Criteria:** Recipients will be selected based on submitted application.

Funds Avail.: Amount not specified. **To Apply:** Applicants must provide a brief statement outlining the reasons for the nomination, current curriculum vitae and two letters of support. **Deadline:** July 1. **Contact:** Electronic submissions should be forwarded to Sonia Holiad, Director of Communications at sonia@advocates.ca.

66 ■ David Stockwood Memorial Prize *(Professional development/Prize)*

Purpose: To honor individuals who made contributions to advocacy-ralated fields. **Focus:** General studies. **Qualif.:** Applicants must be the authors of a previously unpublished, advocacy-related article. **Criteria:** Papers will be evaluated based on their merit.

Funds Avail.: $1,000. **To Apply:** Articles must be a maximum of 3,500 words in length and should be submitted in Word format. **Deadline:** September 30. **Contact:** Electronic submissions should be forwarded to Sonia Holiad, Director of Communications at sonia@advocates.ca.

67 ■ Aerospace States Association (ASA)
107 S West St., Ste. 510
Alexandria, VA 22314
Ph: (202) 257-4872
Fax: (703) 548-8784
URL: aerostates.org

68 ■ Edward A. O'Connor Founder's Scholarships *(Undergraduate/Scholarship)*

Purpose: To help students pursue their education in an aerospace-related education. **Focus:** Aerospace sciences.

Awards are arranged alphabetically below their administering organizations

Qualif.: Applicants must be sophomore or junior undergraduate students pursuing an aerospace-related field. **Criteria:** Selection will be based on submitted materials.

Funds Avail.: $1,500. **Number Awarded:** 2. **To Apply:** Applicants must complete the application form; must submit a copy of official transcript; must submit a two-page, typed statement describing the educational career goals and interests, and how this can be related to aerospace fields; must also submit one letter of recommendation. **Deadline:** April 30. **Contact:** Dr. Stephanie Wright at 5 Essex Dr., Bear, DE 19701; E-mail: swright@udel.edu.

69 ■ AFL-CIO (UWUA) - Utility Workers Union of America (UWUA)

815 16th St. NW
Washington, DC 20006
Ph: (202) 974-8200
Fax: (202) 974-8201
Free: 888-843-8982
E-mail: webmaster@uwua.net
URL: uwua.net

70 ■ Utility Workers Union of America Scholarship Program *(Undergraduate/Scholarship)*

Purpose: To identify and honor exceptionally able high school students; to provide a system of services for corporations, foundations and other organizations that wish to sponsor college undergraduate scholarships for outstanding students who interest them. **Focus:** General studies. **Qualif.:** Applicants must be high school students who are sons and daughters of active members of UWUA; must be a U.S. citizens and have a permanent residence in the United States. **Criteria:** Recipients will be selected based on academic record throughout high school, significant activities and contributions to the school community, test scores, recommendations and the student's essay about personal characteristics, activities, plan and goals.

Funds Avail.: $500-$2,000. **To Apply:** Applicants must fill out the application form; must take the PSAT/NMSQT; must obtain a copy of the Official Student Guide to the PSAT/NMSQT from the high school counselor and make arrangements with the school to take the PSAT/NMSQT. **Deadline:** December 31.

71 ■ African American Success Foundation

7027 W Broward Blvd., Ste. 313
Fort Lauderdale, FL 33317
Ph: (954) 792-1117
E-mail: info@blacksuccessfoundation.org
URL: www.blacksuccessfoundation.org

72 ■ Lydia Donaldson Tutt-Jones Memorial Research Grant *(Graduate, Professional development/Grant)*

Purpose: To provide financial support to students and professionals who conduct research study of African American success, particularly in the area of education. **Focus:** African-American studies. **Qualif.:** Applicants must be graduate students and professionals. Students must be recommended by a faculty mentor who agrees to oversee the project and the submission of a publishable caliber paper upon its completion. **Criteria:** Selection will be based on the committee's criteria.

Funds Avail.: $3,000. **To Apply:** Applicants must submit

the following: a letter of interest in applying for the award; curriculum vitae; a description of the proposed research project (please give project a title) including a timeline; a letter of recommendation from their faculty mentor, if students, or from their department chairperson, agency head or officer of their professional association, if professionals. An original and five copies of the application materials should be submitted along with a stamped, self-addressed post card that will be used to acknowledge receipt of their application. **Deadline:** June. **Contact:** Cynthia Wilson, PhD, Chair, Grant Selection Committee at the above address.

73 ■ Agricultural Institute of Canada

9 Corvus Ct., Ste. 900
Ottawa, ON, Canada K2E 7Z4
Ph: (613) 232-9459
Fax: (613) 594-5190
Free: 888-277-7980
E-mail: office@aic.ca
URL: www.aic.ca

74 ■ Dr. Karl C. Ivarson Scholarships *(Postgraduate/Scholarship)*

Purpose: To support students pursuing studies in soil science. **Focus:** Soil Science. **Qualif.:** Applicants must hold Canadian citizenship or landed immigrant status; must be registered full-time in a master or doctorate program in the area of soil science. Applicants may pursue course electronically or by attending classes on campus. **Criteria:** Recipients are selected on the basis of scholastic ability, areas of study, leadership and career interests.

Funds Avail.: $3,000. **Number Awarded:** 2. **To Apply:** Applicants must submit an official transcript; and letter from the university confirming that their enrollment in current program are required. Application form and other required documents should be sent to Agricultural Institute of Canada Foundation, c/o Brenda Millar, 9 Corvus Court, Ottawa, Ontario K2E 7Z4. **Deadline:** November 4. **Contact:** Brenda Millar, aicf@aic.ca.

75 ■ Douglas McRorie Memorial Scholarships *(Postgraduate/Scholarship)*

Purpose: To provide financial support for post-graduate masters or PhD students specializing in agricultural business, economics, finance or trade. **Focus:** Agribusiness; Economics; Finance. **Qualif.:** Applicants must hold Canadian citizenship or landed immigrant status; must be postgraduates in the area of agricultural business, economics, finance or trade. **Criteria:** Selection will be based on the following criteria: agricultural post-graduate; emphasis in agricultural business/commerce/trade; strong academic record; good leadership potential; excellence in previous performance.

Funds Avail.: $1,500. **Number Awarded:** 6. **To Apply:** Applicants must submit a completed application form; official transcript of records; letter of enrollment verification; and letters of recommendation from faculty advisors. Application form and other required documents should be sent to Agricultural Institute of Canada Foundation, c/o Brenda Millar, 9 Corvus Court, Ottawa, Ontario K2E 7Z4. **Deadline:** March 2. **Contact:** Brenda Millar, aicf@aic.ca.

76 ■ Agriculture Future of America (AFA)

PO Box 414838
Kansas City, MO 64141

Awards are arranged alphabetically below their administering organizations

Ph: (816) 472-4232
Fax: (816) 472-4239
Free: 888-472-4232
E-mail: afa@agfuture.org
URL: www.agfuture.org

77 ■ Agriculture Future of America Community Scholarships *(Undergraduate/Scholarship)*

Purpose: To support local students preparing for a career in the agriculture and food industry. **Focus:** Agricultural economics. **Qualif.:** Applicants must be graduating high school seniors planning to pursue a bachelor's degree in an agriculture-related program. **Criteria:** Recipients are selected based on an interview; an essay of 300-500 words describing the student's perception on the future of agriculture; community service; study group activities; general factors; GPA of 3.0/4.0.

Funds Avail.: No specific amount. **To Apply:** Applicants must contact AFA to request an application form.

78 ■ Agriculture Future of America Scholarship Program *(Undergraduate/Scholarship)*

Purpose: To support academic development through partnerships with rural communities, agriculture organizations, colleges and universities. **Focus:** Agricultural economics. **Qualif.:** Applicants must be students who plan to pursue a four year degree in an agriculture-related field. **Criteria:** Recipients are selected based on academic performance.

Funds Avail.: No specific amount. **To Apply:** Applicants must contact AFA to request an application form.

79 ■ AGS Foundation for Health in Aging (FHA)

40 Fulton St., 18th Fl.
New York, NY 10038
Ph: (212) 308-1414
Fax: (212) 832-8646
Free: 800-563-4916
URL: www.healthinaging.org

80 ■ Hartford Geriatrics Health Outcomes Research Scholars Award Program *(Professional development/Grant)*

Purpose: To support physician-scientists committed to improving the health care of older adults during the critical transition from junior faculty to independent researcher. **Focus:** Geriatric medicine. **Qualif.:** Applicant must: have an MD or DO degree; hold a full-time faculty appointment at the level of assistant professor for no longer than two years at the time the grant becomes effective; demonstrate motivation and ability to devote the majority (75%) of his/her time to conduct research with the goal of devoting his/her research career to this area; be either: (1) a geriatrician or geriatric psychiatrist who has completed all of the requirements to be eligible to sit for a Certificate of Added Qualifications by the time the award commences, or (2) a general internist, family physician, neurologist, or subspecialist of internal medicine who is pursuing a career devoted to aging research and who has completed all the requirements to be eligible to sit for Board Certification in his/her discipline; have at least two years of prior experience; have a primary sponsor who is committed to providing guidance and collaboration throughout the course of the proposed project; and be a citizen or a lawfully admitted permanent resident of the United States. **Criteria:** Selection is based

on potential of applicant to become an independently funded investigator; applicant's commitment to an academic research career devoted to improving the care of older adults; scientific merit of the research proposal; likelihood that the research proposal will lead to future funded research projects; impact of the proposed project on the applicant's career; evidence of the primary sponsor's commitment to the applicant; training plan provided by the sponsor; and the applicant's institutional commitment to the area of research outlined in the research proposal.

Funds Avail.: $200,000. **Number Awarded:** Up to 4. **To Apply:** Applicants may request an application online. **Remarks:** Sponsored by The John A. Hartford Foundation, in collaboration with the AGS Foundation for Health in Aging. **Contact:** long@americangeriatrics.org.

81 ■ T. Franklin Williams Research Scholars Award Program *(Professional development/Grant)*

Purpose: To support the academic career development of a promising geriatrics physician-scientist. **Focus:** Geriatric medicine. **Qualif.:** Applicant must have an MD or DO degree; be within four years of the first faculty appointment at the time the grant becomes effective; must devote 75% of his/her time to conduct research with 40% specifically devoted to this project; be an internal medicine geriatrician who has completed all of the requirements to be eligible to sit for a Certificate of Added Qualifications by the time the award commences; have at least two sponsors committed to providing guidance and collaboration throughout the course of the proposed project (at least one sponsor should represent geriatrics and at least one sponsor should represent a subspecialty of internal medicine); and must be a citizen or a lawfully admitted permanent resident of the United States. **Criteria:** Selection is based on the qualifications of the applicant; impact of the proposed project on the applicant's career; the applicant's commitment to an academic research career devoted to improving the care of older adults; scientific merit of the research proposal and its relevance to improving subspecialty care of older adults; evidence of the sub-specialty and geriatrics sponsors' commitment to the applicant as well as the sponsors' experience in research and training in the applicant's area of research interest; and commitment of the applicant's institution to supporting the career development of the junior faculty member.

Funds Avail.: $75,000. **Number Awarded:** 1. **To Apply:** Applicants may request for an application online. **Contact:** Li-Chia Ong at long@americangeriatrics.org.

82 ■ Aha Punana Leo

96 Pu'uhonu Pl.
Hilo, HI 96720
Ph: (808) 935-4304
Fax: (808) 969-7512
E-mail: contact@ahapunanaleo.org
URL: www.ahapunanaleo.org

83 ■ Lamaku Post-Secondary Scholarships *(Undergraduate/Scholarship)*

Purpose: To support native Hawaiians in their pursuit of post-secondary education. **Focus:** General studies. **Qualif.:** Applicant must show proof of Hawaiian ancestry; must be a United States citizen residing in the State of Hawaii; must show proof of a high school diploma or equivalent. Students in Bachelor degree programs must satisfactorily complete four years of Hawaiian language, which is

Awards are arranged alphabetically below their administering organizations

required for entrance into the Hawaiian Medium Teacher Certification Program. Undergraduate students and Hawaiian Medium Teacher Certification students are expected to maintain a cumulative GPA of at least 2.75 and at least 3.0 in Post-Baccalaureate students. **Criteria:** Selection will be based on the submitted application.

Funds Avail.: No specific amount. **To Apply:** Applicants may apply online or download an application from the website. Applicants must submit a personal essay stating goals and contributions related to the Native Hawaiian Medium Education; letter of recommendation from a family member or a non-family member showing the applicant's interest and goals in Native Hawaiian Medium Education. **Deadline:** March 1. **Contact:** lamaku@ahapunanaleo.org.

84 ■ Ahepa Buckeye Scholarship Foundation

6437 Tylers Crossing
West Chester, OH 45069
Ph: (513) 779-0842
URL: www.ahepadistrict11.org

85 ■ Ahepa Buckeye Scholarship Awards
(Undergraduate/Scholarship)

Purpose: To provide financial assistance to deserving students entering college or in undergraduate school. **Focus:** General studies. **Qualif.:** Applicant must be an active member of the AHEPA, Daughters of Penelope, Sons of Pericles, Maids of Athena, or whose parent(s) have been active members of the Senior Orders for three consecutive years. **Criteria:** Recipient is selected based on scholastic achievement and financial need.

Funds Avail.: No amount mentioned. **To Apply:** Applicant must submit the completed application form along with a verification of eligibility, high school or college transcript and letter of recommendation from the counselor, principal, or other appropriate school official. **Contact:** Applications and related materials should be mailed to AHEPA Buckeye Scholarship Foundation, 25590 W County Line Rd., Sunman, IN 47041.

86 ■ Air Force Association (AFA)

1501 Lee Hwy.
Arlington, VA 22209-1198
Ph: (703) 247-5800
Fax: (703) 247-5853
Free: 800-727-3337
E-mail: membership@afa.org
URL: www.afa.org

87 ■ AFROTC Scholarships *(Undergraduate/Scholarship)*

Purpose: To educate the public about the critical role of aerospace power in the defense of the nation. **Focus:** Aerospace Sciences. **Qualif.:** Applicants must be current Air Force ROTC cadets in good standing, enrolled full-time as incoming juniors or seniors for the academic year; and must be committed to studying in the fields of science, technology, engineering or math. **Criteria:** Selection of the recipients must be made by a selection board. The selection board must consider a combination of both academic merit and financial need. AFROTC will verify the applicant's financial need. AFROTC may select a prior award winner to receive this scholarship. AFROTC will make arrangements and at their expense, make the cadets available to

receive their scholarship at the Air Force Associations' Air and Space Conference and Technology Exhibition. Cadets must appear in uniform to receive their scholarship.

Funds Avail.: $5,000. **Number Awarded:** 2. **To Apply:** Applicants must submit complete application package to Captain Douglas Huttenlocker. **Contact:** Lieutenant Thomas Brannen; thomas.brannen@maxwell.af.mil.

88 ■ Air Force Association Excellence Scholarships *(Graduate, Master's, Undergraduate/Scholarship)*

Purpose: To educate the public about the critical role of aerospace power in the defense of the nation. **Focus:** Science; Technology; Engineering; Mathematics and mathematical sciences. **Qualif.:** Applicants must be enrolled or planning to enroll, full-time or part-time in an undergraduate or graduate program of studies leading to an associate's, bachelor's or master's degree at an accredited college or university. **Criteria:** Scholarship is given based on the committee's criteria and applicant's eligibility.

Funds Avail.: $3,000. **Number Awarded:** 5. **To Apply:** Applicants must submit completed scholarship application form and three essays to the Air Force Association. **Deadline:** April 30. **Contact:** Lynette Cross at 703-247-5800 Ext. 4807; fax: 703-247-5853; or lcross@afa.org.

89 ■ Air Force Association/Grantham Scholarships *(Undergraduate/Scholarship)*

Purpose: To promote aerospace education, specifically the study of science, mathematics and technology. **Focus:** Aerospace Sciences. **Qualif.:** Candidates must have a high school diploma or GED and must be members of AFA or their dependents. **Criteria:** Selection will be based on the committee's criteria.

Funds Avail.: $36,000. **To Apply:** Applicants must submit a completed application form; a two-page, double-spaced essay describing the applicant's academic and career goals and explaining why he/she is interested in pursuing his/her degree via an online degree program, an explanation why this is the right time in the applicant's life and why he/she would be committed to continuing his/her education to get a degree; two letters of recommendation (These should be character references with descriptions of the applicant's performance and his/her potential as a student); and proof of GED completion or high school transcripts (or college transcripts if applicable). College transcript(s) and proof of undergraduate degree are required for the graduate programs. Applicants will be required to provide the information requested on a feedback form six months after the scholarship is awarded. **Deadline:** June 15. **Contact:** Lynette Cross at the above address.

90 ■ Air Force Association Spouse Scholarships *(Undergraduate/Scholarship)*

Purpose: To encourage Air Force spouses worldwide to pursue associates/bachelor undergraduate or graduate/postgraduate degrees. **Focus:** Aerospace. **Qualif.:** Applicants must be spouses of Air Force Active Duty, Air National Guard or Air Force Reserve. Spouses who are themselves Air Force members, or in ROTC, are not eligible. **Criteria:** Selection will be based on the committee's criteria and applicant's eligibility.

Funds Avail.: $2,500. **To Apply:** Applicants must include the following in their application: an original or copy of the most recent college/university transcript or a report card from the applicant's last semester verifying his/her minimum

---

Awards are arranged alphabetically below their administering organizations

3.5 GPA or higher; proof of acceptance into a regionally accredited community college/ college/ university (this may consist of a short letter on college/university stationery from either the admissions office or the registrar); a two-page double-spaced essay, describing the applicant's academic and career goals and the motivation which led him/her to this decision and describing how Air Force and other local community activities in which he/she is involved will enhance his/her goals; two letters of recommendation (should be character references and descriptions of performance and potential as a student, employee or volunteer); a letter of endorsement from the local AFA Chapter would be welcomed and encouraged (the two letters must be from the different sources). Letters from previous or present professors, employers and volunteer organizations referencing the work the applicant has done are encouraged. **Deadline:** April 30.

91 ■ Jodi Callahan Memorial Scholarships
(Undergraduate/Scholarship)

Purpose: To provide scholarships for active duty of Air Force, full-time Air National Guard or full-time Air Force Reserve. **Focus:** Aerospace Sciences. **Qualif.:** Applicants must be enrolled in the current or upcoming semester with a minimum of 3 credit hours or the equivalent. Proof of acceptance may consist of a short letter on college/university stationery from either the admissions office or the registrar. A minimum Grade Point Average of 3.0 is required. **Criteria:** Selection will be based on the committee's criteria.

Funds Avail.: $1,000. **To Apply:** Applicants must complete both online portion and mail required documents by the deadline to be considered: one letter of recommendation from the Air Force supervisor or commander; proof of acceptance into an accredited college/university; and proof of Grade Point Average. Applicant's essay should describe academic goals and how he/she expects his/her degree to enhance his/her service to the Air Force. The letter of recommendation should include a character reference, a description of applicant's performance and an assessment of his/her potential as an Air Force leader and volunteer. **Deadline:** June 30. **Contact:** Lynetter Cross 800-727-3337 ext. 4807.

92 ■ Lt. Colonel Romeo and Josephine Bass Ferretti Scholarships *(Undergraduate/ Scholarship)*

Purpose: To provide educational assistance for graduating high school students. **Focus:** Science; Technology; Engineering. **Qualif.:** Applicants must be in their final year of high school and must be entering an accredited institute of higher learning. Applicants must state an intent to study in the area of science, technology, engineering or math. **Criteria:** Selection will be based on the committee's criteria.

Funds Avail.: $2,500. **Number Awarded:** 2. **To Apply:** Applicants must submt a completed application form, a two-page essay dscribing the academic achievements and goals, one letter of recommendation, an official and original high school transcript, proof of acceptance and a photo. **Contact:** Lynette Cross, lcross@afa.org.

93 ■ Pitsenbarger Awards *(Undergraduate/ Scholarship)*

Purpose: To provide a one-time grant to selected top USAF enlisted personnel. **Focus:** Aerospace Sciences. **Qualif.:** Applicants must be USAF personnel and graduating from the Community College of the Air Force (CCAF) who plan to pursue a baccalaureate degree. **Criteria:** Recipient

selection is determined at the base level by a committee of the Base Education Officer, Senior Enlisted Advisor and a local Air Force Association (AFA) representative. Committee considers job performance, scholastic achievement, educational goals and leadership qualities. Total achievements will be carefully considered by the selection committee.

Funds Avail.: $400. **To Apply:** Applicants must complete the application form; must submit a proof of current enrollment or intent to enroll in an accredited program leading to baccalaureate degree; citations and awards representing activities and narrave statement describing the extracurricular activities. **Contact:** lcross@afa.org.

94 ■ Air Force Sergeants Association
5211 Auth Rd.
Suitland, MD 20746
Ph: (301) 899-3500
Fax: (301) 899-8136
Free: 800-638-0594
E-mail: staff@hqafsa.org
URL: www.hqafsa.org

95 ■ Air Force Sergeants Association Scholarship Program *(Undergraduate/Scholarship)*

Purpose: To financially assist the undergraduate studies of eligible, dependent children of the Air Force Sergeants Association. **Focus:** General studies. **Qualif.:** Applicants must be dependent youth of AFSA or AFSA Auxillary members and must be students attending an accreited academic institution. **Criteria:** Recipients are selected based on applicant's academic record, character, leadership skills, writing ability, versatility and potential for success.

Funds Avail.: $500-$3,000. **To Apply:** Applicants must submit a completed application form; a copy of proof of sponsor's military status (copy of DD 214, copy of the sponsor's ID and discharge letter); official transcript of grades (high school graduates must include all grades from 9th to 12th grades, college applicants must include cumulative record of grades); a letter of recommendation written on the official school stationary with original signature (for high school graduate, letter must be written by the school principal or counselor; for college student, letter must be written by a college professor); a typed paragraph of the applicant's objectives (double-spaced) answering the question, "What do you plan to do with the education you receive?"; essay (double-spaced) answering the question, "What is the most urgent problem facing society today?" and a typed, double-spaced two-page essay about a current, controversial issue; two self-addressed, stamped, blank postcards. High school graduates must include a valid record of combined SAT I or ACT scores (must be recorded on an official school transcript). **Deadline:** March 31. **Contact:** AFSA/CMSAF/AMF Scholarship Program, 5211 Auth Rd., Suitland, MD 20746.

96 ■ Air Force Sergeants Association-Chapter 155 (AFSA)
419 Ocean Rd.
Portsmouth, NH 03801-6020
Ph: (603) 498-0135
URL: www.afsa155.org

97 ■ AFSA Chapter 155 Division 1 Scholarships - Category 1 *(Undergraduate/Scholarship)*

Purpose: To enhance education opportunities for AFSA members and their families. **Focus:** General studies. **Qua-**

Awards are arranged alphabetically below their administering organizations

lif.: Applicants must be graduating high school senior entering 1st year college, whose parents, grandparents and/or guardians are current members of AFSA/Auxiliary; have a GPA of 3.0. **Criteria:** Recipients are selected based on their submitted applications.

Funds Avail.: $500. **Number Awarded:** 1. **To Apply:** Applicants must submit a completed application form (available at the website) and a 5"x7" photograph. **Deadline:** April 15. **Contact:** Clifford Wittman, SMSgt., 1617 Santa Fe St., Schenectady, NY 12303; Email: wittmancm@yahoo.com.

98 ■ AFSA Chapter 155 Division 1 Scholarships - Category 2 *(Undergraduate/Scholarship)*

Purpose: To enhance education opportunities for AFSA members and their families. **Focus:** General studies. **Qualif.:** Applicants must be 2nd, 3rd and 4th year college students up to 26 years age, whose parents, grandparents and/or guardians are current members of AFSA/Auxiliary; have a GPA of 3.0. **Criteria:** Recipients are selected based on their submitted applications.

Funds Avail.: $500. **Number Awarded:** 1. **To Apply:** Applicants must submit a completed application form (available at the website) and a 5"x7" photograph. **Deadline:** April 15. **Contact:** Clifford Wittman, SMSgt., 1617 Santa Fe St., Schenectady, NY 12303; Email: wittmancm@yahoo.com.

99 ■ AFSA Chapter 155 Division 1 Scholarships - Category 3 *(Undergraduate/Scholarship)*

Purpose: To enhance education opportunities for AFSA members and their families. **Focus:** General studies. **Qualif.:** Applicants must be AFSA/Auxiliary members seeking to complete advanced schooling at a credited college or trade school; must have a GPA of 2.0. **Criteria:** Recipients are selected based on their submitted applications.

Funds Avail.: $500. **Number Awarded:** 1. **To Apply:** Applicants must submit a completed application form (available at the website) and a 5"x7" photograph. **Deadline:** April 15. **Contact:** Clifford Wittman, SMSgt., 1617 Santa Fe St., Schenectady, NY 12303; Email: wittmancm@yahoo.com.

100 ■ Master Sergeant Neal E. Powers Memorial Scholarships *(Undergraduate/Scholarship)*

Purpose: To enhance education opportunities for AFSA members and their families. **Focus:** General studies. **Qualif.:** Applicants must be members or dependents of members of Chapter 155/A155; accepted and will be entering first post secondary education program. **Criteria:** Recipients are selected based on their submitted applications.

Funds Avail.: $500. **Number Awarded:** 2. **To Apply:** Applicants must submit a completed application form (available at the website). **Deadline:** April 15. **Contact:** Susan L. Williams, Scholarship Chair, 419 Ocean Rd. Portsmouth, NH 03801-6020.

101 ■ Master Sergeant William Sowers Memorial Scholarships *(Undergraduate/Scholarship)*

Purpose: To enhance education opportunities for AFSA members and their families. **Focus:** General studies. **Qualif.:** Applicants must be members or dependents of members of Chapter 155/A155; enrolled in an accredited institution and have completed at least one semester or term. **Criteria:** Recipients are selected based on their submitted applications.

Funds Avail.: $500. **Number Awarded:** 2. **To Apply:** Applicants must submit a completed application form (available at the website). **Deadline:** April 15. **Contact:** Susan L. Williams, Scholarship Chair, 419 Ocean Rd. Portsmouth, NH 03801-6020.

102 ■ Air Traffic Control Association (ATCA)

1101 King St., Ste. 300
Alexandria, VA 22314
Ph: (703) 299-2430
Fax: (703) 299-2437
E-mail: info@atca.org
URL: www.atca.org

103 ■ Air Traffic Control Association Full-time Employee Student Scholarships *(Professional development/Scholarship)*

Purpose: To provide financial assistance to full-time employees enrolled in advanced study programs that enhance employee's skills in aviation-related position. **Focus:** Aviation; Traffic management. **Qualif.:** Applicants must have attendance equal to at least half-time (6 semester hours or the equivalent) and a minimum of 30 semester or 45 hours still to be completed before graduation; must be enrolled or accepted in a two-year or greater air traffic control program at an institution approved and/or listed by the Federal Aviation Administration as directly supporting the FAA's college training initiative; must be enrolled or accepted in an accredited college or university and planning to continue the following academic year; must be enrolled in course work related to his/her aviation-related career and leading to a bachelor's degree or greater; must be engaged in full-time employment in an aviation-related field; must be enrolled in course work designed to enhance the applicant's skill in an air traffic control or other aviation-related discipline. **Criteria:** Recipient will be selected by the Scholarship Selection Committee based on set of criteria.

Funds Avail.: No amount mentioned. **To Apply:** Applicants must provide two letters of recommendation (from present or previous teachers, professors, instructors, supervisors, or managers) from within the last 12 months; submit certified transcript of all college coursework. If less than 30 semester or 45 quarter hours of college coursework have been completed, all high school transcripts are also required, work or experience that supports the applicant's educational and/or aviation career goals must be addressed in the application and/or essay; financial need must be addressed in the application and/or essay; submit a paper on the subject, "How My Education Efforts Will Enhance My Potential Contribution To Aviation." which should be typed, doubled spaced, 400 words maximum. **Deadline:** May 1. **Contact:** Brian Courter, brian.courter@atca.org.

104 ■ Air Traffic Control Association Non-employee Student Scholarships *(Undergraduate/Scholarship)*

Purpose: To provide financial assistance to students enrolled in an aviation related program of study leading to a bachelor's degree or greater. **Focus:** Aviation. **Qualif.:** Applicants must have attendance equal to at least half-time (6 semester hours or the equivalent) and a minimum of 30 semester or 45 hours still to be completed before graduation; must be enrolled or accepted in a two-year or greater air traffic control program at an institution approved and/or listed by the Federal Aviation Administration as directly

Awards are arranged alphabetically below their administering organizations

supporting the FAA's college training initiative; must be enrolled or accepted in an accredited college or university and planning to continue the following academic year; must be enrolled in course work related to his/her aviation-related career and leading to a bachelor's degree or greater; must be engaged in full-time employment in an aviation-related field; must be enrolled in course work designed to enhance the applicant's skill in an air traffic control or other aviation-related discipline. **Criteria:** Recipient will be selected by the Scholarship Selection Committee based on set of criteria.

Funds Avail.: No amount mentioned. **To Apply:** Applicants must provide two letters of recommendation (from present or previous teachers, professors, instructors, supervisors, or managers) from within the last 12 months; submit certified transcript of all college coursework. If less than 30 semester or 45 quarter hours of college coursework have been completed, all high school transcripts are also required, work or experience that supports the applicant's educational and/or aviation career goals must be addressed in the application and/or essay; financial need must be addressed in the application and/or essay; submit a paper on the subject, "How My Education Efforts Will Enhance My Potential Contribution To Aviation." which should be typed, doubled spaced, 400 words maximum. **Deadline:** May 1. **Contact:** Brian Courter, brian.courter@atca.org.

105 ■ Gabe A. Hartl Scholarships
(Undergraduate/Scholarship)

Purpose: To provide financial assistance to students enrolled in air traffic control curriculum at FAA approved institution. **Focus:** Traffic management. **Qualif.:** Applicants must have attendance equal to at least half-time (6 semester hours or the equivalent) and a minimum of 30 semester or 45 hours still to be completed before graduation; must be enrolled or accepted in a two-year or greater air traffic control program at an institution approved and/or listed by the Federal Aviation Administration as directly supporting the FAA's college training initiative; must be enrolled or accepted in an accredited college or university and planning to continue the following academic year; must be enrolled in course work related to his/her aviation-related career and leading to a bachelor's degree or greater; must be engaged in full-time employment in an aviation-related field; must be enrolled in course work designed to enhance the applicant's skill in an air traffic control or other aviation-related disciplines. **Criteria:** Recipient will be selected by the Scholarship Selection Committee based on this set of criteria.

Funds Avail.: No amount mentioned. **To Apply:** Applicants must provide two letters of recommendation (from present or previous teachers, professors, instructors, supervisors, or managers) from within the last 12 months; submit certified transcript of all college coursework. If less than 30 semester or 45 quarter hours of college coursework have been completed, all high school transcripts are also required, work or experience that supports the applicant's educational and/or aviation career goals must be addressed in the application and/or essay; financial need must be addressed in the application and/or essay; submit a paper on the subject, "How My Education Efforts Will Enhance My Potential Contribution To Aviation." which should be typed, doubled spaced, 400 words maximum. **Deadline:** May 1. **Contact:** Brian Courter, brian.courter@atca.org.

106 ■ Air and Waste Management Association (A&WMA)
1 Gateway Ctr., 3rd Fl.
420 Ft. Duquesne Blvd.
Pittsburgh, PA 15222-1435
Ph: (412) 232-3444
Fax: (412) 232-3450
Free: 800-270-3444
E-mail: info@awma.org
URL: www.awma.org

107 ■ A&WMA Scholarships *(Graduate/ Scholarship)*

Purpose: To promote education in air quality and waste management. **Focus:** Air pollution; Waste management; Environmental law. **Qualif.:** Applicant must be a full-time graduate student pursuing courses of study and research leading to careers in air quality, waste management, environmental management/policy/law and/or sustainability. **Criteria:** Selection is based on the application materials submitted.

Funds Avail.: $2,500-$7,500. **To Apply:** Applicants are required to create a scholarship account online, and upload supporting documents. **Deadline:** January 3.

108 ■ Air and Waste Management Association - Genesee Finger Lakes Chapter (GFLC-A&WMA)
PO Box 92006
Rochester, NY 14692
Ph: (585) 388-1040
E-mail: info@gflawma.com
URL: www.awmanfs.org/gfl.htm

109 ■ GFLC-A&WMA Scholarships *(Graduate, Undergraduate/Scholarship)*

Purpose: To promote environmental awareness and education. **Focus:** Environmental science. **Qualif.:** Applicant must be an undergraduate or graduate student in an environmental engineering, environmental science or environmental management program attending a recognized college/university located within the New York counties of Allegany, Chemung, Genesee, Livingston, Monroe, Orleans, Schuyler, Seneca, Steuben, Wyoming or Yates. **Criteria:** Award is given based on academic records, leadership in academics and in the community and future academic and career potential.

Funds Avail.: $2,500. **Number Awarded:** 1. **To Apply:** Applicants must submit a completed scholarship application form along with two most recent academic transcripts. **Contact:** Jim Carpenter at the above address.

110 ■ Air and Waste Management Association - Golden West Section (A&WMA-GWS)
c/o John Koehler
AECOM Environment
2101 Webster St., Ste. 1900
Oakland, CA 94612
Ph: (510) 847-9747
E-mail: info@awma-gws.org
URL: awma-gws.baaqmd.gov

111 ■ A&WMA-GWS Scholarships *(Graduate, Undergraduate/Scholarship)*
Purpose: To promote better understanding of problems in the fields of air pollution and hazardous waste manage-

Awards are arranged alphabetically below their administering organizations

ment within the geographic area and to provide a means for exchanging information directed toward solving those problems. **Focus:** Atmospheric science; Environmental science; Air pollution; Waste management; Water resources; Toxicology; Public health. **Qualif.:** Applicant must be a graduate or undergraduate student accepted into a full-time program pursuing courses of study and/or research leading to careers ranging from atmospheric science, environmental science and engineering, air pollution, waste management and water resources to toxicology and public health; must be attending a college/university in the Section's geographic area. **Criteria:** Awards will be given based on academic record and career goals. Consideration may also be given to financial need.

Funds Avail.: Up to $3,500. **Number Awarded:** 1 or more. **To Apply:** Applicants must submit a completed scholarship application together with the statement of professional goals; transcripts/grade point average; a resume/work experience and letters of recommendation. Application package must be submitted in duplicate (do not staple duplicate copy). **Deadline:** December 31. **Contact:** Wileen Sweet-Dodge at 650-520-8039, email: wsweetdodge@yahoo.com.

112 ■ Air and Waste Management Association - Louisiana Section

c/o Carol Murphy, Facilities Chair
PO Box 640608
Kenner, LA 70064
Ph: (504) 472-9993
Fax: (504) 472-9963
E-mail: karen.blakemore@phelps.com
URL: la-awma.org

113 ■ A&WMA Louisiana Section Scholarships
(Graduate, Undergraduate/Scholarship)

Purpose: To promote education in air quality and waste management. **Focus:** Engineering; Physical sciences; Natural sciences; Public health. **Qualif.:** Applicant must be a full-time student attending a college/university located within the geographical area of the Louisiana section; at least a junior (undergraduate) and no higher than a master's level graduate student; must have at least two semesters (or three quarters) of schooling remaining at the time of the award; pursuing a bachelors or master's degree with a major in engineering, physical or natural science, or public health; show through course work, projects, personal interest, etc. a desire to promote air pollution control and/or solid or hazardous waste management and must have at least an overall "B" average (3.00 or higher on a scale of 4.00) including all course work through the last completed semester. **Criteria:** Awards will be made based on academic record, plan of study, career goals, recommendations, and financial status.

Funds Avail.: $1,000 or more, and one year student membership in the Air & Waste Management Association. **Number Awarded:** 2 or more. **To Apply:** Applicants must submit a completed General Application Information Sheet together with a 1-2 page resume; 1-2 page interest and award statement; current transcripts; letter or recommendation from a major professor or department head (envelope should be signed across) and a list of current financial awards. **Deadline:** March 30. **Contact:** Karen J. Blakemore, PO Box 4412, Baton Rouge, LA 70821-4412.

114 ■ Air and Waste Management Association - Niagara Frontier Section (AWMA-NFS)
PO Box 384
Williamsville, NY 14231
Ph: (716) 684-8060
E-mail: bwattle@ene.com
URL: www.awmanfs.org

115 ■ AWMA Niagara Frontier Section College Scholarships *(Graduate, Undergraduate/Scholarship)*

Purpose: To support students in their educational pursuits. **Focus:** General studies. **Qualif.:** Applicant must be a full time undergraduate or graduate student attending a recognized college/university located within the NY State counties (Allegany, Cattaraugus, Chautauqua, Erie, Niagara and Wyoming). A child or spouse of a current member is eligible to apply. **Criteria:** Selection is based on applicant's environmental interests, academic record, leadership in school and the community, future academic and career potential, without consideration of sex, race, national origin, financial need, age or physical disability.

Funds Avail.: $500-$1,000. **Number Awarded:** Varies. **To Apply:** Applicants must submit a completed application form (Section I, Section II, and Section III) along with grade transcripts. **Deadline:** March. **Contact:** Submit completed application form and all required attachments to Mr. Paul Van Kerkhove, Ecology & Environment Inc., 368 Pleasant View Dr., Lancaster, New York 14086; Phone: 716-684-8060; Fax: 716-684-0844; E-mail: pvankerkhove@ene.com.

116 ■ Dave Sauer Memorial College Scholarships *(Undergraduate/Scholarship)*

Purpose: To support students in their educational pursuits. **Focus:** General studies. **Qualif.:** Applicant must be a high school senior in good academic standing, attending a recognized high school located within the New York State counties (Allegany, Cattaraugus, Chautauqua, Erie, Niagara or Wyoming) and will attend a recognized college/university. **Criteria:** Selection is based on academic record, leadership in school and community activities and future academic and career potential, without consideration of sex, race, religion, national origin, financial need, age or physical disability.

Funds Avail.: $500-$1,000. **Number Awarded:** Varies. **To Apply:** Applicants must submit a completed application form (Sections I through IV) together with a high school transcript(s) covering the sophomore and junior years. **Deadline:** March. **Contact:** Submit completed application form and all required attachments to Mr. Paul Van Kerkhove, Ecology & Environment Inc., 368 Pleasant View Dr., Lancaster, New York 14086; Phone: 716-684-8060; Fax: 716-684-0844; E-mail: pvankerkhove@ene.com.

117 ■ Air and Waste Management Association - Northern and Central New Jersey Chapter (A&WMA NCNJ)
c/o Mr. Jerry Marcus
Stonehenge Associates, LLC
304 Highland Ave.
Upper Montclair, NJ 07043
Ph: (973) 746-2372
E-mail: jaziem@aol.com
URL: www.mass-awma.net/NCNJ.html

Awards are arranged alphabetically below their administering organizations

118 ■ A&WMA NCNJ Chapter Scholarships
(Graduate, Undergraduate/Scholarship)

Purpose: To encourage qualified students to enter careers in environmental science. **Focus:** Environmental science; Environmental technology. **Qualif.:** Applicant must be a full-time (9 credits or more) undergraduate college student; pursuing courses of study leading to a career (or post-graduate study) in the environmental sciences/engineering or environmental management or related fields; a resident of New Jersey within the chapter area (Northern and Central New Jersey); or attending a college/university within the chapter area. **Criteria:** Selection is based on the application materials submitted for review.

Funds Avail.: $500-$1,000. **Number Awarded:** 2. **To Apply:** Applicants must submit a complete the application form or a copy of the applicant's resume, along with college transcript; letter of recommendation; and one page essay on the applicant's experience and interest in environmental issues. **Deadline:** April 25.

119 ■ Air and Waste Management Association - Southern Section (SSAWMA)
c/o Justice A. Manning
133 Rolling Hill Dr.
Daphne, AL 36526
Ph: (251) 625-0513
E-mail: jmanning1@bellsouth.net
URL: www.ss-awma.org

120 ■ SSAWMA Scholarships *(Graduate/Scholarship)*

Purpose: To assist students pursuing careers in the areas of air and water pollution control and hazardous waste management. **Focus:** Air pollution; Waste management; Environmental law. **Qualif.:** Applicants must be pursuing a graduate-level course of study and research leading to a career related to air or water quality, waste management, pollution prevention, environmental policy/compliance/law, or sustainability. **Criteria:** Awards will be given based on academic records and career goals.

Funds Avail.: $1,500. **Number Awarded:** 3. **To Apply:** Applicants must submit a completed scholarship application form along with the statement of professional goals, transcripts, verification of graduate school attendance, TOEFL or MELAB scores (optional), professional or non-professional work experience and two letters of recommendation. Submit application package in duplicate (must be clipped, not stapled). **Deadline:** June 15. **Remarks:** Recipients are encouraged to be student members of the Southern Section of A&WMA or environmental professionals returning to school for graduate study. **Contact:** Justice Manning at the above address.

121 ■ Aircraft Electronics Association (AEA)
3570 NE Ralph Powell Rd.
Lee's Summit, MO 64064
Ph: (816) 347-8400
Fax: (816) 347-8405
E-mail: info@aea.net
URL: www.aea.net

122 ■ Aircraft Owners and Pilots Association Scholarships *(Undergraduate/Scholarship)*
Purpose: To provide support to individuals intending to pursue their career in aircraft electronics and aviation maintenance industry. **Focus:** Aviation. **Qualif.:** Applicants must be high school seniors and/or college students planning to or attending an accredited school in an avionics or aircraft repair program. **Criteria:** Selection of candidates will be based on their application materials.

Funds Avail.: $2,000. **To Apply:** Applicants are advised to contact the foundation for application forms and other required materials. **Deadline:** February 15.

123 ■ David Arver Memorial Scholarships
(Undergraduate/Scholarship)

Purpose: To provide support for individuals intending to pursue their career in aircraft electronics and aviation maintenance industry. **Focus:** Aviation. **Qualif.:** Applicants must be high school seniors and/or college students planning to or attend an accredited school in an avionics or aircraft repair program. **Criteria:** Selection of candidates will be based on their application materials.

Funds Avail.: $1,000. **To Apply:** Applicants must submit the completed application form; official transcript of grades; one 300-word essay. **Deadline:** February 15. **Remarks:** Scholarship given by Dutch and Ginger Arver in memory of their son, David. Dutch Arver was a strong supporter of the AEA for many years and served on the board of Directors until his retirement.

124 ■ Dutch and Ginger Arver Scholarships
(Undergraduate/Scholarship)

Purpose: To provide support to individuals intending to pursue their career in aircraft electronics and aviation maintenance industry. **Focus:** Aviation. **Qualif.:** Applicants must be seniors and/or college students planning to attend an accredited school in an avionics or aircraft repair program. **Criteria:** Selection of candidates will be based on the criteria of the scholarship committee.

Funds Avail.: $1,000. **To Apply:** Applicants must submit the completed application form; official transcript of grades; one 300-word essay. **Deadline:** February 15.

125 ■ Johnny Davis Memorial Scholarships
(Undergraduate/Scholarship)

Purpose: To provide support to individuals intending to pursue their career in aircraft electronics and aviation maintenance industry. **Focus:** Aviation. **Qualif.:** Applicants must be high school seniors and/or college students planning to or attending an accredited school in an avionics or aircraft repair program. **Criteria:** Selection of candidates will be based on their application materials.

Funds Avail.: $1,000. **To Apply:** Applicants are advised to contact the foundation for application forms and other required materials. **Deadline:** February 15. **Remarks:** Scholarship is named in memory of Johnny Davis, president of Dallas Avionics, Dallas, Texas, who supported general aviation for over 30 years and served as an AEA Associate Board Member.

126 ■ Duncan Aviation Scholarships
(Undergraduate/Scholarship)

Purpose: To provide support to the individuals intending to pursue their career in aircraft electronics and aviation maintenance industry. **Focus:** Aviation. **Qualif.:** Applicant must be a high school senior and/or college student planning to or currently attending an accredited school in an avionics or aircraft repair program. **Criteria:** Selection of candidates will be based on the criteria of the scholarship committee.

Awards are arranged alphabetically below their administering organizations

Funds Avail.: $1,000. **To Apply:** For further information about the scholarship, applicants are advised to contact the foundation at Aircraft Electronics Association, 4217 S Hocker, Independence, MO 64055. **Deadline:** February 15.

127 ■ Field Aviation Co., Inc. Scholarships
(Undergraduate/Scholarship)

Purpose: To provide support to individuals intending to pursue their career in aircraft electronics and aviation maintenance industry. **Focus:** Aviation. **Qualif.:** Applicants must be high school seniors and/or college students planning to or attending an accredited college/university in an aircraft repair program. The educational institutions must be located in Canada. **Criteria:** Selection of candidates will be based on the decision of the Scholarship Committee.

Funds Avail.: $1,000. **To Apply:** Applicants are advised to contact the foundation for application forms and other required materials. **Deadline:** February 15.

128 ■ Garmin Scholarships *(Undergraduate/Scholarship)*

Purpose: To provide support to individuals intending to pursue their career in aircraft electronics and aviation maintenance industry. **Focus:** Aviation. **Qualif.:** Applicants must be seniors and/or college students planning to or attending an accredited school in an avionics or aircraft repair program. **Criteria:** Selection of candidates will be based on their application materials.

Funds Avail.: $2,000. **To Apply:** Applicants are advised to contact the foundation for application forms and other required materials. **Deadline:** February 15.

129 ■ Lowell Gaylor Memorial Scholarships
(Undergraduate/Scholarship)

Purpose: To provide support to individuals intending to pursue their career in aircraft electronics and aviation maintenance industry. **Focus:** Aviation. **Qualif.:** Applicants must be high school seniors and/or college students who plan to or attending an accredited school in an avionics or aircraft repair program. **Criteria:** Selection of candidates will be based on their application materials.

Funds Avail.: $1,000. **To Apply:** Applicants are advised to contact the foundation for application forms and other required materials. **Deadline:** February 15. **Remarks:** Scholarship is named in memory of Lowell Gaylor, President of AvEL Co., Dallas, Texas who supported general aviation and the AEA for over 25 yrs.

130 ■ Bud Glover Memorial Scholarships
(Undergraduate/Scholarship)

Purpose: To provide support for individuals intending to pursue their career in aircraft electronics and aviation maintenance industry. **Focus:** Aviation. **Qualif.:** Applicants must be high school seniors and/or college students who are planning to attend an accredited school in an avionics or aircraft repair program. **Criteria:** Selection of candidates will be based on their application materials.

Funds Avail.: $1,000. **To Apply:** Applicants must submit the completed application form; official transcript of grades; one 300-word essay. **Deadline:** February 15. **Remarks:** Scholarship is named in memory of Bud Glover, former vice president of general aviation sales for Bendix/King. Bud was a 25-year contributor to our avionics industry.

131 ■ Leon Harris/Les Nichols Memorial Scholarships to Spartan College of Aeronautics & Technology *(Undergraduate/Scholarship)*

Purpose: To provide support for individuals intending to pursue a career in aircraft electronics and aviation maintenance industry. **Focus:** Aviation. **Qualif.:** Applicant must be a student planning to pursue an Associate's Degree in Applied Science in Aviation Electronics (avionics) at Spartan College of Aeronautics and Technology campus in Tulsa, Oklahoma. **Criteria:** Selection of candidates will be based on their application materials.

Funds Avail.: $35,000. **To Apply:** Applicant must submit a completed application form; official transcript of grades; one 300-word essay. **Deadline:** February 15. **Remarks:** Award will cover all tuition expenses for eight quarters or until the recipient completes an Associate's Degree.

132 ■ Don C. Hawkins Memorial Scholarships
(Undergraduate/Scholarship)

Purpose: To provide support to individuals who wants to pursue their career in aircraft electronics and aviation maintenance industry. **Focus:** Aviation. **Qualif.:** Applicants must be high school seniors and/or college students planning to or attending an accredited school in an avionics or aircraft repair program. **Criteria:** Selection of candidates will be based on their application materials.

Funds Avail.: $1,000. **To Apply:** Applicants are advised to contact the foundation for application forms and other required materials. **Remarks:** Scholarship is named in memory of Don C. Hawkins.

133 ■ Honeywell Avionics Scholarships
(Undergraduate, Vocational/Occupational/Scholarship)

Purpose: To provide support to individuals intending to pursue their career in aircraft electronics and aviation maintenance industry. **Focus:** Aviation. **Qualif.:** Applicants must be high school, college, or vocational/technical school students planning to or attending an accredited school in an avionics or aircraft repair program. **Criteria:** Selection of candidates will be based on the decision of the Scholarship Committee.

Funds Avail.: $1,000. **To Apply:** Applicants are advised to contact the foundation for application forms and other required materials. **Deadline:** February 15.

134 ■ L-3 Avionics Systems Scholarships
(Undergraduate, Vocational/Occupational/Scholarship)

Purpose: To provide support to individuals intending to pursue their career in aircraft electronics and aviation maintenance industry. **Focus:** Aviation. **Qualif.:** Applicants must be high school, college, or vocational/technical school students planning to or attending an accredited school in an avionics or aircraft repair program. **Criteria:** Selection of candidates will be based on the decision of the Scholarship Committee.

Funds Avail.: $2,500. **To Apply:** Applicants are advised to contact the foundation for application forms and other required materials.

135 ■ Mid-Continent Instrument Scholarships
(Undergraduate/Scholarship)

Purpose: To provide support to individuals intending to pursue their career in aircraft electronics and aviation

Awards are arranged alphabetically below their administering organizations

maintenance industry. **Focus:** Aviation. **Qualif.:** Applicants must be high school seniors and/or college students planning to or attending an accredited school in an avionics or aircraft repair program. **Criteria:** Selection of candidates will be based on the criteria of the Scholarship Committee.

Funds Avail.: $1,000. **To Apply:** Applicants are advised to contact the foundation for application forms and other required materials. **Deadline:** February 15.

136 ■ Monte R. Mitchell Global Scholarships
(Undergraduate/Scholarship)

Purpose: To provide support to the individuals intending to pursue their career in aircraft electronics and aviation maintenance industry. **Focus:** Aviation. **Qualif.:** Applicant must be a European student pursuing a degree in aviation maintenance technology, avionics or aircraft repair at an accredited school located in Europe or the United States. **Criteria:** Selection of candidates will be based on the criteria of the scholarship committee.

Funds Avail.: $1,000. **To Apply:** For further information about the scholarship, applicants are advised to contact the foundation at Aircraft Electronics Association, 4217 S Hocker, Independence, MO 64055.

137 ■ Chuck Peacock Memorial Scholarships
(Undergraduate/Scholarship)

Purpose: To recognize the importance of management skills. **Focus:** Aviation. **Qualif.:** Applicants must be high school seniors and/or college students who are planning to attend an accredited school in an aviation management program. **Criteria:** Selection of candidates will be based on their application materials.

Funds Avail.: $1,000. **To Apply:** Applicants must submit the completed application form; official transcript of grades; one 300-word essay. **Deadline:** February 15. **Remarks:** Scholarship is given by Wanda Peacock in memory of her late husband Chuck. As the founder of the Aircraft Electronics Association, Chuck credited his aviation and business management skills as the cornerstones for his success in the industry.

138 ■ Rockwell Collins Scholarships
(Undergraduate/Scholarship)

Purpose: To provide support to individuals intending to pursue their career in aircraft electronics and aviation maintenance industry. **Focus:** Aviation. **Qualif.:** Applicants must be high school seniors and/or college students planning to or attending an accredited school in an avionics or aircraft repair program. **Criteria:** Selection of candidates will be based on the criteria of the Scholarship Committee.

Funds Avail.: $1,000. **To Apply:** Applicants are advised to contact the foundation for application forms and other required materials. **Deadline:** February 15.

139 ■ Thomas J. Slocum Memorial Scholarships to Westwood College of Aviation Technology *(Undergraduate/Scholarship)*

Purpose: To provide support for individuals intending to pursue their career in aircraft electronics and aviation maintenance industry. **Focus:** Aviation. **Qualif.:** Applicant must be a student who plans to attend Westwood College of Aviation Technology in Broomfield, Colorado in the avionics program. **Criteria:** Selection of candidates will be based on their application materials.

Funds Avail.: $6,000. **Number Awarded:** 3. **To Apply:** Applicants must submit the completed application form; of-

ficial transcript of grades; one 300-word essay. **Deadline:** February 15.

140 ■ Southeast Aerospace Inc. Scholarships
(Undergraduate/Scholarship)

Purpose: To provide support for individuals intending to pursue their career in aircraft electronics and aviation maintenance industry. **Focus:** Aviation. **Qualif.:** Applicants must be high school seniors and/or college students who are planning to attend an accredited school in an avionics or aircraft repair program. **Criteria:** Selection of candidates will be based on the criteria of the scholarship committee.

Funds Avail.: $1,000. **To Apply:** Applicants must submit the completed application form; official transcript of grades; one 300-word essay. **Deadline:** February 15.

141 ■ Sporty's Pilot Shop/Cincinnati Avionics Scholarships *(Undergraduate, Vocational/ Occupational/Scholarship)*

Purpose: To provide support to individuals intending to pursue their career in aircraft electronics and aviation maintenance industry. **Focus:** Aviation. **Qualif.:** Applicants must be high school, college, or vocational/technical school students planning to or attending an accredited school in an avionics or aircraft repair program. **Criteria:** Selection of candidates will be based on the decision of the Scholarship Committee.

Funds Avail.: $2,000. **To Apply:** Applicants are advised to contact the foundation for application forms and other required materials. **Deadline:** February 15.

142 ■ Kei Takemoto Memorial Scholarships
(Undergraduate/Scholarship)

Purpose: To provide support to individuals intending to pursue their career in aircraft electronics and aviation maintenance industry. **Focus:** Aviation. **Qualif.:** Applicants must be high school seniors and/or college students planning to or are attending an accredited school in an avionics or aircraft repair program. **Criteria:** Candidates will be selected based on the scholarship criteria.

Funds Avail.: $500. **To Apply:** Applicants are advised to contact the foundation for application forms and required materials. **Deadline:** February 15. **Remarks:** Scholarship is named in memory of Kei Takemoto whose technical expertise, engineering skill and passion for customer service was an inspiration to the avionics industry for many years.

143 ■ Lee Tarbox Memorial Scholarships
(Undergraduate/Scholarship)

Purpose: To provide support for individuals intending to pursue a career in aircraft electronics and aviation maintenance industry. **Focus:** Aviation. **Qualif.:** Applicants must be high school seniors and/or college students who are planning to attend an accredited school in an avionics or aircraft repair program. **Criteria:** Selection of candidates will be based on their application materials.

Funds Avail.: $2,500. **To Apply:** Applicants must submit the completed application form; official transcript of grades; one 300-word essay. **Deadline:** February 15. **Remarks:** Scholarship is given by Pacific Southwest Instruments.

144 ■ Tom Taylor Memorial Scholarships to Spartan College of Aeronautics and Technology *(Undergraduate/Scholarship)*

Purpose: To encourage young individuals to pursue study in Applied Science or in Aviation Maintenance Technology.

Awards are arranged alphabetically below their administering organizations

Focus: Aviation. **Qualif.:** Applicants must have desire to pursue their associates degree in Applied Science or a diploma in Aviation Maintenance Technology at Spartan College of Aeronautics & Technology's campus in Tulsa, Oklahoma; must not be currently enrolled in the AMT program at Spartan. **Criteria:** Selection of applicants will be based on the scholarship criteria.

Funds Avail.: $35,000. **To Apply:** Applicants must submit the completed application form; official transcript of grades; one 300-word essay. **Deadline:** February 15.

145 ■ Texas State Technical College Scholarships (Undergraduate/Scholarship)

Purpose: To provide support to individuals intending to pursue their career in aircraft electronics and aviation maintenance industry. **Focus:** Aviation. **Qualif.:** Applicants must be students intending to pursue an associate's degree in avionics. **Criteria:** Selection of candidates will be based on the criteria of the scholarship committee.

Funds Avail.: $1,000. **Number Awarded:** 10. APP Applicants must submit the completed application form; official transcript of grades; one 300-word essay. **Deadline:** February 15.

146 ■ Airport Minority Advisory Council Educational and Scholarship Program (AMAC-ESP)

R2345 Crystal Dr., Ste. 902
Arlington, VA 22202
Ph: (703) 414-2622
Fax: (703) 414-2686
E-mail: amac.info@amac-org.com
URL: amac-org.com

147 ■ AMACESP Student Scholarships (Undergraduate/Scholarship)

Purpose: To provide financial assistance for education and outreach to full-time college students interested in pursuing aviation careers. **Focus:** Aviation. **Qualif.:** Applicant must be a U.S. citizen; must be admitted by an accredited school or university for the current school term in which he/she is applying for; must have a cumulative 3.0 GPA; must demonstrates involvement in community activities, extracurricular activities, interest and desire to pursue a career in the aviation/airport industry; and must be seeking a degree in aviation, business administration, accounting, architecture, engineering or finance. **Criteria:** Recipient will be selected by the AMACESP Scholarship Selection Committees based on a set of criteria.

Funds Avail.: $2,000. **Number Awarded:** 8 or more. **To Apply:** Applicant must complete a current Scholarship Application; enclose transcripts to show proof of 3.0 GPA; a one-page essay on career goals and why he/she have chosen his/her particular field of study; and two letters of recommendation from persons who are not relatives that can comment on his/her academic and career goals. **Deadline:** August 5.

148 ■ Airports Council International North America (ACI-NA)

1775 K St. NW, Ste. 500
Washington, DC 20006
Ph: (202) 293-8500
Fax: (202) 331-1362

Free: 888-424-7767
E-mail: memberservices@aci-na.org
URL: www.aci-na.org

149 ■ Airports Council International-North America Scholarships (Graduate, Undergraduate/Scholarship)

Purpose: To provide educational assistance to students at an accredited educational institution working towards a degree and a career in airport management or airport administration. **Focus:** Aviation. **Qualif.:** Applicants must be officially enrolled in an accredited college or university in either an undergraduate program focused on airport management and/or airport operations, or a graduate program focused on research on airport management or airport operations; must reside and attend school in U.S. or Canada; and must maintain a minimum GPA of 3.0 at the time of application. **Criteria:** Applicants are evaluated based on demonstrated academic excellence and leadership; economic needs; and impact of the airport industry.

Funds Avail.: $2,500. **Number Awarded:** 3. **To Apply:** Applicants must submit scholarship application (Form 101-06); official school transcript; two recent letters of recommendation, with one from a former or current professor/instructor and the other letter from someone other than a professor/instructor that has knowledge of the student's leadership qualities; a (300-500 word) personal statement which emphasizes the applicant's interest in airport management or airport operations; and a current resume (maximum of two pages). **Deadline:** December 15 for the Fall term and April 15 for the Spring term.

150 ■ Akron Bar Association Foundation

57 S Broadway
Akron, OH 44308
Ph: (330) 253-5007
Fax: (330) 253-2140
E-mail: dlong@akronbar.org
URL: www.akronbar.org

151 ■ Akron Bar Association Foundation Scholarships (Undergraduate/Scholarship)

Purpose: To provide scholarships to students enrolled in a law school. **Focus:** Law. **Qualif.:** Applicants must be citizens of the United States and in good academic standing with their respective schools; must demonstrate financial need; must have an affiliation with Summit County; must demonstrate an established history of community involvement; and must be admitted to a law school in Ohio. **Criteria:** Application will be considered based on applicant's written formal letter indicating the following: (1) statement of how and why applicants became law students; (2) connection to Summit County; (3) previous and current volunteer and community involvement; and (4) reasons stating why they deserve the award.

Funds Avail.: No specific amount. **To Apply:** Applicants must submit the following requirements: a completed, typed application form; a certified transcript from school(s); a copy of 2011 Federal Income Tax Return; an updated resume; and two letters of recommendation from people who are familiar with applicant's character. Applicant's 2010 Federal Income Tax Return will be considered if 2011 is unavailable. **Deadline:** April 5. **Contact:** Application form and other supporting documents should be submitted to Linda M. Foster at the above address.

Awards are arranged alphabetically below their administering organizations

152 ■ Alabama Architectural Foundation (AAF)

961 Lake Cir.
Hoover, AL 35244
Ph: (205) 985-7002
E-mail: info@aaf.org
URL: www.alabamaarchitecturalfoundation.org

153 ■ Alabama Architectural Foundation Scholarships *(Postgraduate, Undergraduate/ Scholarship)*

Purpose: To provide financial assistance to worthy candidates. **Focus:** Landscape architecture and design. **Qualif.:** Applicants must be students of architecture or related design disciplines in any field of the visual or performing arts and who are enrolled in any institution of higher learning in Alabama in the completion stages of a bachelor's degree or in postgraduate work. **Criteria:** Selection will be based on academic performance, record of activities, awards and recognition, letter of recommendation and written materials from the group of candidates.

Funds Avail.: No specific amount. **To Apply:** Applicants may contact the foundation for the application process.

154 ■ Alabama Commission on Higher Education

PO Box 302000
Montgomery, AL 36130-2000
Ph: (334) 242-1998
Fax: (334) 242-0268
URL: www.ache.alabama.gov

155 ■ ACHE/American Legion Auxiliary Scholarships *(Undergraduate/Scholarship)*

Purpose: To support the education of Alabama students. **Focus:** General studies. **Qualif.:** Applicants must be either the son, daughter, grandson, granddaughter of veterans of World War I, World War II, Korea, or Vietnam and who are residents of Alabama; and must be attending an institutions having on-campus housing. **Criteria:** Selection is based on the application.

Funds Avail.: No specific amount. **To Apply:** Applications are available from the American Legion Department Headquarters, American Legion Auxiliary, 120 North Jackson Street, Montgomery, AL 36104. **Deadline:** April 1. **Contact:** 334-262-1176.

156 ■ ACHE/American Legion Scholarships *(Undergraduate/Scholarship)*

Purpose: To support the education of Alabama students. **Focus:** General studies. **Qualif.:** Applicants must be either the son, daughter, grandson, granddaughter of veterans of World War I, World War II, Korea, or Vietnam and who are residents of Alabama; and must be attending an institutions having on-campus housing. **Criteria:** Selection is based on the application.

Funds Avail.: No specific amount. **To Apply:** Applications are available from the Department Adjutant, The American Legion, P.O. Box 1069, Montgomery, AL 36192. **Deadline:** May 1. **Contact:** 334-262-6638.

157 ■ ACHE Junior and Community College Athletic Scholarships *(Undergraduate/ Scholarship)*

Purpose: To support the education of Alabama students. **Focus:** General studies. **Qualif.:** Applicants must be full-time students enrolled in public junior and community colleges in Alabama. **Criteria:** Selection is based on demonstrated athletic ability determined through try-outs.

Funds Avail.: No specific amount. **To Apply:** Applicants must contact the coach, athletic director, or financial aid officer at any public junior or community college in Alabama in order to be considered.

158 ■ ACHE Junior and Community College Performing Arts Scholarships *(Undergraduate/ Scholarship)*

Purpose: To support the education of Alabama students. **Focus:** Performing arts. **Qualif.:** Applicant must be a full-time student enrolled in public junior and community colleges in Alabama. **Criteria:** Selection is based on demonstrated talent determined through competitive auditions.

Funds Avail.: No specific amount. **To Apply:** Applicant must contact the financial aid office at any public junior or community college in Alabama. Competitive auditions will also be scheduled as part of the application process.

159 ■ ACHE Police Officers and Firefighters Survivors' Educational Assistance Programs *(Undergraduate/Scholarship)*

Purpose: To assist the education of the dependents or spouses of police officers or firefighters killed in the line of duty in Alabama. **Focus:** General studies. **Qualif.:** Applicant must be the dependent or the spouse of a police officer or firefighter killed in the line of duty; enrolled in an undergraduate program at a public post-secondary educational institution in Alabama. **Criteria:** Selection is based on the application.

Funds Avail.: No specific amount. **To Apply:** Application forms may be obtained from the Alabama Commission on Higher Education, PO Box 302000, Montgomery, AL 36130-2000. **Contact:** 334-242-2273.

160 ■ ACHE Senior Adult Scholarships *(Undergraduate/Scholarship)*

Purpose: To support Alabama senior citizens with educational pursuits. **Focus:** General studies. **Qualif.:** Applicant must be a senior citizen (aged 60 and over) who meets the admission requirements to attend a public two-year post-secondary institution in Alabama. **Criteria:** Preference will be given to an applicant who meet the admission requirements.

Funds Avail.: No specific amount. **To Apply:** Applicant must contact the financial aid office at any public two-year post-secondary educational institutions in Alabama in order to be considered.

161 ■ ACHE Two-Year College Academic Scholarships *(Undergraduate/Scholarship)*

Purpose: To support students with educational pursuits. **Focus:** General studies. **Qualif.:** Applicant must be a student accepted for enrollment at public two-year post-secondary educational institutions in Alabama. **Criteria:** Selection is based on demonstrated academic merit as determined by the institutional scholarship committee. Priorities will be given to in-state residents.

Funds Avail.: No specific amount. **To Apply:** Application forms are available at the financial aid office at any public two-year post-secondary educational institution in Alabama.

162 ■ Alabama Gi Dependents Educational Benefit Program *(Undergraduate/Scholarship)*

Purpose: To support the education of Alabama students. **Focus:** General studies. **Qualif.:** Applicant must be a

Awards are arranged alphabetically below their administering organizations

dependent or spouses of eligible Alabama veterans attending a public postsecondary educational institutions in Alabama; enrolled as an undergraduate student. **Criteria:** Selection is based on the application.

Funds Avail.: Tuition, fees and book assistance. **To Apply:** Application forms may be obtained from the Alabama State Department of Veterans Affairs, PO Box 1509, Montgomery, AL 36102-1509, or from any county veterans service officer. **Contact:** Alabama State Department of Veterans Affairs, at 334-242-5077.

163 ■ Alabama National Guard Educational Assistance Program (Undergraduate/Scholarship)

Purpose: To assist Alabama National Guard members to attend a public postsecondary educational institution in Alabama. **Focus:** General studies. **Qualif.:** Applicants must be a student who is an active member in good standing with a federally recognized unit of the Alabama National Guard. **Criteria:** Selection is based on the application.

Funds Avail.: $500-$1000. **To Apply:** Applications are available from Alabama National Guard units. Forms must be signed by a representative of the Alabama Military Department and the financial aid officer at the college/university the applicant plans to attend.

164 ■ Alabama Scholarships for Dependents of Blind Parents (Undergraduate/Scholarship)

Purpose: To support the education of students from families in which the head of the family is blind and whose family income is insufficient to provide educational benefits. **Focus:** General studies. **Qualif.:** Applicant must be an Alabama resident; having a family in which the head of the family is blind or with family income is insufficient to provide educational benefits for attendance at an Alabama postsecondary institution. **Criteria:** Selection is based on need.

Funds Avail.: Covers instructional fees and tuition. **To Apply:** Applications are available from Debra Culver, Rehab. Specialist, Alabama Department of Rehabilitation Services, 2129 East South Blvd., Montgomery, AL 36116-2455. **Remarks:** Students must apply within two years of high school graduation. **Contact:** 800-441-7607, 334-613-2248, or 256-362-0638.

165 ■ Alabama Student Assistance Programs (Undergraduate/Scholarship)

Purpose: To support the education of Alabama students. **Focus:** General studies. **Qualif.:** Applicants must be undergraduate students; and must be Alabama residents attending an eligible Alabama institution. **Criteria:** Selection is based on need.

Funds Avail.: $300-$2,500. **To Apply:** Applicants must submit the Free Application for Federal Student Aid available from high school guidance office or the financial aid office at the institution planning to attend.

166 ■ Alabama Student Grant Programs (Undergraduate, Vocational/Occupational/Grant)

Purpose: To support the education of Alabama students. **Focus:** General studies. **Qualif.:** Applicant must be a part-time or a full-time undergraduate student; an Alabama resident; and attending Birmingham-Southern College, Concordia College, Faulkner University, Huntingdon College, Judson College, Miles College, Oakwood College, Samford University, Selma University, Southeastern Bible College, Southern Vocational College, Spring Hill College, Stillman College, or the University of Mobile. **Criteria:** Selection is based on the application.

Funds Avail.: Up to $1,200. **To Apply:** Applications are available to the financial aid office of the institution where applicant is planning to attend.

167 ■ Alabama Dietetic Association (ALDA)

PO Box 240757
Montgomery, AL 36124
Ph: (334) 260-7970
Fax: (334) 272-7128
E-mail: alda@gmsal.com
URL: www.eatrightalabama.org

168 ■ Birmingham District Alabama Dietetic Association Scholarships (Graduate, Undergraduate/Scholarship)

Purpose: To encourage and reward students majoring in the field of human nutrition, dietetics, foods, nutrition, or food systems management or admitted or enrolled in a dietetic internship who have demonstrated ability and potential in the field of dietetics and nutrition by aiding them financially. **Focus:** Dietetics; Nutrition. **Qualif.:** Applicant must be a junior or senior undergraduate, graduate student, or dietetic intern majoring in the field of human nutrition, dietetics, foods, nutrition, or food systems management or admitted or enrolled in a dietetic internship; a legal resident of one of the following counties: Jefferson, Cullman, Walker, Tuscaloosa, Bibb, Chilton, Shelby, Talladega, St. Clair and/or an active member in the Birmingham District Dietetic Association and a student member of the American Dietetic Association; have a cumulative GPA of 3.0 or above on a 4.0 scale, and a 3.0 or above on a 4.0 scale in major courses of study. **Criteria:** Selection is based on the scholarship; potential in the field of dietetics and nutrition ascertained by, for example: leadership in activities within and outside school, professional interest, honors, activities, and work or volunteer experience; financial need; letters of recommendation; and letter of application.

Funds Avail.: $500. **To Apply:** Applicants must submit a completed application form together with the official computed cumulative GPA (all post secondary work related to dietetics) authenticated by a faculty member; a letter of application including statements relating to financial need, immediate and future goals, leadership activities, and personal attributes such as initiation and motivation for meeting physical, emotional, and family demands as well as graduate school requirements; and resume including personal contact data, education, honors, and awards, involvement in clubs and organizations including offices held, professional and leadership activities, and work on volunteer experience. **Deadline:** February 15. **Remarks:** Sponsored by Birmingham Dietetic Association. **Contact:** Linda Knol, PhD, University of Alabama, Department of Human Nutrition and Hospitality Management, Doster Hall 206, Box 870158, Tuscaloosa, AL 35487-0158.

169 ■ North Alabama Dietetic Association Scholarships (Graduate, Undergraduate/Scholarship)

Purpose: To encourage and reward students majoring in the field of human nutrition, dietetics, foods, nutrition, or food systems management or admitted or enrolled in a dietetic internship who have demonstrated ability and potential in the field of dietetics and nutrition by aiding them financially. **Focus:** Dietetics; Nutrition. **Qualif.:** Applicant must be a junior or senior majoring in the field of human

Awards are arranged alphabetically below their administering organizations

nutrition, dietetics, foods, nutrition or food systems management or admitted or enrolled in a dietetic internship; a legal resident of North Alabama; and have a cumulative GPA of 2.5 or above on a 4.0 scale, and a 3.0 or above on a 4.0 scale in major sources of study. **Criteria:** Selection is based on the scholarship; potential in the field of dietetics and nutrition ascertained by, for example: leadership in activities within and outside school, professional interest, honors, activities, and work or volunteer experience; financial need; letters of recommendation; and letter of application.

Funds Avail.: $500. **To Apply:** Applicants must submit a completed application form together with the official computed cumulative GPA (all post secondary work related to dietetics) authenticated by a faculty member; a letter of application including statements relating to financial need, immediate and future goals, leadership activities, and personal attributes such as initiation and motivation for meeting physical, emotional, and family demands as well as graduate school requirements; and resume including personal contact data, education, honors, and awards, involvement in clubs and organizations including offices held, professional and leadership activities, and work on volunteer experience. **Deadline:** February 15. **Remarks:** Sponsored by the North Alabama Dietetic Association. **Contact:** Linda Knol, PhD, University of Alabama, Department of Human Nutrition and Hospitality Management, Doster Hall 206, Box 870158, Tuscaloosa, AL 35487-0158.

170 ■ Northeast Alabama District Dietetic Association Scholarships *(Graduate, Undergraduate/Scholarship)*

Purpose: To encourage and reward students majoring in the field of human nutrition, dietetics, foods, nutrition, or food systems management or admitted or enrolled in a dietetic internship who have demonstrated ability and potential in the field of dietetics and nutrition by aiding them financially. **Focus:** Dietetics; Nutrition. **Qualif.:** Applicant must be a junior or senior majoring in the field of human nutrition, dietetics, food, nutrition, or food systems management or admitted or enrolled in a dietetic internship; have a cumulative GPA of 2.5 or above on a 4.0 scale, and a 3.0 or above on a 4.0 scale in major sources of study; and a legal resident of one of the following counties: Calhoun, DeKalb, Cherokee, Celburne, Etowah, Marshall, St. Clair, or Talladega or volunteered in a healthcare facility in one of the stated counties. **Criteria:** Selection is based on the scholarship; potential in the field of dietetics and nutrition ascertained by, for example: leadership in activities within and outside school, professional interest, honors, activities, and work or volunteer experience; financial need; letters of recommendation; and letter of application.

Funds Avail.: $500. **To Apply:** Applicants must submit a completed application form together with the official computed cumulative GPA (all post secondary work related to dietetics) authenticated by a faculty member; a letter of application including statements relating to financial need, immediate and future goals, leadership activities, and personal attributes such as initiation and motivation for meeting physical, emotional, and family demands as well as graduate school requirements; and resume including personal contact data, education, honors, and awards, involvement in clubs and organizations including offices held, professional and leadership activities, and work on volunteer experience. **Deadline:** February 15. **Remarks:** Sponsored by the Northeast Alabama Dietetic Association. **Contact:** Linda Knol, PhD, University of Alabama, Department of Human Nutrition and Hospitality Management, Doster Hall 206, Box 870158, Tuscaloosa, AL 35487-0158.

171 ■ William E. Smith Scholarships *(Graduate/Scholarship)*

Purpose: To reward full time graduate students who have demonstrated ability and potential in the field of dietetics and nutrition by aiding them financially during graduate study. **Focus:** Dietetics; Nutrition. **Qualif.:** Applicant must be a full-time graduate student in the field of dietetics and nutrition. **Criteria:** Selection is based on the scholarship; potential in the field of dietetics and nutrition ascertained by, for example: leadership in activities within and outside school, professional interest, honors, activities, and work or volunteer experience; financial need; letters of recommendation; and letter of application.

Funds Avail.: $1,000. **Number Awarded:** 1. **To Apply:** Applicants must submit a completed application form together with the official computed cumulative GPA (all post secondary work related to dietetics) authenticated by a faculty member; a letter of application including statements relating to financial need, immediate and future goals, leadership activities, and personal attributes such as initiation and motivation for meeting physical, emotional, and family demands as well as graduate school requirements; and resume including personal contact data, education, honors, and awards, involvement in clubs and organizations including offices held, professional and leadership activities, and work on volunteer experience. **Deadline:** February 15. **Remarks:** Sponsored by the Royal Cup Coffee Company. **Contact:** Linda Knol, PhD, University of Alabama, Department of Human Nutrition and Hospitality Management, Doster Hall 206, Box 870158, Tuscaloosa, AL 35487-0158.

172 ■ Southeast Alabama Dietetic Association Scholarships *(Graduate, Undergraduate/Scholarship)*

Purpose: To encourage and reward students majoring in the field of human nutrition, dietetics, foods, nutrition, or food systems management or admitted or enrolled in a dietetic internship who have demonstrated ability and potential in the field of dietetics and nutrition by aiding them financially. **Focus:** Dietetics; Nutrition. **Qualif.:** Applicant must be a junior or senior majoring in the field of human nutrition, dietetics, foods, nutrition, or food systems management or admitted or enrolled in a dietetic internship; a legal resident of one of the following counties: Houston, Geneva, Covington, Coffee, Dale, Henry, Pike, or Barbour; or must have been employed or volunteered in a healthcare facility in one of the stated counties; or must be the child or grandchild of an active or former member of the SE Alabama Dietetic Association; and must have a cumulative GPA of 2.5 or above on a 4.0 scale, and a 3.0 or above on a 4.0 scale in major courses of study. **Criteria:** Selection is based on the scholarship; potential in the field of dietetics and nutrition ascertained by, for example: leadership in activities within and outside school, professional interest, honors, activities, and work or volunteer experience; financial need; letters of recommendation; and letter of application.

Funds Avail.: $750. **To Apply:** Applicants must submit a completed application form together with the official computed cumulative GPA (all post secondary work related to dietetics) authenticated by a faculty member; a letter of application including statements relating to financial need, immediate and future goals, leadership activities, and personal attributes such as initiation and motivation for meeting physical, emotional, and family demands as well as graduate school requirements; and resume including

Awards are arranged alphabetically below their administering organizations

personal contact data, education, honors, and awards, involvement in clubs and organizations including offices held, professional and leadership activities, and work on volunteer experience. **Deadline:** February 15. **Remarks:** Sponsored by the Southeast Alabama Dietetic Association. **Contact:** Linda Knol, PhD, University of Alabama, Department of Human Nutrition and Hospitality Management, Doster Hall 206, Box 870158, Tuscaloosa, AL 35487-0158.

173 ■ Wood Fruitticher Grocery Company, Inc. Scholarships *(Graduate, Undergraduate/ Scholarship)*

Purpose: To encourage and reward junior level undergraduate students or full or part time graduate students in American Dietetic Association (ADA) accredited Alabama colleges and universities who have demonstrated ability and potential in the field of dietetics and nutrition by aiding them financially. **Focus:** Dietetics; Nutrition. **Qualif.:** Applicant must have been enrolled in an ADA accredited Alabama college/university for at least one quarter or one semester. **Criteria:** Selection is based on the scholarship; potential in the field of dietetics and nutrition ascertained by, for example: leadership in activities within and outside school, professional interest, honors, activities, and work or volunteer experience; financial need; letters of recommendation; and letter of application.

Funds Avail.: $500. **To Apply:** Applicants must submit a completed application form together with the official computed cumulative GPA (all post secondary work related to dietetics) authenticated by a faculty member; a letter of application including statements relating to financial need, immediate and future goals, leadership activities, and personal attributes such as initiation and motivation for meeting physical, emotional, and family demands as well as graduate school requirements; and resume including personal contact data, education, honors, and awards, involvement in clubs and organizations including offices held, professional and leadership activities, and work on volunteer experience. **Deadline:** February 15. **Remarks:** Sponsored by The Wood Fruitticher Grocery Company, Inc. **Contact:** Linda Knol, PhD, University of Alabama, Department of Human Nutrition and Hospitality Management, Doster Hall 206, Box 870158, Tuscaloosa, AL 35487-0158.

174 ■ Alabama Horse Council (AHC)

PO Box 260
Morris, AL 35116
Free: 800-945-8033
E-mail: info@alabamahorsecouncil.org
URL: www.alabamahorsecouncil.org

175 ■ Alabama Horse Council Scholarships *(Undergraduate/Scholarship)*

Purpose: To support the education of an AHC members and their children. **Focus:** Equine studies. **Qualif.:** Applicants or their parents/grandparents must be current members of AHC; must be majoring in a field of study for a career in the equine industry; must have demonstrated record of activity in the equine industry prior to college application. **Criteria:** Recipients are selected based on their submitted applications.

Funds Avail.: $1000. **To Apply:** Applicants must submit 4 copies of: one page-cover form; two letters of references attesting to the applicant's commitment to the equine industry, activity in the industry and character; short (500 word maximum) essay about how horses have shaped the

lives and the goals that applicant want to pursue in the horse industry; and a list of activities and honors received. **Deadline:** June 1. **Contact:** Charlotte Collins at the above address.

176 ■ Auburn Animal Science Department Graduate Student Scholarships *(Graduate/ Scholarship)*

Purpose: To support students studying Animal Science. **Focus:** Animal science and behavior. **Qualif.:** Applicants must be graduate students in Auburn's Department of Animal Science; have strong background in Alabama's livestock industry; and have current research project involving beef or beef cattle. **Criteria:** Selection is based on merit.

Funds Avail.: $1,500. **To Apply:** Applicants must submit a completed application form.

177 ■ Auburn University College of Veterinary Medicine Scholarships *(Undergraduate/ Scholarship)*

Purpose: To promote Veterinary Medicine education in Alabama. **Focus:** Veterinary science and medicine. **Qualif.:** Applicants must be currently enrolled at Auburn's College of Veterinary Medicine; must have strong background in Alabama's livestock industry; and intending to pursue a career involving large animal medicine. **Criteria:** Selection is based on merit.

Funds Avail.: $1,500. **To Apply:** Applicants must submit a completed application form. **Deadline:** December 5.

178 ■ Cecil Lane Family Scholarships *(Undergraduate/Scholarship)*

Purpose: To provide financial assistance and recognition to students with strong ties to the beef cattle industry. **Focus:** Agricultural sciences. **Qualif.:** Applicants must be resident of Alabama; must be incoming freshman at the Auburn University College of Agriculture; and must be children or grandchildren of ACA members for two consecutive years. **Criteria:** Recipients are selected based on their submitted applications.

Funds Avail.: $1750. **To Apply:** Applicants must submit a completed application form. **Deadline:** December 5. **Contact:** Martha Davis.

179 ■ Ina E. Powell Memorial Scholarships *(Undergraduate/Scholarship)*

Purpose: To provide financial assistance for female students. **Focus:** Agricultural sciences; Forestry; Education-Curricula. **Qualif.:** Applicants must be female students from Alabama; must be high school seniors accepted at the Auburn University; must be planning to pursue agricultural-related courses at the College of Agriculture, School of Forestry and Wildlife sciences, College of Human Sciences or College of Education; must demonstrate leadership abilities; must have GPA of 3.0 or above; and must be children or grandchildren of ACA members for two consecutive years. **Criteria:** Recipients are selected based on their submitted applications.

Funds Avail.: $1500. **To Apply:** Applicants must submit a completed application form. **Deadline:** December 5. **Contact:** Martha Davis.

180 ■ Tagged for Greatness Scholarships *(Undergraduate/Scholarship)*

Purpose: To support the education of AHC members and their children. **Focus:** General studies. **Qualif.:** Applicants

Awards are arranged alphabetically below their administering organizations

must be high school senior and accepted to a 4-year university; must be children or grandchildren of ASA members for two consecutive years. **Criteria:** Recipients are selected based on academic excellence and leadership skills.

Funds Avail.: $1000-$1500. **To Apply:** Applicants must submit a completed application form. **Deadline:** December 5. **Remarks:** Funded by the Alabama Cattlemen's Foundation through the sale of the "Cowboy Tag". **Contact:** Martha Davis.

181 ■ Troy University Rodeo Team Scholarships *(Graduate/Scholarship)*

Purpose: To assist Alabama students with their education. **Focus:** General studies. **Qualif.:** Applicants must be current members of the Troy University Rodeo Team; have strong background in Alabama's livestock industry; and must be children or grandchildren of ASA members for two consecutive years. **Criteria:** Recipients are selected based on academic excellence and leadership skills.

Funds Avail.: $1000. **To Apply:** Applicants must submit a completed application form. **Deadline:** December 5. **Contact:** Martha Davis.

182 ■ University of West Alabama Rodeo Team Scholarships *(Graduate/Scholarship)*

Purpose: To support the education of University of West Alabama Rodeo Team members. **Focus:** General studies. **Qualif.:** Applicants must be current members of the University of West Alabama Rodeo Team; have strong background in Alabama's livestock industry; and must be children or grandchildren of ASA members for two consecutive years. **Criteria:** Recipients are selected based on academic excellence and leadership skills.

Funds Avail.: $1000. **To Apply:** Applicants must submit a completed application form. **Deadline:** December 5. **Contact:** Martha Davis.

183 ■ Samuel Upchurch Memorial Scholarships *(Undergraduate/Scholarship)*

Purpose: To support the education of AHC members and their children. **Focus:** Agricultural economics; Animal science and behavior. **Qualif.:** Applicants must be children or grandchildren of ACA members for two consecutive years; and must be accepted in Animal Science or Agriculture Economics at Auburn University. **Criteria:** Preference is given to applicants whose parents are members of the Alabama Santa Gertrudis Association.

Funds Avail.: $4000. **To Apply:** Applicants must submit a completed application form. **Deadline:** December 5. **Contact:** Martha Davis.

184 ■ Ed Wadsworth Memorial Scholarships *(Undergraduate/Scholarship)*

Purpose: To support the education of AHC members and their children. **Focus:** Animal science and behavior. **Qualif.:** Applicants must be resident of Alabama; must be junior or senior in the Animal Sciences Department at Auburn University; involved in beef cattle production; have demonstrated leadership abilities; have a GPA of 3.0 and above; and must be children or grandchildren of ACA members for two consecutive years. **Criteria:** Recipients are selected based on their submitted applications.

Funds Avail.: $1500. **To Apply:** Applicants must submit a completed application form. **Deadline:** December 5. **Contact:** Martha Davis.

185 ■ The Wax Company Scholarships *(Undergraduate/Scholarship)*

Purpose: To financially support students studying agriculture at the Auburn University. **Focus:** Agricultural sciences. **Qualif.:** Applicants must be high senior or college students studying agriculture at the Auburn University; and must be children of ACA members. **Criteria:** Recipients are selected based on their submitted applications.

Funds Avail.: $1000. **To Apply:** Applicants must submit a completed application form. **Deadline:** December 5. **Remarks:** Funded through the sale of Marshall and Jackson ryegrass seed. **Contact:** Martha Davis.

186 ■ Alabama Law Foundation
PO Box 4129
Montgomery, AL 36101
Ph: (334) 269-1515
E-mail: tdaniel@alfinc.org
URL: www.alfinc.org

187 ■ William Verbon Black Scholarships *(Undergraduate/Scholarship)*

Purpose: To assist full-time students at the University of Alabama School of Law. **Focus:** Law. **Qualif.:** Applicants must be students at the University of Alabama School of Law. **Criteria:** Selection will be based on academic achievement, but consideration is also given to consciousness, dependability, civic involvement, financial need and dedication to the highest ethical standards.

Funds Avail.: No specific amount. **To Apply:** Interested students must contact the foundation for the application process and other information. **Contact:** Tracy Daniel at tdaniel@alfinc.org.

188 ■ Johnston Cabaniss Scholarships *(Undergraduate/Scholarship)*

Purpose: To recognize and assist outstanding second-year law students in their academic pursuits. **Focus:** Law. **Qualif.:** Applicants must be residents of Alabama and must be law students entering second year at any accredited law school in the United States. **Criteria:** Selection will be based on the committee's criteria.

Funds Avail.: $5,000-first place; $1,000-second place. **To Apply:** Applicants may download an application form via ALFINC website. Applicants must submit a completed application form with school transcript attached. **Deadline:** First Friday of June. **Contact:** ALFINC at the above address.

189 ■ Justice Janie L. Shores Scholarships *(Undergraduate/Scholarship)*

Purpose: To award scholarship to female Alabama residents. **Focus:** Law. **Qualif.:** Applicants must be female Alabama residents attending an Alabama law school. **Criteria:** Selection will be based on the committee's criteria.

Funds Avail.: No specific amount. **To Apply:** Applicants must visit the website for the online application process. **Contact:** Tracy Daniel at tdaniel@alfinc.org.

190 ■ Alaska Airmen Association
4200 Floatplane Dr.
Anchorage, AK 99502
Ph: (907) 245-1251
Fax: (907) 245-1259

Awards are arranged alphabetically below their administering organizations

Free: 800-464-7030
E-mail: info@alaskaairmen.com
URL: alaskaairmen.org

191 ■ John P. Culhane Memorial Scholarships
(Undergraduate/Scholarship)

Purpose: To promote development in aviation careers. **Focus:** Aviation. **Qualif.:** Applicants must be enrolled in an aviation-related program at an accredited college, university, trade school or approved training center or be in current training with a certified Flight Instructor or A&P Mechanic; must have completed one year of a commercial aviation training program or at least 25% of the work toward it; must maintain a minimum GPA of 3.0 if enrolled in an accredited college, university or trade school program; must be legal U.S. residents and have no felony convictions. **Criteria:** Recipients are selected based on commitment to aviation goals; interest in both general and commercial aviation in Alaska; evidence of financial need; personal and career goals.

Funds Avail.: $2,500. **To Apply:** Applicants must provide a letter of recommendation from one of their current instructors attesting to the commitment of the applicant to the program; must submit a completed application form; school transcripts; proof of U.S. citizenship. **Deadline:** May 31. **Contact:** Applications should be sent to: AK Airmen's Scholarship Committee at the above address.

192 ■ F. Atlee Dodge Maintenance Scholarships
(Undergraduate/Scholarship)

Purpose: To promote development in aviation careers. **Focus:** Aviation. **Qualif.:** Applicants must be enrolled in an aviation-related program at an accredited college, university, trade school, approved training center or be in current training with a certified Flight Instructor or A&P Mechanic; must have completed one year of a commercial aviation training program or at least 25% of the work; must maintain a minimum GPA of 3.0 if enrolled in an accredited college, university or trade school program; must be legal U.S. residents and have no felony convictions. **Criteria:** Recipients are selected based on commitment to aviation goals; interest in both general and commercial aviation in Alaska; evidence of financial need; personal and career goals.

Funds Avail.: $2,500. **To Apply:** Applicants must provide a letter of recommendation from one of their current instructors attesting to the commitment of the applicant to the program; must submit a completed application form; school transcripts; proof of U.S. citizenship. **Deadline:** March 31.

193 ■ Bob Reeve Aviation Management Scholarships *(Undergraduate/Scholarship)*

Purpose: To promote development in aviation careers. **Focus:** Aviation. **Qualif.:** Applicants must be enrolled in an aviation-related program with an accredited college, university, trade school, approved training center or be in current training with a certified Flight Instructor or A&P Mechanic; must have completed one year of a commercial aviation training program or at least 25% of the work; must maintain a minimum GPA of 3.0 if enrolled in an accredited college, university or trade school program; must be legal U.S. residents and have no felony convictions. **Criteria:** Recipients are selected based on commitment to aviation goals; interest in both general and commercial aviation in Alaska; evidence of financial need; personal and career goals.

Funds Avail.: $2,500. **To Apply:** Applicants must provide

a letter of recommendation from one of their current instructors attesting to the commitment of the applicant to the program; must submit a completed application form; school transcripts; proof of U.S. citizenship. **Deadline:** March 31. **Contact:** Completed applications should be sent to: AK Airmen's Scholarship Committee at the above address.

194 ■ Alaska Broadcasters Association (ABA)
c/o Darlene Simono, Exec. Dir.
700 W 41st St.
Anchorage, AK 99503
Ph: (907) 258-2424
Fax: (907) 258-2414
Free: 888-749-8008
E-mail: akba@gci.net
URL: www.alaskabroadcasters.org

195 ■ Linda Simmons Memorial Scholarships
(Undergraduate/Scholarship)

Purpose: To provide encouragement and financial assistance to students who have demonstrated their interest in the communications arts and their abilities in the area of academic performance, attendance and discipline. **Focus:** Broadcasting. **Qualif.:** Candidate must be pursuing a degree or certified course of study in an accredited junior/community college, college, university or professional trade school; must be pursuing radio and/or television broadcasting or broadcast engineering as a major course of study. Application from candidates pursuing major studies in journalism, public relations or advertising will be considered if there are no qualified candidates with broadcast communications or broadcast engineering majors; must be residents of the State of Alaska. Student must demonstrate excellence in the following areas: academic performance; discipline/attitude; attendance. **Criteria:** Selection will be based on the submitted application materials.

Funds Avail.: $2,000. **To Apply:** Applicants must submit a formal application sheet; short written essay expressing applicant's personal goals; and three letters of reference that address the following criteria: academic performance, discipline/attitude and attendance. **Deadline:** April 1. **Contact:** ABA at the above address.

196 ■ Alaska Community Foundation
400 L St., Ste. 100
Anchorage, AK 99501
Ph: (907) 334-6700
Fax: (907) 334-5780
E-mail: info@alaskacf.org
URL: www.alaskacf.org/index.php

197 ■ Nordic Ski Association of Anchorage Scholarships *(Undergraduate/Scholarship)*

Purpose: To encourage scholastic performance, cross-country skiing and participation in community ski activities. **Focus:** General studies. **Qualif.:** Applicants must be Alaska residents who are high school seniors or currently enrolled college students; must be members of the high school cross-country ski team during their junior and senior years and must have individual or family memberships in the NSAA; and must have a cumulative GPA of at least 2.7 on a 4.0 scale. **Criteria:** Preference will be given to students attending college in Alaska. Applicants will be selected based on their academic performance and application materials.

Awards are arranged alphabetically below their administering organizations

Funds Avail.: $1,500. **To Apply:** Application forms are available at Nordic Skiing Association of Anchorage, 203 W 15th Ave., No. 204, Anchorage, AK 99501. Applicants must have a letter of recommendation, list of personal achievements and honors, a brief statement describing any community service, a maximum 500-word essay on the "benefits you have received from skiing", and a copy of official transcripts from all high school or university works. **Deadline:** April 1.

198 ■ Alberta 4-H
97 E Lake Ramp NE
Airdrie, AB, Canada T4A 0C3
Ph: (403) 948-8510
Fax: (403) 948-2069
E-mail: marquerite.stark@gov.ab.ca
URL: www.4h.ab.ca

199 ■ Grande Prairie 4-H District Scholarships
(Undergraduate/Scholarship)

Purpose: To financially support deserving student members of the Organization who seek for continuing education. **Focus:** General studies. **Qualif.:** Applicant must be a Grande Prairie 4-H District member student and a resident of Alberta based on Student Finance Regulations who have minimum year residency in Alberta immediately prior to the application date and enrolled full-time in a post secondary program recognized by Alberta Advanced Education. **Criteria:** Applicants will be evaluated based on their financial need, commitment to living and working in northern Alberta for a specified amount of time upon graduation, and reasonable good prospects for employment in northern Alberta after graduation.

Funds Avail.: $1,500. **Number Awarded:** 2. **To Apply:** Applicants must submit complete Provincial 4-H Scholarship application and NADC scholarship application. **Deadline:** May 5. **Remarks:** In partnership with Northern Alberta Development Council (NADC). **Contact:** Grande Prairie 4-H District, Scholarship Committee, Unit 90, 10001 - 101 Ave., Grande Prairie, AB, T8V 0X9.

200 ■ Provincial and Regional 4-H Scholarships
(Undergraduate/Scholarship)

Purpose: To financially support deserving student members of the Organization who seek to continue their education. **Focus:** General studies. **Qualif.:** Applicant must be a past or present member of Alberta 4-H Club and/or a full-time post-secondary student at an officially recognized institution. **Criteria:** Recipients are selected based on a set of criteria designed by the Selection Committee made up of representatives from Alberta 4-H Council, 4-H Foundation of Alberta, 4-H Branch.

Funds Avail.: $85,000. **Number Awarded:** 105. **To Apply:** Applicant must submit a completed type-written scholarship application form; and must include an original photo along with the official transcript request for the last year's education. **Deadline:** May 5. **Contact:** Application form and other supporting documents should be submitted to 4-H Foundation of Alberta or call 877-682-2153, Fax: 780-682-3784, E-mail: jackie.mann@4hab.com or foundation@4hab.com.

201 ■ Servus Credit Union 4-H Scholarships
(Undergraduate/Scholarship)

Purpose: To provide financial assistance for Alberta 4-H members to further education. **Focus:** General studies.

Qualif.: Applicants must be Alberta 4-H members who have been involved for a minimum of three years; entering their first year of study at a postsecondary institution in Alberta within one year of graduation from high school; and reside in the following Servus Credit Union trade areas: Andrew, Devon, Drayton Valley, Elk Point, Entwistle, Fort Saskatchewan, Gibbons, Lamont, Leduc, Legal, Morinville, Mundare, Myrnam, Plamondon, Sangudo, St. Paul, Stony Plain and Wabamun. **Criteria:** Recipients are selected based on their demonstrated outstanding 4-H achievement, leadership skills, community involvement and academic standing.

Funds Avail.: $500. **Number Awarded:** 2. **To Apply:** Applicants must submit application form and the complete materials needed to avail the scholarship. **Deadline:** May 5.

202 ■ Alberta Agricultural Economics Association (AAEA)
University of Alberta
515 General Services Bldg.
Edmonton, AB, Canada T6G 2H1
Ph: (780) 492-4562
E-mail: info@aaea.ab.ca
URL: www.aaea.ab.ca

203 ■ Alberta Agricultural Economics Association Masters Scholarships *(Graduate/Scholarship)*

Purpose: To recognize the deserving students in Alberta. **Focus:** Agribusiness, Agricultural economics. **Qualif.:** Applicants must be students enrolled in an M.Sc program in Agricultural Economics or Agri-Food Business Management or Natural Resource Economics in the Department of Rural Economy; must have GPA of 7.5 in their first year of their Masters program. **Criteria:** Selection of applicants will be based on academic achievement; commitment, contribution; initiative and leadership at the University in the community and in Alberta's agri-business.

Funds Avail.: $1,000. **To Apply:** For further information about the scholarship and requirements, applicants are advice to contact the Association at AAEA, 515 General Services Bldg., University of Alberta, Edmonton, AB T6G 2H1.

204 ■ Alberta Agricultural Economics Association Undergraduate Scholarships
(Undergraduate/Scholarship)

Purpose: To recognize the deserving students in Alberta. **Focus:** Economics; Agribusiness. **Qualif.:** Applicants must be full-time students enrolled in the third or fourth year of a B.Sc. Applied Economics or Agri-Food Business Management program in the faculty of Agriculture, Forestry and Home Economics; must have GPA of 7.5 in their most recent academic year. **Criteria:** Selection of applicants will be based on academic achievement; commitment; contribution; initiative and leadership at the University in the community and in Alberta's agri-business.

Funds Avail.: $500. **To Apply:** For further information about the scholarship and requirements, applicants are advised to contact the Association at AAEA, 515 General Services Bldg., University of Alberta, Edmonton, AB T6G 2H1.

205 ■ Alberta Association of Gerontology (AAG)
10216-124 St., No. 300
Edmonton, AB, Canada T5N 4A3

Awards are arranged alphabetically below their administering organizations

E-mail: info@aagweb.ca
URL: www.aagweb.ca

206 ■ Alberta Association of Gerontology Student Awards *(Graduate/Award)*

Purpose: To assist with the costs associated with a student's coursework, research or attendance at a workshop or conference. **Focus:** Gerontology. **Qualif.:** Applicants must be an Albertan registered in a graduate degree program in an accredited post secondary institution; must not be in the last term of their program; demonstrate interest in any aspect of aging; agree to contribute an article for an edition of the AAGmag (e.g., a written summary of research). **Criteria:** Selection will be based on academic merit as illustrated by grades and educational attainment, relevant work/volunteer, current studies/research plans, future commitment to the field of gerontology and an indication of how this award will be used to support the applicant's interest in gerontology.

Funds Avail.: $1,000. **To Apply:** A complete application package consists of: a two-page cover letter that includes a description of the applicant's current studies or research, relevant volunteer/work experience and future plans in gerontology (academic, research, practice); a completed award application form; a copy of the applicant's curriculum vitae; a copy of post-secondary education transcripts (they do not need to be original); a letter from the student's supervisor. **Deadline:** March 31. **Contact:** Lynne Mansell at the above address.

207 ■ Alberta Association of Gerontology Student Awards - Edmonton Chapter *(Graduate, Undergraduate/Award)*

Purpose: To assist with the costs associated with a student's coursework, research or attendance at a workshop or conference. **Focus:** Gerontology. **Qualif.:** Applicants must be registered in a degree, diploma or certificate program in an accredited post-secondary institution (undergraduate, graduate, and diploma students); reside in Edmonton or surrounding communities; not be in the last term of their program; demonstrate an interest in any aspect of aging; agree to contribute an article for an edition of the AAGmag (e.g., a written summary of their research or studies). **Criteria:** Selection will be based on academic merit as illustrated by grades and educational attainment, relevant work/volunteer, current studies/research plans, future commitment to the field of gerontology and an indication of how this award will be used to support the applicant's interest in gerontology. Preference will be given to full-time students, graduate students and current AAG members.

Funds Avail.: $500. **To Apply:** A complete application package consists of: a one-page cover letter that includes a description of the applicant's current studies or research as well as future plans in gerontology (academic, research, practice); a completed award application form; a copy of the applicant's curriculum vitae; a copy of post-secondary education transcripts (they do not need to be original) or verification of the student's studies or research (e.g., current timetable, a letter from the student's supervisor). **Deadline:** April 30. **Contact:** Suzanne Maisey, 6620-28 Ave., Edmonton, AB T6K 2R1.

208 ■ Alberta Barley Commission

3601A 21 St. NE, No. 200
Calgary, AB, Canada T2E 6T5
Ph: (403) 291-9111

Fax: (403) 291-0190
Free: 800-265-9111
E-mail: barleyinfo@albertabarley.com
URL: www.albertabarley.com

209 ■ Eugene Boyko Scholarships *(Undergraduate/Scholarship)*

Purpose: To provide scholarship opportunity to the students of Alberta, Canada. **Focus:** Agricultural sciences. **Qualif.:** Applicants must be: Canadian citizens or permanent Canadian residents living in Alberta; attending a post-secondary institution in Alberta; enrolled full-time in the second or subsequent year of post-secondary study. **Criteria:** Selection will be based on academic achievement in their previous year of post-secondary studies.

Funds Avail.: $500. **To Apply:** Application forms are available from Alberta Scholarship Programs and from Alberta post-secondary institutions. Mail completed application and an official transcript to: Alberta Scholarship Programs 4th Floor - 9940 106 St. Box 28000 Station Main, Edmonton, AB T6J 4R4. **Deadline:** August 1. **Contact:** Alberta Scholarship Program, 780-427-8640, scholarships@gov.ab.ca.

210 ■ Alberta Blue Cross

10009 108th St. NW
Edmonton, AB, Canada T5J 3C5
Ph: (780) 498-8000
Fax: (780) 425-4627
Free: 800-661-6995
URL: www.ab.bluecross.ca

211 ■ Alberta Blue Cross Scholarships for Aboriginal Students *(Undergraduate/Scholarship)*

Purpose: To provide support for young Albertans in their quest for higher skills and meaningful employment. **Focus:** General studies. **Qualif.:** Applicant must be a registered Indian, Inuit or Metis; have been a resident of Alberta the during previous year of study; have completed the final year of high school and be entering into the first year of post-secondary studies at an accredited Alberta post-secondary institute. **Criteria:** Selection is based on scholastic achievement in Alberta Grade 12 diploma examinations, financial need and community involvement.

Funds Avail.: $375-$1,250. **Number Awarded:** 3. **To Apply:** Applicants must submit a completed application form along with a copy of Alberta Education High School transcript; a list or description of involvement in the community and school-sponsored events over the past two years; two letters of reference on letterhead paper; proof of Aboriginal status; a letter confirming attendance from one of the accredited post-secondary educational institution; and a short essay about the application and the reasons for applying for the scholarship. **Deadline:** September 30.

212 ■ Alberta Child Care Association (ACCA)

10025 - 106 St., Ste. 110
Edmonton, AB, Canada T5J 1G4
Ph: (780) 421-7544
Fax: (780) 428-0080
E-mail: nataliew.accna@telus.net
URL: www.albertachildcare.org

Awards are arranged alphabetically below their administering organizations

213 ■ Alberta Child Care Association Professional Development Grants *(Professional development/Grant)*

Purpose: To support the education of child care professionals. **Focus:** Child care. **Qualif.:** Grant is open to all child development supervisors and must meet the following requirements: work as a paid staff member or family child care consultants/coordinators for a licensed and approved child care program or family child care agency in Alberta; work 80 hours each month in a licensed day care, or family child care or for 40 hours each month in a licensed out-of-school care program. **Criteria:** Selection will be based on the committee's criteria.

Funds Avail.: No specific amount. **To Apply:** Candidates' centre will apply on their behalf and must submit the following: completed Alberta Child Care Association Professional Development funding form; a copy of Child Development Supervisor Certificate; Proof of payment for the conference/workshop or course that is requested for reimbursement to be submitted along with the PD application. **Deadline:** December 15. **Remarks:** Funded by Alberta Children and Youth Services and administered by the Alberta Child Care Association.

214 ■ Alberta Foundation for the Arts

10708 - 105 Ave.
Edmonton, AB, Canada T5H 0A1
Ph: (780) 427-9968
URL: www.affta.ab.ca

215 ■ Aboriginal Traditional Arts Project Grants *(Professional development/Grant)*

Purpose: To raise the profile of Aboriginal artists to express and share their culture and perspectives primarily in a traditional cultural art media, and to support traditional art that is passed from one generation to the next. **Focus:** Culture; Media arts. **Qualif.:** Applicants must be Canadian citizens or landed immigrants; have their primary residence in Alberta for one full year before applying for a grant; ensembles must be made up of members who meet the individual criteria; applicants, including ensembles, must not be incorporated with provincial or federal corporate registries. **Criteria:** Selection will be based on the submitted application and supporting materials.

Funds Avail.: $15,000 and may include up to $3,000 per month subsistence allowance. **To Apply:** Applicants must provide the following in the application package: a completed application form and signed Applicant Agreement with original signature. Ensembles must designate one member who is the contact person for all requirements of the grant; must submit the required materials if the applicants are under the age of 18 years at the time of application; an application checklist must be completed and submitted with the application; a detailed description of the project, which demonstrates the project's connection to historical practice in a specific Aboriginal community. Protocols and permission from the community to use traditional tribal knowledge must be addressed. Include a letter of agreement with mentor, elder or cultural resource person, and an outline of the objectives, planned activities, expected results and benefits; a balanced project budget detailing revenues and expenditures in Canadian dollars. Total revenues must equal total expenditures; a professional resume. Applicants must also include the following: for art production, a list of all principals involved in the project and their resumes; for marketing or research, of-ficial invitations, confirmation or itineraries, as applicable; for marketing, a detailed marketing plan; for mentorship, training or career development. Applicants who have been accepted into a mentorship must provide a letter of agreement as proof of acceptance and support from the mentor, elder or cultural resource person and a detailed description, schedule and budget for the course of study. Applicants are encourage to submit additional support materials that may assist in the assessment process. These may include press clippings, invitations, reference letters, reviews, catalogues, scripts, published books or storyboards. Applicants must submit applications in the following format to allow for ease of use by juries: submit four complete, assembled application packages (one original and three copies of the application forms and all printed attachments) along with one copy of audio and/or visual support materials; assemble the parts of the packages in the same order as the checklist for this grant; clip applications into four packages. Do not bind or use folders, page covers or binders; remember to make one additional copy of the complete application package and keep it for your records. Audio and/or visual support materials such as CD, videocassette or DVD must be clearly labelled with the applicant's name on the media. All media must be compatible with Microsoft Windows operating system and NTSC VHS video standards. The applicant is responsible for providing support materials that comply with the viewing capabilities of the AFA. Only one copy of these support materials is required. **Deadline:** February 1 or September 1. **Contact:** ATA at the above address.

216 ■ Art Acquisition by Application Project Grants *(Professional development/Grant)*

Purpose: To provide support for individual artists through the purchase of art produced by Albertan artists and offers an opportunity for Albertans to experience the legacy of Alberta's visual arts community. **Focus:** Arts. **Qualif.:** Artists must be Canadian citizens or landed immigrants; have their primary residence in Alberta for one full year before applying to the program; have met the reporting requirements of any previously applied for AFA grant programs; have had at least one public exhibition featuring their work. Interested artists may submit artworks in one or more of the following categories: painting; sculpture; fibre art; ceramics; drawing; printmaking (excluding reproductions); photography; glass; mixed media (including new media). **Criteria:** Selection will be based on the expert jury's criteria.

Funds Avail.: No specific amount. **To Apply:** Applicants must submit one copy of the complete, assembled application package (application form and all attachments). Staple or clip applications and do not use folders, page covers or binders. Applicants to this program must provide the following in the application package: A completed and signed Application Form and Artist Agreement. If a galley/agent is submitting on the artists' behalf, they must designate one person as the contact for all requirements of the submission and must complete the Application Form, or the artist must complete and sign with an original signature the Authorization for Submission by a Commercial Gallery/Agent and the Artist Agreement; the artists' current resume and an artist statement including background information on the works submitted. A visual representation of the proposed artworks to be purchased by the AFA. This must be submitted as follows: digital image files on CD-ROM. Submission of artwork images on CD-ROM, available for purchase, must be compatible with Microsoft Windows operating system; images must be provided on one CD-ROM clearly labeled with the name of the artist who produced the artworks and the name of the gallery or agent

Awards are arranged alphabetically below their administering organizations

if applicable; each image on the disc must be labelled with the artists name, title of the work and be ordered and numbered corresponding to the Artwork Submission List ("1_Lastname_title.jpg"); image must be in JPEG format, 2280 x 1750 pixel range and between 1-2MB in size; for galleries submitting multiple submissions on one disk, each artist's images must be in a separate folder and labeled; images may represent from 1 to 5 artworks as listed on the Artwork Submission List; an artwork comprised of more than one part/component where the individual parts/components can also be sold separately is considered to be more than one artwork. Applicants must also submit a completed Artwork Submission List. Applicants requesting the return of their CD-ROM must provide a stamped, self-addressed envelope. **Deadline:** April 1.

217 ■ Cultural Relations Project Grants *(Professional development/Grant)*

Purpose: To support professional artists and arts organizations in any arts discipline that will represent Alberta at a national or international level, and to encourage professional artists in community residencies in partnership with an Albertan or Western Canadian community organization. **Focus:** Arts; Culture. **Qualif.:** Applicants must be Canadian citizens or landed immigrants; have their primary residence in Alberta for one full year before applying for a grant. In order to be eligible for a project grant from this fund, an organization must: be incorporated as a not-for-profit and be in good standing with Corporate Registry in Alberta, Saskatchewan, Manitoba or British Columbia; demonstrate responsible fiscal management. Eligible projects include: projects taking place outside of Canada that, in the opinion of the AFA support the development and promotion of Alberta art internationally; projects taking place in Canada but outside of Alberta that, in the opinion of the AFA, support the development and promotion of Alberta art Nationally; artists in the community residencies: (i) applications jointly submitted by an Alberta artist or arts organization and an incorporated not-for-profit Western Canadian organization for a community residency of up to 12 months; (ii) up to three months of collaborative research and development for a 10-12 months residency program; (iii) applications serving more than one community; (iv) applications between an artist and an incorporated for-profit company or organization. **Criteria:** Preference will be given to projects that meet any of the following criteria: projects destined for those countries designated as a priority by the Government of Alberta; projects with confirmed support from the Government of Canada and/or the Canada Council for the Arts; project with clearly demonstrated support from the host community; projects that introduce Alberta artists to new audiences; increase artistic activity in a community, encourage development of future artists and arts audiences, or encourage linkages between artists and the broader community.

Funds Avail.: No specific amount. **To Apply:** Applicants to this program must provide the following in the application package: A complete Application Form, Applicants Agreement, and Application checklist (Attachment VII of the Individual Artists Project Grant Program Application Form or Attachment XII of the Organization Project Grant Program Application Form). Organizations must designate one member who is the contact person for all requirements of the grant. Projects involving more than one artist must be submitted by an organization or by an individual submitting as an ensemble/group. Separate individual artist applications will not be accepted for the same project; the organization's most recent annual financial statement, approved and signed by two board members other than the

Treasurer, demonstrating responsible fiscal management; a copy of the organization's most recent return to a Western Canadian Corporate Registry; a detailed description of the project, including an outline of the objectives, planned activities, and expected results and benefits (for Development applications for Artists in the Community projects, a description of the proposed community needs assessment must be included); a balanced project budget detailing revenues (including the amount requested from the AFA) and expenditures. Total revenues must equal total expenditures; artists in the Community Residencies must provide a signed contract or Memorandum of Understanding between the artist and the organization or municipality that clearly outlines the terms and conditions of the residency and the rights and obligations of each party; a resume of the artist(s) or arts company profile of those representing Alberta in the project; applicants must also include any applicable itinerary, travel confirmations and funding confirmations. Applicants must also include letter(s) or invitation from the host organization. Applicants are encouraged to submit additional support materials that may assist in the assessment process. These may include press clippings, invitations, reference letters, reviews, catalogues, scripts, CD's, DVD's and storyboards. Only one copy of these materials is required. First time applicants must include three letters of reference from recognized peers who attest that the applicant maintains a standard of professionalism that will represent Alberta artists in a positive light. Applicants must submit one original copy of the complete, assembled application package (Application Form, Applicant Agreement and all printed attachments). Staple or clip applications and do not use folders, page covers or binders. Audio and/or visual support materials such as CD, videocassette or DVD must be clearly labelled with the applicant's name. Use separate discs for different file types. All media must be compatible with Microsoft Windows operating system and NTSC VHS video standards. The applicant is responsible for providing support materials that comply with the viewing capabilities of the AFA. An Application Checklist must be completed and submitted with the application.

218 ■ Dance Project Grants *(Professional development/Grant)*

Purpose: To support the development of individual Alberta artists, arts administrators or an ensemble of artists by providing a grant from a specific dance project in a limited time period. **Focus:** Arts; Dance. **Qualif.:** Applicants must be Canadian citizens or landed immigrants; have their primary residence in Alberta for one full year before applying for a grant. In order to be eligible from a project grants, ensembles must be made up of members who meet the individual criteria. Applicants, including ensembles, must not be incorporated with provincial or federal corporate registries. Eligible projects must meet the criteria in one of the following categories: Art production includes the development, creation and production of any dance work. Alberta individual artists that have been contracted by commissioners to create a specific work may apply under this category; Training and career development includes a workshop, master class summer program, professional development or professional course of study in dance. Dancers, dance instructors, designers, arts administrators and technicians may apply; Marketing includes projects that promote, market or distribute the work of Alberta dance artists; Research includes activities that support or result in the development of a dance project. **Criteria:** Selection will be based on the jury's criteria.

Funds Avail.: $15,000 and may include up to $3,000 per month subsistence allowance. **To Apply:** Applicants must

Awards are arranged alphabetically below their administering organizations

provide the following in the application package: a completed Application Form and signed Applicant Agreement with original signature. Ensembles must designate one member who is the contact person for all requirements of the grant. This applicant must sign the Applicant Agreement and complete the Application Form; must submit the required materials if the applicants are under the age of 18 years at the time of application; an application checklist must be completed and submitted with the application; a detailed description of the project, including an outline of the objectives, planned activities, timelines and expected results and benefits; a balanced project budget detailing revenues (including the amount requested from the AFA) and expenditures in Canadian dollars. Total revenues must equal total expenditures; an artistic resume of no more than four pages. Students may submit a description of their dance background, including level of training, performing arts activities and other relevant dance history. Applicants must also include: for art production, a list of all principals involved in the project and their resumes. To assist in the assessment process, applicants are encouraged to submit a video of previous productions of their work, or of the work-in-progress. Commission applicants are encouraged to submit a completed and signed contract with the commissioner and a plan for the exhibition, presentation, display, publication, screening or performance of the commissioned work; for marketing or research, official invitations, confirmations or itineraries, as applicable; for marketing, a detailed marketing plan; for training or career development: (i) applicants who have been accepted into a specific course must provide proof of acceptance and a detailed description, schedule and budget for the study program; applicants who have not already been accepted into a course must submit a detailed description, schedule and budget for the preferred choice. In addition, two alternate program choices should be submitted, with detailed description, schedules and budgets for each choice; (iii) for dance training programs, artists must submit two audition pieces on one VHS NTSC video cassette or DVD that is playable in a commercial DVD player. The two audition pieces together must not exceed 4 minutes in length, and must duplicate the experience of a live audition, including full body shot composition, without props or costume. One audition piece must relate to the program of study, such as classical, contemporary, jazz, modern, folk or heritage dance. The second piece must be in a contrasting style; (iv) non-performing artists must provide a resume, portfolio or videocassette/DVD of their work. Applicants are encouraged to submit additional support materials that may assist in the assessment process. These may include press clippings, invitations, reference letters, reviews, catalogues, scripts published books or storyboards. Applicants must submit applications in the following format to allow ease of use by juries: submit four complete, assembled application packages (one original and three copies of the application forms and all printed attachments) along with one copy of audio and/or visual support materials; assemble the parts of the packages in the same order as the checklist for this grant; clip application into four packages. Do not bind or use folders, page covers or binders; remember to make one additional copy of the complete application package and keep it for your records. Audio and/or visual support materials such as CD, videocassette or DVD must be clearly labelled with the applicant's name on the media. Use separate discs for different file types. All media must be compatible with Microsoft Windows operating system and NTSC VHS video standards. **Deadline:** February 1 and September 1.

219 ■ Film and Video Arts Project Grants
(Professional development/Grant)

Purpose: To support the development of individual Alberta artists, arts administrators or an ensemble of artists by providing a grant for a specific film and video arts project. **Focus:** Arts; Video; Filmmaking. **Qualif.:** Appicants must be Canadian citizens or landed immigrants; have their primary residence in Alberta for one full year before applying for a grant. In order to be eligible for a project grant, an ensemble must be made up of members who meet the individual criteria. Applicants, including ensembles, must not be incorporated with provincial or federal corporate registries. Eligible projects must meet the criteria in one of the following categories: (a) Art production: the creation of a new work in film and video arts. Eligible projects may be a distinct phase of a new work, such as script or screenplay writing, pre-production, production and post-production. Eligible genres include, but are not limited to, narrative shorts and features, experimental shorts, documentary and animation; (b) Marketing: a program of activity for a specific period of time to disseminate a completed film and video arts work and/or to develop audiences and markets for an artist's work. Eligible projects include, but are not limited to, film festival submissions, on-line distribution and promotion initiatives, attendance at screenings, exhibitions, presentations or conferences featuring the artist's work and award presentations by invitations; (c) Research: a program of activity for a specific period of time that supports or results in the development of new work in film and video arts. Eligible projects include, but are not limited to, experimentation, exploration and research (including research for documentaries) related to production; (d) Training and career development: a course or program of study to develop an artist's training in film and video arts. Eligible projects include, but are not limited to, workshops, master classes, retreats, mentorship programs and professional courses. **Criteria:** Selection will be based on the jury's criteria.

Funds Avail.: $15,000 and may include up to $3,000 per month subsistence allowance. **To Apply:** Applicants must provide the following in the application package: a completed Application Form and signed Applicant Agreement with original signature. Ensembles must designate one member who is the contact person for all requirements of the grant. Applicants must sign the Applicant Agreement and complete the Application Form; must submit the required materials if the applicants are under the age of 18 years at the time of application; an application checklist must be completed and submitted with the application; a detailed description of the project, including an outline of the objectives, planned activities, timelines and expected results and benefits; a balanced project budget detailing revenues (including the amount requested from the AFA) and expenditures in Canadian dollars. Total revenues must equal total expenditures; an artistic resume of no more than four pages. Students may submit a description of their dance background, including level of training, performing arts activities and other relevant dance history. Applicants must also include: for all categories, film and video work, scripts or storyboards of previous productions or of the work in progress to aid the assessment process. Video submissions must be a JPEG or GIF video file on VHS NTSC videocassette or one CD or DVD compatible with Microsoft Windows operating system; for art production, a list of all principals involved in the project and their resumes. Commission applicants are encouraged to submit a completed and signed contract with the commissioner and a plan for the screening, exhibition or presentation of

Awards are arranged alphabetically below their administering organizations

the commissioned work; for marketing ore research, official invitations, confirmation or itineraries, as applicable; for training or career development: (i) applicants who have been accepted into a specific course must provide proof of acceptance and a detailed description, schedule and budget for the study program; applicants who have not already been accepted into a course must submit a detailed description, schedule and budget for the preferred choice. In addition, two alternate program choices should be submitted, with detailed description, schedules and budgets for each choice. Applicants are encouraged to submit additional support materials that may assist in the assessment process. These may include press clippings, invitations, reference letters, reviews, catalogues, scripts published books or storyboards. Applicants must submit applications in the following format to allow ease of use by juries: submit four complete, assembled application packages (one original and three copies of the application forms and all printed attachments) along with one copy of audio and/or visual support materials; assemble the parts of the packages in the same order as the checklist for this grant; clip application into four packages. Do not bind or use folders, page covers or binders; remember to make one additional copy of the complete application package and keep it for your records. Audio and/or visual support materials such as CD, videocassette or DVD must be clearly labelled with the applicant's name on the media. Use separate discs for different file types. All media must be compatible with Microsoft Windows operating system and NTSC VHS video standards. **Deadline:** February 1 and September 1.

220 ■ Literary Arts Project Grants *(Professional development/Grant)*

Purpose: To support the development of individual Alberta artists, arts administrators or an ensemble of artists by providing a grant for a specific literary arts project in a limited time period. **Focus:** Arts; Literature. **Qualif.:** Applicants must be Canadian citizens or landed immigrants; have their primary residence in Alberta for one full year before applying for a grant. In order to be eligible from a project grants, ensembles must be made up of members who meet the individual criteria. Applicants, including ensembles, must not be incorporated with provincial or federal corporate registries. Eligible projects must meet the criteria in one of the following categories: (a) Art production: the creation of a new literary work. Eligible projects may be a distinct phase of a new work, such as a first draft or a final draft, in one of the eligible literary genres; (b) Marketing: a program of activity for a specific period of time to disseminate a completed literary work and/or to develop audiences and markets for an artists' work. Eligible projects include, but are not limited to, promotional reading tours and book launches; on-line marketing initiatives such as book trailers; attendance at literary festivals, non-academic conference or award presentation by invitation; (c) Research: a program of activity for a specific period of time that supports or results in the development of new work in the literary arts. Eligible projects include, but are not limited to, experimentation, exploration and research of primary materials; (d) training and career development: a course or program of study to develop a writer's training in one or more of the eligible literary genres, including literary translation. Eligible projects include, but are not limited to, workshops, master classes, retreats, mentorship programs and professional courses. Except for projects in the training and career development category, eligible applicants must be professional writers who have had literary works professional published or produced. Professional literary publications or productions are literary works: (a) that have gone

through an editorial process made by an independent editor/editorial board or that have gone through a dramaturgical process; (b) that have been published or produced by organizations with a majority of paid contributors who are not principals of the publishing or producing organization; (c) for which the writer has received compensation either as royalties, fees or honoraria, or as in-kind remuneration in the form of complimentary copies or a complimentary subscription; (d) of which the writer owns copyright; (e) that are available and accessible to the general public. Eligible literary arts genres are defined as the following: novels, short fiction, poetry, literary non-fiction, graphic novels, plays, young adult fiction and picture books. Professional writers of literary work are those who meet at least one of the following publication or production requirements: (a) a literary book published in print or as an e-book by a professional publishing house; (b) a minimum of two texts of short fiction, such as short stories or excerpts from a novel, published on two separate occasions in print or online literary magazines or periodicals, or in print or e-book anthologies published by professional publishing houses; (c) a minimum of five poems published on at least two separate occasions in print or online literary magazines or periodicals, or in print or e-book anthologies published by professional publishing houses; (d) a minimum of two texts of literary non-fiction published on two separate occasions in print or online literary magazines or periodicals, or in print or e-book anthologies published by professional publishing houses; (e) a play professionally produced. Applicants with a publishing or producing history established outside of Canada must provide in their artistic resumes evidence that their publications or productions are professional literary work. A statement of editorial and copyright policy of the publishes or producers may be required. **Criteria:** Selection will be based on the jury's criteria.

Funds Avail.: $15,000 and may include up to $3,000 per month subsistence allowance. **To Apply:** Applicants must provide the following in the application package: a completed Application Form and signed Applicant Agreement with original signature. Ensembles must designate one member who is the contact person for all requirements of the grant. Applicants must sign the Applicant Agreement and complete the Application Form; must submit the required materials if the applicants are under the age of 18 years at the time of application; an application checklist must be completed and submitted with the application; a detailed description of the project, including an outline of the objectives, planned activities, timelines and expected results and benefits; a balanced project budget detailing revenues (including the amount requested from the AFA) and expenditures in Canadian dollars. Total revenues must equal total expenditures; an artistic resume of no more than four pages that includes a current list of literary works professionally published and produce. Applicants must identify the title, publisher, genre, year published/produced, and length/duration for each work. The artistic resume should also include other literary arts activities such as level of training, readings, performances and self-published works, if applicable. Applicants must also include the following: for all categories, a writing sample of no more than 15 pages, preferably from a work in progress. The writing sample must be a clean copy on white, 8.5 x 11 paper, single-sided, 1.5 or double-spaced and in 12-pt. font; for art production or research involving literary translation projects, a sample manuscript of original text along with a translated version in English; for art production or research involving anthology projects, an agreement with, or expression of interest from, a publisher including a clear statement that

Awards are arranged alphabetically below their administering organizations

identifies the publisher's proposed financial contribution for such costs as editing, legal fees and postage, as well as the publisher's role in the selection of anthology materials; for marketing or research, official invitations, confirmations or itineraries, as applicable; for marketing, a detailed marketing plan; for training or career development: (a) applicants who have been accepted into a specific course must provide proof of acceptance and a detailed description, schedule and budget for the program; (b) applicants who have not already been accepted into a specific course must submit a detailed description, schedule and budget for the preferred choice. In addition, at least two alternate program choices should be submitted, with detailed descriptions, schedules and budgets for each choice. Applicants are encouraged to submit additional support materials that may assist in the assessment process. These may include press clippings, invitations, reference letters, reviews, catalogues, scripts, published books or storyboards. Applicants must submit applications in the following format to allow for ease of use by juries: submit four complete, assembled application packages (one original and three copies of the application forms and all printed attachments) along with one copy of audio and/or visual support materials; assemble the parts of the packages in the same order as the checklist for this grant; clip applications into four packages. Do not bind or use folders, page covers or binders; remember to make one additional copy of the complete application package and keep it for your records. Audio and/or visual support materials such as CD, videocassette or DVD must be clearly labelled with the applicant's name on the media. Use separate discs for different file types. All media must be compatible with Microsoft Windows operating system and NTSC VHS video standards. **Deadline:** February 1 or September 1.

221 ■ Music Project Grants (Professional development/Grant)

Purpose: To support the development of individual Alberta artists, arts administrators or an ensemble of artists by providing a grant for a specific music project in a limited time period. **Focus:** Music. **Qualif.:** Applicants must be Canadian citizens or landed immigrants; have their primary residence in Alberta for one full year before applying for a grant. In order to be eligible for a project grants, ensembles must be made up of members who meet the individual criteria. Applicants, including ensembles, must not be incorporated with provincial or federal corporate registries. Eligible projects must meet the criteria in one of the following categories: (a) Art production demo recording project, not intended for sale, including full production support and basic press kit expenses, or commercial recording projects, intended for sale, including support for pre-production and song development (basic recording); (b) Marketing includes, but is not limited to, marketing and promotion of a commercial release, costs associated with performances at special events by invitation, and promotional tours. Recording artists marketing a commercial recording or producing a music video must have released a commercial recording prior to applying; (c) Research includes activities that support or result in the development of a music project; (d) Training and career development includes a course or program of study to develop an artist's training in music. Eligible projects include, but are not limited to, workshop, master classes, summer program mentorship program, or professional course of study in performance, recording arts or composition. **Criteria:** Selection will be based on the jury's criteria.

Funds Avail.: $15,000 and may include up to $3,000 per month subsistence allowance. **To Apply:** Applicants must

provide the following in the application package: A completed application form and signed Applicant Agreement with original signature. Ensembles must designate one member who is the contact person for all requirements of the grant. Applicants must sign the Applicant Agreement and complete the Application Form; must submit the required materials if the applicants are under the age of 18 years at the time of application; an application checklist must be completed and submitted with the application; a detailed description of the project, including an outline of the objectives, planned activities, timelines and expected results and benefits; a balanced project budget detailing revenues (including the amount requested from the AFA) and expenditures in Canadian dollars. Total revenues must equal total expenditures; an artistic resume of no more than four pages that includes past training, most recent performance highlights, compositions, discography, and ensemble experience. Applicants must also include the following: (a) for art production, include a demo recording, commercial recording, signed contract with the commissioner and a plan for the exhibition, presentation, display, publication, screening or performance of the commissioned work (commission applicants); for all other art production projects include one copy of audio material, including two musical selections; (b) for marketing, include: any official invitations, confirmations or itineraries; a detailed marketing plan; one copy of audio material, including two musical selection, A final copy of a commercially released recording is required for the marketing of commercial recordings or music videos; (c) for research, include: any official invitations, confirmations or itineraries; one copy of audio material, including two musical selections, if applicable; (d) for training or career development: (i) applicants who have been accepted into a specific course must submit: proof of acceptance; a detailed description; a program schedule; budget for the study program; one copy of audio material, including two musical selections. For performance programs, the two selections must be of contrasting style; (ii) applicants who have not already been accepted into a course must submit the following information for the preferred study programs including: a detailed description; a program schedule; budget for each study program; one copy of audio material, including two musical selections. For performance programs, the two selections must be of contrasting style. Applicants are encouraged to submit additional support materials that may assist in the assessment process. These may include press clippings, invitations, reference letters, reviews, catalogues, scripts, published books or storyboards. Applicants must submit applications in the following format to allow for ease of use by juries: submit four complete, assembled application packages (one original and three copies of the application form and all printed attachments) along with one copy of audio and/or visual support materials; assemble the parts of the packages in the same order as the checklist for this grant; clip applications into four packages. Do not bind or use folders, page covers or binders; remember to make one additional copy of the complete application package and keep it for your records. Audio and/or visual support materials such as CD, videocassette or DVD must be clearly labelled with the applicant's name on the media. Use separate discs for different file types. All media must be compatible with Microsoft Windows operating system and NTSC VHS video standards. The applicant is responsible for providing support materials that comply with the viewing capabilities of the AFA. **Deadline:** February 1 and September 1.

Awards are arranged alphabetically below their administering organizations

222 ■ Theatre and Performance Art Project Grants *(Professional development/Grant)*

Purpose: To support the development of individual Alberta artists, arts administrators or an ensemble of artist by providing a grant for a specific theatre and/or performance art project in a limited time period. **Focus:** Theater arts; Performing arts. **Qualif.:** Applicants must be Canadian citizens or landed immigrants; have their primary residence in Alberta for one full year before applying for a grant. In order to be eligible for project grants, ensembles must be made up of members who meet the individual criteria. Applicants, including ensembles, must not be incorporated with provincial or federal corporate registries. Eligible projects must meet the criteria in one of the following categories: Art production includes the development, creation and production of any theatre/performance art work. Alberta individual artists/ensembles that have been contracted by commissioners to create a specific work; Marketing includes projects that promote, market or distribute the work of Alberta theatre/performance arts artists; Research includes activities that support or result in the development of a theatre/performance arts project; Training and career development includes a workshop, master class, summer program, professional development or professional course of study in theatre/performance art Theatre/Performance artists, drama instructors, designers and technicians. **Criteria:** Selection will be based on the jury's criteria.

Funds Avail.: $15,000 and may include up to $3,000 per month subsistence allowance. **To Apply:** Applicants must provide the following in the application package: a completed Application Form and signed Applicant Agreement with original signature. Ensembles must designate one member who is the contact person for all requirements of the grant. Applicants must sign the Applicant Agreement and complete the Application Form; must submit the required materials if the applicants are under the age of 18 years at the time of application; an application checklist must be completed and submitted with the application; a detailed description of the project, including an outline of the objectives, planned activities, timelines and expected results and benefits; a balanced project budget detailing revenues (including the amount requested from the AFA) and expenditures in Canadian dollars. Total revenues must equal total expenditures; an artistic resume of no more than four pages that includes a description of their theatre/performance art background, including level of training, performing arts activities and other relevant artistic history. Applicants must also include the following: for art production, a list of all principals involved in the project and their resumes. To assist in the assessment process, applicants are encouraged to submit a video of previous productions of their work, or of the work-in-progress. Commission applicants are encourage to submit a completed and signed contract with the commissioner and a plan for the workshop, exhibition, presentation, display, publication, screening or performance of the commissioned work; for marketing or research, official invitations, confirmations or itineraries, as applicable; for marketing, a detailed marketing plan; for training or career development: (i) applicants who have been accepted into a specific course must provide proof of acceptance and a detailed description, schedule and budget for the study program; (ii) applicants who have not already been accepted into a course must submit a detailed description, schedule and budget for the preferred choice. In addition, at least two alternate program choices should be submitted, with detailed descriptions, schedules and budgets for each choice. Applicants are encouraged to

submit additional support materials that may assist in the assessment process. These may include press clippings, invitations, reference letters, reviews, catalogues, scripts, published books or storyboards. Applicants must submit applications in the following format to allow for ease of use by juries: submit four complete, assembled application packages (one original and three copies of the application form and all printed attachments) along with one copy of audio and/or visual support materials; assemble the parts of the packages in the same order as the checklist for this grant; clip applications into four packages. Do not bind or use folders, page covers or binders; remember to make one additional copy of the complete application package and keep it for your records. Audio and/or visual support materials such as CD, videocassette or DVD must be clearly labelled with the applicant's name on the media. Use separate discs for different file types. All media must be compatible with Microsoft Windows operating system and NTSC VHS video standards. The applicant is responsible for providing support materials that comply with the viewing capabilities of the AFA. **Deadline:** February 1 and September 1.

223 ■ Visual Arts and New Media Project Grants *(Professional development/Grant)*

Purpose: To support the development of individual Alberta artists, arts administrators or an ensemble of artists by providing a grant for a specific literary arts project in a limited time period. **Focus:** Visual arts; Media arts. **Qualif.:** Applicants must be Canadian citizens or landed immigrants; have their primary residence in Alberta for one full year before applying for a grant. In order to be eligible from a project grants, ensembles must be made up of members who meet the individual criteria. Applicants, including ensembles, must not be incorporated with provincial or federal corporate registries. Eligible projects must meet the criteria in one of the following categories: Art production includes creation of new work in any visual arts medium. Visual arts media may include but are not limited to drawing, painting, sculpture, printmaking, clay, glass, wood, metal fibre or any combination of media. New media may include CD-ROM, Internet and other computer-assisted art; Marketing includes, but is not limited to, attending an exhibition opening, visual arts festival, workshop or award presentation by invitation and projects that promote and market the work of new media artists; Research includes activities that support or result in the development of a visual arts/new media project; training and career development includes a workshop, master class, mentorship program or professional course of study in visual arts or new media. **Criteria:** Selection will be based on the jury's criteria.

Funds Avail.: $15,000 and may include up to $3,000 per month subsistence allowance. **To Apply:** Applicants must provide the following in the application package: A completed application form and signed Applicant Agreement with original signature. Ensembles must designate one member who is the contact person for all requirements of the grant. Applicants must sign the Applicant Agreement and complete the Application Form; must submit the required materials if the applicants are under the age of 18 years at the time of application; an application checklist must be completed and submitted with the application; a detailed description of the project, including an outline of the objectives, planned activities, timelines and expected results and benefits; a balanced project budget detailing revenues (including the amount requested from the AFA) and expenditures in Canadian dollars. Total revenues must equal total expenditures; an artistic resume of no more

Awards are arranged alphabetically below their administering organizations

than four pages. Applicants must also include the following: (a) for art production, one set of no more than ten images of completed work in JPEG or GIF format. Images should be of recent work completed within last five years. The selection must be clearly marked with the applicant's name, Provide a numbered inventory of the images, including title, medium, size and year of execution. Present the images chronologically. Acceptable formats are: (i) one CD or DVD compatible with Microsoft operating system. Images must be JPEG format with a resolution of 72 dpi. A maximum size of 1024 x 798 pixels and 500K (o.5MG). Use RGB or SRGB color mode only (no CMYK). DVDs must be plug and play; (ii) one JPEG or GIF video file of no more than 5 minutes in length on VHS NTSC videocassette, CD or DVD compatible with Microsoft Windows operating system; (iii) an audio CD sample. Commission applicants are encouraged to submit a completed and signed contract with the commissioner and a plan for the exhibition, presentation, display, publication, screening or performance of the commissioned work; (b) for marketing or research, official invitations, confirmations or itineraries, as applicable; (c) for marketing, a detailed marketing plan; (d) for training or career development: (i) applicants who have been accepted into a specific course must provide proof of acceptance and a detailed description, schedule and budget for the study program; (ii) applicants who have not already been accepted into a course must submit a detailed description, schedule and budget for the preferred choice. In addition, at least two alternate program choices should be submitted, with detailed descriptions, schedules and budgets for each choice. Applicants are encouraged to submit additional support materials that may assist in the assessment process. These may include press clippings, invitations, reference letters, reviews, catalogues, scripts, published books or storyboards. Applicants must submit applications in the following format to allow for ease of use by juries: submit four complete, assembled application packages (one original and three copies of the application form and all printed attachments) along with one copy of audio and/or visual support materials; assemble the parts of the packages in the same order as the checklist for this grant; clip applications into four packages. Do not bind or use folders, page covers or binders; remember to make one additional copy of the complete application package and keep it for your records. Audio and/or visual support materials such as CD, videocassette or DVD must be clearly labelled with the applicant's name on the media. Use separate discs for different file types. All media must be compatible with Microsoft Windows operating system and NTSC VHS video standards. The applicant is responsible for providing support materials that comply with the viewing capabilities of the AFA. **Deadline:** February 1 and September 1.

224 ■ Alberta Holstein Association

R.R.1
Didsbury, AB, Canada T0M 0W0
Ph: (403) 335-5916
Fax: (403) 335-4751
E-mail: info@albertaholstein.ca
URL: www.albertaholstein.ca

225 ■ Alberta Holstein Association Scholarships *(Undergraduate/Scholarship)*

Purpose: To encourage students to pursue their education by providing educational funds for deserving undergraduate students. **Focus:** Agriculture, Economic aspects. **Qualif.:**

Applicant must have completed at least the first year of university/college; must be returning to school within the calendar year; must be a regular or junior member of the Alberta Branch Holstein Canada, or a son/daughter of a member. **Criteria:** Recipient will be selected based on farm involvement, community participation, extracurricular activities and academic standing.

Funds Avail.: $500. **Number Awarded:** 4. **To Apply:** Applicant must submit a completed application form available from the website; a 500 to 1000-word essay explaining their farm involvement, volunteer experience along with future employment ambitions. **Deadline:** October 31. **Contact:** Heidi Voegeli-Bleiker, 403-335-5916.

226 ■ Alberta Indian Investment Corporation (AIIC)

PO Box 180
Enoch, AB, Canada T7X 3Y3
Ph: (780) 470-3600
Fax: (780) 470-3605
Free: 888-308-6789
E-mail: info@aiicbusiness.org
URL: www.aiicbusiness.org

227 ■ Sam Bull Memorial Scholarships *(Undergraduate/Scholarship)*

Purpose: To provide scholarship assistance to qualified individuals who want to pursue their education. **Focus:** Law; Political science. **Qualif.:** Applicant must be a First Nation native who has resided in Alberta for at least one year; must demonstrate interest in law or political science education. **Criteria:** Recipient will be evaluated by the selection committee based on academic performance, chosen area of study in relation to First Nation community development and future career aspirations.

Funds Avail.: $1,000. **To Apply:** Applicant must prepare a 100 to 200 word statement of personal and academic objectives, which should emphasize how their proposed course of study will contribute to First Nation community development in Canada. Application forms are available online and must be sent together with other supporting documents to General Manager, PO Box 180, Enoch, AB T7X 3Y3. **Deadline:** February 15.

228 ■ Senator James Gladstone Memorial Scholarships *(Graduate, Undergraduate/ Scholarship)*

Purpose: To provide scholarship assistance to qualified individuals who want to pursue their education. **Focus:** Law; Political science. **Qualif.:** Applicant must be a First Nation native who has resided in Alberta for at least one year; must demonstrate interest in law or political science education. **Criteria:** Recipient will be evaluated by the selection committee based on strong academic performance, chosen area of study in relation to First Nation business/economic development and future career aspirations.

Funds Avail.: $750-$1,000. **To Apply:** Applicant must submit a transcript of record; must prepare a 100 to 200 word statement of personal and academic objectives which should emphasize how their proposed course of study will contribute to First Nation economic and business development in Canada. Application form and other supporting documents must be sent to General Manager, Alberta Indian Investment Corporation, PO Box 180, Enoch, AB

Awards are arranged alphabetically below their administering organizations

T7X 3Y3. **Deadline:** February 15.

229 ■ Alberta Ingenuity Fund

250 Karl Clark Rd.
Edmonton, AB, Canada T6N 1E4
Ph: (780) 450-5111
Fax: (780) 450-5333
E-mail: info@albertaingenuity.ca
URL: www.albertaingenuity.ca/welcome

230 ■ Alberta Ingenuity Graduate Student Scholarships *(Doctorate, Graduate/Scholarship)*

Purpose: To enable academically superior graduate students, in a natural science or engineering discipline, to undertake full-time research training at an Alberta university, leading to a research-based Master's or Doctoral degree. **Focus:** Science; Engineering. **Qualif.:** Applicant must be entering or currently in a full-time graduate program at an Alberta university in a science or engineering-related discipline working towards a research-based master's or doctoral degree. **Criteria:** Selection is based on excellence of the student and the proposed research.

Funds Avail.: Up to $23,000 for a Master's student or up to $26,000 for a Doctoral student per year and a $1,500 yearly research allowance. **To Apply:** Applicants must submit an original, signed application form along with official transcripts or certified copies of transcripts in sealed envelopes (if not sent directly to Alberta Ingenuity office); and three letters of reference in sealed envelopes (if not sent directly to Alberta Ingenuity office). **Deadline:** December 1. **Contact:** Kelly French at kelly.french@albertainnovates.ca or 780-701-3324.

231 ■ Alberta Ingenuity Graduate Student Scholarships in Nanotechnology *(Doctorate, Graduate/Scholarship)*

Purpose: To help Alberta attract and retain world class Master's and Doctoral students in the nanotechnology field. **Focus:** Science; Engineering. **Qualif.:** Applicant must be entering or currently in a full-time graduate program at an Alberta university in a science or engineering-related discipline working towards a research-based master's or doctoral degree. **Criteria:** Selection is based on excellence of the student and the proposed research.

Funds Avail.: Up to $30,000 for a Master's student or up to $45,000 for a Doctoral student. **To Apply:** Applicants must submit an original, signed application form along with official transcripts or certified copies of transcripts in sealed envelopes (if not sent directly to Alberta Ingenuity office); and three letters of reference in sealed envelopes (if not sent directly to Alberta Ingenuity office). **Deadline:** December 1. **Contact:** Kelly French at kelly.french@albertainnovates.ca or 780-701-3324.

232 ■ iCORE ICT Graduate Student Scholarships *(Doctorate, Graduate, Master's/Scholarship)*

Purpose: To help Alberta attract and retain world-class graduate students studying in an ICT related area. **Focus:** Information science and technology. **Qualif.:** Applicant must be entering or currently in a full-time graduate program at an Alberta university, in any discipline, working towards a research-based master's or doctoral degree. **Criteria:** Selection is based on the excellence of the student and the proposed research.

Funds Avail.: Up to $30,000 for a Master's student or up to $36,000 for a Doctoral student. **To Apply:** Applicants must submit an original, signed application form along with official transcripts or certified copies of transcripts in sealed envelopes (if not sent directly to Alberta Ingenuity office); and three letters of reference in sealed envelopes (if not sent directly to Alberta Ingenuity office). **Deadline:** December 1. **Remarks:** In partnership with iCORE and Alberta Advanced Education and Technology (AET). **Contact:** Lilly Wong at wong@icore.ca or 403-210-5340.

233 ■ Alberta Innovates Technology Futures

250 Karl Clark Rd.
Edmonton, AB, Canada T6N 1E4
Ph: (780) 450-5111
Fax: (780) 450-5333
E-mail: referral@albertainnovates.ca
URL: www.albertatechfutures.ca

234 ■ Alberta Innovates Graduate Student Scholarship *(Graduate/Scholarship)*

Purpose: To enable promising students to succeed in areas of scientific research which are strategically important to Alberta. **Focus:** Information science and technology; Health sciences; Energy-related areas; Environmental technology. **Qualif.:** Candidate must be Canadian citizens who hold a new NSERC (Natural Sciences and Engineering Research Council of Canada) or international and Canadian candidates who do not hold an NSERC award, studying at an Alberta university to do graduate work in one of the following research areas: Information and Communication Technology, Nanotechnology and Omics; in and of themselves or additionally which support the areas of Health, Bio-industries, Energy and Environment. If candidates are not yet registered at an Alberta university, their eligibility to apply for the GSS is contingent upon meeting all eligibility requirements for admission to an Alberta university. The candidate should contact the university of their choice for information on those requirements. **Criteria:** Each Alberta university will review all applications and evaluate them based on excellence and strategic alignment in areas of scientific research important to Alberta.

Funds Avail.: Varies. **To Apply:** Application processes are specific to the applicant's university of choice. **Contact:** Sarah Lee, Program Associate, 780-450-5553, sarah.lee@albertainnovates.ca.

235 ■ Alberta Learning Information Service (ALIS) - Alberta Scholarship Program

Box 28000 Main Sta.
Edmonton, AB, Canada T5J 4R4
Ph: (780) 427-8640
Free: 800-661-3753
E-mail: info@alis.gov.ab.ca
URL: www.alis.alberta.ca

236 ■ Alberta Award for the Study of Canadian Human Rights and Multiculturalism *(Doctorate, Graduate/Award)*

Purpose: To encourage the pursuit of studies in Canadian human rights, cultural diversity and multiculturalism. **Focus:** Human rights. **Qualif.:** Applicant must be: a Canadian citizen or permanent resident; enrolled or planning to enroll as a full-time graduate student (Master's or Doctoral level) at an Alberta public post-secondary institution; taking a

Awards are arranged alphabetically below their administering organizations

program of study that supports the purpose of this scholarship; planning to do research that is within a Canadian context and will ultimately benefit Albertans. **Criteria:** Recipients will be selected based on information provided on application form; submitted essay; and curriculum vitae.

Funds Avail.: $10,000. **Number Awarded:** 2. **To Apply:** Applicants may obtain an application form from Graduate and Awards Offices at post-secondary institutions and through Alberta Scholarship Programs at Alberta Learning Information Service's website. Applicant must submit an application form; essay; curriculum vitae and any attachment. **Deadline:** February 1. **Remarks:** Funded by an endowment from the Human Rights Education and Multiculturalism Fund and public contributions made in memory of Pardeep Singh Gundara. **Contact:** Alberta Scholarship Programs at the above address.

237 ■ Alberta Centennial Premier's Scholarships - Alberta *(Undergraduate/Scholarship)*

Purpose: To commemorate the Province of Alberta's Centennial. **Focus:** General studies. **Qualif.:** Applicants must: be Canadian citizens or permanent residents of Canada and Alberta; entering any level of post-secondary study at any university, college, technical institute or apprenticeship program in Canada. **Criteria:** Scholarship recipients are selected from nominations received for the Premier's Citizenship Award. Each high school in Alberta nominates a recipient for the Premier's Citizenship Award and each recipient is considered a nominee for the Alberta Centennial Scholarship. A selection committee will meet and review the nominations and select 25 recipients.

Funds Avail.: $2,005. **Number Awarded:** 25. **To Apply:** Nominations are submitted by high school counselors. **Deadline:** June 15. **Contact:** Alberta Scholarship Program at the above address.

238 ■ Janet and Horace Allen Scholarships *(Undergraduate/Scholarship)*

Purpose: To recognize the academic excellence of a student from Crowsnest Pass high School in the area of the sciences. **Focus:** Science. **Qualif.:** Applicants must be Alberta residents and plan to enroll full-time in a post-secondary program of at least one semester in length. **Criteria:** Recipient will be selected on the basis of achieving the highest average on two of the following Grade 12 courses at the 30 level: Biology, Chemistry, Physics or Science.

Funds Avail.: $1,500. **To Apply:** Applicants may obtain an application form from Alberta Scholarship Programs and Crowsnest Pass High School. **Deadline:** June 1.

239 ■ Art Graduate Scholarships *(Graduate/Scholarship)*

Purpose: To reward outstanding students pursuing full-time study at the masters or equivalent level. **Focus:** Arts. **Qualif.:** Applicants must be residents of Alberta enrolled or planning to enroll full-time either in music, dance, literary arts or visual arts at a Master's level or equivalent level; must demonstrate an outstanding ability in arts; and must be Canadian Citizens or permanent residents. There is a lifetime maximum of two awards per student. Scholarships are for study at graduate faculties and equivalent institutions anywhere in the world. **Criteria:** Recipients are chosen by a Selection Committee appointed by the presidents of the universities in Alberta. Applicants are judged on previous academic accomplishments; program of study; appraiser's evaluations; answers to the essay question; and general impressions from the application form.

Funds Avail.: $15,000. **Number Awarded:** 7. **To Apply:** Applicants must submit a completed application form; and two letters of reference. Original and four signed unstapled copies of application form and attachments must be submitted. **Deadline:** February 1. **Contact:** Alberta Scholarship Program at the above address.

240 ■ Theodore R. Campbell Scholarships *(Undergraduate/Scholarship)*

Purpose: To reward the accomplishments of an aboriginal student from Blue Quills First Nations College. **Focus:** General studies. **Qualif.:** Applicants must be Alberta residents and have completed the first year towards an Education degree at Blue Quills First Nations College. **Criteria:** Selection will be based on the academic achievement during first year of study.

Funds Avail.: $1,500. **To Apply:** Application forms are available from Alberta Scholarship Programs and from the Research and Planning Office at Blue Quills First Nations College. **Deadline:** June 1. **Contact:** Alberta Scholarship Program at the above address.

241 ■ Carmangay Home and School Association Scholarships *(Undergraduate/Scholarship)*

Purpose: To recognize the accomplishments of students who attended Carmangay School and to commemorate the closing of the school. **Focus:** General studies. **Qualif.:** Applicants must: be Canadian citizens or landed immigrants and residents of Alberta according to Alberta Heritage Scholarship Fund regulations; have attended Carmangay School for at least one complete school year; have achieved a high academic standing in their Grade 12 year at an Alberta high school; and plan on entering full-time studies at a recognized post-secondary institution. **Criteria:** Selection will be based on the academic achievement in Grade 12, demonstrated leadership and community involvement. Applicants must provide proof of attendance at Carmangay School either by reference letter or other documentation.

Funds Avail.: $2,500. **To Apply:** Application forms are available from regional school counselors and from the office of Alberta Scholarship Programs. Applicants must mail their application form to Alberta Scholarship Programs. **Deadline:** August 1. **Contact:** Alberta Scholarship Programs at the above address.

242 ■ Robert C. Carson Memorial Bursary *(Undergraduate/Scholarship)*

Purpose: To provide financial assistance to aboriginal students who have successfully completed the first year of a program relating to criminal justice, criminology or law. **Focus:** Criminal justice; Criminology; Law. **Qualif.:** Applicants must be Alberta residents and full-time students enrolled in the second year of either Law Enforcement or Criminal Justice. The qualifying Alberta institutions are: Lethbridge Community College, Mount Royal College, Grant MacEwan College, the University of Calgary or the University of Alberta. **Criteria:** Recipients are nominated by the educational institution they are attending. Preference will be given to non-sponsored aboriginal students.

Funds Avail.: $500. **Number Awarded:** 5. **To Apply:** Application forms are available from the Institution's Student Award Office. **Deadline:** October 1. **Remarks:** Established by Alberta Justice and Solicitor General and Alberta

Awards are arranged alphabetically below their administering organizations

Scholarship Programs. **Contact:** Alberta Scholarship Program at the above address.

243 ■ Laurence Decore Awards for Student Leadership *(Undergraduate/Scholarship)*

Purpose: To recognize those post-secondary students who have demonstrated outstanding dedication and leadership to fellow students and to their community. **Focus:** General studies. **Qualif.:** Applicants must be Alberta residents who are currently enrolled in a minimum of three courses at a designated Alberta post-secondary institution. **Criteria:** Recipients will be selected based on applicant's involvement in either government or student societies, clubs or organization.

Funds Avail.: $500. **To Apply:** Applicants do not need to apply. Schools may submit a nomination for this scholarship. **Deadline:** March 1. **Contact:** Alberta Scholarship Programs at the above address.

244 ■ Earl and Countess of Wessex - World Championships in Athletics Scholarships *(Undergraduate/Scholarship)*

Purpose: To recognize the top male and female Alberta students who have excelled in track and field. **Focus:** Athletics. **Qualif.:** Applicants must be Canadian citizens or landed immigrants and residents of Alberta, according to Alberta Scholarship Programs regulations; must have completed Grade 12 in Alberta in the same year they apply for the scholarship; must be planning on continuing their studies at a post-secondary institution in Alberta; and participating on that institution's track and field team. **Criteria:** Selection will be based on placement in provincial and national championships, AADP standards, best performances, Mercier scores and recommendations from the applicants' coaches. Academic achievement will also be a consideration.

Funds Avail.: $3,000. **To Apply:** Applicants may obtain an application form from all Alberta high schools and from Alberta Scholarship Programs. **Deadline:** October 1. **Contact:** Alberta Scholarship Program at the above address.

245 ■ Fellowships for Full-time Studies in French *(Undergraduate/Fellowship)*

Purpose: To assist Albertans in pursuing post-secondary studies taught in French. **Focus:** French studies. **Qualif.:** Applicants must be Alberta residents, Canadian citizens or landed immigrants enrolled full-time in a post-secondary program. In addition, applicants must be enrolled in a minimum of three courses per semester which have French as the language of instruction. **Criteria:** Selection will be based on academic achievement.

Funds Avail.: $500-$1,000. **To Apply:** Applicants may obtain a fillable application form from the website or from the Students Awards Office at Alberta post-secondary institutions that offer programs taught in French and from Alberta Scholarship Programs. Applicants must include proof of Canadian citizenship: either a photocopy of Canadian birth certificate, passport or immigration papers. College applicants must include a transcript. **Deadline:** November 15. **Contact:** Alberta Scholarship Programs at the above address.

246 ■ Graduate Student Scholarships *(Graduate/Scholarship)*

Purpose: To reward the outstanding academic achievement of students studying at the Masters level. **Focus:** General studies. **Qualif.:** Applicants must be enrolled in the second year of a Masters program. Students must be Canadian citizens or landed immigrants and attending a post-secondary institution in Alberta. **Criteria:** Selection will be based on the committee's criteria.

Funds Avail.: $3,000. **Number Awarded:** 1,000. **To Apply:** No application required. Students are nominated by the faculty of graduate studies. **Contact:** Alberta Scholarship Programs at the above address.

247 ■ Lois Hole Humanities and Social Sciences Scholarships *(Undergraduate/Scholarship)*

Purpose: To recognize student's leadership and community service. **Focus:** Humanities; Social sciences. **Qualif.:** Applicants must be students enrolled full-time in the second or subsequent year of post-secondary study in the Faculty of Humanities, the Faculty of Social Sciences or the Faculty of Arts, at the University of Alberta, the University of Calgary, the University of Lethbridge, Athabasca University, MacEwan University or Mount Royan University. **Criteria:** Selection will be based on academic merit, demonstrated leadership and community service.

Funds Avail.: $5,000. **Number Awarded:** 6. **To Apply:** Applicants may contact the Student Awards Office at participating educational institutions for other application requirements. **Deadline:** October 15 for University of Alberta and Athabasca University; November 15 for University Lethbridge and the University of Calgary. **Contact:** scholarships@gov.ab.ca.

248 ■ Informatics Circle of Research Excellence Scholarships *(Doctorate, Graduate/Scholarship)*

Purpose: To foster a strong graduate student population and support the development of strong informatics research teams. **Focus:** Computer and information sciences; Engineering. **Qualif.:** Applicants must be graduate students in information science and engineering attending an Alberta university. **Criteria:** Selection will be based on the committee's criteria.

Funds Avail.: $30,000-Masters level; $35,000-Doctoral level. **To Apply:** Applicants may contact the Faculty of Graduate Studies for other requirements. The institution will nominate a student to receive this award. **Contact:** Alberta Scholarship Program at the above address.

249 ■ International Education Awards - Ukraine *(Undergraduate/Scholarship)*

Purpose: To recognize the accomplishments of intern, co-op, practicum, apprenticeship and research students. **Focus:** General studies. **Qualif.:** Applicant must be a post-secondary student or an apprenticeship student taking a practicum, internship, co-op or apprenticeship program, or may be a student conducting research. **Criteria:** The student will be selected based on demonstrated past accomplishments and potential for improving relations between Ukraine and Alberta.

Funds Avail.: $5,000. **Number Awarded:** 5. **To Apply:** Application forms will also be available from the Alberta Scholarship Programs' office, Alberta Colleges and Universities, the Canadian Embassy in Kyiv and the Ministry of Education of Ukraine. In total, five copies of the completed application form must be submitted (an original plus four photocopies). This requirement does not apply to academic transcripts and reference letters. **Deadline:** February 1. **Remarks:** Established in 2003. **Contact:** Alberta Scholar-

Awards are arranged alphabetically below their administering organizations

ship Program at the above address.

250 ■ Helen and George Kilik Scholarships
(Undergraduate/Scholarship)

Purpose: To assist student from Olds High School to pursue a post-secondary education. **Focus:** General studies. **Qualif.:** Candidate must be an Alberta resident; have completed all high school studies at Olds High school and intend to pursue post-secondary studies; must demonstrate financial need; and involvement in extracurricular activities. **Criteria:** Selection will be based on academic achievement particularly in math and science.

Funds Avail.: $1,000. **Number Awarded:** One. **To Apply:** Applicants may obtain an application from Olds High School or Alberta Scholarship Programs. **Deadline:** June 1. **Contact:** Alberta Scholarship Programs at the above address.

251 ■ Anna and John Kolesay Memorial Scholarships *(Undergraduate/Scholarship)*

Purpose: To recognize and reward the academic excellence of a student entering a Faculty of Education. **Focus:** General studies. **Qualif.:** Applicant must be: a Canadian citizen or permanent resident and an Alberta resident; from a family where neither parent obtained a university degree; enrolling full-time in the first year of a program in a Faculty of Education. **Criteria:** Selection is based on the highes average obtained on three Grade 12 subjects: one of English 30, or English 30-1, 30-2, or Francais 30 30-2 and two other subjects at the 30 level; Social studies, Mathematics, Science, Biology, Chemistry, Physics and a language.

Funds Avail.: $1,500. **Number Awarded:** One. **To Apply:** Application form can be obtained from Alberta Scholarship Programs and at Alberta high schools. **Deadline:** July 1. **Contact:** Alberta Scholarship Program at the above address.

252 ■ Jason Lang Scholarships *(Undergraduate/ Scholarship)*

Purpose: To reward the outstanding academic achievement of Alberta post-secondary students who are continuing full-time in an undergraduate program in Alberta. **Focus:** Law; Medicine; Pharmacy; Dentistry. **Qualif.:** Nominees must be enrolled full-time in an undergraduate or professional program, such as Law, Medicine, Pharmacy or Dentistry at an eligible Alberta post-secondary institution. These include publicly-funded colleges, technical institutes, universities, private colleges accredited to grant degrees and the Banff Centre. Also, they must be progressing in their post-secondary program and continuing their full-time post-secondary studies at an eligible Alberta educational institution. Nominees must be Canadian citizens or permanent residents and Alberta residents. **Criteria:** Selection will be based on Committee's criteria. Recipients are nominated on the basis of achieving a minimum GPA of 3.2 on a 4.0 scale in the previous academic year while maintaining enrollment in at least 80% of a full course load.

Funds Avail.: $1,000. **To Apply:** Recipients are nominated by the Awards Office at participating Alberta institutions where they have obtained qualifying grades. For information on the nomination process and eligibility, contact the Awards Office. **Deadline:** October 15 and February 15. **Contact:** Alberta Scholarship Programs at the above address.

253 ■ Language Teacher Bursary Program Awards *(Professional development/Award)*

Purpose: To assist certified Alberta teachers to take a summer post-secondary program in a language other than English or language pedagogy course at an institution outside of Canada. **Focus:** Languages. **Qualif.:** Applicants must: be Canadian citizens or individuals lawfully admitted to Canada for permanent residence and residents of Alberta; hold a valid Alberta professional teaching certificate; have been teaching in Alberta for a minimum of three years by the end of the current school year; demonstrate a background in language learning or have recently initiated the study of this language; plan to take a summer program of at least four weeks duration in a language/language teaching methodology other than English, or related field at an institution outside of Canada; must have not previously been awarded a Language Teacher Bursary. **Criteria:** Recipients will be selected based on statement of the program; course rigour; school authority endorsement; and potential benefit for both teacher and the school authority.

Funds Avail.: $2,500-$5,000. **To Apply:** Application form can be obtained from the website. Completed application form must be submitted to your local school authority for endorsement. Once endorsement has been given, the school authority will mail your application to Alberta Scholarship Programs. **Deadline:** February 10. **Contact:** scholarships@gov.ab.ca.

254 ■ Languages In Teacher Education Scholarships *(Undergraduate/Scholarship)*

Purpose: To reward Alberta students enrolled in a recognized Alberta teacher preparation program taking courses that will allow them to teach languages other than English in Alberta schools. **Focus:** Languages. **Qualif.:** Applicants must be: Canadian citizens or individuals lawfully admitted to Canada for permanent residence in Alberta. Visa students are not eligible for this award. Applicants must be registered full-time in their final two years of a recognized Alberta teacher preparation program at an Alberta faculty of education and intend to teach in Alberta schools upon completion of their program. **Criteria:** Selection will be based on the committee's criteria.

Funds Avail.: $2,500. **Number Awarded:** 14. **To Apply:** No applications required. Students will be nominated by their post-secondary institution. **Contact:** scholarships@gov.ab.ca.

255 ■ Sir James Lougheed Awards of Distinction *(Doctorate, Graduate/Award)*

Purpose: To recognize academic achievement and provide Albertans with the opportunity for advanced study at institutions outside of Alberta. Students studying in Alberta should apply for the Ralph Steinhauer Awards for Distinction. **Focus:** General studies. **Qualif.:** Applicants must be: Canadian citizens or landed immigrants; Alberta residents; enrolled or planning to enroll full-time in a graduate program at an institution outside of Alberta. Doctoral students must have completed at least one full year of graduate study or a master's degree. **Criteria:** Recipients will be selected based on previous academic achievements; program of study; appraiser's evaluations; answers to the essay question; and general impression of application form. Recipients will also assessed in the following quantifiable areas: GPA; number of research contributions; number of other contributions such as academic, community, professional activities; and number of previous awards.

Funds Avail.: $15,000 for Masters level; $20,000 for Doctoral level. **Number Awarded:** 7 for Masters Level; 8 for Doctoral Level. **To Apply:** An application form can be obtained from Alberta Scholarship Program, however, applicants cannot send their application electronically. Submit

Awards are arranged alphabetically below their administering organizations

the original and four signed unstapled copies of the completed application form and attachments. This requirement does not apply to academic transcripts and appraisals, these documents must be sent directly to Alberta Scholarship Programs. **Deadline:** Application form should be submitted by February 1; Academic transcripts and appraisals should be submitted by February 15. **Contact:** scholarships@gov.ab.ca.

256 ■ Louise McKinney Post-secondary Scholarships *(Undergraduate/Scholarship)*

Purpose: To recognize exceptional academic achievement and encourage outstanding students to continue their studies at the post-secondary level. **Focus:** General studies. **Qualif.:** Applicants must be residents of Alberta and in their second or subsequent year of full-time study; must have plan to enroll in a university, college, or technical institute; and class standing must be in the top two percent of their program. Alberta students studying outside the province because their program of study is not offered in Alberta will be considered for a scholarship if their class standing is in the top two percent of their program. **Criteria:** Selection will be based on the committee's criteria.

Funds Avail.: $2,500. **To Apply:** Students studying in-province are nominated by the Student Awards Office at participating Alberta post-secondary institutions. Other students may contact the Awards Office to determine their eligibility. **Remarks:** Established by Alberta Scholarship Programs in honour of Louise McKinney. **Contact:** Alberta Scholarship Programs at the above address.

257 ■ Dr. Ernest and Minnie Mehl Scholarships *(Undergraduate/Scholarship)*

Purpose: To encourage students to pursue a post-secondary education and to recognize and reward exceptional academic at the senior high school level. **Focus:** General studies. **Qualif.:** Applicants must be Canadian citizens or landed immigrants who have completed their Grade 12 in Alberta at a school that follows the Alberta Education Curriculum. Applicants must be continuing their studies at a degree granting post-secondary institution in Canada. University transfer programs are acceptable. **Criteria:** Selection will be based on the average obtained on Diploma Examinations in one of English 30-1, 30-2 or Francais 30, 30-2 and Social Studies 30, 30-1 or 30-2 plus any three other subjects: Pure Mathematics 30, Applied Mathematics 30, Biology 30, Chemistry 30, Physics 30 or Science 30. Financial need will aslo be considered

Funds Avail.: $3,500. **Number Awarded:** 1. **To Apply:** No application is required. The recipient will be selected from applications received for an Alexander Rutherford Scholarship. **Deadline:** June 1. **Contact:** Alberta Scholarship Programs at the above address.

258 ■ Charles S. Noble Scholarships for Study at Harvard *(Undergraduate/Scholarship)*

Purpose: To reward academic excellence and provide opportunities for Albertans to pursue studies at Harvard University. **Focus:** General studies. **Qualif.:** Applicants must be Alberta residents who plan to apply or enrolled full-time in any year of study in an undergraduate program at Harvard. **Criteria:** Selection will be based on the committee's criteria.

Funds Avail.: $10,000. $5,000 is disbursed by Alberta Scholarship Programs and $5,000 is disbursed by Harvard. **Number Awarded:** 3. **To Apply:** Applicants may obtain an application form from the Office of Admissions at Harvard

and from the Alberta Heritage Scholarship Fund. **Deadline:** May 15. **Contact:** Alberta Scholarship Programs at the above address.

259 ■ Northern Alberta Development Council Bursary Awards *(Undergraduate/Award)*

Purpose: To increase the number of trained professionals in Northern Alberta and to encourage students from Northern Alberta to obtain a post-secondary education. **Focus:** General studies. **Qualif.:** Applicants must be residents of Alberta, and planning to enroll in a full-time post-secondary program. Applicants must also be within two years of completion of their post-secondary program. **Criteria:** Selection will be based on the committee's criteria.

Funds Avail.: $6,000-$12,000. **To Apply:** Applicants may obtain an application form from www.benorth.ca. Application forms for these bursaries are also available from Alberta Scholarship Programs, Student Awards Offices and from the Northern Alberta Development Council. **Deadline:** April 30. **Contact:** Northern Alberta Development Council, 2nd Fl., Provincial Bldg. 9621 - 96 Ave. Postal Bag 900-14 Peace River, AB T8S 1T4; 780-624-6545; nadc.council@gov.ab.ca.

260 ■ Northern Alberta Development Council Bursary Partnership Program *(Undergraduate/Award)*

Purpose: To assist students in pursuing a post-secondary education. **Focus:** General studies. **Qualif.:** Applicants must be residents of Alberta and plan to enroll full-time in a post-secondary program. In addition, applicants must demonstrate financial need and be willing to live and work in northern Alberta after completion of the program. **Criteria:** Selection will be based on the committee's criteria.

Funds Avail.: $3,000. **To Apply:** Applicants may obtain an application form from www.benorth.ca. Application form for these bursaries are also available from Alberta Scholarship Programs, Student Awards Offices and from the Northern Alberta Development Council. **Deadline:** May 15. **Contact:** Northern Alberta Development Council, 2nd Fl., Provincial Bldg. 9621 - 96 Ave. Postal Bag 900-14 Peace River, AB T8S 1T4; 780-624-6545; nadc.council@gov.ab.ca.

261 ■ Persons Case Scholarships *(Undergraduate, Graduate/Scholarship)*

Purpose: To assist students whose studies will ultimately contribute to the advancement of women, or who are studying in fields where members of their gender are traditionally few in number. **Focus:** General studies. **Qualif.:** Applicants must be residents of Alberta and enrolled full-time at a post-secondary institution in Alberta. In addition, applicants must be enrolled in a program that is either non-traditional for their sex, or a program that will contribute to the advancement of women. Students studying out-of-province may be considered for this award if their program of study is not available in Alberta. **Criteria:** Recipients will be selected based on program of studies; academic achievement; and personal essay.

Funds Avail.: Up to $5,000. **To Apply:** Application form can be obtained from the website. Applicants must submit the following requirements with their complete application form: official transcript of all-post secondary studies; short essay of two or three pages outlining why the issues they are studying are important to them and how their studies, activities and community contribute to the advancement of women; curriculum vitae/resume outlining academic achievement, volunteer experience, awards won, etc. In

Awards are arranged alphabetically below their administering organizations

total, submit six copies of the completed application form, and six copies of all attachments (the original and five photocopies). **Deadline:** September 30. **Remarks:** Established in 1979. **Contact:** Alberta Scholarship Program at the above address.

262 ■ Prairie Baseball Academy Scholarships (Undergraduate/Scholarship)

Purpose: To reward the athletic and academic excellence of baseball players and to provide an incentive and means for these players to continue with their post-secondary education. **Focus:** General studies. **Qualif.:** Applicants must be Alberta residents and enrolled full-time at a post-secondary institution in Alberta; must be participants in the Prairie Baseball Academy; and must have achieved a minimum GPA of 2.0 on a 4.0 scale in the previous semester. **Criteria:** Selection will be based on academic achievement, community involvement and baseball achievements.

Funds Avail.: $500-$2,500. **To Apply:** Applicants may obtain an application form from Alberta Scholarship Programs and from the Prairie Baseball Academy. **Deadline:** October 15. **Contact:** Alberta Scholarship Programs at the above address.

263 ■ Queen Elizabeth II Graduate Scholarship Program (Doctorate, Graduate/Scholarship)

Purpose: To reward the achievement of students pursuing graduate studies in Alberta. **Focus:** General studies. **Qualif.:** Applicants must be Canadian citizens or landed immigrants and enrolled full-time in a faculty of graduate studies in Alberta. **Criteria:** Selection will be based on the committee's criteria.

Funds Avail.: $10,800-Masters level; $15,000-Doctoral level. **To Apply:** Applicants may contact the faculty of graduate studies at their institution for more information about the nomination process. **Contact:** Alberta Scholarship Program at the above address.

264 ■ Registered Apprenticeship Program Scholarships (RAP) (Undergraduate/Scholarship)

Purpose: To recognize the accomplishments of Alberta high school students taking the Registered Apprenticeship Program (RAP) and to encourage recipients to continue their apprenticeship training after completing high school. **Focus:** General studies. **Qualif.:** Applicant must: be a Canadian citizen or landed immigrant and a resident of Alberta; have completed the requirements for a high school diploma of the current year or earlier; be registered as an Alberta apprentice in a trade while still attending high school; have completed a minimum of 250 hours of on-the-job training and work experience in their chosen trade; plan to continue in an approved regular apprenticeship program after completing high school; have at least one period of technical training left to complete the apprenticeship. **Criteria:** Selection will be based on the committee's criteria.

Funds Avail.: $1,000. **To Apply:** Application form can be obtained from Alberta Scholarship Program. Applications must be supported by: one or two paragraph (written or typed) autobiography confirming plans to continue their apprenticeship program and detailing why a career in that trade is a good fit for them; completed employer recommendation form; recommendation letter from a high school teacher or counselor. **Deadline:** June 29. **Contact:** scholarships@gov.ab.ca.

265 ■ Rutherford Scholars (Undergraduate/Scholarship)

Purpose: To reward the best Alexander Rutherford Scholarship recipients. **Focus:** General studies. **Qualif.:** Applicants must be in the top ten students as determined on the first writing of Diploma Examination. **Criteria:** Recipients are selected on the basis of results obtained on Diploma Examinations in one of: English 30-1, 30-2 or Francais 30, 30-2, Social Studies 30 plus three other subjects. Averages normally are in the 96.0 to 98.8 percent range. Only the first writing of the diploma exam will be considered.

Funds Avail.: $2,500. **To Apply:** No application is required. Recipients are selected from all Alexander Rutherford Scholarship applications received before the deadline. **Deadline:** August 1. **Contact:** Alberta Scholarship Programs at the above address.

266 ■ Alexander Rutherford Scholarships for High School Achievement (Undergraduate/Scholarship)

Purpose: To recognize and reward academic achievement at the senior high school level and to encourage students to pursue post-secondary studies. **Focus:** General studies. **Qualif.:** Applicants must be Canadian citizens or permanent residents and Alberta residents and plan to enroll full-time in a post-secondary program or apprenticeship program. Students must have a minimum combined average based on five designated courses in at least one grade: Grade 10, 11 or 12. The minimum average, value of the award and courses that can be used depend on the student's graduation year. **Criteria:** Selection will be based on the committee's criteria.

Funds Avail.: $2,500. **To Apply:** Applicants must provide the following: (1) Alberta Student Number; (2) High School Code; (3) Social Insurance Number; (4) photocopy of permanent resident card or landed immigration long form; (5) Alberta residency; (6) post-secondary studies; and (7) signed and dated application form. There is no limit to apply for the scholarship except that the applicant must be planning to pursue post-secondary studies. Students who apply after the application deadline may not be recognized at their high school awards ceremony. High school grades obtained through upgrading at a post-secondary institution are not accepted. Eligible students who complete high school outside of Alberta must submit an official transcript of their high school marks from that province. **Deadline:** May 1 and December 1. **Contact:** Alberta Scholarship programs at the above address.

267 ■ Dr. Robert and Anna Shaw Scholarships (Undergraduate/Scholarship)

Purpose: To recognize and reward the academic and leadership accomplishments of three students graduating from Sexsmith Secondary School who are entering post-secondary studies. **Focus:** Agriculture; Engineering; Art industries and trade; Fine arts. **Qualif.:** Applicants must be Alberta residents and plan to enroll full-time in a post-secondary program related to agriculture, engineering/trades or fine arts; and must have completed their grade 12 at Sexsmith secondary school. **Criteria:** Selection will be based on academic accomplishments, leadership qualities, community spirit; involvement in extracurricular activities and a student's commitment to place the welfare of others above their own needs.

Funds Avail.: $500. **Number Awarded:** 3. **To Apply:** Applicants may obtain application form from Alberta Scholar-

Awards are arranged alphabetically below their administering organizations

ship Programs and from the Counseling Office at Sexsmith Secondary School. **Deadline:** June 1. **Contact:** Alberta Scholarship Programs at the above address.

268 ■ Dr. Robert Norman Shaw Scholarships
(Undergraduate/Scholarship)

Purpose: To recognize and reward the exceptional achievement of a student graduating from Sexsmith Secondary School who is entering post-secondary studies in a health-related field. **Focus:** Health sciences. **Qualif.:** Applicants must have completed Grade 12 at Sexsmith Secondary School; be Alberta residents and plan to enroll full-time in a health-related post-secondary program of at least one semester in length. **Criteria:** Selection will be based on the highest average on five 30 level Grade 12 subjects: English or Francais, Mathematics, Social Studies, Biology, Chemistry, Physics or Science.

Funds Avail.: $1,500. **To Apply:** Applicants may obtain an application form from the Counseling Office at Sexsmith Secondary School and also from Alberta Scholarship Programs at Alberta Learning Information Service's website. **Deadline:** June 1. **Contact:** Alberta Scholarship Programs at the above address.

269 ■ Alberta Press Council
PO Box 2576
Medicine Hat, AB, Canada T1A 8G8
Ph: (403) 580-4104
Fax: (403) 580-4010
Free: 888-580-4104
E-mail: abpress@telus.net
URL: www.albertapresscouncil.ca

270 ■ Alberta Press Council Scholarships
(Undergraduate/Scholarship)

Purpose: To assist high school students in pursuing post-secondary studies. **Focus:** General studies. **Qualif.:** Applicants must be Canadian citizens or permanent residents; must have been residents of Alberta for at least one year prior to time of application; must be students currently attending Grade 12 in a recognized school in Alberta or students who are enrolled full-time in a post-secondary degree or diploma program. Family members of newspaper staff are eligible to apply; relatives of current Press Council Members are not. Scholarship is open to any field of study. Applicants must agree to allow the publishing of their essay on the Alberta Press Council's website and on Newswire Services. **Criteria:** Selection will be based on a 1000-1100 word essay on a pre-determined topic. Essays will be judged based on creativity, style and content.

Funds Avail.: No specific amount. **To Apply:** Essay must be typed, double spaced, 12 point font, 1,000-1,100 words. It is essential that essays be carefully checked/proofread before submission, and neat and tidy word processed on standard size paper (8 1/2 x 11). Six copies of the essay and the application form, with only one cover page, are to be sent to the Selection Committee, Alberta Press Council. Please submit by regular mail or express post, faxed applications will not be accepted. **Contact:** Alberta Press council at the above address.

271 ■ Alberta Teachers' Association (ATA)
11010 142 St. NW
Edmonton, AB, Canada T5N 2R1
Ph: (780) 447-9400

Fax: (780) 455-6481
E-mail: ms@ata.ab.ca
URL: www.teachers.ab.ca/Pages/home.aspx

272 ■ Alberta Teachers Association Doctoral Fellowships in Education *(Doctorate/Fellowship)*

Purpose: To recognize academic excellence and to help defray the financial costs of university study. **Focus:** Education. **Qualif.:** Applicants must hold a permanent Alberta teaching certificate and have at least five years of successful teaching; must be at the highest level of membership (associate, if applicants are not qualified for active membership); be entering or enrolled first year of full-time study in a doctoral program in education at an accredited or recognized Alberta public university; must have plan to continue a career in Alberta; not have received a previous award; and be members in good standing. **Criteria:** Recipients will be selected based on academic standing, contribution to the association and commitment to public and excellence in teaching.

Funds Avail.: $15,000. **Number Awarded:** 2. **To Apply:** Applicants must obtain and complete the application form; official transcripts of all post-secondary academic and professional courses; three letters of reference attesting the applicant's excellence as a teacher and contributions to the association; and any proof that will provide information of entering the full-time study in a doctoral program. **Deadline:** March 4. **Contact:** Application form and supporting documents must be sent to Corrine Anderson at the above address; Phone: 780-447-9470; Toll Free: 800-232-7208; E-mail: corinne.anderson@ata.ab.ca.

273 ■ Alberta Teachers Association Educational Research Awards *(Professional development/Grant)*

Purpose: To support academic research in Alberta's universities to improve teaching and learning. **Focus:** Education. **Qualif.:** Applicants must be faculty of education members or seasonal lecturers at an Alberta university who have undertaken quality research on classroom teaching and learning. **Criteria:** To qualify for an award, the research must meet the following categories: 1) be directly related to school and classroom practice; 2) be focused on school teaching and/or learning; 3) research must be current, ongoing or completed within the last two years; 4) be related to critical issues; 5) have involved classroom teachers and/or students; 6) be applicable to the Alberta context; 7) have practical benefits to teachers; and 8) have high quality in terms of purpose, methodology and originality.

Funds Avail.: $5,000. **To Apply:** Applicants must fill-out the application form and attach a detailed description of the research. **Deadline:** May 16. **Remarks:** Faxed or e-mailed applications will not be accepted. **Contact:** For submission and further information, applicants must contact Dr. J-C Couture at the above address; Phone: 780-447-9470; Toll Free: 800-232-7208; E-mail: jc.couture@ata.ab.ca.

274 ■ John Mazurek Memorial-Morgex Insurance Scholarships *(Professional development/ Scholarship)*

Purpose: To help students pursue their professional development in the field of business education and/or the use of computer technology in education from a Canadian public institution. **Focus:** Business; Computer and information sciences. **Qualif.:** Applicants must hold a permanent Alberta teaching certificate; have completed at least five years of successful teaching; be at the highest level of

Awards are arranged alphabetically below their administering organizations

membership (associate, if applicants are not qualified for active membership); and be members in good standing. The area of study must focus on business education and computer technology in education from a recognized Canadian public institution. **Criteria:** Scholarship will be awarded to applicants who possess the following: 1) area of study focusing on business education or the use of computer technology in education; 2) contributions to association and commitment to public education; and 3) excellence in teaching.

Funds Avail.: $1,000. **To Apply:** Applicants must complete the application form and include two letters of reference attesting the excellence of teaching and contributions to the association. **Deadline:** March 4. **Remarks:** Faxed or e-mailed applications will not be accepted. **Contact:** Application form and supporting documents must be sent to Corrine Anderson at the above address; Phone: 780-447-9470; Toll Free: 800-232-7208; E-mail: corinne.anderson@ata.ab.ca.

275 ■ Nadene M. Thomas Graduate Research Scholarships *(Graduate/Scholarship)*

Purpose: To financially assist graduate students conducting research on health issues. **Focus:** Education. **Qualif.:** Applicants must hold a permanent Alberta teaching certificate; have completed at least five years of successful teaching in Alberta; be the highest level of membership (associate, if applicants are not qualified for active membership); must intend to continue a career in education; must be registered graduate students in an education degree program at a recognized Canadian university; conduct research focusing on health issues affecting teacher's working conditions; not be previous awardees; and must be members in good standing. **Criteria:** Recipients will be selected based on the following categories: 1) applicant's academic standing; 2) contributions to the association and commitment to the public; 3) excellence in teaching; and 4) applicability of the research on health issues affecting teacher's working condition.

Funds Avail.: $5,000. **To Apply:** Applicants must complete the application form; include official transcripts of all post-secondary academic and professional courses; include three letters of reference attesting the excellence of teaching, contributions to the association and post-secondary work; and must provide a written proof that they have been accepted into a graduate program in education at a recognized Canadian university. **Deadline:** March 4. **Remarks:** Faxed or e-mailed application will not be accepted. **Contact:** Application form and supporting documents must be sent to: Corrine Anderson at the above address; Phone: 780-447-9470; Toll Free: 800-232-7208; E-mail: corinne.anderson@ata.ab.ca.

276 ■ Albuquerque Community Foundation (ACF)

PO Box 25266
Albuquerque, NM 87125-5266
Ph: (505) 883-6240
Fax: (505) 883-3629
E-mail: foundation@albuquerquefoundation.org
URL: www.albuquerquefoundation.org

277 ■ Robby Baker Memorial Scholarships
(Undergraduate/Scholarship)

Purpose: To provide financial support to those deserving students. **Focus:** General Studies. **Qualif.:** Applicants must

be coping with dyslexia or other reading disability; must have earned a minimum of 2.0 GPA and must be enrolled as full time students in an accredited college or university. **Criteria:** Preference will be given to those students who meet the criteria.

Funds Avail.: $750. **Number Awarded:** 1. **To Apply:** Applicants must submit a completed application form and two references from teachers or counselors. **Deadline:** March 6.

278 ■ Notah Begay III Scholarship Program
(Undergraduate/Scholarship)

Purpose: To provide financial assistance to those students who are in need. **Focus:** General Studies. **Qualif.:** Applicants must be Native American scholar athletes; must have a minimum GPA 3.0; must attend a community college, four-year college or university on a full time basis. **Criteria:** Preference will be given to those students who meet the criteria.

Funds Avail.: $2,000. **Number Awarded:** 2. **To Apply:** Applicants must submit the following: copy of FAFSA, Student Aid Report or statement of financial aid; proof of tribal enrollment or Certificate of Indian Blood (minimum 25%); one reference from a current academic teacher or counselor; one reference from an athletic coach; include in your personal statement how you plan to give back to your community after college; high school transcript; copy of SAT and/or ACT scores; resume; and personal essay stating the following: 1) reason(s) of pursuing a post-secondary education; 2) plans of study; 3) career goals; and 4) challenges have been experienced in continuing education. **Deadline:** March 6.

279 ■ Bryan Cline Memorial Soccer Scholarship Program *(Undergraduate/Scholarship)*

Purpose: To support the education of graduating senior varsity soccer players. **Focus:** General Studies. **Qualif.:** Applicants must attend a college or university full time. **Criteria:** Preference will be given to those students who meet the criteria.

Funds Avail.: $1,000. **Number Awarded:** 2. **To Apply:** Applicants must submit a completed application form including the name of your varsity soccer team coach and two letters of reference- one from a teacher or counselor and one from a soccer coach. **Deadline:** March 6. **Remarks:** This scholarship is for Eldorado High School students only. **Contact:** Albuquerque Community Foundation at the above address.

280 ■ Excel Staffing Companies Scholarships for Excellence in Continuing Education
(Undergraduate/Scholarship)

Purpose: To assist individuals who demonstrate a commitment towards reaching a career goal. **Focus:** General Studies. **Qualif.:** Applicants must be individuals who are employed full time while attending school part time; must be residents of Albuquerque; must have a minimum of 3.0 GPA; must be working with a minimum of 30 hours per week. **Criteria:** Preference will be given to those students who meet the criteria.

Funds Avail.: $500-$1,000. **Number Awarded:** 4. **To Apply:** Applicants must submit a completed application form along with a resume including employment, community service, and awards or honors (maximum 4 pages); statement outlining career goals in relation to academic pursuits and financial need (grammar, spelling and punctuation do

Awards are arranged alphabetically below their administering organizations

count); current/most recent transcript verifying minimum 3.0 cumulative GPA; letter from employer verifying employment of at least 30 hours per week; and letter of reference verifying community service and/or volunteer commitment (optional). Attached (sealed) or sent under separate cover: up to two letters of reference from a current or recent instructor or counselor (1-page, 1-side). **Deadline:** June 14.

281 ■ New Mexico Manufactured Housing Association Scholarship Program *(Undergraduate/Scholarship)*

Purpose: To provide scholarship awards to New Mexico high school graduates residing in a manufactured home. **Focus:** General Studies. **Qualif.:** Applicants must live in a mobile/manufactured home; must have earned a minimum GPA 3.0; must attend a college or university full time. **Criteria:** Preference will be given to those students who meet the criteria.

Funds Avail.: $1,000. **Number Awarded:** 1 or 2. **To Apply:** Applicants must submit the following: written statement of financial need; proof of residency in a mobile/manufactured home: a copy of title or rental agreement or retail installment contract or county tax assessment; one reference from a teacher or counselor (1 page, 1 side only). **Deadline:** March 6.

282 ■ Barnes W. Rose, Jr. and Eva Rose Nichol Scholarship Fund *(Undergraduate/Scholarship)*

Purpose: To provide financial assistance to those students who are in need. **Focus:** Engineering. **Qualif.:** Applicants must be a graduate of Albuquerque High School who demonstrate math and/or science interest and skill through SAT/ACF scores and/or strong grades in appropriate high school classes; must have a minimum of 3.6 GPA; must demonstrate financial need; must attend a college or university in pursuit of an engineering degree. **Criteria:** Preference will be given to those students who meet the criteria.

Funds Avail.: $750. **To Apply:** Applicants must submit a completed application form and a minimum of one reference from an Albuquerque High School Math or Science teacher. **Deadline:** March 6. **Contact:** Albuquerque Community Foundation at the above address.

283 ■ Sussman-Miller Educational Assistance Award Program *(Undergraduate/Scholarship)*

Purpose: To provide financial assistance to address the gap in financial aid packages for both students beginning their college careers and those continuing their undergraduate work. **Focus:** General Studies. **Qualif.:** Applicants must attend a college or university full-time; must be graduating high school seniors or currently enrolled in college/university; must be federal financial aid recipients. **Criteria:** Preference will be given to those students who meet the criteria.

Funds Avail.: $500-$2,000. **To Apply:** Applicants must check the available website for the required materials. **Deadline:** April 25; June 26. **Contact:** Albuquerque Community Foundation at the above address.

284 ■ Woodcock Family Education Scholarship Program *(Undergraduate/Scholarship)*

Purpose: To support students of exceptional promise in the fields of science and math. **Focus:** Math; Science. **Qualif.:** Applicants must be Albuquerque graduating high school

seniors; with strong math and/or science credentials; must attend a college or university full time; must have a minimum GPA of 3.8; **Criteria:** Preference will be given to those students who meet the criteria.

Funds Avail.: $11,000. **Number Awarded:** 2. **To Apply:** Applicants must attach these to their application packet: career goals in personal statement MUST include those in the field of math or science; one reference from a math or science teacher; one or more references from other teachers, internship or work programs, or community services. **Deadline:** March 6. **Contact:** Albuquerque Community Foundation at the above address.

285 ■ Alden Kindred of America (AKA)
PO Box 2754
Duxbury, MA 02331-2754
Ph: (781) 934-9092
Fax: (781) 934-9149
E-mail: aldenhouse@comcast.net
URL: www.alden.org

286 ■ Donnell B. Young Scholarships *(Undergraduate/Scholarship)*

Purpose: To provide educational assistance to incoming college students. **Focus:** General studies. **Qualif.:** Applicants must be members of the Alden Kindred of America, Inc.; must be graduating high school students who are lineage members of the Alden Kindred of America, Inc. **Criteria:** Recipient will be selected based on the submitted research paper.

Funds Avail.: No specific amount. **Number Awarded:** 1. **To Apply:** Applicants must submit their high school transcripts (mailed directly by their school). A typewritten research paper of 750-1000 words is a strict requirement. The topic must be extracted from the Early American Period (1620-1750). The preface of the research paper should contain a short paragraph about the reason of the application for the scholarship. Footnotes and bibliography of references should be included. Volunteer work and personal information including hobbies and interests must also be provided. All application forms must have two references (one personal and one from the school). **Deadline:** March 1.

287 ■ Aleut Foundation
703 W Tudor Rd., Ste. 102
Anchorage, AK 99503-6650
Ph: (907) 646-1929
Fax: (907) 646-1949
Free: 800-232-4882
E-mail: taf@thealeutfoundation.org
URL: www.thealeutfoundation.org

288 ■ Andrew Gronholdt Arts Scholarship Awards *(Undergraduate, Vocational/Occupational, Graduate, Master's/Scholarship)*

Purpose: To help students pursue their education in the Arts field. **Focus:** Arts. **Qualif.:** Applicants must be two-year/vocational, undergraduate, graduate and master's degree students; must have at least 3.0 GPA and must be full-time majoring in the Arts field. **Criteria:** Recipients will be selected based on submitted materials.

Funds Avail.: No specific amount. **To Apply:** Applicants

Awards are arranged alphabetically below their administering organizations

must complete the application form; must submit a letter of acceptance, two letters of recommendation, personal statement, birth certificate, class schedule and an official transcript. **Deadline:** June 30. **Contact:** taf@thealeutfoundation.org.

289 ■ Lillie Hope-McGarvey Health Scholarship
Awards *(Undergraduate, Vocational/Occupational, Graduate, Master's/Scholarship)*

Purpose: To provide financial assistance to students entering the fall semester. **Focus:** Medicine. **Qualif.:** Applicants must be two-year/vocational, undergraduate, graduate and master's degrees; must maintain at least 3.0 GPA; must be enrolled full-time majoring in the medical field. **Criteria:** Recipients will be selected based on submitted materials.

Funds Avail.: Amount not specified. **To Apply:** Applicants must complete the application form; must submit an official transcript, letter of acceptance, two letters of recommendation, personal statement, birth certificate, class schedule and an official transcript. **Deadline:** June 30. **Contact:** taf@thealeutfoundation.org.

290 ■ Gabe Stepetin Business Scholarship
Awards *(Undergraduate, Vocational/Occupational, Graduate, Master's/Scholarship)*

Purpose: To provide financial assistance to students interested in pursuing a business field. **Focus:** Business. **Qualif.:** Applicants must be two-year/vocational, undergraduate, graduate and master's degree students; must have at least 3.0 GPA; must be enrolled full-time majoring in the business field. **Criteria:** Recipients will be chosen based on submitted materials.

Funds Avail.: Amount not specified. **To Apply:** Applicants must complete an application form; must submit a letter of acceptance, two letters of recommendation, personal statement, birth certificate, class schedule and an official transcript. **Deadline:** June 30. **Contact:** taf@thealeutfoundation.org.

291 ■ Alex's Lemonade Stand Foundation
333 E Lancaster Ave., Ste. 414
Wynnewood, PA 19096
Ph: (610) 649-3034
Fax: (610) 649-3038
Free: 866-333-1213
URL: www.alexslemonade.org

292 ■ Alex's Lemonade Stand Foundation
Epidemiology Grants *(Doctorate, Professional development/Grant)*

Purpose: To support research of investigators who have a specific focus on the epidemiology, early detection or the prevention of childhood cancer. **Focus:** Cancer; Epidemiology. **Qualif.:** Applicants should be at least at the Assistant, Associate or Full Professor level; must be MD or PhD; must have a history of formal training in disciplines that are relevant to the proposed research or a track record of conducting similar research; critical to these application are innovative proposals that have the potential to generate new insight into the causes of childhood cancer; must demonstrate feasibility. **Criteria:** Selection will be based on the committee's criteria.

Funds Avail.: $100,000. **To Apply:** Applicants must first complete the online form then upload the application in one PDF. Applicants can request a password or sign in by go-

ing to the Guidelines and Submission page of www.alsf-grants.org. All applications must be submitted using the ALSF's online submission process. **Deadline:** December 15. **Contact:** Kay Schaul at 610-649-3034 or e-mail grants@alexslemonade.org.

293 ■ Alex's Lemonade Stand Foundation Innovation Grants *(Professional development/Grant)*

Purpose: To eradicate childhood cancer through basic research, career development and helping to streamline translational clinical research. **Focus:** Cancer. **Qualif.:** Applicants must be experienced investigators with a novel and promising approach in finding causes and cures for childhood cancers. **Criteria:** Selection will be based on the committee's criteria.

Funds Avail.: $100,000. **To Apply:** Applicants must submit an approved letter of intent before application will be submitted. All requests must be submitted using ALSF's online application process. Applicants can request a password or sign in by going to the Guidelines and Submission page of www.alsfgrants.org. **Deadline:** March 1. **Contact:** Lisa Towry, 610-649-3034, grants@alexslemonade.org.

294 ■ Alex's Lemonade Stand Foundation Young Investigator Grants *(Doctorate, Professional development/Grant)*

Purpose: To eradicate childhood cancer through basic research, career development and helping to streamline translational clinical research. **Focus:** Cancer. **Qualif.:** Applicants must be researchers and physicians who have promising research ideas; must be at the early stages of their research careers; must hold an MD or PhD either in an accredited fellowship program or within six years from the completion of a three-year fellowship program at the time the funding will start. PhD applicants must be within six years granting the PhD at the time the funding will start. Post-doctoral are encouraged to apply, but must also be within the six-year time frame; must not currently hold an independent NIH grant. Applicants may currently have a NIH K Award; research mentors must be identified and the application must document their involvement in experimental design and execution. **Criteria:** Selection will be based on the committee's criteria.

Funds Avail.: $40,000. **To Apply:** Applicants can request a password or sign in by going to the Guidelines and Submission page of www.alsfgrants.org. All requests must be submitted using ALSF's online application process. **Deadline:** December. **Contact:** Lisa Towry,610-649-3034, grants@alexslemonade.org.

295 ■ Horatio Alger Association
99 Canal Center Plz., Ste. 320
Alexandria, VA 22314
Ph: (703) 684-9444
Fax: (703) 548-3822
Free: 866-763-9228
URL: www.horatioalger.com

296 ■ Ak-Sar-Ben Scholarships *(Undergraduate/Scholarship)*

Purpose: To provide financial assistance to students in the state of Iowa. **Focus:** General studies. **Qualif.:** Applicants must be enrolled full time as high school seniors, progress-

Awards are arranged alphabetically below their administering organizations

ing normally toward graduation and planning to enter college not later than the fall following graduation; must have a strong commitment to pursue a bachelor's degree at an accredited institution (students may start their studies at a two-year institution and then transfer to a four-year institution); must have critical financial need ($50,000 or less adjusted gross income per family is preferred; if higher, an explanation must be provided); must be involved in co-curricular and community activities; must have a minimum grade point average of 2.0; must be residents of Nebraska and western Iowa; and be citizens or permanent residents of the United States. **Criteria:** Recipients will be selected based on financial need.

Funds Avail.: $6,000. **Number Awarded:** 50. **To Apply:** Applicants must submit an official high school transcript; a copy of parents/guardians federal income tax return; have one letter of support and must be logged in to the application process at the HAA website. Faxes/e-mails will not be accepted. Students must download the certification page from the HAA web site, complete it and obtain the proper signatures prior to mailing.

297 ■ Horatio Alger Ak-Sar-Ben Scholarships
(Undergraduate/Scholarship)

Purpose: To provide financial assistance to students in the state of Nebraska and western Iowa. **Focus:** General studies. **Qualif.:** Applicants must be enrolled full time as high school seniors, progressing normally toward graduation and planning to enter college not later than the fall following graduation; must have a strong commitment to pursue a bachelor's degree at an accredited institution (students may start their studies at a two-year institution and then transfer to a four-year institution); must have critical financial need ($50,000 or less adjusted gross income per family is preferred; if higher, an explanation must be provided); must be involved in co-curricular and community activities; must have a minimum grade point average of 2.0; must be residents of Nebraska or western Iowa; be citizens or permanent residents of the United States. **Criteria:** Recipients will be selected based on financial need.

Funds Avail.: $5,000. **Number Awarded:** 50. **To Apply:** Applicants must submit an official transcript; a copy of parents/guardians federal tax return; have one letter of support and must be logged in to the application process at the HAA website. Faxes/e-mails will not be accepted. Students must download the certification page from the HAA web site, complete it and obtain the proper signatures prior to mailing.

298 ■ Horatio Alger Delaware Scholarships
(Undergraduate/Scholarship)

Purpose: To provide financial assistance to students in the state of Delaware. **Focus:** General studies. **Qualif.:** Applicants must be full time high school seniors, progressing normally toward graduation and planning to enter college no later than the fall following graduation; must have a strong commitment to pursue a bachelor's degree at an accredited institution (students may start their studies at a two-year institution and then transfer to a four-year institution); must have critical financial need ($50,000 or less adjusted gross income per family is preferred; if higher, an explanation must be provided); must be involved in co-curricular and community activities; must have a minimum grade point average of 2.0; be residents of Delaware and be citizens of the United States. **Criteria:** Recipients will be selected based on financial need.

Funds Avail.: $5,000. **Number Awarded:** 5. **To Apply:**

Applicants must have one letter of support and must be logged in to the application process at the HAA website. Faxes/e-mails will not be accepted. Students must download the certification page from the HAA web site, complete it and obtain the proper signatures prior to mailing. **Remarks:** Funded through the generosity of Michele Rollins and her children Michele, Monique, Michael and Marc.

299 ■ Horatio Alger District of Columbia, Maryland and Virginia Scholarships
(Undergraduate/Scholarship)

Purpose: To recognize deserving students from the Washington D.C., Metro area in the following counties: District of Columbia, Maryland, Virginia. **Focus:** General studies. **Qualif.:** Applicants must be full time high school seniors, progressing normally toward graduation and planning to enter college no later than the fall following graduation; must have a strong commitment to pursue a bachelor's degree at an accredited institution (students may start their studies at a two-year institution and then transfer to a four-year institution); must have critical financial need ($50,000 or less adjusted gross income per family is preferred; if higher, an explanation must be provided); must be involved in co-curricular and community activities; must have a minimum grade point average of 2.0; must be residents of DC, MD and VA; and be citizens or permanent residents of the United States. **Criteria:** Recipients will be selected based on financial need.

Funds Avail.: $5,000. **Number Awarded:** 20. **To Apply:** Applicants must have one letter of support and must be logged in to the application process at the HAA website. Faxes/e-mails will not be accepted. Students must download the certification page from the HAA web site, complete it and obtain the proper signatures prior to mailing.

300 ■ Horatio Alger Florida Scholarships
(Undergraduate/Scholarship)

Purpose: To provide financial assistance to students in the counties of Broward, Martin and St. Lucie in the state of Florida. **Focus:** General studies. **Qualif.:** Applicants must be full time high school seniors, progressing normally toward graduation and planning to enter college not later than the fall following graduation; must have a strong commitment to pursue a bachelor's degree at an accredited institution (students may start their studies at a two-year institution and then transfer to a four-year institution); must have critical financial need ($50,000 or less adjusted gross income per family is preferred; if higher, an explanation must be provided); must be involved in co-curricular and community activities; must have a minimum grade point average of 2.0; must attend and residents of Broward, Martin, or St. Lucie counties in the state of Florida. **Criteria:** Recipients will be selected based on financial need.

Funds Avail.: $5,000. **Number Awarded:** 23. **To Apply:** Applicants must have one letter of support and must be logged in to the application process at the HAA website. Faxes/e-mails will not be accepted. Students must download the certification page from the HAA web site, complete it and obtain the proper signatures prior to mailing.

301 ■ Horatio Alger Franklin Scholarships
(Undergraduate/Scholarship)

Purpose: To provide financial assistance to high school seniors in the state of Pennsylvania. **Focus:** General studies. **Qualif.:** Applicants must reside and attend high school in the state of Pennsylvania; must be full time high school seniors, progressing normally toward graduation and plan-

---

Awards are arranged alphabetically below their administering organizations

ning to enter college no later than the fall following graduation; must have a strong commitment to pursue a bachelor's degree at an accredited institution (students may start their studies at a two-year institution and then transfer to a four-year institution); must have critical financial need ($50,000 or less adjusted gross income per family is preferred; if higher, an explanation must be provided); must be involved in co-curricular and community activities; must have a minimum grade point average of 2.0; and be citizens or permanent residents of the United States. **Criteria:** Recipients will be selected based on financial need.

Funds Avail.: $10,000. **Number Awarded:** 25. **To Apply:** Applicants must have one letter of support and must be logged in to the application process at the HAA website. Faxes/e-mails will not be accepted. Students must download the certification page from the HAA web site, complete it and obtain the proper signatures prior to mailing.

302 ■ Horatio Alger Georgia Scholarships
(Undergraduate/Scholarship)

Purpose: To provide financial assistance to students in the state of Georgia. **Focus:** General studies. **Qualif.:** Applicants must be full time high school seniors, progressing normally toward graduation and planning to enter college not later than the fall following graduation; must have a strong commitment to pursue a bachelor's degree at an accredited institution (students may start their studies at a two-year institution and then transfer to a four-year institution); must have critical financial need ($50,000 or less adjusted gross income per family is preferred; if higher, an explanation must be provided); must be involved in co-curricular and community activities; must have a minimum grade point average of 2.0; and must be Georgia residents or citizens of the United States. **Criteria:** Recipients will be selected based on financial need.

Funds Avail.: $5,000. **Number Awarded:** 50. **To Apply:** Applicants must have one letter of support and must be logged in to the application process at the HAA website. Faxes/e-mails will not be accepted. Students must download the certification page from the HAA web site, complete it and obtain the proper signatures prior to mailing.

303 ■ Horatio Alger Idaho University Scholarships *(Undergraduate/Scholarship)*

Purpose: To provide financial assistance to students entering their final two years of study in the College of Business at Idaho State University. **Focus:** General studies. **Qualif.:** Applicants must attend Idaho State University and be enrolled in the College of Business; must have critical financial need based on the Student Aid Report; must be residents of the State of Idaho; must have a minimum cumulative grade point average of 2.25 or better. **Criteria:** Recipients will be selected based on the committee's review of all applications.

Funds Avail.: $5,000. **Number Awarded:** 5. **To Apply:** Applicants must submit an official high school and college transcript of records; a copy of parents/guardians federal income tax return; must provide a copy of Student Aid Report (SAR); and have one letter of support and must be logged in to the application process at the HAA website. Faxes/e-mails will not be accepted. Students must download the certification page from the HAA web site, complete it and obtain the proper signatures prior to mailing. **Deadline:** March 21. **Remarks:** This scholarship program is exclusively for students who plan to enroll in the ISU Business School in the Fall 2011.

304 ■ Horatio Alger Illinois Scholarships
(Undergraduate/Scholarship)

Purpose: To provide financial assistance to students in the state of Illinois. **Focus:** General studies. **Qualif.:** Applicants must be enrolled full time as high school seniors, progressing normally toward graduation and planning to enter college not later than the fall following graduation; must have a strong commitment to pursue a bachelor's degree at an accredited institution (students may start their studies at a two-year institution and then transfer to a four-year institution); must have critical financial need ($50,000 or less adjusted gross income per family is preferred; if higher, an explanation must be provided); must be involved in co-curricular and community activities; must have a minimum grade point average of 2.0; be residents of Illinois; and be citizens or permanent residents of the United States. **Criteria:** Recipients will be selected based on financial need.

Funds Avail.: $5,000. **Number Awarded:** 20. **To Apply:** Applicants must submit an official high school transcript; a copy of parents/guardians federal income tax return; and have one letter of support and must be logged in to the application process at the HAA website. Faxes/e-mails will not be accepted. Students must download the certification page from the HAA web site, complete it and obtain the proper signatures prior to mailing.

305 ■ Horatio Alger Indiana Scholarships
(Undergraduate/Scholarship)

Purpose: To financial assistance to students in the state of Indiana. **Focus:** General studies. **Qualif.:** Applicants must be enrolled full time as high school seniors, progressing normally toward graduation and planning to enter college not later than the fall following graduation; must have a strong commitment to pursue a bachelor's degree at an accredited institution (students may start their studies at a two-year institution and then transfer to a four-year institution); must have critical financial need ($50,000 or less adjusted gross income per family is preferred; if higher, an explanation must be provided); must be involved in co-curricular and community activities; must have a minimum grade point average of 2.0; be residents of Indiana; and be citizens or permanent residents of the United States. **Criteria:** Recipients will be selected based on financial need.

Funds Avail.: $5,000. **Number Awarded:** 10. **To Apply:** Applicants must submit an official high school transcript; one copy of parents/guardians federal income tax return; and have one letter of support and must be logged in to the application process at the HAA website. Faxes/e-mails will not be accepted. Students must download the certification page from the HAA web site, complete it and obtain the proper signatures prior to mailing. **Remarks:** Funded through the generosity of Linda and Jack Gill.

306 ■ Horatio Alger Kentucky Scholarships
(Undergraduate/Scholarship)

Purpose: To provide financial assistance to students in the state of Kentucky. **Focus:** General studies. **Qualif.:** Applicants must be enrolled full time as high school seniors, progressing normally toward graduation and planning to enter college not later than the fall following graduation; must have a strong commitment to pursue a bachelor's degree at an accredited institution (students may start their studies at a two-year institution and then transfer to a four-year institution); must have critical financial need ($50,000 or less adjusted gross income per family is preferred; if higher, an explanation must be provided); must be involved in co-curricular and community activities; must have a

Awards are arranged alphabetically below their administering organizations

minimum grade point average of 2.0; be residents of Kentucky; and be citizens or permanent residents of the United States. **Criteria:** Recipients will be selected based on financial need.

Funds Avail.: $5,000. **Number Awarded:** 8. **To Apply:** Applicants must submit an official high school transcript; a copy of parents/guardians federal income tax return; have one letter of support and must be logged in to the application process at the HAA website. Faxes/e-mails will not be accepted. Students must download the certification page from the HAA web site, complete it and obtain the proper signatures prior to mailing.

307 ■ Horatio Alger Lola and Duane Hagadone Idaho Scholarships *(Undergraduate/Scholarship)*

Purpose: To provide scholarships to students in the State of Idaho. **Focus:** General studies. **Qualif.:** Applicants must be enrolled full time as high school seniors, progressing normally toward graduation and planning to enter college not later than the fall following graduation; must have a strong commitment to pursue a bachelor's degree at an accredited institution (students may start their studies at a two-year institution and then transfer to a four-year institution); must have critical financial need ($50,000 or less adjusted gross income per family is preferred; if higher, an explanation must be provided); must be involved in co-curricular and community activities; must have a minimum grade point average of 2.0; and be residents of Benewah, Boundary, Bonner, Kootenai, Latah, or Shoshone counties in the State of Idaho; and must citizens of United States. Recipients must pursue a bachelor's degree at the University of Idaho or Lewis-Clark State College. **Criteria:** Recipients will be selected based on the Committee's review of all applications.

Funds Avail.: $5,000. **Number Awarded:** 25. **To Apply:** Applicants must submit an official high school transcript; a copy of parents/guardians federal income tax return; and have one letter of support and must be logged in to the application process at the HAA website. Faxes/e-mails will not be accepted. Students must download the certification page from the HAA web site, complete it and obtain the proper signatures prior to mailing.

308 ■ Horatio Alger Louisiana Scholarships *(Undergraduate/Scholarship)*

Purpose: To provide financial assistance to students in the state of Louisiana. **Focus:** General studies. **Qualif.:** Applicants must be enrolled full time as high school seniors, progressing normally toward graduation and planning to enter college not later than the fall following graduation; must have a strong commitment to pursue a bachelor's degree at an accredited institution (students may start their studies at a two-year institution and then transfer to a four-year institution); must have critical financial need ($50,000 or less adjusted gross income per family is preferred; if higher, an explanation must be provided); must be involved in co-curricular and community activities; must have a minimum grade point average of 2.0; must be residents of Louisiana; and be citizens or permanent residents of the United States. Students must plan to attend and enroll in one of the following five schools to be awarded the Louisiana Scholarship: Loyola University - New Orleans; McNeese State University; Tulane University; University of New Orleans; Xavier University. **Criteria:** Recipients will be selected based on financial need.

Funds Avail.: $10,500. **Number Awarded:** 50. **To Apply:** Applicants must submit an official high school transcript; a

copy of parents/guardians federal income tax return; have one letter of support and must be logged in to the application process at the HAA website. Faxes/e-mails will not be accepted. Students must download the certification page from the HAA web site, complete it and obtain the proper signatures prior to mailing.

309 ■ Horatio Alger Minnesota Scholarships *(Undergraduate/Scholarship)*

Purpose: To provide financial assistance to students in the state of Minnesota. **Focus:** General studies. **Qualif.:** Applicants must be enrolled full time as high school seniors, progressing normally toward graduation and planning to enter college not later than the fall following graduation; must have a strong commitment to pursue a bachelor's degree at an accredited institution (students may start their studies at a two-year institution and then transfer to a four-year institution); must have critical financial need ($50,000 or less adjusted gross income per family is preferred; if higher, an explanation must be provided); must be involved in co-curricular and community activities; must have a minimum grade point average of 2.0; must be residents of Anoka, Carver, Dakota, Hennepin, Ramsey, Scott and Washington counties; and be citizens or permanent residents of the United States. **Criteria:** Recipients will be selected based on financial need.

Funds Avail.: $4,000. **Number Awarded:** 10. **To Apply:** Applicants must submit an official high school transcript; a copy of parents/guardians federal tax return; have one letter of support and must be logged in to the application process at the HAA website. Faxes/e-mails will not be accepted. Students must download the certification page from the HAA web site, complete it and obtain the proper signatures prior to mailing.

310 ■ Horatio Alger Missouri Scholarships *(Undergraduate/Scholarship)*

Purpose: To provide financial assistance to students in the state Missouri. **Focus:** General studies. **Qualif.:** Applicants must be enrolled full time as high school seniors in Missouri, progressing normally toward graduation and planning to enter college not later than the fall following graduation; must have a strong commitment to pursue a bachelor's degree at an accredited institution (students may start their studies at a two-year institution and then transfer to a four-year institution); must have critical financial need ($50,000 or less adjusted gross income per family is preferred; if higher, an explanation must be provided); must be involved in co-curricular and community activities; must have a minimum grade point average of 2.0; must be residents of Missouri; and be citizens or permanent residents of the United States. **Criteria:** Recipients will be selected based on financial need.

Funds Avail.: $5,000. **Number Awarded:** 10. **To Apply:** Applicants must submit an official high school transcript; a copy of parents/guardians federal income tax return; have one letter of support and must be logged in to the application process at the HAA website. Faxes/e-mails will not be accepted. Students must download the certification page from the HAA web site, complete it and obtain the proper signatures prior to mailing.

311 ■ Horatio Alger Montana Scholarships *(Undergraduate/Scholarship)*

Purpose: To provide financial assistance to students in the state of Montana. **Focus:** General studies. **Qualif.:** Applicants must be enrolled full time as high school seniors,

Awards are arranged alphabetically below their administering organizations

progressing normally toward graduation and planning to enter college not later than the fall following graduation; must have a strong commitment to pursue a bachelor's degree at an accredited institution (students may start their studies at a two-year institution and then transfer to a four-year institution); must have critical financial need ($50,000 or less adjusted gross income per family is preferred; if higher, an explanation must be provided); must be involved in co-curricular and community activities; must have a minimum grade point average of 2.0; must be residents of Montana; and be citizens or permanent residents of the United States. Recipients must pursue a bachelor's degree at the University of Montana, The University of Montana-Western, The University of Montana-Missoula College of Technology, Helena College of Technology of The University of Montana, or Montana Tech of The University of The University of Montana. **Criteria:** Recipients will be selected based on financial need.

Funds Avail.: $5,000. **Number Awarded:** 50. **To Apply:** Applicants must submit an official high school transcript; a copy of parents/guardians federal tax return; have one letter of support and must be logged in to the application process at the HAA website. Faxes/e-mails will not be accepted. Students must download the certification page from the HAA web site, complete it and obtain the proper signatures prior to mailing.

312 ■ Horatio Alger National Scholarships
(Undergraduate/Scholarship)

Purpose: To assist high school students who have faced and overcome great obstacles in their young lives. **Focus:** General studies. **Qualif.:** Applicants must be enrolled full time as high school seniors, progressing normally toward graduation and planning to enter college not later than the fall following graduation; must have a strong commitment to pursue a bachelor's degree at an accredited institution (students may start their studies at a two-year institution and then transfer to a four-year institution); must have critical financial need ($50,000 or less adjusted gross income per family is preferred; if higher, an explanation must be provided); must be involved in co-curricular and community activities; must have a minimum grade point average of 2.0; and be citizens or permanent residents of the United States. **Criteria:** Recipients will be selected based on the Committee's review of all applications.

Funds Avail.: $20,000. **Number Awarded:** 104. **To Apply:** Applicants must submit an official high school transcript; a copy of parents/guardian federal income tax return; and have one letter of support and must be logged in to the application process at the HAA website. Faxes/e-mails will not be accepted. Students must download the certification page from the HAA web site, complete it and obtain the proper signatures prior to mailing.

313 ■ Horatio Alger North Dakota Scholarships
(Undergraduate/Scholarship)

Purpose: To provide financial assistance to students in the state of North Dakota. **Focus:** General studies. **Qualif.:** Applicants must be enrolled full time as high school seniors, progressing normally toward graduation and planning to enter college not later than the fall following graduation; must have a strong commitment to pursue a bachelor's degree at an accredited institution (students may start their studies at a two-year institution and then transfer to a four-year institution); must have critical financial need ($50,000 or less adjusted gross income per family is preferred; if higher, an explanation must be provided); must be involved in co-curricular and community activities; must have a

minimum grade point average of 2.0; be residents of North Dakota; and be citizens or permanent residents of the United States. **Criteria:** Recipients will be selected based on financial need.

Funds Avail.: $5,000. **Number Awarded:** 5. **To Apply:** Applicants must submit an official high school transcript; a copy of parent's/guardian's federal tax return; have one letter of support and must be logged in to the application process at the HAA website. Faxes/e-mails will not be accepted. Students must download the certification page from the HAA web site, complete it and obtain the proper signatures prior to mailing.

314 ■ Horatio Alger Pennsylvania Scholarships
(Undergraduate/Scholarship)

Purpose: To provide financial assistance to students in the State of Pennsylvania. **Focus:** General studies. **Qualif.:** Applicants must be enrolled full time as high school seniors, progressing normally toward graduation and planning to enter college not later than the fall following graduation; must have a strong commitment to pursue a bachelor's degree at an accredited institution (students may start their studies at a two-year institution and then transfer to a four-year institution); must have critical financial need ($50,000 or less adjusted gross income per family is preferred; if higher, an explanation must be provided); must be involved in co-curricular and community activities; must have a minimum grade point average of 2.0; be residents of Pennsylvania; and be citizens or permanent residents of the United States. **Criteria:** Recipients will be selected based on financial need.

Funds Avail.: $5,000. **Number Awarded:** 50. **To Apply:** Applicants must submit an official high school transcript; have one letter of support and must be logged in to the application process at the HAA website. Faxes/e-mails will not be accepted. Students must download the certification page from the HAA web site, complete it and obtain the proper signatures prior to mailing. **Remarks:** Funded through the generosity of Joseph and Jeanette Neubauer of the Neubauer Family Foundation.

315 ■ Horatio Alger South Dakota Scholarships
(Undergraduate/Scholarship)

Purpose: To provide financial assistance to students in the state of South Dakota. **Focus:** General studies. **Qualif.:** Applicants must be enrolled full time as high school seniors, progressing normally toward graduation and planning to enter college not later than the fall following graduation; must have a strong commitment to pursue a bachelor's degree at an accredited institution (students may start their studies at a two-year institution and then transfer to a four-year institution); must have critical financial need ($50,000 or less adjusted gross income per family is preferred; if higher, an explanation must be provided); must be involved in co-curricular and community activities; must have a minimum grade point average of 2.0; be residents of South Dakota; and be citizens or permanent residents of the United States. **Criteria:** Recipients will be selected based on financial need.

Funds Avail.: $5,000. **Number Awarded:** 25. **To Apply:** Applicants must submit an official high school transcript; a copy of parents/guardians federal tax return; have one letter of support and must be logged in to the application process at the HAA website. Faxes/e-mails will not be accepted. Students must download the certification page from the HAA web site, complete it and obtain the proper signatures prior to mailing.

Awards are arranged alphabetically below their administering organizations

316 ■ Horatio Alger Texas - Fort Worth Scholarships (*Undergraduate/Scholarship*)

Purpose: To provide financial assistance to students from Fort Worth, Texas. **Focus:** General studies. **Qualif.:** Applicants must be full time high school seniors, progressing normally toward graduation and planning to enter college no later than the fall following graduation; must have a strong commitment to pursue a bachelor's degree at an accredited institution (students may start their studies at a two-year institution and then transfer to a four-year institution); must have critical financial need ($50,000 or less adjusted gross income per family is preferred; if higher, an explanation must be provided); must be involved in co-curricular and community activities; must have a minimum grade point average of 2.0; must live and attend high school in Forth Worth, Texas; and must be citizens of the United States. **Criteria:** Recipients will be selected based on financial need.

Funds Avail.: $5,000. **Number Awarded:** 12. **To Apply:** Applicants must have one letter of support and must be logged in to the application process at the HAA website. Faxes/e-mails will not be accepted. Students must download the certification page from the HAA web site, complete it and obtain the proper signatures prior to mailing.

317 ■ Horatio Alger Texas Scholarships (*Undergraduate/Scholarship*)

Purpose: To provide financial assistance to students in the state of Texas. **Focus:** General studies. **Qualif.:** Applicants must be full time high school seniors, progressing normally toward graduation and planning to enter college no later than the fall following graduation; must have a strong commitment to pursue a bachelor's degree at an accredited institution (students may start their studies at a two-year institution and then transfer to a four-year institution); must have critical financial need ($50,000 or less adjusted gross income per family is preferred; if higher, an explanation must be provided); must be involved in co-curricular and community activities; must have a minimum grade point average of 2.0; must be residents of Texas; and must be citizens or permanent residents of the United States. **Criteria:** Recipients will be selected based on financial need.

Funds Avail.: $5,000. **Number Awarded:** 7. **To Apply:** Applicants must have one letter of support and must be logged in to the application process at the HAA website. Faxes/e-mails will not be accepted. Students must download the certification page from the HAA web site, complete it and obtain the proper signatures prior to mailing.

318 ■ Horatio Alger Utah Scholarships (*Undergraduate/Scholarship*)

Purpose: To provide financial assistance to students in the state of Utah. **Focus:** General studies. **Qualif.:** Applicants must be full time high school seniors, progressing normally toward graduation and planning to enter college no later than the fall following graduation; must have a strong commitment to pursue a bachelor's degree at an accredited institution (students may start their studies at a two-year institution and then transfer to a four-year institution); must have critical financial need ($50,000 or less adjusted gross income per family is preferred; if higher, an explanation must be provided); must be involved in co-curricular and community activities; must have a minimum grade point average of 2.0; must be residents of Utah; and must be citizens or permanent residents of the United States. **Criteria:** Recipients will be selected based on financial need.

Funds Avail.: $5,000. **Number Awarded:** 15. **To Apply:** Applicants must have one letter of support and must be logged in to the application process at the HAA website. Faxes/e-mails will not be accepted. Students must download the certification page from the HAA web site, complete it and obtain the proper signatures prior to mailing.

319 ■ Horatio Alger Washington Scholarships (*Undergraduate/Scholarship*)

Purpose: To provide financial assistance to students in the state of Washington. **Focus:** General studies. **Qualif.:** Applicants must be full time high school seniors, progressing normally toward graduation and planning to enter college no later than the fall following graduation; must have a strong commitment to pursue a bachelor's degree at an accredited institution (students may start their studies at a two-year institution and then transfer to a four-year institution); must have critical financial need ($50,000 or less adjusted gross income per family is preferred; if higher, an explanation must be provided); must be involved in co-curricular and community activities; must have a minimum grade point average of 2.0; must be residents of Washington; and must be citizens or permanent residents of the United States. **Criteria:** Recipients will be selected based on financial need.

Funds Avail.: $5,000. **Number Awarded:** 10. **To Apply:** Applicants must have one letter of support and must be logged in to the application process at the HAA website. Faxes/emails will not be accepted. Students must download the certification page from the HAA web site, complete it and obtain the proper signatures prior to mailing.

320 ■ Horatio Alger Wyoming Scholarships (*Undergraduate/Scholarship*)

Purpose: To provide financial assistance to students in the state of Wyoming. **Focus:** General studies. **Qualif.:** Applicants must be full time high school seniors, progressing normally toward graduation and planning to enter college no later than the fall following graduation; must have a strong commitment to pursue a bachelor's degree at an accredited institution (students may start their studies at a two-year institution and then transfer to a four-year institution); must have critical financial need ($50,000 or less adjusted gross income per family is preferred; if higher, an explanation must be provided); must be involved in co-curricular and community activities; must have a minimum grade point average of 2.0; must be residents of Wyoming; and must be citizens or permanent residents of the United States. **Criteria:** Recipients will be selected based on financial need.

Funds Avail.: $5,000. **Number Awarded:** 15. **To Apply:** Applicants must have one letter of support and must be logged in to the application process at the HAA website. Faxes/e-mails will not be accepted. Students must download the certification page from the HAA web site, complete it and obtain the proper signatures prior to mailing.

321 ■ All-Ink.com

1460 N Main St., Ste. 2
Spanish Fork, UT 84660
Ph: (801) 794-0123
Fax: (801) 794-0124
Free: 888-567-6511
E-mail: wecare@all-ink.com
URL: www.all-ink.com

Awards are arranged alphabetically below their administering organizations

322 ■ All-Ink Scholarships *(Graduate, Undergraduate/Scholarship)*

Purpose: To support students in pursuing their goal of a higher education. **Focus:** General studies. **Qualif.:** Applicant may be a high school senior, undergraduate or graduate student; a U.S. citizen or permanent resident; have a minimum 2.5 GPA and enrolled or planning to participate in an accredited college/university program. **Criteria:** Selection is based on the applications.

Funds Avail.: $5,000. **To Apply:** Applicants are required to apply online. **Deadline:** December 31. **Contact:** csp@all-ink.com or cspadmin@all-ink.com.

323 ■ All Star Association
PO Box 911050
Lexington, KY 40591-1050
Fax: (859) 255-3647
Free: 800-930-3644
URL: www.allstardairy.com

324 ■ John D. Utterback Scholarship Program *(Undergraduate/Scholarship)*

Purpose: To provide support for dependents of association members. **Focus:** Food science and technology. **Qualif.:** Applicants must be high school or college students enrolled in food science, marketing, business, nutrition, packaging, or AG education programs; must be employees and/or their dependents. **Criteria:** Applicants will be selected based on their academic performance, courses related to food science, apparent commitment to a career in dairy/beverage/food industry; involvement in extra-curricular activities, and by the evidence of leadership ability, initiative, character and integrity.

Funds Avail.: $5,000. **Number Awarded:** 5. **To Apply:** Applicants must complete and print the online questionnaire; must have the official transcript from all high schools, colleges and universities attended; must submit a request letter of recommendation from a faculty member familiar with the applicant's scholastic performance; must have a recent photograph. Application form and other supporting documents must be sent to: All Star Dairy Association Inc., 1050 Monarch St., Ste. 101, Lexington, KY 40513. **Deadline:** June 1.

325 ■ Allegheny County Bar Foundation (ACBF)
400 Koppers Bldg.
436 Seventh Ave.
Pittsburgh, PA 15219
Ph: (412) 402-6641
E-mail: dblaner@acba.org
URL: www.acbf.org

326 ■ Daniel B. Dixon Scholarships *(Undergraduate/Scholarship)*

Purpose: To support a law student attending the University of Pittsburgh School of Law. **Focus:** Law. **Qualif.:** Applicant must be a law student attending the University of Pittsburgh School of Law who has completed his/her first or second year and who has demonstrated an interest in real estate law. **Criteria:** Selection is based on academic excellence and financial need.

Funds Avail.: $500. **Number Awarded:** 1. **To Apply:** Applicants must submit a completed application form together with the essay, recommendation, transcripts and proof of class rank (most recent grade reports). **Deadline:** June 15. **Remarks:** Established in 2007. **Contact:** Lorrie K. Albert at 412-402-6640 (Phone), 412-261-3622 (Fax) or lalbert@acba.org.

327 ■ Kennedy T. Friend Scholarships *(Graduate, Undergraduate/Scholarship)*

Purpose: To support the education of the son/daughter of a "member of the Bar of Allegheny County". **Focus:** General studies. **Qualif.:** Applicant must be a son/daughter of a "member of the Bar of Allegheny County", and enrolled at Yale University in New Haven, Connecticut or at the University of Paris in France. **Criteria:** Applicant must meet the qualification to receive the award.

Funds Avail.: $9,000-$17,000. **To Apply:** Applicants must submit an application form together with a copy of Attorney's Annual Fee application, written confirmation of registration from the school, and a list of courses to be taken. **Deadline:** May 1. **Remarks:** Established on May 26, 1929. **Contact:** Trust Administrator, PNC Institutional Investments, Kennedy T. Friend, 2 PNC Plz. - 7th Fl., 620 Liberty Ave., Pittsburgh, PA 15222 or 1-888-231-6082.

328 ■ F.C. Grote Fund Scholarships *(Graduate, Undergraduate/Scholarship)*

Purpose: To support the education of a student at the University of Pittsburgh School of Law and the University of Pennsylvania Law School. **Focus:** Law. **Qualif.:** Applicant must be a student at the University of Pittsburgh School of Law or the University of Pennsylvania Law School. **Criteria:** Selection is based on the application materials submitted.

Funds Avail.: $5,000. **To Apply:** Applicants must submit a completed application form. **Deadline:** April 16. **Contact:** Lorrie K. Albert at 412-402-6640 (Phone), 412-261-3622 (Fax) or lalbert@acba.org.

329 ■ Honorable Carol Los Mansmann Memorial Scholarships *(Graduate, Undergraduate/Scholarship)*

Purpose: To support an outstanding female law student attending Duquesne University School of Law. **Focus:** Law. **Qualif.:** Applicant must be a female law student attending Duquesne University School of Law who demonstrates a potential for leadership and a commitment to the advancement of women; must be enrolled in the School of Law and must have completed first year of the day division or second year of the evening or part-time day division; must be ranked in the top half of the class. **Criteria:** Selection is based on a combination of academic achievement, involvement in extracurricular and other activities, financial need and an essay.

Funds Avail.: $3,000. **Number Awarded:** One or more. **To Apply:** Applicants must submit a completed application including transcripts and proof of class rank (most recent grade reports). **Deadline:** April 16. **Contact:** Lorrie K. Albert at 412-402-6640 (Phone), 412-261-3622 (Fax) or lalbert@acba.org.

330 ■ Honorable Joseph H. Ridge Memorial Scholarships *(Undergraduate/Scholarship)*

Purpose: To support the education of a student at Duquesne Law School. **Focus:** Law. **Qualif.:** Applicant must be a student of Duquesne Law School and must also be a graduate of Central Catholic High School. **Criteria:** Scholarship will be awarded to the highest ranking member of the

Awards are arranged alphabetically below their administering organizations

graduating class at Duquesne Law School.

Funds Avail.: No specific amount. **To Apply:** Students may contact the Allegheny County Bar Foundation for more information.

331 ■ James I. Smith, III Notre Dame Law School Scholarship Fund *(Graduate, Undergraduate/Scholarship)*

Purpose: To provide scholarships to law students from Allegheny County enrolled at Notre Dame Law School. **Focus:** Law. **Qualif.:** Applicant must be an Allegheny County student enrolled at Notre Dame Law School. **Criteria:** Selection is based on the application materials submitted.

Funds Avail.: No specific amount. **To Apply:** Applicants must submit completed applications and include an estimated budget. Application must be signed by an authorized representative of the law school. **Deadline:** April 16. **Remarks:** Created in 2001 in honor of the retirement of James I. Smith. **Contact:** Lorrie K. Albert at 412-402-6640 (Phone), 412-261-3622 (Fax) or lalbert@acba.org.

332 ■ Alliance Defending Freedom (ADF)

15100 N 90th St.
Scottsdale, AZ 85260
Ph: (480) 444-0020
Fax: (480) 444-0028
Free: 800-TELL-ADF
E-mail: grants@telladf.org
URL: www.alliancedefendingfreedom.org

333 ■ Alliance Defense Fund - Blackstone Legal Fellowships *(Undergraduate/Fellowship)*

Purpose: To train law students who will rise to positions of influence and leadership as legal scholars, litigators, policy makers and judges. **Focus:** Law. **Qualif.:** Applicants must be exceptionally capable and highly motivated first year law students (second year law students are also welcome to apply). **Criteria:** Selection is based on demonstrated Christian commitment, motivation to engage in popular legal culture, leadership potential in a legal context, evidence of oral and written communication skills, and academic achievement.

Funds Avail.: $6,300. **Number Awarded:** At least 110. **To Apply:** Applicants must complete the application online. **Deadline:** January 21.

334 ■ Alliance for Equality of Blind Canadians (AEBC)

RPO Town Centre
Kelowna, BC, Canada V1Y 9H2
Free: 800-561-4774
E-mail: info@blindcanadians.ca
URL: www.blindcanadians.ca

335 ■ AEBC Toronto Chapter Scholarships *(Graduate, Undergraduate, Vocational/ Occupational/Scholarship)*

Purpose: To support outstanding blind, deaf-blind and partially blind Canadian students in their educational pursuits. **Focus:** General studies. **Qualif.:** Applicant must be blind, deaf-blind or partially sighted; a Canadian citizen or landed immigrant; attending a post-secondary program (college, university or vocational) with a full-time course load or at a 40% course load if accompanied by an explanation; and an Ontario resident studying in Ontario. **Criteria:** Selection is based on academic performance, community involvement and overcoming adversity.

Funds Avail.: $1,500. **Number Awarded:** 1. **To Apply:** Applicants must complete the application form online. In addition, applicants must submit a current or most recent average academic grade, calculated in percent; a personal letter; and a reference letter. **Deadline:** November 1. **Contact:** scholarship@blindcanadians.ca.

336 ■ Business, Education and Technology Scholarships *(Graduate, Undergraduate, Vocational/Occupational/Scholarship)*

Purpose: To support outstanding blind, deaf-blind and partially blind Canadian students in their educational pursuits. **Focus:** General studies. **Qualif.:** Applicant must be blind, deaf-blind or partially sighted; a Canadian citizen or landed immigrant; and attending a post-secondary program (college, university or vocational) with a full-time course load or at a 40% course load if accompanied by an explanation. **Criteria:** Selection is based on academic performance, community involvement and overcoming adversity.

Funds Avail.: $1,500. **Number Awarded:** 1. **To Apply:** Applicants must complete the application form online. In addition, applicants must submit a current or most recent average academic grade, calculated in percent; a personal letter; and a reference letter. **Deadline:** November 1. **Contact:** scholarship@blindcanadians.ca.

337 ■ Alan H. Neville Memorial Scholarships *(Graduate, Undergraduate, Vocational/ Occupational/Scholarship)*

Purpose: To support outstanding blind, deaf-blind and partially blind Canadian students in their educational pursuits. **Focus:** General studies. **Qualif.:** Applicant must be blind, deaf-blind or partially sighted; a Canadian citizen or landed immigrant; and attending a post-secondary program (college, university or vocational) with a full-time course load or at a 40% course load if accompanied by an explanation. **Criteria:** Selection is based on academic performance, community involvement and overcoming adversity.

Funds Avail.: $1,000. **Number Awarded:** 1. **To Apply:** Applicants must complete the application form online. In addition, applicants must submit a current or most recent average academic grade, calculated in percent; a personal letter; and a reference letter. **Deadline:** November 1. **Contact:** scholarship@blindcanadians.ca.

338 ■ AEBC Rick Oakes Scholarships for the Arts *(Graduate, Undergraduate, Vocational/ Occupational/Scholarship)*

Purpose: To support outstanding blind, deaf-blind and partially blind Canadian students in their educational pursuits. **Focus:** General studies. **Qualif.:** Applicant must be blind, deaf-blind or partially sighted; a Canadian citizen or landed immigrant; and attending a post-secondary program (college, university or vocational) with a full-time course load or at a 40% course load if accompanied by an explanation. **Criteria:** Selection is based on academic performance, community involvement and overcoming adversity.

Funds Avail.: $1,000. **Number Awarded:** 1. **To Apply:** Applicants must complete the application form online. In

Awards are arranged alphabetically below their administering organizations

addition, applicants must submit a current or most recent average academic grade, calculated in percent; a personal letter; and a reference letter. **Deadline:** November 1. **Contact:** scholarship@blindcanadians.ca.

339 ■ Alliance of Technology and Women (ATW)

PO Box 800868
Dallas, TX 75380
Free: 888-895-1566
E-mail: info@dfwatw.org
URL: www.dfwatw.org

340 ■ GREAT MINDS Collegiate Scholarship Program *(Undergraduate/Scholarship)*

Purpose: To provide financial assistance to women whose academic and professional goals include work in science, math, engineering or technology. **Focus:** Science; Math; Engineering; Technology. **Qualif.:** Applicants must be first-time students or adult learners returning to school to pursue a new career; must be enrolled in an Associate's or Bachelor's Degree program; may have diverse levels of life experience, academic merit, age, race and religion. **Criteria:** Recipients are chosen on the basis of volunteer service, passion for technology, leadership activities, scholastic grades, letters of recommendation and previous awards. Demonstrated passion and spirit is weighted most heavily in the selection process.

Funds Avail.: No specific amount. **To Apply:** Applicants must submit a completed application form. **Contact:** Alliance of Technology and Women at the above address.

341 ■ Alpha Chi (AX)

915 E Market Ave.
Searcy, AR 72149
Ph: (501) 279-4443
Fax: (501) 279-4589
Free: 800-477-4225
E-mail: tyarbrough@alphachihonor.org
URL: www.alphachihonor.org

342 ■ H. Y. Benedict Fellowships *(Graduate/ Fellowship)*

Purpose: To provide financial support to individuals for their first year of graduate study toward the master's, doctorate, or professional degree at any recognized institution. **Focus:** General studies. **Qualif.:** Nominee must be enrolled as graduate student with the baccalaureate degree during the school year in which application is made and must identify the graduate or professional school(s) to which he/she has applied for study the following fall. **Criteria:** Nominee must be enrolled for the following fall semester as a full-time student in graduate or professional study.

Funds Avail.: $2,500. **Number Awarded:** 10. **To Apply:** Nominee must submit the official nomination form completed, signed by the sponsor and included with the entry; a letter of application from the student outlining his/her plans for study and detailing his/her extracurricular activities, maximum length of two pages, double-spaced; an academic paper or other appropriate work in the student's major field; one letter of recommendation/evaluation from a faculty member in the field represented by the paper or project addressed to the significance of the work; a self-addressed, stamped envelope. **Deadline:** February 22.

343 ■ Edwin W. Gaston Scholarships *(Undergraduate/Scholarship)*

Purpose: To provide financial support for the education of senior undergraduate students. **Focus:** General studies. **Qualif.:** Nominee must be a senior year undergraduate student. **Criteria:** Nominee must be enrolled for the fall semester as a full-time student in undergraduate study toward the baccalaureate degree.

Funds Avail.: $2,500. **Number Awarded:** 2. **To Apply:** Nominee must submit the official nomination form completed, signed by the sponsor and included with the entry; a letter of application from the student outlining his/her plans for study and detailing his/her extracurricular activities, maximum length of two pages, double-spaced; an academic paper or other appropriate work in the student's major field; one letter of recommendation/evaluation from a faculty member in the field represented by the paper or project addressed to the significance of the work; a self-addressed, stamped envelope. **Deadline:** February 22.

344 ■ Alfred H. Nolle Scholarships *(Undergraduate/Scholarship)*

Purpose: To provide financial support for the education of senior undergraduate students. **Focus:** General studies. **Qualif.:** Nominee must be a full-time undergraduate senior student. **Criteria:** Nominee must be enrolled for the fall semester as a full-time student in undergraduate study toward the baccalaureate degree.

Funds Avail.: $1,500. **Number Awarded:** 10. **To Apply:** Nominee must submit the official nomination form completed, signed by the sponsor and included with the entry; a letter of application from the student outlining his/her plans for study and detailing his/her extracurricular activities, maximum length of two pages, double-spaced; an academic paper or other appropriate work in the student's major field; one letter of recommendation/evaluation from a faculty member in the field represented by the paper or project addressed to the significance of the work; a self-addressed, stamped envelope. **Deadline:** February 22.

345 ■ Pryor Graduate Fellowships *(Graduate/ Fellowship)*

Purpose: To provide financial assistance individuals for full-time graduate or professional study (beyond the baccalaureate level). **Focus:** General studies. **Qualif.:** Applicant must be an active alumni member and a graduate student member at Alpha Chi institutions at the time of application. **Criteria:** Candidates will be evaluated based on criteria by the Pryor Fellowship Committee. Only complete applications will be given consideration.

Funds Avail.: $5,000 to a student who has completed at least two years of graduate or professional study and $3,000 to a first or second year student of graduate or professional study. **Number Awarded:** 2. **To Apply:** Applicants must submit evidence of outstanding scholarship; 300-500 word essay introducing their academic/ professional goals, but not indicating financial need; two letters of recommendation from employers or professors or other persons qualified to give an evaluation; two complete official transcripts sealed by registrar; copy of official results of GRE, LSAT, MCAT or equivalent to applicant's discipline; and completed application form. **Deadline:** February 1.

346 ■ Robert W. Sledge Fellowships *(Graduate/ Fellowship)*

Purpose: To provide financial support to individuals for their first year of graduate study toward the master's,

Awards are arranged alphabetically below their administering organizations

doctorate or professional degree at any recognized institution. **Focus:** General studies. **Qualif.:** Nominee must be enrolled as graduate with the baccalaureate degree during the school year in which application is made and must identify the graduate or professional school(s) to which he/she has applied for study the following fall. **Criteria:** Nominee must be enrolled for the following fall semester as a full-time student in graduate or professional study.

Funds Avail.: $3,500. **Number Awarded:** 2. **To Apply:** Nominee must submit the official nomination form completed, signed by the sponsor and included with the entry; a letter of application from the student outlining his/her plans for study and detailing his/her extracurricular activities, maximum length of two pages, double-spaced; an academic paper or other appropriate work in the student's major field; one letter of recommendation/evaluation from a faculty member in the field represented by the paper or project addressed to the significance of the work; a self-addressed, stamped envelope. **Deadline:** February 22.

347 ■ Alpha Chi Sigma
2141 N Franklin Rd.
Indianapolis, IN 46219-2435
Ph: (317) 357-5944
Fax: (317) 351-9702
Free: 800-ALCHEMY
E-mail: national@alphachisigma.org
URL: www.alphachisigma.org

348 ■ Alpha Chi Sigma Scholarship Awards
(Graduate, Undergraduate/Scholarship)

Purpose: To encourage and recognize outstanding scholarship among Collegiate members of Alpha Chi Sigma Fraternity. **Focus:** General studies. **Qualif.:** Nominees must have been members of Alpha Chi Sigma Fraternity for at least one year, and enrolled in an institution of higher learning at the time of nomination. Undergraduate nominees must have completed the Junior year at the time of nomination. Graduate nominees may be nominated based upon their undergraduate and graduate records upon the completion of their first year of graduate study. Graduate students may also be nominated, based upon their graduate records alone, after admission to candidacy for the terminal degree in the field of graduate study. **Criteria:** Nominees will be evaluated by the appointed award committee with established criteria.

Funds Avail.: $1,000. **To Apply:** Application process is done through nomination. Nominee must submit the following checklist: 1) biographical sketch; 2) two letters of recommendation by faculty of the institution from where the student is enrolled; 3) transcripts of all academic works; 4) photograph; 5) address and telephone number of a candidate including summer address if different; and 6) other information that may support the application of a nominee such as abstracts of presentations of meetings, or reprints of scientific publications.

349 ■ Alpha Delta Gamma (ADG)
946 Sanders Dr.
St. Louis, MO 63126
E-mail: council@alphadeltagamma.org
URL: www.alphadeltagamma.org

350 ■ Alpha Delta Gamma Educational Foundation Scholarships (ADGEF) *(All/Scholarship)*
Purpose: To support and promote educational opportunities for the members of Alpha Delta Gamma National

Fraternity. **Focus:** General studies. **Qualif.:** Applicant must be a member of Alpha Delta Gamma National Fraternity. **Criteria:** Selection is based on the application.

Funds Avail.: No specific amount. **To Apply:** Applicants must submit a statement from the financial office of the college or university attended; one letter of recommendation from Chapter moderator; one letter of recommendation from a current instructor; no larger than 5X7 photo; a letter from the ADG National Treasurer stating the applicant's membership standing; one-page biographical sketch; and one copy of transcript of records. **Remarks:** The scholarship is payable to the present school to be used for tuition, books, or housing, unless otherwise noted in the application. **Contact:** All applications must be sent to: Wayne Palmer-Ball, 7553 Hwy. V, Caledonia, WI 53108; E-mail: topadg@aol.com.

351 ■ Alpha Kappa Alpha (AKA) - Educational Advancement Foundation (EAF)
5656 S Stony Island Ave.
Chicago, IL 60637
Ph: (773) 947-0026
Fax: (773) 947-0277
Free: 800-653-6528
E-mail: akaeaf@akaeaf.net
URL: www.akaeaf.org

352 ■ Alpha Kappa Alpha - Educational Advancement Foundation Financial Need-Based Scholarships *(Graduate, Undergraduate/Scholarship)*

Purpose: To provide financial support to undergraduate and graduate students for the advancement of education and to promote life-long learning. **Focus:** General studies. **Qualif.:** Applicants must be full-time undergraduate students, sophomores or beyond, currently enrolled in an accredited campus-based degree-granting institution of higher learning or currently enrolled, full-time graduate students; must have a minimum 2.5 GPA or C+ average. **Criteria:** Recipients are selected based on financial need.

Funds Avail.: $750 to $2,500. **To Apply:** Applicants must submit all the required application information. **Deadline:** April 15 for the undergraduates' applications; August 15 for graduates' applications.

353 ■ Alpha Kappa Alpha - Educational Advancement Foundation Merit Scholarships *(Graduate, Undergraduate/Scholarship)*

Purpose: To provide financial support to undergraduate and graduate students for the advancement of education and to promote life-long learning. **Focus:** General studies. **Qualif.:** Applicants must be full-time and currently enrolled undergraduate students with at least sophomore standing at an accredited campus-based degree-granting institution or full-time and currently enrolled graduate students at an accredited campus-based degree-granting institution. Both must possess a minimum grade point average of 3.0. **Criteria:** Applicants are evaluated based on academic achievement and demonstrated community service and involvement.

Funds Avail.: $750-$2,500. **To Apply:** Applicants must submit all the required application information. **Deadline:** April 15 for undergraduates' applications; August 15 for graduates' applications.

Awards are arranged alphabetically below their administering organizations

354 ■ Youth Partners Accessing Capital (PAC) (Graduate, Undergraduate/Scholarship)

Purpose: To provide financial support to undergraduate and graduate students for the advancement of education and to promote life-long learning. **Focus:** General studies. **Qualif.:** Applicants must be members of the Alpha Kappa Alpha Sorority, Inc.; at least college sophomores who have a minimum 3.0 of GPA. **Criteria:** Applicants are evaluated based on demonstrated exceptional academic achievement; financial need; and leadership or volunteerism in civic or campus activities.

Funds Avail.: $750-$1,500. **To Apply:** Applicants must submit all the required application information. **Deadline:** April 15.

355 ■ Alpha Phi Sigma
3301 College Ave.
Fort Lauderdale, FL 33314
Ph: (954) 262-7004
Fax: (954) 262-3646
E-mail: headquarters@alphaphisigma.org
URL: www.alphaphisigma.org

356 ■ Commander James Carr Forensic Science Scholarships (Undergraduate/Scholarship)

Purpose: To assist students in their educational pursuits. **Focus:** General studies. **Qualif.:** Applicants must be Alpha Phi Sigma members. **Criteria:** Recipients are selected based on academic achievement, professional recommendations, and extracurricular activities.

Funds Avail.: $1000. **Number Awarded:** 1. **To Apply:** Applicants must submit required materials and documents following the stipulated guidelines. **Deadline:** January 31.

357 ■ V.A. Leonard Scholarships (Graduate, Undergraduate/Scholarship)

Purpose: To assist students in their educational pursuits. **Focus:** General studies. **Qualif.:** Applicants must be Alpha Phi Sigma members. **Criteria:** Recipients are selected based on academic achievement, professional recommendations and extracurricular activities.

Funds Avail.: $1000. **Number Awarded:** 1. **To Apply:** Applicants must submit required materials and documents following the stipulated guidelines. **Deadline:** December 31. **Remarks:** Established in 1982 in honor and recognition of Dr. Leonard's leadership and hard work in the field of Criminal Justice.

358 ■ Public Agency Training Council Criminal Justice Scholarships (Undergraduate/Scholarship)

Purpose: To assist students in their educational pursuits. **Focus:** General studies. **Qualif.:** Applicants must be Alpha Phi Sigma members. **Criteria:** Recipients are selected based on academic achievement, professional recommendations, and extracurricular activities.

Funds Avail.: $1000. **Number Awarded:** 1. **To Apply:** Applicants must submit required materials and documents following the stipulated guidelines. **Deadline:** January 31. **Remarks:** Established in 1987.

359 ■ Detective Cheryl Seiden Memorial Scholarships (Undergraduate/Scholarship)

Purpose: To assist students in their educational pursuits. **Focus:** General studies. **Qualif.:** Applicants must be Alpha Phi Sigma members. **Criteria:** Recipients are selected based on academic achievement, professional recommendations, and extracurricular activities.

Funds Avail.: $1000. **Number Awarded:** 1. **To Apply:** Applicants must submit required materials and documents following the stipulated guidelines. **Deadline:** January 31. **Remarks:** In memory of Metro-Dade Police Detective Cheryl Seiden, killed in the line of duty.

360 ■ Regina B. Shearn Scholarships (Graduate, Undergraduate/Scholarship)

Purpose: To assist students in their educational pursuits. **Focus:** General studies. **Qualif.:** Applicants must be Alpha Phi Sigma members. Applicants are not eligible to receive the same scholarship two years in succession. **Criteria:** Selection is based on academic performance, leadership and service, personal statement and evaluation reports.

Funds Avail.: $1,000. **Number Awarded:** 1. **To Apply:** Applicants must submit required materials and documents following the stipulated guidelines. **Deadline:** December 31. **Remarks:** Established in 2001, named after the first National Executive Director of Alpha Phi Sigma.

361 ■ Alpha Sigma Alpha
9002 Vincennes Cir.
Indianapolis, IN 46268-3018
Ph: (317) 871-2920
Fax: (317) 871-2924
E-mail: asa@alphasigmaalpha.org
URL: www.alphasigmaalpha.org

362 ■ Special Education Scholarships (Graduate, Undergraduate/Scholarship)

Purpose: To support female students pursuing graduate and undergraduate work in the field of Special Education. **Focus:** Special education. **Qualif.:** Applicant must be a female graduate or undergraduate student studying in the field of Special Education. **Criteria:** Selection is based on the application materials submitted for review.

Funds Avail.: No specific amount. **Number Awarded:** 2. **To Apply:** Applicants must submit a completed application form together with two letters of recommendation; essay (maximum of 250 words); a recent photo with paragraph; and transcripts. **Deadline:** March 2.

363 ■ Marjorie Anderson Thompson Scholarships (Graduate, Undergraduate/Scholarship)

Purpose: To support the education of a female student with moderate to severe hearing loss. **Focus:** General studies. **Qualif.:** Applicant must have a moderate to severe hearing loss defined as a pure tone average between 55 dB and 75 dB. **Criteria:** Preference will be given to members of Alpha Sigma Alpha.

Funds Avail.: No specific amount. **Number Awarded:** 1. **To Apply:** Applicants must submit a completed application form together with two letters of recommendation; essay (maximum of 250 words); a recent photo with paragraph; a proof of hearing loss; and transcripts. **Deadline:** March 2.

364 ■ Alpha Tau Omega (ATO)
1 N Pennsylvania St., 12th Fl.
Indianapolis, ID 46204
Ph: (317) 684-1865
Fax: (317) 684-1862

Awards are arranged alphabetically below their administering organizations

---

URL: www.ato.org

365 ■ Alpha Tau Omega Graduate Scholarships
(Graduate/Scholarship)

Purpose: To provide educational programs and scholarships of the highest standards. **Focus:** General studies. **Qualif.:** Applicants must be students either enrolled or accepted into an accredited graduate program; must be full-time students during the academic year; must be initiated members of ATO in good standing; must have a minimum cumulative GPA of 3.5 on a 4.0 scale. **Criteria:** Selection will be based on academic achievements; demonstrated leadership in ATO; and demonstrated leadership on campus and in the community.

Funds Avail.: No specific amount. **To Apply:** Applicants must apply online at www.ato.org and answer all questions in essay format. Applicants must also attach their transcript and three letters of recommendation. **Deadline:** March 4.

366 ■ Alpha Tau Omega Undergraduate Scholarships (Undergraduate/Scholarship)

Purpose: To provide educational programs and scholarships of the highest standards. **Focus:** General studies. **Qualif.:** Applicants must be students who have at least one undergraduate year remaining before graduation. **Criteria:** Selection will be based on the committee's criteria.

Funds Avail.: No specific amount. **To Apply:** Applicants must apply online at www.ato.org and answer all questions in essay format. Applicants must also attach their transcript and three letters of recommendation. **Deadline:** March 4. **Remarks:** Funded through a bequest from Alexander Macomber who served for 35 years as the Worthy Grand Keeper of the Exchequer for the ATO Fraternity.

367 ■ William D. Krahling Excellence in Journalism Scholarships (Undergraduate/Scholarship)

Purpose: To provide educational programs and scholarships of the highest standards. **Focus:** Journalism. **Qualif.:** Applicants must be students majoring in journalism or a related field; must have completed one academic year of undergraduate education and have at least one undergraduate year remaining. **Criteria:** Selection will be based on the committee's criteria.

Funds Avail.: No specific amount. **To Apply:** Applicants must apply online at www.ato.org and answer all questions in essay format. Applicants must also attach their transcript and three letters of recommendation. **Deadline:** March 4. **Remarks:** Established to help college journalism students strive for excellence as exemplified by Brother William D. Krahling, Mt. Union '54, who served as the editor of the ATO Palm.

368 ■ Lawrence A. Long Memorial Law Scholarships (Undergraduate/Scholarship)

Purpose: To provide educational programs and scholarships of the highest standards. **Focus:** General studies. **Qualif.:** Applicants must be students who are enrolled or accepted into an accredited law school and must be full-time students during the academic year. **Criteria:** Selection will be based on academic achievements; demonstrated leadership in ATO; and demonstrated leadership on campus and in the community.

Funds Avail.: No specific amount. **To Apply:** Applicants must apply online at www.ato.org and answer all questions in essay format. Applicants must also attach their transcript

and three letters of recommendation. **Deadline:** March 4. **Remarks:** Honors former Worthy Grand Chief Lawrence A. Long who served as Province Chief, Worthy Grand Keeper of the Annals, member of the National Fraternity Board of Directors, Worthy Grand Chief and Worthy High Chancellor.

369 ■ J. Milton Richardson Theological Fellowships (Graduate/Fellowship)

Purpose: To provide educational programs and scholarships of the highest standards. **Focus:** Theology. **Qualif.:** Applicant must be an ATO member who plans to attend or is enrolled in an accredited graduate school in theology or the seminary, and who intends to become a member of the clergy. **Criteria:** Selection will be based on the committee's criteria.

Funds Avail.: No specific amount. **To Apply:** Applicants must apply online at www.ato.org and answer all questions in essay format. Applicants must also attach their transcript and three letters of recommendation. **Deadline:** March 4. **Remarks:** Established in 1981 to honor J. Milton Richardson who served as ATO's National Chaplin and Spiritual advisor for four decades.

370 ■ Ambucs Resource Center
PO Box 5127
High Point, NC 27262
Fax: (336) 852-6830
Free: 800-838-1845
E-mail: ambucs@ambucs.org
URL: www.ambucs.org

371 ■ AMBUCS Scholarships for Therapists Program (Graduate, Undergraduate/Scholarship)

Purpose: To ensure that a new generation of therapists will continue to enhance the lives of people with disabilities. **Focus:** Physical therapy; Occupational therapy; Speech and language pathology/audiology. **Qualif.:** Applicant must be a citizen of the United States; with documented financial need; with good scholastic standing; be accepted at the junior or senior undergraduate, or graduate level in a program which qualifies the applicant for clinical practice in occupational therapy, physical therapy, speech and language pathology and hearing audiology; and must express an intent to enter clinical practice in chosen field of therapy in the United States upon completion of course of study for which aid is requested. **Criteria:** Awards are based on financial need, US citizenship, commitment to local community, demonstrated academic accomplishment, character for compassion integrity and career objectives.

Funds Avail.: $500-$1,500. **To Apply:** Applicants must may visit the website for the online application. Applicants must also submit the following supporting documents: most current IRS 1040 form; personal statement (one-page double-spaced, at least 10 pt. font); program acceptance/enrollment certification. **Deadline:** April 15.

372 ■ American Academy of Neurology (AAN)
1080 Montreal Ave.
St. Paul, MN 55116
Ph: (651) 695-2717
Fax: (651) 695-2791
Free: 800-879-1960
E-mail: memberservices@aan.com

Awards are arranged alphabetically below their administering organizations

URL: www.aan.com

373 ■ Clinical Research Training Fellowships
(Professional development/Fellowship)

Purpose: To support clinical research training in the neurosciences. **Focus:** Neurology. **Qualif.:** Applicants must be neurologists and clinical investigators interested in academic careers in clinical research; and must be AAN members who have completed less than five years of residency. **Criteria:** Candidates' applications are evaluated by the Clinical Research Subcommittee of the Science Committee of the AAN based on the applicant's ability and promises as clinician-scientists based on prior record of achievement and career plan, letters of reference and curriculum vitae; quality and nature of the training to be provided and the institutional, departmental and mentor-specific training environment; quality and originality of the research plan. Priorities will be given to those applicants who have taken their research career at an early stage.

Funds Avail.: $55,000 per year plus $10,000 for tuition fee. **To Apply:** Applicants must submit one complete copy of the letter of nomination from the Chair of the department of neurology, including assurance that clinical service responsibilities will be restricted to no more than 20 percent of the fellow's time; (three-page) research plan; copy of a current curriculum vitae; two letters of reference supporting applicant's potential for a clinical, academic research career and qualifications for the fellowship; listing of the applicant's and mentor's current and pending for support, other than this fellowship, using NIH format; letter from proposed mentor detailing the support of and commitment to the applicant and the proposed research and training plan; copy of the proposed mentor's NIH Biosketch; and document describing arrangements for formal course work including quantitative clinical epidemiology, biostatistics, study design, data analysis and ethics. **Contact:** Terry Heinz, theinz@aan.com, 651-695-2746.

374 ■ Medical Student Summer Research Scholarships *(Undergraduate/Scholarship)*

Purpose: To provide financial support for projects in either institutional, clinical or laboratory setting where there are ongoing programs of research, service or training or a private practice. **Focus:** Neurology. **Qualif.:** Applicants must be first or second-year medical student members who have a supporting preceptor and a project with clearly defined goals; or either third-year medical student members who are on the official summer break will also be considered with accompanying documentation, whose project is conducted through U.S. or Canadian institution of the students' choice and jointly designed by the students and sponsoring institutions. **Criteria:** Preference will be given to those applicants from schools with established SIGN chapters. More than one student from an institution may apply, but only one student will be selected from an institution.

Funds Avail.: $3,000. **Number Awarded:** 20. **To Apply:** Applicants must submit completed application form; (1-2 page) project proposal and curriculum vitae; two letters of recommendation: one from the project preceptor and one from the SIGN faculty advisor; and completed tax form with institution information. **Deadline:** February. **Contact:** Cheryl Alementi at the above address, Phone: 651-695-2737, E-mail: calementi@aan.com.

375 ■ American Academy of Nurse Practitioners (AANP)
PO Box 12846
Austin, TX 78711
Ph: (512) 442-4262
Fax: (512) 442-6469
E-mail: admin@aanp.org
URL: www.aanp.org

376 ■ CFIDS Association of America NP Student Scholarships *(Graduate/Scholarship)*

Purpose: To assist an AANP student and members in their education. **Focus:** Nursing. **Qualif.:** Applicants must be an AANP student and full member; an MSN-NP student pursuing a Master's in Nursing with NP specialty; have a minimum MSN-NP study GPA of 3.5. **Criteria:** Recipients are selected based on the Selection Committee's review of the application materials.

Funds Avail.: $1,000. **Number Awarded:** 2. **To Apply:** Applicants must request an application at scholarship@aanp.org. **Deadline:** September 26. **Remarks:** Post-MS NP, DNP and doctoral students are not qualified. Scholarship is sponsored by the Chronic Fatigue and Immune Dysfunction Syndrome (CFIDS) Association of America.

377 ■ National Heartburn Alliance NP Student Scholarships *(Graduate/Scholarship)*

Purpose: To assist an AANP student and members in their education. **Focus:** Nursing. **Qualif.:** Applicants must be AANP student members; MSN-NP students pursuing Master's in Nursing with NP specialty; have APAminimum MSN-NP study GPA of 3.5; must have completed at least one course of their Post-MS NP educational program at the time of application submission; and must be US citizens. **Criteria:** Recipients are selected based on the Selection Committee's review of the application materials.

Funds Avail.: $1,000. **Number Awarded:** 1. **To Apply:** Applicants must request an application form at scholarship@aanp.org. **Deadline:** September 26. **Remarks:** Post-MS NP, DNP and doctoral students are not qualified for the scholarship.

378 ■ Pfizer Inc. NP Student Scholarships
(Graduate/Scholarship)

Purpose: To assist an AANP student and members in their education. **Focus:** Nursing. **Qualif.:** Applicants must be AANP student members; MSN-NP students pursuing Master's in Nursing with NP specialty; have a minimum MSN-NP study GPA of 3.5; must have completed at least one course of their Post-MS NP educational program at the time of application submission; and must be US citizens. **Criteria:** Recipients are selected based on the Selection Committee's review of the application materials.

Funds Avail.: $1,000. **Number Awarded:** 1. **To Apply:** Applicants must request an application form at scholarship@aanp.org. **Deadline:** September 26. **Remarks:** Post-MS NP, DNP and doctoral students are not qualified. Scholarship is sponsored by Pfizer Inc.

379 ■ Pharmavite LLC NP Doctoral Education Scholarships *(Doctorate/Scholarship)*

Purpose: To assist an AANP student and members in their education. **Focus:** Medical education; Nursing. **Qualif.:** Applicants must be an AANP student and full member; U.S. citizen; an NP pursuing a Doctoral degree; currently

Awards are arranged alphabetically below their administering organizations

licensed practicing NP in the United States; have a minimum Doctoral study GPA of 3.75 and above. **Criteria:** Recipients are selected based on the Selection Committee's review of the application materials.

Funds Avail.: $2,000. **Number Awarded:** 1. **To Apply:** Applicants must request an application form at scholarship@aanp.org. **Deadline:** September 26. **Remarks:** MSN-NP and Post-MS NP students are not qualified for the scholarship.

380 ■ UCB, Inc. NP Student Scholarships
(Graduate/Scholarship)

Purpose: To assist an AANP student and members in their education. **Focus:** Nursing. **Qualif.:** Applicants must be AANP student members; MSN-NP students pursuing Master's in Nursing with NP specialty; have a minimum MSN-NP study GPA of 3.5; must have completed at least one course of their Post-MS NP educational program at the time of application submission; and must be US citizens. **Criteria:** Recipients are selected based on the selection Committee's review of the application materials.

Funds Avail.: $1,000. **Number Awarded:** 1. **To Apply:** Applicants must request an application form at scholarship@aanp.org. **Deadline:** September 26. **Remarks:** Post-MS NP, DNP and doctoral students are not qualified. Scholarship is sponsored by the UCB Inc.

381 ■ American Academy of Nursing (BAGNC) - Building Academic Geriatric Nursing Capacity Coordinating Center
Cordinating Ctr.
1000 Vermont Ave. NW, Ste. 910
Washington, DC 20005
Ph: (202) 777-1170
Fax: (202) 777-0107
E-mail: bagnc@aannet.org
URL: www.geriatricnursing.org

382 ■ BAGNC Predoctoral Scholarships
(Doctorate, Graduate/Scholarship)

Purpose: To increase academic geriatric nursing capacity in the United States. **Focus:** Geriatric medicine. **Qualif.:** Applicant must be a registered nurse; hold degree(s) in nursing; a U.S. citizen or permanent U.S. resident; plan an academic and research career; and demonstrate potential for long-term contributions to geriatric nursing. **Criteria:** Selection is based on applicants' qualifications, proposed Professional Development Plan and research area and the selected mentor(s) and institution of study.

Funds Avail.: $100,000. **Number Awarded:** 9. **To Apply:** The application must: provide the qualifications of the faculty mentor and detailed evidence of the mentor's commitment to, and involvement with, the applicant's professional development throughout the 2-year award program; include primary mentor's agreement to participate in program activities and the Annual Leadership Conference when possible; provides evidence of school's commitment to the applicant's academic career and professional development during the applicant's scholarship period; provides plan for continued support to ensure completion of doctoral program after grant term ends. **Deadline:** January 11.

383 ■ Claire M. Fagin Fellowships *(Doctorate/Fellowship)*

Purpose: To advance well-qualified applicants from under-represented minority groups to improve the nation's ability to provide culturally competent care to its increasingly diverse aging population. **Focus:** Geriatric medicine. **Qualif.:** Applicant must be a doctorally-prepared registered nurse; hold degree(s) in nursing; be a U.S. citizen or permanent U.S. resident; have potential to develop into independent investigators; and demonstrated potential for long-term contributions to geriatric nursing. **Criteria:** Selection is based on applicants' qualifications, proposed Professional Development Plan and research area and the selected mentor(s) and institution of study.

Funds Avail.: $120,000. **Number Awarded:** 9. **To Apply:** Selected Mentor(s) and Institutions of Study - the proposal must: include qualifications of the faculty mentor and detailed evidence of the mentor's commitment to and involvement with the applicant's professional development and activities throughout the two-year award program; demonstrate a match between the mentor's area of gerontological nursing research and the applicant's research interest area; confirm the primary mentor's agreement to participate in BAGNC Program activities including the Annual Leadership Conference when possible; show evidence of school's commitment to the applicant's academic career and professional development during the applicant's fellowship period. **Deadline:** January 11.

384 ■ American Academy of Optometry (AAO)
2909 Fairgreen St.
Orlando, FL 32803
Ph: (321) 710-3937
Fax: (407) 893-9890
E-mail: aof@aaoptom.org
URL: www.aaopt.org

385 ■ The William C. Ezell Fellowships
(Postgraduate/Fellowship)

Purpose: To encourage talented persons to pursue full-time careers in optometric research and education. **Focus:** Optometry. **Qualif.:** Applicants must be post-graduate students, continuing a full-time study and training in research that leads to a Masters or PhD degree. **Criteria:** Applicants fellowship applications will be reviewed by the Research Committee of the American Academy of Optometry and recommendations will then be sent to the AOF Board which approves and funds the Ezell Fellowships.

Funds Avail.: $8,000 plus $750 travel fellowships. **To Apply:** Applicants must submit application form together with three letters of recommendation from the persons qualified to comment on his/her educational qualifications, research abilities and potential and current and future teaching capabilities; one-page statement describing the applicant's educational objectives, future research and/or teaching interest and career objectives; and a copy of scientific publications, copies of papers in press must be included. Applications and documents must be submitted electronically indicating the Ezell Fellowship (+ applicant's last name) in the subject line. Attachments in .pdf are highly preferred, although MS Word is acceptable. **Deadline:** March. **Remarks:** Named after the founding President of the AOF, William C. Ezell, OD. **Contact:** Applications and supporting materials must be emailed at aof@aaoptom.org.

386 ■ Terrance Ingraham Pediatric Optometry Residency Awards *(Graduate/Award)*

Purpose: To promote the practice and development of the field of pediatric optometry by providing incentive and support to talented optometric residents who demonstrate a

Awards are arranged alphabetically below their administering organizations

passion and commitment to practice, research and education in the field of children's vision. **Focus:** Optometry. **Qualif.:** Applicant must be an optometrist continuing a pediatric/vision therapy residency at an accredited school or college of optometry. **Criteria:** Applicants will be evaluated on the basis of their educational background and their ability and potential as teachers, researchers, and practitioners in the field of pediatric optometry. Preference will be given to applicants with an interest in the utilization of soft contact lenses in pediatric populations.

Funds Avail.: $4,000. **Number Awarded:** 2. **To Apply:** Applicant must submit an application which includes applicant's education, research and teaching experience; a description of the applicant's residency program and his/her plans for the next academic year; a one-page statement of the applicant's career goals; three letters of recommendation from persons qualified to comment on educational qualifications, research abilities and potential. **Deadline:** January 25. **Contact:** Tracy Kitts, Foundation Coordinator, 301-984-4734; aof@aaoptom.org.

387 ■ VISTAKON George Mertz and Sheldon Wechsler Residency Awards *(All/Award)*

Purpose: To promote the practice and development of the field of optometry by providing incentive and support to talented optometric residents who demonstrate a passion and commitment to practice, research, and education. **Focus:** Optometry. **Qualif.:** Applicant must be an optometrist continuing a contact lens residency program at an accredited school or college of optometry. **Criteria:** Applicants will be evaluated primarily on the basis of their educational background and their ability and potential as teachers, researchers and practitioners in the field of contact lenses.

Funds Avail.: $4,000. **To Apply:** Applicants must submit a summary of the their education, research and teaching experience; description of the residency program and plans for the next academic year; one-page statement of the applicant's career goals; and three letters of reference. **Deadline:** January. **Contact:** Tracy Kitts, phone: 301-984-4734; email: aof@aaoptom.org.

388 ■ Antoinette M. Molinari Memorial Scholarships *(Doctorate/Scholarship)*

Purpose: To assist an exceptional student who has extraordinary financial needs and would have difficulty meeting the financial requirements of attending an optometry school. **Focus:** Optometry. **Qualif.:** Applicants must be students pursuing a doctorate of optometry through a full-time course of study and who maintain a grade point average of 3.5 (4 point scale) or higher for all course work taken in optometry school. **Criteria:** Recipient will be selected based on academic and leadership potential and financial need.

Funds Avail.: $6,000. **Number Awarded:** 1. **To Apply:** Applicants must submit a completed application form; three letters of reference from persons who can attest the applicant's educational qualifications, leadership potential, and financial needs; one-page statement describing the educational and career objectives; and an official transcript of optometry course work. **Deadline:** June.

389 ■ VISTAKON Research Grants *(All/Grant)*

Purpose: To encourage talented persons to pursue their full-time careers in optometry. **Focus:** Optometry. **Qualif.:** The $25,000 award will be open to individuals in optometry and vision science and $10,000 award will be available to graduate students and postdoctoral fellows no more than

five years from their terminal degree. **Criteria:** Applicants will be judged by the VISTAKON Research Grants Selection Committee based on some criteria. Applications that do not follow the required outline will not be considered.

Funds Avail.: $25,000. **Number Awarded:** 2. **To Apply:** Applicants must submit a proposal electronically and must contain the following components: introduction; background and significance; specific aims; preliminary studies; and study design and methods. These sections should total no more than five pages. References (maximum of one page) Budget and budget justification (maximum of one page) Biographical sketch(es) of Principal and one co-investigator only (maximum of two pages for each investigator) Education/training; research and professional experience; honors and awards publications (refereed) for the last three years and representative earlier publications. **Deadline:** July. **Contact:** Proposals must be submitted by email at aof@aaoptom.org.

390 ■ VSP Research Grants *(All/Grant)*

Purpose: To support the research into the efficacy of optometric care and optometric medical interventions. **Focus:** Optometry. **Qualif.:** Applicants must be individuals who are research-oriented, including but not limited to individual researchers; corporations; schools and colleges of optometry; schools and colleges of public health; schools and colleges of medicine; professional associations; and private foundations. **Criteria:** Applicants will be evaluated by the American Academy of Optometry's Research Committee.

Funds Avail.: $42,000. **To Apply:** Applicants must submit proposals, electronically, which must contain the following components: introduction; background and significance; specific aims; preliminary studies; and study design and methods. These sections should total no more than five pages. References (maximum of one page); budget and budget justification (maximum of one page); biographical sketch(es) of principal and one co-investigator only (maximum of two pages for each investigator); education/training; research and professional experience; honors and awards. Publications (refereed) for the last three years and representative earlier. **Contact:** Mark Bullimore, 614-292-4724, bullimore.1@osu.edu.

391 ■ American Academy of Periodontology (AAP)

737 N Michigan Ave., Ste. 800
Chicago, IL 60611-6660
Ph: (312) 787-5518
Fax: (312) 787-3670
Free: 800-282-4867
E-mail: member.services@perio.org
URL: www.perio.org

392 ■ American Academy of Periodontology Educator Scholarships *(Postdoctorate/Scholarship)*

Purpose: To provide financial relief to students intending to pursue a career as a full-time teacher at a U.S. periodontal program upon graduation from a U.S. periodontal postdoctoral training program. **Focus:** Dentistry. **Qualif.:** Applicants must be student members of the AAP who have been accepted into or are currently enrolled in a U.S. periodontal postdoctoral training program and who intend to enter full-time teaching in a U.S. program. **Criteria:** Applicants are evaluated based on merit and financial need.

Funds Avail.: $25,000. **To Apply:** Applicants must submit

Awards are arranged alphabetically below their administering organizations

completed application form; dental school transcripts; periodontal program transcripts; curriculum vitae; letter of nomination from the periodontal program director or the designated mentor; two letters of recommendation; and essay of approximately 1,000 words which addresses their commitment to education. **Deadline:** June 1.

393 ■ American Academy of Periodontology Foundation Education Fellowships
(Postdoctorate/Fellowship)

Purpose: To support research projects focused on the prevention of periodontitis. **Focus:** Dentistry. **Qualif.:** Applicants must be first or second year students of a U.S. periodontal postdoctoral program and must be student members of the American Academy of Periodontology. **Criteria:** Applicants are evaluated based on financial need.

Funds Avail.: $15,000. **To Apply:** Applicants must submit completed application form; proposal for research project focusing on the prevention of periodontitis; dental school and periodontal postdoctoral transcripts; letter of support from the periodontal institution's Program Director; and essay of approximately 750 words in which the applicant discusses their future plans in periodontal education and research.

394 ■ American Academy of Periodontology Teaching Fellowships *(Postdoctorate/Fellowship)*

Purpose: To support the young periodontal educators' commitment to a career in academia by providing debt relief to qualified applicants. **Focus:** Dentistry. **Qualif.:** Applicants must be in the first three years of their full-time teaching employment as defined by the institution at a U.S. periodontal program or have accepted a full-time faculty position at a U.S. periodontal program; must be students or active members of American Academy of Periodontology (AAP). Individuals who have not yet begun working as educators but who present a letter stating they have accepted a full-time teaching position may also apply. **Criteria:** Applications will be reviewed by a Selection Committee appointed by the Foundation President. Finalists will be invited to attend a mandatory personal interview during the Annual Meeting. If applicants will reach the final level, Selection Committee will call writers of recommendation letters and individuals mentioned by name in the applicant's personal statements and/or application letters.

Funds Avail.: $50,000. **To Apply:** Applicants must submit completed application form; dental school transcripts; periodontal program transcripts; curriculum vitae; letter of nomination from the periodontal chair or other appropriate individual from their employing institution; two letters of recommendation; and essay of approximately 1,000 words which addresses their commitment to education. **Deadline:** June 1. **Contact:** For questions, please contact Robert Vitas, Executive Director; Phone: 312-573-3256; Fax: 312-787-3983; Toll free: 800-282-4867; E-mail: bob@perio.org or aapf_ed@perio.org.

395 ■ Abram and Sylvia Chasens Teaching and Research Fellowships *(Postdoctorate/Fellowship)*

Purpose: To encourage periodontal students to enter the teaching field. **Focus:** Dentistry. **Qualif.:** Applicants must be periodontal postgraduate students in their third year of a non-military accredited periodontal post-doctoral training program in the United States; must intend to pursue a career in periodontal teaching and research in the United States; and must have strong interest in periodontal education. **Criteria:** Applicants are evaluated based on demon-

strated excellence of character and integrity; record of academic and personal achievements; and aptitude for teaching and research.

Funds Avail.: No specific amount. **To Apply:** Applicants must submit completed application form; transcript of grades from dental school and postgraduate work; curriculum vitae; personal statement of 750 words that addresses the special qualities they will bring to education, their philosophy of education, research interests, extracurricular and community activities, financial need and career plans; and three letters of reference. **Contact:** Application form and other supporting documents should be sent to Robert Vitas, Executive Director; Phone: 312-573-3256; Fax: 312-787-3983; Toll free: 800-282-4867; E-mail: bob@perio.org or aapf_ed@perio.org.

396 ■ Richard J. Lazzara Fellowships in Advanced Implant Surgery *(Postdoctorate/Fellowship)*

Purpose: To provide educational and clinical experiences that reflect the most current techniques in implant dentistry. **Focus:** Dentistry. **Qualif.:** Applicants must be third year students in an accredited periodontal post-doctoral training program in the United States; must be recommended by the students' periodontal program director. **Criteria:** Applications will be judged by the Selection Committees appointed by the Foundation President. If applicants will reach the final level, Selection Committees will call writers of recommendation letters and individuals mentioned by name in the applicant's personal statements and/or application letters.

Funds Avail.: $50,000. **To Apply:** Applicants must submit completed application form; three letters of recommendation, one letter must be from the periodontal program director, another from a periodontist and the third from a personal reference; transcript of grades from both dental school and postgraduate work; curriculum vitae; and personal essay. **Deadline:** February 1. **Contact:** Application form and other supporting documents should be submitted to Robert Vitas, Executive Director; Phone: 312-573-3256; Fax: 312-787-3983; Toll free: 800-282-4867; E-mail: bob@perio.org or aapf_ed@perio.org.

397 ■ Bud and Linda Tarrson Fellowships *(Postdoctorate/Fellowship)*

Purpose: To provide financial assistance to the brightest scientific and clinical minds with demonstrated facility for teaching and to encourage these individuals to pursue an academic career in periodontology. **Focus:** Dentistry. **Qualif.:** Applicants must be either full-time or part-time faculty members at the instructor or assistant level; must be affiliated with a U.S. training institution for 10 years or less; must have the goal of teaching and research in periodontology. **Criteria:** Applicants are evaluated based on their work on academic field.

Funds Avail.: Maximum of $36,000. **To Apply:** Applicants must submit completed application form; letter of nomination; recommendations; curriculum vitae; and personal statement. **Deadline:** May 1. **Contact:** For questions, please contact Robert Vitas, Executive Director, Toll free: 800-282-4867, E-mail: bob@perio.org or aapf_ed@perio.org.

398 ■ Tarrson Regeneration Scholarships *(Postdoctorate/Scholarship)*

Purpose: To provide financial assistance to students doing research in regeneration. **Focus:** Medical research. **Qua-**

Awards are arranged alphabetically below their administering organizations

lif.: Applicants must be students who have been accepted in an accredited U.S. periodontal postdoctoral training program or first-year residents within the first six months of their periodontal postdoctoral training program. **Criteria:** Applications will be judged by the Selection Committees appointed by the Foundation President. Finalists must be available for personal interviews during the Annual Meeting.

Funds Avail.: $37,000. **Number Awarded:** 2. **To Apply:** Applicants must submit a completed Tarrson Regeneration Scholarship application form; a proposal abstract describing their clinical research project relevant to clinical or translational regeneration studies; dental school transcripts; two letters of reference; personal essay; and curriculum vitae. **Deadline:** July 15.

399 ■ American Academy in Rome

7 E 60 St.
New York, NY 10022
Ph: (212) 751-7200
Fax: (212) 751-7200
E-mail: info@aarome.org
URL: www.aarome.org

400 ■ Rome Prize *(Doctorate, Graduate/Prize)*

Purpose: To foster the pursuit of advanced research and independent study in the fine arts and humanities. **Focus:** Arts; Humanities **Qualif.:** Applicants must be U.S. citizens at the time of application. U.S. citizens and foreign nationals who have lived in the United States for three years may apply for the National Endowment for the Humanities post-doctoral fellowships. Graduate students in the humanities may apply for pre-doctoral fellowships. **Criteria:** Selection will be based on the applicant's achievements and the potential for future development. Jurors will consider the quality of submitted application materials and what interviews reveal about an applicant's past achievements and future goals.

Funds Avail.: A stipend of $13,000-$26,000. **To Apply:** Applicants may visit the website to get the online application. **Deadline:** November 1.

401 ■ American Advertising Federation-Cleveland

20325 Ctr. Ridge Rd., Ste. 670
Cleveland, OH 44116
Ph: (440) 673-0020
Fax: (440) 673-0025
E-mail: adassoc@aafcleveland.com
URL: clevead.com

402 ■ American Advertising Federation-Cleveland College Scholarships *(Undergraduate/ Scholarship)*

Purpose: To bring advertising, public relations, sales and marketing professionals together to build networks and create business solutions. **Focus:** Advertising. **Qualif.:** Applicants must be Ohio college students majoring in advertising, marketing and communications; must be Ohio residents and enrolled on a full-time basis; must have a current minimum cumulative 3.0 GPA; must be seniors, juniors or in the last semester of the sophomore year. **Criteria:** Recipients are selected on a financial need and merit basis.

Funds Avail.: No specific amount. **To Apply:** Applicants

must submit a completed application form, transcript of records, two letters of recommendation from faculty and/or professionals and a one-page, double-spaced essay essay stating their career goals. **Deadline:** October 29.

403 ■ American Advertising Federation-Cleveland High School Scholarships *(Undergraduate/Scholarship)*

Purpose: To provide opportunity for students who plan to pursue careers in advertising, marketing, communication, photography and graphic design. **Focus:** Advertising. **Qualif.:** Applicants must be enrolled in a Cleveland Municipal School District high school; must be planning to enroll in a communication/marketing-related major at an accredited college or university with the goal of pursuing a degree; must carry a full course load and hold a current minimum cumulative GPA of 2.5 or higher on a 4.0 scale; must be in their senior year. **Criteria:** Recipients are selected on a financial need and merit basis.

Funds Avail.: No specific amount. **To Apply:** Applicants must submit a completed application form, two letters of recommendation from teachers or other professionals and a typed one-page, double-spaced essay describing their career goals. **Deadline:** January 22.

404 ■ The American Anthropological Association (AAA)

2200 Wilson Blvd., Ste. 600
Arlington, VA 22201
Ph: (703) 528-1902
Fax: (703) 528-3546
E-mail: bdavis@aaanet.org
URL: www.aaanet.org

405 ■ AAA Leadership Mentoring/Shadow Award Program *(Graduate/Award)*

Purpose: To provide opportunities for young professional anthropologists. **Focus:** Anthropology. **Qualif.:** Applicants must be anthropologists three to five years beyond completion of their terminal graduate degree and must be members of the American Anthropological Association. **Criteria:** Awards will be given to those applicants who best meet the requirements.

Funds Avail.: Awardees will be granted a travel subsidy worth $500. **To Apply:** Applicants will be paired to a mentor chosen from among the AAA leadership. **Deadline:** May 1. **Contact:** Questions should be addressed to Joseph Jones at jjones@aaanet.org.

406 ■ AAA Minority Dissertation Fellowship Program *(Doctorate/Fellowship)*

Purpose: To encourage members of ethnic minorities to complete their doctoral degrees in anthropology. **Focus:** Anthropology. **Qualif.:** Applicants must be U.S. citizens; must be members of an underrepresented ethnic minority group including, but not limited to: African Americans, Alaskan Natives, American Indians or Native Americans, Asian Americans, Latinos, Chicanos and Pacific Islanders; must be enrolled in a full-time academic program leading to a doctoral degree in anthropology; must be admitted to degree candidacy before the dissertation fellowship is awarded; and be members of the American Anthropological Association. **Criteria:** Applicants will be evaluated based on financial need.

Funds Avail.: $10,000. **Number Awarded:** 1. **To Apply:**

Awards are arranged alphabetically below their administering organizations

Applicants must submit an application cover form, cover letter, research plan, curriculum vitae, statement regarding employment attesting the applicant's ability and commitment to complete the writing of the dissertation during the fellowship period, disclosure statement, three letters of recommendation, bibliography and an official transcript. Materials should not be stapled. **Contact:** Applicants must contact Kathleen Terry-Sharp of the Department of Academic Relations at academic@aaanet.org.

407 ■ Margaret Mead Awards *(Professional development/Award)*

Purpose: To recognize young scholars for a book, film, monograph or service which interprets anthropological data and principles in ways that make them meaningful to a broadly concerned public. **Focus:** Anthropology. **Qualif.:** Applicants must have received their PhD degree after January 1 (ten years or less). **Criteria:** Nominees contributions will be judged based on intellectual quality, clarity and understandability, extent or depth of the impact and breadth of the impact.

Funds Avail.: Amount not specified. **To Apply:** Applicants must include a curriculum vitae, two letters of recommendation and must submit a four copies of the book or film. **Deadline:** March. **Contact:** Nominations and four copies of supporting materials must be submitted to the Society of Applied Anthropology, PO Box 2436, Oklahoma City, OK 73101-2436; Phone: 405-843-5113; Fax: 405-843-8553; E-mail: info@sfaa.net.

408 ■ David M. Schneider Awards *(Doctorate/Award)*

Purpose: To recognize an essay that treats the topics of kinship, cultural theory and American culture in a fresh and innovative fashion. **Focus:** Anthropology. **Qualif.:** Authors must be graduate students in anthropology who have been admitted to candidacy for, but have not yet received their PhD by June; and must be members of the American Anthropological Association. **Criteria:** Students will be evaluated based on the submitted essay.

Funds Avail.: $1,000. **To Apply:** Applicants must submit a two-page curriculum vitae, one-page abstract, a letter from dissertation Advisor, Director of graduate studies, or department Chair; and must submit an unpublished essay no more than 30 pages in length (double-spaced, 12 point font, inclusive of notes and bibliography). **Deadline:** June 1. **Contact:** Four copies of the materials should be sent to Kathy Ano at the above address; E-mail: kano@aanet.org.

409 ■ American Antiquarian Society (AAS)

185 Salisbury St.
Worcester, MA 01609-1634
Ph: (508) 755-5221
Fax: (508) 753-3311
E-mail: edunlap@mwa.org
URL: www.americanantiquarian.org

410 ■ AAS-American Historical Print Collectors Society Fellowships *(Doctorate/Fellowship)*

Purpose: To enable scholars, advanced graduate students and others to spend an uninterrupted block of time doing research in the AAS library. **Focus:** American Studies. **Qualif.:** Applicants must be enrolled in doctoral degree of accredited institutions or universities. **Criteria:** Recipients are selected based on: significance or importance of the

project; appropriateness of the proposed study to AAS collections.

Funds Avail.: $1,200-$1,700. **To Apply:** Applicants must fill out the online application form. **Deadline:** January 15. **Contact:** Mr. Paul Erickson, academicfellowships@mwa.org.

411 ■ AAS-American Society for Eighteenth Century Studies Fellowships *(Postdoctorate/Fellowship)*

Purpose: To enable scholars, advanced graduate students and others to spend an uninterrupted block of time doing research in the AAS library. **Focus:** General Studies. **Qualif.:** Applicants are not necessarily members of ASECS; must be an ABD graduate students or postdoctorals, holding the PhD or equivalent degree at the time of the application. **Criteria:** Recipients are selected based on: significance or importance of the project; appropriateness of the proposed study to the AAS collections.

Funds Avail.: $1,200-$1,700. **To Apply:** Applicants must fill out the online application form. **Deadline:** January 15. **Contact:** Mr. Paul Erickson, academicfellowships@mwa.org.

412 ■ AAS Fellowships for Creative and Performing Artists and Writers *(All/Fellowship)*

Purpose: To improve the ways in which an understanding of history is communicated to the American people. **Focus:** American History; Culture; Performing Arts; Writing; Filmmaking; Journalism. **Qualif.:** Applicants must have work for the general public which produces imaginative, non-formulaic works dealing with pre-twentieth century American history. **Criteria:** Recipients are selected based on the quality of performed task.

Funds Avail.: $1,100. **Number Awarded:** 3. **To Apply:** Applicants must provide a cover sheet; two letters of reference; a current resume including a listing of any awards, scholarship, or grant received; a statement of not more than five-typed, double spaced pages briefly summarizing the applicants educational and professional background and goals, describing the research for the project including readings in primary and secondary sources, and indicating the nature of the research program proposed for the AAS fellowship; ten copies of representative samples of previous works must included for the distribution of the committee. **Deadline:** October 5.

413 ■ AAS National Endowment for the Humanities Long-Term Fellowships *(Postdoctorate/Fellowship)*

Purpose: To enable scholars, advanced graduate students and others to spend an uninterrupted block of time doing research in the AAS library. **Focus:** Humanities. **Qualif.:** Applicants must have completed their formal professional training; maybe foreign nationals who have been residents in the United States for at least three years immediately preceding the application deadline. **Criteria:** Recipients are selected based on: significance or importance of the project; appropriateness of the proposed study to the AAS collections.

Funds Avail.: $50,400. **Number Awarded:** 3. **To Apply:** Applicants must fill out the online application form. **Deadline:** January 15. **Contact:** Mr. Paul Erickson, academicfellowships@mwa.org.

414 ■ AAS-Northeast Modern Language Association Fellowships *(All/Fellowship)*

Purpose: To enable scholars, advanced graduate students and others to spend an uninterrupted block of time doing

Awards are arranged alphabetically below their administering organizations

research in the AAS library. **Focus:** American History. **Qualif.:** Applicants are not necessarily members of NEMLA. **Criteria:** Recipients are selected based on: significance or importance of the project; appropriateness of the proposed study to the AAS collections.

Funds Avail.: $1,200-$1,700. **To Apply:** Applicants must fill out the online application form. **Deadline:** January 15. **Contact:** Mr. Paul Erickson, academicfellowships@mwa.org.

415 ■ Stephen Botein Fellowships *(Doctorate/Fellowship)*

Purpose: To enable scholars, advanced graduate students and others to spend an uninterrupted block of time doing research in the AAS library. **Focus:** American History; Culture. **Qualif.:** Applicants must be enrolled in doctoral degree of accredited institution or universities; must be engaged in scholarly research and writing including doctoral dissertation in any field of American history and culture. **Criteria:** Recipients are selected based on: significance or importance of the project; appropriateness of the proposed study to the AAS collections.

Funds Avail.: $1,200-$1,700. **To Apply:** Applicants must fill out the online application form. **Deadline:** January 15. **Contact:** Mr. Paul Erickson, academicfellowships@mwa.org.

416 ■ ACLS Frederick Burkhardt Residential Fellowships *(Professional development/Fellowship)*

Purpose: To support an academic year (normally nine months) of residence at any one of the national residential research centers participating in the program. **Focus:** Humanities; Social Sciences. **Qualif.:** Applicants must be recently tenured humanists; must be employed in a tenured position at a degree granting academic institution in the United States. **Criteria:** Recipients are selected based on the quality of the proposal and required qualifications.

Funds Avail.: $75,000. **Number Awarded:** 11. **To Apply:** Applicants must visit the website for the online fellowship application system. Applicants must submit no more than ten pages, double-spaced proposal; no more than three pages bibliography; no more than two pages publications list; three reference letters. Applicants must provide an institutional statement. **Deadline:** October 2.

417 ■ The "Drawn to Art" Fellowships *(Doctorate/Fellowship)*

Purpose: To enable scholars, advanced graduate students and others to spend an uninterrupted block of time doing research in the AAS library. **Focus:** Art; Culture. **Qualif.:** Applicants must be enrolled in doctoral degree of accredited institution or universities. **Criteria:** Recipients are selected based on: significance or importance of the project; appropriateness of the proposed study to the AAS collections.

Funds Avail.: $1,200-$1,700. **To Apply:** Applicants must fill out the online application form. **Deadline:** January 15. **Contact:** Mr. Paul Erickson, academicfellowships@mwa.org.

418 ■ The Christoph Daniel Ebeling Fellowships *(Doctorate/Fellowship)*

Purpose: To enable scholars, advanced graduate students and others to spend an uninterrupted block of time doing research in the AAS library. **Focus:** American Studies. **Qualif.:** Applicants must be scholars in American Studies doing

dissertation or rehabilitation research at universities in Germany. **Criteria:** Recipients are selected based on: significance or importance of the project; appropriateness of the proposed study to the AAS collections.

Funds Avail.: $1,200-$1,700. **To Apply:** Applicants must fill out the online application form. **Deadline:** January 20. **Contact:** Mr. Paul Erickson, academicfellowships@mwa.org.

419 ■ Hench Post-Dissertation Fellowships *(Postdoctorate/Fellowship)*

Purpose: To provide scholars with time and resources to extend research and/or to revise the dissertation for publication. **Focus:** History; Literature; American Studies; Political Science; Music. **Qualif.:** Applicants must have more than three years beyond receipt of the doctorate. **Criteria:** Recipients are selected based on: appropriateness of the project to the AAS collections and interests; likelihood that the revised dissertation will make a highly significant books.

Funds Avail.: $35,000. **To Apply:** Applicant must fill out the on-line application form. **Deadline:** October 15. **Contact:** Paul Erickson at perickson@mwa.org; academicfellowships@mwa.org.

420 ■ Jay and Deborah Last Fellowships *(Doctorate/Fellowship)*

Purpose: To enable scholars, advanced graduate students and others to spend an uninterrupted block of time doing research in the AAS library. **Focus:** Art; Culture. **Qualif.:** Applicants must be enrolled in doctoral degree of accredited institution or universities. **Criteria:** Recipients are selected based on: significance or importance of the project; appropriateness of the proposed study to the AAS collections.

Funds Avail.: $1,200-$1,700. **To Apply:** Applicants must fill out the online application form. **Deadline:** January 15. **Contact:** Mr. Paul Erickson, academicfellowships@mwa.org.

421 ■ The Legacy Fellowships *(Doctorate/Fellowship)*

Purpose: To enable scholars, advanced graduate students and others to spend an uninterrupted block of time doing research in the AAS library. **Focus:** American History; Culture. **Qualif.:** Applicants must be enrolled in doctoral degree of accredited institution or universities; must be engaged in scholarly research and writing including doctoral dissertation in any field of American history and culture. **Criteria:** Recipients are selected based on: significance or importance of the project; appropriateness of the proposed study to the AAS collections.

Funds Avail.: $1,200-$1,700. **To Apply:** Applicants must fill out the online application form. **Deadline:** January 15. **Contact:** Mr. Paul Erickson, academicfellowships@mwa.org.

422 ■ Kate B. and Hall J. Peterson Fellowships *(Doctorate/Fellowship)*

Purpose: To enable scholars, advanced graduate students and others to spend an uninterrupted block of time doing research in the AAS library. **Focus:** American History; Culture. **Qualif.:** Applicants must be enrolled in doctoral degree of accredited institution or universities; must be engaged in scholarly research and writing including doctoral dissertation in any field of American history and culture. **Criteria:** Recipients are selected based on: significance or

Awards are arranged alphabetically below their administering organizations

importance of the project; appropriateness of the proposed study to the AAS collections.

Funds Avail.: $1,200-$1,700. **To Apply:** Applicants must fill out the online application form. **Deadline:** January 15. **Contact:** Mr. Paul Erickson, academicfellowships@ mwa.org.

423 ■ The Reese Fellowships *(Doctorate/ Fellowship)*

Purpose: To enable scholars, advanced graduate students and others to spend an uninterrupted block of time doing research in the AAS library. **Focus:** American Studies. **Qualif.:** Applicants must be enrolled in doctoral degree of accredited institution or universities. **Criteria:** Recipients are selected based on: significance or importance of the project; appropriateness of the proposed study to the AAS collections.

Funds Avail.: $1,200-$1,700. **To Apply:** Applicants must fill out the online application form. **Deadline:** January 15. **Contact:** Mr. Paul Erickson, academicfellowships@ mwa.org.

424 ■ The Joyce Tracy Fellowships *(Doctorate/ Fellowship)*

Purpose: To enable scholars, advanced graduate students and others to spend an uninterrupted block of time doing research in the AAS library. **Focus:** American History; Culture. **Qualif.:** Applicants must be enrolled in doctoral degree of accredited institution or universities; must be engaged in scholarly research and writing including doctoral dissertation in any field of American history and culture. **Criteria:** Recipients are selected based on: significance or importance of the project; appropriateness of the proposed study to the AAS collections.

Funds Avail.: $1,200-$1,700. **To Apply:** Applicants must fill out the online application form. **Deadline:** January 15. **Contact:** Mr. Paul Erickson, academicfellowships@ mwa.org.

425 ■ American Art Therapy Association (AATA)

225 N Fairfax St.
Alexandria, VA 22314
Ph: (703) 548-5860
Fax: (703) 783-8468
Free: 888-290-0878
E-mail: info@arttherapy.org
URL: www.arttherapy.org

426 ■ American Art Therapy Association Anniversary Scholarships (AATA) *(Graduate/ Scholarship)*

Purpose: To promote education in Art therapy. **Focus:** Art therapy. **Qualif.:** Applicant must be an active student member of AATA; accepted or attending an AATA approved graduate art therapy program; have a GPA of 3.25; and demonstrated financial need. **Criteria:** Selection is based on the application.

Funds Avail.: No specific amount. **Number Awarded:** 1. **To Apply:** Applicants must submit a completed application form. **Deadline:** May 1. **Contact:** Application form and supporting documents must be sent to 225 N Fairfax St., Alexandria, VA 22314; E-mail: sbolouri@arttherapy.org.

427 ■ Myra Levick Scholarships *(Graduate/ Scholarship)*

Purpose: To promote education in art therapy. **Focus:** Art therapy. **Qualif.:** Applicant must be an active student member of AATA; accepted or attending an AATA approved graduate art therapy program; have a GPA of 3.0; and demonstrated financial need. **Criteria:** Selection is based on the application.

Funds Avail.: No specific amount. **Number Awarded:** 1. **To Apply:** Applicant must submit a completed application form; one official academic transcript; two academic or work-related, signed letters of recommendation; student financial information form; one essay (maximum of two pages, double spaced, typewritten) including the biography and stating the future role as an art therapist; and documentation of acceptance or enrollment in an American Art Therapy Association approved art therapy program. **Deadline:** May 1. **Contact:** Application form and supporting documents must be sent to 225 N Fairfax St., Alexandria, VA 22314; E-mail: sbolouri@arttherapy.org.

428 ■ Rawley Silver Awards for Excellence *(Graduate/Scholarship)*

Purpose: To promote education in art therapy. **Focus:** Art therapy. **Qualif.:** Applicant must be an active student member of AATA; accepted or attending an AATA approved graduate art therapy program; and have an excellent academic record. **Criteria:** Selection is based on the application.

Funds Avail.: $100 (no financial need); full scholarship (with financial need). **Number Awarded:** 1. **To Apply:** Applicants must submit a completed application form together with official academic transcripts; two academic/work related letters of recommendations; student financial information form; a two-page essay (biography); and proof of acceptance in an AATA approved graduate art therapy program. Submit the original and four more copies of the complete required application packets. **Deadline:** May 1. **Contact:** Application form and supporting documents must be sent to 225 N Fairfax St., Alexandria, VA 22314; E-mail: sbolouri@arttherapy.org.

429 ■ American Association for the Advancement of Science (AAAS)

1200 New York Ave. NW
Washington, DC 20005
Ph: (202) 326-6400
Fax: (202) 371-9526
E-mail: membership@aaas.org
URL: www.aaas.org

430 ■ AAAS Mass Media Science and Engineering Fellowships *(Graduate, Postgraduate, Undergraduate/Fellowship)*

Purpose: To increase public understanding of science and technology. **Focus:** Media Art; Science Technologies; Engineering. **Qualif.:** Applicants must be undergraduates in their senior year; must be graduate or post-graduate students. **Criteria:** Recipients are selected based on telephone interview made by the AAAS staff.

Funds Avail.: $450. **To Apply:** Applicants must fill out the application form. Applicants must submit a copy of resume including honors, awards and relevant activities; one brief sample of their writing (two-to-three pages on any subject written in terms appropriate for the general public); journal articles; three letters of recommendation; transcript of the undergraduate and graduate work. **Deadline:** January 15.

431 ■ AAAS Science and Technology Policy Fellowships *(Postdoctorate/Fellowship)*

Purpose: To provide professional development opportunity to individuals interested in learning about the science-policy

Awards are arranged alphabetically below their administering organizations

interface while applying their scientific and technical knowledge and analytical skills to the federal policy realm. **Focus:** Engineering; Science; Science Technologies. **Qualif.:** Applicants must hold a doctoral-level degree in any physical, biological, health/medical or behavioral science, any field of engineering, or any interdisciplinary field; must demonstrate exceptional competence in their specialty appropriate to their career stage; must show an understanding of the opportunities for science and engineering to support a broad range of non-scientific issues, and display commitment to apply their scientific or technical expertise to serve society; must exhibit awareness and sensitivity to the political, economic and social issues that influence policy; must be articulate communicators, both in verbal and written, to decision-makers and non-scientific audiences; must have the ability to work effectively with the individual and groups outside the scientific community; must demonstrate initiative, problem solving ability, leadership capacity, flexibility and willingness to address policy issues outside their scientific realm; must be U.S. citizens or hold a dual citizenship with the another country. **Criteria:** Recipients are selected based on the scientific/technical background and professional accomplishment, leadership and potential, analytical and problem solving abilities, communication, interpersonal and outreach skills.

Funds Avail.: No stated amount. **Number Awarded:** 2. **To Apply:** Applicants must provide a profile indicating name and contact information; candidates' data; candidates' statement providing the qualifications for the fellowship and career goals; reasons for applying for the fellowship. Applicants must also submit curriculum vitae; extracurricular activities; and references including three recommendation letters. **Contact:** 202-326-6700; fellowships@aaas.org.

432 ■ American Association of Advertising Agencies

405 Lexington Ave., 18th Fl.
New York, NY 10174-1801
Ph: (212) 682-2500
Fax: (212) 682-8391
URL: www.aaaa.org

433 ■ AAAA Operation Jumpstart III Scholarships *(Graduate/Scholarship)*

Purpose: To provide financial assistance to aspiring multicultural art directors and copywriters. **Focus:** Advertising. **Qualif.:** Applicants must be registered as incoming graduates or portfolio school students at one of six designated OJS III portfolio schools: Miami Ad School, Ad Center at Virginia Commonwealth University, Portfolio Center, Creative Circus, University of Texas at Austin, or Pratt Institute; either be full-time juniors at one of two designated OJS III colleges (Minneapolis College of Art and Design or the Art Center College of Design at Pasadena); must be African Americans, Asian Americans, Hispanic Americans, Native Americans, multiracial or multiethnic; must show a creative talent and promise; must be U.S. citizens or permanent residents. **Criteria:** Awards will be given to those applicants who best meet the criteria and demonstrated financial need.

Funds Avail.: $10,000. **To Apply:** Applicants must request an application form from the aforementioned schools.

434 ■ Bill Bernbach Diversity Scholarships *(Undergraduate/Scholarship)*

Purpose: To recognize excellence in art direction, copywriting and design. **Focus:** Advertising. **Qualif.:** Applicants

must be African Americans, Native Americans, or Hispanic Americans; must be full-time students in their final year at one of the following 4A's participating portfolio schools: Miami Ad School, Ad Center at Virginia Commonwealth University, Portfolio Center, Creative Circus, University of Texas at Austin, Art Center of Design at Pasadena; must be U.S. citizens or permanent residents; must hold a bachelor's degree from an accredited college or university. **Criteria:** Awards will be given to those applicants who best meet the criteria.

Funds Avail.: $5,000. **Number Awarded:** 5. **To Apply:** Applicants must the tuition office of the participating schools.

435 ■ Multicultural Advertising Intern Program *(Graduate, Undergraduate/Internship)*

Purpose: To encourage students to strongly consider advertising as a career. **Focus:** Advertising. **Qualif.:** Applicants must be undergraduate and graduate students; must be African Americans, Asian Americans, Hispanic Americans and Native Americans. **Criteria:** Recipients will be selected based on submitted materials.

Funds Avail.: Amount not specified. **To Apply:** Applicants must contact AAAA office to clarify guidelines and required procedures.

436 ■ American Association of Ambulatory Care Nursing (AAACN)

PO Box 56
Pitman, NJ 08071-0056
Free: 800-262-6877
E-mail: aaacn@ajj.com
URL: www.aaacn.org

437 ■ AAACN Scholarships *(Undergraduate/Scholarship)*

Purpose: To provide financial support for researches. **Focus:** Nursing. **Qualif.:** Applicants must be members of American Academy of Ambulatory Care Nursing (AAACN) for a minimum of two years; currently enrolled in an accredited school of nursing or a program deemed by the committee to advance the profession of nursing; request for payment of tuition, books, academic supplies; proof of acceptance in course; must submit a research abstract and proof of acceptance of research study by academic institution or Investigational Review Board employing or sponsoring institutions; willing to present research findings at AAACN Annual Conference following receipt of award; willing to publish article in Viewpoint describing a research study and outcome. **Criteria:** Recipient will be selected by the AAACN Committee.

Funds Avail.: $100 to $1,000. **To Apply:** Applicants must complete an application form and must provide a current enrollment or proof of acceptance in an accredited school of nursing or other academic program. Applicants are required to submit two copies of the application form. **Deadline:** January 15. **Contact:** Applications can be addressed to A.J. Jannetti at the above address or email reichartp@ajj.com.

438 ■ American Association of Attorney-Certified Public Accountants (AAA-CPA)

3921 Old Lee Hwy., Ste. 71A
Fairfax, VA 22030
Ph: (703) 352-8064

Awards are arranged alphabetically below their administering organizations

Fax: (703) 352-8073
Free: 888-288-9272
E-mail: info@attorney-cpa.com
URL: www.attorney-cpa.com

439 ■ Attorney-CPA Foundation Scholarships
(Undergraduate/Scholarship)

Purpose: To promote the study and understanding of the fields of Law and Accounting and other related professions. **Focus:** Law. **Qualif.:** Applicants must be graduating law students who have obtained CPA Certificate. **Criteria:** Recipients must be graduating law school students, must have commitment to the profession of accounting as evidenced by a CPA certificate, must have outstanding academic performance, and must have shown leadership in school and community.

Funds Avail.: $250-$2,500. **To Apply:** Applicants must submit the completed application form. **Deadline:** April 15.

440 ■ American Association of Blacks in Energy (AABE)

1625 K St. NW, Ste. 405
Washington, DC 20006
Ph: (202) 371-9530
Fax: (202) 371-9218
Free: 800-466-0204
E-mail: info@aabe.org
URL: www.aabe.org

441 ■ American Association of Blacks in Energy Scholarships *(Undergraduate/Scholarship)*

Purpose: To help increase the number of African Americans and other misrepresented minorities in energy-related fields. **Focus:** Energy-related areas. **Qualif.:** Applicants must have at least an overall "B" academic average and a "B" average in mathematics and science courses; must be graduating high school seniors who have applied to one or more accredited colleges/universities; must be planning to major in engineering, mathematics, or the physical sciences; must demonstrate financial need; and must be members of one of the underrepresented minority groups in the sciences and related areas of technology. **Criteria:** Applicants are evaluated based on criteria designed by the organization's National Scholarship Committee.

Funds Avail.: $1,500. **Number Awarded:** 6. **To Apply:** Applicants must submit completed AABE application form; high school transcript; two letters of reference (one academic, one non-academic); and parent(s) or guardian(s) official verification of income (copy of signed tax return for previous year or W2 or a verified FAFSA form). **Deadline:** March 16.

442 ■ American Association of Bovine Practitioners (AABP)

PO Box 3610
Auburn, AL 36831-3610
Ph: (334) 821-0442
Fax: (334) 821-9532
Free: 800-269-2227
E-mail: aabphq@aabp.org
URL: www.aabp.org

443 ■ AABP Amstutz Scholarships
(Undergraduate/Scholarship)

Purpose: To enhance the professional lives of its members through relevant continuing education that will improve the well-being of cattle and the economic success of the owners; increase awareness; to promote leadership for issues critical to cattle industries; to improve opportunities for careers in bovine medicine. **Focus:** Veterinary science and medicine. **Qualif.:** Applicant must be enrolled in a college of veterinary medicine located in Canada and United States; and must be in second year of the veterinarian curriculum at the time of the application. **Criteria:** Applicants will be evaluated for the overall interest of the applicant in bovine practice, involvement in bovine medicine and bovine-related extracurricular activities, ability to express oneself in writing, and insightful answers to the essay questions.

Funds Avail.: $7,500. **Number Awarded:** 9. **To Apply:** Applicants must submit a current cumulative school GPA and class rank; he/she must submit a biographical account that outlines the background of the cattle industry; an applicant must prepare a one-page or less list factors that stimulate the interest and involvement in bovine medicine and extracurricular activities; 500 characters or less description of plans following graduation from veterinary school; 2500 characters or less answer about the experiences that stimulate in pursuing a career in food/animal/bovine medicine; 2500 characters or less answering the question "What is our role today and in the future as a veterinarian in shaping public perception of food animal welfare in United States or Canada?"; an essay about the plans in using the money acquired from the award if considered; applicant must submit two letters of recommendation from either veterinarian or faculty members regarding the applicant's worthiness for the award. **Deadline:** May.

444 ■ AABP Bovine Veterinary Student Recognition Awards *(Undergraduate/Scholarship)*

Purpose: To provide awards to 3rd and/or 4th year veterinary students who are interested in dairy and/or beef veterinary medicine. **Focus:** Veterinary science and medicine. **Qualif.:** Applicant must be a student member of AABP enrolled at Veterinary Colleges and Schools during the 2nd year and/or 3rd year. **Criteria:** Award committee will evaluate the student's application based on interest in bovine medicine, work experience, academic and professional experience, career goals, and recommendation letter.

Funds Avail.: $1,500. **Number Awarded:** 8. **To Apply:** Applicant must fill out the on-line application form which outlines the background, work, and academic experience, primary interests in veterinary medicine, career goals and providing the name of a faculty sponsor. **Deadline:** March 15.

445 ■ AABP Education Grants *(Undergraduate/Grant)*

Purpose: To help expand the skills and knowledge base of the cattle production medicine practitioner. **Focus:** Veterinary science and medicine. **Qualif.:** Applicant must be a member or student member of the AABP; must be incoming senior student or new graduate attending an accredited veterinary college or an AABP approved continuing education. **Criteria:** Recipients will be evaluated based on their academic awards.

Funds Avail.: $750. **To Apply:** Applicant must fill out the online application form including the career goal, current job description, prior experience with food animal production medicine, and goals of advanced education program; a brief course outline, letter of recommendation, signed hold

---

Awards are arranged alphabetically below their administering organizations

harmless agreement release form; and must obtain a completion of the advanced training. Successful applicants will be required to submit an evaluation from detailing the experience. **Deadline:** April 15.

446 ■ AABP Research Assistantships
(Doctorate/Scholarship)

Purpose: To enhance the professional lives of its members through continuing relevant education that will improve the well-being of cattle and economic success of the owners; to increase the awareness; to promote leadership for issues critical to cattle industries; to improve opportunities for careers in bovine medicine. **Focus:** Veterinary science and medicine. **Qualif.:** Applicant must be enrolled at an accredited North American veterinary college (school) pursuing a concurrent master's or doctoral degree; applicant must be a student AABP member. **Criteria:** Scholarship Committee will evaluate the student's application based on academic qualifications and experience; justification and relevance to the concerns of private practice and the cattle industry; clarity of objectives and probability of completing the research; methodology and scientific merit; budget; site suitability for proposed research.

Funds Avail.: $10,000. **To Apply:** Applicants must fill out the online application form; applicant must submit an evaluation criteria and scoring system, and a progress report. **Deadline:** February 1. **Contact:** 334-821-9532.

447 ■ AABP Student Externship Program
(Undergraduate/Scholarship)

Purpose: To support veterinary students. **Focus:** Veterinary science and medicine. **Qualif.:** Applicant must be admitted to a veterinary school and completed his/her externship of at least two weeks in bovine practice; must be a student and AABP member; must be a full-time veterinary student at an American, Canadian, or Caribbean veterinary college or be a newly admitted freshman at such college. **Criteria:** Scholarship will be given to students who have an interest in food animal practice but who may not have extensive exposure to bovine practice or cattle industry; awards will be given to underclassmen and to externships where the practice provides some tangible support for the student, such as room or board.

Funds Avail.: $750. **To Apply:** Applicant must complete the online application form including the dates of expected externship, practice where it is to take place, projected cost support to be provided by the practice and amount of aid requested, and student's career interests, prior experience with food producing animals, and goals for the externship; must provide a letter from the practice describing what the students will be doing; a letter from a faculty member at the student's veterinary college; and must submit a completed release agreement. **Deadline:** April 1 and October 1.

448 ■ American Association for Cancer Research
615 Chestnut St., 17th Fl.
Philadelphia, PA 19106
Ph: (215) 440-9300
Fax: (215) 440-9313
Free: 866-423-3955
E-mail: aacr@aacr.org
URL: www.aacr.org

Awards are arranged alphabetically below their administering organizations

449 ■ American Association for Cancer Research - GlaxoSmithKline Clinical Cancer Research Scholar Awards *(Graduate, Postdoctorate/Award)*

Purpose: To support young cancer researchers who are the first authors and presenters of highly meritorious abstracts related to clinical cancer research. **Focus:** Oncology. **Qualif.:** Applicants must be graduate students, medical students and residents, clinical fellows or equivalent, and postdoctoral fellows who are traveling from any country in the world; must be the first author and presenter of an abstract of clinical cancer research; must be AACR members. Nonmembers must complete an application for Associate Membership prior to the abstract submission deadline to be considered. **Criteria:** Selection will be based upon the novelty, quality and significance of the abstract submitted.

Funds Avail.: $4,000. **To Apply:** Eligible individuals should check the appropriate box in the Online Abstract Submission System and must submit their abstracts by the deadline. A letter of support (not more than one page) must be sent from the applicant's mentor, supervisor or department head to elizabeth.martin@aacr.org. The letter should confirm that the applicant meets the eligibility requirements; describe the applicant's clinical cancer research to be presented at the Annual Meeting; and attest that the mentor, supervisor or department head will permit the applicant to attend future AACR meetings or conferences to be supported by this Award. **Deadline:** November 15.

450 ■ American Association for Cancer Research Minority Scholar Awards *(Graduate/Award)*

Purpose: To provide opportunities and support for research training and career development of minorities and for involving minority institutions in cancer research, research training, education and outreach. **Focus:** Oncology. **Qualif.:** Candidates must be full-time graduate students, medical students, residents, clinical or postdoctoral fellows, or junior faculty members; must be in the minority groups that have been defined by the National Cancer Institute as being traditionally underrepresented in cancer and biomedical research; must be citizens or permanent residents of the United States or Canada. **Criteria:** Selection will be based on the committee's criteria.

Funds Avail.: No specific amount. **To Apply:** Applicants may visit the website for the online application or to download a copy of the application. **Deadline:** November 15. **Contact:** micr@aacr.org.

451 ■ Thomas J. Bardos Science Education Awards for Undergraduate Students *(Undergraduate/Award)*

Purpose: To inspire young science students to enter the field of cancer research and provide a unique educational opportunity for these students in the development of their careers in science. **Focus:** Science. **Qualif.:** Candidates must be full-time, third-year undergraduate students majoring in science; must be AACR members at the time of application. Student membership is free of charge. **Criteria:** Selection will be based on the committee's criteria.

Funds Avail.: No specific amount. **To Apply:** Applicants may visit the website for the online application or to download a copy of the application. **Deadline:** December 1. **Contact:** Amy Cranston Bowers, 215-440-9300, scienceeducation@aacr.org.

452 ■ Minority-Serving Institution Faculty Scholar Awards *(Doctorate/Award)*

Purpose: To increase the scientific knowledge base of faculty members at Minority-Serving Institutions, and to encourage them and their students to pursue careers in cancer research. **Focus:** Oncology. **Qualif.:** Candidates must have completed doctoral studies or clinical fellowships and hold full-time faculty status at an institution designated as a Minority-Serving Institution; must have acquired doctoral degrees in fields relevant to cancer research; must be citizens or permanent residents of the United States or Canada. **Criteria:** Selection will be based on the committee's criteria.

Funds Avail.: No specific amount. **To Apply:** Applicants may visit the website for the online application or to download a copy of the application. **Deadline:** December 10. **Contact:** micr@aacr.org.

453 ■ Women in Cancer Research Scholar Awards *(Graduate, Postdoctorate/Award)*

Purpose: To support Women in Cancer Research scientists-in-training and presenters of meritorious scientific papers. **Focus:** Oncology. **Qualif.:** Applicants must be members of Women in Cancer Research; must be full time scientists-in-training who are graduate students, medical students, residents, clinical fellows or equivalent, or postdoctoral fellows; may be travelling from within the United States or abroad. There are no citizenship or residency requirements; must be first authors on abstracts submitted for consideration for presentation at the AACR Annual Meeting. **Criteria:** Selection will be based on the committee's criteria.

Funds Avail.: No specific amount. **To Apply:** Eligible individuals should check the appropriate box in the Online Abstract Submission System and must submit their abstracts by the deadline. A letter of support (no more than one page) must be sent from the applicant's mentor, supervisor or department head to wicr@aacr.org. **Deadline:** November 15.

454 ■ American Association of Cereal Chemists (AACC)

3340 Pilot Knob Rd.
Saint Paul, MN 55121
Ph: (651) 454-7250
Fax: (651) 454-0766
E-mail: aacc@scisoc.org
URL: www.aaccnet.org

455 ■ American Association of Cereal Chemists Graduate Fellowships *(Graduate/Fellowship)*

Purpose: To encourage graduate research in grain-based food science and technology. **Focus:** Food science and technology. **Qualif.:** Applicants must be current AACC International Student Division members; must be enrolled in a graduate study by the time the fellowship becomes effective or be current graduate students pursuing a course of study leading to an MS or a PhD degree; educational institutions where recipients have been enrolled must be conducting fundamental investigations for the advancement of cereal science and technology, including oilseeds; must be enrolled in an academic schedule that meets the minimum requirements of the university involved, for full-time graduate studies. **Criteria:** Selection will be made by a jury consisting of six individual AACC International

members with a non-voting chair appointed by the President of AACC International.

Funds Avail.: $2,000-$3,000. **To Apply:** Applicants may visit the website to download an application form; must submit copies of transcripts, letter of application describing the career plans, and three letters of recommendation. **Deadline:** March 1.

456 ■ American Association of Colleges of Nursing (AACN)

1 Dupont Cir. NW, Ste. 530
Washington, DC 20036
Ph: (202) 463-6930
Fax: (202) 785-8320
E-mail: ccrowell@aacn.nche.edu
URL: www.aacn.nche.edu

457 ■ AACN Minority Nurse Faculty Scholarships *(Graduate/Scholarship)*

Purpose: To diversify the faculty population to the field of nursing education. **Focus:** Nursing. **Qualif.:** Applicant must be enrolled full-time in an accredited graduate nursing program; a U.S. citizen, permanent resident, refugee or qualified immigrant; an underrepresented Minority, (Caucasian/non-Hispanic applicants are not eligible); committed to teach nursing in the United States after successful completion of graduate studies. **Criteria:** Applications will be judged based on following criteria: 1) applicant's ability to contribute in nursing education field; 2) commitment to nursing education career in United States which includes mentoring, recruiting, and retaining underrepresented minority nurses; 3) ability to work with a mentor/advisor throughout the award period; 4) potential as a leader; 5) development of goals which reflect education, research, and professional involvement; 6) quality, feasibility and innovativeness of the proposed research; and 7) school has made commitment to his/her academic career and professional development.

Funds Avail.: $18,000. **Number Awarded:** 5. **To Apply:** Applicants must submit an application data sheet; three letters of reference with signatures; one-page letter (no more than 500 words) describing the personal and professional interest in nursing education; budget outline; Dean's Commitment statement; letter of acceptance to a Nursing school; original transcript of records; outlined program of study; curriculum vitae; goal identification form; and applicant's signature form. **Deadline:** May 2. **Remarks:** Awardees will be required to sign a letter of commitment that they will provide a one-year payback in a teaching role for each year of scholarship support provided. Failure to complete the payback requirement will require that funding be repaid to the program by the recipient. **Contact:** Application form and supporting documents must be sent to Project Coordinator, Debbit Latimer at the above address; E-mail: dlatimer@aacn.nche.edu.

458 ■ AfterCollege/AACN Nursing Scholarships *(Graduate, Undergraduate/Scholarship)*

Purpose: To promote education in nursing. **Focus:** Nursing. **Qualif.:** Applicant must be enrolled at an AACN member institution; seeking baccalaureate, master's or doctoral degree in nursing; and have a GPA of 3.25 or higher. **Criteria:** Consideration is given to students enrolled in a master's or doctoral program and pursuing a nursing faculty career; completing an RN to baccalaureate program (BSN); or enrolled in an accelerated baccalaureate or

Awards are arranged alphabetically below their administering organizations

master's degree nursing program.

Funds Avail.: $2,500. **Number Awarded:** 2. **To Apply:** Applicants are advised to visit the website for the application forms. **Deadline:** January 31, April 30, July 31, and October 31. **Remarks:** In partnership with AfterCollege, the leading employment website for nursing/allied health care student. **Contact:** scholarship@aacn.nche.edu.

459 ■ The California Endowment and AACN Minority Nurse Faculty Scholarships *(Graduate/ Scholarship)*

Purpose: To increase the number of minority faculty teaching in California Nursing schools. **Focus:** Nursing. **Qualif.:** Applicant must be enrolled full-time in an accredited graduate nursing program; a U.S. citizen, permanent resident, refugee or qualified immigrant; resident of the state of California; an underrepresented Minority, (Caucasian/non-Hispanic applicants are not eligible); committed to teach nursing in the United States after successful completion of graduate studies. **Criteria:** Selection is based on contribution to the advancement of nursing education, leadership potential, evidence of commitment to a career in nursing education, nature and extent goals of reflecting education, research, and professional activities.

Funds Avail.: $18,000. **To Apply:** Applicants must submit a completed application form together with the required materials. **Contact:** Application form and supporting documents must be sent to: Debbie Latimer at the above address; E-mail: dlatimer@aacn.nche.edu.

460 ■ American Association of Colleges of Osteopathic Medicine (AACOM)

5550 Friendship Blvd., Ste. 310
Chevy Chase, MD 20815-7231
Ph: (301) 968-4100
Fax: (301) 968-4101
E-mail: sshannon@aacom.org
URL: www.aacom.org/Pages/default.aspx

461 ■ AACOM Scholar in Residence Program *(Graduate, Undergraduate/Scholarship)*

Purpose: To promote leadership roles in the profession and positions of influence in health policy. **Focus:** Osteopathic medicine. **Qualif.:** Individuals with a professional connection to the osteopathic profession. Applicants must be undergraduates, graduates or continuing medical students; and must be nominated by their dean. **Criteria:** Recipients will be selected based on application materials submitted.

Funds Avail.: $2,225. **To Apply:** Applicants must submit a proposal focusing the following areas of study: a) outcomes-centered medical education; b) best evidence medical education; c) integration of osteopathic medical principles into standard medical practices; d) linkage of medical practices to healthcare outcomes; and e) application of continuous quality improvement. **Deadline:** March 31, June 30, September 30, and December 31. **Contact:** Linda Heun 5550 Friendship Blvd., Ste. 310, Chevy Chase, MD 20815; Phone: 301-968-4143, Fax: 301-968-4101; meded@.aacom.org.

462 ■ American Association of Colleges for Teacher Education (AACTE)

1307 New York Ave. NW, Ste. 300
Washington, DC 20005-4721

Ph: (202) 293-2450
Fax: (202) 457-8095
E-mail: aacte@aacte.org
URL: www.aacte.org

463 ■ AACTE Outstanding Book Awards *(Professional development/Award)*

Purpose: To recognize authors and publications that make a significant contribution to the knowledge base of teacher education or teaching and learning with implications for teacher education. **Focus:** Teaching. **Qualif.:** Applicants must be authors or editors of a publication that has been published between July 2009 and June of the current year. **Criteria:** Recipients will be selected based on submitted published book. Priority will be given to works that address the four areas and eight action items identified in AACTE's research agenda and whose focus and style of presentation are consistent with the principles set forth in Research Standards and Guidelines.

Funds Avail.: Amount not specified. **To Apply:** Applicants must submit a letter of nomination addressing the criteria, seven copies of the book, brief professional biography at least 150 words and must include the contact information of the author(s) or the publisher's representative(s). **Deadline:** June. **Contact:** For more information about this award, applicants must contact Kristin McCabe; Phone: 207-899-1309; E-mail: kmccabe@aacte.org.

464 ■ AACTE Outstanding Dissertation Awards *(Doctorate/Award)*

Purpose: To recognize excellence in doctoral dissertation research that contributes to the knowledge base of teacher education or teaching and learning with implications for teacher education. **Focus:** Teaching. **Qualif.:** Applicants must be individuals receiving a doctorate in education from January 1 through June 30. **Criteria:** Evaluation will be based on quality of submitted research. Priority will be given to works that address the four areas and eight action items identified in AACTE's research agenda and whose focus and style of presentation are consistent with the principles set forth in Research Standards and Guidelines.

Funds Avail.: Amount not specified. **To Apply:** Applicants must submit an information sheet providing the dissertation adviser's contact information; letter of support from the dissertation's adviser and explaining the importance of dissertation's question, appropriateness and completeness of the study design and significance of the analysis and interpretations; a copy of dissertation's abstract and narrative (not to exceed 10 pages, double-spaced) that answers questions stated on the online application procedures. **Deadline:** August. **Contact:** For more information about this award, applicants must contact Kristin McCabe; Phone: 207-899-1309; E-mail: kmccabe@aacte.org.

465 ■ David G. Imig Awards for Distinguished Achievement in Teacher Education *(Professional development/Award)*

Purpose: To recognize achievements in the field of policy or research in teacher education. **Focus:** Teaching. **Qualif.:** Applicants must be individuals or team of individuals who are responsible for the achievement. **Criteria:** Recipients will be selected based on qualifications and submitted materials.

Funds Avail.: Amount not specified. **To Apply:** Applicants must complete the online entry form. Nomination must contain a letter of recommendation describing how nomi-

Awards are arranged alphabetically below their administering organizations

nees fulfill the selection criteria and must include their curriculum vitae. **Deadline:** October 7. **Contact:** For more information about this award, applicants must contact Matthew Wales at 202-293-2450 or e-mail mwales@aacte.org.

466 ■ Edward C. Pomeroy Awards for Outstanding Contributions to Teacher Education *(Professional development/Award)*

Purpose: To recognize outstanding contributions to teacher education, either through distinguished service to the teacher education community through the development and promotion of outstanding practices in teacher education at the collegiate, state or national level. **Focus:** Teaching. **Qualif.:** Applicants must be individuals who have made exceptional contributions to AACTE, to a national or state organization involved in teacher education, or to persons responsible for the development of exemplary teacher education initiatives. **Criteria:** Award will be given to applicants who best meet the qualifications.

Funds Avail.: Amount not specified. **To Apply:** Applicants must complete the online entry form. Nomination must contain a letter of recommendation describing how nominees fulfill the selection criteria and curriculum vitae. **Deadline:** October 7. **Contact:** For more information about this award, applicants must contact Matthew Wales at 202-293-2450 or e-mail mwales@aacte.org.

467 ■ Margaret B. Lindsey Awards for Distinguished Research in Teacher Education *(Professional development/Award)*

Purpose: To recognize individuals whose research over the last decade has made a major impact on the field of teacher education. **Focus:** Teaching. **Qualif.:** Nominee's works must include at least a decade of cumulative research. **Criteria:** Recipients will be selected based on submitted work.

Funds Avail.: Amount not specified. **To Apply:** Applicants must complete the online entry form found on the website; must include a letter of nomination that describes nominee's accomplishments and explaining why they deserve to receive the award. **Deadline:** October 7. **Contact:** For more information about this award, applicants must contact Matthew Wales at 202-293-2450 or e-mail mwales@aacte.org.

468 ■ American Association of Critical-Care Nurses (AACN)

101 Columbia
Aliso Viejo, CA 92656-4109
Ph: (949) 362-2000
Fax: (949) 362-2020
Free: 800-899-2273
E-mail: info@aacn.org
URL: www.aacn.org

469 ■ AACN Continuing Professional Development Scholarships *(Graduate, Professional development/Scholarship)*

Purpose: To provide financial assistance to students who want to acquire knowledge and skills beyond traditional academic nursing education. **Focus:** Nursing. **Qualif.:** Applicants must be current active members of AACN at the time of application and throughout the term of the funded activity. **Criteria:** Selection will be based on how applicants would assess and articulate gaps in their own knowledge and skills; how they set professional learning goals on the basis of identified gaps; how they identify and evaluate learning opportunities that will move them toward achieving their goals; and how they present a budget of expenses for funding the proposed learning activity.

Funds Avail.: No specific amount. **To Apply:** Applicants must submit a completed application form and curriculum vitae in a separate Word document or PDF file. **Deadline:** January 16. **Contact:** E-mail at scholarships@aacn.org.

470 ■ American Association of Endodontists (AAE)

211 E Chicago Ave., Ste. 1100
Chicago, IL 60611-2691
Ph: (312) 266-7255
Fax: (312) 266-9867
Free: 800-872-3636
E-mail: info@aae.org
URL: www.aae.org

471 ■ Endodontic Educator Fellowship Awards *(Graduate/Fellowship)*

Purpose: To recognize the critical role that endodontic educators play in strengthening their specialty and to address the need for more endodontic specialists to teach in dental schools. **Focus:** Dentistry. **Qualif.:** Applicant must be a citizen or hold a permanent residency card for the United States or Canada. Applicant must have been accepted for the next academic year or enrolled in the first or second year of an Advanced Specialty Education Program in Endodontics that is accredited by, or has a reciprocal agreement with, the Commission on Dental Accreditation of the American Dental Association; and has been accepted into a Master's, Doctorate or postdoctoral training program (the degree-granting institution must be an accredited U.S. university). **Criteria:** Fellows are selected based on: meeting the eligibility requirements for applicant and school/program; strength of recommendations; strength of applicant's essay; accuracy of information on the application form; official transcripts from previous degree or certificate programs; degree of support from program director/dean of current institution; and strength of interview with committee members.

Funds Avail.: Full tuition plus $2,500 per month. **To Apply:** Applicants must submit a completed application form along with three letters of recommendation; a typed essay; and official transcripts from all undergraduate and graduate programs. **Deadline:** December 31.

472 ■ Endodontic Research Grants *(Graduate/Grant)*

Purpose: To inspire and support research and the genesis of new knowledge in endodontics. **Focus:** Dentistry. **Qualif.:** Applicant must be a student of an advanced specialty education program in endodontics at a dental school that is accredited by or has a reciprocal agreement with the Commission on Dental Accreditation of the American Dental Association; faculty or researcher in endodontology or related fields (microbiology, pathology and physiology) of a dental school that is accredited by or has a reciprocal agreement with the Commission on Dental Accreditation of the ADA; active member of the AAE. Dental school faculty or research staff who are not endodontists are strongly encouraged to include an endodontist as a consultant or co-investigator. Postgraduate students must be AAE members. **Criteria:** Applications are evaluated based on:

Awards are arranged alphabetically below their administering organizations

significance of research and its relation to the AAE Research Priorities; scientific merit and potential for discovering new information; excellence of research design and statistical methods and probability of successful completion; extent to which the project has been previously funded; extent to which alternative funding sources were sought; and extent to which the research can lead to future innovations in clinical endodontics, or future research that is funded by national or federal funding agencies.

Funds Avail.: No specific amount. **To Apply:** Applicants must submit a CD containing the application form and all proposal materials. **Deadline:** Spring/Summer: February 16; Fall/Winter: August 18;. **Contact:** Development coordinator at 800-872-3636 x-3008.

473 ■ American Association of Equine Practitioners (AAEP)
4075 Iron Works Pkwy.
Lexington, KY 40511
Ph: (859) 233-0147
Fax: (859) 233-1968
E-mail: aaepoffice@aaep.org
URL: www.aaep.org

474 ■ AAEP/ALSIC Scholarships
(Undergraduate/Scholarship)

Purpose: To advance the health and welfare of horses by promoting the discovery and sharing of new knowledge; to enhance awareness of the need to the targeted research; to educate the public; to expand fundraising opportunities; to facilitate cooperation among funding agencies. **Focus:** Veterinary science and medicine. **Qualif.:** Applicants must be senior veterinary students who have indicated a strong desire to pursue a career in equine medicine at schools nationwide. **Criteria:** Consideration will be given to students who have demonstrated leadership qualities in any of a variety of equine-related areas including, but not limited to, involvement with the AAEP, community organizations or equined industry programs.

Funds Avail.: $2,500. **Number Awarded:** 8. **To Apply:** An applicant must fill out the online application form. Applicants must attach completed AAEP/ALSIC Scholarship Program Cover Sheet; one essay, not to exceed 1,500 words that answers the three questions, "Why do you plan to enter equined practice and what events and/or individuals influenced your decision?", "What characteristics do you possess that uniquely qualify?"; a curriculum vitae, not to exceed two pages; a 2-page curriculum vitae. Evaluation form must be completed by a clinical instructor familiar with the applicant's performance and the other evaluation form must be completed by an equine practitioner in private practice; a self-addressed, stamped postcard by the AAEP as confirmation of receipt. **Deadline:** October 1.

475 ■ AAEP Foundation Past Presidents' Research Fellowships *(Doctorate/Scholarship)*

Purpose: To emphasize the importance of equine research; to reward a researcher for his or her contributions. **Focus:** Veterinary science and medicine. **Qualif.:** An applicant must be a graduate of an AVMA-accredited school/college of veterinary medicine; must be current AAEP member; graduate student or resident, or have completed a doctorate or residency program within the past 2 years. **Criteria:** Scholarship Committee will evaluate application based on the potential for proposed research to contribute to equine veterinary medicine; sincere intent for long-term career in

equine veterinary research; experience within horse industry; experience and activity in equine veterinary medicine; experience with equine research; academic performance; and based on the professional accomplishments before and after graduation.

Funds Avail.: $5,000. **To Apply:** An applicant must attach the complete filled out AAEP Research Fellow Cover Sheet; he/she must prepare a maximum one-page cover letter outlining long-term research intent, as well as how it will impact equine veterinary medicine and positively affect horse health; an applicant must include how the scholarship will help in doing the research; a maximum two-page scientific abstract and budget of the intent research project; an applicant must obtain a curriculum vitae, a completed evaluation form, a signed and sealed letter of recommendations;; and an applicant must provide a self-addressed, stamped postcard to be returned as confirmation of receipt; an applicant must attend the AAEP Convention; he/she must provide information to AAEP for AAEP Foundation Publications such as biographical sketch, benefits of fellowship, impact of research result, **Deadline:** July 30.

476 ■ American Association of Family and Consumer Sciences (AAFCS)
400 N Columbus St., Ste. 202
Alexandria, VA 22314
Ph: (703) 706-4600
Fax: (703) 706-4663
Free: 800-424-8080
E-mail: staff@aafcs.org
URL: www.aafcs.org

477 ■ American Association of Family and Consumer Sciences Scholarships
(Undergraduate/Scholarship)

Purpose: To encourage undergraduate study in family and consumer sciences and its subspecialties. **Focus:** Sciences. **Qualif.:** Applicants must be citizens or permanent residents of the United States; must be planning to pursue or currently pursuing a degree in family and consumer sciences or its specialties at the undergraduate level on a full-time basis; must be currently enrolled in an undergraduate program that will continue into the coming academic year or have been admitted to an undergraduate program for the coming academic year; must be willing to commit themselves to meet the specific requirements of the scholarship for which they are applying. **Criteria:** Recipients are selected based on ability to pursue undergraduate study; experience in relation to preparation for study in proposed field; special recognition and awards; participation in professional/community organizations and activities; evidence of professional commitment and leadership; significance of proposed area of study to families and individuals; professional goals; written communication and evaluation of applicant's recommendations.

Funds Avail.: $5,000. **Number Awarded:** 1. **To Apply:** Applicants must complete the application form; must have maximum of three evaluators; must obtain official or unofficial copies of transcript; must mail five hard copies of labeled CDs of the completed application form. **Deadline:** January 15.

478 ■ American Association for Hand Surgery (AAHS)
500 Cummings Ctr., Ste. 4550
Beverly, MA 01915

Awards are arranged alphabetically below their administering organizations

Ph: (978) 927-8330
Fax: (978) 524-8890
Free: 800-333-8835
E-mail: contact@handsurgery.org
URL: www.handsurgery.org

479 ■ American Association for Hand Surgery Annual Research Awards *(Professional development/Award)*

Purpose: To foster creativity and innovation in basic and/or clinical research in all areas pertinent to hand surgery. **Focus:** Surgery. **Qualif.:** Applicants must be residents, fellows, therapists and AAHS members. **Criteria:** Applicants are selected according to the potential of their research project.

Funds Avail.: $10,000. **Number Awarded:** 1. **To Apply:** Applicants must submit an application form plus seven copies of investigators' demographic information, description of research and curriculum vitae for each researcher. **Deadline:** December 1. **Contact:** Mail application to American Association for Hand Surgery office or e-mail at efreeman@plasticsurgery.org.

480 ■ American Association on Health and Disability (AAHD)

110 N Washington St., Ste. 328-J
Rockville, MD 20850
Ph: (301) 545-6140
Fax: (301) 545-6144
E-mail: rcarlin@aahd.us
URL: www.aahd.us

481 ■ AAHD Scholarships *(Graduate, Undergraduate/Scholarship)*

Purpose: To promote health and wellness in people with disabilities. **Focus:** Public health; Health education; Disabilities. **Qualif.:** Applicant must be enrolled in undergraduate or graduate school; have a documented disability and must provide documentation; a US citizen or legal resident living in the US; and enrolled in, or accepted by, an accredited US four year university or graduate school on a full-time basis. **Criteria:** Preference will be given to students majoring in public health, disability studies, health promotion or a field related to disability and health.

Funds Avail.: $1,000. **To Apply:** Applicant must submit a completed application form together with a personal statement (maximum 3 pages-double spaced), including brief personal history, educational/career goals, extra-curricular activities, and reasons why he/she should be selected by the AAHD Scholarship Committee; three letters of recommendation (one must be from a teacher or academic advisor); and an official copy of high school transcript as well as college transcript (if applicable). Applicant must agree to allow AAHD to use his/her name, picture and/or story in future scholarship materials. **Deadline:** November 15. **Contact:** Roberta Carlin, AAHD Executive Director at rcarlin@aahd.us or 301-545-6140 x-206.

482 ■ American Association of Healthcare Administrative Management

11240 Waples Mill Rd., Ste. 200
Fairfax, VA 22030
Ph: (703) 281-4043
Fax: (703) 359-7562

E-mail: moayad@aaham.org
URL: www.aaham.org

483 ■ National AAHAM Scholarships *(Undergraduate/Scholarship)*

Purpose: To provide educational scholarship to individual AAHAM members and their dependents. **Focus:** General studies. **Qualif.:** Applicants must be individuals who have been National AAHAM members for at least one year and have paid their current dues by March 30 of the year in which applications are submitted. **Criteria:** Applicants are judged based on the established criteria by the review and selection committee comprised of the Chairmen of the Board and the current chairs of the Education and Finance Committees.

Funds Avail.: $2,500. **Number Awarded:** 2. **To Apply:** Applicants must submit all the required application information. **Deadline:** May 31. **Contact:** moayad@aaham.org.

484 ■ American Association for the Improvement of Boxing (AAIB)

86 Fletcher Ave.
Mount Vernon, NY 10552-3319
Ph: (914) 664-4571
Fax: (914) 664-3164
E-mail: aaib@verizon.net
URL: www.aaib.org

485 ■ AAIB Scholarships *(Undergraduate/Scholarship)*

Purpose: To provide educational opportunities and financial assistance to working students. **Focus:** General Studies. **Qualif.:** Program is open to high school seniors who must be accepted by an accredited college or university; must be nominated by a current paid member; must be current or former amateur boxers in the United States who have been accepted by a bona fide college or university. **Criteria:** Recipient is chosen based on scholastic achievement, athletic achievement and community service.

Funds Avail.: $8,000. **Number Awarded:** 1. **To Apply:** Application form is available in the website. **Deadline:** June 15.

486 ■ American Association of Japanese University Women (AAJUW)

3253 Calle De Debesa
Camarillo, CA 93010
E-mail: president@aajuw.org
URL: www.aajuw.org

487 ■ AAJUW Scholarships *(Graduate, Undergraduate/Scholarship)*

Purpose: To assist the advancement of women in education. **Focus:** General studies. **Qualif.:** Applicant must be a female student enrolled in an accredited California college/university; have junior, senior or graduate standing by Fall; attend (at own expense) the award ceremony; and shall be a contributor to U.S.-Japan relations, cultural exchanges and the development of leadership in the area of her designated field. **Criteria:** Selection is based on the application materials submitted.

Funds Avail.: %1,500. **Number Awarded:** 2 or 3. **To Apply:** Applicants must submit a completed application form

Awards are arranged alphabetically below their administering organizations

together with a current resume; official transcript for the past two years of study (sealed and sent directly by the college/university to AAJUW); two letters of recommendation (addressed to AAJUW); and the essay (maximum to 2 typewritten pages, double-spaced, 8 1/2 x 11). All required documents must be sent to: Masako Mera, AAJUW Scholarship Committee, 445 Surfview Dr., Pacific Palisades, CA 90272.

488 ■ American Association for Justice (AAJ)

777 6th St. NW, Ste. 200
Washington, DC 20001
Ph: (202) 965-3500
Fax: (202) 298-6849
Free: 800-424-2725
E-mail: membership@justice.org
URL: www.justice.org

489 ■ AAJ Trial Advocacy Scholarships
(Undergraduate/Scholarship)

Purpose: To assist law students in furthering their studies. **Focus:** Law. **Qualif.:** Applicants must be second and third year AAJ law student members; must be enrolled in an ABA-accredited law school. **Criteria:** Scholarships are given to applicants who: exhibit an interest and proficiency of skills in trial advocacy; express a desire to represent victims; demonstrate a commitment and dedication to AAJ mission through involvement in an AAJ student chapter and minority caucus activities; and show financial need.

Funds Avail.: $2,500. **To Apply:** Applicants must submit resume; 500-word essay on how the applicants will meet the criteria; up to three recommendations from a faculty adviser, trial advocacy professor, Dean, AAJ member, or trial lawyer; and a completed form verifying applicant's student status. **Deadline:** May 1. **Contact:** Brandon Grubesky at brandon.grubesky@justice.org.

490 ■ Mike Eidson Scholarships *(Graduate, Undergraduate/Scholarship)*

Purpose: To provide a support system of women lawyers to network, socialize, form professional relationships and develop female leadership for AAJ. **Focus:** Law. **Qualif.:** Applicants must be 3L (or rising 4L in a night program) female students who have demonstrated a commitment to a career as a plaintiffs lawyer or criminal defense lawyer, along with dedication to upholding and defending the principles of the Constitution, and to the concept of a fair trial, the adversary system, and a just result for the injured, the accused and those whose rights are jeopardized. **Criteria:** Selection will be based on the committee's criteria.

Funds Avail.: $5,000. **To Apply:** Applicants must contact the Association for the application process.

491 ■ The Richard D. Hailey AAJ Law Student Scholarships *(Undergraduate/Scholarship)*

Purpose: To assist law students in furthering their studies. **Focus:** Law. **Qualif.:** Applicants must be incoming first, second or third year African American, Hispanic American, Asian American, Native American and bi-racial AAJ law student members; must be enrolled in an ABA-accredited law school. **Criteria:** Scholarships are given to applicants who: exhibit an interest and proficiency of skills in trial advocacy; express a desire to represent victims; demonstrate a commitment and dedication to AAJ mission through involvement in an AAJ student chapter and minority caucus

activities; and show financial need.

Funds Avail.: $1,000. **Number Awarded:** 6. **To Apply:** Applicants must submit resume; 500-word essay on how the applicants will meet the criteria; up to three recommendations from a faculty adviser, trial advocacy professor, Dean, AAJ member or trial lawyer; and a completed form verifying applicant's student status. **Deadline:** May 1. **Contact:** Brandon Grubesky at brandon.grubesky@justice.org.

492 ■ Alia Herrera Memorial Scholarships
(Undergraduate/Scholarship)

Purpose: To assist law students in furthering their studies. **Focus:** Law. **Qualif.:** Applicants must be students entering second or third year of law school, or having the equivalent of one year to complete; must be attending law schools in the Philadelphia, PA area; must be members of the law student section of AAJ; must be children of AAJ members. **Criteria:** Recipients are selected based on the Scholarship Committee's review of academic records.

Funds Avail.: $3,000. **To Apply:** Applicants must submit cover letter; resume; transcript; letter of recommendation from a law professor or Dean of law school; 500-word essay on the topic ("Damage Caps": Limiting Damage awards in Civil cases by State and/or federal statutes, compared to juries making damage awards, with judicial review; Who should bare the risk or loss, and why?). **Deadline:** May 1. **Contact:** Crystal D. Gilreath, 1591 Vinton Ave., Memphis, TN 38104; higginsgilreath@yahoo.com.

493 ■ The Leesfield/AAJ Law Student Scholarships *(Undergraduate/Scholarship)*

Purpose: To assist law students in furthering their studies. **Focus:** Law. **Qualif.:** Applicants must be first and second year AAJ law student members. **Criteria:** Recipients are selected based on submitted application materials.

Funds Avail.: $2,500. **To Apply:** Applicants must submit resume; statement of financial need; 500-word written request substantiating the applicant's commitment to preserving the civil justice system; three recommendations from a faculty adviser, trial advocacy professor, dean AAJ member, or trial lawyer; and a completed form verifying applicant's student status. **Contact:** Brandon Grubesky at brandon.grubesky@justice.org.

494 ■ American Association of Law Libraries (AALL)

105 W Adams St., Ste. 3300
Chicago, IL 60603-6225
Ph: (312) 939-4764
Fax: (312) 431-1097
E-mail: support@aall.org
URL: www.aallnet.org

495 ■ AALL Research Funds *(Professional development/Grant)*

Purpose: To fund one or more projects of value to those professions that create, disseminate or use legal and law-related information. **Focus:** Law; Paralegal studies. **Qualif.:** Applicants should have experience with research projects, and an understanding of the creation, dissemination and/or use of legal and law related information. Applicants may be individuals or partnerships. **Criteria:** Preference will be given to members of AALL, working individually or in partnership with others. Selection will be based on the following: the pertinence of the research ques-

Awards are arranged alphabetically below their administering organizations

tion, the appropriateness of the research and the feasibility of the work plan; the intellectual significance of the project, including its potential contribution to scholarship in librarianship, law librarianship or legal fields, and the likelihood that it will encourage research in a new direction; the qualification, expertise and level of commitment of the project director, and appropriateness of chosen staff; the promise of quality, usefulness and impact on scholarship of any resulting research product; the potential for success of the project.

Funds Avail.: $1,100. **To Apply:** Applicants must provide a resume and statement of their qualifications for carrying out the project. The AALL grant proposal cover sheet must accompany all applications. Applicants must submit two copies of the proposal to the Research Committee Chair. Grant recipients will submit their final report and project results by the scheduled date. The project proposal must: demonstrate significance and originality in the context of existing literature and research; propose appropriate strategies for conducting the research based on the topic or issue selected, including a plan for systematic analysis that will produce objective and reliable results; show feasibility to be completed within the established time frame and budget; include a preferred means of disseminating project results. **Deadline:** March 30. **Remarks:** An endowment established by LexisNexis®. **Contact:** Kate Hagan, Executive Dir.; Phone: 312-939-4764; Fax: 312-939-4770; Email: khagan@aall.org.

496 ■ AALL Scholarships for Continuing Education Classes *(Postgraduate/Scholarship)*

Purpose: To provide financial assistance to individuals who wish to pursue courses related to law librarianship. **Focus:** Library and archival sciences. **Qualif.:** Applicants must be law librarians with a degree from an ALA-accredited library school or an ABA-accredited law school, who are registered in continuing education courses related to law librarianship. Applicants must also be AALL members. **Criteria:** Applicants who are permanent residents of United States and Canada will be given preference.

Funds Avail.: $500. **To Apply:** Applicants must submit a completed application form; course description and registration; personal statement; and letters of recommendation. **Deadline:** April 1. **Contact:** Email: scholarships@aall.org.

497 ■ AALL Scholarships for Library School Graduates Seeking a Non-Law Degree *(Postgraduate/Scholarship)*

Purpose: To assist individuals who wish to develop a professional career in law librarianship and who intend to have a career as law librarians. **Focus:** Library and archival sciences. **Qualif.:** Applicants must be library school graduates who are degree candidates in an area other than law. Scholarship is restricted to members of AALL. **Criteria:** Recipients are selected based on the application packet and financial need.

Funds Avail.: No specific amount. **To Apply:** Applicants must submit an application form; transcript of records; letters of recommendation; and a personal statement. **Deadline:** April 1. **Contact:** Application form and other required documents may send electronically at scholarship@aall.org.

498 ■ American Association of Law Libraries Library School Scholarships *(Graduate, Postgraduate/Scholarship)*

Purpose: To help individuals achieve their goal as law librarians. **Focus:** Library and archival sciences; Law. **Qua-**

lif.: Applicant must be a law school graduate working towards a degree in an accredited library school or a college graduate with meaningful law library experience and a degree candidate in an accredited library school. Applicant must have the intention of having a career as a law librarian. **Criteria:** Applicants who are law school graduates with meaningful library experience or college graduates working for degrees with emphasis on courses in law are given preference.

Funds Avail.: Exact scholarship amount is not specified. **To Apply:** Applicants must submit an application form; transcripts; three letters of recommendation; and a personal statement. Evidence of financial need must be submitted. Applicants must also provide a stamped self-addressed postcard and envelope to be use by the Committee in notifying them regarding their application form. **Deadline:** April 1. **Contact:** scholarships@aall.org.

499 ■ Foreign, Comparative & International Law - Schaffer Grants for Foreign Law Librarians *(Professional development/Grant)*

Purpose: To provide financial assistance to ensure the presence and participation of a foreign librarian at the AALL Annual Meeting. **Focus:** Library and archival sciences; Law. **Qualif.:** Applicants must be law librarians or other professional working in the legal information field, who is currently employed in a country other than the United States. Applicants must be in a position of significant responsibility for the dissemination, preservation and/or organization of legal information. Applicants may be from any type of law library. An applicant who would not otherwise have the opportunity to attend the AALL Annual Meeting is invited and encouraged to apply. Applicants must have sufficient English proficiency to fully participate in the conference without an interpreter. **Criteria:** Applications will be evaluated on the basis of the law librarian's ability to add to the Association's knowledge of law, legal information and law librarianship from a foreign perspective. Preference will be given to an applicant from an under-represented country or region, to someone who demonstrates financial need or to an applicant who has never attended an AALL Annual Meeting.

Funds Avail.: $2,000. **To Apply:** Applicants must submit an Application Form and a resume of their professional qualifications. The Application Form should be filled out as completely as possible. Simultaneous electronic submission of a completed Application and resume is preferred but not required. All documents should be in English and should be sent together either electronically or traditional mail. **Deadline:** March 1. **Contact:** Ryan Harrington, Reference Librarian for Foreign and International Law, Yale Law School, Lillian Goldman Law Library, PO Box 208215, New Haven, CT 06520; Phone: 203-432-7371; Fax: 203-432-4604; Email: ryan. harrington@yale.edu.

500 ■ Alan Holoch Memorial Grants *(Professional development/Grant)*

Purpose: To assist individuals with travel or registration expenses for the American Association of Law Libraries Annual Meeting. **Focus:** Library and archival sciences; Law. **Qualif.:** Applicants must be members of the Social Responsibilities Special Interest Section at the time of the application. **Criteria:** Selection will be based on the committee's criteria.

Funds Avail.: No specific amout. **To Apply:** Applicants must submit a completed application together with one letter of recommendation from either an employer or a col-

Awards are arranged alphabetically below their administering organizations

league or peer. Recommendations should be sought from those who are familiar with the applicants. **Deadline:** April 12.

501 ■ AALL/Wolters Kluwer Law & Business Grants (*Professional development/Grant*)

Purpose: To fund one or more projects of value to those professions that create, disseminate or use legal and law-related information. **Focus:** Law; Paralegal studies. **Qualif.:** Applicants should have experience with research projects, and an understanding of the creation, dissemination and/or use of legal and law related information. Applicants may be individuals or partnerships. **Criteria:** Preference will be given to members of AALL, working individually or in partnership with others. Selection will be based on the following: the pertinence of the research question, the appropriateness of the research and the feasibility of the work plan; the intellectual significance of the project, including its potential contribution to scholarship in librarianship, law librarianship or legal fields, and the likelihood that it will encourage research in a new direction; the qualification, expertise and level of commitment of the project director, and appropriateness of chosen staff; the promise of quality, usefulness and impact on scholarship of any resulting research product; the potential for success of the project.

Funds Avail.: No specific amount. **To Apply:** Applicants must provide a resume and statement of their qualifications for carrying out the project. The proposal must: demonstrate significance and originality in the context of existing literature and research; propose appropriate strategies for conducting the research based on the topic or issue selected, including a plan for systematic analysis that will produce objective and reliable results; show feasibility to be completed within the established time frame and budget; include a preferred means of disseminating project results. Applicants must submit two copies of the project proposal to the Research Committee Chair. **Deadline:** December 12. **Contact:** Paula Davidson, Dir. of Finance and Administration; Phone: 312-205-8012; Fax: 312-431-1097; Email: pdavidson@aall.org.

502 ■ Marcia J. Koslov Scholarships (*Professional development/Scholarship*)

Purpose: To provide funding for members to attend live seminars and conferences presented by the Institute for Court Management, the Center for Legal and Court Technology, the Equal Justice Conference or other programs that provide continuing education for state, court or county law librarians. **Focus:** Library and archival sciences; Law. **Qualif.:** Candidates must be current member of AALL who serve as librarians in state, court or county libraries. **Criteria:** Selection will be based on the committee's criteria.

Funds Avail.: No specific amount. **To Apply:** Candidates must provide the following information: submit a copy of the seminar or conference information, which provides detail as to the content, faculty and educational goals of the program. Be sure that it also provides the registration and/or other fees necessary for attendance; submit a statement explaining why the applicant wants to pursue continuing professional education and why the live seminar or conference they are interested in attending will meet their objectives. The statement should also summarize the applicant's primary duties, responsibilities and career goals. This statement will help gauge the fit between what the course offers and the benefits the applicant hopes to receive from attendance; submit a resume providing evidence of work experience, academic achievement and

professional participation. **Deadline:** April 1. **Contact:** membership@aall.org.

503 ■ Minority Leadership Development Awards (*Graduate/Award*)

Purpose: To introduce minority law librarians to leadership opportunities within the Association. **Focus:** Library and archival sciences; Law. **Qualif.:** Applicants must be: members of a minority groups as defined by current US government guidelines; have a strong academic record and have earned a Master's degree in Library/Information Science; have no more than 5 years of professional (post-MLS or post-JD) library or information service work experience; be current members of AALL at the time application is submitted; have been members of AALL for at least 2 years or have 2 years of full time, professional law library work experience; demonstrate leadership potential. **Criteria:** Selection will be based on the committee's criteria.

Funds Avail.: No specific amount. **To Apply:** Applicants must submit the application package containing the following: completed application form; current resume or curriculum vitae; three letters of recommendation from individuals who can evaluate their law library employment experience or relevant graduate education commenting on their present and potential contributions to AALL and the field of law librarianship; a brief essay on how belonging to a minority group has influenced their career to date and on how the profession benefits from encouraging the leadership development of law librarians from minority groups; a brief essay on what leadership means to them and how this grant will help them realize their personal leadership goals. **Deadline:** April 1.

504 ■ Marla Schwartz Grants (*Professional development, Graduate/Grant*)

Purpose: To support attendance at any events related to technical services, including cataloging, preservation, acquisitions, collection development, serials and management and/or to support attendance at CONELL. **Focus:** Library and archival sciences; Law. **Qualif.:** Applicants do not need to be members of either AALL or TS-SIS. Applicants must be new law librarians and graduate students in library/information studies programs. **Criteria:** Selection will be based on the following: financial need; individuals who have not previously attended an AALL sponsored educational event; individuals who have not previously received a TS-SIS sponsored educational grant; new or student members of TS-SIS who have demonstrated potential for professional development or scholarly activity; students in library science/information studies program who may not be a member of either AALL or TS-SIS, but who plan careers in technical services law librarianship.

Funds Avail.: No specific amount. **To Apply:** Applicants must submit an application which includes: current position and relevant previous positions; estimate of expenses for attending the event; statement of how much financial support will be provided by the applicant's employer; expected graduation date; maximum of 200 words brief statement explaining why the applicant is applying for the grant; two references supporting the application by individuals who are familiar with the applicant's work or the applicant's interest in professional development as a technical services law librarian. **Remarks:** Established to honor Marla's memory and achievements.

Awards are arranged alphabetically below their administering organizations

505 ■ AALL & Thomson West - George A. Strait Minority Scholarship Endowments (Postgraduate/Scholarship)

Purpose: To support the education of minority students who wish to pursue their career goals in law librarianship. **Focus:** Library and archival sciences. **Qualif.:** Applicants must be college graduates with meaningful law library experience; members of a minority group as defined by current U.S. Government guidelines; degree candidates in an ALA-accredited library school or an ABA-accredited law school; intend to have a career in law librarianship; must have at least one quarter/semester remaining after the scholarship is awarded. **Criteria:** Recipients are selected based on application materials submitted and financial need.

Funds Avail.: Exact scholarship amount is not specified. **To Apply:** Applicants must submit a completed application form; course description and registration; personal statement; and three letters of recommendation. **Deadline:** April 1. **Contact:** Application form and other required documents may send electronically at scholarships@all.org.

506 ■ Technical Services Special Interest Section Grants (Professional development/Grant)

Purpose: To provide financial assistance to librarians who might not otherwise be able to attend an AALL-sponsored workshop due to limited financial resources. **Focus:** Library and archival sciences; Law. **Qualif.:** Applicants for general grants must be current members of TS-SIS. **Criteria:** Selection will be based on the following: financial need; individuals who have not previously attended an AALL sponsored educational event; individuals who have not previously received a TS-SIS sponsored educational grant; new or student members of TS-SIS who have demonstrated potential for professional development or scholarly activity.

Funds Avail.: No specific amount. **To Apply:** Applicants must submit an application which includes: current position and relevant previous positions; estimate of expenses for attending the event; statement of how much financial support will be provided by the applicant's employer; expected graduation date; maximum of 200 words brief statement explaining why the applicant is applying for the grant; two references supporting the application by individuals who are familiar with the applicant's work or the applicant's interest in professional development as a technical services law librarian.

507 ■ AALL Leadership Academy Grants (Professional development/Grant)

Purpose: To provide a forum for the exchange of ideas and information on academic law libraries and to represent its members interests and concerns within the Association. **Focus:** Library and archival sciences; Law. **Qualif.:** Applicants must be ALL-SIS members who are accepted into the AALL Leadership Academy and who have not received and used any ALL-SIS grants in the past. **Criteria:** Preference is given to newer members of ALL-SIS who are active participants in the ALL-SIS, AALL and/or AALL Chapters.

Funds Avail.: $1,000. **To Apply:** Applicants must submit a completed application packet, available at the website, to the Chair of the ALL-SIS Awards Committee. The application packet must include the following: completed application; two letters of recommendation commenting on your potential to contribute to ALL-SIS, AALL and the field of law librarianship, and addressing the applicant's financial need for the grant; personal statement; current resume.

508 ■ ALL-SIS CONELL Grants (Professional development/Grant)

Purpose: To promote participation by newer academic law librarians in AALL and the ALL-SIS. **Focus:** Library and archival sciences; Law. **Qualif.:** Recipients must be ALL-SIS members with demonstrated financial need and agree to become a member of the New Academic Law Librarians Meeting (NALLM)/Mentoring Committee for the year following the grant. **Criteria:** Grant recipients will be chosen, in large part, based on demonstrated financial need.

Funds Avail.: $500. **Number Awarded:** Two. **To Apply:** Interested applicants must submit the following: a current resume; two letters of recommendation from current or former teachers or employers that discuss your potential to contribute to the field of academic law librarianship and your need for the grant.

509 ■ Government Documents Special Interest Section - Veronica Maclay Student Grants (Master's/Grant)

Purpose: To promote and enhance the value of law libraries to the legal and public communities, to foster the profession of law librarianship, and to provide leadership in the field of legal information. **Focus:** Library and archival sciences; Law. **Qualif.:** Applicants must be students currently enrolled in an ALA accredited library and information studies master's program. **Criteria:** Preference will be given to LIS students who demonstrate interest in government information and a career in law librarianship.

Funds Avail.: $1,000. **To Apply:** Applicants must submit a completed application and recommendation letter in electronic format. **Deadline:** March 26.

510 ■ American Association for Marriage and Family Therapy (AAMFT)

112 S Alfred St.
Alexandria, VA 22314-3061
Ph: (703) 838-9808
Fax: (703) 838-9805
E-mail: central@aamft.org
URL: www.aamft.org

511 ■ AAMFT Minority Fellowships (Doctorate, Graduate/Fellowship)

Purpose: To provide financial assistance to graduate students who wish to pursue their doctoral degrees in Marriage and Family therapy. **Focus:** Family/Marital therapy. **Qualif.:** Applicants must be American citizens or permanent residents with permanent resident registration card; must demonstrate a strong commitment to a career in ethnic minority mental health and substance abuse services; must be enrolled full-time in a Marriage and Family Therapy doctoral program; must be an African American, Alaskan Native, American Indian, Asian American, Hispanic/Latino, Native Hawaiian or Pacific Islander. **Criteria:** Selection is based on the submitted application materials and financial need.

Funds Avail.: $20,000 used for all related costs of doctoral program attendance and training. **To Apply:** Applicants must complete the application form available in the website; must submit two essays containing the following: (1) specific training interest and career goals and (2) the choice of university, training program, and advisor/mentor, and how their choices relate to minority mental health or specific training interest and career goals; must provide a curriculum

Awards are arranged alphabetically below their administering organizations

vita/resume, three recommendation letters, and transcript for any college/university attended for at least a full academic year within the last 10 years. **Deadline:** March 18.

512 ■ American Association of Medical Assistants (AAMA)

20 N Wacker Dr., Ste. 1575
Chicago, IL 60606
Ph: (312) 899-1500
Fax: (312) 899-1259
URL: www.aama-ntl.org

513 ■ Maxine Williams Scholarships
(Postdoctorate/Scholarship)

Purpose: To support students in a medical assisting program. **Focus:** Medical assisting. **Qualif.:** Applicants must be currently enrolled, and have completed a minimum of one quarter or a semester at a postsecondary medical assisting program accredited by (CAAHEP); and have a GPA of 3.0 or higher. **Criteria:** Selection is based on academic ability and financial need.

Funds Avail.: $1,000 and one-year membership in AAMA. **To Apply:** Applicants must request an application form electronically to boardservices@aama-ntl.org, including applicant's name; accreditation code; and program's institution name, city and state. **Deadline:** February 15. **Remarks:** Established in 1959, named after the first president and founder of the AAMA, Maxine Williams. **Contact:** Application form can be requested by sending an e-mail at boardservices@aama-ntl.org.

514 ■ American Association of Neurological Surgeons (AANS) (AANS)

5550 Meadowbrook Dr.
Rolling Meadows, IL 60008-3852
Ph: (847) 378-0500
Fax: (847) 378-0600
Free: 888-566-2267
E-mail: info@aans.org
URL: www.aans.org

515 ■ AANS Medical Student Summer Research Fellowships (MSSRF) *(Undergraduate/Fellowship)*

Purpose: To provide first or second year medical students the opportunity to participate in neurosurgical research through a summer fellowship within an academic department of neurosurgery in the United States or Canada. **Focus:** Neurology. **Qualif.:** Applicants must be American or Canadian medical students. **Criteria:** Candidates will be judged based upon the scientific merits of the proposed project, the credentials of the applicant, letters of reference, the preceptor statement and the support provided by the sponsoring program/laboratory.

Funds Avail.: $2,500. **Number Awarded:** 20. **To Apply:** Applicants must submit applications which include the curriculum vitae and bio-sketch, a description of future plans, and a statement of why this fellowship is of interest to the applicants and why it would be beneficial to them. **Deadline:** February 1.

516 ■ William P. Van Wagenen Fellowships
(Undergraduate/Fellowship)

Purpose: To provide financial support to a post neurosurgical resident for foreign travel for scientific enrichment, prior to beginning an academic career in neurological surgery. **Focus:** Neurology. **Qualif.:** Applicants must be senior neurosurgical residents whose country of study is different from the country of residence in approved neurosurgery residency programs and whose intent is to pursue an academic career in neurological surgery. **Criteria:** Candidates will be evaluated by the Van Wagenen Selection Committee based on the originality and quality of proposal, thoroughness with which the plan for a period abroad has been designed, personal attributes, and the quality of the research environment.

Funds Avail.: $120,000. **To Apply:** Applicants must submit a completed application together with the letter of reference. **Deadline:** May 1.

517 ■ American Association of Neuroscience Nurses (AANN)

4700 W Lake Ave.
Glenview, IL 60025
Ph: (847) 375-4733
Fax: (847) 375-6430
Free: 888-557-2266
E-mail: info@aann.org
URL: www.aann.org

518 ■ Certified Neuroscience Registered Nurse Recertification Grant Program (CNRN) *(Professional development/Grant)*

Purpose: To award financial assistance to nurses seeking recertification as a CNRN during their 5th year after CNRN certification. **Focus:** Neuroscience; Nursing. **Qualif.:** Open to all CNRNs in their 5th year of certification. The applicants must meet the requirements for recertification as delineated by the ABNN. One letter of recommendation from a supervisor in support of applicant is to accompany the application. **Criteria:** Selection will be based on the committee's criteria.

Funds Avail.: $215. **To Apply:** Applicants must provide one complete original (with Form A) and four blinded (no identifying information, such as name, institution name, city, etc. Use generic terms instead), collated copies of the application (without Form A). The Agreement Statement and letter of recommendation should be included with the complete original application. **Deadline:** October 7. **Contact:** For further information, applicants must contact Neuroscience Nursing Foundation (NNF) by calling 509-738-2542 or by e-mail jdmeacham1@gotsky.com.

519 ■ Integra Foundation NNF Research Grant Awards *(Professional development/Grant)*

Purpose: To encourage qualified nurses to contribute to the advancement of neuroscience nursing through research. **Focus:** Neuroscience; Nursing. **Qualif.:** Principal investigator must be a registered nurse. Investigators must be ready to start the research project, or are already in the process of conducting the research, which must be congruent with NNF research priorities and must be significant to neuroscience nursing. **Criteria:** Selection will be based on the quality of the proposed research and the NNF research fund budget.

Funds Avail.: $10,000. **To Apply:** Applicants must submit the following requirements: Application Form - One copy of the application form with all information included, six copies of the application form with all identifying information removed; Investigator Information Form - One copy of investigator information form (Form A) with all information

---

Awards are arranged alphabetically below their administering organizations

included (one for each investigator), six copies of each investigator information form (Form B) for use in blind review; Budget Page - Six copies of the budget page; The Proposal - One copy of the proposal which may include names and identifying information, six additional copies of the proposal without names or identifying information; Local Institution Approval from local institutional review board indicating approval of protection of human participants (if Local institutional approval is pending, submit it when obtained). Study must have been submitted to local review committee prior to the time of application. **Deadline:** July 31. **Contact:** Application form and supporting documents must be sent to Neuroscience Nursing Foundation (NNF) Grant Application Department, 3007 Marx Rd, Rice, WA 99167.

520 ■ NNF Scholarship Program (Graduate, Undergraduate/Scholarship)

Purpose: To promote excellence in neuroscience nursing. **Focus:** Neuroscience; Nursing. **Qualif.:** Applicants must be registered nurses pursuing a career in neuroscience nursing at the undergraduate or graduate level. **Criteria:** Selection will be based on the committee's criteria.

Funds Avail.: $1,500. **To Apply:** Applications must be typed or word-processed. The application is available at the NNF website, www.aann.org. Complete all information as requested. Incomplete applications will not be considered and will be returned to the applicants. School which the applicant attends, or plans to attend must be accredited. Submit one copy of Form A, four copies of Form B (including personal statement).

521 ■ American Association of Occupational Health Nurses (AAOHN)

7794 Grow Dr.
Pensacola, FL 32514
Ph: (850) 474-6963
Fax: (850) 484-8762
Free: 800-241-8014
E-mail: aaohn@aaohn.org
URL: www.aaohn.org

522 ■ AAOHN Professional Development Scholarships - Academic Study (Graduate, Undergraduate/Scholarship)

Purpose: To provide opportunities to further professional education for occupational and environment health professionals. **Focus:** Occupational safety and health. **Qualif.:** Undergraduate candidate must be a registered nurse enrolled full or part time in a nationally accredited school of nursing baccalaureate program and demonstrate an interest in, and commitment to, occupational and environmental health. Graduate candidate must be a registered nurse enrolled full or part time in a graduate program that has application to occupational and environmental health. Applicants must submit documentation of enrollment status. **Criteria:** Selection will be based on the committee's criteria.

Funds Avail.: $2,500. **Number Awarded:** 2. **To Apply:** Applicants must submit a 500 word or less narrative (double-spaced with one-inch margins in 12-point font) addressing: professional goals as they pertain to academic activity and the field of occupational and environmental health; impact of education on career. Completed application must be emailed to tracy.goodbred@dancyamc.com. **Deadline:** January 6.

523 ■ AAOHN Professional Development Scholarships - Continuing Education (Professional development/Scholarship)

Purpose: To support occupational and environmental health professionals in attending and successfully completing continuing education activities. **Focus:** Occupational safety and health. **Qualif.:** Candidates must be employed in the field of occupational and environmental health nursing and demonstrate an interest in, and commitment to, occupational and environmental health. **Criteria:** Selection will be based on the committee's criteria.

Funds Avail.: $1,000-$1,500. **Number Awarded:** 4. **To Apply:** Applicants must submit a 500 word or less narrative (double-spaced with one-inch margins in 12-point font) addressing: career goals as they pertain to applicant's professional development and continued competence; how continuing education will further applicant's goals; need for financial support; commitment to ongoing continuing education activities. Applicants must also submit a letter of support from their employer/supervisor and copy of continuing education activity brochure or other printed information describing the activity. Completed application must be emailed to tracy.goodbred@dancyamc.com. **Deadline:** January 6.

524 ■ Leadership Development Scholarships (Professional development/Scholarship)

Purpose: To support volunteer leadership development in occupational and environmental health nursing. **Focus:** Occupational safety and health. **Qualif.:** Candidates must be employed in the field of occupational and environmental health nursing and demonstrate an interest in, and commitment to, occupational and environmental health **Criteria:** Selection will be based on the committee's criteria.

Funds Avail.: $1,000. **To Apply:** This scholarship is to be applied to leadership development activity/program registration, travel and/or associated travel-related expenses. Types of activities that will be considered for funding include the AAOHN Conference of Leaders, Nurse in Washington Internship Program, mentoring development program, etc. Applicant must submit a 500-word or less narrative (double-spaced with one-inch margins in 12-point font) addressing: why the applicant considers him/herself an emerging leader in volunteer service; leadership skills applicant would develop by participating in the selected leadership development activity/program; how learned skills will be applied serving in a volunteer leadership role within the profession of occupational and environment health nursing; quality/relevance of leadership development activity/program to stated goals. Applicants must also submit a letter of support from employer/supervisor. **Deadline:** August 1. **Contact:** Don Bollmer, Dir. of Business Affairs, at the above address.

525 ■ American Association for Paralegal Education (AAFPE)

19 Mantua Rd.
Mount Royal, NJ 08061
Ph: (856) 423-2829
Fax: (856) 423-3420
E-mail: info@aafpe.org
URL: www.aafpe.org

526 ■ AAFPE LEX Scholarships (Undergraduate/Scholarship)

Purpose: To help students pursue their education in legal studies. **Focus:** Paralegal studies. **Qualif.:** Applicants must

---

Awards are arranged alphabetically below their administering organizations

be full or part-time students who have a LEX chapter. **Criteria:** Applicants will be evaluated based on submitted materials.

Funds Avail.: $500. **Number Awarded:** 3 to 5. **To Apply:** Candidates must submit a completed LEX application form with a 500-word essay; transcript of records showing at least "B" average; and a letter of recommendation from a faculty member in the paralegal or legal assistant studies department of the qualifying institution. **Deadline:** February 29.

527 ■ American Association of Physicists in Medicine (AAPM)

1 Physics Ellipse
College Park, MD 20740
Ph: (301) 209-3350
Fax: (301) 209-0862
E-mail: 2011.aapm@aapm.org
URL: www.aapm.org/default.asp

528 ■ AAPM Fellowships for Graduate Study in Medical Physics *(Graduate/Fellowship)*

Purpose: To support students pursuing graduate studies leading to a doctoral degree in Medical Physics. **Focus:** Physics. **Qualif.:** Applicants must be graduates of an undergraduate program in physics or equivalent majors (engineering-physics, math-physics, or nuclear engineering or applied physics) from an accredited university or college in North America; have an undergraduate GPA of greater than 3.5; and must have submitted an application for graduate study to one of the accredited programs with subsequent acceptance. **Criteria:** Selection is based on the submitted application and materials.

Funds Avail.: $13,000/year plus tuition support not exceeding $5,000/year. **To Apply:** Applicants must submit a completed application form. **Contact:** Jackie Ogburn at 301-209-3394 or jackie@aapm.org.

529 ■ AAPM Minority Undergraduate Summer Experience Fellowships (MUSE) *(Undergraduate/Fellowship)*

Purpose: To expose minority undergraduate university students to the field of medical physics by performing research or assisting with clinical service at a U.S. institutions. **Focus:** Physics. **Qualif.:** Applicant must have completed at least 2 years of undergraduate studies, but shall not have graduated; must be a U.S. citizen, permanent resident, or eligible to live and work in the U.S. Non-citizens and non-permanent residents must provide evidence at the time of application (e.g. visas and permits issued by INS) that they are authorized to work in the USA during the period of the fellowship. **Criteria:** Preference will be made to applicants who have declared a major or are eligible to declare a major in physics, engineering, or other science, which requires mathematics at least through differential equations and junior level courses in modern physics/ quantum mechanics and electricity and magnetism or equivalent courses in engineering sciences.

Funds Avail.: $4,500. **Number Awarded:** 6. **To Apply:** Applicant must complete the AAPM-provided student application and all required supplementary information. **Contact:** Jacqueline Ogburn at 301-209-3394 or jackie@ aapm.org.

530 ■ AAPM Summer Undergraduate Fellowships *(Undergraduate/Fellowship)*

Purpose: To provide opportunities for undergraduate university students to gain experience in medical physics by performing research in a medical physics laboratory or assisting with clinical service at a clinical facility. **Focus:** Physics; Mathematics and mathematical sciences. **Qualif.:** Applicant must have completed at least 2 years of undergraduate studies, but shall not have graduated; have declared a major or be eligible to declare a major in physics, engineering, or other science, which requires mathematics at least through differential equations and junior level courses in modern physics/quantum mechanics and electricity and magnetism or equivalent courses in engineering sciences; and must be a U.S. citizen, permanent resident, or eligible to live and work in the U.S. Non-citizens and non-permanent residents must provide evidence at the time of application (e.g. visas and permits issued by INS) that they are authorized to work in the USA during the period of the fellowship. **Criteria:** Selection is based on the submitted application and materials.

Funds Avail.: $4,000. **To Apply:** Applicants must submit a completed application form and materials. **Contact:** Jacqueline Ogburn at 301-209-3394 or jackie@aapm.org.

531 ■ RSNA/AAPM Fellowships for Graduate Study in Medical Physics *(Graduate/Fellowship)*

Purpose: To support students pursuing graduate studies leading to a doctoral degree in Medical Physics. **Focus:** Physics. **Qualif.:** Applicant must be a graduate of an undergraduate program in physics or equivalent major from an accredited university or college in North America; have an undergraduate GPA of greater than 3.5; and must have submitted an application for graduate study at one of the accredited programs with subsequent acceptance. **Criteria:** Selection is based on the submitted application and materials.

Funds Avail.: $13,000/year plus tuition support not exceeding $5,000/year. **To Apply:** Applicants must submit a completed application form together with all post-secondary study transcripts; Graduate Record Exam results; two or three reference letters; and acceptance letter from the intended AAPM Accredited Program. **Contact:** Jacqueline Ogburn at 301-209-3394 or jackie@aapm.org.

532 ■ American Association of Physics Teachers (AAPT)

1 Physics Ellipse
College Park, MD 20740-3845
Ph: (301) 209-3311
Fax: (301) 209-0845
E-mail: eo@aapt.org
URL: www.aapt.org

533 ■ Barbara Lotze Scholarships for Future Teachers *(Undergraduate/Scholarship)*

Purpose: To provide scholarships for future high school physics teachers. **Focus:** Physics. **Qualif.:** Applicants must be U.S. citizens attending U.S. schools. Undergraduate students who are enrolled or planning to enroll in physics teacher preparation curricula or high school seniors entering such programs are eligible to apply. **Criteria:** Recipients are selected based on merit.

Funds Avail.: $2,000. **Number Awarded:** 2. **To Apply:** Applicants must submit a completed application form; transcripts of all relevant academic works; a letter to the Scholarship Committee; and proof of U.S. citizenship. **Deadline:** December 1.

Awards are arranged alphabetically below their administering organizations

534 ■ American Association of Plastic Surgeons (AAPS)

500 Cummings Ctr., Ste. 4550
Beverly, MA 01915
Ph: (978) 927-8330
Fax: (978) 524-8890
URL: www.aaps1921.org

535 ■ American Association of Plastic Surgeons Academic Scholars Program
(Graduate/Grant)

Purpose: To assist surgeons in establishing a new and independent research program. **Focus:** Plastic surgery. **Qualif.:** Applicants must be plastic and reconstructive surgeons who have: (1) completed the chief residency year within the preceding five years; and (2) received a full-time faculty appointment in a department of surgery/plastic surgery at a medical school accredited by the Liaison Committee on Graduate Medical Education in the United States or by the Committee for Accreditation of Canadian Medical Schools in Canada. **Criteria:** Applicants who are not current recipients of major research grants are given preference.

Funds Avail.: $30,000. **To Apply:** Applicants must complete application online; must submit the research plan and budget; and supporting letters from the Chair of the Department/Division of Plastic Surgery. **Deadline:** November 1.

536 ■ American Association of Poison Control Centers

515 King St., Ste. 510
Alexandria, VA 22314
Ph: (703) 894-1858
Fax: (703) 683-2812
Free: 800-222-1222
E-mail: info@aapcc.org
URL: www.aapcc.org

537 ■ Clinical Toxicology Fellowships
(Doctorate/Fellowship)

Purpose: To train doctors of pharmacy graduates to function in a professional, administrative and research capacity. **Focus:** Toxicology. **Qualif.:** Applicants must possess a Pharm.D. degree from accredited schools or College of Pharmacy. **Criteria:** Selection will be based on the committee's review of application materials.

Funds Avail.: No specific amount. **To Apply:** Applicants must submit letters of reference; and letters of application with curriculum vitae attached. **Contact:** Wendy Klein-Scwartz.

538 ■ American Association of Police Polygraphists (AAPP)

PO Box 657
Waynesville, OH 45068-0657
Fax: (937) 488-1046
Free: 888-743-5479
E-mail: nom@policepolygraph.org
URL: www.policepolygraph.org

539 ■ William "Buddy" Sentner Scholarship Awards *(Undergraduate/Scholarship)*

Purpose: To provide financial assistance for deserving graduating high school senior or student currently attending college. **Focus:** General studies. **Qualif.:** Applicants must be graduating high school seniors or currently attending college; must be the children, grandchildren, nieces, nephews, adopted or dependents of an AAPP member; or have at least one parent, grandparent and other legal guardian who is a full, life, or honorably retired member. Applicants who have a deceased member will be accepted as long as he/she was in good standing with the AAPP at the time of death. **Criteria:** Recipients are selected based on Selection Committee's review of the application materials.

Funds Avail.: Scholarship amount not specified. **To Apply:** Applicants must submit a completed application form; a recent official transcript of all courses and grades; and two character reference letters (from current institution's faculty and from a non-relative). Completed application package must be sent to the AAPP's Office. **Deadline:** February 15.

540 ■ American Association of Professional Apiculturists (AAPA)

College of Agriculture
Atwood Research Facility
400 E Main St.
Frankfort, KY 40601
Ph: (502) 597-6351
Fax: (502) 597-6551
E-mail: thomas.webster@kysu.edu
URL: www.masterbeekeeper.org/aapa

541 ■ American Association of Professional Apiculturists Research Scholarships *(Graduate, Undergraduate/Scholarship)*

Purpose: To recognize and promote outstanding research by students in the field of apiculture. **Focus:** Entomology. **Qualif.:** Applicants must be undergraduate or graduate students working in North America with completed research on Apis; must be active AAPA members. **Criteria:** Award Committee will review proposals and rank them to the top three. Ranks will be based on scientific merit, presentation, originality and the overall value of the work within the field of apiculture.

Funds Avail.: $1,000. **To Apply:** Research proposal package must include a curriculum vitae of the nominee, one letter of recommendation, and a summary of the research problem not exceeding three pages including: objectives, significance, and methods. Nominees may also include: up to three publication reprints, submitted manuscripts or abstracts of theses or dissertations. Four copies of the proposal package should be sent to the Chair of the AAPA Student Award Committee at least one month prior to the annual meeting.

542 ■ American Association of Railroad Superintendents (AARS)

PO Box 200
LaFox, IL 60147-0200
Ph: (630) 762-0754
Fax: (630) 762-0755
E-mail: aars@railroadsuperintendents.org
URL: www.railroadsuperintendents.org

543 ■ Frank J. Richter Scholarships *(Graduate, Undergraduate/Scholarship)*

Purpose: To support the education of students enrolled at an accredited college or university in the U.S. or Canada.

Awards are arranged alphabetically below their administering organizations

Focus: Transportation. **Qualif.:** Applicant must be enrolled full-time undergraduate or graduate student at an accredited college or university; demonstrated successful completion of the previous year's study by maintaining at least a 2.75 accumulated GPA on a scale of 1 to 4 with an "A" equal to 4; have accumulate enough credits from accredited schools in time for the Fall Semester to have obtained at least a sophomore level standing at the college or university of enrollment. **Criteria:** Preference will be given to applicants enrolled in the transportation field and all applicants will be considered.

Funds Avail.: $1,000. **To Apply:** Applicants must submit a completed application form together with an official transcript from the schools attended; and two letters of recommendation. The application and narrative statement are to be submitted in one envelope. The transcripts and letters of recommendation must be sent directly to AARS from the appropriate person. **Deadline:** July 1.

544 ■ American Association of School Administrators. (AASA)

1615 Duke St.
Arlington, VA 22203-1730
Ph: (703) 528-0700
Fax: (703) 841-1543
E-mail: info@aasa.org
URL: www.aasa.org

545 ■ Educational Administration Scholarship Awards *(Postgraduate/Scholarship)*

Purpose: To provide incentive, honor and financial assistance for outstanding graduate students in school administration intending to make school superintendency a career. **Focus:** General studies. **Qualif.:** Applicants must be recommended by the chair of the school of education in which the applicant is currently enrolled. Only one application may be submitted from each college or university campus. **Criteria:** Recipients are selected based on academic performance.

Funds Avail.: $2,500. **To Apply:** Applicants must submit completed application form available on the website; a declaration of mission consisting of no more than three separate statements (single-spaced, typewritten) addressing the following: an account of how you came to be interested in school administration, what you conceive the job of a school superintendent to be, what aspects of it chiefly appeal to you, what type of contribution you would like to make in this field, the particular kind of further training and experience which you believe most essential to your best performance, and how you would apply a scholarship toward achieving your professional goals; a succinct statement of an administrative problem you have already encountered, a description of how you met it, and what, on reflection, you wish you had done about it. If you have had no administrative experience, select a problem in the field of classroom teaching or of student activities or discipline; no more than two paragraphs in which you describe specific instances in your training and experience which highlight your individual strengths and focus on your successes. These paragraphs should help the reader know you as an administrator; also submit a letter of recommendation (one original and five photocopies) from the dean of the school of education where applicant is currently enrolled; and letters of endorsement. **Deadline:** July 30. **Contact:** Kay Dillon at kdillon@aasa.org; 703-875-0761.

546 ■ Stop Hunger Scholarships *(Undergraduate/Scholarship)*

Purpose: To recognize students involved in the fight against hunger in America. **Focus:** General studies. **Qualif.:** Applicants must be enrolled in an accredited education institution (kindergarten through college) in the United States; and must have demonstrated ongoing commitment to their community by performing volunteer services impacting hunger in the United States at least within the last 12 months. **Criteria:** Recipients are selected based on academic performance.

Funds Avail.: $3,000. **Number Awarded:** 5. **To Apply:** Applicants and nominators must supply a valid e-mail address; applicants must submit a completed application form.

547 ■ American Association of School Personnel Administrators (AASPA)

11863 W 112th St., Ste. 100
Overland Park, KS 66210
Ph: (913) 327-1222
Fax: (913) 327-1223
E-mail: aaspa@aaspa.org
URL: www.aaspa.org

548 ■ Leon Bradley Scholarships *(Undergraduate/Scholarship)*

Purpose: To assist minorities seeking their initial teaching certification and/or endorsement. **Focus:** Teaching. **Qualif.:** Applicants must be minority college students such as: American Indians, Asian or Pacific Islanders, Black or Hispanic Americans; must be in their final year of student teaching or teaching preparation; must have at least 3.0 GPA; and must reside and currently be enrolled in schools in the following states or provinces: Connecticut, Delaware, Maine, Maryland, Massachusetts, New Brunswick, Newfoundland, New Hampshire, New Jersey, New York, Nova Scotia, Pennsylvania, Prince Edward Island, Quebec, Rhode Island, Vermont, or West Virginia. **Criteria:** Selection will be based on the submitted application materials.

Funds Avail.: $2,000 for student who is taking the student teaching program; $1,000 for student who is taking the teaching preparation program. **Number Awarded:** 2. **To Apply:** Applicants must complete an application form available in website. **Deadline:** April 13. **Contact:** Mail application and supporting documents to Sandy Tonkin, Professional Development Coordinator at the above address or e-mail at sandy@aaspa.org for further information.

549 ■ American Association of State Troopers (AAST)

1949 Raymond Diehl Rd.
Tallahassee, FL 32308
Ph: (850) 385-7904
Fax: (850) 385-8697
Free: 800-765-5456
E-mail: ada@statetroopers.org
URL: www.statetroopers.org

550 ■ American Association of State Troopers Scholarship Foundation First Scholarships *(Undergraduate/Scholarship)*

Purpose: To provide financial assistance for the education of students who are dependents of the members of

---

Awards are arranged alphabetically below their administering organizations

American Association of State Troopers, Inc. **Focus:** Law enforcement. **Qualif.:** Applicants must be high school or college students who are sons or daughters of a trooper by natural birth, legal adoption, step child, or legal guardian. **Criteria:** Applicants will be evaluated based on academic performance and financial need.

Funds Avail.: $500. **To Apply:** Applicants must submit an official transcript indicating a minimum 2.5 GPA (4.0 scale) at an accredited school; for high school students: final four-year high school transcripts; for college students: a current official college transcripts indicating all grades earned through the current year which he or she is applying for; letter of acceptance from an accredited college, state university or community college for the academic year; a 500-word, typed essay entitled, "How my Education Will Advance My Career Plans"; and a small photo attached to the bottom of the application as indicated. **Deadline:** July 31. **Contact:** Joan Breeding, joan@statetroopers.org.

551 ■ American Association of State Troopers Scholarship Foundation Second Scholarships
(Undergraduate/Scholarship)

Purpose: To provide financial assistance for the education of students who are dependents of the members of American Association of State Troopers, Inc. **Focus:** Law enforcement. **Qualif.:** Applicants must be high school or college students who are sons or daughters of trooper members by natural birth, legal adoption, step child, or legal guardian. **Criteria:** Applicants will be evaluated based on academic performance and financial need.

Funds Avail.: $1,000. **To Apply:** Applicants must submit an original and official transcript indicating the minimum 3.5 GPA (4.0 scale) maintained during the fall through spring semesters for which the scholarship award was granted; a letter or registration notice as proof of enrollment for the academic year; and a small photo attached to the bottom of the application as indicated. **Deadline:** July 31. **Contact:** Joan Breeding, joan@statetroopers.org.

552 ■ V.J. Johnson Memorial Scholarships
(Undergraduate/Scholarship)

Purpose: To provide financial assistance to a student who intends to use his or her education to pursue a career in law enforcement. **Focus:** Law enforcement. **Qualif.:** Applicants must be high school or college students who are sons or a daughters of trooper members by natural birth, legal adoption, step child, or legal guardian (in Florida only). **Criteria:** Recipients are selected based on academic performance and financial need.

Funds Avail.: $1,500. **Number Awarded:** 1. **To Apply:** Applicants must submit an original and official transcript indicating the minimum of 3.8 GPA (4.0 scale) maintained during the fall through spring semesters for which the second scholarship award was granted; a letter or registration notice as proof of enrollment for the academic year; a 500-word, typed essay entitled, "How my Education Will Advance My Plans for a Career in Law Enforcement"; and a small photo attached to the bottom of the application as indicated. **Deadline:** July 31. **Contact:** Joan Breeding, joan@statetroopers.org.

553 ■ American Association for the Surgery of Trauma (AAST)
633 N St. Clair St., Ste. 2600
Chicago, IL 60611
Ph: (312) 202-5252

Fax: (312) 202-5064
Free: 800-789-4006
E-mail: aast@aast.org
URL: www.aast.org

554 ■ AAST/ACS/NIGMS Scholarships *(Professional development/Scholarship)*

Purpose: To facilitate the career development of individuals pursuing careers in trauma surgery research. **Focus:** Surgery. **Qualif.:** Applicants must be surgeon-scientists working in the early stages of their research careers; must be members in good standing of the ACS and eligible for membership in AAST. **Criteria:** Recipients are selected based on the committee's review of application materials.

Funds Avail.: $75,000. **To Apply:** Applicants must submit K08 or K23 application simultaneously to NIGMS and ACS Scholarship administrators. **Deadline:** October 12. **Contact:** kearly@facs.org.

555 ■ AAST/KCI Research Grants *(All/Grant)*

Purpose: To sponsor clinical research in the area of wound care. **Focus:** Surgery. **Qualif.:** Program is open to individuals intending to conduct clinical research in the area of wound care only. **Criteria:** Recipients are selected based on the Scholarship Committee's review of application materials.

Funds Avail.: $50,000. **To Apply:** Applicants must submit a completed application form including curriculum vitae, bibliography and research proposals. Applicants are also required to submit one typed original copy of the application form and four 3-hole punched photocopies. **Deadline:** February 1. **Contact:** Robert C. Mackersie, M.D., AAST Sec.-Treas., Phone: 415-206-4622; Fax: 415-206-5484.

556 ■ AAST Medical Student Scholarships *(All/Scholarship)*

Purpose: To sponsor medical research in the fields of burns, trauma and acute care surgery. **Focus:** Surgery. **Qualif.:** Program is open for medical students who attend the AAST annual meeting. **Criteria:** Recipients are selected based on the Scholarship Committee's review of application materials.

Funds Avail.: $200 stipend for food/misc items. **To Apply:** Applicants must submit letters of recommendation and curriculum vitae to L. D. Britt, MD, MPH. **Deadline:** June 1. **Contact:** Tamara Jenkins, tjenkins@aast.org; L. D. Britt, MD, MPH, Chair, Scholarship Committee, 633 N Saint Clair St., Suite 2600, Chicago, IL 60611.

557 ■ Local Wound Haemostatics and Hemorrhage Control Scholarships *(All/Scholarship)*

Purpose: To support post residency research of surgeons with a major commitment in trauma surgery. **Focus:** Surgery. **Qualif.:** Program is open for individuals intending to conduct clinical research in the areas of hemeostasis and resuscitation only; must have commitment to trauma surgery academic research. **Criteria:** Recipients are selected based on the Scholarship Committee's review of application materials.

Funds Avail.: $50,000. **To Apply:** Applicants must submit a completed application form including curriculum vitae, bibliography and research proposals. Applicants are also required to submit one typed original copy of the application form and 4 3-hole punched photocopies. Submit completed application to Robert C. Mackersie, M.D., AAST Sec.-Treas., Trauma/Critical Care, UCSF-San Francisco

Awards are arranged alphabetically below their administering organizations

Gen. Hospital, 1001 Potrero Ave., Ward 3A, San Francisco, CA 94110. **Deadline:** February 1. **Contact:** Robert C. Mackersie, M.D., AAST Sec.-Treas., Phone: 415-206-4622; Fax: 415-206-5484.

558 ■ American Association of Textile Chemists and Colorists (AATCC)

PO Box 12215
Research Triangle Park, NC 27709-2215
Ph: (919) 549-8141
Fax: (919) 549-8933
E-mail: danielsj@aatcc.org
URL: www.aatcc.org

559 ■ Charles H. Stone Scholarships
(Undergraduate/Scholarship)

Purpose: To provide financial assistance to juniors or senior students who reside in NC, SC, VA or WV and attend North Carolina State University or Clemson University. **Focus:** Textile science. **Qualif.:** Applicants must be U.S. citizens; juniors or senior students in an undergraduate program; must have minimum GPA of 2.85 on a 4.0 scale; must be Textile Chemistry undergraduates in Dyeing/Fiber Science/Polymers/Color Science; must be Piedmont Section Textile employees. **Criteria:** Recipients are selected based on extracurricular activities; employment experience and financial need.

Funds Avail.: $5,000. **Number Awarded:** 4. **To Apply:** Applicants must submit all the required application information.

560 ■ American Association for Thoracic Surgery (AATS)

900 Cummings Ctr., Ste. 221-U
Beverly, MA 01915
Ph: (978) 927-8330
Fax: (978) 524-8890
URL: www.aats.org

561 ■ Advanced Cardiovascular Surgery Fellowships *(Graduate, Postdoctorate/Fellowship)*

Purpose: To provide exposure in the field of advanced cardiovascular surgery. **Focus:** Medicine. **Qualif.:** Applicants must have already successfully completed an approved thoracic surgery residency or its equivalent and desire an additional one or two years to supplement their training in cardiothoracic surgery. **Criteria:** Priority is given to applicants who passed the United States Medical Licensing Examination (USMLE) or the former Foreign Medical Graduate Exam in the Medical Sciences (FMGEMS) and the ECFMG English examination.

Funds Avail.: No specific amount. **To Apply:** Applicants must submit: completed online application; curriculum vitae; personal statement of professional goals; copy of graduate school and or medical/dental school diploma. Postdoctoral fellowship applications includes: official transcripts; three letters of recommendation from faculty members. Other residency and fellowship program applications includes: dean's letter; official transcripts; official test transcripts for all applicable examinations; valid ECFMG certificate; three original letters of recommendation. **Deadline:** December 31. **Contact:** Carla MacLean, 507-255-702-69.

562 ■ Edward D. Churchill Research Scholarships *(Professional development/Scholarship)*

Purpose: To provide an opportunity for research, training and experience for North American surgeons committed to pursuing academic career in cardiothoracic surgery. **Focus:** Medicine. **Qualif.:** Applicants must be in the final year of cardiothoracic residency or in their first two years in an academic position. **Criteria:** Recipients are selected based on the submitted research proposals.

Funds Avail.: $80,000. **To Apply:** Applicants must submit a proposal for the research; and a statement of career plans and how the research activity will relate to the applicant's academic career. **Deadline:** July 1. **Remarks:** The scholarship will be funded by the Association and administered by the Graham Education and Research Foundation.

563 ■ Summer Intern Scholarships in Cardiothoracic Surgery *(Undergraduate/Scholarship)*

Purpose: To introduce the field of cardiothoracic surgery. **Focus:** Medicine. **Qualif.:** Applicants must have the approval of the prospective sponsoring institutions; must be a member of the AATS; must be first or second-year medical students. **Criteria:** Recipients are selected based on the committee's review of application materials.

Funds Avail.: $2,500. **To Apply:** Applicants must complete an online application and include a one-page outline of what they hope to accomplish during their eight weeks internship. Applicants must also submit a letter of support from the host sponsor. **Deadline:** January 15. **Remarks:** Established in 2007.

564 ■ American Association for Women in Community Colleges (AAWCC)

PO Box 3098
Gaithersburg, MD 20885
Ph: (301) 442-3374
E-mail: info@aawccnatl.org
URL: www.aawccnatl.org

565 ■ American Association for Women in Community Colleges Regional Scholarships *(Undergraduate/Scholarship)*

Purpose: To help students maximize their potential. **Focus:** General studies. **Qualif.:** Applicants must be currently enrolled. **Criteria:** Recipients will be selected based on submitted application.

Funds Avail.: $500. **Number Awarded:** 10. **To Apply:** Applicants are advised to contact the Regional Director of Mercer County Community College for the application form and other required documents. **Deadline:** March 2. **Contact:** Application form and supporting documents must be sent to: Ms. Beverly Walker-Griffea, AAWCC Vice President for Resource and Development, 757-825-3810 or e-mail at walkergriffeab@tncc.edu.

566 ■ American Association for Women in Community Colleges Scholarship Leaders Institute *(Professional development/Scholarship)*

Purpose: To support the advancement of community college women into leadership positions. **Focus:** General studies. **Qualif.:** Applicants must be faculty members who work in a community college. **Criteria:** Selection of recipients will be based on commitment to AAWCC, leadership plans, and the endorsement of a mentor from their home institution.

Funds Avail.: $3,000 including registration fee and travel expenses. **To Apply:** Applicants must complete the application form available at the website. **Deadline:** March

Awards are arranged alphabetically below their administering organizations

31. **Contact:** Applications should be sent to: Dr. Barbara L. Tower, 7201 Rossville Blvd., Baltimore, MD 21237.

567 ■ American Astronomical Society (AAS)

2000 Florida Ave. NW, Ste. 400
Washington, DC 20009-1231
Ph: (202) 328-2010
Fax: (202) 234-2560
E-mail: aas@aas.org
URL: www.aas.org

568 ■ American Astronomical Society Small Research Grants *(Doctorate/Grant)*

Purpose: To promote research related to astronomy. **Focus:** Astronomy and astronomical sciences. **Qualif.:** Applicant must be a U.S. citizen or foreign astronomer with Ph.D. or equivalent and must not be connected to the institution. **Criteria:** Recipients are evaluated based on: scientific merit, student participation, budget, other funds available for the proposed project.

Funds Avail.: $500-$7,000. **Number Awarded:** 2. **To Apply:** Applicants must submit the proposal (maximum of four pages); curriculum vitae (maximum of two pages); and a cover letter. Send four copies of the proposal and must mail a hardcopy of the cover page. **Deadline:** May 7 and November 28. **Contact:** Application form and a hard copy of the proposal's cover page must be submitted to Rick Fienberg at the above address, content of the proposal may send electronically at rick.fienberg@aas.org.

569 ■ Annie J. Cannon Awards in Astronomy *(Doctorate/Award)*

Purpose: To fund outstanding research and promise for future research by a postdoctoral woman researcher. **Focus:** Astronomy and astronomical sciences. **Qualif.:** Applicants must be North American female astronomers within five years of receiving their PhD in the year designated for the award. **Criteria:** Selection will be based on the committee's criteria.

Funds Avail.: $1,500. **To Apply:** Nominators should request that the nominee submit a research plan of no more than three pages describing their anticipated course of work for the next five years. The plan should be broadly accessible to astronomers with a range of scientific interests. **Contact:** aassec@aas.org.

570 ■ Chambliss Astronomy Achievement Student Awards *(Undergraduate, Graduate/Award)*

Purpose: To recognized exemplary research by undergraduate and graduate students who present at one of the poster sessions at the meetings of the AAS. **Focus:** Astronomy and astronomical sciences. **Qualif.:** Participants must be undergraduate and graduate students and must be members of the AAS. **Criteria:** Judging criteria are based on presentation and content, weighted so that content is 60% of the score.

Funds Avail.: No specific amount. **To Apply:** Work must have been done while the presenters were undergraduate or graduate students. Participants must submit the correct abstract form indicating that the poster is being submitted for consideration for the award. Participants must be present at their posters at the scheduled judging time to be eligible.

571 ■ Chretien International Research Grants *(Doctorate, Professional development/Grant)*

Purpose: To promote research or projects related to astronomy. **Focus:** Astronomy and astronomical sciences. **Qualif.:** Applicants must be astronomers with PhD or equivalent. **Criteria:** Recipients are selected based on submitted proposals. Decisions will be made on the basis of quality research; importance of the proposed research to the international astronomy; ability of the applicant to carry out the research; and prudence of the budget estimates. Letters of reference will greatly affect the committee's decision. Preference will be given to individuals of high promise who are otherwise unfunded.

Funds Avail.: $20,000. **Number Awarded:** Varies. **To Apply:** Applicants must submit a description of research (maximum of three pages); a statement on the applicant's ability to finish the project; a proposed budget; description of other financial resources (if applicable); curriculum vitae and bibliography of recent papers; two reference letters from astronomers who know the applicant's work; other circumstances that might help in the selection process. **Deadline:** April 1. **Contact:** Application form and all supporting materials should be submitted electronically to Kelly Clark at grants@aas.org.

572 ■ Rodger Doxsey Travel Prizes *(Graduate, Postdoctorate/Prize)*

Purpose: To provide graduate students or postdocs within one year of receiving or receipt of their PhD a monetary prize to enable the oral presentation of their dissertation research at a meeting of the AAS. **Focus:** Astronomy and astronomical sciences. **Qualif.:** Applicants must be graduate students or postdocs; must be planning to present their dissertation research at a meeting of the AAS in the form of an oral dissertation talk; must be attending a North American university or have recently graduated from a North American university. **Criteria:** Selection will be based on the scientific merit of the dissertation research of the PhD.

Funds Avail.: No specific amount. **To Apply:** Applicants must submit their abstract by the "on-time" abstract submission deadline. Advisors of the applicants must submit a letter indicating that the applicant is within one year of receiving or receipt of the PhD. **Deadline:** October 1.

573 ■ American Australian Association (AAA)

50 Broadway, Ste. 2003
New York, NY 10004
Ph: (212) 338-6860
Fax: (212) 338-6864
E-mail: information@aaanyc.org
URL: www.americanaustralian.org

574 ■ American Australian Association Neurological Fellowships *(Graduate/Fellowship)*

Purpose: To provide financial support to students registered in a program of study and research focused on neurology. **Focus:** Neurology. **Qualif.:** Applicant must be an Australian citizen or permanent resident of Australia; must be a neurosurgeon or neurosurgeon-in-training educated/training at an Australian University; must intend to devote full time to research or study and be fluent in English; must be supported by their Program Director and Chairman. **Criteria:** Applications will be reviewed by the Association's Chairman, and a panel of appointed judges

Awards are arranged alphabetically below their administering organizations

based on the following criteria: (1) Quality of proposed research/study of neuroscience/surgery. Applicants should display intellect, vision and innovation. (2) Candidate's ability to communicate clearly and concisely to a Selection Committee which may or may not have formal training in subject matter. (3) Clarity, specificity and feasibility of educational/research goals. (4) Neurosurgery Residents must have support of their Program Director. (5) Practicing Neurosurgeons must have support of their Chairman.

Funds Avail.: $25,000 to cover travel, living and some project related expenses. **To Apply:** Applicants must complete the application form available on the website; must submit three professional/academic references, including one from their program director at home school/ hospital, limited to 1,000 words; must prepare essays regarding with their career plans and aspirations (limit 300 words), statement of purpose (limit 1,200 words), and other interests (limit 50 words). **Deadline:** April 15. **Contact:** Applications may submit via email to diane.sinclair@ aaanyc.org.

575 ■ Morgan Stanley Pediatrics Fellowships (Doctorate, Postdoctorate/Fellowship)

Purpose: To support Australian or American researchers who wish to conduct research in pediatrics at a top U.S. or Australian educational or research institution. **Focus:** Medicine; Early childhood education. **Qualif.:** Applicant must be an Australian citizen or permanent resident; must be conducting post-graduate or post-doctoral research in the area of medicine particularly with a focus on early childhood. **Criteria:** Selection will be based on the committee's criteria.

Funds Avail.: $25,000. **To Apply:** Application form may be obtained online at www.americanaustralian.org. Applicant must submit a completed application form, budget for the research/study period, essays and letters of reference. **Deadline:** April 15. **Contact:** leizel.vergara@aaanyc.org.

576 ■ American Bar Foundation (ABF)
750 N Lake Shore Dr., 4th Fl.
Chicago, IL 60611-4403
Ph: (312) 988-6500
Fax: (312) 988-6579
E-mail: fellows@abfn.org
URL: www.americanbarfoundation.org/index.html

577 ■ ABF Doctoral Fellowships (Doctorate, Graduate/Fellowship)

Purpose: To encourage original and significant research on law, the legal profession, and legal institutions. **Focus:** Law. **Qualif.:** Applicant must be a Doctoral or Post-Doctoral candidate in social sciences; have completed all doctoral requirements except the dissertation; or students who will complete their dissertation prior to the beginning of the award. Research must be in the general area of socio-legal studies or in social scientific approaches to law. Dissertations must address issues in the field and show major contribution to social scientific understanding of law and legal process. **Criteria:** Selection is based on the submitted dissertation abstract or proposal.

Funds Avail.: $27,000. **To Apply:** Applicants must submit a dissertation abstract or proposal; two letters of reference; a curriculum vitae; a transcript of graduate records; and a short sample of written work (optional). **Deadline:** December 15. **Contact:** Kathryn Harris, Admin. Associate for

Academic Affairs and Research at 312-988-6515 or kharris@abfn.org.

578 ■ Law and Social Science Dissertation Fellowship and Mentoring Program (Doctorate, Graduate/Fellowship)

Purpose: To promote education in Law and Social Sciences. **Focus:** Law; Social sciences. **Qualif.:** Applicant must be a U.S. citizen and permanent resident; a third year or fourth year graduate student in the field of law and social science; a student in a PhD program in a social science department; or humanities student pursuing a dissertation with relation to social science. **Criteria:** Selection is based on the application.

Funds Avail.: $27,000 and $1,500 for research and travel expenses. **To Apply:** Applicants must submit a 1-2 page application; a 2-3 page description of research project; a resume or curriculum vitae; a writing sample; three letters of recommendation from faculty members; and undergraduate and graduate transcripts. A complete set of application materials must be sent. **Deadline:** December 1. **Contact:** Laura Beth Nielsen, lnielsen@abfn.org.

579 ■ Summer Research Diversity Fellowships in Law and Social Science (Undergraduate/ Fellowship)

Purpose: To promote education in social sciences. **Focus:** Law; Social sciences. **Qualif.:** Applicant must be an American citizen and permanent resident; an African American, Hispanic/Latino, Native American, or Puerto Rican, or individuals who will add diversity to the field of law and social science; a sophomore or junior student who have not yet received a degree; have a GPA of 3.0; and pursuing an academic major in the social sciences or humanities. **Criteria:** Selection is based on the application materials.

Funds Avail.: $3,600. **To Apply:** Applicants must send the completed application form together with the essay, official transcripts, and a letter of recommendation from a faculty member. **Deadline:** February 15. **Contact:** fellowships@ abfn.org.

580 ■ American Birding Association (ABA)
1618 W Colorado Ave.
Colorado Springs, CO 80904
Ph: (719) 578-9703
Fax: (719) 578-1480
Free: 800-850-2473
E-mail: member@aba.org
URL: www.aba.org

581 ■ ABA Scholarships (Undergraduate/ Scholarship)

Purpose: To recognize and stimulate interest in birds. To promote the pursuit of educational and other bird-related activities. **Focus:** Animal science and behavior; Animal rights. **Qualif.:** Scholarship is open to American Birding Association active members only. **Criteria:** Scholarship recipients will be selected based on scholastic ability, professional interest, character and financial need.

Funds Avail.: No specific amount. **To Apply:** Applicants must submit a completed application form available from the ABA office and can be downloaded from the website; an essay about the importance of a bird; a letter of recommendation from a teacher, bird club member or mentor.

Awards are arranged alphabetically below their administering organizations

Deadline: May 13. **Contact:** Send complete documents to: Chip Clouse at the above address or e-mail cclouse@aba.org.

582 ■ Richard E. Andrews Memorial Scholarships *(Undergraduate/Scholarship)*

Purpose: To provide financial assistance for young birders. **Focus:** Animal science and behavior; Animal rights. **Qualif.:** Scholarship is open to American Birding Association active members. **Criteria:** Scholarship recipients will be selected based on scholastic ability, professional interest, character and financial need.

Funds Avail.: No specific amount. **To Apply:** Applicants must submit a complete application form (available at the ABA office and can be downloaded from the website); an essay explaining why he/she deserves the Andrews Scholarships; and a letter of recommendation from a teacher, bird club member or mentor. **Deadline:** May 13. **Contact:** Send complete documents to: Chip Clouse at the above address or e-mail cclouse@aba.org.

583 ■ American Board of Funeral Service Education (ABFSE)

3414 Ashland Ave., Ste. G
St. Joseph, MO 64506
Ph: (816) 233-3747
Fax: (816) 233-3793
E-mail: exdir@abfse.org
URL: www.abfse.org

584 ■ ABFSE National Scholarship Program
(Undergraduate/Scholarship)

Purpose: To provide financial awards to students enrolled in funeral service or mortuary science programs to assist them in obtaining their professional education. **Focus:** Funeral services; Mortuary science. **Qualif.:** Applicant must have at least completed one semester (or quarter) of study in a funeral service or mortuary science education accredited by the American Board of Funeral Service Education; must have one term or semester remaining in his/her program which will commence after the award date in order to be considered for a full award; must be a citizen of the United States. **Criteria:** Selection of scholarship recipients is competitive. Awards are made by the Scholarship Committee of ABFSE.

Funds Avail.: $500 - $2,500. **To Apply:** Applicants must apply online. Applicant must submit the email confirmation, tax forms, letter of recommendation and transcript of records to: ABFSE Scholarship Committee. **Deadline:** March 1 or September 1. **Contact:** scholarships@abfse.org.

585 ■ American Brain Tumor Association (ABTA)

8550 W Bryn Mawr Ave., Ste. 550
Chicago, IL 60631
Ph: (773) 577-8750
Fax: (773) 577-8738
Free: 800-886-2282
E-mail: info@abta.org
URL: www.abta.org

586 ■ Basic Research Fellowships
(Postdoctorate/Fellowship)

Purpose: To encourage talented scientists early in their careers to enter, or remain in, the field of brain tumor research. **Focus:** Oncology. **Qualif.:** Applicant must be post-doctorate student intending to pursue a career in neuro-oncology. **Criteria:** Candidates will be evaluated based on some criteria by members of the Association's distinguished Scientific Advisory Council which include the caliber of the applicants, training program, and proposed research.

Funds Avail.: $100,000. **To Apply:** Applicants must seek application form from the ABTA office. **Contact:** Deneen Hesser at the above address.

587 ■ American Bus Association (ABA)

111 K St. NE, 9th Fl.
Washington, DC 20002
Ph: (202) 842-1645
Fax: (202) 842-0850
Free: 800-283-2877
E-mail: abainfo@buses.org
URL: www.buses.org

588 ■ ABA Diversity Scholarships
(Undergraduate/Scholarship)

Purpose: To promote understanding and to mobilize greater involvement in the transportation industry. **Focus:** Transportation; Travel and tourism. **Qualif.:** Applicants must have completed first year of studies; must be majoring or have a course of study relevant to the transportation, travel, and tourism industry at an accredited university; and must have a minimum of 3.0 GPA. **Criteria:** Recipients are selected on the basis of academic merit, character, leadership and financial need and dedication to advancing the transportation, travel and tourism industry.

Funds Avail.: $2,500. **Number Awarded:** 2. **To Apply:** Application process is online (please visit the website). **Contact:** Andrea Glass, Program Manager; Phone: 615-627-9686; Fax: 615-627-9693; E-mail: aglass@applyists.com.

589 ■ ABA Members Scholarships for ABA Bus and Tour Operators Only *(Undergraduate/Scholarship)*

Purpose: To financially assist deserving students who have potentials to be future leaders in the transportation, travel and tourism industry. **Focus:** Transportation; Travel and tourism. **Qualif.:** Applicant must be an employee or a dependent of ABA bus and tour member companies employed for at least one year; must be entering first year of college, university or professional training school by fall; must have a minimum of 3.0 GPA or an average of "B". **Criteria:** Applicants will be selected based on their academic merit, community service, extracurricular activities, leadership and anticipated financial need.

Funds Avail.: $2,500. **Number Awarded:** 13. **To Apply:** Application process is online (please visit the website). **Contact:** Andrea Glass, Program Manager; Phone: 615-627-9686; Fax: 615-627-9693; E-mail: aglass@applyists.com.

590 ■ ABA Members Scholarships for All ABA Member Companies *(Undergraduate/Scholarship)*

Purpose: To financially assist deserving students who have potentials to be future leaders in the transportation, travel and tourism industry. **Focus:** Transportation; Travel and tourism. **Qualif.:** Applicants must be employees or dependent of ABA members companies employed for at least

Awards are arranged alphabetically below their administering organizations

one year; must have completed their first year of studies and pursuing with reference to the field of transportation, travel and tourism industry; must have a minimum of 3.0 GPA or an average of "B". **Criteria:** Applicants will be selected based on their academic merit, community service, extracurricular activities, leadership and anticipated financial need.

Funds Avail.: $2,500. **Number Awarded:** 13. **To Apply:** Application process is online (please visit the website). **Contact:** Andrea Glass, Program Manager; Phone: 615-627-9686; Fax: 615-627-9693; E-mail: aglass@applyists.com.

591 ■ American Bus Association Academic Merit Scholarships (Undergraduate/Scholarship)

Purpose: To financially assist deserving students who have a potential to be future leaders in the transportation, travel, and tourism industry. **Focus:** Transportation; Travel and tourism. **Qualif.:** Applicants must have completed first year of studies and majoring or have a course of study relevant to the transportation, travel and tourism industry at an accredited university; must have a minimum of 3.4 GPA or higher. **Criteria:** Applicants will be selected based on their academic record, personal promise, character and financial need. Applicants affiliated with ABA-member companies will be given priority.

Funds Avail.: $2,500. **Number Awarded:** 2. **To Apply:** Application process is online (please visit the website). Applicants must also submit an essay (500 words) discussing the role they will play in advancing the future of the transportation, motorcoach, travel, and tourism/hospitality industry. **Contact:** Andrea Glass, Program Manager; Phone: 615-627-9686; Fax: 615-627-9693; E-mail: aglass@applyists.com.

592 ■ Peter L. Picknelly Honorary Scholarships (Undergraduate/Scholarship)

Purpose: To honor the contribution of bus drivers, mechanics and maintenance personnel to the motorcoach industry. **Focus:** Transportation; Travel and tourism. **Qualif.:** Applicant must be a bus driver or maintenance personnel, or dependent of ABA operator member; must be in a technical school with two-years or more transportation-related education programs; must maintain a 3.0 GPA; must have demonstrated desire and ability to participate in a learning program. **Criteria:** Recipients are selected on the basis of academic merit; extracurricular activities; commitment to complete the transportation program; and financial need.

Funds Avail.: $2,500. **Number Awarded:** 1. **To Apply:** Application process is online (please visit the website). **Contact:** Andrea Glass, Program Manager; Phone: 615-627-9686; Fax: 615-627-9693; E-mail: aglass@applyists.com.

593 ■ American Cancer Society Inc. (American Society for the Control of Cancer)

1599 Clifton Rd. NE
Atlanta, GA 30329
Ph: (404) 929-6824
Fax: (404) 325-9341
Free: 866-228-4327
E-mail: ca.edoff@cancer.org
URL: www.cancer.org

594 ■ American Cancer Society - Postdoctoral Fellowships (Doctorate/Fellowship)

Purpose: To support the training of researchers who have received a doctoral degree to provide initial funding leading to an independent career in cancer research. **Focus:** Health care services. **Qualif.:** Applicants must have obtained their doctoral degree prior to activation of the fellowship; must be US citizens, non-citizen nationals or permanent residents of the United States. **Criteria:** Selection will be based on the committee's criteria.

Funds Avail.: $44,000-$48,000 plus $4,000 per year fellowship allowance. **To Apply:** Interested applicants must visit the website for the electronic grant application process. **Deadline:** April 1 and October 15.

595 ■ American Cancer Society - Research Scholar Grants (Doctorate, Professional development/Grant)

Purpose: To provide resources for investigator-initiated research in a variety of cancer-relevant areas. **Focus:** Medical research. **Qualif.:** Applicants must have an independent research or faculty position and meet one of the following criteria: must be independent investigators within first 6 years of independent career with no more than one current R01-like support; must be independent investigators at any stage of their career with any level of prior funding; or independent investigators at any stage of their career with any level of prior funding. **Criteria:** Selection will be based on the following: demonstrated intellectual independence and committed research facilities; time limit on applicants' eligibility; and current grant support.

Funds Avail.: $200,000. **To Apply:** Applicants must visit the website for the electronic grant application process. **Deadline:** April 1 and October 15.

596 ■ Doctoral Degree Scholarships in Cancer Nursing (Doctorate/Scholarship)

Purpose: To strengthen nursing practice by providing assistance for advance preparation in the field of cancer nursing research. **Focus:** Nursing. **Qualif.:** Applicants must be currently enrolled in or applying to a doctoral degree program in nursing or a related field of research; must meet the requirements for doctoral study and must have been accepted by the institution to which they have applied at the time of funding; must have a current license to practice as registered nurses; must project a program of study that integrates cancer nursing and provides evidence of faculty support for the program of study. Scholarship recipients must take a minimum of 18 credit hours or 6 courses per year; must demonstrate a commitment to cancer nursing as evidenced by recent experience, education and/or research in the specialty area. **Criteria:** Selection will be based on the following criteria: relevant professional experience in oncology; involvement in professional organizations, including leadership roles; involvement in activities of the American Cancer Society or other relevant volunteer organizations; clear, explicit and realistic professional goals; consideration of program components, particularly oncology content, in selecting a doctoral program; conduct or plan to conduct research that is important, methodologically sound, and relevant to the health of persons affected with cancer or at risk for cancer; commitment from a faculty advisor who is experienced in the student's area of study and will provide guidance in academic and research activities; selection of a doctoral program which will support the student's professional goals and research; and dedication to cancer nursing research.

Funds Avail.: $15,000. **Number Awarded:** Two. **To Apply:** Interested applicants must visit the website for the electronic application process. **Deadline:** October 15.

Awards are arranged alphabetically below their administering organizations

597 ■ Graduate Scholarships in Cancer Nursing Practice (Master's, Doctorate/Scholarship)

Purpose: To support graduate students pursuing a master's degree in cancer nursing or doctorate of nursing practice. **Focus:** Nursing. **Qualif.:** Applicants must be currently enrolled in or applying to a master's or DNP degree graduate program with demonstrated integration of cancer content; must have a current license to practice as a registered nurse. Students in bridge programs must have passed the N-CLEX examination and updated their status with the ACS Program Office by the time the award begins; must be pursuing an advance degree and not solely a post-master's certificate. **Criteria:** Award will be given to the successful applicants who: have work experience in oncology; are involved in cancer-related professional and academic organizations; are involved in cancer-related volunteer organizations; have published or contributed to scholarly publications, presentations and creative works; are the recipients of professional and academic awards and honors; have considered program content, faculty and clinical resources related to cancer in selecting a graduate program; have a focus for scholarly activity in a specific area of cancer nursing; have strong letters of recommendation from two qualified professionals; have made a career commitment to cancer nursing; have formed explicit and realistic professional goals.

Funds Avail.: $10,000. **To Apply:** Interested applicants must visit the website for the electronic application process **Deadline:** February 1.

598 ■ Mentored Research Scholar Grant in Applied and Clinical Research (Doctorate, Professional development/Grant)

Purpose: To support junior faculty members to become independent investigators as either clinician scientists or cancer control researchers. **Focus:** Medical research. **Qualif.:** Applicants must: be within the first four years of a full-time faculty appointment or the equivalent; not be independent investigators; have four years or less postdoctoral research training/experience at the time of application; have a clinical doctoral degree; have a research doctoral degree in a clinical discipline or equivalent in nursing, nutrition, psychology, social work, etc.; or have a research doctoral degree in a cancer control discipline or equivalent in behavioral, epidemiologic, health policy, health services or psychosocial research. **Criteria:** Selection will be based on the following: applicants' academic and scientific qualifications, potential to succeed as an independent investigator and commitment to research as a career; the appropriateness of the mentors' research qualifications in the proposed project area, the role of the mentors on the project, research productivity and prior success in fostering the development of cancer researchers; submitted research and training plan; documentation of the institutional commitment to the research development of the applicants.

Funds Avail.: Up to $135,000 including $10,000 for the mentors. **To Apply:** Interested applicants must visit the website for the electronic grant application process. **Deadline:** April 1 and October 15.

599 ■ American Center for Mongolian Studies (ACMS)

333 Ingraham Hall
1155 Observatory Dr.
Madison, WI 53706
Ph: (360) 356-1020

E-mail: info@mongoliacenter.org
URL: www.mongoliacenter.org

600 ■ ACMS Faculty Research Fellowships (Professional development/Fellowship)

Purpose: To support faculty members from U.S. colleges and universities who wish to conduct short-term field research in Mongolia. **Focus:** General studies. **Qualif.:** Applicants must be U.S. citizens or permanent residents; must be currently teaching at a college or university in the United States; and must be members of ACMS. **Criteria:** Applicants will be evaluated based on research project.

Funds Avail.: Total amount of $4,000. **Number Awarded:** 5. **To Apply:** Applicants must submit a cover sheet, curriculum vitae, 500 words personal statement, 500 words research statement and a letter of support from a Research Sponsor in Mongolia. All application materials must be submitted in English. **Deadline:** February 15.

601 ■ ACMS Intensive Mongolian Language Fellowship Program (Undergraduate/Fellowship)

Purpose: To provide opportunities to Intermediate-level students to enhance their communicative competence through systematic improvement of reading, writing, listening and speaking skills in an authentic environment. **Focus:** General studies. **Qualif.:** Applicants must be in their intermediate-level of the study and be current members of the ACMS. **Criteria:** Fellowships are awarded to applicants based on merit and need. Criteria for fellowship selection includes: 1) ability to complete coursework at the Intermediate level; 2) importance of learning a Mongolian language for the applicant's academic studies or career plans; and 3) commitment to attend classes and maintain an average minimum grade of B+.

Funds Avail.: Total amount of $3,000. **To Apply:** Applicants must submit a completed application form, resume or CV, short description of applicant's Mongolian Language Proficiency, description on how to further their career or studies through program participation, a letter of recommendation and relevant information on financial need. **Deadline:** February 15.

602 ■ ACMS Library Fellowships (Graduate, Professional development/Fellowship)

Purpose: To support students or faculty members in library science to conduct a short-term project and/or research in Mongolia. **Focus:** Library and archival sciences. **Qualif.:** Applicants must be U.S. citizens or permanent residents currently enrolled in or teaching in a college or university in United States; must be advanced graduate students or faculty members in library science and must be current members of ACMS. **Criteria:** Applicants will be selected based on their submitted research project.

Funds Avail.: $2,000 for travel expenses and $2,000 for a project stipend. **Number Awarded:** Varies. **To Apply:** Applicants must submit a cover sheet, curriculum vitae, (500-word each) personal statement and a research statement, and a letter of support from a Research Sponsor in Mongolia. All application materials should be submitted in English. **Deadline:** February 15.

603 ■ ACMS Research Fellowships (Doctorate, Postdoctorate/Fellowship)

Purpose: To support scholars conducting research in Mongolia. **Focus:** General studies. **Qualif.:** Applicants must be citizens and graduated from a university located in United

Awards are arranged alphabetically below their administering organizations

States and Canada; must have completed the required coursework for their programs and have an accepted dissertation proposal prior to the start of their fellowship program. All postdoctoral fellows must have completed their PhD within seven years of the start of their fellowship program; and must be current members of the ACMS. **Criteria:** Recipients will be selected based on the research project.

Funds Avail.: Maximum award of $27,000 per fellow. **To Apply:** Applicants must submit a research project, two letters of recommendation, transcript of records, (500-word) personal statement, curriculum vitae and a completed application cover sheet. **Deadline:** February 15. **Contact:** Application materials must be submitted to fellowship@mongoliacenter.org.

604 ■ ACMS U.S.-Mongolia Field Research Fellowship Program (Graduate, Undergraduate/Fellowship)

Purpose: To support students who wish to conduct field research in Mongolia. **Focus:** General studies. **Qualif.:** Applicants must be U.S. citizens or permanent residents currently enrolled full-time in a university or college and must be current members of ACMS. Undergraduate applicants must have at least third year standing in their program while graduate applicants can be at a masters or predissertation doctoral level. **Criteria:** Applicants will be evaluated based on submitted research projects.

Funds Avail.: Total amount of $4,000. **Number Awarded:** 4 to 5. **To Apply:** Applicants must submit the required materials and must include a letter of support from their Research Sponsor responsible for overseeing their research program. **Deadline:** February 15.

605 ■ American Ceramic Society (ACerS)
600 N Cleveland Ave., Ste. 210
Westerville, OH 43082
Ph: (614) 794-5855
Fax: (301) 206-9789
Free: 866-721-3322
E-mail: customerservice@ceramics.org
URL: ceramics.org

606 ■ Electronics Division Lewis C. Hoffman Scholarships (Undergraduate/Scholarship)

Purpose: To encourage academic interest and excellence among undergraduate students. **Focus:** Materials research/science; Engineering, Materials. **Qualif.:** Applicant must be a junior-year student, or a student who has recently completed his or her junior year; must have acquired a total of 70 or more semester credits or equivalent quarter credits; must have extracurricular activities. **Criteria:** Applicants will be selected based on the application requirements.

Funds Avail.: $2,000. **To Apply:** Applicant must submit a recommendation letter from a faculty member in the department; must have a 500 word essay on the year's topic. **Deadline:** July 31. **Contact:** Dr. Timothy J. Haugan, Research Team Leader and Physicist, The Air Force Research Laboratory, Propulsion Directorate, Energy Power and Thermal Division, Mechanical Energy, Conversion Branch, AFRL/RZPG, 1950 5th St. Bldg. 450, Wright-Patterson AFB, OH 45433-7251, Tel: 937-255-7163, Fax: 937-255-4307, Email: timothy.haugan@wpafb.af.mil; or Marcia Stout at mstout@ceramics.org.

607 ■ American Clan Gregor Society (ACGS)
238 W 1220 N
American Fork, UT 84003
Ph: (801) 763-0663
E-mail: clangregorsociety@earthlink.net
URL: american-clan-gregor-society.us

608 ■ Harry and Edith Blunt Scholarships (Undergraduate/Scholarship)

Purpose: To provide educational assistance to incoming college students. **Focus:** General studies. **Qualif.:** Applicants must be ACGS members or children of ACGS members. **Criteria:** Priority will be given to children of the members of the society.

Funds Avail.: $1,000. **To Apply:** Applicants must submit their transcript of records, college acceptance and personal letter about activities and educational plans. **Deadline:** April 1. **Contact:** Susan Tichy, Scholarship Committee Chair at stichy@gmu.edu.

609 ■ Dr. Edward May Magruder Medical Scholarships (Undergraduate/Scholarship)

Purpose: To provide educational assistance to the students of the University of Virginia School of Medicine. **Focus:** Medicine. **Qualif.:** Applicants who are ACGHS members, children of members, or others who have lineage to the Clan Gregor are welcome to apply. Applicants must also be enrolled at least half-time or full-time for Federal Title VII programs. Those applicants who are in default on a federal loan or owe a refund on a federal grant are disqualified. Registration in Selective Service is also required for the application. **Criteria:** Recipients will be selected based on their satisfactory academic progress and financial information.

Funds Avail.: The amount will depend on the number of grantees. **Number Awarded:** The number of awards will be based on the selected students. **To Apply:** Applicants must complete both the FAFSA and the UVA School of Medicine Application (refer and download from www.healthsystem.virginia.edu). Previous year U.S Tax Returns is also required for the completion of the requirements. **Deadline:** April 1 for entering students and April 15 for returning students. **Remarks:** Established in honor of Dr. Magruder in 1927. **Contact:** Ms. Nancy L. Zimmer, nlb3w@virginia.edu or UVA SOM Financial Aid Office, PO Box 800730, Charlottesville, VA 22908-0730.

610 ■ The American Classical League (ACL)
Miami University
422 Wells Mill Dr.
Oxford, OH 45056
Ph: (513) 529-7741
Fax: (513) 529-7742
E-mail: info@aclclassics.org
URL: www.aclclassics.org

611 ■ Glenn Knudsvig Memorial Scholarships (Graduate, Undergraduate/Scholarship)

Purpose: To encourage teaching profession of classics by providing educational fund for deserving teacher and undergraduate or graduate member of the American Classical League. **Focus:** Classical studies. **Qualif.:** Applicant must be a current JCL sponsor who has attended the most recent NJCL convention; teacher of Latin, Greek or Classics with less than five years of classroom experience and

Awards are arranged alphabetically below their administering organizations

has never attended an ACL Institute; graduate student who plans to teach K-12 Latin, Greek or Classics; teacher whose student participated in the 2010 National Latin Exam and has never attended an ACL Institute. **Criteria:** Recipient is chosen based on merit.

Funds Avail.: $1,000 covering expenses on registration, room, board on campus and travel for Annual ACL Institute. **To Apply:** Application form and instructions are available at the website. **Deadline:** January 15.

612 ■ Arthur Patch McKinlay Scholarships
(Graduate, Undergraduate/Scholarship)

Purpose: To provide educational fund for deserving teachers, undergraduate or graduate members of the American Classical League as they pursue careers in teaching classics. **Focus:** Classical studies. **Qualif.:** Applicant must be an ACL member for the preceding three years and planning to teach classics at elementary through secondary level for the school year 2011-2012. **Criteria:** Recipient is chosen based on a review of proposed bonafide study program.

Funds Avail.: $1,500 covering expenses on registration, room, board on campus and the cost of transportation. **To Apply:** Application form and instructions are available at the website. **Deadline:** January 15.

613 ■ Ed Phinney Commemorative Scholarships *(Graduate, Undergraduate/Scholarship)*

Purpose: To provide educational fund for deserving teachers, undergraduates or graduate members of the American Classical League. **Focus:** Classical studies. **Qualif.:** Applicant must be a current member of the American Classical League; must have been an ACL member for year prior to applying (if applying to attend ACL Institute for the first time, only current ACL membership required.) **Criteria:** Award is given to an eligible and proficient undergraduate classic major or graduate student of classics intending to teach at the elementary through college level.

Funds Avail.: $1,000 covering expenses on registration, room, board on campus and the cost of transportation. **To Apply:** Application form and instructions are available at the website. **Deadline:** January 15.

614 ■ American College of Chiropractic Orthopedics (ACCO)
c/o Thomas C. Mack, Pres.
35 S Lake St.
North East, PA 16428
Ph: (814) 725-2225
Fax: (814) 665-1032
E-mail: thomasmackdc@gmail.com
URL: www.accoweb.org

615 ■ F. Maynard Lipe Scholarship Awards
(Postdoctorate, Postgraduate/Scholarship)

Purpose: To provide financial assistance to eligible individuals pursuing research in line with chiropractic. **Focus:** Chiropractic. **Qualif.:** Applicants must be doctors enrolled in Post Graduate Orthopedics leading to diplomat status or the masters program in musculoskeletal manipulation and rehabilitation. **Criteria:** Candidates will be evaluated by the ACCO assigned Scholarship Committee.

Funds Avail.: $500. **To Apply:** Applicants must submit application form, recommendation letter from the orthopedic course instructor and an article focusing on the complete

chiropractic management of an orthopedically related clinical problem from initial diagnosis through treatment and long-term management. The article should be 1,000 to 2,500 words in length and should be doubled-spaced. Mail applications to: Jesse R. Rothenberger, Chm., Lipe Scholarship Committee, PO Box 385 Boyertown, PA, 19512. **Deadline:** December 31.

616 ■ American College of Nurse-Midwives Foundation (ACNM)
8403 Colesville Rd., Ste. 1550
Silver Spring, MD 20910
Ph: (240) 485-1800
Fax: (240) 485-1818
URL: www.midwife.org

617 ■ ACNM Foundation, Inc. Fellowships for Graduate Education *(Doctorate, Postdoctorate/Fellowship)*

Purpose: To provide financial assistance for midwives actively enrolled in doctoral or post-doctoral studies. **Focus:** Midwifery. **Qualif.:** Applicants must be certified nurse-midwives (CNM) or certified midwives (CM); must be current members of the American College of Nurse-Midwives (ACNM); must be actively enrolled in a doctoral or post-doctoral education program; and must be graduate students in good standing as verified by the Academic Program Director. **Criteria:** Applicants are evaluated based on financial need and academic achievement.

Funds Avail.: No specific amount. **To Apply:** Applicants must submit application form; academic/career goals and plans; academic director form; and two academic recommendations. **Deadline:** March 13.

618 ■ Basic Midwifery Student Scholarship Program *(Undergraduate/Scholarship)*

Purpose: To provide assistance to students of nurse-midwifery. **Focus:** Nursing; Midwifery. **Qualif.:** Applicants must be students in good standing in an ACNM DOA-accredited basic midwifery education program; must have successfully completed one academic or clinical semester/quarter or clinical module; and must be current members of the American College of Nurse-Midwives (ACNM). **Criteria:** Applicants are judged based on demonstrated academic excellence and financial need.

Funds Avail.: No specific amount. **To Apply:** Applicants must submit application information form; statement of career goals and plans; financial assessment form; statement of financial need; program director form; and the faculty recommendation form. **Deadline:** April 1.

619 ■ Hazel Corbin/Childbirth Connection Grants for Evidence-based Midwifery Care
(Professional development/Grant)

Purpose: To support or augment projects that advance understanding of the safety and/or effectiveness of midwifery practices for mothers and newborns. **Focus:** Nursing; Midwifery. **Qualif.:** Applicants must be professionals involved in furthering understanding of the safety and/or effectiveness of midwifery practices for mothers and newborns; may be professionals from midwifery or any other field that may contribute to such objective (for example, nursing, public health, social science); may be affiliated with an academic institution, an advocacy group, a clinical entity, a professional organization (including ACNM), a

Awards are arranged alphabetically below their administering organizations

public agency, a research or consulting organization, or other group that may be concerned with evidence-based midwifery care; and may be based in the United States or in another country. **Criteria:** Applicants will be evaluated based on completed application form which should clearly describe information needed to address the review criteria including: assessment of the project relevance, excellence and impact.

Funds Avail.: $4,500. **To Apply:** Applicants must submit completed application form and all other required application materials and information to Lisa L. Pain. **Contact:** Lisa L. Pain, PO Box 380315 Cambridge, MA 02238-0315; 617-876-6660 or e-mail at lisa.paine@hutchdyer.com.

620 ■ American College of Nursing Practitioners (ACNP)
1501 Wilson Blvd., Ste. 509
Arlington, VA 22209
Ph: (703) 740-2529
Fax: (703) 740-2533
E-mail: acnp@acnpweb.org
URL: www.acnpweb.org

621 ■ ACNP Nurse Practitioner Student Scholarship Awards *(Undergraduate/Scholarship)*

Purpose: To recognize an outstanding student in the field of nursing. **Focus:** Nursing. **Qualif.:** Applicant must be member of ACNP; enrolled in an accredited NP program; have a GPA of 3.4. **Criteria:** Recipients will be selected based on the Award Committee's review of all applications.

Funds Avail.: $1,000. **To Apply:** Applicants must complete and submit the application form along with the following supporting documents: proof of Student Membership in ACNP; official transcript of an accredited NP program that indicates a 3.4 GPA; curriculum vitae (not more than 2 pages); two letters from professional colleagues indicating leadership roles and involvement in any organizational policy development; statement of the applicant's goals related to the ACNP Mission (not more than 200 words). **Deadline:** July 11.

622 ■ American College of Radiation Oncology (ACRO)
5272 River Rd., Ste. 630
Bethesda, MD 20816
Ph: (301) 718-6515
Fax: (301) 656-0989
URL: www.acro.org

623 ■ American College of Radiation Oncology Resident Scholarships *(Graduate/Scholarship)*

Purpose: To support subspecialty electives at any qualified institution in North America demonstrating expertise in the desired subspecialty area. **Focus:** Oncology. **Qualif.:** Applicant must be ACRO and ARRO radiation oncology resident member; be second, third, or fourth year student of an accredited U.S. residency program; or U.S. citizen attending an accredited residency program in Canada; and have not previously been awarded an ACRO resident scholarship. **Criteria:** Applications are reviewed by the ACRO Resident Scholarship Committee. Recipients will be selected based on merit.

Funds Avail.: No specific amount. **To Apply:** Applicants

must submit an application. **Deadline:** September 21.

624 ■ American Composites Manufacturers Association (ACMA)
3033 Wilson Blvd., Ste. 420
Arlington, VA 22201-3843
Ph: (703) 525-0511
Fax: (703) 525-0743
E-mail: info@acmanet.org
URL: www.acmanet.org

625 ■ American Composites Manufacturers Association Scholarships *(Undergraduate/ Scholarship)*

Purpose: To support individuals involved in the composites industry. **Focus:** General studies. **Qualif.:** Applicants must be graduating high school seniors planning to pursue a degree in accredited four-year colleges or universities. **Criteria:** Recipients are selected based on personal merit and background (merit is demonstrated in academic achievement; leadership in school; civic and other extracurricular activities; and motivations to serve and succeed).

Funds Avail.: $2,000. **To Apply:** Application forms are available at ACMA website (www.acmanet.org).

626 ■ American Composites Manufacturers Association Western Chapter Scholarships *(Undergraduate/Scholarship)*

Purpose: To provide special services and networking opportunities to member companies in the 13 most western states. **Focus:** General Studies. **Qualif.:** Applicants must be employees, spouses, children or grandchildren of individuals who are employed by a company located in the 13 most western states (Alaska, Arizona, California, Colorado, Hawaii, Idaho, Montana, New Mexico, Nevada, Oregon, Utah, Washington, or Wyoming) that is a member of the ACMA; must be registered full-time students (minimum 12 hours) at an accredited college or university. **Criteria:** Recipients are selected based on: scholastic aptitude; career objectives; leadership; and extracurricular activities such as community involvement.

Funds Avail.: $2,000. **To Apply:** Applicants must submit the completed application form; transcript of all college work; statement of educational goals; career intentions and resume of extracurricular activities; work experience; community involvement; and two letters of reference (personal reference and a reference from a professor or teacher). **Deadline:** May 15. **Contact:** ACMA at the above address.

627 ■ American Concrete Institute (ACI)
38800 Country Club Dr.
Farmington Hills, MI 48331
Ph: (248) 848-3700
Fax: (248) 848-3701
URL: www.concrete.org

628 ■ ACI BASF Construction Chemicals Student Fellowships *(Graduate, Undergraduate/ Fellowship)*

Purpose: To support high-potential undergraduate and graduate students whose studies relate to concrete. **Focus:** Construction; Chemical engineering; **Qualif.:** Applicant must be an undergraduate or graduate in the award year

Awards are arranged alphabetically below their administering organizations

with an interest in the area of specialty chemicals for new construction and repair/rehabilitation. Student must be nominated by an ACI-Member Faculty. **Criteria:** Selection is based on the application materials and on the interview.

Funds Avail.: $7,000. **Number Awarded:** 1. **To Apply:** Applicants must submit a completed application form together with a resume; an essay (maximum of 500 words); two completed online reference forms; all undergraduate and graduate transcripts; and Internship Requirement Agreement. **Deadline:** October 18. **Contact:** scholarships@concrete.org.

629 ■ ACI Cagley ACI Student Fellowships
(Graduate, Master's, Undergraduate/Fellowship)

Purpose: To support high-potential undergraduate and graduate students whose studies relate to concrete. **Focus:** Commercial design. **Qualif.:** Applicant must have an interest in a career in design; undergraduate or enrolled in Master's programs; and must be serving an internship with Cagley & Associates prior to the award year. Student must be nominated by an ACI-Member Faculty. **Criteria:** Selection is based on the application materials and on the interview.

Funds Avail.: $7,000. **Number Awarded:** 1. **To Apply:** Applicants must submit a completed application form together with a resume; an essay (maximum of 500 words); two completed online reference forms; all undergraduate and graduate transcripts; and Internship Requirement Agreement. **Deadline:** October 18. **Contact:** scholarships@concrete.org.

630 ■ ACI President's Fellowships *(Doctorate, Master's/Fellowship)*

Purpose: To support high-potential undergraduate and graduate students whose studies relate to concrete. **Focus:** Construction; Commercial design. **Qualif.:** Applicants must be in Master's or Doctoral programs in either construction, design, or education programs and must be nominated by an ACI-Member Faculty. **Criteria:** Selection is based on the application materials and on the interview.

Funds Avail.: $7,000. **Number Awarded:** 1. **To Apply:** Applicants must submit a completed application form together with a resume; an essay (maximum of 500 words); two completed online reference forms; all undergraduate and graduate transcripts; and Internship Requirement Agreement. **Deadline:** October 18. **Contact:** scholarships@concrete.org.

631 ■ ACI Scholarships *(Graduate/Scholarship)*

Purpose: To support high-potential graduate students whose studies relate to concrete. **Focus:** Engineering; Architecture; Materials research/science. **Qualif.:** Applicant must have been accepted for graduate study at an accredited college or university in an engineering, architecture, or materials science program (graduate study program shall be in the area of concrete with an emphasis on structural design, materials, construction, or any combination thereof), and must be a full-time first or second-year graduate student during the entire scholarship year. **Criteria:** Selection is based on the submitted application and materials.

Funds Avail.: $3,000. **Number Awarded:** 1. **To Apply:** Applicants must submit a completed application form along with a resume; an essay (maximum of 500 words); two completed Online Reference Forms; and all undergraduate and graduate transcripts. **Deadline:** October 18. **Contact:** scholarships@concrete.org.

632 ■ ACI Baker Student Fellowships
(Undergraduate/Fellowship)

Purpose: To support high-potential undergraduate and graduate students whose studies relate to concrete. **Focus:** Construction; Civil engineering. **Qualif.:** Applicant must be an undergraduate student with an interest in a career in the construction industry; entering junior or senior year; studying in a civil engineering, structural engineering, or construction industry management program; serving an internship before the award period (this internship may be served with a firm other than Baker Concrete Construction); and must be nominated by an ACI-Member Faculty. **Criteria:** Selection is based on the application materials and on the interview.

Funds Avail.: $7,000. **Number Awarded:** 2. **To Apply:** Applicants must submit a completed application form together with a resume; an essay (maximum of 500 words); two completed online reference forms; all undergraduate and graduate transcripts; and Internship Requirement Agreement. **Deadline:** October 18. **Contact:** scholarships@concrete.org.

633 ■ ACI Elmer Baker Student Fellowships
(Undergraduate/Fellowship)

Purpose: To support high-potential undergraduate and graduate students whose studies relate to concrete. **Focus:** Construction. **Qualif.:** Applicant must be an undergraduate student entering junior or senior year with an interest in a career in the construction industry; serving an internship with Baker Concrete Construction before the award period; and must be nominated by an ACI-Member Faculty. **Criteria:** Selection is based on the application materials and on the interview.

Funds Avail.: $7,000. **Number Awarded:** 1. **To Apply:** Applicants must submit a completed application form together with a resume; an essay (maximum of 500 words); two completed online reference forms; all undergraduate and graduate transcripts; and Internship Requirement Agreement. **Deadline:** October 18. **Contact:** scholarships@concrete.org.

634 ■ ACI W.R. Grace Scholarships *(Graduate/Scholarship)*

Purpose: To support high-potential graduate students whose studies relate to concrete. **Focus:** Engineering; Architecture; Materials research/science. **Qualif.:** Applicant must have been accepted for graduate study at an accredited college or university in an engineering, architecture, or materials science program (graduate study program shall be in the area of concrete with an emphasis on structural design, materials, construction, or any combination thereof), and must be a full-time first or second-year graduate student during the entire scholarship year. **Criteria:** Selection is based on the submitted application and materials.

Funds Avail.: $3,000. **Number Awarded:** 1. **To Apply:** Applicants must submit a completed application form along with a resume; an essay (maximum of 500 words); two completed Online Reference Forms; and all undergraduate and graduate transcripts. **Deadline:** October 18. **Remarks:** The award is the ACI Foundation's first and longest-running industry-sponsored educational scholarship. **Contact:** scholarships@concrete.org.

635 ■ Katharine & Bryant Mather Scholarships
(Graduate/Scholarship)

Purpose: To support high-potential graduate students whose studies relate to concrete. **Focus:** Engineering;

Awards are arranged alphabetically below their administering organizations

Architecture; Materials research/science. **Qualif.:** Applicant must have been accepted for graduate study at an accredited college or university in an engineering, architecture, or materials science program (graduate study program shall be in the area of concrete with an emphasis on structural design, materials, construction, or any combination thereof); must be a full-time first or second-year graduate student during the entire scholarship year; and must be pursuing a research on sustainable development of concrete. **Criteria:** Selection is based on the submitted application and materials.

Funds Avail.: $3,000. **Number Awarded:** 1. **To Apply:** Applicants must submit a completed application form along with a resume; an essay (maximum of 500 words); two completed Online Reference Forms; and all undergraduate and graduate transcripts. **Deadline:** October 18. **Remarks:** Established in 1988 to honor Katharine and Bryant Mather for their exceptional contributions to the knowledge of concrete. **Contact:** scholarships@concrete.org.

636 ■ Kumar Mehta Scholarships *(Graduate/Scholarship)*

Purpose: To support high-potential graduate students whose studies relate to concrete. **Focus:** Engineering; Architecture; Materials research/science. **Qualif.:** Applicant must have been accepted for graduate study at an accredited college or university in an engineering, architecture, or materials science program (graduate study program shall be in the area of concrete with an emphasis on structural design, materials, construction, or any combination thereof); must be a full-time first or second-year graduate student during the entire scholarship year; and must be pursuing a research on sustainable development of concrete. **Criteria:** Selection is based on the submitted application and materials.

Funds Avail.: $3,000. **Number Awarded:** 1. **To Apply:** Applicants must submit a completed application form along with a resume; an essay (maximum of 500 words); two completed Online Reference Forms; and all undergraduate and graduate transcripts. **Deadline:** October 18. **Remarks:** Initiated by Dr. Mehta in 2002. **Contact:** scholarships@ concrete.org.

637 ■ ACI Charles Pankow Foundation ACI Student Fellowships *(Graduate, Undergraduate/Fellowship)*

Purpose: To support high-potential undergraduate and graduate students whose studies relate to concrete. **Focus:** Construction. **Qualif.:** Applicant must be in an undergraduate or graduate class in the award year; serving an internship in a construction environment with the Charles Pankow Company prior to the award year; and must be nominated by an ACI-Member Faculty. **Criteria:** Selection is based on the application materials and on the interview.

Funds Avail.: $10,000. **Number Awarded:** 1. **To Apply:** Applicants must submit a completed application form together with a resume; an essay (maximum of 500 words); two completed online reference forms; all undergraduate and graduate transcripts; and Internship Requirement Agreement. **Deadline:** October 18. **Contact:** scholarships@concrete.org.

638 ■ ACI Bertold E. Weinberg Scholarships *(Graduate/Scholarship)*

Purpose: To support high-potential graduate students whose studies relate to concrete. **Focus:** Engineering; Architecture; Materials research/science. **Qualif.:** Applicant

must have been accepted for graduate study at an accredited college or university in an engineering, architecture, or materials science program (graduate study program shall be in the area of concrete with an emphasis on structural design, materials, construction, or any combination thereof), and must be a full-time first or second-year graduate student during the entire scholarship year. **Criteria:** Selection is based on the submitted application and materials.

Funds Avail.: $3,000. **Number Awarded:** 1. **To Apply:** Applicants must submit a completed application form along with a resume; an essay (maximum of 500 words); two completed Online Reference Forms; and all undergraduate and graduate transcripts. **Deadline:** October 18. **Contact:** scholarships@concrete.org.

639 ■ ACI Richard N. White Student Fellowships *(Master's/Fellowship)*

Purpose: To support high-potential undergraduate and graduate students whose studies relate to concrete. **Focus:** Material and process engineering. **Qualif.:** Applicant must have an interest in materials enrolling in a Master's program during the award year and must be nominated by an ACI-Member Faculty. **Criteria:** Selection is based on the application materials and on the interview.

Funds Avail.: $7,000. **Number Awarded:** 1. **To Apply:** Applicants must submit a completed application form together with a resume; an essay (maximum of 500 words); two completed online reference forms; all undergraduate and graduate transcripts; and Internship Requirement Agreement. **Deadline:** October 18. **Contact:** scholarships@concrete.org.

640 ■ American Congress on Surveying and Mapping (ACSM)
5119 Pegasus Ct., Ste. Q
Frederick, MD 21704
Ph: (240) 439-4615
Fax: (240) 439-4952
E-mail: curtis.sumner@acsm.net
URL: www.acsm.net

641 ■ AAGS Graduate Fellowship Awards *(Undergraduate/Fellowship)*

Purpose: CSM Scholarships are designed to encourage, recognize, and support exceptional surveying and mapping students. **Focus:** Surveying. **Qualif.:** Applicants must be enrolled in or accepted to a graduate program in geodetic surveying or geodesy. **Criteria:** Recipients will be selected based on academic record, applicant's statement, letters of recommendation and professional activities.

Funds Avail.: $2,000. **To Apply:** Applicants must complete the application form; applicants must provide a proof of membership in ACSM; a brief yet complete statement indicating educational objectives, future plans of study or research, professional activities and financial need; at least three letters of recommendation (minimum of two from faculty members familiar with the student's work); a complete original official transcript through year prior to when the award will be presented. **Deadline:** November 2. **Contact:** Dawn James at dawn.james@asm.net.

642 ■ The Berntsen International Scholarships in Surveying Technology *(Undergraduate/Scholarship)*

Purpose: To encourage, recognize and support exceptional surveying and mapping students. **Focus:** Surveying. **Qua-**

Awards are arranged alphabetically below their administering organizations

lif.: Applicant must be enrolled in two-year degree programs in surveying technology. **Criteria:** Recipients will be selected based on academic record, applicant's statement, letters of recommendation and professional activities.

Funds Avail.: $500. **Number Awarded:** 1. **To Apply:** Applicants must complete the application form; applicants must provide a proof of membership in ACSM; a brief yet complete statement indicating educational objectives, future plans of study or research, professional activities and financial need; at least three letters of recommendation (minimum of two from faculty members familiar with the student's work); a complete original official transcript through year prior to when the award will be presented. **Deadline:** November 2. **Contact:** Dawn James at dawn.james@asm.net.

643 ■ Nettie Dracup Memorial Scholarships
(Undergraduate/Scholarship)

Purpose: To provide financial assistance to a United States citizen. **Focus:** Surveying. **Qualif.:** Applicants must be undergraduate student who is enrolled in Geodetic Surveying in an accredited college or university. **Criteria:** Recipients will be selected based on academic record, applicant's statement, letters of recommendation and professional activities.

Funds Avail.: $2,000. **Number Awarded:** 2. **To Apply:** Applicants must complete the application form; applicants must provide a proof of membership in ACSM; a brief yet complete statement indicating educational objectives, future plans of study or research, professional activities and financial need; at least three letters of recommendation (minimum of two from faculty members familiar with the student's work); a complete original official transcript through year prior to when the award will be presented. **Deadline:** November 2. **Contact:** Dawn James at dawn.james@asm.net.

644 ■ AAGS Joseph F. Dracup Scholarship Awards *(Undergraduate/Scholarship)*

Purpose: CSM Scholarships are designed to encourage, recognize, and support exceptional surveying and mapping students. **Focus:** Surveying. **Qualif.:** Applicants must be enrolled in two-year or four-year-surveying (and closely related) degree program, either full or part-time. **Criteria:** Recipients will be selected based on academic record, applicant's statement, letters of recommendation and professional activities.

Funds Avail.: $2,000. **To Apply:** Applicants must complete the application form; applicants must provide a proof of membership in ACSM; a brief yet complete statement indicating educational objectives, future plans of study or research, professional activities and financial need; at least three letters of recommendation (minimum of two from faculty members familiar with the student's work); a complete original official transcript through year prior to when the award will be presented. **Deadline:** November 2. **Contact:** Dawn James at dawn.james@asm.net.

645 ■ Kris M. Kunze Memorial Scholarships
(Undergraduate/Scholarship)

Purpose: To encourage, recognize, and support exceptional surveying and mapping students. **Focus:** Surveying. **Qualif.:** Applicants must be licensed Professional Land Surveyors of Certified Photogrammetrists pursuing college level courses in Business Administration or Business Management or applicants must be full-time students enrolled in a two or four-year degree program in Surveying

and Mapping pursuing a course of study including Business Administration or Business Management. **Criteria:** Recipients will be selected based on academic record, applicant's statement, letters of recommendation and professional activities.

Funds Avail.: $1,000. **To Apply:** Applicants must complete the application form; applicants must provide a proof of membership in ACSM; a brief yet complete statement indicating educational objectives, future plans of study or research, professional activities and financial need; at least three letters of recommendation (minimum of two from faculty members familiar with the student's work); a complete original official transcript through year prior to when the award will be presented. **Deadline:** November 2. **Contact:** Dawn James at dawn.james@asm.net.

646 ■ The Lowell H. and Dorothy Loving Undergraduate Scholarships *(Undergraduate/Scholarship)*

Purpose: To encourage, recognize, and support exceptional surveying and mapping students. **Focus:** Surveying. **Qualif.:** Applicants must be junior or senior standing in a four-year program at a university or college in the United States. **Criteria:** Recipients will be selected based on academic record, applicant's statement, letters of recommendation and professional activities.

Funds Avail.: $2,500. **To Apply:** Applicants must complete the application form; applicants must provide a proof of membership in ACSM; a brief yet complete statement indicating educational objectives, future plans of study or research, professional activities and financial need; at least three letters of recommendation (minimum of two from faculty members familiar with the student's work); a complete original official transcript through year prior to when the award will be presented. **Deadline:** November 2. **Contact:** Dawn James at dawn.james@asm.net.

647 ■ The Cady McDonnell Memorial Scholarships *(Undergraduate/Scholarship)*

Purpose: To encourage, recognize, and support exceptional surveying and mapping students. **Focus:** Surveying. **Qualif.:** Applicants must be a resident of one of the following western states; Montana, Idaho, Washington, Oregon, Wyoming, Colorado, Utah, Nevada, California, Arizona, New Mexico, Alaska, and Hawaii; applicants must be a woman student enrolled in the field of surveying. **Criteria:** Recipients will be selected based on academic record, applicant's statement, letters of recommendation and professional activities.

Funds Avail.: $1,000. **To Apply:** Applicants must complete the application form; applicants must provide a proof of membership in ACSM; a brief yet complete statement indicating educational objectives, future plans of study or research, professional activities and financial need; at least three letters of recommendation (minimum of two from faculty members familiar with the student's work); a complete original official transcript through year prior to when the award will be presented. **Deadline:** November 2. **Contact:** Dawn James at dawn.james@asm.net.

648 ■ NSPS Board of Governors Scholarships
(Undergraduate/Scholarship)

Purpose: To encourage, recognize, and support exceptional surveying and mapping students. **Focus:** Surveying. **Qualif.:** Applicants must be enrolled in studies in surveying entering their junior year of study in a four-year degree program of their choice; applicants must maintain a

Awards are arranged alphabetically below their administering organizations

minimum 3.0 grade point average. **Criteria:** Recipients will be selected based on academic record, applicant's statement, letters of recommendation and professional activities.

Funds Avail.: $1,000. **To Apply:** Applicants must complete the application form; applicants must provide a proof of membership in ACSM; a brief yet complete statement indicating educational objectives, future plans of study or research, professional activities and financial need; at least three letters of recommendation (minimum of two from faculty members familiar with the student's work); a complete original official transcript through year prior to when the award will be presented. **Deadline:** November 2. **Contact:** Dawn James at dawn.james@asm.net.

649 ■ The NSPS Scholarships *(Undergraduate/Scholarship)*

Purpose: To recognize outstanding students enrolled full-time in undergraduate surveying programs. **Focus:** Surveying. **Qualif.:** Applicants must complete the application form; applicants must provide a proof of membership in ACSM; a brief yet complete statement indicating educational objectives, future plans of study or research, professional activities and financial need; at least three letters of recommendation (minimum of two from faculty members familiar with the students work); a complete original official transcript through year prior to when the award. **Criteria:** Recipients will be selected based on academic record, applicant's statement, letters of recommendation and professional activities.

Funds Avail.: $1,000. **Number Awarded:** 2. **To Apply:** Applicants must complete the application form; applicants must provide a proof of membership in ACSM; a brief yet complete statement indicating educational objectives, future plans of study or research, professional activities and financial need; at least three letters of recommendation (minimum of two from faculty members familiar with the student's work); a complete original official transcript through year prior to when the award will be presented. **Deadline:** November 2. **Contact:** Dawn James at dawn.james@asm.net.

650 ■ The Schonstedt Scholarships in Surveying *(Undergraduate/Scholarship)*

Purpose: ACSM Scholarships are designed to encourage, recognize, and support exceptional surveying and mapping students. **Focus:** Surveying. **Qualif.:** Applicant must be junior or senior student enrolled in a college or university. **Criteria:** Recipients will be selected based on academic record, applicant's statement, letters of recommendation and professional activities.

Funds Avail.: 1,500. **Number Awarded:** 2. **To Apply:** Applicants must complete the application form; applicants must provide a proof of membership in ACSM; a brief yet complete statement indicating educational objectives, future plans of study or research, professional activities and financial need; at least three letters of recommendation (minimum of two from faculty members familiar with the student's work); a complete original official transcript through year prior to when the award will be presented. **Deadline:** November 2. **Contact:** Dawn James at dawn.james@acsm.net.

651 ■ American Conifer Society (ACS)

175 Charisma Ln.
Lewisville, NC 27023-9611
Ph: (336) 945-0483
Fax: (336) 945-0484

E-mail: nationaloffice@conifersociety.org
URL: www.conifersociety.org

652 ■ American Conifer Society Scholarships *(Undergraduate/Scholarship)*

Purpose: To provide financial assistance to ACS members to pursue their education. **Focus:** Horticulture. **Qualif.:** Applicant must be a current ACS member. **Criteria:** Selection of applicant is based on merit in the field of agriculture.

Funds Avail.: $2,500. **To Apply:** Application form may be downloaded from The American Conifer Society Web Page; www.conifersociety.org or you may request a form from; The American Conifer Society Scholarship Committee, 900 Winston Rd. N., Rochester, NY 14609. Forms are also available from the National Office. **Deadline:** April 30. **Contact:** ACS Scholarship Committee, Gerald P. Kral, 900 Winton Rd., N, Rochester, NY 14609, Email: gkral1@rochester.rr.com.

653 ■ American Constitution Society for Law and Policy (ACS)

1333 H St. NW, 11th Fl.
Washington, DC 20005
Ph: (202) 393-6181
Fax: (202) 393-6189
E-mail: info@acslaw.org
URL: www.acslaw.org

654 ■ ACS Law Fellowships *(Graduate/Fellowship)*

Purpose: To provide a recent law school graduate a year of legal experience and training. **Focus:** Law. **Qualif.:** Applicant must be a recent law school graduate from a U.S. law school; have a strong academic record; excellent research, writing and oral communication skills; strong interpersonal skills; and demonstrate initiative, organization and attention to detail. **Criteria:** Selection is based on the application materials.

Funds Avail.: No specific amount. **To Apply:** Applicants must send a cover letter; resume; 5-10 page, self-edited writing sample; and three references to ACS via U.S. mail. Applicants may also email jobs@acslaw.org with "Law Fellow Candidate" in the subject line; or fax to 202-393-6189 (Attn: Marlee Waxelbaum). **Deadline:** April 29.

655 ■ American Copy Editors Society Education Fund (ACES)

7 Avenida Vista Grande, Ste. B7, No. 467
Santa Fe, NM 87508
Ph: (415) 704-4884
E-mail: tschmedding@dailyherald.com
URL: www.copydesk.org

656 ■ Aubespin Scholarships *(Undergraduate/Scholarship)*

Purpose: To encourage young individuals to continue their career as potential professional copy editors. **Focus:** Editors and editing. **Qualif.:** Applicant must be a junior, senior or graduate student in the fall, graduating student who will take full-time copy editing jobs or internships. **Criteria:** Applications are evaluated by a panel of five people with copy desk experience.

Funds Avail.: $2,500. **To Apply:** Application forms are

Awards are arranged alphabetically below their administering organizations

available on the website. Applicant must send a list of course work relevant to copy editing, list of copy editing experience, including work on student and professional publications; must provide an essay (750 words, double spaced); must have two recommendation letters: one from a faculty member or adviser and one from someone on a college or professional publication; must have two copies of five to 10 headlines; must submit a copy of a story that demonstrate the applicant's ability. Application form and other supporting documents must be sent to: ACES Scholarships, Milwaukee Journal Sentinel, 333 W State St., Milwaukee, WI 53203. **Deadline:** November 15. **Contact:** Deirdre Edgar at dedgar@copydesk.org.

657 ■ American Council of the Blind (ACB)

2200 Wilson Blvd., Ste. 650
Arlington, VA 22201
Ph: (202) 467-5081
Fax: (703) 465-5085
Free: 800-424-8666
E-mail: info@acb.org
URL: www.acb.org

658 ■ American Council of the Blind Scholarships *(Graduate, Undergraduate/Scholarship)*

Purpose: To support blind students in their educational pursuits. **Focus:** General studies. **Qualif.:** Applicant must be an undergraduate or graduate blind student. **Criteria:** Selection is based on the submitted application and materials.

Funds Avail.: No specific amount. **To Apply:** Application process must be completed online. In addition, applicants must submit a Certification of Legal Blindness from an ophthalmologist, optometrist, physician or other competent authority; certified transcripts; acceptance letter from a university for entering freshmen; high school transcripts (entering freshmen and sophomores) or undergraduate transcripts (graduate students); and a recommendation letter from a current or recent instructor. Send application materials to pcastillo@acb.org. **Deadline:** March 15. **Contact:** Patricia Castillo at pcastillo@acb.org.

659 ■ American Council of Engineering Companies of Illinois (Consulting Engineers Association of Illinois)

5221 S 6th Street Rd., Ste. 120
Springfield, IL 62703
Ph: (217) 529-7430
Fax: (217) 529-2742
E-mail: acec-il@acec-il.org
URL: www.acec-il.org

660 ■ American Council of Engineering Companies of Illinois Scholarships *(Doctorate, Graduate, Undergraduate/Scholarship)*

Purpose: To assist engineering students of Illinois in reaching their goals of higher education. **Focus:** Engineering. **Qualif.:** Applicants must be U.S. citizens, specifically, Illinois engineering students currently enrolled and pursuing a bachelor's, master's or PhD degree in an Accreditation Board for Engineering and Technology (ABET)-accredited engineering program or in an accredited land surveying program located in the state of Illinois; may be students entering their junior, senior, fifth, master's or graduate year

in the fall. **Criteria:** Applicants are evaluated based on academic merit.

Funds Avail.: $1,500. **Number Awarded:** 11. **To Apply:** Applicants must submit the completed application form along with student's GPA; work experience; extracurricular college activities; recommendation from a professor, consulting engineering or land surveyor; and a 500-word essay. **Contact:** Gaye Kick at the above address or e-mail at acecgaye@acec-il.org.

661 ■ American Council on Exercise

4851 Paramont Dr.
San Diego, CA 92123
Ph: (858) 576-6500
Fax: (858) 576-6564
Free: 888-825-3636
URL: www.acefitness.org

662 ■ Joe Q. Bryant American Council on Exercise Educational Scholarships *(Undergraduate/Scholarship)*

Purpose: To provide support to the Penn State students. **Focus:** Health care services. **Qualif.:** Candidates must a student of Penn State; must maintain at least a 3.0 GPA on a 4.0 scale (verified by academic transcript); must meet the eligibility requirements for the ACE Certification Exam; must have perform two (2) hours of community service monthly during any term in which the student is enrolled. **Criteria:** American Council on Exercises will evaluate each application materials.

Funds Avail.: $1,000. **To Apply:** Applicant must submit the following: Applicant information form; Official copy of academic transcript; Two recommendation forms and statements of support: One academic reference and one non-academic reference; Academic/Leadership/Awards Form; Essay form and 500-word essay. **Deadline:** March 15. **Contact:** Cassie McNab at the above address.

663 ■ William J. Merriman American Council on Exercise Educational Scholarships *(Undergraduate/Scholarship)*

Purpose: To provide support to the Manhattan College students. **Focus:** Health care services. **Qualif.:** Applicant must be a student of Manhattan College; must have at least a 3.0 GPA on a 4.0 scale (verified by academic transcript); must meet the eligibility requirements for the ACE Certification Exam; must perform two hours of community service monthly during any term in which the student is enrolled. **Criteria:** American Council on Exercises will evaluate each application.

Funds Avail.: $1.000. **To Apply:** Applicant must have the following: Applicant information form; Official copy of academic transcript; Two recommendation forms and statement of support: One academic reference and One non-academic reference; Activities/Leadership/Awards form; Essay form and 500-word essay. **Deadline:** March 15. **Contact:** Cassie McNab at the above address.

664 ■ William Shannon American Council on Exercise Certification Scholarships *(Professional development, Undergraduate/Scholarship)*

Purpose: To provide support to the students and employees of Duke University. **Focus:** Health care services. **Qualif.:** Applicant must be a student or employee of Duke University; must meet the requirements for the ACE

Awards are arranged alphabetically below their administering organizations

Certification Exam; must perform two hours of community service monthly during any term in which the student is enrolled. **Criteria:** American Council on Exercises will evaluate each application.

Funds Avail.: $1.000. **Number Awarded:** 1. **To Apply:** Application form must consist of the following: applicant information form; official copy of academic transcript; two recommendation forms and statements of support: one academic reference and one non-academic reference; activities/leadership/awards form; essay form and 500-word essay. **Deadline:** March 15. **Contact:** Cassie McNab at the above address.

665 ■ American Council on Germany (ACG)

14 E 60th St., Ste. 1000
New York, NY 10022
Ph: (212) 826-3636
Fax: (212) 758-3445
E-mail: info@acgusa.org
URL: www.acgusa.org

666 ■ Dr. Guido Goldman Fellowships *(Doctorate, Postdoctorate/Fellowship)*

Purpose: To promote the study of German and European issues by American scholars. **Focus:** European studies; German studies. **Qualif.:** Applicants must be U.S. citizens; postgraduate students; or enrolled in PhD programs and finishing their dissertation. **Criteria:** Selection Committee will select applicants based on the contribution the project will make to an understanding of the economics and foreign relations of Germany, Europe and North America; the feasibility of the proposed project; the training of the applicant; and the scholarly potential of the applicant.

Funds Avail.: Covers the cost of pre-approved international and domestic travel and a per diem of $200. **To Apply:** Applicants must submit a cover letter, outlining the applicant's professional and personal objectives for the fellowship; a 2-page project proposal; a current CV; and two letters of reference. **Deadline:** June 29. **Contact:** Robin Cammarota, Fellowship Coordinator at 212-826-3636 or rcammarota@acqusa.org.

667 ■ Dr. Richard M. Hunt Fellowships *(Doctorate, Postdoctorate/Fellowship)*

Purpose: To promote the study of German issues by American scholars. **Focus:** German studies. **Qualif.:** Applicants must be U.S. citizens; postgraduate students; or enrolled in PhD programs and finishing their dissertation. **Criteria:** The selection committee will evaluate applications based on the contribution the project will make to a better understanding of German history; the feasibility of the proposed project; the training of the applicant; and the scholarly potential of the applicant.

Funds Avail.: Covers the cost of pre-approved international and domestic travel and a per diem of $200. **To Apply:** Applicants must submit a cover letter, outlining the applicant's professional and personal objectives for the fellowship; a 2-page project proposal; a current CV; and two letters of reference. **Deadline:** June 29. **Contact:** Robin Cammarota, Fellowship Coordinator at 212-826-3636 or rcammarota@acqusa.org.

668 ■ American Council of Independent Laboratories (ACIL)

1875 I St. NW, Ste. 500
Washington, DC 20006-5425

Ph: (202) 887-5872
Fax: (202) 887-0021
E-mail: info@acil.org
URL: www.acil.org

669 ■ American Council of Independent Laboratories Scholarships *(Undergraduate/ Scholarship)*

Purpose: To provide financial assistance for helping to ensure future generations of skilled employees for the laboratory testing community. **Focus:** Physical sciences. **Qualif.:** Applicants must be students attending their junior year or higher in a four-year, bachelor degree major in any of the physical sciences practiced by ACIL members: physics, chemistry, engineering, geology, biology, or environmental science in granting institution or graduate program within the United States. **Criteria:** Recipient will be selected based on academic achievement, career goals, leadership, and financial need.

Funds Avail.: $4,000. **To Apply:** Applicant must submit a brief resume or personal statement outlining the activities in college, including field of study and future plans; two letters of recommendation from faculty members of the university currently attending; transcript of grades; and information on any other scholarship or grant aid now receiving. **Deadline:** April 6.

670 ■ American Council of Learned Societies (ACLS)

633 Third Ave., 8th Fl.
New York, NY 10017-6795
Ph: (212) 697-1505
Fax: (212) 949-8058
E-mail: paulineyu@acls.org
URL: www.acls.org

671 ■ ACLS Collaborative Research Fellowships *(Doctorate/Fellowship)*

Purpose: To offer small teams of two or more scholars the opportunity to collaborate intensively on a single, substantive project. **Focus:** Humanities; Social sciences. **Qualif.:** A collaborative project must constitute of at least two scholars who are each seeking salary-replacement stipends for six to twelve continuous months of supported research leave to pursue full-time collaborative research during the fellowship tenure. The project coordinator must have an appointment at a US-based institution of higher education. Other project members may be at institutions outside the United States or may be independent scholars; must hold a PhD degree or its equivalent in publications and professional experience at the time of application. **Criteria:** Proposals will be judged along the following criteria: (1) Intellectual significance of the project, including its ambition and scope, and its potential contribution to scholarship in the humanities; (2) Relevance of the research questions being posed, the appropriateness of research methods, the feasibility of the work plan, the appropriateness of the field work to be undertaken, the archival or source materials to be studied and the research site; (3) Qualifications, expertise and commitment of the project coordinator and collaborators; (4) Detail and soundness of the process and product of the collaboration, including dissemination plans; (5). Degree to which the proposed collaboration represents innovative practice in the applicants' disciplines and subfields; (6) Potential for success, including the likelihood that

Awards are arranged alphabetically below their administering organizations

the work proposed will be completed and lead to distance results within the projected timeframe; where appropriate, the collaborators' previous record of success; and the size of the proposed budget in relation to anticipated results.

Funds Avail.: Maximum of $140,000. **To Apply:** Applications must include the following: completed application forms; participant information sheet, listing all collaborators and additional project members; 10-page Proposal (double space, in Times New Roman, 11-point font). The proposal should describe the intellectual significance of the research project and explain in detail the process and product of the collaboration; two-page bibliography that places the project in intellectual context and includes relevant work in all of the disciplines involved in the project; research plan, including a timeline of the proposed research activities that specifies the location, duration and names of individuals involved in each stage. This may be in the form of a graphic timeline or narrative description; budget statement, outlining salary replacement, costs of research assistance, travel and research materials; a no more than three pages publications list for each collaborator; two reference letters that provide explicit information on the proposed collaborative project and the collaborators. **Deadline:** October 2.

672 ■ ACLS Digital Innovation Fellowships
(Doctorate/Fellowship)

Purpose: To provide scholars the means to pursue intellectually significant projects that deploy digital technologies intensively and innovatively. **Focus:** Social sciences; Humanities. **Qualif.:** Applicants must be scholars in all fields of the humanities and the humanistic social sciences; must have a PhD degree conferred prior to the application deadline; must be US citizens or maintain permanent resident status as of the application deadline. **Criteria:** Selection will be based on the following criteria: scholarly excellence, in terms of the project's intellectual ambitions and technological underpinnings; project's feasibility; project's intellectual, technological and institutional sustainability; project's portability, accessibility and scalability; project's articulation with local infrastructure at the applicants' home institution or at the institution hosting the project.

Funds Avail.: $25,000 for the project costs; $60,000 for stipends. **To Apply:** Applications must be submitted online and must include the following: completed application form; 10-page proposal (double spaced, Times New Roman, 11-point font) explaining the applicant's research plan in relation to the objectives of the Digital Innovation Fellowship Program. The narrative statement should explain, briefly but specifically, the applicant's approach, and why, as well as describe progress already made, make clear the relevance of the project to applicant's professional experience, and discuss the significance of this work within the their specific and general fields. Please balance the description of specific work plans against an overview of goals and the contribution this project will make to digital scholarship generally and to the particular scholarly field(s) it engages. Furthermore, proposals should explicitly state the means and tools (software, applications, interfaces) to be used to accomplish the project's goals. Proposals should present plans for how the project will be sustained and preserved over time, and how the applicant will disseminate notice of its availability. Please balance the description of specific work plans against an overview of their goals and the contribution this project will make to digital scholarship generally and to the particular scholarly field(s) it engages. Furthermore, proposals should explicitly state the means and tools (software, applications, interfaces) to be used to

accomplish the project's goals. Proposals should present plans for how the project will be sustained and preserved over time, and how the applicant will disseminate notice of its availability. Please give the applicant's proposal a brief, descriptive title, and label sections of your narrative as appropriate to assist readers. In addition, if the applicant's project is part of a collaborative undertaking, it is essential to explain that context and describe your relationship to the other participants. Please also list the names of the applicant's colleagues and indicate whether or not those individuals are also applying for ACLS fellowships in the current competition; 3-page bibliography providing an overview of the publications central to advancing the project; publication list; project plan, no more than three pages, providing a coherent plan for development of the project, including a description of tasks to be accomplished within the period of the fellowship; budget plan, no more than two pages, providing a detailed account of the proposed use of the research funds; three reference letters; institutional statement from a senior official of their home institution or the institution hosting the project. **Deadline:** October 2.

673 ■ African Humanities Fellowships
(Postdoctorate/Fellowship)

Purpose: To support dissertations and projects in African studies in all disciplines of the humanities. **Focus:** African studies; Humanities. **Qualif.:** Applicants must be nationals and residents of a country in sub-Saharan Africa, with a current affiliation at an institution in Ghana, Nigeria, South Africa, Tanzania or Uganda. Applicants for Dissertation-Completion Fellowships should be in the final year of writing the dissertation at a university in Ghana, Nigeria, Tanzania or Uganda. Dissertation-Completion Fellowships are not available in South Africa. Applicants for Early Career Postdoctoral Fellowships must be working in Ghana, Nigeria, South Africa, Tanzania or Uganda and must have completed the PhD no more than five years ago. **Criteria:** Selection will be based on the committee's criteria.

Funds Avail.: No specific amount. **To Apply:** Projects must be in the humanities and must be carried out in sub-Saharan Africa. Applicants must submit a completed application by email or may be mailed to the AHP/ACLS offices in New York. **Deadline:** November 1.

674 ■ American Council of Learned Societies Fellowships *(Postdoctorate/Fellowship)*

Purpose: To help scholars devote six to twelve continuous months to full-time research and writing. **Focus:** General studies. **Qualif.:** Applicants must have PhD degrees conferred at least two years before the application deadline; must be U.S. citizens or have permanent resident status; must have a lapse of at least two years since the last supported research leave. **Criteria:** Recipients are selected based on academic rank.

Funds Avail.: $35,000 for Assistant Professor; $40,000 for Associate Professor; $60,000 for full professor. **Number Awarded:** 3. **To Apply:** Applicants must complete the application form; a double-spaced proposal of not more than five pages; two pages of supporting materials; not more than two pages of bibliography; not more than two pages of publication list; and two reference letters. **Deadline:** September 29.

675 ■ American Research in the Humanities in China Fellowships *(Doctorate/Fellowship)*

Purpose: To support research that reflects an understanding of the present Chinese academic and research environ-

Awards are arranged alphabetically below their administering organizations

ment. **Focus:** Humanities; Social sciences. **Qualif.:** Applicants must be citizens or permanent residents of the United States who have lived in the United States continuously for at least three years as of the application deadline date; must hold a PhD degree conferred prior to the application deadline. However, an established scholar who can demonstrate the equivalent of the PhD in publications and professional experience may also qualify. **Criteria:** Selection will be based on the committee's criteria.

Funds Avail.: Up to $50,400. **To Apply:** Applicants must submit a carefully formulated research proposal that reflects an understanding of the present Chinese academic and research environment. The proposal should include a persuasive statement of the need to conduct the research in China. Applications must include: completed application form; proposal (no more than five pages, double spaced, in Times New Roman 11-point font); up to three additional pages of images, musical scores or other similar supporting non-text materials; copies of correspondence with Chinese contacts; bibliography (no more than two pages); curriculum vitae (no more than five pages); three reference letters. **Deadline:** October 2.

676 ■ Comparative Perspectives on Chinese Culture and Society Grants (Doctorate/Grant)

Purpose: To promote interchange among scholars who may not otherwise have the opportunity to work together, and to support collaborative work in China studies. **Focus:** Chinese studies. **Qualif.:** The principal organizer must be affiliated with a university or research institution and must hold a PhD. There are no restrictions as to citizenship of participants or location of the project; however, it is expected the scholars from academic institutions in Taiwan will participate in conferences, workshops and planning meetings. **Criteria:** Selection will be based on the committee's criteria.

Funds Avail.: Up to $25,000 for conferences; $10,000-$15,000 for workshops and seminars; up to $6,000 for planning meetings. **To Apply:** All proposals must include the following: application information sheet (available at the website); a description of the project and its purposes. Descriptions should be no more than five double-spaced pages; a budget for the proposed event, including a statement of any other funds available; a short bibliography of relevant sources; two-page CV of principal organizer; a list of those invited with their CVs (two pages maximum). This list should clearly differentiate between those who have agreed to participate in the event and those whose participation is not confirmed. This list should also specify paper writers and discussants. Participation of scholars from academic institutions in Taiwan is expected. Participation of scholars from outside the China field is strongly encouraged; for conferences only: an appendix containing abstracts (of approximately 150-200 words) for each paper to be presented at the conference. Submit the application materials as a single, searchable PDF file. **Deadline:** September 19.

677 ■ Dissertation Fellowships in East European Studies (Doctorate/Fellowship)

Purpose: To support dissertations in East European studies in all disciplines of the humanities and social sciences. **Focus:** European studies; Humanities; Social sciences. **Qualif.:** Applicants must be enrolled in a PhD program at a US university; must have completed all requirements for the PhD except the dissertation; may apply for one-year research and writing fellowships in sequence, but may not apply for a second year of funding in either category.

Criteria: Fellowships will be granted based on the potential of the applicants, the quality and scholarly significance of the proposed work and its importance to the development of the field of East European studies.

Funds Avail.: $18,000. **To Apply:** Applicants project must pertain to at least one of the East European countries; must be in the humanities or social sciences; must aim to produce a PhD dissertation, written in English; must clearly state a plan of work that can be accomplished during the fellowship period. Applications must include the following: completed application form; proposal (no more than five pages, double spaced, in Times New Roman, 11-point font; up to two additional pages of images, musical scores or other similar supporting non-text materials; bibliography (no more than two pages); publications list (no more than two pages); three reference letters; institutional statement; language evaluation form(s). **Deadline:** November 15.

678 ■ Early Career Postdoctoral Fellowships in East European Studies (Postdoctorate/Fellowship)

Purpose: To support postdoctoral research and writing in East European studies in all disciplines of the humanities and social sciences. **Focus:** European studies; Humanities; Social sciences. **Qualif.:** Applicants must be US citizens; PhD must be conferred prior to the application deadline. However, established scholars who can demonstrate the equivalent of the PhD in publications and professional experience may also qualify; must be at an early career stage. **Criteria:** Selection will be based on the scholarly merit of the proposal, its importance to the development of the field and the scholarly potential and accomplishments of the applicants.

Funds Avail.: $25,000. **To Apply:** Applicants' projects must: pertain to at least one of the East European countries; be in the humanities or social sciences and must investigate aspects of East European societies, histories and cultures with a special regard for how they illuminate contemporary issues or the necessary backgrounds for understanding such issues; aim to produce a written scholarly product such as a book manuscript, to be written in English; must clearly state a plan of work that can be accomplished during the fellowship period. Applications must be submitted online and must include: completed application form; a no more than five pages, double spaced, in Times New Roman and 11-point font proposal; up to two additional pages of images, musical scores or other similar supporting non-text materials; no more than two pages bibliography; no more than two pages publications list; two reference letters.

679 ■ Henry Luce Foundation Dissertation Fellowships in American Art (Doctorate/Fellowship)

Purpose: To provide support for young scholars who are in the phase of completing their dissertations and to advance research after being awarded the PhD. **Focus:** Art history. **Qualif.:** Applicants must be PhD candidates in a department of art history in the United States completing their dissertation which focuses on a topic in the history of the visual arts of the United States; must be U.S. citizens or have permanent residency; and must have completed all the requirements for the PhD except the dissertation before the beginning of the fellowship tenure. **Criteria:** Recipients are selected based on academic standing and completed requirements.

Funds Avail.: $25,000. **Number Awarded:** 10. **To Apply:** Applicants must complete the application form including statement of all university and external support received during graduate study; double-spaced proposal including a timeline for the expected completion of the dissertation writing and defense (not more than five pages); up to additional three pages of supporting materials; bibliography of not more than two pages; a completed chapter of the dissertation; three reference letters; a letter from the applicant's institution; and official transcript of graduate records. **Deadline:** November.

680 ■ Andrew W. Mellon Dissertation Completion Fellowships *(Doctorate/Fellowship)*

Purpose: To provide support for young scholars who are in the phase of completing their dissertations; to advance research after being awarded the PhD. **Focus:** Humanities; Social Sciences. **Qualif.:** Applicants must be PhD candidates in a humanities or social science department in the United States; must have all requirements for the PhD except the dissertation completed before beginning fellowship tenure; must be no more than six years in the degree program. **Criteria:** Recipients are selected based on academic standing and completed requirements.

Funds Avail.: $25,000; $3,000 for research cost; $5,000 for university fees. **To Apply:** Applicants must complete the application form including statement of all university and external support received during graduate study; a double-spaced proposal including a timeline for the expected completion of the dissertation writing and defense (not more than five pages); up to additional three pages of supporting materials; not more than two pages of bibliography; a completed chapter of the dissertation; two reference letters; and a letter from the applicant's institution. **Deadline:** November.

681 ■ Charles A. Ryskamp Research Fellowships *(Doctorate/Fellowship)*

Purpose: To support advanced assistant professors and untenured associate professors in the humanities and related science. **Focus:** Humanities; Science. **Qualif.:** Applicants must be tenured-track assistant professors and untenured associate professors; must hold the PhD or equivalent and be employed in tenure-track positions at degree granting academic institutions in the United States. **Criteria:** Recipients are selected based on academic standing.

Funds Avail.: $64,000; $2,500 for research and travel. **To Apply:** Applicants must submit completed application form; double-spaced proposal (not more than ten pages); bibliography (not more than two pages); publication list (not more than two pages); and four reference letters. **Deadline:** September.

682 ■ American Counsel Association (ACA)
2500 Wachovia Capitol Ctr.
150 Fayetteville St.
Raleigh, NC 27601
Ph: (919) 821-1220
E-mail: jdorsett@smithlaw.com
URL: www.amcounsel.org

683 ■ American Counsel Association Scholarships *(Undergraduate/Scholarship)*

Purpose: To provide scholarships to academically gifted and financially needy third-year law students. **Focus:** Law. **Qualif.:** Applicants must be enrolled in a law school located within the Seventh Federal Judicial District. **Criteria:** Selection will be based on the committee's criteria.

Funds Avail.: No specific amount. **To Apply:** The law school deans are invited to submit nominations which are reviewed by the Committee.

684 ■ American Counseling Association (ACA)
5999 Stevenson Ave.
Alexandria, VA 22304
Ph: (703) 823-6862
Fax: (703) 823-0252
Free: 800-347-6647
E-mail: ryep@counseling.org
URL: www.counseling.org

685 ■ Ross Trust Graduate Student Scholarships *(Graduate, Postdoctorate/Scholarship)*

Purpose: To provide support to students preparing for counseling roles in the nation's elementary, middle and secondary schools. **Focus:** Counseling/Guidance. **Qualif.:** Applicants must be currently enrolled in either master's level or in doctoral level program of studies in preparation to work as professional counselors at the elementary, middle or secondary education level. **Criteria:** Selection of applicants will be based on the following: (a) Master's-level students must have an outstanding academic performance (based on a minimum of 15 graduate hours completed) and exemplary volunteer activities; (b) Doctoral-level students must have an outstanding academic performance (based on a minimum of 15 graduate hours completed), exemplary volunteer activities in schools and/or community, and scholarly research, writing and presentations.

Funds Avail.: $1,375. **Number Awarded:** 15. **To Apply:** Applicants must have statement of career goals; must provide a description of volunteer experiences in schools and/or the community. For doctoral level scholarships, applicants must have statement reflecting research, writing and presentation activities. **Contact:** For additional information, applicants can direct their questions via e-mail to hclubb@counseling.org.

686 ■ American Criminal Justice Association (ACJA-LAE) - Lambda Alpha Epsilon (ACJA-LAE)
PO Box 601047
Sacramento, CA 95860-1047
Ph: (916) 484-6553
Fax: (916) 488-2227
E-mail: acjalae@aol.com
URL: www.acjalae.org

687 ■ American Criminal Justice Association Scholarships *(Graduate, Undergraduate/Scholarship)*

Purpose: To provide financial support to members who are upper or lower division students or graduate students enrolled in a course of study in the criminal justice field. **Focus:** Criminal Justice. **Qualif.:** Applicants must be US citizens or eligible non-citizens; must be ACJA/LAE chapter members; must be currently enrolled in a recognized course of study directly or indirectly associated with the criminal justice field; must have achieved a minimum overall GPA of 3.0 on a scale of 4.0; must be currently enrolled with a minimum course of at least two-thirds of full-time loads. **Criteria:** Recipients are selected based on: overall GPA of 3.0 or better on a scale of 4.0; GPA of basic courses completed in criminal justice or related field of study; and

Awards are arranged alphabetically below their administering organizations

statement of career and educational goals.

Funds Avail.: $400; $200; $100. **To Apply:** Applicants must fill out application form. Applicants must submit: five copies of school transcript; five copies of letters of recommendation from chapter officers and faculty advisors; career and educational goal statement. **Deadline:** December 31. **Contact:** Dr. Archie Rainey at the above address.

688 ■ American Culinary Federation (ACF)

180 Center Place Way
St. Augustine, FL 32095
Ph: (904) 824-4468
Fax: (904) 825-4758
Free: 800-624-9458
E-mail: acf@acfchefs.net
URL: www.acfchefs.org

689 ■ American Culinary Federation Chair's Scholarship Grants *(All/Scholarship)*

Purpose: to provide financial assistance to those studying culinary arts. **Focus:** Culinary arts. **Qualif.:** Applicants must be a student hot food team sponsored by an ACF Chapter; have already won their state competition and are ready to go to the regional competition, or have won their regional competition and are ready to go to the national competition; must be ACF Student Members in good standing and have held at least one fundraiser. **Criteria:** Recipient will be selected based on the American Academy of Chefs Scholarship Committee's review of the application materials.

Funds Avail.: No specific amount. **To Apply:** Applicants must submit a completed application form; proof of fundraiser and amount raised; and signed images release to use the team's names and/or photos in ACF publications. **Deadline:** For state teams going to Regionals: the application is due at least 15 days before the regional competition. For Regional teams going to Nationals: the application is due by June 1.

690 ■ Balestreri/Cutino Scholarships
(Undergraduate/Scholarship)

Purpose: to provide financial assistance to those studying culinary arts. **Focus:** Culinary arts. **Qualif.:** Applicant must be an exemplary student currently enrolled in an accredited, post-secondary college, with a major in either culinary or pastry arts, or be an ACF registered apprentice. Applicant must have completed a grading or marking period (trimester, semester or quarter) and must have a career goal of becoming a chef or pastry chef. **Criteria:** Scholarship recipient will be selected based on the American Academy of Chefs Scholarship Committee's review of the application materials.

Funds Avail.: No specific amount. **To Apply:** Applicants must submit a completed application form; two letters of recommendation from industry and/or culinary professionals (may not be related to the applicant in any manner); a Financial Aid Release Form completed by the financial aid office; sealed official transcript showing current GPA; and signed photo and/or photo in ACF publications. **Deadline:** May 1 or September 1.

691 ■ Chaine des Rotisseurs Scholarships
(Undergraduate/Scholarship)

Purpose: to provide financial assistance to those studying culinary arts. **Focus:** Culinary arts. **Qualif.:** Applicant must

be an exemplary student (have and maintain a cumulative GPA of 2.5 of higher) currently enrolled in an accredited, post-secondary college, with a major in either culinary or pastry arts, or be an ACF registered apprentice. Applicant must have completed a grading or marking period (trimester, semester or quarter) and must have a career goal of becoming a chef or pastry chef. **Criteria:** Scholarship recipient will be selected based on the American Academy of Chefs Scholarship Committee's review of the application materials.

Funds Avail.: No specific amount. **To Apply:** Applicants must submit a completed application form; two letters of recommendation from industry and/or culinary professionals (may not be related to the applicant in any manner); a Financial Aid Release Form completed by the financial aid office; sealed official transcript showing current GPA; and signed photo and/or photo in ACF publications. **Deadline:** May 1 or September 1.

692 ■ Julia Child Memorial Scholarships
(Undergraduate/Scholarship)

Purpose: to provide financial assistance to those studying culinary arts. **Focus:** Culinary arts. **Qualif.:** Applicant must be an exemplary student (have and maintain a cumulative GPA of 2.5 of higher) currently enrolled in an accredited, post-secondary college, with a major in either culinary or pastry arts, or be an ACF registered apprentice. Applicant must have completed a grading or marking period (trimester, semester or quarter) and must have a career goal of becoming a chef or pastry chef. **Criteria:** Scholarship recipient will be selected based on the American Academy of Chefs Scholarship Committee's review of the application materials.

Funds Avail.: No specific amount. **To Apply:** Applicants must submit a completed application form; two letters of recommendation from industry and/or culinary professionals (may not be related to the applicant in any manner); a Financial Aid Release Form completed by the financial aid office; sealed official transcript showing current GPA; and signed photo and/or photo in ACF publications. **Deadline:** May 1 or September 1.

693 ■ Linda Cullen Memorial Scholarships
(High School/Scholarship)

Purpose: to provide financial assistance to those studying culinary arts. **Focus:** Culinary arts. **Qualif.:** Applicant must be an exemplary senior high school student eligible to graduate the same year as the scholarship is applied for. Applicant must be currently accepted to an accredited, post-secondary college, with a major in either culinary or pastry arts, or must be an ACF registered apprentice; have a career goal of becoming a chef or pastry chef. **Criteria:** Scholarship recipient will be selected based on the American Academy of Chefs Scholarship Committee's review of the application materials.

Funds Avail.: No specific amount. **To Apply:** Applicants must submit a completed application form; two letters of recommendation from industry and/or culinary professionals (may not be related to the applicant in any manner); a Financial Aid Release Form completed by the financial aid office; sealed official high school transcript showing current GPA; and signed photo and/or photo in ACF publications. **Deadline:** March 31.

694 ■ Stanley "Doc" Jensen Scholarships *(High School/Scholarship)*

Purpose: to provide financial assistance to those studying culinary arts. **Focus:** Culinary arts. **Qualif.:** Applicant must

Awards are arranged alphabetically below their administering organizations

be an exemplary senior high school student eligible to graduate the same year as the scholarship is applied for. Applicant must be currently accepted to an accredited, post-secondary college, with a major in either culinary or pastry arts, or must be an ACF registered apprentice; have a career goal of becoming a chef or pastry chef. **Criteria:** Scholarship recipient will be selected based on the American Academy of Chefs Scholarship Committee's review of the application materials.

Funds Avail.: No specific amount. **To Apply:** Applicants must submit a completed application form; two letters of recommendation from industry and/or culinary professionals (may not be related to the applicant in any manner); a Financial Aid Release Form completed by the financial aid office; sealed official high school transcript showing current GPA; and signed photo and/or photo in ACF publications. **Deadline:** March 31.

695 ■ Andrew Macrina Scholarships (High School/Scholarship)

Purpose: to provide financial assistance to those studying culinary arts. **Focus:** Culinary arts. **Qualif.:** Applicant must be an exemplary senior high school student eligible to graduate the same year as the scholarship is applied for. Applicant must be currently accepted to an accredited, post-secondary college, with a major in either culinary or pastry arts, or must be an ACF registered apprentice; have a career goal of becoming a chef or pastry chef. **Criteria:** Scholarship recipient will be selected based on the American Academy of Chefs Scholarship Committee's review of the application materials.

Funds Avail.: No specific amount. **To Apply:** Applicants must submit a completed application form; two letters of recommendation from industry and/or culinary professionals (may not be related to the applicant in any manner); a Financial Aid Release Form completed by the financial aid office; sealed official high school transcript showing current GPA; and signed photo and/or photo in ACF publications. **Deadline:** March 31.

696 ■ Ray and Gertrude Marshall Scholarships (Undergraduate/Scholarship)

Purpose: to provide financial assistance to those studying culinary arts. **Focus:** Culinary arts. **Qualif.:** Applicant must be an exemplary student (have and maintain a cumulative GPA of 2.5 of higher) currently enrolled in an accredited, post-secondary college, with a major in either culinary or pastry arts, or be an ACF registered apprentice. Applicant must have completed a grading or marking period (trimester, semester or quarter) and must have a career goal of becoming a chef or pastry chef. **Criteria:** Scholarship recipient will be selected based on the American Academy of Chefs Scholarship Committee's review of the application materials.

Funds Avail.: No specific amount. **To Apply:** Applicants must submit a completed application form; two letters of recommendation from industry and/or culinary professionals (may not be related to the applicant in any manner); a Financial Aid Release Form completed by the financial aid office; sealed official transcript showing current GPA; and signed photo and/or photo in ACF publications. **Deadline:** May 1 or September 1.

697 ■ Hermann G. Rusch Scholarships (Professional development/Scholarship)

Purpose: To support professional chefs who wished to continue education or initial certification class. **Focus:** Culi-

nary arts. **Qualif.:** For initial certification, applicants must pass an initial ACF certification class with a "C" grade or better. For continuing education, applicants must be certified by the American Culinary Federation as a Certified Chef d' Cuisine or higher; enrolled in a state accredited educational institution for the purpose of enhancing culinary skills or knowledge; an active member of the American Culinary Federation in good standing for three or more years. **Criteria:** Scholarship recipient will be selected based on the American Academy of Chefs Scholarship Committee's review of the application materials.

Funds Avail.: $750 for approved courses only. **To Apply:** Applicants must submit a completed application form, proof of certification, proof of ACF membership and total cost of class.

698 ■ Spice Box Grants (Professional development/Grant)

Purpose: To support professional chefs who wish to continue their education or initial certification class. **Focus:** Culinary arts. **Qualif.:** For initial certification, applicants must pass an initial ACF certification class with a "C" grade or better. For continuing education, applicants must be certified by the American Culinary Federation as a Certified Chef d' Cuisine or higher; enrolled in a state accredited educational institution for the purpose of enhancing culinary skills or knowledge; an active member of the American Culinary Federation in good standing for three or more years. **Criteria:** Scholarship recipient will be selected based on the American Academy of Chefs Scholarship Committee's review of the application materials.

Funds Avail.: $750 for approved courses only. **To Apply:** Applicants must submit a completed application form, proof of certification, proof of ACF membership and total cost of class.

699 ■ Tomato Fest Scholarship Grants (Undergraduate/Scholarship)

Purpose: To provide financial assistance to those studying culinary arts. **Focus:** Culinary arts. **Qualif.:** Applicant must be an exemplary student (have and maintain a cumulative GPA of 2.5 of higher) currently enrolled in an accredited, post-secondary college, with a major in either culinary or pastry arts, or be an ACF registered apprentice. Applicant must have completed a grading or marking period (trimester, semester or quarter) and must have a career goal of becoming a chef or pastry chef. **Criteria:** Scholarship recipient will be selected based on the American Academy of Chefs Scholarship Committee's review of the application materials.

Funds Avail.: No specific amount. **To Apply:** Applicants must submit a completed application form; two letters of recommendation from industry and/or culinary professionals (may not be related to the applicant in any manner); a Financial Aid Release Form completed by the financial aid office; sealed official transcript showing current GPA; and signed photo and/or photo in ACF publications. **Deadline:** May 1 or September 1.

700 ■ American Dental Association (ADA)
211 E Chicago Ave.
Chicago, IL 60611-2678
Ph: (312) 440-2500
Fax: (312) 440-7494
E-mail: affiliates@ada.org
URL: www.ada.org

Awards are arranged alphabetically below their administering organizations

701 ■ American Dental Association Dental Assisting Scholarship Program (Undergraduate/Scholarship)

Purpose: To provide financial assistance for furthering education of students in pursuing the field of dentistry. **Focus:** Dentistry. **Qualif.:** Applicants must be U.S. citizens (permanent resident status does not qualify); must be entering students at the time of application and enrolled in a dental assisting program accredited by the Commission on Dental Accreditation of the American Dental Association; enrolled as full-time students with minimum of 12 credit hours; demonstrate a minimum financial need of $1,000; have minimum accumulative grade point average of 3.0 based on a 4.0 scale; and two reference forms: one from a dentist or dental assisting representative and/or one from a school representative which must be submitted as part of the application form. **Criteria:** Applicants will be evaluated based on demonstrated financial need; academic achievement; biographical sketch questionnaire; and two completed reference forms.

Funds Avail.: $1,000. **Number Awarded:** 10. **To Apply:** Applicants must submit an application form that is typed or printed in black ink, completed and signed by school officials; completed application form including the Academic Achievement Record Form and Financial Needs Assessment Form signed by school official; a copy of the school's letter of acceptance for those incoming first-year students; two completed reference forms, sealed and signed on the back flap of the envelope by the referrers (required forms must be used which are a part of the scholarship application form); typed, biographical sketch questionnaire (required form must be used which is a part of the scholarship application form); a self-addressed, stamped postcard which can be mailed upon receipt of the application (if the applicant wishes to have verification that the application was received). **Deadline:** September 5.

702 ■ American Dental Association Dental Hygiene Scholarship Program (Undergraduate/Scholarship)

Purpose: To provide financial assistance for furthering education of students in pursuing the field of dentistry. **Focus:** Dentistry. **Qualif.:** Applicants must be U.S. citizens (permanent resident status does not qualify); must be entering final year at the time of application and currently attending a dental hygiene program accredited by the Commission on Dental Accreditation of the American Dental Association; enrolled as full-time students with minimum of 12 credit hours; demonstrate a minimum financial need of $1,000; have a minimum accumulative grade point average of 3.0 based on a 4.0 scale; and two reference forms from two dental hygiene program representatives which must be submitted as part of the application form. **Criteria:** Applicants will be evaluated based on demonstrated financial need; academic achievement; biographical sketch questionnaire; and two completed reference forms.

Funds Avail.: $1,000. **To Apply:** Applicants must submit an application form that is typed or printed in black ink, completed and signed by school officials; completed application form including the Academic Achievement Record Form and Financial Needs Assessment Form signed by school official; a copy of the school's letter of acceptance for those incoming first-year students; two completed reference forms, sealed and signed on the back flap of the envelope by the referrers (required forms must be used which are a part of the scholarship application form); typed, biographical sketch questionnaire (required form must be

used which is a part of the scholarship application form); a self-addressed, stamped postcard which can be mailed upon receipt of the application (if the applicant wishes to have verification that the application was received). **Deadline:** June 2.

703 ■ American Dental Association Dental Laboratory Technology Scholarship Program (Undergraduate/Scholarship)

Purpose: To provide financial assistance for students to further their education in the field of dentistry. **Focus:** Dentistry. **Qualif.:** Applicants must be U.S. citizens (permanent resident status does not qualify); entering their final year as students at the time of application; must be currently attending a dental laboratory technology program accredited by the Commission on Dental Accreditation of the American Dental Association; must be enrolled as full-time students with minimum of 12 credit hours; must demonstrate financial need of $1,000; have a minimum accumulative grade point average of 3.0 based on a 4.0 scale; and must have two reference forms from two dental laboratory technology program representatives which must be submitted as part of the application form. **Criteria:** Applicants will be evaluated based on demonstrated financial need; academic achievement; biographical sketch questionnaire; and two completed reference forms.

Funds Avail.: $1,000. **To Apply:** Applicants must submit an application form that is typed or printed in black ink, completed and signed by school officials; completed application form including the Academic Achievement Record Form and Financial Needs Assessment Form signed by school official; a copy of the school's letter of acceptance for those incoming first-year students; two completed reference forms, sealed and signed on the back flap of the envelope by the referrers (required forms must be used which are a part of the scholarship application form); typed, biographical sketch questionnaire (required form must be used which is a part of the scholarship application form); a self-addressed, stamped postcard which can be mailed upon receipt of the application (if applicants wish to have verification that their application was received). **Deadline:** September 5.

704 ■ American Dental Association Dental Student Scholarships (Undergraduate/Scholarship)

Purpose: To provide financial assistance for furthering education of dental students. **Focus:** Dentistry. **Qualif.:** Applicant must be a U.S. citizens (permanent resident status does not qualify); entering second year student at the time of application and currently attending or enrolled at a dental school accredited by the Commission on Dental Accreditation of the American Dental Association; enrolled as a full-time student with a minimum of 12 credit hours; must demonstrate a financial need of $2,500; have a minimum accumulative grade point average of 3.0 based on a 4.0 scale; and two reference forms from two dental school representatives. **Criteria:** Applicant will be evaluated based on demonstrated financial need; academic achievement; biographical sketch questionnaire; and two completed reference forms.

Funds Avail.: $2,500. **To Apply:** Applicant must submit an application form that is typed or printed in black ink, completed and signed by school officials; completed application form, including the Academic Achievement Record Form and Financial Needs Assessment Form signed by school official; a copy of the school's letter of acceptance,

Awards are arranged alphabetically below their administering organizations

for entering first-year students; two completed reference forms, sealed and signed on the back flap of the envelope by the referrers (required forms must be used which are a part of the scholarship application form); typed, biographical sketch questionnaire (required form must be used which is a part of the scholarship application form); a self-addressed, stamped postcard, which can be mailed upon receipt of the application (if the applicant wishes to have verification that the application was received). **Deadline:** December 3.

705 ■ American Dental Association Minority Dental Student Scholarships (Undergraduate/Scholarship)

Purpose: To provide financial assistance for furthering education of the minority dental students. **Focus:** Dentistry. **Qualif.:** Applicants must be U.S. citizens (permanent resident status does not qualify); entering second year students at the time of application and currently attending or enrolled at a dental school accredited by the Commission on Dental Accreditation of the American Dental Association; enrolled as a full-time student, a minimum of 12 credit hours; demonstrate a minimum financial need of $2,500; have a minimum accumulative grade point average of 3.0 based on a 4.0 scale; and two reference forms from two dental school representatives (i.e., professor or academic advisor) in support of the application must be submitted as part of the application form. **Criteria:** Applicant will be evaluated based on applicant's demonstrated financial need, academic achievement, biographical sketch questionnaire and two completed reference forms.

Funds Avail.: $2,500. **Number Awarded:** 25. **To Apply:** Applicant must submit an application form that is typed or printed in black ink, completed and signed by school officials; completed application form, including the Academic Achievement Record Form and Financial Needs Assessment Form, which are a part of the application form, and signed by school official; a copy of the school's letter of acceptance, if entering first-year student; two completed reference forms, sealed and signed on the back flap of the envelopes by the referrers (required forms must be used which are a part of the scholarship application form); typed, biographical sketch questionnaire (required form must be used which is a part of the scholarship application form); a self-addressed, stamped postcard, which can be mailed upon receipt of the application (if the applicant wishes to have verification that the application was received). **Deadline:** December 3.

706 ■ American Dental Hygienists' Association Institute for Oral Health (ADHA IOH)

c/o American Dental Hygienists' Association
444 N Michigan Ave., Ste. 3400
Chicago, IL 60611
Ph: (312) 440-8900
E-mail: institute@adha.net
URL: www.adha.org/ioh

707 ■ ADHA IOH Sigma Phi Alpha Graduate Scholarships (Graduate/Scholarship)

Purpose: To provide financial assistance to dental hygiene students and dental hygienists who can demonstrate a commitment to further knowledge through academic achievement, professional excellence and desire to improve the public's overall health. **Focus:** Dental hygiene. **Qualif.:** Applicants must be Sigma Phi Alpha members pursuing a

graduate degree in dental hygiene or any related fields; must demonstrate a cumulative GPA of at least 3.5 on a 4.0 scale; must be members of ADHA. **Criteria:** Applicants will be chosen based on submitted materials.

Funds Avail.: Amount not specified. **To Apply:** Applicants are required to have a specific goals statement and must submit a manuscript upon completion of the program. **Deadline:** February 1.

708 ■ American Dental Hygienists' Association Institute for Oral Health Fellowships (Master's/Fellowship)

Purpose: To support professional advancement of dental hygiene educators. **Focus:** Dental hygiene. **Qualif.:** Applicants must be faculty members pursuing a Master's degree in dental hygiene education or doctoral work; must hold a valid license to practice dental hygiene; must be active members of ADHA. **Criteria:** Recipients will be selected based on demonstrated commitment to dental hygiene education, research, advancement of dental hygiene practice and academic record.

Funds Avail.: $5,000. **Number Awarded:** 2. **To Apply:** Applicants must contact ADHA Institute for Oral Health for application process.

709 ■ Wilma Motley Memorial California Merit Scholarships (Undergraduate, Master's, Doctorate, Professional development/Scholarship)

Purpose: To provide financial assistance to dental hygiene students and dental hygienists who can demonstrate a commitment to further knowledge through academic achievement, professional excellence and desire to improve the public's overall health. **Focus:** Dental hygiene. **Qualif.:** Applicants must be Registered Dental Hygienists in Alternative Practice (RDHAP) or individuals pursuing associate/certificate, baccalaureate, master's or doctorate degree in dental hygiene or related field; must be residents and attending a dental hygiene program in California; must demonstrate leadership experience and have GPA of at least 3.5 on a 4.0 scale; must be active members of ADHA. **Criteria:** Applicants will be awarded based on merit.

Funds Avail.: $2,000. **Number Awarded:** 3. **To Apply:** Applicants must contact ADHA Institute for Oral Health office to request an application form and to ask further information. **Deadline:** February 1.

710 ■ Irene Woodall Graduate Scholarships (Master's/Scholarship)

Purpose: To provide financial assistance to dental hygiene students and dental hygienists who demonstrate a commitment to further knowledge through academic achievement, professional excellence and desire to improve the public's overall health. **Focus:** Dental hygiene. **Qualif.:** Applicants must be pursuing a Master's degree in dental hygiene or any related fields; must have a minimum GPA of 3.5 on a 4.0 scale; must be members of American Dental Hygienist's Association. **Criteria:** Scholarship will be awarded based on how well the applicant demonstrates the goal or achievement described.

Funds Avail.: $1,000-$2,000. **To Apply:** Applicants must contact ADHA Institute for Oral Health office for further information. **Deadline:** February 1.

711 ■ American Division Veterans Association (ADVA)

503 Avalon Way
Shrewsbury, MA 01545

Awards are arranged alphabetically below their administering organizations

E-mail: spen@juno.com
URL: www.americal.org

712 ■ American Division Veterans Association Scholarships *(Undergraduate, Vocational/Occupational/Scholarship)*

Purpose: To provide college and vocational scholarships to the children and grandchildren, including those by adoption, of current and deceased ADVA members, provided the deceased member held good membership standing at the time of death, and to any child or adopted child of an American Division soldier who was killed or died while on active duty with the division. **Focus:** General studies. **Qualif.:** Applicant must be a high school graduate and planning to attend college. **Criteria:** Recipients will be selected based on financial need.

Funds Avail.: No specific amount. **To Apply:** Applicant must submit a letter from the sponsor attesting to the applicant's eligibility according to ADVA Scholarship Fund Purpose and By-Laws; a letter of admission from the applicant's college or vocational school of choice; a letter from the applicant's high school principal attesting to the applicant's character if applicant is attending or has graduated from high school (If currently attending a college education, applicant may disregard this reference letter); two letters of recommendation from current teachers concerning the applicant's progress in current classes or subjects; a photocopy of the applicant's high school or college transcript; a detailed statement of the applicant's academic accomplishments, extracurricular activities, and community service involvement; an applicant must submit a 200-300 word essay on subjects pertaining to American Division history, national pride, loyalty to the nation, and patriotism. **Deadline:** April 1.

713 ■ American Educational Research Association (AERA)

1430 K St. NW, Ste. 1200
Washington, DC 20005-2504
Ph: (202) 238-3200
Fax: (202) 238-3250
E-mail: webmaster@aera.net
URL: www.aera.net

714 ■ AERA-AIR Fellows Program
(Postdoctorate/Fellowship)

Purpose: To support early career scholars by providing intensive research and training opportunities to recent doctoral recipients in the fields and disciplines related to the scientific study of education and education processes; to increase the number of underrepresented minority professionals conducting advanced research or providing technical assistance. **Focus:** Education. **Qualif.:** Applicants must be U.S citizens and permanent residents; must have completed their PhD/EdD degrees within the three years prior to application. **Criteria:** Selection of applicants will be based on their research proposal.

Funds Avail.: $45,000-$50,000. **Number Awarded:** Up to three. **To Apply:** Applicants must complete the application form available online; must submit a letter of recommendation; transcript of records; personal statement; dissertation abstract; dissertation/doctoral thesis summary; writing sample; and curriculum vitae. **Deadline:** December 1. **Contact:** Submit application to: George Wimberly at the above address.

715 ■ AERA-ETS Fellowship Program in Measurement *(Postdoctorate/Fellowship)*

Purpose: To increase the involvement of women and underrepresented minority professionals in measurement, psychometric, assessment and related fields. **Focus:** Testing, educational/psychological. **Qualif.:** Applicants must be U.S citizens and permanent residents; must have completed their PhD/EdD degrees within the three years prior to application. **Criteria:** Selection of applicants will be based on the scholarship selection criteria.

Funds Avail.: $55,000. **To Apply:** Applicants must complete the application form available online; must submit a letter of recommendation; transcript of records; personal statement; dissertation abstract; dissertation/doctoral thesis summary; writing sample; and curriculum vitae. **Deadline:** December 1. **Contact:** Applications should be sent to: George Wimberly at the above address.

716 ■ AERA Minority Fellowship Program in Education Research *(Postdoctorate/Fellowship)*

Purpose: To provide support for doctoral dissertation research and to advance education research by outstanding minority graduate students and to improve the quality and diversity of university faculties. **Focus:** Education. **Qualif.:** Applicant must be a U.S citizen and permanent resident; must work full-time on his or her dissertations and course requirements. **Criteria:** Selection will be based on the submitted application.

Funds Avail.: Stipend of $12,000 and up to $1,000 in travel support to attend the AERA Annual Meeting. **Number Awarded:** Up to three. **To Apply:** Applicants must complete the application form available online; must submit a letter of recommendation and transcript of record. Application form and other supporting documents must be sent to AERA-AIR Fellows Program, American Educational Research Association, 1430 K St. NW, Ste. 1200, Washington, DC 20005. **Deadline:** December 1.

717 ■ American Enterprise Institute

1150 17th St. NW
Washington, DC 20036
Ph: (202) 862-5800
Fax: (202) 862-7177
E-mail: webmaster@aei.org
URL: www.aei.org

718 ■ American Enterprise Institute National Research Initiative Fellowships (NRI) *(Graduate/Fellowship)*

Purpose: To promote sound policy research by enabling talented students to spend an academic year in residence at AEI, pursuing domestic public policy research independently or in conjunction with an AEI scholar. **Focus:** Economics; Political science; Social sciences; Law. **Qualif.:** Applicant must be a recent law school and business school graduate wishing to pursue public policy whose areas of study are economics, political and social science, law, or public policy. **Criteria:** Selection is based on academic performance, writing ability and references.

Funds Avail.: No specific amount. **To Apply:** Applicants must submit a statement of purpose; two letters of reference; curriculum vitae; graduate school transcripts; and one writing sample. **Deadline:** December 4. **Contact:** Emily Batman at nri@aei.org.

Awards are arranged alphabetically below their administering organizations

719 ■ American Epilepsy Society (AES)

342 N Main St., Ste. 301
West Hartford, CT 06117-2507
Ph: (860) 586-7505
Fax: (860) 586-7550
E-mail: info@aesnet.org
URL: www.aesnet.org

720 ■ Robert S. Morison Fellowships *(Doctorate, Graduate/Fellowship)*

Purpose: To promote study and research on epilepsy. **Focus:** Epilepsy. **Qualif.:** Applicant must possess an M.D. degree and must have an intention to continue training in basic science in an epilepsy research laboratory. **Criteria:** Selection is based on the application materials submitted.

Funds Avail.: $40,000/year, with $10,000/year for institutional fringe benefits, and $1,000 for travel to the AES Annual Meeting. **To Apply:** Applicants must apply for the post-doctoral fellowships and research and training fellowships at the Epilepsy Foundation. Student must note on the application the desire to be considered for the Morison Fellowship. **Remarks:** In partnership with The Grass Foundation.

721 ■ American Federation of Police and Concerned Citizens (AFP&CC)

6350 Horizon Dr.
Titusville, FL 32780
Ph: (321) 264-0911
Fax: (321) 264-0033
E-mail: policeinfo@aphf.org
URL: www.afp-cc.org

722 ■ American Federation of Police and Concerned Citizen Scholarships *(Undergraduate, Vocational/Occupational/Scholarship)*

Purpose: To assist family members and children of officers killed in the line of duty. **Focus:** Law Enforcement. **Qualif.:** Applicants must be high school graduates attending a traditional four-year college, university, technical or vocational educational institutions. **Criteria:** Recipients are selected based on financial need.

Funds Avail.: $1,000. **To Apply:** Applicants must submit an application form.

723 ■ American Floral Endowment (AFE)

1601 Duke St.
Alexandria, VA 22314
Ph: (703) 838-5211
Fax: (703) 838-5212
E-mail: afe@endowment.org
URL: endowment.org

724 ■ Ball Horticultural Company Scholarships *(Undergraduate/Scholarship)*

Purpose: To further the advancement of education and science in the floriculture and environmental horticulture field by funding research and studies and financing scholarships and other educational activities for individuals interested in the field. **Focus:** Horticulture. **Qualif.:** Applicants must be students currently enrolled in their third to fourth year of college; must be pursuing a career in commercial floriculture. **Criteria:** Recipients are selected based on academic performance.

Funds Avail.: No specific amount. **To Apply:** Applicants must send a completed online application form; must submit two letters of recommendation and transcript of records.

725 ■ Vic and Margaret Ball Student Intern Scholarships *(Undergraduate/Internship)*

Purpose: To further the advancement of education and science in the floriculture and environmental horticulture field by funding research and studies and financing scholarships and other educational activities for individuals interested in the field; to assure continuance of practical experience opportunities. **Focus:** Horticulture. **Qualif.:** Applicants must be full-time undergraduate students who are currently enrolled in a floriculture/environmental horticulture program at a two or four year college/university within the United States; must be U.S. citizens; must maintain "C" or better GPA with satisfactory progress in a degree or certificate program. **Criteria:** Recipients are selected based on academic performance, financial need and interest in a horticulture career.

Funds Avail.: varies. **To Apply:** Applicants must submit a completed and signed application form, official transcript from all institutions attended, a statement explaining the reasons for applying and future career goals, a letter of recommendation and endorsement by a faculty member. Applicants must submit a 500 word report evaluating the experience within 30 days of completing the program; pictures of the student working at the intern location must be included. Applicants must have permission to interrupt studies for the length of the training period. **Deadline:** March 1 and October 1.

726 ■ Harold Bettinger Scholarships *(Undergraduate/Scholarship)*

Purpose: To further the advancement of education and science in the floriculture and environmental horticulture field by funding research and studies and financing scholarships and other educational activities for individuals interested in the field. **Focus:** Horticulture. **Qualif.:** Applicants must be sophomore or graduate students pursuing a career in business and/or marketing with the intent to apply it to a horticulture-related business. **Criteria:** Recipients are selected based on academic performance.

Funds Avail.: No specific amount. **To Apply:** Applicants must send a completed online application form; must submit two letters of recommendation and transcript of records.

727 ■ Leonard Bettinger Vocational Scholarships *(Undergraduate, Vocational/Occupational/Scholarship)*

Purpose: To further the advancement of education and science in the floriculture and environmental horticulture field by funding research and studies and financing scholarships and other educational activities for individuals interested in the field. **Focus:** Horticulture. **Qualif.:** Applicants must be vocational students in a one or two-year program who intend to become growers or greenhouse managers. **Criteria:** Recipients are selected based on academic performance.

Funds Avail.: No specific amount. **To Apply:** Applicants must send a completed online application form; must submit two letters of recommendation and transcript of records.

728 ■ James Bridenbaugh Memorial Scholarships *(Undergraduate/Scholarship)*

Purpose: To further the advancement of education and science in the floriculture and environmental horticulture field

Awards are arranged alphabetically below their administering organizations

by funding research and studies and financing scholarships and other educational activities for individuals interested in the field. **Focus:** Horticulture. **Qualif.:** Applicants must be sophomore to senior students pursuing a career in floral design and marketing fresh flowers and plants. **Criteria:** Recipients are selected based on academic performance.

Funds Avail.: No specific amount. **To Apply:** Applicants must send a completed online application form; must submit two letters of recommendation and transcript of records.

729 ■ John Carew Memorial Scholarships
(Undergraduate/Scholarship)

Purpose: To further the advancement of education and science in the floriculture and environmental horticulture field by funding research and studies and financing scholarships and other educational activities for individuals interested in the field. **Focus:** Horticulture. **Qualif.:** Applicants must be graduate students with an interest in greenhouse crops. **Criteria:** Recipients are selected based on academic performance.

Funds Avail.: No specific amount. **To Apply:** Applicants must send a completed online application form; must submit two letters of recommendation and transcript of records.

730 ■ Earl Deadman Memorial Scholarships
(Undergraduate/Scholarship)

Purpose: To further the advancement of education and science in the floriculture and environmental horticulture field by funding research and studies and financing scholarships and other educational activities for individuals interested in the field. **Focus:** Horticulture. **Qualif.:** Applicants must be sophomore to fifth-year students who plan to become greenhouse growers; must be from the Northwestern area of the U.S. **Criteria:** Recipients are selected based on academic performance.

Funds Avail.: No specific amount. **To Apply:** Applicants must send a completed online application form; must submit two letters of recommendation and transcript of records.

731 ■ Dosatron International Inc. Scholarships
(Undergraduate/Scholarship)

Purpose: To further the advancement of education and science in the floriculture and environmental horticulture field by funding research and studies and financing scholarships and other educational activities for individuals interested in the field. **Focus:** Horticulture. **Qualif.:** Applicants must be third to fifth year students who are interested in floriculture production and plan to work in the greenhouse environment. **Criteria:** Recipients are selected based on academic performance.

Funds Avail.: $500. **To Apply:** Applicants must send a completed online application form; must submit two letters of recommendation and transcript of records.

732 ■ Paris Fracasso Production Floriculture Scholarships *(Undergraduate/Scholarship)*

Purpose: To further the advancement of education and science in the floriculture and environmental horticulture field by funding research and studies and financing scholarships and other educational activities for individuals interested in the field. **Focus:** Horticulture. **Qualif.:** Applicants must have junior or senior status and to express a career goal in production floriculure. **Criteria:** Recipients are selected based on academic performance.

Funds Avail.: No specific amount. **To Apply:** Applicants must send a completed online application form; must submit

two letters of recommendation and transcript of records.

733 ■ Ed Markham International Scholarships
(Undergraduate/Scholarship)

Purpose: To further the advancement of education and science in the floriculture and environmental horticulture field by funding research and studies and financing scholarships and other educational activities for individuals interested in the field. **Focus:** Horticulture. **Qualif.:** Applicants must be sophomore to graduate students pursuing a career in horticulture marketing through international travel. **Criteria:** Recipients are selected based on academic performance.

Funds Avail.: $3,500. **To Apply:** Applicants must send a completed online application form; must submit two letters of recommendation and transcript of records. **Deadline:** June.

734 ■ National Greenhouse Manufacturers Association Scholarships *(Undergraduate/ Scholarship)*

Purpose: To further the advancement of education and science in the floriculture and environmental horticulture field by funding research and studies and financing scholarships and other educational activities for individuals interested in the field. **Focus:** Horticulture. **Qualif.:** Applicants must be junior, senior or graduate students pursuing a career in horticulture and bio-engineering or the equivalent at a four-year college. Applicants must maintain a 3.0 GPA. **Criteria:** Recipients are selected based on academic performance.

Funds Avail.: No specific amount. **To Apply:** Applicants must send a completed online application form; must submit two letters of recommendation and transcript of records.

735 ■ Mike and Flo Novovesky Scholarships
(Undergraduate/Scholarship)

Purpose: To further the advancement of education and science in the floriculture and environmental horticulture field by funding research and studies and financing scholarships and other educational activities for individuals interested in the field. **Focus:** Horticulture. **Qualif.:** Applicants must be second year to graduating married students with a GPA of 2.5 or higher. **Criteria:** Recipients are selected based on academic performance.

Funds Avail.: No specific amount. **To Apply:** Applicants must send a completed online application form; must submit two letters of recommendation and transcript of records.

736 ■ Lawrence "Bud" Ohlman Memorial Scholarships *(Undergraduate/Scholarship)*

Purpose: To further the advancement of education and science in the floriculture and environmental horticulture field by funding research and studies and financing scholarships and other educational activities for individuals interested in the field. **Focus:** Horticulture. **Qualif.:** Applicant must be in his or her third to final year in college, with a career goal to become a bedding plant grower for an established business. **Criteria:** Recipients are selected based on academic performance.

Funds Avail.: $500. **To Apply:** Applicants must send a completed online application form; must submit two letters of recommendation and transcript of records.

737 ■ Jim Perry Vocational Scholarships
(Undergraduate, Vocational/Occupational/ Scholarship)

Purpose: To further the advancement of education and science in the floriculture and environmental horticulture field

Awards are arranged alphabetically below their administering organizations

by funding research and studies and financing scholarships and other educational activities for individuals interested in the field. **Focus:** Horticulture. **Qualif.:** Applicant must be a vocational student in a one or two-year program with the intent of becoming a grower or greenhouse manager. **Criteria:** Recipients are selected based on academic performance.

Funds Avail.: No specific amount. **To Apply:** Applicants must send a completed online application form; must submit two letters of recommendation and transcript of records.

738 ■ James K. Rathmell Jr. Scholarships
(Undergraduate/Scholarship)

Purpose: To further the advancement of education and science in the floriculture and environmental horticulture field by funding research and studies and financing scholarships and other educational activities for individuals interested in the field. **Focus:** Horticulture. **Qualif.:** Applicants must be in their third to final year of undergraduate studies or be graduate students; must plan to work or study outside of the United States. **Criteria:** Recipients are selected based on academic performance.

Funds Avail.: No specific amount. **To Apply:** Applicants must send a completed online application form; must submit two letters of recommendation, transcript of records, and specific plan for horticulture work/study outside of the USA.

739 ■ Seed Companies Scholarships
(Undergraduate/Scholarship)

Purpose: To further the advancement of education and science in the floriculture and environmental horticulture field by funding research and studies and financing scholarships and other educational activities for individuals interested in the field. **Focus:** Horticulture. **Qualif.:** Applicants must be third to final year or graduate students who are pursuing a career in the seed industry in sales, breeding, research or marketing. **Criteria:** Recipients are selected based on academic performance.

Funds Avail.: No specific amount. **To Apply:** Applicants must send a completed online application form; must submit two letters of recommendation and transcript of records.

740 ■ John Tomasovic, Sr. Scholarships
(Undergraduate/Scholarship)

Purpose: To further the advancement of education and science in the floriculture and environmental horticulture field by funding research and studies and financing scholarships and other educational activities for individuals interested in the field. **Focus:** Horticulture. **Qualif.:** Applicants must be in their second to final year in college and pursuing a career in a horticulture-related field; must have 3.0-3.5 GPA. **Criteria:** Recipients are selected based on financial need and GPA.

Funds Avail.: No specific amount. **To Apply:** Applicants must send a completed online application form; must submit two letters of recommendation and transcript of records.

741 ■ Edward Tuinier Memorial Scholarships
(Undergraduate/Scholarship)

Purpose: To further the advancement of education and science in the floriculture and environmental horticulture field by funding research and studies and financing scholarships and other educational activities for individuals interested in the field. **Focus:** Horticulture. **Qualif.:** Applicants must be in their second to final year in a floriculture program at Michigan State University. **Criteria:** Recipients are selected

based on academic performance.

Funds Avail.: No specific amount. **To Apply:** Applicants must send a completed online application form; must submit two letters of recommendation and transcript of records.

742 ■ Jacob VanNamen-Vans Marketing Scholarships *(Undergraduate/Scholarship)*

Purpose: To further the advancement of education and science in the floriculture and environmental horticulture field by funding research and studies and financing scholarships and other educational activities for individuals interested in the field. **Focus:** Horticulture. **Qualif.:** Applicants must be in their second to final year in college; must be interested in agribusiness marketing and distribution of floral products. **Criteria:** Recipients are selected based on academic performance.

Funds Avail.: No specific amount. **To Apply:** Applicants must send a completed online application form; must submit two letters of recommendation and transcript of records.

743 ■ American Foreign Service Association (AFSA)
2101 E St. NW
Washington, DC 20037
Ph: (202) 338-4045
Fax: (202) 338-6820
Free: 800-704-AFSA
E-mail: afsa@afsa.org
URL: www.afsa.org

744 ■ American Foreign Service Association Scholarship Fund *(Undergraduate/Scholarship)*
Purpose: To provide financial assistance for college education of deserving students who are dependents of the active, retired with pension, deceased or separated US government Foreign Service employees who served or serving at least a year abroad in a foreign affairs agencies. **Focus:** General studies. **Qualif.:** Applicants must be students who attended or will be attending full-time (12 credit hours or more) as an undergraduate at a 2 or 4 year accredited college, university, community college, art school or conservatory (stateside or overseas); have cumulative 2.0 GPA on a 4.0 scale; must complete undergraduate in four years; and must demonstrate financial need. **Criteria:** Applicants will be evaluated on the basis of academic record and financial need.

Funds Avail.: $1,000 to $4,000. **Number Awarded:** 70. **To Apply:** Applicants must submit the Scholarship Application accompanied with a copy of high school/college transcripts; students or parents must complete the CSS PROFILE. **Deadline:** February 6. **Contact:** Lori Dec, Scholarship Director, dec@afsa.org.

745 ■ American Foundation for Aging Research (AFAR)
University of Albany
Dept. of Biological Sciences
1400 Washington Ave.
Albany, NY 12222
Ph: (518) 437-4448
E-mail: afar@agingresearchfoundation.org
URL: www.agingresearchfoundation.org

746 ■ AFAR Scholarships *(Graduate, Undergraduate/Scholarship)*
Purpose: To provide educational assistance to qualified students pursuing careers in biological aspects of aging.

Awards are arranged alphabetically below their administering organizations

Focus: Aging. **Qualif.:** Applicants must be undergraduate, graduate, or pre-doctoral students enrolled in degree programs at colleges or universities in the United States; must be enrolled in a U.S. institution at the time an application is submitted. **Criteria:** Recipient is chosen based on reviewed quality of full application.

Funds Avail.: $500 undergraduates; $1000 graduates. **To Apply:** Applicants must submit a recent academic transcript and letters of reference (one from their adviser and two from their instructors). **Contact:** afar@agingresearchfoundation.org.

747 ■ American Foundation for the Blind (AFB)

2 Penn Plz., Ste. 1102
New York, NY 10001
Ph: (212) 502-7600
Fax: (888) 545-8331
Free: 800-232-5463
E-mail: afbinfo@afb.net
URL: www.afb.org

748 ■ Gladys C. Anderson Memorial Scholarships *(Graduate, Undergraduate/Scholarship)*

Purpose: To provide scholarships in the field of classical or religious music to persons who are blind or visually impaired. **Focus:** Classical music. **Qualif.:** Applicant must be blind or visually impaired; be a female undergraduate or graduate student studying classical or religious music. **Criteria:** The scholarship committee will review only those applications that are complete with supporting documents and meet all scholarship requirements.

Funds Avail.: $1,000. **Number Awarded:** 1. **To Apply:** Applicants must complete the online application. In addition, applicants must submit official transcripts; proof of post-secondary acceptance; two letters of recommendation; proof of U.S. citizenship; proof of legal blindness; and a performance tape/CD not to exceed 30 minutes. Supporting documents are to be collected and sent in one envelope to the AFB Scholarship Committee. **Deadline:** April 30.

749 ■ Karen D. Carsel Memorial Scholarships *(Graduate/Scholarship)*

Purpose: To financially support the education of a blind or visually impaired graduate student. **Focus:** General studies. **Qualif.:** Applicant must be blind or visually impaired; and must be a full-time graduate student who presents evidence of economic need. **Criteria:** The scholarship committee will review only those applications that are complete with supporting documents and meet all scholarship requirements.

Funds Avail.: $500. **Number Awarded:** 1. **To Apply:** Applicants must complete the online application. In addition, applicants must submit official transcripts; proof of post-secondary acceptance; two letters of recommendation; proof of U.S. citizenship; and proof of legal blindness. Supporting documents are to be collected and sent in one envelope to the AFB Scholarship Committee. **Deadline:** April 30.

750 ■ Rudolph Dillman Memorial Scholarships *(Graduate, Undergraduate/Scholarship)*

Purpose: To provide scholarships in the field of rehabilitation and/or education to persons who are blind or visually impaired. **Focus:** Rehabilitation, Physical/Psychological; Education. **Qualif.:** Applicant must be blind or visually

impaired; and an undergraduate or graduate student in the field of rehabilitation or education. **Criteria:** The scholarship committee will review only those applications that are complete with supporting documents and meet all scholarship requirements. One of the awards is reserved specifically for a student who presents proof of economic need (Student Aid Report required).

Funds Avail.: $2,500. **Number Awarded:** 4. **To Apply:** Applicants must complete the online application. In addition, applicants must submit official transcripts; proof of post-secondary acceptance; two letters of recommendation; proof of U.S. citizenship; and proof of legal blindness. Supporting documents are to be collected and sent in one envelope to the AFB Scholarship Committee. **Deadline:** April 30.

751 ■ R.L. Gillette Scholarships *(Undergraduate/ Scholarship)*

Purpose: To provide scholarships in the field of literature or music to persons who are blind or visually impaired. **Focus:** Literature; Music. **Qualif.:** Applicant must be blind or visually impaired; must be a female student enrolled in a full-time four-year undergraduate degree program in literature or music. **Criteria:** The scholarship committee will review only those applications that are complete with supporting documents and meet all scholarship requirements.

Funds Avail.: $1,000. **Number Awarded:** 2. **To Apply:** Applicants must complete the online application. In addition, applicants must submit official transcripts; proof of post-secondary acceptance; two letters of recommendation; proof of U.S. citizenship; proof of legal blindness; and a performance tape/CD not to exceed 30 minutes, or a creative writing sample. Supporting documents are to be collected and sent in one envelope to the AFB Scholarship Committee. **Deadline:** April 30.

752 ■ Delta Gamma Foundation Florence Margaret Harvey Memorial Scholarships *(Graduate, Undergraduate/Scholarship)*

Purpose: To provide scholarships in the field of rehabilitation and/or education to persons who are blind or visually impaired. **Focus:** Rehabilitation, Physical/Psychological; Education. **Qualif.:** Applicant must be blind or visually impaired; and an undergraduate or graduate student in the field of rehabilitation or education. **Criteria:** The scholarship committee will review only those applications that are complete with supporting documents and meet all scholarship requirements.

Funds Avail.: $1,000. **Number Awarded:** 1. **To Apply:** Applicants must complete the online application. In addition, applicants must submit official transcripts; proof of post-secondary acceptance; two letters of recommendation; proof of U.S. citizenship; and proof of legal blindness. Supporting documents are to be collected and sent in one envelope to the AFB Scholarship Committee. **Deadline:** April 30.

753 ■ Paul and Ellen Ruckes Scholarships *(Graduate, Undergraduate/Scholarship)*

Purpose: To provide scholarships in the field of engineering or in computer, physical or life sciences to persons who are blind or visually impaired. **Focus:** Engineering; Computer and information sciences; Life sciences; Physical sciences. **Qualif.:** Applicant must be blind or visually impaired; and an undergraduate or graduate student in the field of engineering or in computer, physical or life sciences. **Criteria:** The scholarship committee will review only those

Awards are arranged alphabetically below their administering organizations

applications that are complete with supporting documents and meet all scholarship requirements.

Funds Avail.: $1,000. **Number Awarded:** 1. **To Apply:** Applicants must complete the online application. In addition, applicants must submit official transcripts; proof of post-secondary acceptance; two letters of recommendation; proof of U.S. citizenship; and proof of legal blindness. Supporting documents are to be collected and sent in one envelope to the AFB Scholarship Committee. **Deadline:** April 30.

754 ■ Ferdinand Torres Scholarships *(Graduate, Undergraduate/Scholarship)*

Purpose: To financially support the education of a blind or visually impaired student. **Focus:** General studies. **Qualif.:** Applicant must be a blind or visually impaired full-time undergraduate or graduate student. **Criteria:** Strong preference will be given to new immigrants to the United States, and to those residing in the New York City metropolitan area.

Funds Avail.: $2,500. **Number Awarded:** 1. **To Apply:** Applicants must complete the online application. In addition, applicants must submit official transcripts; proof of post-secondary acceptance; two letters of recommendation; proof of U.S. citizenship; proof of legal blindness; evidence of economic need; and proof of residence in the United States (e.g. telephone bill; utility bill). Immigrants must include a description of country of origin and reason for coming to the U.S. (To be included in Part Four of the application essay). Supporting documents are to be collected and sent in one envelope to the AFB Scholarship Committee. **Deadline:** April 30.

755 ■ American Foundation for Pharmaceutical Education (AFPE)

1 Church St., Ste. 400
Rockville, MD 20850
Ph: (301) 738-2160
Fax: (301) 738-2161
E-mail: info@afpenet.org
URL: www.afpenet.org

756 ■ American Foundation for Pharmaceutical Education Gateway Research Scholarships *(Professional development/Scholarship)*

Purpose: To increase the number of students who undertake a faculty-mentored research program and decide to enroll in graduate programs leading to a Ph.D. in the basic, clinical, or administrative pharmaceutical sciences. **Focus:** Pharmaceutical sciences. **Qualif.:** Scholar must be selected and nominated by a faculty member; must be enrolled in a Pharm.D. program; must have completed at least two years of college; must be enrolled in at least the first year of the professional pharmacy curriculum; be enrolled in a baccalaureate degree program; have completed at least one year of the degree program; must be enrolled for at least one full academic year after initiation of the award; and must be U.S. citizens. **Criteria:** Preference will be given to applications from students who need relevant research experience in order to have the basis to decide whether to pursue the Ph.D. degree in the pharmaceutical sciences.

Funds Avail.: $5,000. **Number Awarded:** 11. **To Apply:** Applicants must complete the application form, in MS Word format, which can be downloaded from the website or requested by letter, telephone, or fax from AFPE. Forms

may also be available in the Dean's office at US schools/colleges of pharmacy. The faculty member seeking support and who will be responsible for mentoring the research scholar must provide: a copy of the faculty member's curriculum vitae including education and training, experience in research and bibliography/publications; official copies of all of the student's college transcripts; a typewritten letter by the student (not more than one page) explaining his/her interest in a pharmaceutical science research experience and his/her potential career goal(s); two fully completed statements of recommendation and evaluation forms from the faculty applicant and a professor who is familiar with both the faculty member and the student's work. **Deadline:** January 23.

757 ■ American Foundation for Pharmaceutical Education Pre-Doctoral Fellowships in the Pharmaceutical Sciences *(Doctorate/Fellowship)*

Purpose: To encourage outstanding pre-doctoral students who have completed at least three semesters of graduate study and have no more than three years remaining to continue their studies and earn a Ph.D. in the pharmaceutical sciences at a U.S. school or college of pharmacy. **Focus:** Pharmaceutical sciences. **Qualif.:** Applicants must have completed at least three semesters of graduate study toward a Ph.D. and have no more than three years remaining to obtain a Ph.D. degree in a graduate program in the pharmaceutical sciences administered by, or affiliated with a U.S. school or college of pharmacy. Students enrolled in joint Pharm.D./Ph.D programs are eligible to apply if they have completed the equivalent of three full semesters of graduate credit toward Ph.D., and if the Ph.D. degree will be awarded within three additional years; must be U.S. citizens or permanent residents. **Criteria:** Recipients will be selected by the Board of grant based on completed requirements.

Funds Avail.: $6,000. **Number Awarded:** 10. **To Apply:** Applicants must complete the pre-doctoral fellowship form; statements of recommendation and evaluation forms from three college faculty members who are acquainted with the student's progress in graduate study; and official transcripts of all collegiate grades. Application must be signed by the Dean of the Pharmacy Department. **Deadline:** March 15.

758 ■ Clinical Pharmacy Post-Pharm.D. Fellowships in the Biomedical Research Sciences *(Postdoctorate/Fellowship)*

Purpose: To enable a Pharm.D. level clinical pharmacist to obtain advanced education, training and expertise in relevant areas of the biomedical and related basic sciences in order to become a competent clinical scientist in academia, the pharmaceutical industry, institutional settings, or government, able to create and maintain a prominent peer-reviewed research program and make major contributions to the biomedical and pharmaceutical sciences; to generate skilled clinical scientists capable of conducting and teaching clinically-oriented research, advanced training is required in disciplines beyond those provided in a Pharm.D. program. **Focus:** Biomedical research. **Qualif.:** Applicants must have received the Pharm.D. degree within the past ten years; must have received a postdoctoral clinical residency and/or clinical fellowship program of at least one year duration; must agree to carry out the fellowship on a full-time basis and not engage in any part-time work; must be able to provide evidence of acceptance for the desired postdoctoral training by a suitable mentor at a recognized academic/research institution, which is not necessarily a college of pharmacy; and must be U.S. citizens or perma-

Awards are arranged alphabetically below their administering organizations

nent residents. **Criteria:** Recipients are selected by an Advisory Committee who will review applications and submit finalists to the AFPE Board of Grants who will make the final decision.

Funds Avail.: $27,500. **Number Awarded:** 2. **To Apply:** Applicants must submit description which includes: course work and research project to be taken; mentor's research program; resources and facilities to be use; a curriculum vitae of both applicant and mentor; statement from the applicant outlining career aspirations and expected impact of the fellowship on career goals; agreements concerning progress reports, financial support, full-time commitment to the program, publications, acknowledgement of AFPE support; letters of recommendation; and letters from Dean and Department Chair assuring that the fellowship recipient will be relieved of all teaching, advisory, service, clinical and administrative responsibilities during the two-year fellowship.

759 ■ Minority Pharmacy Faculty New Investigator Grants *(Professional development/ Grant)*

Purpose: To serve the needs of new minority investigators by providing initial funding for their research programs. **Focus:** Pharmaceutical sciences; Pharmacy. **Qualif.:** Applicants must be African-American/Black students who have earned terminal degrees in their disciplines (Pharm.D., Ph.D.); must have regular full-time faculty appointment at the assistant professor or higher level at a U.S. School or College of Pharmacy. **Criteria:** Recipients are selected based on the proposal review and recommendation for funding.

Funds Avail.: $10,000. **Number Awarded:** 1. **To Apply:** Applicants must submit a proposal including title page, abstract, research narrative, budget, biographical sketch, animal research approval letter, human subjects research approval letter, and other supporting documents. **Deadline:** March 2.

760 ■ Minority Student Gateway to Research Scholarships *(Professional development/ Scholarship)*

Purpose: To increase the number of African American/ Black Pharm.D. students and baccalaureate science students who graduate and enroll in graduate programs leading to a Ph.D. in the basic, clinical, or administrative pharmaceutical sciences. **Focus:** Pharmacy. **Qualif.:** Scholars must be selected and nominated by a faculty member; must be African American/Black; must be enrolled in a Pharm.D. program; must have completed at least two years of college; must be enrolled in at least the first year of the professional pharmacy curriculum or in a baccalaureate degree program; must have completed at least one year of the degree program; must be U.S. citizens or permanent residents; and must be enrolled for at least one full academic year after initiation of the award. Students enrolled in joint Pharm.D./Ph.D. programs may not apply. The student award recipient must not accept any other concurrent research support (e.g., from AACP, AFAR, ASHP, PhRMA, or any other external organization) during the 1-year scholarship period. In case of multiple source awards, the student must choose only one. **Criteria:** Preference will be given to applications from students who need relevant research experience in order to have a basis to decide whether to pursue the Ph.D. degree in the pharmaceutical sciences.

Funds Avail.: $5,000. **Number Awarded:** 1. **To Apply:**

Faculty member seeking support and who will be responsible for mentoring the research scholar must provide: a copy of the faculty/member's curriculum vitae including education and training, experience in research, and bibliography/publications; official copies of all of the student's college transcripts; completed application; a letter written by the student (must be not more than one page and typewritten); and two fully completed statements of recommendation and evaluation forms from the faculty applicant and a professor who is familiar with both the faculty member and the student's work.

761 ■ Minority Student Pre-Doctoral Fellowship Program *(Doctorate, Graduate/Fellowship)*

Purpose: To encourage outstanding African-American/ Black pre-doctoral students who have completed at least three semesters of graduate study and have not more than three years remaining to continue their studies and earn their Ph.D. in the pharmaceutical sciences at a U.S. school or college of pharmacy. To identify and support those students who have the potential to become leaders in the pharmaceutical profession. **Focus:** Pharmaceutical sciences. **Qualif.:** Applicants must be Africa-American/Black students who have completed at least three semesters of graduate study toward the Ph.D. and who have no more than three years remaining to obtain the Ph.D. degree in a graduate program in the pharmaceutical sciences administered by, or affiliated with a U.S. school or college of pharmacy. Students enrolled in joint Pharm.D./Ph.D programs are eligible if they have completed the equivalent of three semesters of graduate credit toward Ph.D., and if the Ph.D. degree will be awarded within three additional years. Applicants must be U.S. citizens or permanent residents. **Criteria:** Recipients are selected based on academic achievement as decided by the Board of Grant based on the completed requirements.

Funds Avail.: $6,000. **Number Awarded:** 5. **To Apply:** Applicants must complete the pre-doctoral fellowship form; statements of recommendation and evaluation forms from three college faculty members who are acquainted with applicant's progress in graduate study; and official transcripts of all collegiate grades. **Deadline:** March 15.

762 ■ Pharmacy Faculty Fellowships in Community Pharmacy Practice *(Postdoctorate/ Fellowship)*

Purpose: To increase the number of full-time faculty at schools/colleges of pharmacy with specific expertise in community pharmacy practice teaching and/or research; to develop pharmacy college teaching faculty and/or researchers capable of making major contributions to curriculum design, experiential education, clinical research and/or basic research in the area of community pharmacy practice. **Focus:** Pharmacy; Pharmaceutical sciences. **Qualif.:** Applicants must have received the Pharm.D. degree, preferably within the past ten years and may also hold a B.S. and/or M.S; must have completed post-doctoral work in community pharmacy practice as documented by curriculum development, publications, community pharmacy experiential education activities and/or basic research; must agree to carry out the fellowship on a full-time basis and not engage in any part-time work; and must be U.S. citizens or permanent residents. **Criteria:** Recipients are selected based on proposals.

Funds Avail.: $25,000. **Number Awarded:** 1. **To Apply:** Applicants must provide description which includes: fellowship program or research project to be taken, mentor's research program, resources and facilities to be use; cur-

Awards are arranged alphabetically below their administering organizations

riculum vitae; statement outlining career aspirations and impact on career goals; agreement based on: progress report, financial support, publications and commitment; letters of recommendation; and letter from the Dean or Department Chair assuring that recipients will be relieved of all teaching, advisory, service, clinical and administrative responsibilities.

763 ■ Pharmacy Faculty Fellowships in Geriatric Pharmacy/Geriatric Pharmaceutical Science (Postdoctorate/Fellowship)

Purpose: To increase the number of full-time faculty at schools/colleges of pharmacy with specific expertise in geriatric pharmacy and/or geriatric pharmaceutical sciences; to generate pharmacy college faculty teachers and/or researchers capable of making major contributions to curriculum design, experiential education, clinical research, and basic research in priority areas of geriatric pharmacy and/or geriatric pharmaceutical sciences. **Focus:** Medicine, Geriatric; Pharmaceutical sciences. **Qualif.:** Applicants must have received the Pharm.D. degree preferably within the past ten years and may also hold a B.S. and/or M.S; must have completed post-doctoral work in geriatric pharmacy and/or geriatric pharmaceutical science as documented by curricula development, publications, geriatric clinical pharmacy service delivery and/or basic research; must agree to carry out the fellowship on a full-time basis and not engage in any part-time work; and must be U.S. citizens or permanent residents. **Criteria:** Recipients are selected based on the review by an Advisory Committee and submit finalists to AFPE Board of Grants who will make the final decision.

Funds Avail.: $25,000. **Number Awarded:** 1. **To Apply:** Applicants must provide a letter with his/her application from his/her Dean, or Department Chair assuring that the applicant will be relieved of all teaching or clinical responsibilities; a letter with his/her application form from his/her Dean assuring that the applicant's educational institution will provide a minimum of $25,000 in matching financial support for the applicants during the six-month fellowship period; and evidence of acceptance for the desired fellowship training by a suitable mentor at a recognized academic and/or research institution, not necessarily a school/college of pharmacy. **Deadline:** April 1.

764 ■ Pharmacy Faculty New Investigator Grants Program (Doctorate/Grant)

Purpose: To serve the needs of new investigators by providing initial funding for their research programs; to financially assist pharmacy faculty members to establish a program of research. **Focus:** Pharmacy. **Qualif.:** Applicants must have earned terminal degrees in their disciplines; have regular full-time faculty appointment at the assistant professor level. **Criteria:** Recipients are selected based on the review of the proposals.

Funds Avail.: $10,000. **Number Awarded:** 15. **To Apply:** Applicants must submit a title page with signatures of Department Chair and Dean; abstract page; research narrative; budget page; biographical sketch; animal research approval letter (if applicable); and other supporting documents. Successful applicants must submit two copies of a final report and any reprints of abstract/papers published in referred journals. **Deadline:** May 23. **Contact:** Send application to: Amy B. Connelly, Project Manager at 1426 Prince St., Alexandria, VA 22314-2481. Phone: 703-739-2330 ext. 1036, Fax: 703-836-8982.

765 ■ American Foundation for Suicide and Prevention (AFSP)

120 Wall St., 29th Fl.
New York, NY 10005
Ph: (212) 363-3500
Fax: (212) 363-6237
Free: 888-333-2377
E-mail: inquiry@afsp.org
URL: www.afsp.org

766 ■ AFSP - Distinguished Investigator Grants (Postgraduate/Grant)

Purpose: To support the work of investigators from all disciplines that contribute to the understanding of suicide and suicide prevention. **Focus:** Suicide. **Qualif.:** Investigators from all academic disciplines are eligible to apply, and both basic science and applied research projects will be considered, providing the study has an essential focus on suicide prevention. Applicants must be at the level of associate professor or higher with an established record of research and publication on suicide. **Criteria:** Awards are given based on the research proposals.

Funds Avail.: $100,000. **To Apply:** Applicant may fill-up an application form online. The application must include the following sections: Cover sheet; Principal Investigator Assurance Form; Abstract; Certification for Protection of Human Subjects; Budget; Budget Justification; Biographical Information; Project Description; Project Timeline; References; and Appendices. Completed grant applications must be submitted electronically to grants@afsp.org. A compact disc (CD) containing the completed application must also be submitted to the American Foundation for Suicide Prevention, 120 Wall St., 22nd Floor, New York, NY 10005. **Contact:** grantsmanager@afsp.org.

767 ■ AFSP Postdoctoral Research Fellowships (Postgraduate/Fellowship)

Purpose: To support the work of investigators from all disciplines that contribute to the understanding of suicide and suicide prevention. **Focus:** Suicide. **Qualif.:** Applicant must have received a Ph.D., M.D., or other doctoral degree within the preceding years and have not had more than three years of fellowship support. **Criteria:** Applicants are chosen based on his/her research proposal.

Funds Avail.: Fellows receive a progressive stipend of $42,000 in the first year and $46,000 in the second, with an institutional allowance of $6,000. **To Apply:** Applicants may go online to fill out an application form. The application must include the following sections: Cover sheet; Principal Investigator Assurance Form; Abstract; Certification for Protection of Human Subjects; Budget; Budget Justification; Biographical Information; Project Description; Project Timeline; References; Research Training Plan; and Recommendation of Mentor. Completed grant applications must be submitted electronically to grants@afsp.org. A compact disc (CD) containing the completed application must also be submitted to the American Foundation for Suicide Prevention, 120 Wall St., 22nd Floor, New York, NY 10005. **Contact:** grantsmanager@afsp.org.

768 ■ AFSP Standard Research Grants (Postgraduate/Grant)

Purpose: To support the work of investigators from all disciplines that contribute to the understanding of suicide and suicide prevention. **Focus:** Suicide. **Qualif.:** Investigators from all academic disciplines are eligible to apply, and

Awards are arranged alphabetically below their administering organizations

both basic science and applied research projects will be considered, providing the study has an essential focus on suicide prevention. **Criteria:** Awards are given based on the research proposals.

Funds Avail.: $75,000. **To Apply:** Applicant may fill-up an application form online. The application must include the following sections: Cover sheet; Principal Investigator Assurance Form; Abstract; Certification for Protection of Human Subjects; Budget; Budget Justification; Biographical Information; Project Description; Project Timeline; References; and Appendices. Completed grant applications must be submitted electronically to grants@afsp.org. A compact disc (CD) containing the completed application must also be submitted to the American Foundation for Suicide Prevention, 120 Wall St., 22nd Floor, New York, NY 10005. **Contact:** grantsmanager@afsp.org.

769 ■ AFSP Young Investigator Grants
(Postgraduate/Grant)

Purpose: To support the work of investigators from all disciplines that contribute to the understanding of suicide and suicide prevention. **Focus:** Suicide. **Qualif.:** Applicant must be at the level of assistant professor or lower. **Criteria:** Awards is given based on the submitted research proposals.

Funds Avail.: $75,000. Additional $5,000 per year for a mentor, who serves as an advisor to the applicant. **To Apply:** Applicants may apply and fill out the application form online. The application must include the following sections: Cover sheet; Principal Investigator Assurance Form; Abstract; Certification for Protection of Human Subjects; Budget; Budget Justification; Biographical Information; Project Description; Project Timeline; References; and Recommendation of Mentor. Completed grant applications must be submitted electronically to grants@afsp.org. A compact disc (CD) containing the completed application must also be submitted to the American Foundation for Suicide Prevention, 120 Wall St., 22nd Floor, New York, NY 10005. **Deadline:** December 1. **Contact:** Vinita Ling, Grants Manager; 212-363-3500 ext. 15.

770 ■ American Foundation for Suicide and Prevention Pilot Grants *(Postgraduate/Grant)*

Purpose: To support the work of investigators from all disciplines that contribute to the understanding of suicide and suicide prevention. **Focus:** Suicide. **Qualif.:** Any investigator at any level. **Criteria:** Grants are given based on the submitted research proposals.

Funds Avail.: $15,000-$30,000. **To Apply:** Applicant may fill out an application form online. **Deadline:** June 1 and December 1. Vinita Ling, Grants Manager; 212-363-3500 ext. 15. **Contact:** grantsmanager@afsp.org.

771 ■ American Foundry Society, Inc.
505 State St.
Des Plaines, IL 60016-8399
Ph: (847) 824-0181
Fax: (847) 824-7848
Free: 800-537-4237
E-mail: lsmolecki@afsinc.org
URL: www.afsinc.org

772 ■ H.H. Harris Foundation Scholarships
(Undergraduate/Scholarship)

Purpose: To provide educational aid to students and professionals in the metallurgical and casting of metals field. **Focus:** Metallurgy. **Qualif.:** Applicants must be students or professionals pursuing a career in the field of metallurgy or any related fields; and must be U.S. citizens. **Criteria:** Recipients will be selected based on submitted application.

Funds Avail.: No specific amount. **To Apply:** Applicants must fill out the application form and are required to submit two letters of reference. **Deadline:** May 31. **Remarks:** Unsigned applications will not be considered. **Contact:** Charles Michod, Jr., H.H. Harris Foundation, 33 W Wacker Dr., Ste. 2000, Chicago, IL 60606; Phone: 312-236-6700; Fax: 312-346-0904; E-mail: cmichod@komdr.com.

773 ■ American Galvanizers Association (AGA)
6881 S Holy Cir., Ste. 108
Centennial, CO 80112-1145
Ph: (720) 554-0900
Fax: (720) 554-0909
Free: 800-468-7732
E-mail: aga@galvanizeit.org
URL: www.galvanizeit.org

774 ■ Galvanize the Future: Edgar K. Schutz Scholarships *(Graduate, Undergraduate/Prize, Scholarship)*

Purpose: To teach future specifiers about hot-dip galvanizing while providing them with funding for their education. **Focus:** Architecture; Engineering, Civil; Material and process engineering. **Qualif.:** Applicant must be a full- or part-time, undergraduate or graduate student of any age enrolled at an accredited 4-year college/university only in North America. **Criteria:** Selection is based on relevance, accuracy, conciseness and ingenuity.

Funds Avail.: 1st place: $2,500; 2nd place: $1,500; 3rd place: $1,000. **Number Awarded:** 3. **To Apply:** Applicants must submit a completed application form along with the essay (1000-2000 words). **Deadline:** March 31. **Contact:** scholarship@galvanizeit.org.

775 ■ American Geographical Society (AGS)
32 Court St., Ste. 201
Brooklyn, NY 11201-4404
Ph: (718) 624-2212
Fax: (718) 624-2239
E-mail: ags@amergeog.org
URL: www.amergeog.org

776 ■ McColl Family Fellowships *(Professional development/Fellowship)*

Purpose: To promote the study of geology. **Focus:** Geology. **Qualif.:** Applicants must be geographers. **Criteria:** Recipient will be selected by the selection committee.

Funds Avail.: No specific amount. **To Apply:** Applicants must submit a curriculum vitae; a cover letter (maximum of 3 pages); and a statement of the sum request. **Deadline:** October 17. **Contact:** Peter Lewis at the above address.

777 ■ American Geosciences Institute (AGI)
4220 King St.
Alexandria, VA 22302-1502
Ph: (703) 379-2480
Fax: (703) 379-7563

Awards are arranged alphabetically below their administering organizations

E-mail: ls@agiweb.org
URL: www.agiweb.org

778 ■ AGI Minority Participation Program Geoscience Student Scholarships (AGI-MPP)
(Graduate, Undergraduate/Scholarship)

Purpose: To develop the professional corps of underrepresented ethnic-minority students in the geosciences. **Focus:** Geosciences. **Qualif.:** Applicant must be a U.S. citizen; and a member of an ethnic group that is underrepresented in the geosciences. **Criteria:** Selection is based on academic performance, work experience and interest in the geosciences.

Funds Avail.: No specific amount. **To Apply:** Applicants must submit a completed scholarship application form along with the required materials. **Deadline:** March 15.

779 ■ American GI Forum of San Jose
322 S 1st St.
San Jose, CA 95113
Ph: (408) 288-9470
Fax: (408) 288-9473
E-mail: sjgif@sjgif.org
URL: www.sjgif.org

780 ■ American GI Forum of San Jose Scholarships *(Undergraduate/Scholarship)*

Purpose: To provide financial assistance to qualified students of Hispanic descent who reside in the County of Santa Clara, California. **Focus:** General Studies. **Qualif.:** Applicants must be graduating high school students located in Santa Clara County; must be enrolled or plan to enroll in an accredited college or university leading to an associate or bachelor's degree; and must have a minimum grade point average of 2.5. **Criteria:** Recipients are selected based on academic achievement, career goals and aspirations, community school activities and financial need; and quality of the essay based on its content, clarity, grammar and experience. Priority will be given to students of Mexican-American Descent.

Funds Avail.: No specific amount. **To Apply:** Applicants must submit completed application form; wallet size senior picture; official copy of high school transcript; biographical data sheet; an autobiographical essay; and a copy of parent's most recent Federal Income Tax or Student Aid Application for California. Essay must be typed and not exceeding two pages. **Deadline:** March.

781 ■ American Handel Society (AHS)
c/o Marjorie Pomeroy
49 Christopher Hollow Rd.
Sandwich, MA 02563
E-mail: info@americanhandelsociety.org
URL: www.americanhandelsociety.org

782 ■ J. Merrill Knapp Research Fellowships
(Undergraduate/Fellowship)

Purpose: To support work in the area of Handel or other related research. **Focus:** General studies. **Qualif.:** Applicant must be students at North American universities and residents of North America. **Criteria:** Preference will be given to advanced graduate student who has not previously held this fellowship.

Funds Avail.: $2,000. **To Apply:** Applicant must submit a

curriculum vitae, a description of the project (not to exceed 750 words), a budget showing how and when the applicant plans to use the funds, and a description of other grants applied for or received for the same project; must have two recommendation letters. Application and other materials must be sent to: School of Music, University of Maryland, College Park **Deadline:** March 1. **Contact:** Richard King.

783 ■ American Head and Neck Society (AHNS)
11300 W Olympic Blvd., Ste. 600
Los Angeles, CA 90064
Ph: (310) 437-0559
Fax: (310) 437-0585
E-mail: admin@ahns.info
URL: www.ahns.info

784 ■ AHNS-ACS Career Development Awards
(Professional development/Grant)

Purpose: To support clinical, basic science or translational researches in neoplastic disease of the head and neck. **Focus:** Medical research. **Qualif.:** Applicants must be members of both ACS and AHNS. **Criteria:** Applicant who is within five years of completion of training, and is a full-time faculty member will receive the award.

Funds Avail.: $40,000.

785 ■ AHNS Pilot Research Grants *(Professional development/Grant)*

Purpose: To support basic, translational or clinical researches in head and neck oncology. **Focus:** Medical research. **Qualif.:** Applicants must be residents, fellows or junior faculty for pilot research in head and neck related topics; must be residents of U.S. or Canada, medical students, PhD or faculty members at the rank of associate professor or below. **Criteria:** Recipient is chosen based on reviewed quality of research project.

Funds Avail.: $10,000. **Number Awarded:** 1. **To Apply:** Applicants may contact the Society for the application process and other requirements.

786 ■ AHNS Young Investigator Awards *(Professional development/Grant)*

Purpose: To support clinical, basic science or translational research in the study of neoplastic disease of the head and neck. **Focus:** Medical research. **Qualif.:** Applicants must be AHNS members (may be a candidate member). Also open to fellows and assistant professors. **Criteria:** Priority is given to investigators with outstanding research.

Funds Avail.: $10,000 per year. **Number Awarded:** 1. **To Apply:** Applicants may contact the society for the application process and other requirements.

787 ■ Ballantyne Resident Research Grants
(Professional development/Grant)

Purpose: To support basic, translational or clinical researches in head and neck oncology. **Focus:** Medical research. **Qualif.:** Applicants must be residents, fellows or junior faculty for pilot research in head and neck related topics; must be residents of U.S. or Canada; must be medical students, Ph.D.s or faculty members at the rank of associate professor or below. **Criteria:** Recipient is chosen based on ability to meet mentioned criteria and potential of proposed research.

Funds Avail.: $10,000. **Number Awarded:** 1. **To Apply:**

Awards are arranged alphabetically below their administering organizations

Applicants may contact the Society for the application process and other requirements.

788 ■ Surgeon Scientist Career Development Awards (Professional development/Grant)

Purpose: To support a collaborative American Head and Neck Society and American Academy of Otolaryngology-Head and Neck Surgery Foundation research project by fostering the development of contemporary basic or clinical research skills focused on neoplastic disease of the head and neck among new full-time academic surgeons. **Focus:** Medical research. **Qualif.:** Candidates must be full-time academic surgeons in faculty positions at the rank of assistant professor or instructor who: are citizens of the United States, noncitizen nationals or have been lawfully admitted for permanent residency at the time of application; must hold a Doctor of Medicine (MD) degree from an accredited institution; must have demonstrated the capacity or potential for highly productive independent research career with an emphasis in head and neck surgical oncology; are members or candidate members of the American Academy of Otolaryngology-Head and Neck Surgery and/or the American head and Neck Society; have completed residency or fellowship training no longer than four (4) years prior to submitting an application. **Criteria:** Selection will be based on the criteria of the Research Committee.

Funds Avail.: $35,000 per year. **Number Awarded:** 1. **To Apply:** Applicants are advised to consult their institution's offices of research administration or sponsored projects for information on processing in requirement for an application prior to its submission.

789 ■ American Hellenic Educational Progressive Association - District No. 1 Scholarship Foundation

18 Riverdale Dr.
Charleston, SC 29407
Ph: (843) 670-7728
E-mail: melvazin@aol.com
URL: www.ahepadistrict1.org

790 ■ Ahepa District No. 1 Scholarship Program (Graduate, Undergraduate/Scholarship)

Purpose: To promote, encourage, induce and advance education at the college, university and graduate school level. **Focus:** General studies. **Qualif.:** Applicant must be a student in the graduating class of his/her high school and planning to attend full-time in an accredited college or university during the current calendar year; a high school graduate planning to attend full time in an accredited college or university during the calendar year; or attending an accredited college or university and will continue to attend full time during the calendar year. **Criteria:** Recipient is selected based on financial need, scholastic achievement, extra-curricular activities, athletic achievements, work and community service.

Funds Avail.: $500 to $1,500. **To Apply:** Applicants must complete the application form; must submit transcript of records; must provide the name of the college or university to which they have been accepted or which they are planning to attend; must submit a typewritten and not to exceed 500 words essay; and must include two letters of recommendation which have been obtained within the past six months. **Deadline:** March 31. **Contact:** Application form and other supporting documents should be sent to Melvia Zinaich, Co-Chair, PO Box 1011, Charleston, SC 29402.

791 ■ American Historical Association (AHA)

400 A St. SE
Washington, DC 20003-3889
Ph: (202) 544-2422
Fax: (202) 544-8307
E-mail: info@historians.org
URL: www.historians.org

792 ■ Fellowships in Aerospace History (Doctorate/Fellowship)

Purpose: To provide funding support for a research project related to aerospace history; to encourage engagement in significant and sustained advanced research in all aspects of the history of aerospace from the earliest human interest in flight to the present including cultural and intellectual history, economic history, history of law and public policy, history of science, engineering and management. **Focus:** History. **Qualif.:** Applicants must possess a doctorate degree in history or in a closely related field; may either be enrolled as students having completed all coursework in a doctoral degree-granting program. **Criteria:** Recipients are selected based on the significance of the research project.

Funds Avail.: $20,000. **To Apply:** Applicants must complete the application form and submit along with seven copies (each copy should contain one application form, proposal and CV, collated and paper clipped together); and letter of recommendations sealed in a separate envelope. **Deadline:** April 1.

793 ■ The J. Franklin Jameson Fellowships in American History (Doctorate/Fellowship)

Purpose: To support significant scholarly research in the collections of the Library Congress for one semester for scholars who are at an early stage in their careers in history. **Focus:** History. **Qualif.:** Applicants must hold a Ph.D. degree or equivalent; must have received this degree within the past seven years; and must have not published or had accepted for publication a book-length historical work. **Criteria:** Recipients are selected based on academic performance.

Funds Avail.: $5,000. **To Apply:** Applicants must submit an original and six copies of complete application including applicant's vita (not more than three to five pages in length); a statement concerning the proposed project and its relationship to the Library of Congress holdings; tentative schedule for residence of the fellowship; and three letters of recommendation. Letters should be written by individuals qualified to judge the project and address the applicant's fitness to undertake it. **Deadline:** March 15.

794 ■ American Hotel and Lodging Educational Foundation (AH&LEF)

1201 New York Ave. NW, No. 600
Washington, DC 20005-3931
Ph: (202) 289-3100
Fax: (202) 289-3199
E-mail: cboatman@ahlef.org
URL: www.ahlef.org

795 ■ The American Automobile Association Five Diamond Hospitality Scholarships (AAA) (Undergraduate/Scholarship)

Purpose: To provide educational assistance for hospitality management students. **Focus:** Hotel, institutional, and

Awards are arranged alphabetically below their administering organizations

restaurant management. **Qualif.:** Applicants must be enrolled in at least 12 credit hours for the upcoming Fall and Spring semesters; at least a sophomore at the time of nomination; have a minimum 3.0 GPA; and must be U.S. citizens or permanent U.S. residents. **Criteria:** Recipients are selected based on academic performance, hospitality work experience, financial need, extracurricular/professional attributes and honors, as well as personal attributes as defined in their career goal statement.

Funds Avail.: $5,000. **Number Awarded:** 1. **To Apply:** Applicants must complete all the required sections of the application and enclose publicity materials including a colored photograph; must prepare (one-to-two) sentences stating the importance of scholarship to them; a quote from the Dean or Director of the nominating school; and nominating school must send a nomination form confirming its nominee. **Deadline:** May 1.

796 ■ American Express Professional Development Scholarships (Professional development/ Scholarship)

Purpose: To enhance the skills of hospitality professionals. **Focus:** Hotel, institutional, and restaurant management. **Qualif.:** Applicants must be working a minimum of 35 hours per week at an AH&LA member hotel and with at least 12 months hotel experience. If applying for a certification, applicants must qualify the certification program. **Criteria:** Applicants are selected based on professional, community and extracurricular activities; industry-related work experience; and personal attributes including career goals and their response to questions.

Funds Avail.: $2,000 (Baccalaureate full-time); $1,000 (Baccalaureate part-time; Associate full-time); and $500 (Associate part-time). **Number Awarded:** 4. **To Apply:** Applicants must submit an application form and attach the appropriate EI distance learning enrollment form or professional certification form. **Deadline:** January 1, April 1, July 1 and October 1. **Remarks:** Founded by American Express in 1994. **Contact:** E-mail Crystal Hammond, Manager of the Foundation's programs at chammond@ahlef.org or call 202-289-3188.

797 ■ The American Express Scholarship Competition (Undergraduate/Scholarship)

Purpose: To provide educational assistance for current lodging employees and their dependents. **Focus:** Hotel, institutional and restaurant management. **Qualif.:** Applicants must be enrolled full-time or part-time; must be working a minimum of 20 hours per week at an AH & LA member hotel and with at least 12 months hotel experience. **Criteria:** Recipients are selected based on academic performance, hospitality work experience, financial need, extracurricular/professional attributes and honors, as well as personal attributes as defined in their career goal statement.

Funds Avail.: Baccalaureate Majors - $2,000 full-time enrollment; or $1,000 part-time; Associate Majors - $1,000 full-time enrollment; or $500 part- time. **To Apply:** Applicants must complete all the required sections of the application. **Deadline:** May 1. **Remarks:** Founded by American Express in 1994.

798 ■ The Hyatt Hotels Fund For Minority Lodging Management Students (Undergraduate/ Scholarship)

Purpose: To provide financial aid for minority students pursuing a degree in hotel management. **Focus:** Hotel,

institutional, and restaurant management. **Qualif.:** Applicant must be enrolled in at least 12 credit hours for the upcoming Fall and Spring semesters, or just the Fall semester if graduating this December; at least a sophomore in a four-year program at the time of application; a minority descent: African-American, Hispanic, American Indian, Alaskan Native, Asian or Pacific Islander; a U.S. citizen or permanent U.S. resident. **Criteria:** Recipients are selected based on academic performance, hospitality work experience, financial need, extracurricular/professional attributes and honors, as well as personal attributes as defined in their career goal statement.

Funds Avail.: $2,000. **To Apply:** Applicants must complete all the required sections of the application. **Deadline:** January 1 to May 1. **Remarks:** Established by Hyatt in 1988.

799 ■ The Steve Hymans Extended Stay Scholarship Program (Undergraduate/ Scholarship)

Purpose: To provide educational assistance for hospitality management students. **Focus:** Hotel, institutional, and restaurant management. **Qualif.:** Applicant must be enrolled full-time or part-time; have a minimum of 3.0 GPA; be a U.S. citizen or permanent U.S. resident; and have at least some experience either working or interning (paid or unpaid) at a lodging property. **Criteria:** Applicants with experience at an extended stay property will be given preference.

Funds Avail.: $1,000 to $3,000. **To Apply:** Students will be nominated by their respective school. Student nominees must complete all the required sections of the application. Additionally, under separate cover, participating schools are required to send a nomination form confirming their nominees and providing suggested award amounts. **Deadline:** January 1 to May 1. **Remarks:** Established in honor of Steve Hymans. **Contact:** Christa Boatman, 202-289-3139; cboatman@ahlef.org or Michelle Poinelli, 202-289-3181; mpoinelli@ahlef.org.

800 ■ Lodging Management Program Scholarships (LMP) (Undergraduate/Scholarship)

Purpose: To provide educational assistance to students pursuing a degree in hospitality-related degree programs. **Focus:** Hotel, institutional, and restaurant management. **Qualif.:** Applicants must be graduating high school seniors and have completed Year 1 and 2 of the LMP; must have a minimum 2.0 GPA. **Criteria:** Awards are given based on merit.

Funds Avail.: $1,000 per scholarship. **To Apply:** Applications are self nominated which means students do not have to attend a particular school or be nominated by their respective schools. Applicants must complete all sections of the AH&LEF scholarship application form. **Contact:** Questions can be addressed to Christa Boatman at the above address.

801 ■ The Arthur J. Packard Memorial Scholarship Competition (Undergraduate/Scholarship)

Purpose: To provide educational assistance for lodging management students. **Focus:** Hotel, institutional, and restaurant management. **Qualif.:** Applicants must be enrolled full-time for the upcoming Fall and Spring semesters majoring Hospitality Management; have a minimum GPA of 3.5 or higher; and must be U.S. residents. **Criteria:** Recipient are selected based on academic performance, hospitality work experience, financial need, extracurricular/ professional attributes and honors, as well as personal at-

Awards are arranged alphabetically below their administering organizations

tributes as defined in their career goal statement.

Funds Avail.: First-place winner $5,000; Second-place $3,000; Third-place $2,000. **To Apply:** Applicants must complete all the required sections of the application. **Deadline:** January 1 to May 1. **Remarks:** Established in honor of Arthur J. Packard. **Contact:** Christa Boatman, 202-289-3139; cboatman@ahlef.org or Michelle Poinelli, 202-289-3181; mpoinelli@ahlef.org.

802 ■ Pepsi Scholarships (Undergraduate/ Scholarship)

Purpose: To provide educational assistance for students pursuing a degree in hospitality-related degree programs. **Focus:** Hotel, institutional, and restaurant management. **Qualif.:** Applicants must be graduates of the Hospitality High School in Washington, D.C.; enrolled in at least 12 credit hours for the upcoming Fall and Spring semesters; worked at least 250 hours in the hotel/hospitality industry; and have a minimum 3.0 GPA. **Criteria:** Recipients are selected based on academic performance, hospitality work experience, financial need, extracurricular/professional attributes and honors, as well as personal attributes as defined in their career goal statement.

Funds Avail.: $500-$3,000 depending upon enrollment. Funds must be used exclusively for tuition, fees and books. **To Apply:** Applicants must complete all the required sections of the application; participating school must send a nomination form confirming its nominees and suggested award amount(s). **Deadline:** May 1. **Remarks:** Created by PepsiCo Foundation.

803 ■ Rama Scholarships for the American Dream (Graduate, Undergraduate/Scholarship)

Purpose: To provide educational assistance for lodging management students. **Focus:** Hotel, institutional, and restaurant management. **Qualif.:** Applicants must be enrolled in at least nine credit hours for the upcoming Fall and Spring semesters or just the Fall semester if graduating in December; must be undergraduate or graduate hospitality management majors; must have a minimum 2.5 GPA; and must be U.S. citizens or permanent U.S. residents. **Criteria:** Applicants who are students of Asian-Indian descent and other minority groups, as well as JHM employees and their dependents will be given preference.

Funds Avail.: $1,000-$3,000. **To Apply:** Applicants must complete all the required sections of the application. **Deadline:** January 1 to May 1. **Remarks:** Established by JHM Hotels, Inc. **Contact:** Christa Boatman, 202-289-3139; cboatman@ahlef.org or Michelle Poinelli, 202-289-3181; mpoinelli@ahlef.org.

804 ■ American Indian College Fund

8333 Greenwood Blvd.
Denver, CO 80221
Ph: (303) 426-8900
Fax: (303) 426-1200
Free: 800-776-3863
E-mail: info@collegefund.org
URL: www.collegefund.org

805 ■ Citi Foundation Scholarship Program (Undergraduate/Scholarship)

Purpose: To provide students with exposure to career options, leadership skills and information on the education and commitment necessary to succeed in the business world. **Focus:** General studies. **Qualif.:** Applicants must have at least a 3.0 grade point average; must commit to organizing and participating in a career exploration day; must be American Indian or Alaskan Native with proof of enrollment or descendancy; must be enrolled full-time at an eligible tribal college; and must have demonstrated exceptional academic achievement and financial need. **Criteria:** Preference will be given to those students who meet the criteria.

Funds Avail.: $4,000. **To Apply:** Applicants must complete the application process online. **Deadline:** May 31. **Contact:** Debra Reed at 800-776-3863 or dreed@collegefund.org.

806 ■ Coca-Cola First Generation Scholarships (Undergraduate/Scholarship)

Purpose: To provide financial assistance for students who are in need. **Focus:** General studies. **Qualif.:** Applicants must have at least a 3.0 grade point average; must be in first or second semester of college; must be the first member of their immediate family to attend college; must be American Indian or Alaskan Native with proof of enrollment or descendancy; must be enrolled full-time at an eligible tribal college; and must have demonstrated exceptional academic achievement and financial need. **Criteria:** Preference will be given to those students who meet the criteria.

Funds Avail.: $5,000. **To Apply:** Applicants must complete the application process online. **Deadline:** May 31. **Contact:** Debra Reed at 800-776-3863 or dreed@collegefund.org.

807 ■ Vine Deloria Jr. Memorial Scholarships (Graduate/Scholarship)

Purpose: To provide financial support for outstanding American Indian students who are pursuing a graduate degree. **Focus:** General studies. **Qualif.:** Applicants must be pursuing an advanced degree (MA, MS, JD, PhD, MD, other); must be able to demonstrate financial need; and must be American Indian or Alaskan Native with proof of enrollment or descendancy. **Criteria:** Preference will be given to students who meet the criteria.

Funds Avail.: $1,000. **To Apply:** Applicants must complete the application process online. **Deadline:** May 31. **Contact:** Susie Mitchell at 800-776-3863 or smitchell@collegefund.org.

808 ■ General Mills Foundation Scholarships (Undergraduate/Scholarship)

Purpose: To provide need-based scholarships for outstanding American Indian students who are currently enrolled at a tribal college in Minnesota or New Mexico. **Focus:** General studies. **Qualif.:** Applicants must have at least a 2.5 grade point average; must be American Indian or Alaskan Native with proof of enrollment or descendancy; must be enrolled full-time at an eligible Minnesota or New Mexico tribal college; and must have demonstrated exceptional academic achievement and financial need. **Criteria:** Preference will be given to those who meet the criteria.

Funds Avail.: $2,500. **To Apply:** Applicants must complete the application process online. **Deadline:** May 31. **Contact:** Debra Reed at 800-776-3863 or dreed@collegefund.org.

809 ■ Nissan North America, Inc. Scholarships (Undergraduate/Scholarship)

Purpose: To award scholarships to outstanding American Indian students who are currently enrolled in tribal colleges. **Focus:** General studies. **Qualif.:** Applicants must have at

Awards are arranged alphabetically below their administering organizations

least a 2.5 grade point average; must be enrolled full-time at an eligible tribal college; must be American Indian or Alaskan Native with proof of enrollment or descendancy; and must have demonstrated exceptional academic achievement. **Criteria:** Preference will be given to students who meet the criteria.

Funds Avail.: $3,000. **To Apply:** Applicants must complete the application process online. **Deadline:** May 31. **Contact:** Debra Reed at 800-776-3863 or dreed@collegefund.org.

810 ■ Sovereign Nations Scholarships
(Undergraduate/Scholarship)

Purpose: To award scholarships to American Indian students who are enrolled in a tribal college. **Focus:** General studies. **Qualif.:** Applicants must have demonstrated exceptional academic achievement by maintaining a 3.0 or higher G.P.A.; must commit to working for their tribe or an Indian organization upon completion of their degree; must be enrolled full-time at an eligible tribal college; and must be American Indian or Alaskan Native with proof of enrollment or descendancy. **Criteria:** Preference will be given to those students who meet the criteria.

Funds Avail.: $2,000. **To Apply:** Applicants must complete the application process online. **Deadline:** May 31. **Contact:** Debra Reed at 800-776-3863 or dreed@collegefund.org.

811 ■ Morgan Stanley Tribal Scholars Program
(Undergraduate/Scholarship)

Purpose: To award scholarships to outstanding American Indian students who are currently enrolled at a tribal college and who have an interest in business or the financial services industry. **Focus:** Business or related field. **Qualif.:** Applicants must have at least a 3.0 grade point average; must have declared a major in business or a related field; must be enrolled full-time at an eligible tribal college; must be American Indian or Alaskan Native with proof of enrollment or descendancy; and must have demonstrated exceptional academic achievement. **Criteria:** Preference will be given to those students who meet the criteria.

Funds Avail.: $2,500. **To Apply:** Applicants must complete the application process online. **Deadline:** May 31. **Contact:** Debra Reed at 800-776-3863 or dreed@collegefund.org.

812 ■ Time Warner Tribal Scholars Program
(Undergraduate/Scholarship)

Purpose: To award scholarships for outstanding American Indian students who are enrolled in a tribal college. **Focus:** General studies. **Qualif.:** Applicants must have at least a 2.5 grade point average; must be enrolled full time at an eligible tribal college; and must be American Indian or Alaskan Native with proof of enrollment or descendancy. **Criteria:** Preference will be based on exceptional academic achievement.

Funds Avail.: $2,500. **To Apply:** Applicants must complete the application process online. **Deadline:** May 31. **Contact:** Debra Reed at 800-776-3863 or dreed@collegefund.org.

813 ■ Woksape Oyate: "Wisdom of the People" Distinguished Scholars Awards *(Undergraduate/ Scholarship)*

Purpose: To award a scholarship to the best and the brightest American Indian student attending a tribal college. **Focus:** General studies. **Qualif.:** Program is open to valedictorians or salutatorians of their high school class; must be American Indian or Alaskan Native with proof of enrollment or descendancy; must be enrolled full-time at an eligible

tribal college; and must have demonstrated exceptional academic achievement. **Criteria:** Preference will be given to students who meet the criteria.

Funds Avail.: $8,000. **Number Awarded:** 1. **To Apply:** Applicants must complete the application process online. **Deadline:** May 31. **Contact:** Debra Reed at 800-776-3863 or dreed@collegefund.org.

814 ■ American Indian Education Foundation
2401 Eglin St.
Rapid City, SD 57703
Ph: (605) 342-9968
Fax: (605) 342-4113
Free: 866-866-8642
E-mail: info@aiefprograms.org
URL: www.nrcprograms.org

815 ■ Association on American Indian Affairs Emergency Aid Scholarships *(Undergraduate/ Scholarship)*

Purpose: To award scholarship to Native American undergraduates of any major. **Focus:** General studies. **Qualif.:** Applicants must be enrolled members of a federally recognized tribe. **Criteria:** Awards will be given based on financial need and severity of the emergency.

Funds Avail.: $100-$400. **Number Awarded:** 20. **To Apply:** Applicants must: complete AIEF Scholarship Application; provide documentation of tribal enrollment for themselves or their parents; provide transcripts with ACT and GPA scores; attach an essay that outlines the following information: introduction, academics, career plans, service to the Native American community, leadership/community service, financial needs and unique circumstances. **Contact:** Association on American Indian Affairs, ENA Scholarship, 966 Hungerford Dr. Ste. 12 B Rockeville, MD 20850. 240-314-7155.

816 ■ Brown Foundation College Scholarships
(Undergraduate/Scholarship)

Purpose: To award scholarship to the students of Native American ancestry wishing to attend college. **Focus:** Education. **Qualif.:** Applicants must be students wishing to attend college and major in education. **Criteria:** Selection will be based on the committee's criteria.

Funds Avail.: $1,000. **Number Awarded:** 10. **To Apply:** Applicants must: complete AIEF Scholarship Application; provide documentation of tribal enrollment for themselves or their parents; provide transcripts with ACT and GPA scores; attach an essay that outlines the following information: introduction, academics, career plans, service to the Native American community, leadership/community service, financial needs and unique circumstances. **Contact:** Brown Foundation Scholarship Program, 1515 SE Monroe, Topeka, KS 66612; Phone: 785-235-3939; brownfoundation@juno.com.

817 ■ Catching the Dream Scholarships *(Graduate, Undergraduate/Scholarship)*

Purpose: To give American Indian students the tools, resources and opportunities to learn and succeed. **Focus:** Education; Business; Science; Engineering. **Qualif.:** Applicants must be enrolled members of a federally recognized tribe; both undergraduate and graduate students may apply. **Criteria:** Selection will be based on the committee's criteria.

Awards are arranged alphabetically below their administering organizations

Funds Avail.: $500-$5,000. **To Apply:** Applicants may submit an application to the Scholarship Affairs Office of Catching the Dream. **Deadline:** March 15-Summer; April 15-Fall; September 15-spring. **Contact:** Catching the Dream 8200 Mountain Rd. NE Ste. 203 Albuquerque, NM 87110; 505-262-2351 x 116; nscholarsh@aol.com.

818 ■ Daughters of the American Revolution American Indian Scholarships *(Undergraduate/Scholarship)*

Purpose: To give American Indian students the tools, resources and opportunities to learn and succeed. **Focus:** General studies. **Qualif.:** Applicants must be: Native Americans who can show proof of ancestry; undergraduate or graduate students who have a GPA of 2.75 or higher; may be in any major. **Criteria:** Selection will be based on the committee's criteria.

Funds Avail.: $500. **Number Awarded:** 60. **Deadline:** April 1-fall; October 1-spring.

819 ■ Indian Health Service Scholarship Program *(Undergraduate/Scholarship)*

Purpose: To give American Indian students the tools, resources and opportunities to learn and succeed. **Focus:** Health sciences. **Qualif.:** Applicants must be enrolled members of state or federally recognized tribes; must be undergraduate or graduate students who are majoring in any health-related pre-professional program. **Criteria:** Selection will be based on the committee's criteria.

Funds Avail.: No specific amount. **Deadline:** February.

820 ■ International Order of the King's Daughters and Sons North American Indian Scholarship Program *(Undergraduate/Scholarship)*

Purpose: To give American Indian students the tools, resources and opportunities to learn and succeed. **Focus:** General studies. **Qualif.:** Applicants must be: Native Americans who have (or whose parents have) a reservation number; undergraduates of any major. **Criteria:** Selection will be based on the committee's criteria.

Funds Avail.: $650. **To Apply:** Applicants must: complete AIEF Scholarship Application; provide documentation of tribal enrollment for themselves or their parents; provide transcripts with ACT and GPA scores; attach an essay that outlines the following information: introduction, academics, career plans, service to the Native American community, leadership/community service, financial needs and unique circumstances. **Deadline:** April 1. **Contact:** International Order of the King's Daughters and Sons. Attn: Director, North American Indian Department PO Box 1040 Chautauqua, NY 14722-1040; 716-357-4951.

821 ■ Native American Education Grants *(Graduate, Undergraduate/Grant)*

Purpose: To give American Indian students the tools, resources and opportunities to learn and succeed. **Focus:** General studies. **Qualif.:** Applicants must be: enrolled members of federally recognized tribes; undergraduate or graduate students of any major. **Criteria:** Selection will be based on the committee's criteria.

Funds Avail.: $200-$3,000. **To Apply:** Applicants must: complete AIEF Scholarship Application; provide documentation of tribal enrollment for themselves or their parents; provide transcripts with ACT and GPA scores; attach an essay that outlines the following information: introduction,

academics, career plans, service to the Native American community, leadership/community service, financial needs and unique circumstances. **Deadline:** June 1. **Contact:** Frances Cook, Native American Education Grants, Presbyterian Church-USA, 100 Witherspoon St. Rm M052B, Louisville, KY 40202; 888-728-7228 x 5776.

822 ■ Jackie Robinson Foundation Minority Scholarships *(Undergraduate/Scholarship)*

Purpose: To give American Indian students the tools, resources and opportunities to learn and succeed. **Focus:** General studies. **Qualif.:** Applicants must be high school seniors entering an accredited college or university as freshmen. **Criteria:** Selection will be based on the committee's criteria.

Funds Avail.: $6,000. **To Apply:** Applicants must: complete AIEF Scholarship Application; provide documentation of tribal enrollment for themselves or their parents; provide transcripts with ACT and GPA scores; attach an essay that outlines the following information: introduction, academics, career plans, service to the Native American community, leadership/community service, financial needs and unique circumstances. **Deadline:** April 1. **Contact:** Jackie Robinson Foundation, Attn: Scholarship Coordinator, 3 W 35th St. 11th Fl. New York, NY 10001; 212-290-8600; www.jackierobinson.org.

823 ■ U.S. BIA Indian Higher Education Grants *(Undergraduate/Grant)*

Purpose: To give American Indian Students the tools, resources and opportunities to learn and succeed. **Focus:** General studies. **Qualif.:** Applicants must be: Native American undergraduate students of any major; enrolled in a federally recognized tribe. **Criteria:** Awards will be given based on financial need.

Funds Avail.: $300-$900. **Number Awarded:** 1,200. **To Apply:** Applicants must: complete AIEF Scholarship Application; provide documentation of tribal enrollment for themselves or their parents; provide transcripts with ACT and GPA scores; attach an essay that outlines the following information: introduction, academics, career plans, service to the Native American community, leadership/community service, financial needs and unique circumstances. Applicants may contact their tribe's education office for more information.

824 ■ American Indian Graduate Center (AIGC)

3701 San Mateo Blvd. NE, Ste. 200
Albuquerque, NM 87110
Ph: (505) 881-4584
Fax: (505) 884-0427
Free: 800-628-1920
E-mail: web@aigcs.org
URL: www.aigc.com

825 ■ Accenture American Indian Scholarship Program *(Graduate, Undergraduate/Scholarship)*

Purpose: To provide financial assistance to undergraduate and graduate American Indians in furthering their education. **Focus:** Technology; Engineering; Medicine; Law; Business. **Qualif.:** Applicants must be American Indians who are incoming freshmen with a cumulative GPA of 3.25 or greater on a 4.0 scale at the end of the seventh semester of high school or graduates/professionals who have attained a cumulative GPA of 3.25 or greater on a 4.0 scale,

Awards are arranged alphabetically below their administering organizations

as measured by undergraduate transcripts; must be enrolled members of a U.S. federally-recognized American Indian tribe or Alaska Native group; must be seeking a degree and career in fields of study including technology, engineering, medicine, law and business. **Criteria:** Applicants are evaluated on the basis of demonstrated character; personal merit evident through leadership in school, civic and extracurricular activities, academic achievement and motivation to serve and succeed; and commitment to the American Indian Community, locally and/or nationally.

Funds Avail.: No amount specified. **To Apply:** Applicants must submit completed application form; copy of certificate of Indian Blood (CIB); unofficial undergraduate and/or graduate academic transcripts; biographical data and/or resume; essay describing their character, personal merit and commitment to community and heritage; two personal letters of recommendation (one must come from an education professional who is familiar with their academic work and the other one must come from an individual having knowledge of their leadership and community service activities); and financial aid award letter from the institution they will attend. **Deadline:** May 11.

826 ■ AIGC Fellowships - Graduate *(Graduate/ Fellowship)*

Purpose: To provide financial assistance to Native Americans and Alaska Native graduates or professional degree-seeking students in furthering their education. **Focus:** General studies. **Qualif.:** Applicants must be pursuing a post-baccalaureate graduate or professional degree as full-time students at an accredited institution in the U.S.; must be enrolled members of a federally-recognized American Indian or Alaska Native group or provide documentation of descendency; must possess one-fourth federally-recognized Indian blood. **Criteria:** Recipients are selected based on financial need.

Funds Avail.: $1,000 up to $5,000. **Number Awarded:** 375. **To Apply:** Applicants must submit all the required application information including the Tribal Eligibility Certificate and Financial Need Form. **Deadline:** June 1. **Contact:** Marveline Vallo Gabbard at marveline@aigcs.org.

827 ■ BIE-Loan for Service for Graduates *(Graduate/Loan)*

Purpose: To provide financial assistance to eligible American Indians and Alaska Natives seeking graduate and professional degrees. **Focus:** General studies. **Qualif.:** Applicant must be an enrolled member of a United States federally-recognized American Indian tribe or Alaska Native group or possess one-fourth federally-recognized Indian blood; must have 3.0 grade point average; and must be pursuing a graduate or a professional degree as a full-time student at an accredited institution in the United States. **Criteria:** Applicants are evaluated based on financial need.

Funds Avail.: No specific amount. **To Apply:** Applicants must submit all the required application information. **Deadline:** June 1.

828 ■ Wells Fargo American Indian Scholarships - Graduate *(Graduate/Scholarship)*

Purpose: To provide financial assistance to American Indian graduates in furthering their education. **Focus:** Banking; Gaming industry; Management; Accounting; Finance; Information science and technology. **Qualif.:** Applicants must be enrolled members of a United States federally-recognized American Indian tribe or Alaska Native group;

must be pursuing career and degree fields relating to banking, resort management, gaming operations, management and administration, including accounting, finance, information technology and human resources; must be full-time graduate students at a U.S. accredited college or university; and must have a cumulative average GPA of 3.0 on a 4.0 scale at the time of application. **Criteria:** Applicants are evaluated based on financial need.

Funds Avail.: No specific amount. **To Apply:** Applicants must submit all the required application information. **Deadline:** June 1.

829 ■ American Indian Library Association (AILA)

12 Highfield Rd., No. 2
Roslindale, MA 02131
E-mail: kellypster@gmail.com
URL: www.ailanet.org

830 ■ AILA Scholarships *(Graduate/Scholarship)*

Purpose: To encourage the entry of qualified American Indians and Alaskan Natives into the library profession. **Focus:** Library and archival sciences. **Qualif.:** Applicant must be a member of a federally recognized tribe as evidenced by the CIBC card of the applicant, or be a tribal member with official documentation; demonstrate involvement in the American Indian community and sustained commitment to American Indian concerns and initiatives; admitted to a graduate program in library and/or information sciences accredited by the American Library Association and must be enrolled for a minimum of 6 hours each semester. **Criteria:** Preference will be given to applicants who are employed in a tribal library or who are currently employed in a library serving American Indian populations. Financial need will be considered.

Funds Avail.: $2,000. **Number Awarded:** 1. **To Apply:** Applicants must submit a completed scholarship application together with two letters of recommendation; evidence of enrollment in a federally recognized tribe or Alaskan village or a similar official document; a personal statement (maximum of 250 words) addressing past and future sustained involvement in American Indian communities and a resume. Submit complete application package to American Indian Library Association Treasurer, Dean Joan S. Howland. **Deadline:** May 1. **Contact:** Holly Tomren, UCI Libraries, Cataloging Dept., PO Box 19557 Irvine, CA 92623.

831 ■ American Indian Science and Engineering Society (AISES)

PO Box 9828
Albuquerque, NM 87119-9828
Ph: (505) 765-1052
Fax: (505) 765-5608
E-mail: pam@aises.org
URL: www.aises.org

832 ■ AISES Intel Scholarships *(Graduate, Undergraduate/Scholarship)*

Purpose: To financially assist ethnic students in furthering their education. **Focus:** Computer and information sciences; Engineering, Computer; Electrical engineering. **Qualif.:** Applicant must be a member of an American Indian tribe or otherwise considered to be an American Native by

Awards are arranged alphabetically below their administering organizations

the tribe with which affiliation is claimed; or is at least 1/4 American Indian or Alaskan Native blood or considered to be an Alaskan Native by an Alaskan Native group to which affiliation is claimed; must be a full-time undergraduate or graduate student with at least 3.0 GPA at an accredited four-year college or university; must be majoring one of the following disciplines: a) Computer Science; b) Computer Engineering; or c) Electrical Engineering; and must be a current member of AISES. **Criteria:** Judges will evaluate the applications based on information that is provided, including but not limited to: 1) which school within the college/university the student is attending; 2) student's current or expected course curriculum; and 3) AISES current year funding levels.

Funds Avail.: $5,000 for undergraduates and $10,000 for graduate students. **To Apply:** Applicants must complete an application form; must submit the most recent transcript and proof of tribal enrollment; two letters of recommendation; online resume. On a separate sheet, applicants must provide a personal statement of no more than 500 words. **Deadline:** June. **Contact:** Questions should be directed to Liz Encinias at collegerelations@aises.org.

833 ■ AISES Summer Internships (Graduate, Undergraduate/Internship)

Purpose: To promote an advanced study to the graduate level and assist students in developing professional networks. **Focus:** General studies. **Qualif.:** Applicants must be U.S. citizens or permanent residents; must be college/university sophomores, juniors, seniors, or graduate students at the time of application; must be enrolled on a full-time basis; must have 3.0 GPA on a 4.0 scale; and must be current AISES members. **Criteria:** Recipients will be selected based on submitted materials.

Funds Avail.: No specific amount. **To Apply:** Applicants must submit a completed and signed application form; must submit two letters of recommendation; most recent official transcript(s); professional resume; proof of citizenship; essay; and two letters of recommendation. **Deadline:** February. **Contact:** Questions should be directed to Liz Encinias at collegerelations@aises.org.

834 ■ A.T. Anderson Memorial Scholarships (Graduate, Undergraduate/Scholarship)

Purpose: To financially assist ethnic students in furthering their education. **Focus:** Science; Engineering; Medicine; Natural resources; Mathematics and mathematical sciences. **Qualif.:** Applicant must be a memebr of an American Indian tribe, an Alaska Native, or Native Hawaiian otherwise considered to be an American Indian by the tribe with which affiliation is claimed; or at least 1/4 American Indian blood or at least 1/4 Alaskan Native; must be a current AISES member; and have a 3.0 on a 4.0 scale cumulative GPA. **Criteria:** Judges will evaluate the applications based on information that is provided, including but not limited to: 1) which school within the college/university the student is attending; 2) student's current or expected course curriculum; and 3) AISES current year funding levels.

Funds Avail.: $1,000 for undergraduates; $2,000 for graduate students. **To Apply:** Applicants must complete an application form; must submit the most recent transcript and proof of tribal enrollment; two letters of recommendation; online resume. On a separate sheet, applicants must provide a personal statement with no more than 500 words. **Deadline:** June. **Contact:** Questions should be directed to Liz Encinias at collegerelations@aises.org.

835 ■ American Institute of Aeronautics and Astronautics Foundation
1801 Alexander Bell Dr., Ste. 500
Reston, VA 20191-4344
Ph: (703) 264-7500
Fax: (703) 264-7551
Free: 800-639-AIAA
E-mail: custserv@aiaa.org
URL: www.aiaa.org

836 ■ AIAA Foundation Scholarship Program
(Graduate, Undergraduate/Scholarship)

Purpose: To advance the arts, sciences, and technology of aeronautics and astronautics. **Focus:** Aeronautics; Astronautics. **Qualif.:** Applicant must: have completed at least one academic quarter or semester of full-time college work; have a college GPA of not less than the equivalent of a 3.3 on a 4.0 scale; be enrolled in an accredited college or university. Applicant does not have to be an AIAA student member in good standing to apply, but must become one before receiving a scholarship. Applicant's scholarship plan shall be such as to provide entry into some field of science or engineering encompassed by the technical activities of AIAA. Applicants shall not have, or subsequently receive, any other scholarship/award which, when combined with the AIAA Foundation award covers more than the cost of tuition. Applicant may be students of any nationality, not restricted by the US State Department, in full-time study at any accredited college or university within the United States. **Criteria:** Selection will be based on the committee's criteria.

Funds Avail.: No specific amount. **To Apply:** The completed application must be received on or before the deadline. Students submitting their applications should include the essay and also make arrangements to have their official college transcripts sent directly to AIAA. Sophomore and junior students who have received one of these scholarship awards and wish to be considered for continuation of this award should arrange to have transcripts of their college academic record, and letters of recommendation from their faculty members and others supporting their continuance in the program sent to AIAA.

837 ■ American Institute of Architects - Alaska
PO Box 240625
Anchorage, AK 99524
Ph: (907) 276-2834
Fax: (907) 688-4658
E-mail: info@aiaak.org
URL: aiaalaska.org

838 ■ AIA Alaska Scholarships (Graduate, Undergraduate/Scholarship)

Purpose: To help Alaska resident students enroll in an accredited architectural program. **Focus:** Architecture. **Qualif.:** Students must be permanent residents of the State of Alaska and have completed six or more semesters in a program leading to a Bachelor's Degree in Architecture or enrolled in a Master's Program in Architecture. **Criteria:** Selection will be based on overall ability, desire, determination and potential for successfully completing an architecture education and entering into architecture as a profession.

Funds Avail.: A total fo $4,000. **Number Awarded:** 3. **To**

Awards are arranged alphabetically below their administering organizations

Apply: Applicants must submit an application packet containing a personal letter stating need, qualifications and desire. In addition, a completed application form, resume and transcript, as well as a letter of recommendation from a faculty member, must be included in the package. **Deadline:** September 30.

839 ■ American Institute of Architects Northeast Illinois (AIA NEI)

c/o Corda Murphy, Exec. Dir.
412 Green Valley Dr.
Naperville, IL 60540
Ph: (630) 527-8550
Fax: (630) 357-4818
E-mail: exec@aianei.org
URL: www.aianei.org

840 ■ AIA/NEI Scholarships *(Graduate, Undergraduate/Scholarship)*

Purpose: To support students enrolled in an accredited architecture program. **Focus:** Architecture. **Qualif.:** Applicant must be a U.S. citizen; enrolled at one of the East Central or West Central accredited Architecture schools; and have a home residence of record within the AIA/NEI Chapter boundaries (Cook, DuPage, Kane, and Kendall Counties, except that the territory shall not include the area within the city limits of Chicago, nor south of Interstate 55, nor east of the Edens Expressway). **Criteria:** Selection is based on the application materials submitted for review.

Funds Avail.: $3,000. **Number Awarded:** 3. **To Apply:** Applicants must submit a completed application form including two letters of recommendation and a self-addressed, stamped postcard. **Deadline:** March 31.

841 ■ Arnold Les Larsen, FAIA, Memorial Scholarships *(Graduate, Master's/Scholarship)*

Purpose: To recognize students accepted into the Master of Architecture program of the University of Illinois at Urbana-Champaign or Chicago. **Focus:** Architecture. **Qualif.:** Applicant must be a U.S. citizen and enrolled in the Master's of Architecture program at either the University of Illinois at Chicago or at Urbana-Champaign. **Criteria:** Preference will be given to students who are participants in an AIAS chapter, demonstrated financial need and with a permanent residence within the AIA/NEI Chapter boundaries (DuPage, Kane, Kendall and suburban Cook Counties).

Funds Avail.: $1,000. **Number Awarded:** 1. **To Apply:** Applicants must submit a completed application form including two letters of recommendation and a self-addressed, stamped postcard. **Deadline:** March 31.

842 ■ American Institute of Bangladesh Studies (AIBS)

University of Wisconsin-Madison
203 Ingraham
1155 Observatory Dr.
Madison, WI 53706
Ph: (608) 265-4304
Fax: (608) 265-3062
E-mail: aibsinfo@aibs.net
URL: www.aibs.net

843 ■ AIBS Junior Fellowships *(Doctorate/Fellowship)*

Purpose: To provide funds for a junior research fellowship in Bangladesh. **Focus:** General studies. **Qualif.:** Applicants must be U.S. citizens or permanent residents; must be in the ABD phase of their Ph.D. programs; and must be in the stage of data collection and writing. **Criteria:** Recipients are selected based on submitted applications and supporting materials.

Funds Avail.: Round trip transportation, $920 and allowances per month. **To Apply:** Applicants must send five copies each of application form (available on the website), curriculum vitae (maximum of three pages) and research proposal (maximum of ten pages).

844 ■ AIBS Senior Fellowships *(Doctorate, Postdoctorate/Fellowship)*

Purpose: To provide funding for a senior research fellowship in Bangladesh. **Focus:** General studies. **Qualif.:** Applicants must be U.S. citizens or permanent residents and must have a PhD degree. **Criteria:** Recipients are selected based on submitted applications and supporting materials.

Funds Avail.: Round trip transportation, $1,150 and allowances per month. **To Apply:** Applicants must send five copies each of application form (available at the website), curriculum vitae (maximum of three pages), research proposal (maximum of ten pages) and transcript of records.

845 ■ American Institute of Chemical Engineers (AIChE)

3 Park Ave.
New York, NY 10016-5991
Ph: (646) 495-1380
Fax: (203) 775-5177
Free: 800-242-4363
E-mail: xpress@aiche.org
URL: www.aiche.org

846 ■ John J. McKetta Undergraduate Scholarships *(Undergraduate/Scholarship)*

Purpose: To provide financial assistance for chemical engineering undergraduate students planning a career in the chemical engineering process industries. **Focus:** Engineering, Chemical. **Qualif.:** Nominees must be national student members of AIChE attending an ABET accredited schools in the US, Canada or Mexico who are in their junior or senior year of a 4-year program in Chemical Engineering or equivalent for a 5-year co-op program. Nominees must have maintained a minimum of 3.0/4.0 GPA. **Criteria:** Preference is given to nominees from Mexican universities participating in ABET's Equivalent Education Program.

Funds Avail.: $5,000. **To Apply:** Nominees must submit a maximum two-page essay outlining career goals in the chemical engineering process industries (2 single-sided, single-spaced typed pages) and nominations must be accompanied by a minimum of two letters of recommendation, one from AIChE student advisor and the other from either a departmental faculty member or technical work supervisor. **Deadline:** June 15. **Contact:** awards@aiche.org.

847 ■ Minority Scholarship Awards for College Students *(Undergraduate/Scholarship)*

Purpose: To provide educational assistance for chemical engineering undergraduate students. **Focus:** Engineering, Chemical. **Qualif.:** Applicants must be AIChE national student members at the time of application. **Criteria:** Selection of recipients will be based on academic record, participation in AIChE student and professional activities,

Awards are arranged alphabetically below their administering organizations

career objectives and financial need.

Funds Avail.: $1,000. **Number Awarded:** 10. **To Apply:** Nominations must be submitted containing the following items: from the students: a) a completed application form; b) a career essay not to exceed 300 words outlining the following: immediate plans after graduation and area(s) of chemical engineering of most interest; long-range career objectives; official transcript of college grades. Nominations from the college financial aid office must contain: a letter indicating that the student is eligible for financial aid based on their records; a letter of recommendation from the AIChE student chapter advisor, department chair, or chemical engineering faculty member containing, but not limited to, the following: verification of nominee's GPA and projected completion date; evaluation of the student's academic performance and participation in AIChE and other professional or civic activities. **Deadline:** June 15. **Contact:** Donia Elsherbeni, donie@aiche.org.

848 ■ Minority Scholarship Awards for Incoming College Freshmen (Undergraduate/ Scholarship)

Purpose: To provide educational assistance for chemical engineering college freshmen. **Focus:** Engineering, Chemical. **Qualif.:** Applicants must be members of a minority group (i.e. African-American, Hispanic, Native American, or Alaskan Native) that is underrepresented in chemical engineering; must be high school graduates during the previous academic year and plan to enroll during the following academic year in a four-year university offering a science/engineering degree. **Criteria:** Recipients are selected based on academic record, participation in school and work activities, reason for choosing science or engineering, and financial need.

Funds Avail.: $1,000. **Number Awarded:** 10. **To Apply:** Nominations must be submitted containing the following items from the student: a) completed application form; b) career essay not to exceed 300 words outlining the following: (1) college or university chosen to attend, (2) reasons for choosing science/engineering, (3) possible career choices that may be of interest; c) official transcript of high school grades. Nominations must also include documents from the parent/guardian which should contain a letter verifying financial need which includes a list of financial resources for educational support; and a letter of recommendation from the high school counselor, math teacher or science teacher containing, but not limited to, the following: a) verification of student's GPA and graduation date; b) verification of high school senior class average grade (if confidential, high school counselor statement is required); c) confirmation of minority group of student; d) information about the student's school, job and/or other activities. **Deadline:** June 15. **Contact:** Donia Elsherbeni, donie@aiche.org.

849 ■ AIChE/Donald F. and Mildred Topp Othmer National Scholarship Awards (Undergraduate/Scholarship)

Purpose: To provide financial assistance for AIChE national student members for their undergraduate education in chemical engineering. **Focus:** Engineering, Chemical. **Qualif.:** Nominees must be AIChE national student members at the time of the nomination. **Criteria:** Recipients are selected based on academic record; participation in AIChE Student Chapter and other professional activities as outlined by the Student Chapter Advisor in their nomination letter; support of the nominee by the Student Chapter Advisor; and

nominees' career objectives and plans as outlined in their letter.

Funds Avail.: $1,000. **Number Awarded:** 15. **To Apply:** Nominators must submit completed nomination form; letter of nomination from the AIChE Student Chapter Advisor containing, but not limited to, the following: a) verification of the nominees' GPAs and projected completion date; b) an evaluation of the nominees' academic performance and participation in AIChE Student Chapter and other professional activities; statement from the nominees (not to exceed 300 words) outlining their career plans and objectives in chemical engineering and including, but not limited to, the following: a) immediate plans after graduation and area(s) of chemical engineering of most interest; b) long-range career objectives. **Deadline:** June 15.

850 ■ The American Institute for Conservation of Historic and Artistic Works (AIC)
1156 15th St. NW, Ste. 320
Washington, DC 20005-1714
Ph: (202) 452-9545
Fax: (202) 452-9328
E-mail: info@conservation-us.org
URL: www.conservation-us.org

851 ■ FAIC Latin American and Caribbean Scholars Program (Professional development/ Scholarship)

Purpose: To provide financial support for conservation professionals from Latin America and the Caribbean to participate in the annual meeting. **Focus:** Latin American Studies. **Qualif.:** Applicants must be Latin Americans. **Criteria:** Recipients will be selected based on quality of the essay, opportunities to attend international meetings, number of applicants, ability to communicate in English and availability of the financial support.

Funds Avail.: No specific amount. **To Apply:** Applicants must complete the application form and submit a curriculum vitae and an essay. For further information, applicants are advised to visit www.conservation-us.org/grants. **Deadline:** September (paper) and October (poster). **Contact:** Application form, supporting documents and questions can be sent at becas@conservation-us.org.

852 ■ Foundation of American Institute for Conservation Lecture Grants (Professional development/Grant)

Purpose: To provide funds and presentations of public lectures to help advance public awareness of conservation. **Focus:** Latin American Studies. **Qualif.:** Applicants must be Latin American. **Criteria:** Recipients are selected based on the ability of the project to advance public awareness of conservation; number of people reached, other project outcomes; speaker's ability to communicate the proposed topic; and feasibility of project.

Funds Avail.: $500. **To Apply:** Applicants must complete the online application form and are asked to wait for the application packet that will be sent by the award committee. **Deadline:** February 15 and September 15.

853 ■ American Institute for Economic Research (AIER)
PO Box 1000
Great Barrington, MA 01230

Awards are arranged alphabetically below their administering organizations

Ph: (413) 528-1216
Fax: (413) 528-0103
Free: 888-528-1216
E-mail: info@aier.org
URL: www.aier.org

854 ■ American Institute for Economic Research Student Summer Fellowships *(Doctorate, Graduate, Undergraduate/Fellowship)*

Purpose: To train graduating college seniors who plan to enter doctoral programs in economics or an affiliated field, and those enrolled in such programs for no longer than two years. **Focus:** Economics; Political science. **Qualif.:** Applicant must be a graduating college senior planning to pursue a PhD in economics or in a related field; or, a current graduate student enrolled in such program for no longer than two years. **Criteria:** Selection is based on academic achievement, interest in current economic problems, plans for future study, and potential for success.

Funds Avail.: $1,500. **To Apply:** Applicants must submit a completed application form together with a vita/resume; personal statement (not to exceed three double-spaced typewritten pages); writing sample; outline of proposed course of study; official transcripts; and scholastic references. **Deadline:** March 23. **Contact:** fellowship@aier.org.

855 ■ American Institute of Iranian Studies (AIIrS)

c/o Dr. Erica Ehrenberg, Exec. Dir.
118 Riverside Dr.
New York, NY 10024
E-mail: aiis@nyc.rr.com
URL: www.simorgh-aiis.org

856 ■ Persian Language Study in Tehran Scholarships *(Doctorate, Graduate/Fellowship)*

Purpose: To help graduate students with advanced learning in Persian studies. **Focus:** Humanities; Social sciences. **Qualif.:** Applicants should be U.S. citizens enrolled in a doctoral program in humanities or social sciences; must have an approved research topic that requires use of Persian, and must have completed at least one full academic year of Persian language study. **Criteria:** Mastery of Persian language study is not required but could be prioritized.

Funds Avail.: No specific amount. **To Apply:** Applications must include a letter-form curriculum vitae, with the following information: citizenship, research plans, level of Persian study attained, academic affiliation, and status. Recommendation letters mentioning the relevance of Persian study to the dissertation should be sent directly to AIIrS. Applications must be sent to aiis@nyc.rr.com or mailed to Dr. Erica Ehrenberg. **Deadline:** Applications must be submitted on January 10 and letters of recommendation must be on January 15. **Contact:** Dr. Erica Ehrenberg, Executive Director.

857 ■ Research Fellowships in Iranian Studies, Resident Director-Tehran *(Doctorate, Graduate/Fellowship)*

Purpose: To help graduate students with advanced learning in Persian studies. **Focus:** Persian studies. **Qualif.:** Applicants should be U.S. citizens, have completed a doctoral program and be proficient in Persian. **Criteria:** Applications will be considered in a rolling basis.

Funds Avail.: No specific amount. **To Apply:** Applicants must submit a detailed description of research plans including the names, addresses, e-mail addresses of two references and a curriculum vitae. Applications must be sent to aiis@nyc.rr.com or mailed to Dr. Erica Ehrenberg. **Contact:** Dr. Erica Ehrenberg, Executive Director.

858 ■ Short-term Senior Fellowships in Iranian Studies *(Doctorate, Graduate/Fellowship)*

Purpose: To promote research in the field of Iranian Studies. **Focus:** Humanities; Social sciences; Interracial studies. **Qualif.:** Applicants must be U.S. citizens, scholars, faculty members, or museum staff. **Criteria:** Preference will be given to applicant with knowledge of Persian study and a record of research in the humanities or the social sciences relating to Iran. Applications will be considered in a rolling basis.

Funds Avail.: No specific amount. **To Apply:** Applicants must submit a curriculum vitae; and a detailed letter explaining how the fellowship would benefit the applicant's work, the names and addresses of the relevant contacts in Iran who have provided permission to research, and the names and e-mail addresses of two referees. Applicant must specify preferred dates of travel. **Contact:** Applications must be sent to aiis@nyc.rr.com or mailed to Dr. Erica Ehrenberg.

859 ■ American Institute for Maghrib Studies (AIMS)

Center for Middle Eastern Studies
Marshall Bldg.
845 N Park Ave., Rm. 470
Tucson, AZ 85721-0158
Ph: (520) 626-6498
Fax: (520) 621-9257
E-mail: aimscmes@u.arizona.edu
URL: aimsnorthafrica.org

860 ■ AIMS Long-term Research Grants *(Doctorate, Postdoctorate/Grant)*

Purpose: To render fund for US scholars interested in conducting research on North Africa in any Maghrib country. **Focus:** General studies. **Qualif.:** Applicant must be a U.S. citizen graduate student, independent scholar and faculty in all disciplines currently enrolled in a M.A. or Ph.D. program; and must be a member of AIMS at the time of application. **Criteria:** Recipients will be selected based on submitted application and proposal.

Funds Avail.: $15,000. **Number Awarded:** 1. **To Apply:** Applicant must submit completed grant application, proposal or research design (no more than 1500 words), proposed itinerary with approximate dates, budget, vitae indicating language proficiency and institutional affiliation, letters of recommendation from two referees, including the candidate's dissertation advisor, or in the case of applicants holding a Ph.D., the names of two persons who may be contacted for references, and one page summary of the proposed research in either French or Arabic. **Deadline:** December 31. **Contact:** For further information, applicants may e-mail aimscmes@email.arizona.edu.

861 ■ AIMS Short-term Research Grants *(Doctorate, Postdoctorate/Grant)*

Purpose: To render fund for US scholars interested in conducting research on North Africa in any Maghrib country.

Awards are arranged alphabetically below their administering organizations

Focus: General studies. **Qualif.:** Applicant must be a U.S. citizen graduate student, independent scholar and faculty in all disciplines currently enrolled in a M.A. or Ph.D. program; and must be a member of AIMS at the time of application. **Criteria:** Recipients will be selected based on submitted application and proposal.

Funds Avail.: $6,000. **Number Awarded:** 1. **To Apply:** Applicant must submit a completed grant application, proposal or research design, proposed itinerary with approximate dates, budget, vitae indicating language proficiency and institutional affiliation, letters of recommendation from two referees, including the candidate's dissertation advisor, or in the case of applicants holding a Ph.D., the names of two persons who may be contacted for references, and one page summary of the proposed research in either French or Arabic. **Deadline:** December 31. **Contact:** Original application form and four copies of supporting documents must be submitted to AIMS office.

862 ■ American Institute of Pakistan Studies (AIPS)
203 Ingraham Hall
1180 Observatory Dr.
Madison, WI 53706
Ph: (608) 261-1194
E-mail: aips@pakistanstudies-aips.org
URL: www.pakistanstudies-aips.org

863 ■ AIPS Post-Doctoral Fellowships
(Doctorate/Fellowship)

Purpose: To encourage and support research on issues relevant to Pakistan and the promotion of scholarly exchange between the United States and Pakistan. **Focus:** Pakistani studies. **Qualif.:** Applicant must be a U.S. citizen or enrolled/employed full-time in an institution of higher education in the U.S.A. **Criteria:** Selection is based on the application materials submitted for review.

Funds Avail.: $3,000-$25,000. **Number Awarded:** Varies. **To Apply:** Applicant must submit a complete application package which includes: application checklist; application processing fee of $30; signed and dated application form; abstract; project statement (maximum of 5 pages); bibliography; budget proposal; curriculum vitae (maximum of 2 pages); three letters of recommendation (if submitted via email, the letters should come from the referees' own email account); and letter of affiliation. Complete application package must be submitted via email at aips@pakistanstudies-aips.org, or via regular mail. **Deadline:** June 15, September 1 and January 1. **Contact:** Laura Hammond at the above address.

864 ■ AIPS Pre-Doctoral Fellowships *(Doctorate, Graduate/Fellowship)*

Purpose: To encourage and support research on issues relevant to Pakistan and the promotion of scholarly exchange between the United States and Pakistan. **Focus:** Pakistani studies. **Qualif.:** Applicant must be a U.S. citizen or enrolled/employed full-time in an institution of higher education in the U.S.A. Pre-doctoral applicant should have completed all requirements for the PhD except the dissertation. **Criteria:** Selection is based on the application materials submitted for review.

Funds Avail.: $3,000-$25,000. **Number Awarded:** Varies. **To Apply:** Applicant must submit a complete application package which includes: application checklist; application

processing fee of $30; signed and dated application form; abstract; project statement (maximum of 5 pages); bibliography; budget proposal; curriculum vitae (maximum of 2 pages); three letters of recommendation (if submitted via email, the letters should come from the referees' own email account); letter of affiliation; and graduate transcripts. Complete application package must be submitted via email at aips@pakistanstudies-aips.org, or via regular mail. **Contact:** Laura Hammond at the above address.

865 ■ American Institute of Physics
1 Physics Ellipse
College Park, MD 20740-3843
Ph: (301) 209-3100
Fax: (301) 209-0843
E-mail: aipinfo@aip.org
URL: www.aip.org

866 ■ American Institute of Physics Congressional Science Fellowships *(Doctorate/Fellowship)*

Purpose: To help scientists broaden their experience through direct involvement with the legislative and policy processes. **Focus:** Physics. **Qualif.:** Applicants must be members in one or more of the 10 AIP Member Societies at the time of application; must be U.S. citizens; must have a PhD in physics or closely-related field prior to start of Fellowship term; must have an interest or experience in applying scientific knowledge to the solution of societal problems; must have excellent scientific credentials, outstanding interpersonal and communications skills and sound judgment and maturity in decision-making. **Criteria:** Selection will be based on the committee's criteria.

Funds Avail.: $70,000. **To Apply:** Applicants must submit the following application materials: letter of intent, providing information regarding their reason for applying, scientific training and professional background, science policy interest and experience, attributes and experiences that would make applicants more effective in this position; a resume limited to two pages, with up to one additional page allowed for a list of key publications; three letters of recommendation to be submitted directly by applicant's references. Letters should be from those having direct knowledge of the applicant's character, professional competence and particular attributes or experience that would enhance the candidate's suitability for this position. Applicants must visit the website for the on-line application and instructions on submitting the application materials. **Deadline:** January 15.

867 ■ American Institute of Physics State Department Science Fellowships *(Doctorate/Fellowship)*

Purpose: To contribute scientific and technical expertise to the department and raise awareness of the value of scientific input. **Focus:** Physics. **Qualif.:** Applicants must be members in one or more of the 10 AIP Member Societies at the time of application; must be U.S. citizens; must have a PhD in physics or closely-related field prior to start of Fellowship term; must be eligible for security clearance; must have an interest or experience in S&T aspects of foreign policy; must have excellent scientific credentials, outstanding interpersonal and communications skills and sound judgment and maturity in decision-making. **Criteria:** Selection will be based on the committee's criteria.

Funds Avail.: $70,000. **To Apply:** Applicants must submit

Awards are arranged alphabetically below their administering organizations

the following application materials: letter of intent, providing information regarding their reason for applying, scientific training and professional background, science policy interest and experience, attributes and experiences that would make applicants more effective in this position; a resume limited to two pages, with up to one additional page allowed for a list of key publications; three letters of recommendation to be submitted directly by applicant's references. Letters should be from those having direct knowledge of the applicant's character, professional competence and particular attributes or experience that would enhance the candidate's suitability for this position. Applicants must visit the website for the on-line application and instructions on submitting the application materials. **Deadline:** November 1.

868 ■ American Institute of Polish Culture (AIPC)

1440 79th St. Causeway, Ste. 117
Miami, FL 33141
Ph: (305) 864-2349
Fax: (305) 865-5150
E-mail: info@ampolinstitute.org
URL: www.ampolinstitute.org

869 ■ Harriet Irsay Scholarships *(Graduate, Undergraduate/Scholarship)*

Purpose: To provide financial support for American students of Polish descent who wish to continue their education after high school. **Focus:** Communications; Education; Media arts; History; International affairs and relations; Journalism; Liberal arts; Polish studies; Public relations. **Qualif.:** Applicant must be of Polish heritage; an American citizen or permanent resident; full-time graduate or undergraduate student in the field of communication, education, film, history, International Relation, journalism, liberal arts, polish studies, public relations; or graduate student in business programs with a thesis related to Poland, or graduate student with a thesis with Polish subject. **Criteria:** Recipients are selected on the basis of merits.

Funds Avail.: $1,000. **Number Awarded:** 10-15. **To Apply:** Applicants must submit a completed application form; school transcripts; resume; essay (200-400 words) about "Why should I receive the scholarship"; an article about Poland (maximum of 700 words); and three signed recommendation letters on a letterhead stationary from teachers or other person knowledgeable about the applicant's academic background. A non-refundable $10 processing fee (check or money order) must also be included. **Deadline:** July 1. **Contact:** For further information, applicants may e-mail admin@ampolinstitute.org.

870 ■ American Institute of Steel Construction (AISC)

1 E Wacker Dr., Ste. 700
Chicago, IL 60601-1802
Ph: (312) 670-2400
Fax: (312) 670-5403
E-mail: solutions@aisc.org
URL: www.aisc.org

871 ■ AISC/Great Lakes Fabricators and Erectors Association Fellowships *(Graduate/ Fellowship)*

Purpose: To provide financial assistance to those studying civil engineering. **Focus:** Civil engineering; Architectural engineering. **Qualif.:** Applicants must be full-time civil or architectural engineering students who are currently/or will be doing masters-level work at any graduate school in Michigan. **Criteria:** Applicants will be selected based on academic merit, faculty recommendation and jury's review of application materials.

Funds Avail.: $5,000. **Number Awarded:** 1. **To Apply:** Applicants must submit an official transcript; a reference and optional letter of reference; and a one-page detailed answers to the following: (a) Demonstrate concentration on steel related course work and/or thesis with a strong steel orientation, or (b) Demonstrate proposed course work and proposed thesis concentration in structural steel. **Deadline:** May 1. **Contact:** For further information, applicants must contact Shanna Quinn at the above address; E-mail: quinn@aisc.org.

872 ■ AISC/Rocky Mountain Steel Construction Association Fellowships *(Graduate/Fellowship)*

Purpose: To provide financial assistance to those studying civil engineering. **Focus:** Civil engineering; Architectural engineering. **Qualif.:** Applicants must be full-time civil or architectural engineering students who are currently/or will be doing masters-level work in either Colorado or Wyoming. Applicants must be U.S. citizens. **Criteria:** Applicants will be selected based on academic merit, faculty recommendation and jury's review of the application materials.

Funds Avail.: $3,000. **Number Awarded:** 1. **To Apply:** Applicants must submit an official transcript; a reference and optional letter of reference; and a one-page detailed answers to the following: (a) Demonstrate concentration on steel related course work and/or thesis with a strong steel orientation, or (b) Demonstrate proposed course work and proposed thesis concentration in structural steel. **Deadline:** May 1. **Contact:** For further information, applicants must contact Shanna Quinn at the above address; E-mail: quinn@aisc.org.

873 ■ AISC/Southern Association of Steel Fabricators Fellowships *(Graduate/Fellowship)*

Purpose: To provide financial assistance to those studying civil engineering. **Focus:** Civil engineering; Architectural engineering. **Qualif.:** Applicants must be full-time civil or architectural engineering students who are currently/or will be doing masters-level work at any graduate school in Alabama, Arkansas, Florida, Georgia, Kentucky, Louisiana, Mississippi and Tennessee. Applicants must be U.S. citizens. **Criteria:** Applicants will be selected based on academic merit, faculty recommendation and jury's review of the application materials.

Funds Avail.: $2,500. **Number Awarded:** 2. **To Apply:** Applicants must submit an official transcript; a reference and optional letter of reference; and one-page detailed answers to the following: (a) Demonstrate concentration on steel related course work and/or thesis with a strong steel orientation, or (b) Demonstrate proposed course work and proposed thesis concentration in structural steel. **Deadline:** May 1. **Contact:** For further information, applicants must contact Shanna Quinn at the above address; E-mail: quinn@aisc.org.

874 ■ AISC/Southern Association of Steel Fabricators Scholarships *(Undergraduate/ Scholarship)*

Purpose: To encourage greater interest in structural steel design. **Focus:** Civil engineering; Architectural engineering. **Qualif.:** Applicants must be full-time civil or architectural

Awards are arranged alphabetically below their administering organizations

engineering students who are U.S. Citizens entering their 3rd or 4th year of study with an interest in structural steel from a university in Alabama, Arkansas, Florida, Georgia, Kentucky, Louisiana, Mississippi and Tennessee. **Criteria:** Applicants are selected based on academic merit and faculty recommendation. Preference will be given to those students who have selected a concentration in structural steel.

Funds Avail.: $2,500. **Number Awarded:** 2. **To Apply:** Applicants must submit an official transcript; a reference and optional letter of reference; and a short essay on overall career objective. **Deadline:** May 1. **Contact:** Nancy Gavlin at the above address.

875 ■ AISC/Structural Steel Education Council Fellowships *(Graduate/Fellowship)*

Purpose: To provide financial assistance to those studying civil engineering. **Focus:** Civil engineering; Architectural engineering. **Qualif.:** Applicants must be residents of/and full-time civil or architectural engineering students undertaking masters-level work in any graduate program from universities in California and Nevada. **Criteria:** Applicants will be selected based on academic merit and faculty recommendation. Preference will be given to applicants who are legal residents from either California or Nevada.

Funds Avail.: $2,500. **Number Awarded:** 2. **To Apply:** Applicants must submit an official transcript; a reference and optional letter of reference; and a one-page detailed answers to the following: (a) Demonstrate concentration on steel related course work and/or thesis with a strong steel orientation, or (b) Demonstrate proposed course work and proposed thesis concentration in structural steel. **Deadline:** May 1. **Contact:** For further information, applicants must contact Shanna Quinn; E-mail: quinn@aisc.org.

876 ■ AISC/US Steel Fellowships *(Graduate/ Fellowship)*

Purpose: To provide financial assistance to those studying civil engineering. **Focus:** Civil engineering; Architectural engineering. **Qualif.:** Applicants must be full-time civil or architectural engineering students who are currently/will be doing masters-level work at universities in Alaska, Delaware, Hawaii, Iowa, Maryland, Minnesota, Nebraska, Ohio, Texas and Wisconsin. Applicants must be U.S. citizens. **Criteria:** Applicants will be selected based on academic merit, faculty recommendation and jury's review of the application materials.

Funds Avail.: $2,500. **Number Awarded:** 1. **To Apply:** Applicants must submit an official transcript; a reference and optional letter of reference; and a one-page detailed answers to the following: (a) Demonstrate concentration on steel related course work and/or thesis with a strong steel orientation, or (b) Demonstrate proposed course work and proposed thesis concentration in structural steel. **Deadline:** September 30. **Contact:** Nancy Gavlin at the above address; E-mail: gavlin@aisc.org.

877 ■ AISC/Fred R. Havens Fellowships *(Graduate, Undergraduate/Fellowship)*

Purpose: To provide financial assistance to those studying civil engineering. **Focus:** Civil engineering; Architectural engineering. **Qualif.:** Applicants must be U.S. citizens studying civil or architectural engineering full-time at universities in Missouri, Kansas or at MIT. Applicants must be graduates or undergraduate students who have completed one steel design course. **Criteria:** Undergraduate applicants are selected based on academic merit, faculty

recommendation and evaluation of short essay and steel design analysis/designs submitted while graduate students applying are evaluated.

Funds Avail.: $5,000. **Number Awarded:** 2. **To Apply:** Undergraduate applicants must submit an official transcript; a reference and optional letter of reference; a two-page essay on their interest in steel structures and an original sample steel design analysis/design solution with calculations. In addition to the mentioned requirements, graduate applicants must submit an official transcript; a reference and optional letter of reference; and a one-page detailed which answers the following: (a) Demonstrate concentration on steel related course work and/or thesis with a strong steel orientation, or (b) Demonstrate proposed course work and proposed thesis concentration in structural steel. **Deadline:** May 1. **Contact:** For further information, applicants must contact Shanna Quinn at the above address; Phone: 312-670-5418; E-mail: quinn@aisc.org.

878 ■ American Institute of Wine and Food - Rhode Island

PO Box 1016
Portsmouth, RI 02871
Ph: (401) 683-2490
Fax: (401) 683-1949
E-mail: jadeeast33@juno.com
URL: www.aiwf.org/rhodeisland

879 ■ Patricia Tillinghast Memorial Scholarships *(Graduate, Undergraduate/Scholarship)*

Purpose: To provide educational financial support to a culinary arts student, a baking and pastry student and a continuing education student. **Focus:** Culinary arts. **Qualif.:** Applicant must be a Rhode Island resident for a minimum of 5 years; maintain a 3.5 - 4.0 GPA; a full-time student enrolled and attending a university/college; and be available to receive the scholarship at the annual Meet the Board event if chosen as a recipient. **Criteria:** Selection is based on academic standing and financial need.

Funds Avail.: No specific amount. **Number Awarded:** 3. **To Apply:** Applicants must write a letter to: The Board of Directors, AIWF Rhode Island Chapter, c/o John Philcox, 969 W Main Rd., Apt 6404, Middletown, RI 02842. The letter (1 page, 250 words) should contain experiences or future dreams in the culinary arts field and why you deserve to receive the scholarship. Applicants must include two letters of recommendation from faculty. **Deadline:** November 1.

880 ■ American Intellectual Property Law Education Foundation (AIPLEF)

241 18th St. S, Ste. 700
Arlington, VA 22202
Ph: (703) 415-0780
Fax: (703) 415-0786
E-mail: admin@aiplef.org
URL: www.aiplef.org

881 ■ Jan Jancin Competition Awards *(Undergraduate/Award)*

Purpose: To promote the study of intellectual property law. **Qualif.:** Candidates must be law students nominated by their schools who have excelled in the study of intellectual property law. **Criteria:** Selection will be based on the committee's criteria.

Awards are arranged alphabetically below their administering organizations

Funds Avail.: $2,500 and $5,000. **Number Awarded:** Two. **To Apply:** Any law school may submit one nomination of a law student enrolled in their institution of the current year. The nomination should be no more than two pages and completed by a member of the faculty who has a direct knowledge of the student's work. Submit a nomination in the form of a letter of recommendation on Law School letterhead, enclosing a one-page written summation of the achievements from the nominee along with student's application summary and all of the following items: best grades in IP courses overall; outstanding achievement in specified IP courses; best IP paper written by a student; determination by a faculty consensus; or membership and activity in student IP organizations. **Deadline:** June 15.

882 ■ Sidney B. Williams, Jr. Scholarships
(Undergraduate/Scholarship)

Purpose: To increase the number of underrepresented minority groups serving as intellectual property law practitioners in law firms and departments of corporations. **Focus:** Law. **Qualif.:** Applicants must be entering or attending law school; **Criteria:** Recipients are selected based on: demonstrated commitment to developing a career in intellectual property law; academic performance during the undergraduate, graduate and law school levels; financial need; leadership Skills, community activities or special accomplishments.

Funds Avail.: $10,000. **To Apply:** Applicants must submit completed scholarship application form; FAFSA form (or similar form) and other supporting documentation required. Applicants must also submit undergraduate transcript and graduate law transcript(if applicable); two letters of recommendation from, but not limited to former teachers, college administrators, community leaders, or other similar persons concerning the academic ability, character, reputation or professional aptitude of the applicant; evidence of being a US citizen; personal or telephonic interview; and recent resume. **Deadline:** March 15. **Contact:** Sophia Rogers Thurgood Marshall College Fund at 80 Maiden Lane, Ste. 2204, New York, NY 10038; srogers@tmcfund.org.

883 ■ American Jersey Cattle Association (National All-Jersey Inc.)
6486 E Main St.
Reynoldsburg, OH 43068-2362
Ph: (614) 861-3636
Fax: (614) 861-8040
E-mail: info@usjersey.com
URL: www.usjersey.com

884 ■ Cedarcrest Farms Scholarships *(Graduate, Undergraduate/Scholarship)*

Purpose: To financially support secondary students entering college freshmen through graduate school. **Focus:** General studies. **Qualif.:** Applicants must be junior member or lifetime member of the American Jersey Cattle Association. **Criteria:** Applicants must have minimum grade point average of 2.5 on a 4 point scale.

Funds Avail.: $10,000. **To Apply:** Applicants must submit complete scholarship application form and a copy of most recent transcript listing all completed coursework. **Deadline:** July 1.

885 ■ Reuben R. Cowles Youth Awards
(Undergraduate/Award)

Purpose: To financially support secondary students entering as college freshmen through graduate school. **Focus:**

General studies. **Qualif.:** Applicants must be junior member or lifetime member of the American Jersey Cattle Association, and residents of Florida, Georgia, North Carolina, South Carolina, Tennessee or Virginia. **Criteria:** Applicants must have minimum grade point average of 2.5 on a 4 point scale.

Funds Avail.: $10,000. **To Apply:** Applicants must submit complete scholarship application form and a copy of most recent transcript listing all completed coursework. **Deadline:** July 1.

886 ■ American Jewish Historical Society (AJHS)
15 W 16th St.
New York, NY 10011-6301
Ph: (212) 294-6160
Fax: (212) 294-6161
Free: 866-740-8013
E-mail: info@ajhs.cjh.org
URL: www.ajhs.org

887 ■ Ruth B. Fein Prize *(Graduate/Prize)*

Purpose: To encourage interested students to undertake research in the field of American Jewish history. **Focus:** Area and ethnic studies. **Qualif.:** Applicants must be graduate students who will help undertake research at the American Jewish Historical Society. **Criteria:** Recipients will be selected based on qualifications.

Funds Avail.: $1,000. **To Apply:** Applicants must submit a two-page description of the project, a letter of support from a graduate mentor and a detailed budget for travel expenses. **Deadline:** April. **Contact:** feinprize@ajhs.cjh.org.

888 ■ Pokross/Curhan Family Fund Prize
(Graduate, Undergraduate/Prize)

Purpose: To help students undertake research using the collections held at AJHS/Boston, the Newton Centre home of the American Jewish Historical Society. **Focus:** Area and ethnic studies. **Qualif.:** Applicants must be undergraduates and graduate students pursuing an academic degree at an accredited academic institution. **Criteria:** Recipients will be selected based on qualifications.

Funds Avail.: $1,000. **To Apply:** Applicants must send a two-page description of plans to produce an essay, thesis, dissertation, documentary, exhibition or other form of public program on an aspect of the American Jewish experience; and must submit a letter of support from an undergraduate or graduate mentor. **Deadline:** April. **Contact:** pokrosscurhanprize@ajhs.cjh.org.

889 ■ American Judges Association (AJA)
300 Newport Ave.
Williamsburg, VA 23185-4147
Ph: (757) 259-1841
Fax: (757) 259-1520
E-mail: aja@ncsc.dni.us
URL: aja.ncsc.dni.us

890 ■ American Judges Association Law Student Essay Competition *(Undergraduate/Prize)*

Purpose: To honor students who have original and unpublished work. **Focus:** Law. **Qualif.:** Applicants must

Awards are arranged alphabetically below their administering organizations

be full-time law students enrolled in and attending an accredited law school in the United States or Canada. **Criteria:** Papers will be evaluated based on the following category: 1) writing quality and clarity; 2) interest of the topic and content to a broad segment of the judiciary; 3) analysis and reasoning; 4) timeliness, originality and creativity; 5) quality and use of the research; and 6) compliance with these rules.

Funds Avail.: $3,000 (1st Prize); $1,500 (2nd Prize); $1,000 (3rd Prize). **Number Awarded:** 3. **To Apply:** Applicants must submit a paper (double-spaced, 10-25 pages in length) discussing the topic given by the Committee. The cover page must be submitted in a separate document which includes the title, author's name and contact information. **Deadline:** June 1. **Contact:** Entries should be e-mailed to aja@ncsc.org.

891 ■ American Lebanese Engineering Society (ALES)
PO Box 585
Norwood, MA 02062
Ph: (617) 435-8687
E-mail: info@alesonline.org
URL: www.alesonline.org

892 ■ American Lebanese Engineering Society Scholarship Program *(Graduate, Undergraduate/ Scholarship)*

Purpose: To provide scholarships and educational grants to qualified Lebanese students. **Focus:** Engineering. **Qualif.:** Applicants must be undergraduate and graduate students of an ABET-accredited university. **Criteria:** Candidate must be of Lebanese descent or Lebanese junior, senior, or graduate student that has a GPA of 3.25 on a 4.00 scale.

Funds Avail.: No specific amount. **Number Awarded:** 2. **To Apply:** Applicants must submit completed application form, a copy of most recent academic transcript, two letters of recommendation, a recent clear black or white passport type photo and a one-page essay describing academic background, achievements, and goals and the relevance of studies to ALES goals and the reason why he/she should be the recipient of the award. **Deadline:** February 11.

893 ■ American Legion (AL)
c/o Public Relations Division
PO Box 1055
Indianapolis, IN 46206
Ph: (317) 630-1200
Fax: (317) 630-1223
Free: 800-433-3318
URL: www.legion.org

894 ■ The American Legion Legacy Scholarships *(Undergraduate/Scholarship)*

Purpose: To financially support the education of the dependents of active duty United States military and guard and reserve personnel. **Focus:** General studies. **Qualif.:** Applicant must be the dependent of active duty United States military and guard and reserve personnel who were federalized and killed on active duty on or after September 11, 2001. **Criteria:** Awards are given based on merit.

Funds Avail.: Slightly more than $37,000. **To Apply:** Ap-

plicants must submit a completed scholarship application with a photocopy of the deceased veteran's Certificate of Death (DD 1300). **Deadline:** April 15.

895 ■ The American Legion National High School Oratorical Scholarships Contest *(Undergraduate/Scholarship)*

Purpose: To support the education of deserving high school students. **Focus:** General studies. **Qualif.:** Candidates must be high school students. **Criteria:** Students must win the oratorical contest to acquire the scholarship.

Funds Avail.: 1st place: $18,000; 2nd place: $16,000; 3rd place: $14,000. Each Department (State) winner in the first round will receive a $1,500 scholarship. Each first round winner that does not advance to the Final Round will receive an additional $1,500 scholarship. **Number Awarded:** Varies. **To Apply:** Applicants may contact their Department (State) or the National Organization of the American Legion for more information about the scholarships. **Remarks:** The awards may be used to attend any college or university in the United States.

896 ■ Eight and Forty Lung and Respiratory Disease Nursing Scholarships *(Professional development/Scholarship)*

Purpose: To assist registered nurses (RN) with advanced preparation for positions in supervision, administration or teaching. **Focus:** Nursing, Pediatric. **Qualif.:** Applicant must be a registered nurse with a current state license; must have graduated at a regionally accredited school of nursing or will be graduated by the application deadline; must be a registered nurse pursuing nursing education in the field of pediatric lung and respiratory diseases on a part-time or full-time basis; must be accepted by a regionally accredited school of nursing; must be a U.S. citizen; must have leadership qualities; and must have the ability to pursue full-time employment after school. **Criteria:** Awards are given based on personal and academic qualifications with consideration given to past experience and future employment plans as they relate to pediatric lung and respiratory disease nursing.

Funds Avail.: $3,000 each. **To Apply:** Applicants must submit a completed scholarship application along with a current state Registered Nurse License or registration; three letters of recommendation; transcript of all college credit attempted; and letter of acceptance from an accredited school of nursing. **Deadline:** May 15. **Remarks:** In cooperation with Eight and Forty.

897 ■ Samsung American Legion Scholarships *(Undergraduate/Scholarship)*

Purpose: To assist the education of a child, grandchild, great grandchild, etc. or a legally adopted child of a U.S. wartime veteran. **Focus:** General studies. **Qualif.:** Applicant must be a high school junior who participates in either an American Legion Boys State or American Legion Auxiliary Girls State Program and be a direct descendant (child, grandchild, great grandchild, etc. or a legally adopted child) of a U.S. wartime veteran who served on active duty during one or more of the periods of war officially designated as eligibility dates for membership in The American Legion by the United States government. **Criteria:** Awards are given based on merit.

Funds Avail.: In 2010, 10 $20,000 scholarships and 88 $1,000 scholarships were awarded. **Number Awarded:** Varies. **To Apply:** Applicants must submit a completed

Awards are arranged alphabetically below their administering organizations

scholarship application along with a photocopy of the veteran's Certification of Release or Discharge from Active Duty (DD-214), to Boys/Girls State program. **Remarks:** In cooperation with Samsung.

898 ■ American Library Association (ALA)
50 E Huron St.
Chicago, IL 60611
Ph: (312) 944-6780
Fax: (312) 440-9374
Free: 800-545-2433
E-mail: ala@ala.org
URL: www.ala.org

899 ■ Marshall Cavendish Scholarships
(Graduate/Scholarship)

Purpose: To provide financial assistance for furthering the education of an individual. **Focus:** General studies. **Qualif.:** Applicant must be an American or Canadian or permanent resident attending ALA accredited Master's Program and no more than 12 semester hours towards MLS/MLIS/MIS prior to June 1 of year awarded. **Criteria:** Applicants will be evaluated on the basis of academic excellence, leadership and evidence of commitment to a career in librarianship.

Funds Avail.: $3,000. **To Apply:** Applicants must submit applications and all supporting documents. **Deadline:** March 1. **Contact:** Kimberly Sanders at scholarships@ ala.org or ksanders@ala.org.

900 ■ David H. Clift Scholarships *(Graduate/Scholarship)*

Purpose: To provide financial assistance for furthering the education of a deserving individual. **Focus:** General studies. **Qualif.:** Applicant must be a US or Canadian citizen or permanent resident attending an ALA accredited Master's program and no more than 12 semester hours towards MLS/MLIS/MIS prior to June of year awarded. **Criteria:** Applicants will be evaluated based on academic excellence, leadership and evidence of commitment to a career in librarianship.

Funds Avail.: $3,000. **To Apply:** Applicants must complete the online application. In addition, applications must provide an official academic transcript from institutions. These can be submitted directly from the institution, or mailed in the unopened envelope as received from the degree-granting institutions along with any other materials. Only official (sealed) copies will be accepted. **Deadline:** March 1. **Contact:** scholarships@ala.org.

901 ■ Christopher Hoy/ERT Scholarships
(Graduate, Master's/Scholarship)

Purpose: To provide financial assistance for furthering the education of a deserving individual. **Focus:** General studies. **Qualif.:** Applicant must be a US or Canadian citizen or permanent resident attending ALA accredited Master's Program and no more than 12 semester hours towards MLS/MLIS/MIS prior to June 1 of year awarded. **Criteria:** Applicants will be evaluated based on academic excellence, leadership and evidence of commitment to a career in librarianship.

Funds Avail.: $5,000. **To Apply:** Applicants must submit applications and all supporting documents. **Deadline:** March 1. **Contact:** Kimberly L. Sanders at ksanders@ ala.org.

902 ■ American Liver Foundation (ALF)
39 Broadway, Ste. 2700
New York, NY 10006
Ph: (212) 668-1000
Fax: (212) 483-8179
Free: 800-223-0179
E-mail: info@liverfoundation.org
URL: www.liverfoundation.org

903 ■ American Liver Foundation Liver Scholar Awards *(Doctorate/Award)*

Purpose: To develop the potential of outstanding, young scientists and encouraging research in liver physiology and disease. **Focus:** Medical Research. **Qualif.:** Applicants must be sponsored by a public or private non-profit institution accredited in the United States, Canada or Mexico engaged in health care and health-related research. **Criteria:** Awards are made to eligible institutions and are for salary support only for the awardee.

Funds Avail.: $225,000. **To Apply:** Applicants may download an application form online. Applicants must submit an application which contain the following section: Application Information; Summary and Abstract; Biographical Sketch; Research Plan; Research Facilities; Candidate's Statement; Letters of Commitment; Letters of Recommendation; Institution Review Board; Signatures. Original and eight (8) copies of the completed application must be received at ALF. **Deadline:** October 15. **Contact:** American Liver Foundation Research Department/Liver Scholars 1425 Pompton Avenue, Suite 3 Cedar Grove, NJ 07009.

904 ■ American Liver Foundation Special Research Initiatives *(Doctorate/Award)*

Purpose: To support investigational work relating to liver physiology and disease. **Focus:** Medical Research. **Qualif.:** Applicant can be a faculty member at any level and must be sponsored by a public or private non-profit institution accredited in the United States, Canada or Mexico engaged in healthcare and health-related research. **Criteria:** Award is made to eligible institutions. There are no restrictions on how the monies are to be used on the research but no indirect costs are provided.

Funds Avail.: $100,000. **To Apply:** Applicants may download an application form online. Applicants who hold or have applied for other research grants must provide the abstract page from that grant with this application. Applicants must submit an application which contain the following section: Application Information; Summary and Abstract; Biographical Sketch; Research Plan; Research Facilities; Candidate's Statement; Letters of Commitment; Letters of Recommendation; Institution Review Board; Signatures. Original and eight (8) copies of the completed application must be received at ALF. **Deadline:** October 16. **Contact:** American Liver Foundation Research Department Biliary Atresia Special Research Initiative 1425 Pompton Avenue, Suite 3 Cedar Grove, NJ 07009.

905 ■ Cystic Fibrosis Cholestatic Liver Disease Liver Scholarships *(Doctorate/Award)*

Purpose: To develop the potential of outstanding, young scientists and encouraging research in liver physiology and disease. **Focus:** Medical research. **Qualif.:** Applicants must hold an M.D., Ph.D., or equivalent; must be sponsored by a public or private non-profit institution accredited in the United States, Canada, or Mexico engaged in healthcare and health-related research. Applicants must apply while

Awards are arranged alphabetically below their administering organizations

they are within the first three years of their faculty appointment and commence the award within the first four years of faculty appointment. **Criteria:** Awards are made to eligible institutions and are for salary support only for the awardee.

Funds Avail.: $225,000. **Number Awarded:** 1. **To Apply:** Applicants must download an application form online. Applicants must submit an application which contain the following section: Application Information; Summary and Abstract; Biographical Sketch; Research Plan; Research Facilities; Candidate's Statement; Letters of Commitment; Letters of Recommendation; Institution Review Board; Signatures. Original and eight (8) copies of the completed application must be received at ALF. **Deadline:** October 16. **Contact:** American Liver Foundation Research Department/ Liver Scholars Cystic Fibrosis Cholestatic Liver Scholar 1425 Pompton Avenue, Suite 3 Cedar Grove, NJ 07009.

906 ■ Postdoctoral Research Fellowships
(Postdoctorate/Award)

Purpose: To support investigational work relating to liver physiology and disease. **Focus:** Medical Research. **Qualif.:** Applicants must be sponsored by a public or private non-profit institution accredited in the United States, Canada or Mexico engaged in health care and health-related research; must be in his/her first or second year of first Postdoctoral Research Fellowship at the time of application; must be sponsored by a research mentor. **Criteria:** Award is given on the basis of the applicant's eligibility

Funds Avail.: $12,500. **To Apply:** Applicants may download an application form online. Applicants must submit an application which contain the following section: Application Information; Summary and Abstract; Biographical Sketch; Research Plan; Research Facilities; Candidate's Statement; Letters of Commitment; Letters of Recommendation; Institution Review Board; Signatures. Original and eight (8) copies of the completed application must be received at ALF. **Deadline:** October 15. **Contact:** American Liver Foundation Research Department Postdoctoral Research Fellowship 1425 Pompton Avenue, Suite 3 Cedar Grove, NJ 07009.

907 ■ American Lung Association (ALA)
1301 Pennsylvania Ave. NW, Ste. 800
Washington, DC 20004
Ph: (212) 315-8700
Fax: (202) 452-1805
Free: 800-548-8252
E-mail: info@lungusa.org
URL: www.lungusa.org

908 ■ American Lung Association/AAAAI Allergic Respiratory Diseases Awards *(Doctorate/ Grant)*

Purpose: To support research that will advance the understanding of allergic respiratory disease. **Focus:** Health sciences; Public health. **Qualif.:** Applicants may be at any level of research experience, however, at the time of application, the applicant must hold a doctoral degree, have a faculty appointment in an allergy/immunology division/ section of an academic institution, be undertaking a project related to allergic respiratory disease, and have completed a training fellowship. Applicants must be US citizens or foreign nationals holding one of the following visa immigration statuses: permanent resident (Green Card), student (F-1), exchange visitor (J-1), temporary worker in a specialty occupation (H-1, H-1B), Canadian or Mexican

citizen engaging in professional activities (TC or TN), or temporary worker with extra-ordinary abilities in the sciences (O-1). Non-citizens must submit a notarized copy of proof of possession of a Green Card or F-1, J-1, H-1, H-1B, TC, TN or O-1 visas. **Criteria:** Selection will be based on scientific merit, innovation, and feasibility of the research plan, and its relevance to the mission of the American Lung Association; education and experience; sponsor's program, including the record of training academic scientists, the research productivity of the faculty and the quality of the research training program proposed for the applicant.

Funds Avail.: $50,000. **Number Awarded:** 3. **To Apply:** Applicants may visit the website for the application process. Submit one signed original plus two copies of all application materials to: Research and Program Services, American Lung Association, 14 Wall St., 8th Fl., New York, NY 10005. **Deadline:** October 21. **Contact:** Pat Georgette, pgeorgette@lungusa.org; Phone: 212-315-8724.

909 ■ American Lung Association Biomedical Research Grants *(Doctorate/Grant)*

Purpose: To provide seed monies to junior investigators researching the mechanisms of lung disease and general lung biology. **Focus:** Health sciences; Public health. **Qualif.:** At the time of application, an applicant must hold a doctoral degree, be assured of a faculty appointment or equivalent institutional commitment (salary support, research space) by the start of the award. Applicants must have completed two years of post-doctoral research training by the start of the award. Applicants must be US citizens or foreign nationals holding one of the following visa immigration statuses: permanent resident (Green Card), student (F-1), exchange visitor (J-1), temporary worker in a specialty occupation (H-1, H-1B), Canadian or Mexican citizen engaging in professional activities (TC or TN), or temporary worker with extra-ordinary abilities in the sciences (O-1). Non-citizens must submit a notarized copy of proof of possession of a Green Card or F-1, J-1, H-1, H-1B, TC, TN or O-1 visas. **Criteria:** Selection will be based on scientific merit, innovation, and feasibility of the research plan, and its relevance to the mission of the American Lung Association; education and experience, publications and letters of recommendation; research environment; likelihood that the applicant will continue to have a career in lung and/or other relevant research; Department Chair letter clearly assuring faculty appointment with demonstrated institutional commitment before the start of an award.

Funds Avail.: $40,000. **Number Awarded:** 10-12. **To Apply:** Applicants may visit the website for the application process. Submit one signed original plus two copies of all application materials to: Research and Program Services, American Lung Association, 14 Wall St., 8th Fl., New York, NY 10005. **Deadline:** October 21. **Contact:** Pat Georgette, pgeorgette@lungusa.org; Phone: 212-315-8724.

910 ■ American Lung Association Clinical Patient Care Research Grants *(Doctorate/Grant)*

Purpose: To provide monies to investigators working on traditional clinical studies examining methods for improving patient care and treatment for lung disease. **Focus:** Health sciences; Public health. **Qualif.:** At the time of application, an applicant must hold a doctoral degree, be assured of faculty appointment or equivalent with demonstrated institutional commitment (salary support, research space) by the start of the award. Applicants must have completed two years of post-doctoral research training by the start of the award. Grantee organizations must be recognized academic or other non-profit research entities. **Criteria:**

Awards are arranged alphabetically below their administering organizations

Selection will be based on scientific merit, innovation, and feasibility of the research plan, and its relevance to the mission of the American Lung Association; education and experience, publications and letters of recommendation; research environment; likelihood that the applicant will continue to have a career in lung and/or other relevant research; Department Chair letter clearly assuring faculty appointment with demonstrated institutional commitment before the start of an award.

Funds Avail.: $40,000. **Number Awarded:** 1-2. **To Apply:** Applicants may visit the website for the application process. Submit one signed original plus two copies of all application materials to: Research and Program Services, American Lung Association, 14 Wall St., 8th Fl., New York, NY 10005. **Deadline:** October 21. **Contact:** Pat Georgette, pgeorgette@lungusa.org; Phone: 212-315-8724.

911 ■ American Lung Association Dalsemer Research Grants *(Doctorate/Grant)*

Purpose: To provide seed monies to junior investigators focusing on interstitial lung disease research. **Focus:** Health sciences; Public health. **Qualif.:** At the time of application, an applicant must hold a doctoral degree, be assured of faculty appointment or equivalent with demonstrated institutional commitment (salary support, research space) by the start of the award. Applicants must have completed two years of post-doctoral research training by the start of the award. Grantee organizations must be recognized academic or other non-profit research entities. Applicants must be US citizens or foreign nationals holding one of the following visa immigration statuses: permanent resident (Green Card), student (F-1), exchange visitor (J-1), temporary worker in a specialty occupation (H-1, H-1B), Canadian or Mexican citizen engaging in professional activities (TC or TN), or temporary worker with extra-ordinary abilities in the sciences (O-1). Non-citizens must submit a notarized copy of proof of possession of a Green Card or F-1, J-1, H-1, H-1B, TC, TN or O-1 visas. **Criteria:** Selection will be based on scientific merit, innovation, and feasibility of the research plan, and its relevance to the mission of the American Lung Association; education and experience, publications and letters of recommendation; research environment; likelihood that the applicant will continue to have a career in lung and/or other relevant research; Department Chair letter clearly assuring faculty appointment with demonstrated institutional commitment before the start of an award.

Funds Avail.: $40,000. **Number Awarded:** 1. **To Apply:** Applicants may visit the website for the application process. Submit one signed original plus two copies of all application materials to: Research and Program Services, American Lung Association, 14 Wall St., 8th Fl., New York, NY 10005. **Deadline:** October 21. **Contact:** Pat Georgette, pgeorgette@lungusa.org; Phone: 212-315-8724.

912 ■ American Lung Association DeSousa Awards *(Doctorate/Grant)*

Purpose: To support clinical, laboratory, epidemiological, or any other kind of research that focuses on bronchiectasis, infection with a typical Mycobacteria, and infection with Nocardia species. **Focus:** Health sciences; Public health. **Qualif.:** At the time of application, an applicant must hold a doctoral degree, be assured of faculty appointment or equivalent with demonstrated institutional commitment (salary support, research space) by the start of the award. Applicants must have completed two years of post-doctoral research training by the start of the award. Grantee

organizations must be recognized academic or other non-profit research entities. Applicants must be US citizens or foreign nationals holding one of the following visa immigration statuses: permanent resident (Green Card), student (F-1), exchange visitor (J-1), temporary worker in a specialty occupation (H-1, H-1B), Canadian or Mexican citizen engaging in professional activities (TC or TN), or temporary worker with extra-ordinary abilities in the sciences (O-1). Non-citizens must submit a notarized copy of proof of possession of a Green Card or F-1, J-1, H-1, H-1B, TC, TN or O-1 visas. **Criteria:** Selection will be based on scientific merit, innovation, and feasibility of the research plan, and its relevance to the mission of the American Lung Association; education and experience, publications and letters of recommendation; research environment; likelihood that the applicant will continue to have a career in lung and/or other relevant research; Department Chair letter clearly assuring faculty appointment with demonstrated institutional commitment before the start of an award.

Funds Avail.: $100,000. **Number Awarded:** 1. **To Apply:** Applicants may visit the website for the application process. Submit one signed original plus two copies of all application materials to: Research and Program Services, American Lung Association, 14 Wall St., 8th Fl., New York, NY 10005. **Deadline:** October 21. **Contact:** Pat Georgette, pgeorgette@lungusa.org; Phone: 212-315-8724.

913 ■ American Lung Association Lung Cancer Discovery Awards *(Doctorate/Grant)*

Purpose: To support the development of novel medical treatments, advancing current treatment options and/or finding a cure for lung cancer through clinical, laboratory, epidemiological, or any other king of research. **Focus:** Health sciences; Public health. **Qualif.:** At the time of application, the applicant must be a matriculating student in good standing in a full-time academic program leading to a doctoral degree in one of the above-mentioned fields. Applicants must be US citizens or foreign nationals holding one of the following visa immigration statuses: permanent resident (Green Card), student (F-1), exchange visitor (J-1), temporary worker in a specialty occupation (H-1, H-1B), Canadian or Mexican citizen engaging in professional activities (TC or TN), or temporary worker with extra-ordinary abilities in the sciences (O-1). Non-citizens must submit a notarized copy of proof of possession of a Green Card or F-1, J-1, H-1, H-1B, TC, TN or O-1 visas. **Criteria:** Selection will be based on scientific merit, innovation, and feasibility of the research plan, and its relevance to the mission of the American Lung Association; education and experience; sponsor's program, including the record of training academic scientists, the research productivity of the faculty and the quality of the research training program proposed for the applicant.

Funds Avail.: $100,000. **Number Awarded:** 1. **To Apply:** Applicants are required to submit a Letter of Intent to the American Lung Association. Letter of Intent must be an attached PDF file, no more than 3 pages, which must include: rationale for the project; planned specific aims; brief statement of the overall experimental approach; NIH Biosketch of the applicant (separate attached PDF file). Submit one signed original plus two copies of all application materials to: Research and Program Services, American Lung Association, 14 Wall St., 8th Fl., New York, NY 10005. **Deadline:** October 21. **Contact:** Pat Georgette, pgeorgette@lungusa.org; Phone: 212-315-8724.

Awards are arranged alphabetically below their administering organizations

914 ■ American Lung Association Senior Research Training Fellowships (Doctorate/Fellowship)

Purpose: To support the training of MDs and PhDs seeking further academic training as scientific investigators with the goal of pursuing a career in pulmonary medicine and long biology research. **Focus:** Health sciences; Public health. **Qualif.:** At the time of application, an applicant must hold a doctoral degree and must work in an academic or not-for-profit institution. MD or DO applicants must also have completed their clinical training, have some research experience, and be in their 3rd or 4th year of fellowship training. PhD applicants must be in their 1st or 2nd year of postdoctoral training. Persons with medical degrees, whose credentials show that they are on a career track which will not include the practice of medicine, must be in their 1st or 2nd year of full-time postdoctoral research. Applicants must be US citizens or foreign nationals holding one of the following visa immigration statuses: permanent resident (Green Card), student (F-1), exchange visitor (J-1), temporary worker in a specialty occupation (H-1, H-1B), Canadian or Mexican citizen engaging in professional activities (TC or TN), or temporary worker with extra-ordinary abilities in the sciences (O-1). Non-citizens must submit a notarized copy of proof of possession of a Green Card or F-1, J-1, H-1, H-1B, TC, TN or O-1 visas. **Criteria:** Selection will be based on the committee's criteria.

Funds Avail.: $32,500. **Number Awarded:** 8-10. **To Apply:** Applicants may visit the website for the application process. Submit one signed original plus two copies of all application materials to: Research and Program Services, American Lung Association, 14 Wall St., 8th Fl., New York, NY 10005. **Deadline:** October 21. **Contact:** Pat Georgette, pgeorgette@lungusa.org; Phone: 212-315-8724.

915 ■ American Lung Association Social-Behavioral Research Grants (Doctorate/Grant)

Purpose: To provide seed monies to junior investigators working on various disciplines of social science examining risk factors affecting lung health. **Focus:** Health sciences; Public health. **Qualif.:** At the time of application, an applicant must hold a doctoral degree, be assured of faculty appointment or equivalent with demonstrated institutional commitment (salary support, research space) by the start of the award. Applicants must have completed two years of post-doctoral research training by the start of the award. Grantee organizations must be recognized academic or other non-profit research entities. Applicants must be US citizens or foreign nationals holding one of the following visa immigration statuses: permanent resident (Green Card), student (F-1), exchange visitor (J-1), temporary worker in a specialty occupation (H-1, H-1B), Canadian or Mexican citizen engaging in professional activities (TC or TN), or temporary worker with extra-ordinary abilities in the sciences (O-1). Non-citizens must submit a notarized copy of proof of possession of a Green Card or F-1, J-1, H-1, H-1B, TC, TN or O-1 visas. **Criteria:** Selection will be based on scientific merit, innovation, and feasibility of the research plan, and its relevance to the mission of the American Lung Association; education and experience, publications and letters of recommendation; research environment; likelihood that the applicant will continue to have a career in lung and/or other relevant research; Department Chair letter clearly assuring faculty appointment with demonstrated institutional commitment before the start of an award.

Funds Avail.: $40,000. **Number Awarded:** 1-2. **To Apply:** Applicants may visit the website for the application process.

Submit one signed original plus two copies of all application materials to: Research and Program Services, American Lung Association, 14 Wall St., 8th Fl., New York, NY 10005. **Deadline:** October 21. **Contact:** Pat Georgette, pgeorgette@lungusa.org; Phone: 212-315-8724.

916 ■ Lung Health Dissertation Grants (Graduate/Grant)

Purpose: To support pre-doctoral dissertation research in the various disciplines of social science examining risk factors affecting lung health. **Focus:** Health sciences; Public health. **Qualif.:** At the time of application, the applicant must be a matriculating student in good standing in a full-time academic program leading to a doctoral degree in one of the above-mentioned fields. Applicants must be US citizens or foreign nationals holding one of the following visa immigration statuses: permanent resident (Green Card), student (F-1), exchange visitor (J-1), temporary worker in a specialty occupation (H-1, H-1B), Canadian or Mexican citizen engaging in professional activities (TC or TN), or temporary worker with extra-ordinary abilities in the sciences (O-1). Non-citizens must submit a notarized copy of proof of possession of a Green Card or F-1, J-1, H-1, H-1B, TC, TN or O-1 visas. The sponsor should be a recognized authority in the applicant's field of research and possess the necessary training resources. The sponsor must have an academic affiliated appointment and must be working in a not-for-profit institution. **Criteria:** Selection will be based on scientific merit, innovation, and feasibility of the research plan, and its relevance to the mission of the American Lung Association; education and experience; sponsor's program, including the record of training academic scientists, the research productivity of the faculty and the quality of the research training program proposed for the applicant.

Funds Avail.: $21,000. **To Apply:** Applicants may visit the website for the application process. Submit one signed original plus two copies of all application materials to: Research and Program Services, American Lung Association, 14 Wall St., 8th Fl., New York, NY 10005. **Deadline:** October 21. **Contact:** Pat Georgette, pgeorgette@lungusa.org; Phone: 212-315-8724.

917 ■ American Marketing Association Foundation (AMAF)

311 S Wacker Dr., Ste. 5800
Chicago, IL 60606
Ph: (312) 542-9000
Fax: (312) 542-9001
E-mail: joleniczak@ama.org
URL: www.themarketingfoundation.org

918 ■ Richard A. Hammill Scholarship Fund (Undergraduate/Scholarship)

Purpose: To provide an annual scholarship award for students who are enrolled in the Marketing Program. **Focus:** Marketing and distribution. **Qualif.:** Applicants must be students enrolled at Georgia State University. **Criteria:** Selection will be based on the committee's criteria.

Funds Avail.: No specific amount. **To Apply:** Interested applicants may apply online via the AMAF website. **Contact:** AMA Foundation at the above address.

919 ■ Robert J. Lavidge Nonprofit Marketing Research Scholarships (Professional development/Scholarship)

Purpose: To provide scholarship for marketing professionals working in the nonprofit sector to further their marketing

Awards are arranged alphabetically below their administering organizations

research-related education. **Focus:** Marketing and distribution. **Qualif.:** Applicants must be nonprofit marketing professionals with an interest in furthering their marketing research education. **Criteria:** Individuals will be judged based on how they demonstrate participation in a marketing research educational program.

Funds Avail.: $1,000. **To Apply:** Interested applicants may apply online via the AMAF website. **Deadline:** May 13. **Contact:** AMAF at the above address.

920 ■ Valuing Diversity PhD Scholarships
(Doctorate/Scholarship)

Purpose: To provide scholarship to underrepresented populations in the marketing profession. **Focus:** Marketing and distribution. **Qualif.:** Applicant must be a U.S. citizen or a permanent resident; must be enrolled on campus, in a full-time AACSB-accredited marketing doctoral program and have successfully completed at least one year; must have not previously received a Valuing Diversity Scholarship; must be African American, Hispanic American, or Native American. **Criteria:** Selection will be based on the committee's criteria.

Funds Avail.: $1,000. **To Apply:** Applicants must complete the online application found on the AMAF's website. Essays must be in Microsoft Word format. Essays should be two-pages, double-spaced, in 12 pt. type (approximately 500 words). Sources you mention in your essay should be credited on an additional page and do not count against the two-page maximum. Applicants must also submit two letters of recommendation. **Deadline:** May 1.

921 ■ American Medical Association (AMA)
515 N State St.
Chicago, IL 60610
Ph: (312) 464-4430
Fax: (312) 464-4189
Free: 800-621-8335
E-mail: jasupport@ama-assn.org
URL: www.ama-assn.org

922 ■ AMA Foundation Minority Scholars Awards *(Undergraduate/Scholarship)*

Purpose: To advance healthcare through support of programs in medical education, research and service. **Focus:** Medical Education. **Qualif.:** Applicant must be a current first or second year student and a permanent resident or citizen of the U.S.; must be African American, American Indian, Native American, Alaska Native or Hispanic/Latino. **Criteria:** Recipients are selected based on academic standing.

Funds Avail.: $10,000. **Number Awarded:** 12. **To Apply:** Applicants must complete the application form. Detailed requirement will be sent by the AMA Foundation to each medical school's Office of the Dean, Office of the Student Affairs, and Office of Financial Aid. **Deadline:** April 15.

923 ■ AMA Foundation Physicians of Tomorrow Scholarships *(Undergraduate/Scholarship)*

Purpose: To advance healthcare through support of programs in medical education, research and service. **Focus:** Medical Education. **Qualif.:** Applicants must be current third year medical students who are entering their fourth year of study. **Criteria:** Recipients are selected based on academic standing and financial need.

Funds Avail.: $10,000. **Number Awarded:** 12. **To Apply:**

Applicants must complete the application form. Detailed requirements will be sent by the AMA Foundation to each medical school's Office of the Dean, Office of the Student Affairs, and Office of Financial Aid. **Deadline:** May 31.

924 ■ The Arthur N. Wilson, MD, Scholarships
(Undergraduate/Scholarship)

Purpose: To advance healthcare through support of programs in medical education, research and service. **Focus:** Medical Education. **Qualif.:** Applicants must be medical students who attended high school in Alaska. **Criteria:** Recipients are selected based on academic standing and financial need.

Funds Avail.: $5,000. **To Apply:** Applicants must submit completed application form; a one-page personal statement outlining the career goals in the field of medicine; a curriculum vitae; official transcript from the applicant's high school in Southeast Alaska; official medical school transcript; and letter of recommendation from a faculty member at the medical school or office of the dean. Applicants may apply directly to the American Medical Association (AMA) Foundation. **Deadline:** June 15. **Contact:** dina.lindenberg@ama-assn.org; 312-464-4193.

925 ■ American Men's Studies Association (AMSA)
1080 S University Ave.
Ann Arbor, MI 48109
Ph: (734) 763-3491
E-mail: mensstudies@umich.edu
URL: mensstudies.org

926 ■ Loren Frankel Memorial Scholarships
(Undergraduate, Graduate/Scholarship)

Purpose: To support students engaged in the critical study of men and masculinities. **Focus:** Sexuality. **Qualif.:** Applicants must be undergraduate or graduate students. **Criteria:** Applicants will be evaluated based on content of the application, quality and the student's potential for making a contribution to the field of men's studies.

Funds Avail.: $500 per year. **To Apply:** Applicants must submit a maximum two-page document that includes brief biographical information, title and abstract of the paper and paragraph describing the importance of the project to professional and intellectual development. **Deadline:** January 15.

927 ■ American Meteorological Society (AMS)
45 Beacon St.
Boston, MA 02108-3693
Ph: (617) 227-2425
Fax: (617) 742-8718
E-mail: amsinfo@ametsoc.org
URL: www.ametsoc.org

928 ■ AMS Freshman Undergraduate Scholarships *(Undergraduate/Scholarship)*

Purpose: To encourage high school students to study in the atmospheric and related sciences. **Focus:** Meteorology. **Qualif.:** Applicant must be a U.S. citizen or hold a permanent resident status; entering the freshman year of college as a full-time student; and plan to pursue a degree in the atmospheric or related oceanic or hydrologic sciences. **Criteria:** Selection is based on the applicant's

Awards are arranged alphabetically below their administering organizations

performance in high school including academic records, recommendation, scores from a national college exam and a written essay.

Funds Avail.: $2,500/year. **To Apply:** Applicants must submit a completed application form together with an official high school transcript showing grades from the past three years; a letter of recommendation from a high school teacher or guidance counselor; and a copy of scores from a SAT or similar national college entrance exam. **Deadline:** February 10. **Remarks:** Students eligible to apply for both the AMS Minority Scholarship Program and the AMS Freshman Scholarship Program may apply to both programs, but may only accept one AMS scholarship. **Contact:** Donna Fernandez at 617-227-2426 x-246 or Stephanie Armstrong at 617-227-2426 x-235.

929 ■ AMS Graduate Fellowships in the History of Science (Graduate/Fellowship)

Purpose: To support students who wish to complete a dissertation on the history of science. **Focus:** History of science. **Qualif.:** Applicant must be a graduate student in good standing who proposes to complete a dissertation in the history of the atmospheric or related oceanic or hydrologic sciences. **Criteria:** Selection is based on the submitted application materials.

Funds Avail.: $15,000. **To Apply:** Applicants must submit a cover letter with a curriculum vitae; official transcripts from undergraduate and graduate institutions; a typewritten, detailed description of the dissertation topic and proposed research plan (10 page maximum); and three letters of recommendation (including one from dissertation advisor). **Deadline:** February 10. **Contact:** Donna Fernandez at 617-227-2426 x-246 or Stephanie Armstrong at 617-227-2426 x-235.

930 ■ AMS Industry/Government Graduate Fellowships (Graduate/Fellowship)

Purpose: To attract promising young scientists to prepare for careers in the atmospheric and related oceanic and hydrologic fields. **Focus:** Meteorology. **Qualif.:** Applicant must be entering the first year of graduate school and provide evidence of acceptance as a full-time student at an accredited U.S. institution at the time of the award; must pursue a related full-time course of study in the atmospheric or related oceanic or hydrologic sciences over a full academic year; have a minimum GPA of 3.25 on a 4.0-point scale; and a U.S. citizen or hold permanent resident status. **Criteria:** Selection is based on the applicant's performance as an undergraduate student including academic records, recommendations and Graduate Record Examinations (GRE) scores.

Funds Avail.: $24,000. **To Apply:** Applicants must submit a completed application form along with the written references, official transcripts and GRE score reports. **Deadline:** February 10. **Contact:** Donna Fernandez at 617-227-2426 x-246 or dfernandez@ametsoc.org.

931 ■ AMS/Industry Minority Scholarships (Undergraduate/Scholarship)

Purpose: To help further the education of outstanding students pursuing a career in the atmospheric and related oceanic or hydrologic sciences. **Focus:** Meteorology. **Qualif.:** Applicant must be a minority student entering the freshman year of college; planning to pursue a career in the atmospheric or related oceanic and hydrologic sciences; a U.S. citizen or hold permanent resident status; and must be pursuing a degree at a U.S. institution. **Criteria:** Selec-

tion is based on the submitted application materials.

Funds Avail.: $3,000/year. **To Apply:** Applicants must submit a completed application form along with an official high school transcript showing grades from the past three years; a letter of recommendation from a high school teacher or guidance counselor; and a copy of scores from a SAT or similar national college entrance exam. All original materials should be mailed to the closest local chapter listed at the bottom of the application. Photocopies of the application, transcripts and essay should be mailed to the AMS Headquarters. **Deadline:** February 10. **Contact:** Donna Fernandez at 617-227-2426 ext. 246.

932 ■ AMS Undergraduate Named Scholarships (Undergraduate/Scholarship)

Purpose: To support students majoring in the atmospheric or related oceanic or hydrologic sciences. **Focus:** Meteorology. **Qualif.:** Applicant must be a full-time student entering the final year of undergraduate study; majoring in the atmospheric or related oceanic or hydrologic science, and/or must show clear intent to make the atmospheric or related sciences a career; enrolled full time in an accredited U.S. institution; and must have a cumulative GPA of at least a 3.25 on a scale of 4.0. **Criteria:** Selection is based on the applicant's performance as an undergraduate student including academic records and recommendation.

Funds Avail.: No specific amount. **Number Awarded:** Varies. **To Apply:** Applicants must submit a completed application form along with letters of reference and official transcripts. Written references will be accepted via e-mail and may be sent to dfernand@ametsoc.org. **Deadline:** February 10. **Contact:** Donna Fernandez at 617-227-2426 x-246 or dfernandez@ametsoc.org.

933 ■ American MidEast Leadership Network (AMLN)

PO Box 2156
Long Island City, NY 11102
Ph: (347) 924-9674
Fax: (917) 591-2177
E-mail: info@amln.org
URL: www.amln.org

934 ■ AMLN Scholarships (Graduate, Undergraduate/Scholarship)

Purpose: To encourage Arab students to pursue higher education. **Focus:** General studies. **Qualif.:** Applicant must be of Arab heritage; a U.S. citizen or a legal permanent resident with permanent resident card or passport stamped I-551; and a high school senior or undergraduate/graduate student enrolled full-time in a degree seeking program at an accredited U.S. college/university in the Tri state area (NJ, NY, CT). Undergraduate and graduate students must have earned at least 12 credits at a U.S. accredited college/university; have a minimum cumulative GPA of 3.00 on a 4.00 scale and must be active in the local Arab American community. **Criteria:** Selection is based on the application.

Funds Avail.: $1,000-$3,000. **To Apply:** Applicants must submit a completed scholarship application form along with two letters or recommendation, three essays (do not combine), and 2 passport-sized photos. **Remarks:** Sponsored by Alpha Research and Development.

935 ■ American Military Retirees Association (AMRA)

5436 Peru St., No. 1
Plattsburgh, NY 12901

Awards are arranged alphabetically below their administering organizations

Ph: (518) 563-9479
Fax: (518) 324-5204
Free: 800-424-2969
E-mail: info@amra1973.org
URL: amra1973.org

936 ■ Sergeant Major Douglas R. Drum Memorial Scholarship Fund *(Undergraduate/ Scholarship)*

Purpose: To protect and improve the benefits of the military retirees. **Focus:** General studies. **Qualif.:** Applicant must be a current member of AMRA, his/her dependent, child or grandchild; he/she must be pursuing a degree in an accredited college or university. **Criteria:** Scholarship Committee will evaluate the application based on the student's educational achievements, leadership abilities, character, citizenship, and community service.

Funds Avail.: No specific amount. **To Apply:** Applicants must present the award letter to the college/university and request that AMRA be billed for half the scholarship for the first semester and half the scholarship for the second semester; an applicant must submit a 500 word or less essay telling why an applicant deserve a scholarship from AMRA stating the Educational plans, achievements, leadership abilities, extracurricular and community activities, work experiences, character and citizenship traits, or any other circumstance that assist the committee during the selection process; an applicant must submit a letter of recommendation either from a teacher or professor, non-family member, past or current employer, from a project coordinator or a team leader. **Deadline:** March 1.

937 ■ American Montessori Society (AMS)

281 Park Ave. S
New York, NY 10010
Ph: (212) 358-1250
Fax: (212) 358-1256
E-mail: ams@amshq.org
URL: www.amshq.org

938 ■ AMS Teacher Education Scholarships *(Undergraduate/Scholarship)*

Purpose: To support the growth of Montessori teachers. **Focus:** Education, Teaching. **Qualif.:** Applicant must be accepted or in the process of acceptance by an affiliated AMS teacher education program. **Criteria:** Selection of applicant will not be based on the gender, race, creed, color or national origin or sexual orientation. Applicants are considered on the basis of financial need, a compelling personal statement, three letters of recommendation and official verification of acceptance into an AMS Teacher Education Program.

Funds Avail.: $28,000. **To Apply:** Application forms are available on the website. Applicant must submit a personal statement, three recommendation letters, financial statement and appropriate tax form and verification of TEP acceptance. **Deadline:** May 2. **Contact:** Application form and supporting documents must be sent to Connie Murphy at the above address.

939 ■ American Musicological Society (AMS)

6010 College Sta.
Brunswick, ME 04011
Ph: (207) 798-4243

Fax: (207) 798-4254
Free: 877-679-7648
E-mail: ams@ams-net.org
URL: www.ams-net.org

940 ■ Alvin H. Johnson AMS Dissertation Fellowships *(Graduate/Fellowship)*

Purpose: To provide financial assistance for full-time studies. **Focus:** Music. **Qualif.:** Applicants must be anyone eligibly registered in good standing for a doctorate at a North American university and must have completed all formal degree requirements except the dissertation at the time of full application. **Criteria:** Recipients will be selected on the basis of academic merit.

Funds Avail.: $20,000. **Number Awarded:** 50. **To Apply:** Applicants can apply and submit applications online via the AMS website. Applicants will be requested to upload the following information: A 150-word project description; a current dissertation prospectus of 12-15 pages (c. 3000-4000 words). The prospectus should include a detailed rationale of the project (supported by, but not limited to, an assessment of relevant secondary literature), an overview of each chapter, and a clear statement of progress to date, all written in prose; a bibliography of two to three pages citing the most important relevant primary and secondary sources; a sample chapter (preferably not an introductory chapter reviewing the literature); a curriculum vitae. Applicants should also arrange the following: two supporting letters of recommendation, one of which is from a member of the student's dissertation advisory committee. Letters of support may be sent directly to the Chair of the AHJ AMS 50 Dissertation Fellowship Committee. PDF format is preferred. Send as an email attachment to a50-recomms@ams-net.org, or via fax to the AMS office; A letter from the registrar or departmental Dir. of Graduate Studies attesting to the student's ABD (all-but-dissertation) status. Submit in the same way as letters of recommendation. **Deadline:** December 17.

941 ■ Howard Mayer Brown Fellowships *(Graduate/Fellowship)*

Purpose: To increase the presence of minority scholars and teachers in musicology by providing financial aid. **Focus:** Music. **Qualif.:** Applicants must be students who have completed at least one year of graduate work, intend to pursue a Ph.D. and are in good standing at their home institution. **Criteria:** Recipients are selected based on their academic merit.

Funds Avail.: $20,000. **To Apply:** Applications may be made directly by the student, or the student may be nominated by a faculty member of the institution at which the student is enrolled or by a member of the Society at another institution. Supporting documents must include the following: a personal statement from the student (not to exceed five pages) summarizing his or her musical and academic background and stating why she or he wished to pursue an advanced degree in musicology; a summary statement, not to exceed 250 words, outlining areas of research or specific topics presented in the personal statement; a curriculum vitae; samples of the applicant's work (typically not to exceed 30 pages total), such as term papers, thesis chapters, or any published material; letters of support from three faculty members, one of which may be the letter of nomination. Letters of recommendation should be sent as an email attachment to hmb-apps@ams-net.org, or via fax to the AMS office. **Deadline:** December 17. **Contact:** Prof. Charles Hiroshi Garrett, Committee Chair, at cgarr@umich.edu.

Awards are arranged alphabetically below their administering organizations

942 ■ American Nephrology Nurses' Association (ANNA)

E Holly Ave.
Box 56
Pitman, NJ 08071
Ph: (856) 256-2320
Fax: (856) 589-7463
Free: 888-600-2662
E-mail: anna.webeditor@inurse.com
URL: www.annanurse.org

943 ■ American Nephrology Nurses' Association Evidence-Based Research Grants *(Professional development/Grant)*

Purpose: To encourage the discovery of new knowledge as well as the incorporation of the best scientific evidence currently available into the practice of nephrology nursing, with the ultimate goal of improving patient outcomes. **Focus:** Nephrology. **Qualif.:** The principal or co-principal investigators must be members of ANNA within the duration of the research project; must share equal responsibility with all other co-investigators for the conceptualization and implementation of the proposed research project; must provide an evidence of their experiences and credentials demonstrating the ability to complete the proposed EBP project and commitment to nephrology nursing; must have the option of contacting a member of the ANNA Research Committee to discuss ideas and use the assistance of the committee to connect them with appropriate mentors, if needed. **Criteria:** Funding will be based on established research, clinical practice priorities and availability of funds.

Funds Avail.: $5,000 per proposal. **Number Awarded:** 3. **To Apply:** The proposal must demonstrate the following: significance and applicability of the EBP project to nephrology nursing or related therapies; for EBP research proposals, sound methodology in accordance with recognized nursing research guidelines; for other EBP, sound methodology and implementation strategies depending on the type of project; for EBP research projects, approval by the appropriate institutional review board; for other EBP projects, support from the institution where the project will be implemented; feasibility and likelihood of successful completion. Applicants must submit the following items in the order specified: cover letter; ANNA Evidence-based Practice Grant Application Checklist; cover sheet; Co-investigators/consultants/collaborators sheet; detailed budget and justification; abstract; research or project plan; timeline for the research/project completion; references; appendices; copy of IRB approval for research studies or letter of support for other projects; curriculum vitae; personal research articles if available; 8 x 10 professional headshot (black and white or color). Project proposals should be submitted by e-mail to the ANNA National Office. **Deadline:** August 31 for the first proposal; November 15 for the final proposal. **Contact:** annascholarships@ajj.com.

944 ■ American Nephrology Nurses' Association Research Grants *(Doctorate, Graduate/ Grant)*

Purpose: To recognize outstanding nephrology nurse researchers. **Focus:** Nephrology. **Qualif.:** The principal or co-principal investigators must be members of ANNA within the duration of the research project; must share equal responsibility with all other co-investigators for the conceptualization and implementation of the proposed research project; must provide an evidence of their commitment to nephrology nursing experiences and credentials; must be registered nurses who hold a master's or doctoral degree. The contributions of each of the team members must be identified and the application should describe how each investigator's role fits with their expertise and will facilitate completion of the research project. **Criteria:** Award funding will be based on established research priorities and availability of funds.

Funds Avail.: $15,000 per proposal. **To Apply:** Applicants must complete the entire grant application form according to the instructions. The proposal must demonstrate the following: applicability of investigation to nephrology, transplantation or related therapies; sound methodology in accordance with recognized nursing research guidelines; approval by the appropriate institutional review board; feasibility and likelihood of successful completion; a detailed budget for the proposed project should be outlined including costs that exceed the grant amount. While indirect costs may be included in the budget, ANNA does not fund indirect costs; a detailed timeline from the beginning to completion of the project must be included as awell as list of specific dates and activities. Applicants must also include the following: a cover letter, indicating how the applicant(s) meet the criteria; a completed and signed cover sheet; a 250-word abstract; maximum of 12 pages, double-spaced research plan; references; appendices; budget sheet(s); and curriculum vitae of principal and all co-investigators, collaborators and consultants. **Deadline:** August 31 for the first proposal; November 15 for the final proposal. **Contact:** annascholarships@sjj.com.

945 ■ Nephrology Nurse Researcher Awards *(Doctorate, Graduate/Award)*

Purpose: To recognize outstanding nephrology nurse researchers. **Focus:** Nephrology. **Qualif.:** Candidates must be full members of ANNA, have been members for a minimum of the last two years as of the award application deadline; actively involved in nephrology nursing related health care services; active participants in ANNA at the local, regional and national level; must preferably hold a master's or doctoral degree. **Criteria:** Selection will be based on the committee's criteria.

Funds Avail.: $1,000. **To Apply:** The nomination packet should include documentation of the following: a) nominee has conducted research which contributes towards advancement of nephrology nursing. The packet should include a list of research the nominee has completed with the following information: title of the research study; list of other researchers (if applicable); date of completion of the project or projected completion of the study; b) the nominee has shared his/her research findings, either through presentation at ANNA meeting or publication in appropriate journals. The nomination letter should provide the following: a list of presentations, including any co-presenters, with the title of the presentation, date, type of meeting and site of meeting; a list of publications in APA format, including other authors (if applicable), publication date, title of article, name of the journal, volume and issue and page numbers; c) additional comments that support the nominee as an outstanding nephrology nurse researcher.

946 ■ Barbara F. Prowant Nursing Research Grants *(Graduate/Grant)*

Purpose: To promote nursing research particularly in the area of nephrology. **Focus:** Nephrology. **Qualif.:** Principal investigators must be members of ANNA within the duration of the project; must be currently certified by the Nephrology Nursing Certification Commission; must be currently

Awards are arranged alphabetically below their administering organizations

enrolled in a graduate program on the masters, doctorate or post-doctorate level; must provide evidences of their experiences and credentials demonstrating the ability to complete the proposed project and commitment to nephrology nursing; must have the option of contacting a member of the ANNA Research Committee to discuss ideas and use the assistance of the committee to connect them with appropriate mentors, if needed. **Criteria:** Funding will be based on scientific merit and availability of funds.

Funds Avail.: $5,000. **To Apply:** The proposal must demonstrate the following: significance and applicability of the project to nursing, education or related therapies; for research proposals, sound methodology in accordance with recognized nursing research guidelines; for other proposals, sound methodology and implementation strategies depending on the type of project; approval by the appropriate Institutional Review Board; support from institution where the project will be implemented; feasibility and likelihood of successful completion and support from faculty. Applicants must submit the following items in the order specified: cover letter; ANNA Evidence-based Practice Grant Application Checklist; cover sheet; Co-investigators/consultants/collaborators sheet; detailed budget and justification; abstract; research or project plan; timeline for research/project completion; references; appendices; copy of IRB approval for research studies or letter of support for other projects; curriculum vitae; personal research articles if available; 8 x 10 professional headshot (black and white or color). Project proposals should be submitted by e-mail to the ANNA National Office. **Deadline:** August 31 for the first proposal; November 15 for the final proposal. **Contact:** annascholarships@ajj.com.

947 ■ American Nuclear Society (ANS)

555 N Kensington Ave.
La Grange Park, IL 60526
Ph: (708) 352-6611
Fax: (708) 352-0499
Free: 800-323-3044
E-mail: members@ans.org
URL: www.new.ans.org

948 ■ American Nuclear Society Incoming Freshman Scholarships *(Undergraduate/Scholarship)*

Purpose: To assist students who wish to complete their post-secondary education and prepare for careers in nuclear science and technology (NS&T). **Focus:** Engineering, Nuclear. **Qualif.:** Applicants must be graduating high school seniors who have the intention to pursue a degree in nuclear engineering. **Criteria:** Applicants are evaluated based on high school academic achievement; freshman college courses enrolled in; quality and content of 500-word essay; letters of recommendation by counselors and/or teachers; and other information.

Funds Avail.: $1,000 for each recipient. **Number Awarded:** 4. **To Apply:** Applicants must submit all the required application information. **Deadline:** April 1.

949 ■ American Nuclear Society Undergraduates Scholarships *(Undergraduate/Scholarship)*

Purpose: To help students complete their post-secondary education and prepare for careers in nuclear science and technology (NS&T). **Focus:** Nuclear science; Engineering, Nuclear. **Qualif.:** Applicants must be students who have

completed at least one year in a course of study leading to a degree in nuclear science, nuclear engineering or a nuclear-related field. **Criteria:** Recipients are selected based on merit and financial need.

Funds Avail.: No specific amount. **Number Awarded:** Up to 21. **To Apply:** Applicants must submit all the required application information.

950 ■ American Occupational Therapy Foundation (AOTF)

PO Box 31220
Bethesda, MD 20824-1220
Ph: (301) 652-6611
Fax: (301) 656-3620
Free: 800-729-2682
E-mail: aotf@aotf.org
URL: www.aotf.org

951 ■ Ethel Beard Burstein Scholarship Program *(Postgraduate/Scholarship)*

Purpose: To provide financial assistance for AOTF members to promote research and education in the field of occupational therapy. **Focus:** Occupational therapy. **Qualif.:** Applicant must be a member of the AOTF; must demonstrate a need for financial assistance; sustained a record of outstanding scholastic achievement. Post-baccalaureate applicant must be enrolled as a full-time student at the professional level in an accredited or developing occupational therapy educational program. **Criteria:** Priority will be given to applicants who are enrolled at a Philadelphia school and committed to clinical practice.

Funds Avail.: $1,200. **Number Awarded:** 2. **To Apply:** Applicant must complete online application, (please visit AOTF website); must prepare two personal references; curriculum Director's statement; official transcripts; financial statement; and an essay. **Deadline:** December 2.

952 ■ Kappa Delta Phi Scholarship Program *(Postgraduate/Scholarship)*

Purpose: To provide financial assistance for AOTF members to promote research and education in the field of occupational therapy. **Focus:** Occupational therapy. **Qualif.:** Applicant must be a member of the AOTF; must demonstrate a need for financial assistance; sustained a record of outstanding scholastic achievement. Post-baccalaureate applicant must be enrolled as a full-time student at the professional level in an accredited or developing occupational therapy educational program. **Criteria:** Recipients are selected based on the application and the materials submitted. Priority will be given to the residents of AZ, CA, FL, IA, IN, KY, MO, OH.

Funds Avail.: $2,000. **Number Awarded:** 2. **To Apply:** Applicants must complete the online application, (please visit AOTF website); must prepare two personal references; curriculum Director's statement; official transcripts; financial statement; and an essay. **Deadline:** November 15 for application; January 10 for personal references and program director statement. **Contact:** Jeanne Cooper; jcooper@aotf.org.

953 ■ Mary Minglen Scholarship Program *(Postgraduate/Scholarship)*

Purpose: To provide financial assistance for AOTF members to promote research and education in the field of oc-

Awards are arranged alphabetically below their administering organizations

cupational therapy. **Focus:** Occupational therapy. **Qualif.:** Applicant must be a member of the AOTF; must demonstrate a need for financial assistance; sustained a record of outstanding scholastic achievement. Post-baccalaureate applicants must be enrolled as full-time students at the professional level in an accredited or developing occupational therapy educational program. **Criteria:** Recipients are selected based on the application and the materials submitted.

Funds Avail.: $1,000. **To Apply:** Applicants must complete the online application, (please visit AOTF website); must prepare two personal references; curriculum Director's statement; official transcripts; financial statement; and an essay. **Deadline:** December 2.

954 ■ NorthCoast Medical Scholarship Program
(Postgraduate/Scholarship)

Purpose: To provide financial assistance for AOTF members to promote research and education in the field of occupational therapy. **Focus:** Occupational therapy. **Qualif.:** Applicant must be a member of the AOTF; must demonstrate a need for financial assistance; sustain a record of outstanding scholastic achievement. Post-baccalaureate applicants must be enrolled as full-time students at the professional level in an accredited or developing occupational therapy educational program. **Criteria:** Recipients are selected based on the application and the materials submitted.

Funds Avail.: $5,000. **Number Awarded:** 2. **To Apply:** Applicants must complete the online application, (please visit AOTF website); must prepare two personal references; curriculum Director's statement; official transcripts; financial statement; and an essay. **Deadline:** November 15 for application; January 10 for personal references and program director statement.

955 ■ Frank Oppenheimer Scholarship Program
(Postgraduate/Scholarship)

Purpose: To provide financial assistance for AOTF members to promote research and education in the field of occupational therapy. **Focus:** Occupational therapy. **Qualif.:** Applicant must be a member of the AOTF; must demonstrate a need for financial assistance; sustained a record of outstanding scholastic achievement. Post-baccalaureate applicant must be enrolled as a full-time student at the professional level in an accredited or developing occupational therapy educational program. **Criteria:** Recipients are selected based on the application and the materials submitted.

Funds Avail.: $1,000. **To Apply:** Applicants must complete the online application, (please visit AOTF website); must prepare two personal references; curriculum Director's statement; official transcripts; financial statement; and an essay. **Deadline:** November 15 for application; January 10 for personal references and program director statement.

956 ■ Willard and Spackman Scholarship Program *(Postgraduate/Scholarship)*

Purpose: To provide financial assistance for AOTF members to promote research and education in the field of occupational therapy. **Focus:** Occupational therapy. **Qualif.:** Applicant must be a member of the AOTF; must demonstrate a need for financial assistance; sustained a record of outstanding scholastic achievement. Post-baccalaureate applicant must be enrolled as a full-time student at the professional level in an accredited or developing occupational therapy educational program. **Criteria:** Recipi-

ents are selected based on the application and the materials submitted.

Funds Avail.: $2,000. **Number Awarded:** 2. **To Apply:** Applicants must complete the online application, (please visit AOTF website); must prepare two personal references; curriculum Director's statement; official transcripts; financial statement; and an essay. **Deadline:** November 15 for application; January 10 for personal references and program director statement.

957 ■ Edith Weingarten Scholarship Program
(Postgraduate/Scholarship)

Purpose: To provide financial assistance for AOTF members to promote research and education in the field of occupational therapy. **Focus:** Occupational therapy. **Qualif.:** Applicant must be a member of the AOTF; must demonstrate a need for financial assistance; sustained a record of outstanding scholastic achievement. Post-baccalaureate applicant must be enrolled as a full-time student at the professional level in an accredited or developing occupational therapy educational program. **Criteria:** Recipients are selected based on the application and the materials submitted.

Funds Avail.: $1,000. **To Apply:** Applicants must complete the online application, (please visit AOTF website); must prepare two personal references; curriculum Director's statement; official transcripts; financial statement; and an essay. **Deadline:** November 15 for application; January 10 for personal references and program director statement.

958 ■ American Orff-Schulwerk Association (AOSA)
PO Box 391089
Cleveland, OH 44139-8089
Ph: (440) 543-5366
Fax: (440) 543-2687
E-mail: info@aosa.org
URL: www.aosa.org

959 ■ AOSA Research Grants *(All/Grant)*

Purpose: To promote philosophy and encourage research in varied applications of Orff Schulwerk. **Focus:** Music; Education, Music. **Qualif.:** Applicants must be active and expert AOSA members. **Criteria:** Applicants are evaluated based on merit.

Funds Avail.: $500-$5,000. **To Apply:** Applicants must submit a completed application form, a resume reflecting knowledge of or expertise in Orff Schulwerk, a letter of reference and a project proposal. Abstract should be maximum of 250 words. Requirements must be submitted to the AOSA Research Chair. **Deadline:** January 15 or July 15. **Remarks:** The proposal (limited to 15 pages, double-spaced) must include an introduction and problem, related literature, procedure, bibliography and proposed budget.

960 ■ AOSA Research Partnership Grants *(All/Grant)*

Purpose: To encourage joint research by music teachers and researchers. **Focus:** Music. **Qualif.:** Applicants must be groups consisting of one practicing music teacher (must be a member of the AOSA) of grades P-12 in a school setting and one faculty member with substantial research experience at a college or university. **Criteria:** Applicants are selected based on the panel's review of the application materials.

Awards are arranged alphabetically below their administering organizations

Funds Avail.: $500 to $5,000. **Number Awarded:** 3. **To Apply:** Applicants must submit a completed application form; resume; letter of reference; and a proposal indicating the purpose, procedure, budget summary and timeline of the project. **Deadline:** January 15 and July 15.

961 ■ Barbara Potter Scholarships (All/ Scholarship)

Purpose: To provide financial assistance for members of AOSA who wish to study at the Orff Institute in Salzburg, Austria. **Focus:** Music. **Qualif.:** Applicant must be a U.S. citizen or a resident of the United States for the past five years; must be an AOSA member; must be planning to study at the Orff Institute in Salzburg, Austria; must have completed Level III Orff Schulwerk Training; must demonstrate personal need of financial aid. **Criteria:** Applicants are selected based on the jury's review of application materials.

Funds Avail.: No specific amount. **To Apply:** Applicants must submit a completed application and agreement form; one-page resume; one-to-two pages project description and three reference letters. Submit all requirements to the Office of the Executive Director. **Deadline:** January 25.

962 ■ Shields-Gillespie Scholarships (All, Professional development/Scholarship)

Purpose: To support special creative projects that are associated with Orff Schulwerk and that will benefit the music education of children. **Focus:** Music. **Qualif.:** Applicant must be a U.S. citizen or must have resided in the United States for the past five years; a current member of AOSA and must have been an AOSA member in good standing for one year; must be actively involved in teaching low-income preschool or kindergarten students; must have a strong motivation to study music; and demonstrated financial need. **Criteria:** Applicants are selected based on the jury's review of application materials.

Funds Avail.: No specific amount. **To Apply:** Applicants must submit two copies of completed application and agreement form; one-page resume; one-to-two pages project description and three reference letters. If the application is for professional development, applicants must submit a financial statement and copies of two most recent income tax returns. Submit all requirements to the Office of the Executive Director. **Deadline:** January 25.

963 ■ American Oriental Society (AOS)

University of Michigan, Hatcher Graduate Library
Ann Arbor, MI 48109-1190
Ph: (734) 647-4760
E-mail: jrodgers@umich.edu
URL: www.umich.edu/~aos

964 ■ Louise Wallace Hackney Fellowships for the Study of Chinese Art (Doctorate, Postdoctorate/Fellowship)

Purpose: To permit the study of Chinese art, with special relation to painting and its reflection of Chinese culture, **Focus:** Chinese studies. **Qualif.:** Applicants must have completed three years study of the Chinese language or its equivalent and must be able to demonstrate that they have already committed themselves to the serious study of this important area of oriental art; must be post-doctoral as well as doctoral students. **Criteria:** Applicants are selected by the two committees of specialists in the field.

Funds Avail.: $8,000. **To Apply:** Applicants should submit the following materials in duplicate: (1) transcript of their undergraduate and graduate course work; (2) statement of personal finances; (3) three or four-page summary of the proposed project to be undertaken during the year of the fellowship award, appended with a financial statement explaining the expense involved in this study; (4) no less than three letters of recommendation. **Deadline:** March 1. **Contact:** Jonathan Rodgers, jrodgers@umich.edu.

965 ■ American Orthopedic Foot and Ankle Society (AOFAS)

6300 N River Rd., Ste. 510
Rosemont, IL 60018
Ph: (847) 698-4654
Fax: (847) 692-3315
Free: 800-235-4855
E-mail: aofasinfo@aofas.org
URL: www.aofas.org/Pages/Home.aspx

966 ■ AOFAS Research Grants Program (Graduate/Grant)

Purpose: To assist members and other orthopedists in providing the highest quality foot and ankle care to the public. **Focus:** Medicine, Orthopedic. **Qualif.:** Eligibility for grant funding is a benefit of membership in AOFAS, and the principle or co-principle project investigator must be an AOFAS active, candidate or international member. **Criteria:** Investigator will not be awarded more than two grants in any four consecutive years.

Funds Avail.: $20,000. **To Apply:** The grant application form and administrative policies and procedures are available online. **Deadline:** December 1. **Contact:** For additional questions, applicants must contact the AOFAS office at aofasinfo@aofas.org or call 847-698-4654.

967 ■ Orthopedic Foot and Ankle Fellowships (Graduate/Fellowship)

Purpose: To assist members and other orthopedists in providing the highest quality foot and ankle care to the public. **Focus:** Medicine, Orthopedic. **Qualif.:** Applicants must be orthopedic surgeons. **Criteria:** Recipients will be selected based on a consensus by foot and ankle fellowship directors.

Funds Avail.: No specific amount. **To Apply:** Applicants may download an application form online. Upon completion of the requirements, the applicants must submit their application together with curriculum vitae, personal vitae, personal statement, and check list of programs. **Deadline:** March 1. **Contact:** Daniel Farber, MD, Chair, dfarber@umoa.umm.edu or 410-448-6774.

968 ■ American Osteopathic Foundation (AOF)

142 E Ontario St., Ste. 1450
Chicago, IL 60611
Ph: (312) 202-8234
Fax: (312) 202-8216
Free: 866-455-9383
E-mail: info@aof-foundation.org
URL: www.aof-foundation.org

969 ■ William G. Anderson, DO, Minority Scholarships (Undergraduate/Scholarship)

Purpose: To provide monetary scholarship to help defer the cost of students' osteopathic medical education. **Focus:**

Awards are arranged alphabetically below their administering organizations

Osteopathic medicine. **Qualif.:** Any minority osteopathic student who will be entering his or her second- to fourth-year studies at an AOA accredited college/school of osteopathic medicine. **Criteria:** Applicant shall meet the following criteria: Strong interest in osteopathic medicine, its philosophy and principles; Excellent academic achievement; Demonstrated leadership efforts in addressing the educational, societal, and health needs of minorities; Demonstrated leadership efforts to eliminate inequities in medical education and health care; Noteworthy accomplishments, awards and honors, clerkship or special projects, and extracurricular activities in which the student has shown leadership abilities. Financial need can be considered but not the determinative factor in the selection of a recipient.

Funds Avail.: $5,000. **Number Awarded:** 1. **To Apply:** The following should be sent in one complete packet to the American Osteopathic Foundation: 1) completed, typewritten or computer generated application form; 2) rating sheets and letters of recommendation from two references; 3) maximum of two pages personal statement; 4) one-page personal financial need statement; 5) letter from the Dean certifying the applicant's academic standing and explanation of the eligibility criteria; 6) letter from the Financial Aid Officer; 7) curriculum vitae; 8) official medical school academic transcript (may be mailed separately); and 9) copy of financial aid report (if applicable). **Deadline:** April 27. **Contact:** Vicki Heck, Association Dir. of Communications; vheck@aof-foundation.org or at 312-202-8232.

970 ■ McCaughan Heritage Scholarships
(Undergraduate/Scholarship)

Purpose: To provide monetary scholarship to help defer the cost of students' osteopathic medical education. **Focus:** Osteopathic medicine. **Qualif.:** Any osteopathic medical student who are in their last year of studies in an AOA approved college/school of osteopathic medicine is eligible to be nominated for this scholarship. **Criteria:** Recipients shall meet the following criteria: Demonstrated commitment to the osteopathic profession, medicine and education; Promotes osteopathic ideas and unity within the osteopathic community; Participation in extracurricular activities that promote osteopathic medicine to the public; Demonstrates, by word and deed, the desire to advance osteopathic medicine; Presents a positive image and attitude about the osteopathic profession; Exhibits a unique combination of character, moral, academic and ethical behavior.

Funds Avail.: $5,000. **Number Awarded:** 1. **To Apply:** Applicant must submit the following in one packet: Completed application form; Letters of recommendation from 3 references; Letter from Dean certifying that the applicant is in good academic standing and states the applicant's class ranking; Personal statement from the applicant of not more than 2 pages; Official medical school academic transcript; Curriculum vitae or resume. **Deadline:** April 27. **Contact:** Vicki Heck, Association Dir. of Communications; vheck@aof-foundation.org or at 312-202-8232.

971 ■ Procter and Gamble Complex PE Scholars Grant *(Undergraduate/Award)*

Purpose: To provide monetary aid to osteopathic medical students to help defray the costs involved of taking COMPLEX-USA Level 2-PE. **Focus:** Osteopathic medicine. **Qualif.:** Applicants must be 3rd or 4th year osteopathic medical students to help defray the cost of taking COMPLES-USA Level 2-PE. **Criteria:** Recipients shall meet the following criteria: Strong interest in osteopathic medicine, its philosophy and principle. Excellent academic achievement and successful completion COMPLEX-USA

Level 1; Participation in school/community life outside of class requirements, as well as participation in professionally related activities during osteopathic medical school; Serves as an ambassador for the school and the osteopathic profession.

Funds Avail.: $1,000. **To Apply:** The Dean at each COM/SOM is invited to nominate one student who best meets the eligibility criteria. The following should be sent in own complete packet: Completed, typewritten or computer generated nomination form; Letter of recommendation from the Dean (nominator); One letter of recommendation from someone involved with the nominee's osteopathic education that can speak to the nominee's qualifications for this grant based on the eligibility criteria.

972 ■ Welch Scholars Grants *(Undergraduate/Grant)*

Purpose: To promote education within the osteopathic profession. **Focus:** Osteopathic medicine. **Qualif.:** Any osteopathic student who will be entering his or her second to fourth year of studies at an AOA accredited college/school of osteopathic medicine. **Criteria:** The recipients are chosen based on their outstanding academic achievement, participation in extracurricular activities, strong commitment toward osteopathic medicine, and financial need.

Funds Avail.: $2,000. **To Apply:** Applicant must submit the following in one packet: Completed, typewritten or computer generated Nomination form; Letter from Dean certifying that the applicant is in good academic standing and states the applicant's class ranking; Letter from the Director of Financial Aid verifying the student's financial need for educational assistance; Letters of recommendation from two references who can speak to the applicant's qualification for this grant based on the eligibility criteria; Personal statement of not more than two pages; Personal financial need statement of not more than one page. Official medical school academic transcript (may be mailed separately). **Deadline:** May 14. **Contact:** Vicki Heck, Association Dir. of Communications; vheck@aof-foundation.org or at 312-202-8232.

973 ■ American Otological Society (AOS)
c/o Kristen Bordignon, Admin.
1980 Warson Rd.
Springfield, IL 62704
Ph: (217) 638-0801
Fax: (217) 679-1677
E-mail: otosociety@yahoo.com
URL: www.americanotologicalsociety.org

974 ■ AOS Research Training Fellowships
(Graduate/Fellowship)

Purpose: To further the study on otosclerosis, Meniere's disease, and related ear disorders. **Focus:** Otology; Otosclerosis; Meniere's disease. **Qualif.:** Applicant must be a physician (resident or medical student). **Criteria:** Selection is based on the application materials and documents submitted.

Funds Avail.: $35,000 for stipend, $5,000 for supplies. **To Apply:** Applicants must submit a completed scholarship application together with the required materials. Applications must be accompanied by a documentation from the sponsor and institution that facilities and faculty are appropriate for the research training requested. **Deadline:** January 31. **Contact:** John P. Carey, M.D., Executive

Awards are arranged alphabetically below their administering organizations

Secretary, Research Fund of the American Otological Society, Inc. Johns Hopkins University, School of Medicine, Department of Otolaryngology-Head & Neck Surgery 601 N. Caroline Street, JHOC 6255 Baltimore, MD 21287-0910, Tel: 352-751-0932, or E-mail: segossard@aol.com.

975 ■ American Paint Horse Foundation (APHA)

PO Box 961023
Fort Worth, TX 76161-0023
Ph: (817) 834-2742
Fax: (817) 834-3152
E-mail: rteate@apha.com
URL: www.aphfoundation.org

976 ■ American Paint Horse Foundation Scholarships *(Undergraduate/Scholarship)*

Purpose: To promote educational and social growth of young horsemen and women. **Focus:** General studies. **Qualif.:** Applicants must have at least a B average in high school; must pass the college entrance exam; must be APHA members in good standing; must have at least 3.0 cumulative grade point average; and must be enrolled in at least 12 credit hours per semester. **Criteria:** Recipients are selected based on a review of submitted requirements.

Funds Avail.: No specific amount. **To Apply:** Applicants must provide three letters of reference and an essay explaining their educational plans. **Deadline:** March 1.

977 ■ American Parkinson Disease Association (APDA)

National Office
135 Parkinson Ave.
Staten Island, NY 10305
Ph: (718) 981-8001
Fax: (718) 981-4399
Free: 800-223-2732
E-mail: apda@apdaparkinson.org
URL: www.apdaparkinson.org

978 ■ American Parkinson Disease Association Medical Students Summer Fellowships *(Doctorate/Fellowship)*

Purpose: To provide stipend to enable medical students performing supervised laboratory or clinical research designed to clarify our understanding of Parkinson's disease, its nature, manifestations, etiology or treatment. **Focus:** Medicine. **Qualif.:** Applicants must be full-time medical students in good academic standing in an approved American medical school. The proposed research project must be performed in an academic medical center or recognized research institute in the United States; and be sponsored by a full-time faculty member or established institute scientist. The project must be part of the sponsor's ongoing research which performed under the sponsor's direct supervision. **Criteria:** Preference will be given to those who meet the qualifications.

Funds Avail.: $4,000. **To Apply:** Applicants must provide three pages of proposed work which contains: title, location, sponsors, goals and objectives, investigative methods, data analysis methods, significance of anticipated findings, resources and description of the proposed project. Also, it should be discussing the background rationale including preliminary results of work completed by the sponsors. One

original and two hard copies of application should be submitted electronically. **Deadline:** January 31. **Contact:** Paul Maestrone, DVM, Director of Scientific & Medical Affairs.

979 ■ APDA Postdoctoral Fellowships *(Professional development/Fellowship)*

Purpose: To support postdoctoral scientists whose research training holds promise into new insights of geriatric psychology, pathophysiology, etiology and treatment of Parkinson's disease. **Focus:** Geriatric Medicine; Parkinson's disease. **Qualif.:** Applicants must have completed their MD, DO, PhD, MD/PhD, DO/PhD or clinical residency program within two (2) years of the onset of the proposed study and must perform the research project at an academic institution within the United States. **Criteria:** Preference will be given to those who meet the criteria.

Funds Avail.: Up to $35,000. **To Apply:** Applicants must submit (150 words, three pages) research proposal which includes: background rationale, research plan/methods and goals; letter of reference and support from a mentor or other faculty member; and pending sponsored support. Applicants must provide one original and two hard copies of application and must be sent electronically. **Deadline:** March 1. **Contact:** For further details, applicants must contact Michele Popadynec at mpopadynec@apdaparkinson.org.

980 ■ APDA Research Grants *(Professional development/Grant)*

Purpose: To provide financial support for junior investigators intending to pursue research in Parkinson's disease. **Focus:** Parkinson's disease. **Qualif.:** Applicants must be affiliated with and perform the research project at an academic institution within the United States; and must be junior investigators pursuing research in Parkinson's disease. **Criteria:** Selection of recipients will be based on merit.

Funds Avail.: $50,000. **To Apply:** Applicants must submit the three pages proposal; 150 words abstract of the proposed study; NIH Bio-sketch and references. One (1) original and two (2) hard copies of the completed application must be submitted electronically. **Deadline:** January 31. **Contact:** For further details, applicants must contact Michele Popadynec at mpopadynec@apdaparkinson.org.

981 ■ George C. Cotzias, MD Memorial Fellowships *(Professional development/Fellowship)*

Purpose: To assist promising neurologists in establishing careers in research, teaching and clinical services relevant to the problems, causes, prevention, diagnosis and treatment of Parkinson's disease and related neurological movement disorders. **Focus:** Neurology. **Qualif.:** Applicant must be a physician with an MD or DO degree who has completed clinical training in adult neurology, child neurology, neurosurgery, neuropathology or neuroradiology and demonstrates a promising career trajectory as a clinician scientist; should be in the formative years of career development and must not have achieved tenure status or been promoted to Associate Professor; must have an appointment at an academic institution located within the United States that has shown a clear commitment to the career development of the candidate; must be a U.S. citizen or permanent U.S. resident. **Criteria:** Awards will be given to those who meet the qualifications.

Funds Avail.: $80,000. **To Apply:** Applicant must submit the following requirements: an abstract of the proposed

---

Awards are arranged alphabetically below their administering organizations

study (150 words); a budget for each year; resources provided or to be provided by the sponsoring institution; other sources of funding, to include sponsoring agency, amount and award period (indicate how the other sponsored research complements or supplements the present proposal); two letters of recommendation (one from the applicant's institutional sponsor and one from an academic colleague with knowledge of the applicant's professional performance). One original and two hard copies of application must be sent electronically. **Deadline:** January 31. **Contact:** For further details, applicants must contact Michele Popadynec by e-mail at mpopadynec@apdaparkinson.org.

982 ■ Roger C. Duvoisin, MD Research Grants
(Professional development/Grant)

Purpose: To provide funds for established scientists affiliated with research or academic institutions located within the United States and who presently not working on Parkinson's Disease research. **Focus:** Neurology. **Qualif.:** Applicant must be a physician with an MD or DO degree who has completed clinical training in adult neurology, child neurology, neurosurgery, neuropathology or neuroradiology. **Criteria:** Awards will be given to those who meet the qualifications.

Funds Avail.: $80,000 per year. **To Apply:** Applicant must submit a three pages proposal; a brief abstract of the proposed study (150 words); NIH Bio-Sketch; and budget (a detailed budget should be submitted for the first year and a continuing budget for the second year). Applicants must submit one original and two hard copies of application form. **Deadline:** January 31. **Contact:** For further details, applicants must contact Michele Popadynec at mpopadynec@apdaparkinson.org.

983 ■ American Pediatric Surgical Nurses Association (APSNA)
111 Deer Lake Rd., Ste. 100
Deerfield, IL 60015
Ph: (608) 262-2146
E-mail: webadmin@apsna.org
URL: www.apsna.org

984 ■ American Pediatric Surgical Nurses Association Educational Grants *(Professional development/Grant)*

Purpose: To assist APSNA members to further their professional education. **Focus:** Nursing; Pediatric medicine; Surgery. **Qualif.:** Applicant must be an APSNA member in good standing for at least one year; a registered nurse or advanced practice nurse with two years experience in pediatric surgical nursing involved in pediatric surgery patient care, education or research; must be active in the development of professional pediatric surgical nursing practices and standards. **Criteria:** Recipients will be selected by the Education Committees based on potential leadership.

Funds Avail.: No specific amount. **To Apply:** Applicant must submit a completed application form; a documentation of program, conference or educational needs which the scholarship will be used; description of the program course; a current curriculum vitae; a letter of recommendation from co-worker; a cover letter to the Director at Large stating the applicant's credentials, experience and involvement in the pediatric surgical nursing practices and standards; and an essay about the importance of the award. **Deadline:** No-

vember 1 to February 28. **Contact:** For more information, e-mail the Director at dal@apsna.org.

985 ■ American Philological Association (APA)
University of Pennsylvania
220 S 40th St., Ste. 201E
Philadelphia, PA 19104-3543
Ph: (215) 898-4975
Fax: (215) 573-7874
E-mail: apaclassics@sas.upenn.edu
URL: www.apaclassics.org

986 ■ American Philological Association Minority Student Summer Fellowships
(Undergraduate/Fellowship)

Purpose: To provide financial assistance for undergraduate students who wish to pursue their preparation for graduate work in classical archeology. **Focus:** Archeology; Classical studies. **Qualif.:** Applicant must have (but not limited to) participated in classical summer programs or field schools in Italy, Greece or Egypt or language training at institutions in the U.S., Canada or Europe. **Criteria:** Candidates will be judged based on academic qualifications, quality of proposal and financial need.

Funds Avail.: $3,000. **To Apply:** Applicants must complete the application form together with a letter of application describing the applicant's career goals and plans with a list of other programs applied to; must have an undergraduate transcript; must provide two letters of recommendation by a faculty member or other professionals who have worked with the applicant during the past two years (at least one must be an APA or AIA member). **Deadline:** December 14. **Contact:** Sanjaya Thakur, Classical Department, Colorado College, 14 E Cache la Poudre St., Colorado Springs, CO 80903.

987 ■ Thesaurus Linguae Latinae Fellowships (TTL) *(Doctorate/Fellowship)*

Purpose: To support American scholars who wish to broaden their knowledge in the work of Thesaurus Linguae Latinae Institute in Munich. **Focus:** Philology; Latin American studies. **Qualif.:** Applicant must be a U.S. citizen or permanent resident; must have a PhD. degree or anticipate the degree in the next few months. **Criteria:** Fellowships will be awarded to applicants who possess a thorough familiarity and special interest in the Latin languages, as well as advanced competence in Greek.

Funds Avail.: $50,400. **To Apply:** Applicant must submit a curriculum vitae and a statement of what benefits the applicant expects to derive from the fellowship for his or her research and teaching. Applicant must also provide three references. **Deadline:** November 15. **Contact:** Professor Anthony Corbeill, at corbeill@ku.edu.

988 ■ American Philosophical Society (APS)
104 S 5th St.
Philadelphia, PA 19106-3387
Ph: (215) 440-3400
Fax: (215) 440-3423
E-mail: orders@dianepublishing.net
URL: www.amphilsoc.org

989 ■ Daland Fellowships in Clinical Investigation *(Doctorate/Fellowship)*

Purpose: To provide financial support for research in the several branches of clinical medicine, including internal

Awards are arranged alphabetically below their administering organizations

medicine, neurology, pediatrics, psychiatry and surgery. **Focus:** Clinical sciences; Neurology; Pediatric medicine; Surgery; Psychiatry. **Qualif.:** Candidates must be both U.S. citizens and foreign nationals; have MD or MD/PhD degree for fewer than eight years; do not have more than two years of post-doctoral training and research; expecting to perform the research at an institution in the United States. **Criteria:** Fellowship recipients will be selected on the basis of merits.

Funds Avail.: $40,000 for first year and $40,000 for second year. **To Apply:** Applicants must submit a completed application form and letter of support form. Maintain the application format, do not include additional page. Three references are required. **Deadline:** September 1. **Contact:** Linda Musumeci, Dir. of Grants and Fellowships; Email: lmusumeci@amphilsoc.org; Phone: 215-440-3429.

990 ■ John Hope Franklin Dissertation Fellowships (Doctorate/Fellowship)

Purpose: To support the doctoral projects of minority students. **Focus:** General studies. **Qualif.:** Applicants must have completed all course work and examinations preliminary to the dissertation; devote full-time for twelve months with no teaching obligations-to research on the dissertation. **Criteria:** Fellowship recipients will be selected on the basis of merit.

Funds Avail.: Amount not specified. **To Apply:** Applicants must submit completed on-line application form and letter of support form; must maintain the (three-page) format and must not be in 11pt. font smaller. Applications must be submitted as email attachments to applications@amphilsoc.org. References are required, referees must follow the format (must not exceed one-page) and must be sent electronically to lettersofsupport@amphilsoc.org. **Deadline:** October 1. **Remarks:** The Fellowship is named in honor of a distinguished member of the APS. Recipient of the award is expected to spend a three months in Philadelphia. **Contact:** Linda Musumeci, Dir. of Grants and Fellowships; Email: lmusumeci@amphilsoc.org; Phone: 215-440-3429.

991 ■ Franklin Research Grants (Postgraduate/Grant)

Purpose: To support research in all areas of knowledge leading to publication. **Focus:** General studies. **Qualif.:** Applicants must have a doctorate or have published work of doctoral character and quality. Pre-doctoral graduate students are not eligible. **Criteria:** Recipients will be selected based on the jury's review of the application materials.

Funds Avail.: Maximum of $6,000. **To Apply:** Applicants must submit a completed application form and letter of support form available at the website; must maintain the 4-page format and must not be in 11pt. font smaller. Two references are required, referees must follow the format (must not exceed one page) and must be sent in a sealed envelope with the proposal or sent electronically to lettersofsupport@amphilsoc.org. **Deadline:** October 1 and December 1. **Remarks:** Recipients of the award may re-apply after two years. **Contact:** Linda Musumeci, Dir. of Grants and Fellowships; Email: lmusumeci@amphilsoc.org; Phone: 215-440-3429.

992 ■ Lewis and Clark Fund for Exploration and Field Research (Doctorate/Grant)

Purpose: To provide funds for projects related to the astrobiological field. **Focus:** Biological and clinical sciences. **Qualif.:** Applicant must be a post-doctoral student and a U.S. resident performing research anywhere in the world. Foreign applicant must be based at a U.S. institution or planning to carry out research in the United States. **Criteria:** Grant recipient will be selected on the basis of merits.

Funds Avail.: $5,000. **To Apply:** Applicant must submit a completed application form and letter of support form available at the website; must maintain the 4-page format and must have a font size greater than 11pt. Applicant must also submit two references. Referees must also follow the format (must not exceed one page) and send their letters of support to lettersofsupport@amphilsoc.org. Applications must be submitted as email attachments to applications@amphilsoc.org. **Deadline:** February 1. **Contact:** Linda Musumeci, Dir. of Grants and Fellowships; Email: lmusumeci@amphilsoc.org; Phone: 215-440-3429.

993 ■ Library Resident Research Fellowships (Doctorate/Fellowship)

Purpose: To promote useful knowledge in the field of science and humanities. **Focus:** Science; Humanities. **Qualif.:** Applicants must be US citizens or foreign nationals; must hold a PhD or its equivalent and have passed their preliminary examinations; degreed independent scholars. **Criteria:** Preference will be given to the candidates who live 75 or more miles from Philadelphia.

Funds Avail.: $2,500. **To Apply:** Interested applicants must visit the website for the online application process. **Deadline:** March 1.

994 ■ Phillips Fund Grants for Native American Research (Graduate/Grant)

Purpose: To support research on Native American linguistics, ethnohistory and the history of studies of Native American in the continental United States and Canada. **Focus:** Native American studies. **Qualif.:** Applicant must be a graduate student for research on masters theses or doctoral dissertations. **Criteria:** Grant recipient will be selected on the basis of merits.

Funds Avail.: $2,500-$3,500. **To Apply:** Applicant must submit a completed on-line application form and letter of support form; must maintain the (3-page) format and must not be in 11pt. font smaller. Two references are required, referees must follow the format (must not exceed one page); a brief formal report; copies of any tape recordings; transcriptions; microfilms; and must be sent in a sealed envelope with the proposal or sent electronically to lettersofsupport@amphilsoc.org. Applications must be submitted to: Philips Fund for Native American Research, American Philosophical Society 104 S Fifth St., Philadelphia, PA 19106-3386; or to applications@amphilsoc.org. **Deadline:** March 1. **Contact:** Linda Musumeci, Dir. of Grants and Fellowships; Email: lmusumeci@amphilsoc.org; Phone: 215-440-3429.

995 ■ American Physical Society (APS)

One Physics Ellipse
College Park, MD 20740-3844
Ph: (301) 209-3200
Fax: (301) 209-0865
E-mail: exoffice@aps.org
URL: www.aps.org

996 ■ American Physical Society Minority Undergraduate Scholarships (Undergraduate/Scholarship)

Purpose: To advance and diffuse the knowledge of physics. **Focus:** Physics. **Qualif.:** Applicants must be African

Awards are arranged alphabetically below their administering organizations

American, Hispanic American, or Native American US citizens or permanent residents who are majoring or planning to major in physics; must be high school seniors, college freshmen or sophomores. **Criteria:** Recipients are selected based on financial need and academic standing.

Funds Avail.: Maximum amount of $2,000. **To Apply:** Applicants must apply online. **Deadline:** February 3.

997 ■ M. Hildred Blewett Fellowships
(Postdoctorate/Scholarship)

Purpose: To enable early-career women to return to physics research career after having had to interrupt their careers for family reasons. **Focus:** Physics. **Qualif.:** Applicants must be currently legal residents or resident aliens of the United States or Canada; must be currently in Canada or the United States; must have an affiliation with a research-active educational institution or national laboratory; and must have completed work toward a PhD. **Criteria:** Applicants are selected based on a committee's review of the application materials.

Funds Avail.: $45,000. **To Apply:** Application form is available on the website. Completed application form and other supporting documents must be sent electronically to: blewett@aps.org. **Deadline:** June 1.

998 ■ American Physical Therapy Association (APTA)
1111 N Fairfax St.
Alexandria, VA 22314-1488
Ph: (703) 684-2782
Fax: (703) 706-8536
Free: 800-999-2782
E-mail: memberservices@apta.org
URL: www.apta.org

999 ■ APTA Minority Scholarships - Faculty Development Scholarships (Postdoctorate/Scholarship)

Purpose: To provide doctoral education support for minority faculty members, to acknowledge and reward those who demonstrate commitment to minority services and activities and show superior achievements in the profession of physical therapy. **Focus:** Physical therapy. **Qualif.:** Applicant must be a U.S. citizen or legal permanent resident; a member of one of the racial/ethnic minority groups (African-American or Black, Asian, Native Hawaiian or other Pacific Islander, American Indian/Alaska Native and Hispanic/Latino); be a physical therapist, a full-time faculty member, teaching in an accredited or developing professional physical therapist education program; must possess a license to practice physical therapy in a U.S. jurisdiction or have met all the requirements for licensure in a U.S. jurisdiction; enrolled as a student in a regionally accredited post-professional doctoral program whose content has a demonstrated relationship to physical therapy; must demonstrate continuous progress toward the completion of his/her post-professional doctoral program in a timely fashion; must demonstrate commitment to minority services and activities; must demonstrate a commitment to further the physical therapy profession through teaching and research; and must not have received the award in prior years. **Criteria:** Selection is based on demonstrated evidence of contributions in the area of minority affairs and services, contributions to the profession of physical therapy and scholastic achievement.

Funds Avail.: $8,000 plus plaque and certificate. **Number Awarded:** 1. **To Apply:** Applicants must submit a completed typewritten application form along with a copy of an official transcript from the Registrar's Office of all post-professional doctoral coursework; a personal essay which include a response to the four questions listed on the application; curriculum vitae; plan of study for attaining degree (signed by the applicant's faculty advisor); and the reference forms completed by the faculty advisor or chair of the dissertation committee. One original typewritten (or other computerized format) set and six collated, attached, duplicate sets of all materials must be submitted. **Deadline:** December 1. **Contact:** minority@apta.org.

1000 ■ APTA Minority Scholarships - Physical Therapist Assistant Students (All/Scholarship)

Purpose: To acknowledge and reward demonstrated participation in minority affairs and service, the potential for superior achievements as a physical therapist assistant and academic excellence. **Focus:** Physical therapy. **Qualif.:** Applicant must be a U.S. citizen or legal permanent resident; a member of a racial/ethnic minority group (African-American or Black, Asian, Native Hawaiian or other Pacific Islander, American Indian/Alaska Native or Hispanic/Latino); enrolled in the final academic year of an accredited or developing physical therapist assistant education program; must show evidence of contributions in the areas of minority affairs and services and high scholastic achievement; and must possess potential for excellence as a physical therapist assistant. **Criteria:** Selection is based on demonstrated evidence of contributions in the area of minority affairs and services with an emphasis on contributions made while enrolled in the physical therapy education program; potential to contribute to the profession of physical therapy; and scholastic achievement.

Funds Avail.: No specific amount. **To Apply:** Applicants must submit a completed application form along with one copy of an official transcript from the Registrar's Office of all physical therapist assistant coursework (when possible); a personal essay on professional goals and minority services including a response to the three questions listed on the application; a personal information fact sheet (curriculum vitae); and reference forms completed (typed or other computerized form) by the physical therapy academic program, a physical therapist clinician and from a resource to verify contributions to the minority community. Application package which consist of seven sets of materials (1 original and six duplicate sets collated) and one original transcript of physical therapy coursework must be received in the Department of Minority Affairs. **Deadline:** December 1. **Contact:** minority@apta.org.

1001 ■ APTA Minority Scholarships - Physical Therapist Students (All/Scholarship)

Purpose: To acknowledge and reward demonstrated participation in minority affairs activities and services, the potential for superior achievements in the profession of physical therapy, appropriate display of professionalism as a future physical therapist and academic excellence. **Focus:** Physical therapy. **Qualif.:** Applicant must be a U.S. citizen or a legal permanent resident; a member of one of the racial/ethnic minority group (African-American or Black, Asian, Native Hawaiian or other Pacific Islander, American Indian/Alaska Native and Hispanic/Latino); enrolled in the final academic year of an accredited or developing professional physical therapist education program; must show evidence of contributions in the areas of minority affairs and services and high scholastic achievement; and must

Awards are arranged alphabetically below their administering organizations

possess potential for superior achievements in the profession of physical therapy as well as professional excellence as a physical therapist. **Criteria:** Selection is based on demonstrated evidence of contributions in the area of minority affairs and services with an emphasis on contributions made while enrolled in the physical therapy education program; potential to contribute to the profession of physical therapy; and scholastic achievement.

Funds Avail.: No specific amount. **To Apply:** Applicants must submit a completed application form along with a copy of an official transcript from the Registrar's Office of all physical therapy coursework (when possible); a personal essay on professional goals and minority service including a response to the three questions listed on the first page of the application; a personal information fact sheet (curriculum vitae); and reference forms completed (typed or other computerized form) by the physical therapy academic program, a physical therapist clinician and from a resource to verify contributions to the minority community. Application package which consist of seven sets of materials (1 original and six duplicate sets collated) and one original transcript of physical therapy coursework must be received in the Department of Minority Affairs. **Deadline:** December 1. **Contact:** minority@apta.org.

1002 ■ American Physiological Society (APS)

9650 Rockville Pike
Bethesda, MD 20814-3991
Ph: (301) 634-7118
Fax: (301) 634-7241
E-mail: mfrank@the-aps.org
URL: www.the-aps.org

1003 ■ American Physiological Society Postdoctoral Fellowships in Physiological Genomics (APS) *(Postdoctorate/Fellowship)*

Purpose: To encourage post-doctoral students to enhance their knowledge in the field of physiological sciences. **Focus:** Physiology. **Qualif.:** Applicants must have completed an outstanding work in a top-flight graduate program; must have the intention of employing organ system approaches during their post-doctoral training; must have a project which requires the scientist to use the tools of cellular and molecular biology in setting the whole animal; and must have a sponsor which is a member of the American Physiological Society (APS). **Criteria:** Recipients will be selected based on submitted application.

Funds Avail.: Varies. **To Apply:** Only online applications will be accepted. Applicants must log on to www.the-aps.org/awardapps to apply. **Deadline:** January 16.

1004 ■ APS/NIDDK Minority Travel Fellowship Awards *(Graduate, Postdoctorate/Fellowship)*

Purpose: To increase the participation of pre and postdoctoral minority students in physiological sciences. **Focus:** Physiology. **Qualif.:** Applicants must be graduate, postdoctoral and advanced undergraduate students who obtained their undergraduate education in Minority Biomedical Research Programs (MBRS) or Minority Access to Research Career (MARC) eligible institutions. Minority Faculty members are welcome to apply. **Criteria:** Recipients will be selected based on submitted application.

Funds Avail.: No stated amount. **To Apply:** Applicants must submit a copy of their abstract, reasons for wishing to attend the meeting; reasons for financial need, brief curriculum vitae, letter of recommendation from an advisor and list of estimated expenses. Faculty member applicants must submit a record of current and pending support. Applicants must log on to www.the-aps.org/awardapps for the application form. **Remarks:** Only online applications will be accepted.

1005 ■ Porter Physiology Development Fellowship Awards *(Doctorate/Fellowship)*

Purpose: To encourage PhD students to pursue their education in physiological sciences. **Focus:** Physiology. **Qualif.:** Applicant must be a PhD student majoring physiological sciences; must be an ethnic minority who is a citizen or permanent resident of the United States; and must be a member of American Physiological Society (APS). **Criteria:** Applications will be judged based on potential for success including the following: 1) academic records; 2) statement of interest; 3) previous awards and experiences; and 4) recommendation letters; applicant's proposed training environment; clarity and quality of the research.

Funds Avail.: $23,500. **To Apply:** Applicant must submit an application form; documentation of educational background including transcript of records, a copy of acceptance letter to the graduate training program, current curriculum vitae, list of all undergraduate and graduate institutions have attended; must upload a biographical sketch; must provide the Advisor's or Program Director's contact information; must complete a proposed training or research plan; and must request the uploading of two letters of recommendation from an advisor or Program Director. **Deadline:** January 15. **Contact:** For further information regarding the application and submission, applicants must contact Ms. Brooke Bruthers, Minority Programs Coordinator at bbruthers@the-aps.org.

1006 ■ Caroline tum Suden Professional Opportunity Awards *(Postdoctorate, Professional development/Award)*

Purpose: To encourage professionals, pre-doctoral and post-doctoral students to enhance their knowledge in the field of physiological sciences. **Focus:** Physiology. **Qualif.:** Applicants must be authors of an abstract submitted to American Physiological Society (APS); and must be members in good standing at the time of application. **Criteria:** Awards will be given to applicants who successfully submit their abstract. Abstracts must show a clearly stated hypothesis or aim, technical approach to the study, quantitative and statistical comparisons and clarity of the conclusion including the significance of the study.

Funds Avail.: $500. **Number Awarded:** 38. **To Apply:** Applicants must submit a copy of their abstract; a one-page own composition letter stating the following: 1) career goals; 2) research goals; 3) role in the research described in the abstract; and 4) reason(s) why they deserve to receive the award. Applicants must log on to www.the-aps.org/awardapps for the online application. **Deadline:** March 1. **Remarks:** Exceeding one page and restatement of letter to abstract may be cause for disqualification.

1007 ■ American Planning Association (APA)

205 N Michigan Ave., Ste. 1200
Chicago, IL 60601
Ph: (312) 431-9100
Fax: (312) 431-9985
Free: 800-954-1669

Awards are arranged alphabetically below their administering organizations

E-mail: customerservice@planning.org
URL: www.planning.org

1008 ■ Charles Abrams Scholarships *(Graduate/Scholarship)*

Purpose: To aid students who will pursue careers as practicing planners. **Focus:** Urban affairs/design/planning. **Qualif.:** Applicants must be U.S. citizens, and must be accepted into the graduate planning program of one of the following schools: Columbia University, Harvard University, Massachusetts Institute of Technology, New School University and University of Pennsylvania. A nomination by the department chair is required. **Criteria:** Recipients will be selected based on financial need, interest in pursuing an academic curriculum leading to a career in the planning profession, and applicant's statement of the academic background and extra-curricular activities.

Funds Avail.: $2,000. **To Apply:** Applicants must submit a letter of nomination; a one-to-two-page statement written by the applicants describing their commitment to complete the planning curriculum of the university and to pursue a career in the planning profession, as well as an outline of the applicants' qualifications, extra-curricular activities, and reasons for believing that a scholarship award is justified; a financial aid application; official transcripts of all previous collegiate and academic work; an official copy of all GRE scores. **Deadline:** April 30. **Contact:** Kriss Blank at the above address.

1009 ■ Robert A. Catlin/David W. Long Memorial Scholarships *(Graduate/Scholarship)*

Purpose: To foster increased interest among African American undergraduates in urban planning as a graduate field of study and as a professional career. **Focus:** Urban affairs/design/planning. **Qualif.:** Applicants must be African Americans who are rising juniors and seniors majoring in urban planning and related fields; must have a minimum GPA of 3.0; and must be full time enrolled students. **Criteria:** Recipients will be selected based on the committee's review of all submitted applications.

Funds Avail.: $2,500. **To Apply:** Applicants must submit an application form; a personal statement; two letters of recommendation; one sealed Official Academic Transcript for each college or university attended; self-addressed, stamped postcard for notification of the receipt of a complete application. **Deadline:** March 11. **Contact:** Eric D. Shaw, Vice Chairperson at pbcd.policy@gmail.com.

1010 ■ Economic Development Division Graduate Scholarships *(Graduate/Scholarship)*

Purpose: To provide financial assistance for individuals studying economic development and planning. **Focus:** Urban affairs/design/planning. **Qualif.:** Program is open to master's level students from PAB-accredited planning departments across the United States. **Criteria:** Recipients will be selected based on merit.

Funds Avail.: $1,000. **To Apply:** Applicants must submit a letter of recommendation from a full-time faculty member and (2,000 to 2,500-word) original paper or work having to do with a substantive and relevant topic related to economic development and planning. **Deadline:** February 10. **Contact:** John Provo, PhD. Dir. at jprovo@vt.edu.

1011 ■ Environment, Natural Resource and Energy Division Fellowships (ENRE) *(Graduate/Fellowship)*

Purpose: To provide financial support for students excelling in graduate level studies in planning related to natural resources, energy or the environment. **Focus:** Urban affairs/design/planning; Natural resources; Energy-related areas. **Qualif.:** Applicants must be second year graduate students enrolled in an accredited graduate school planning program focusing on issues related to the environment, natural resources or energy. Candidates must also have a minimum GPA of B or 3.0 on a 4.0 scale and must be in a program or course of study consistent with ENRE's mission. **Criteria:** Recipient will be selected based on the quality of application materials and the connection of the student's course of study to ENRE's mission. Priority will be given to ENRE Division members.

Funds Avail.: $2,500 ($1,250 for each of the two semesters). **To Apply:** Applicants must submit an application form; recommendation letter from the student's thesis/project faculty advisor; an 800-word description of the student's master's thesis or project, including how it relates to the division's mission; a 600-word essay describing interest in environmental planning, experience and future goals; a resume. **Deadline:** February 11.

1012 ■ Judith McManus Price Scholarships *(Graduate, Undergraduate/Scholarship)*

Purpose: To provide partial funding for women and minority students. **Focus:** Urban affairs/design/planning. **Qualif.:** Applicants must be U.S. citizens enrolled in Planning Accreditation Board accredited planning programs. Candidates must also be women members of the following minority groups: African American, Hispanic American or Native American. **Criteria:** Recipients will be selected based on academic achievement, letters of recommendation, financial need, professional presentation and geographic balance of awards for the year.

Funds Avail.: $2000-$4000. **To Apply:** Applicant must submit a two- to five page background statement describing how the applicant's graduate education will be applied to career goals and why he/she chose planning as a career path; a completed and signed APA financial aid application; two letters of recommendation; written verification from the school's financial officer indicating the average cost of one academic year; resume; copy of acceptance letter from a PAB-accredited graduate planning school; a notarized statement of financial independence signed by the applicant's parents; and an official transcript. **Deadline:** April 30. **Remarks:** The award also includes a paid one-year student membership to APA. **Contact:** Kriss Blank at the above address.

1013 ■ American Political Science Association (APSA)

1527 New Hampshire Ave. NW
Washington, DC 20036-1206
Ph: (202) 483-2512
Fax: (202) 483-2657
E-mail: apsa@apsanet.org
URL: www.apsanet.org

1014 ■ American Political Science Association Federal Executives Fellowships *(Professional development/Fellowship)*

Purpose: To give senior-level federal executives an opportunity to learn more about Congress and the legislative process through direct participation. **Focus:** Political Science. **Qualif.:** Applicants must have a minimum grade of GS-13 or equivalent at time of application; must have at least two years of federal service in the executive branch

Awards are arranged alphabetically below their administering organizations

and a long-term career goal relevant to a congressional experience; and must demonstrate a commitment to public service, adaptability to new, diverse working environments, and an interest in the legislative process and public affairs. **Criteria:** Recipients are selected based on the result of the nominations and interviews.

Funds Avail.: No specific amount. **To Apply:** Applicants must submit seven copies of: a detailed resume providing contact information, current grade, work experiences, educational background, languages, and special skills and talents; a statement assessing the nominee's executive potential and need for training by the supervisor(s) or agency Executive Resources Board; and a statement by the nominee presenting a need for training, the relevance of training to career goals, and the utilization of training by agency. **Deadline:** March 31. **Contact:** The American Political Science Association at the above address.

1015 ■ American Political Science Association Journalists Fellowships *(Professional development/Fellowship)*

Purpose: To give early-to mid career journalists an opportunity to learn more about Congress and the legislative process through direct participation. **Focus:** Journalism. **Qualif.:** Applicants must be U.S. citizens or permanent U.S. residents; must demonstrate interest in communications and policy making process; must either be print journalists, or broadcast journalists. Print journalists must have a bachelor's degree and two-ten years of continuous, full-time professional experience in newspaper or magazine at the time of application; Broadcast journalists must have a bachelor's degree and two-ten years of continuous, full-time professional experience in radio or television at the time of the application. They must have a background in reporting, producing, directing or writing. **Criteria:** Recipients are selected based on the result of the interview.

Funds Avail.: $38,000, plus a small travel allowance. **To Apply:** Applicants must submit a detailed resume; around 500-word personal statement explaining how the Congressional Fellowship relates to professional goals; contact information for three professional references who have written letters of recommendation; a sample of the best writing whether published or unpublished for the scholar; seven copies of the five clips of the best writing for print journalist; and seven VHS tapes, CD-ROMS, or DVD's with scripts of the five clips of the best reporting for broadcast journalists. **Deadline:** December 1. **Contact:** American Political Science at the above address.

1016 ■ American Political Science Association/ MCI Scholarships *(Postdoctorate/Scholarship)*

Purpose: To give early-to-mid scholars and journalists an opportunity to learn more about Congress and the legislative process through direct participation. **Focus:** Journalism; Political Science. **Qualif.:** Applicants must be U.S. citizens or permanent U.S. residents; must demonstrate an interest in communications and policy making process; must be either scholars, print journalists or broadcast journalists. Scholars must have a Ph.D. completed within the last 15 years or will have defended their dissertation by November of the fellowship year. Print journalists must have a bachelor's degree and two-ten years of continuous, full-time professional experience in newspaper or magazine at the time of application; Broadcast journalists must have a bachelor's degree and two-ten years of continuous, full-time professional experience in radio or television at the time of the application. They must have a background in reporting, producing, directing or writing. **Criteria:** Recipi-

ents are selected based on the result of the interview.

Funds Avail.: $38,000, plus a small travel allowance. **To Apply:** Applicants must submit a detailed resume; around 500-words personal statement explaining how the Congressional Fellowship relates to his/her professional goals; contact information for three professional references who have written letters of recommendation; a sample of the best writing whether it published or unpublished for the scholar; seven copies of the five clips of the best writing for print journalist; and seven VHS tapes, CD-ROMS, or DVDs with scripts of the five clips of the best reporting for broadcast journalists. **Deadline:** December 1. **Contact:** American Political Science at the above address.

1017 ■ American Political Science Association Political Scientists Fellowships *(Postdoctorate/ Fellowship)*

Purpose: To give early-to-mid career political scientists an opportunity to learn more about Congress and the legislative process through direct participation. **Focus:** Political Science. **Qualif.:** Applicants must be U.S. citizens or permanent U.S. residents; must demonstrate an interest in Congress and policy making process; must have a Ph.D. completed within the last 15 years or a dissertation near completion. **Criteria:** Recipients are selected based on the result of the interview.

Funds Avail.: $38,000, plus a small travel allowance. **To Apply:** Applicants must submit a detailed resume; around 500-words personal statement explaining how the Congressional Fellowship relates to your professional goals; contact information for three professional references who have written letters of recommendation; a sample of the best writing whether it published or unpublished manuscript. **Deadline:** December 1. **Contact:** American Political Science at the above address.

1018 ■ Health and Aging Policy Fellows *(Professional development/Fellowship)*

Purpose: To make a positive contribution to the development and implementation of health policies that affect the older Americans. **Focus:** Health Care Services. **Qualif.:** Applicants must be engaged in all career stages; must be U.S. citizens or permanent residents of the U.S. territories who have career plans that anticipate continued work in the U.S. after the fellowship period. **Criteria:** Recipients are selected based on the commitment to health and aging issues and improving the health and well-being of older Americans; potential for leadership in health policy; professional qualifications and achievements; impact of the fellowship experience on the applicant's career; and interpersonal and communication skills.

Funds Avail.: No specific amount. **Number Awarded:** 6. **To Apply:** Applicants must fill out and submit the application form; an essay stating the reasons why the applicant needs the fellowship, description of his/her experiences or contributions in the health aging field, and plans for continued development of the health policy leadership skills after completing the fellowship; a curriculum vitae; a one-page biographical sketch; and the name and contact information of the institutional references and two professional references. **Deadline:** May 15. **Contact:** Harold Alan Pincus, M.D. at pincush@pi.cpmc.columbia.edu.

1019 ■ The Robert Wood Johnson Health Policy Fellowship Program *(All/Fellowship)*

Purpose: To build and maintain a strong and diverse leadership and workforce in health and health care as well

Awards are arranged alphabetically below their administering organizations

as to develop specific fields. **Focus:** Health Sciences; Health Care Services. **Qualif.:** Applicants must have a background in allied health professions, biomedical sciences, dentistry, economics, or other social sciences, health services and administration, medicine, nursing, public health, or social and behavioral health. Applicants must be citizens or permanent residents of the US or its territories at the time of application. **Criteria:** Recipients are selected based on professional achievements; potential for leadership in health policy; potential for future growth and career advancement; and interpersonal and communication skills.

Funds Avail.: $165,000. **Number Awarded:** 6. **To Apply:** Applicants must submit a cover letter including contact information; most recent curriculum vitae; a one-page biographical sketch; names and contact information of three references; a brief essay stating the reasons why the applicant needs the RWJF Fellowship; a description of the most significant community-related activity that utilized professional expertise; a sample letter to a congressional representative, plans for continued development of health policy leadership (300-words); and a letter from the sponsoring institution. Applicants must visit the fellowship website at www.healthpolicyfellows.org/fellowship.php. **Deadline:** November 9. **Contact:** 500 5th Street, NW, Washington, DC 20001; 202-334-1506; info@healthpolicyfellows.org.

1020 ■ American Polygraph Association (APA)
PO Box 8037
Chattanooga, TN 37414-0037
Free: 800-272-8037
URL: www.polygraph.org

1021 ■ William J. Yankee Memorial Scholarships *(Undergraduate/Scholarship)*

Purpose: To provide financial assistance to deserving students. **Focus:** General studies. **Qualif.:** Applicants must have four-year degree from an accredited college or university; must attend an APA accredited basic polygraph examiner training course; must qualify for APA membership upon completion of training. **Criteria:** Selection of candidates will be based on academic success and a demonstrated interest in the field of polygraphing.

Funds Avail.: $5,000. **To Apply:** Applicants must submit an essay of up to 1000 words on detection of deception, interviewing, interrogation or related fields; must have at least two letters of recommendation. **Deadline:** June 1.

1022 ■ American Psychiatric Association Alliance (APAA)
PO Box 285
North Boston, NY 14110
Ph: (703) 907-7304
E-mail: ang3689@aol.com
URL: www.apaalliance.org

1023 ■ Elsa Barton Educational Scholarship Fund *(Undergraduate, Vocational/Occupational/Scholarship)*

Purpose: To provide financial assistance for post secondary educational needs of a spouse/partner or dependents of impaired, disabled, or deceased physicians unable to provide family income. **Focus:** General Studies. **Qualif.:** Program is open for the spouse, partner, widow, or child of

an impaired, disabled or deceased physician who could exhibit a need for additional financial resources in acquiring a post secondary education or vocational training. **Criteria:** Recipient is selected based on financial need.

Funds Avail.: No specific amount. **To Apply:** Applicants must submit a completed application form available on the website; a brief statement (300 words or less) on the applicant's professional or vocational goals, explanation of financial situation, amount of funding needed and purpose and list of financial aid or scholarships applicant receives or will be receiving; verification of financial need: CSS Financial Aid Profile, or FAFSA and applicant's Federal Income Tax returns (If applicant is a child of a physician, also include copies of both parents' Federal Income Tax Returns); proof of physician's inability to practice or a death certificate; and the applicant's relevant high school, university, or course of study transcripts. **Deadline:** April 15. **Contact:** Angela Poblocki at the above address.

1024 ■ American Psychiatric Publishing Inc. (APPI)
1000 Wilson Blvd., Ste. 1825
Arlington, VA 22209-3924
Ph: (703) 907-7322
Fax: (703) 907-1091
Free: 800-368-5777
E-mail: appi@psych.org
URL: www.appi.org

1025 ■ Minority Medical Student Fellowships in HIV Psychiatry *(Undergraduate/Fellowship)*

Purpose: To support minority medical students who have primary interest in services related to HIV/AIDS and substance abuse and its relationship to the mental health or psychological well-being of ethnic minorities. **Focus:** Psychology. **Qualif.:** Applicants must be minority medical students. **Criteria:** Preference will be given to those who meet the criteria.

Funds Avail.: No specific amount. **To Apply:** Applicants must submit a completed application form. **Deadline:** March 31. **Contact:** More information is available from Carol Svoboda at 703-907-8642 or csvoboda@psych.org; or Diane Pennessi at 703-907-8668 or dpennessi@psych.org.

1026 ■ American Psychoanalytic Association (APSAA)
309 E 49th St.
New York, NY 10017-1601
Ph: (212) 752-0450
Fax: (212) 593-0571
E-mail: info@apsa.org
URL: www.apsa.org

1027 ■ American Psychoanalytic Association Fellowships *(Doctorate, Postdoctorate, Professional development/Fellowship)*

Purpose: To encourage interest and involvement in psychoanalysis among future leaders, researchers and educators of mental health and academia. **Focus:** Psychology. **Qualif.:** Applicants must be nominated by their Department Chairs or Program Directors. Psychiatry applicants must be full-time general or child psychiatry residents, PGY-2 or higher, or fellows or psychiatrists who have

Awards are arranged alphabetically below their administering organizations

become board eligible within the previous three years. Psychology applicants must hold a half-time position with an academic department or clinical training program; must have training, leadership, or research responsibilities. If predoctorate, must have completed the required coursework and be in or beyond the predoctoral internship. If postdoctorate, must have received the doctoral degree within the past five years. Social worker applicants must have an M.S.W., D.S.W., or PhD received within the past five years; must demonstrate a pursuit of applied psychoanalysis in one or more of the following areas: a part-time appointment with an academic department; a position in training, leadership, public policy, or research; an interdisciplinary position (at least part-time) offering an opportunity to teach through didactics or consultation. D.S.W. and PhD applicants must have begun their advanced degrees within five years of M.S.W. Academic and multidisciplinary applicants must be individuals from academia or non-mental health professions; must demonstrate a serious ongoing interest in psychoanalysis and its relationship to their primary field; must be curious about how psychoanalytic theory is used clinically; must be working in a position that influences others through education, writing, public speaking, research organizational leadership, performance, and/or artistic installations; must be no more than eight years postdoctorate (or its equivalent) or, if predoctorate, be nearing completion of degree. **Criteria:** Recipients will be selected based on demonstrated leadership ability in their discipline; have showed special aptitude in research, teaching, artistic, writing and/or clinical endeavors; have special interest in psychodynamics, psychoanalysis, applied psychoanalysis or community outreach/development.

Funds Avail.: Amount not specified. **To Apply:** Applicants must submit a completed application form and other supporting materials.

1028 ■ American Psychological Association of Graduate Students (APAGS)

750 1st St. NE
Washington, DC 20002-4242
Ph: (202) 336-6014
Fax: (202) 336-5694
Free: 800-374-2721
E-mail: apags@apa.org
URL: www.apa.org/apags

1029 ■ APAGS-CLGBTC Grant Program
(Graduate/Grant)

Purpose: To fund a project that promotes training and educational experiences in Lesbian, Gay, Bisexual and Transgender Concerns practice. **Focus:** Psychology. **Qualif.:** Applicant must be a graduate student member of APAGS; enrolled as a student in good standing at an accredited university; must be in a masters or doctoral program. Undergraduates are not eligible for the scholarships. **Criteria:** Scholarship Selection Committee will review applications based on objective, qualitative and quantitative criteria.

Funds Avail.: $1,000. **To Apply:** Applicants must submit a title page; summary of the proposed project; evaluation; organization profile; appendix. **Deadline:** May 1.

1030 ■ APAGS' Committee on Ethic Minority Affairs (CEMA) Grant Program *(Graduate/Grant)*

Purpose: To promote education and training opportunities for ethnic minorities and enhance the recruitment and reten-

tion efforts for ethnic minority students in psychology. **Focus:** Psychology. **Qualif.:** Applicant must be a graduate student member of APAGS; enrolled as a student in good standing at an accredited university; must be in a masters or doctoral program. Undergraduates are not eligible for the scholarships. **Criteria:** Scholarship Selection Committee will review applications based on objective, qualitative and quantitative criteria.

Funds Avail.: $1,000 for Spring Semester and $1,000 for Fall Semester. **Number Awarded:** 5. **To Apply:** Applicants must submit a title page indicating the name of the program; name and address of the applicant and date submitted; summary of the proposed project; evaluation; organizational profile; appendix. **Deadline:** May 1.

1031 ■ ASPPB Larry J. Bass Jr., PhD. Memorial Scholarship Awards *(Graduate, Undergraduate/Grant)*

Purpose: To provide funds for research on the regulation of psychology. **Focus:** Psychology. **Qualif.:** Applicants must be psychology graduate students or advanced undergraduate psychology majors. **Criteria:** Scholarship Selection Committee will review applications based on objective, qualitative and quantitative criteria.

Funds Avail.: $1,000. **To Apply:** Applicants must submit a curriculum vitae/resume; a recommendation from a professor or advisor who will mentor the research; a written proposal that includes: outline of the desired area of research, description of the proposed methodology and estimate of project timeline. **Deadline:** May 1. **Remarks:** The Scholarship was named after the former president of the Association of State and Provincial Psychology Boards (ASPPB), Larry J. Bass Jr. PhD (1999-2000). **Contact:** Larry J. Bass, Jr., PhD. Memorial Scholarship Award, c/o The ASPPB Foundation, 7177 Halcyon Summit Dr., Montgomery, AL 36117.

1032 ■ Diversity Dissertation Scholarships
(Doctorate/Fellowship)

Purpose: To encourage and support graduate students in their research in the field of psychology concerning diversity issues. **Focus:** Psychology. **Qualif.:** Applicant must be a graduate student member of APAGS; enrolled as a student in good standing at an accredited university; must be in a doctoral program. **Criteria:** Recipient is selected based on the relevance of the study to diversity.

Funds Avail.: $1,500. Funds must be used to support proposed research. **To Apply:** Applicants must submit a cover letter that indicates the name of the nominee and the scholarship being applied for; graduate school affiliation; dissertation chair, current address, phone number and email address; a letter of recommendation supporting the application; an abbreviated dissertation proposal; and a curriculum vitae. **Deadline:** May 1.

1033 ■ Nancy B. Forest and L. Michael Honaker Master's Scholarships for Research *(Doctorate, Graduate/Scholarship)*

Purpose: To fund a research in the field of Psychology at the Masters level. **Focus:** Psychology. **Qualif.:** Applicant must be a graduate student member of APAGS; enrolled as a student in good standing at an accredited university; must be in a masters or doctoral program. Undergraduates are not eligible for the scholarships. **Criteria:** Scholarship Selection Committee will review applications based on objective, qualitative and quantitative criteria.

Awards are arranged alphabetically below their administering organizations

Funds Avail.: $1,500. **To Apply:** Applicants must submit a cover letter that indicates the name of the scholarship; a curriculum vitae; a thesis proposal; and two letters of recommendation that supports the application. **Deadline:** May 1. **Remarks:** The scholarship is named in honor of APA staff members Nancy B. Forest and L. Michael Honaker, PhD for their support of APAGS over the years.

1034 ■ Scott Mesh Honorary Scholarships for Research in Psychology (Graduate/Fellowship)

Purpose: To support dissertation research related to the field of psychology. **Focus:** Psychology. **Qualif.:** Applicant must be a graduate student member of APAGS; enrolled as a student in good standing at an accredited university; must be in a masters or doctoral program. Undergraduates are not eligible for the scholarships. **Criteria:** Scholarship Selection Committee will review applications based on objective, qualitative and quantitative criteria.

Funds Avail.: $1,500. **To Apply:** Applicants must submit a cover letter that indicates the name of the scholarship; a curriculum vitae; a dissertation proposal; and two letters of recommendation (not to exceed two pages) that supports the application. **Deadline:** May 1. **Remarks:** The scholarship is named after Scott Mesh, one of the founding co-chairs of APAGS in 1988.

1035 ■ David Pilon Scholarships for Training in Professional Psychology (Doctorate, Graduate/Scholarship)

Purpose: To promote training and educational experiences in professional practice. **Focus:** Psychology. **Qualif.:** Applicant must be a graduate student member of APAGS; must be enrolled as a student in good standing at an accredited university; must be in a masters or doctoral program. Undergraduates are not eligible for the scholarships. **Criteria:** Scholarship Selection Committee will review applications based on objective, qualitative and quantitative criteria.

Funds Avail.: $1,500. **To Apply:** Applicants must submit a cover letter that indicates the name of the scholarship; a curriculum vitae; a statement (500 words) addressing the applicant's short and long-term goals; a formal proposal; and two letters of recommendation that supports the application. **Deadline:** May 1. **Remarks:** Established in honor of David Pilon, one of the founding co-chairs of APAGS in 1988.

1036 ■ American Psychological Foundation (APF)

750 First St. NE
Washington, DC 20002-4242
Ph: (202) 336-5843
Fax: (202) 336-5812
E-mail: foundation@apa.org
URL: www.apa.org/apf

1037 ■ APF/COGDOP Graduate Research Scholarships (Doctorate, Graduate/Scholarship)

Purpose: To help graduate students further their education in psychology. **Focus:** Psychology. **Qualif.:** Applicant must be a graduate student enrolled in an interim master's program or doctoral program. **Criteria:** Selection is based on the research proposal and applicant's background.

Funds Avail.: $5,000, $3,000, $2,000 and $1,000. **Number Awarded:** 13. **To Apply:** Applicants must submit a com-

pleted application form along with a letter of recommendation (maximum of 3 pages) from the student's graduate research advisor with original signature; a brief outline (maximum of 3 pages) of the student's thesis or dissertation research project (even if in progress); a curriculum vitae and a transcript (unofficial/student copy is acceptable) of all graduate coursework completed. Each application must include five collated sets and submitted in one complete package. **Deadline:** June 30. **Contact:** science@apa.org.

1038 ■ Benton-Meier Neuropsychology Scholarships (Graduate/Scholarship)

Purpose: To financially support graduate students in Neuropsychology. **Focus:** Psychology. **Qualif.:** Applicant must be a graduate student in psychology enrolled full time and in good standing at an accredited university. **Criteria:** Selection is based on the submitted proposal and application materials.

Funds Avail.: $2,500. **Number Awarded:** 2. **To Apply:** Applicants must submit a proposal together with a letter of recommendation from a faculty advisor and a curriculum vitae online. **Deadline:** June 1. **Contact:** Emily Leary at eleary@apa.org.

1039 ■ Violet and Cyril Franks Scholarships (Graduate/Scholarship)

Purpose: To support graduate-level scholarly projects that use a psychological perspective to help understand and reduce stigma associated with mental illness. **Focus:** Psychology. **Qualif.:** Applicant must be a graduate student in psychology enrolled full time and in good standing at an accredited university. **Criteria:** Selection is based on the submitted proposal and application materials.

Funds Avail.: $5,000. **To Apply:** Applicants must submit a proposal together with a letter of recommendation from a faculty advisor and a curriculum vitae online. **Deadline:** May 15. **Contact:** Kim Palmer Rowsome, Program Officer, at krowsome@apa.org.

1040 ■ Elizabeth Munsterberg Koppitz Child Psychology Graduate Fellowships (Graduate/Fellowship)

Purpose: To promote the advancement of knowledge and learning in the field of child psychology. **Focus:** Psychology. **Qualif.:** Applicant must have achieved doctoral candidacy. Students may apply before having passed the qualifying exams but proof of having advanced to doctoral candidacy will be required before funds are released. **Criteria:** Selection is based on the submitted proposal and application materials.

Funds Avail.: $25,000 plus $3,000 travel stipend. Runners-up will receive $5,000 travel stipend. **Number Awarded:** 4 and 2 runners-up. **To Apply:** Applicants must submit a proposal (maximum of 7 pages, 1 inch margins, no smaller than 11 pt. font) together with a curriculum vitae, two recommendations (one from a graduate advisor and the other from the department chair or Director of Graduate Studies), and a copy of the IRB approval online. **Deadline:** November 15. **Contact:** Kim Palmer Rowsome, Program Officer, at krowsome@apa.org.

1041 ■ Esther Katz Rosen Fellowships (Graduate/Fellowship)

Purpose: To support activities related to the psychological understanding of gifted and talented children and adoles-

Awards are arranged alphabetically below their administering organizations

cents. **Focus:** Psychology. **Qualif.:** Applicant must be a graduate student who has achieved doctoral candidacy, and in good academic standing at a university in the U.S. or Canada. Students may apply before having passed the qualifying exams but proof of having advanced to doctoral candidacy will be required before funds are released. **Criteria:** Selection is based on the submitted proposal and application materials.

Funds Avail.: $25,000. **Number Awarded:** 1. **To Apply:** Applicants must submit a proposal (maximum of 10 pages, with 1 inch margins, no smaller than 11 pt. font) along with a curriculum vitae, two recommendations (one from a graduate advisor and the other from the department chair or Director of Graduate Studies) and a copy of the IRB approval (if applicable) online. **Deadline:** March 1. **Contact:** Kim Palmer Rowsome, Program Officer, at krowsome@apa.org.

1042 ■ American Psychology-Law Society (AP-LS)

PO Box 11488
Southport, NC 28461-3936
Ph: (910) 933-4018
Fax: (910) 933-4018
Free: 800-255-7792
E-mail: apls@ec.rr.com
URL: www.ap-ls.org

1043 ■ American Psychology-Law Society Dissertation Awards *(Graduate/Award)*

Purpose: To promote the interdisciplinary study of psychology and law. **Focus:** Psychology; Law. **Qualif.:** Applicants must be members of AP-LS and must defend their dissertation. **Criteria:** Selection will be based on the committee's criteria.

Funds Avail.: No specific amount. **To Apply:** Applicants must attach and submit the following items in Word or PDF format to aplsdissertations@gmail.com: the dissertation which was submitted to the student's university; the dissertation with all author, advisor and school identifying information removed; and a letter of support from the dissertation advisor. **Deadline:** December 31. **Contact:** Rachel Kalbeitzer, Chair of the Dissertation Awards Committee, rkalbeitzer@gmail.com.

1044 ■ American Psychology-Law Society Early Career Professional Grants-In-Aid *(Professional development/Grant)*

Purpose: To support AP-LS members who are ECPs in conducting research related to psychology and law. **Focus:** Psychology; Law. **Qualif.:** Applicants must be Early Career professionals, defined by APA as those within seven years of receiving their last degree. **Criteria:** Preference will be given to those applicants who have not ever received an AP-LS ECP Grant-In-Aid.

Funds Avail.: $5,000. **To Apply:** Applicants must submit a cover sheet including all contact information for the primary investigator and the title of the proposal. The cover letter should include the status of the human subject review for the project; an abstract of 150-word or less describing the proposed research; a proposed budget with justifications; a curriculum vitae; a list of at least five suggested outside reviewers for the project with expertise in the area of the proposal. External reviewer suggestions must exclude those with a potential conflict of interest; a five-page

maximum project description including the following: statement of the problem. A clear statement of the research problem and the significance of the problem to psychology and law; relation of the problem to the state of the field. A concise overview of the relevant empirical literature, theoretical background and/or law related to the project; project method. A detailed description of the methodology and analytical strategy to be employed, including an outline for expected completion of the project; anticipated contribution. A statement of the significance of the project within the field of psychology and law. **Deadline:** December 15. **Contact:** Lora Levett, llevett@ufl.edu.

1045 ■ American Psychology-Law Society Student Grants-In-Aid *(Graduate/Grant)*

Purpose: To support empirical graduate research that addresses psycholegal issues. **Focus:** Psychology; Law. **Qualif.:** Applicants must be graduate students who are student affiliate members of AP-LS. **Criteria:** Selection will be based on the committee's criteria.

Funds Avail.: $750. **To Apply:** Applicants must submit a maximum of 1500-word proposal, excluding references, in a Word or PDF format that includes the following: a cover sheet indicating the title of the project, name, address, phone number and email address of the investigator; an abstract of 100 words or less summarizing the project; purpose, theoretical rationale and significance of the project; procedure to be employed; specific amount requested, including a detailed budget; references. Applicants should include a discussion of the feasibility of the research. Applicants must submit a proof that IRB approval has been obtained for the project and the appropriate tax form W-9 for U.S. citizens and W-8BEN for international students. **Deadline:** September 30 and January 31. **Contact:** Dr. Steven Ross, sjross2@uw.edu.

1046 ■ Saleem Shah Early Career Development Awards *(Doctorate/Award)*

Purpose: To recognize early career excellence and contributions to the field of psychology and law. **Focus:** Psychology; Law. **Qualif.:** Applicants must have received the doctoral degree or the law degree, whichever comes later, if both have been earned within the last six years. **Criteria:** Selection will be based on the committee's criteria.

Funds Avail.: A total of $2,000. **To Apply:** Nominators must send a letter detailing the nominee's contributions to psychology and law, copy of the nominee's vita. Self-nominations will not be considered. **Deadline:** December 1. **Remarks:** Sponsored by the American Psychology-Law Society Division 41 and the American Academy of Forensic Psychology. **Contact:** Nominations should be sent to Patty Griffin at pgriffin@navpoint.com.

1047 ■ American Public Power Association (APPA)

1875 Connecticut Ave. NW, Ste. 1200
Washington, DC 20009-5715
Ph: (202) 467-2900
Fax: (202) 467-2910
Free: 800-515-2772
E-mail: info@PublicPower.org
URL: www.appanet.org

1048 ■ DEED Student Research Grant/Internships *(Graduate, Undergraduate/Grant)*

Purpose: To promote the involvement of students in studying energy-related disciplines in the public power industry;

Awards are arranged alphabetically below their administering organizations

and to provide host utilities with technical assistance. **Focus:** Energy-related areas. **Qualif.:** Applicants must be graduate or undergraduate students studying in energy-related disciplines from accredited colleges or universities; must be attending school in a country with at least one sponsor DEED member. **Criteria:** Selection of applicants will be based on the scholarship criteria: (a) Broad applicability of benefits to public power systems; (b) Close involvement of the host utility in project monitoring, sponsorship and guidance; (c) Major in an academic field related to the electric power or energy service industries; (d) Superior academic performance; (e) Special consideration to utilities who have not previously sponsored a student and to small utilities; (f) Educational and learning opportunities for student(s) in public power and utility field.

Funds Avail.: $4,000. **Number Awarded:** 10. **To Apply:** Applicants must complete the information on the DEED Student Research Grant/Internship application cover sheet available online; must submit the original signature of the student, utility authority and school official as well as other information requested in required signature section; must have a single transcript of the student's academic record. **Deadline:** February 15 and October 1. **Contact:** Application form and other requirements must be sent to DEED Administrator, American Public Power Association, 1875 Connecticut Ave. NW, Ste. 1200, Washington, DC 20009-5715, Phone: 202-467-2960, 202-467-2994 or e-mail deed@appanet.org.

1049 ■ American Public Transportation Foundation (APFT)

1666 K St. NW, Ste. 1100
Washington, DC 20006
Ph: (202) 496-4868
Fax: (202) 496-4323
URL: www.aptfd.org

1050 ■ Richard J. Bouchard Scholarships
(Graduate, Undergraduate/Scholarship)

Purpose: To increase and retain the number of young professionals entering the public transportation field as a career in order to sustain growth and improvement throughout the industry. **Focus:** Transportation. **Qualif.:** Applicant must be enrolled in a fully accredited institution; have and maintain at least a 3.0 GPA (B) in course work that is relevant to the industry or required of a degree program; be either employed by or demonstrate a strong interest in entering the public transportation industry; be a college sophomore (30 hours or more satisfactorily completed), junior, senior, or seeking an advanced degree. **Criteria:** Selection is based on demonstrated interest in the public transportation industry as a career, academic achievement, essay content and quality, need for financial assistance and involvement in extracurricular citizenship and leadership activities.

Funds Avail.: No specific amount. **Number Awarded:** 1. **To Apply:** Applicants must submit a completed application form along with a description of internship program or supplemental educational program from nominating/ sponsoring organization for nominee; a typed, double-spaced essay of 1,000 words or less on "In what segment of the public transportation industry will you make a career and why?"; three letters of recommendation; a copy of completed Free Application for Student Aid Form (FAFSA); official college transcript; verification of enrollment; and a copy of the fee schedule from the college/university for the

academic year. **Deadline:** June 15. **Remarks:** The scholarship is awarded to the applicant dedicated to a career in public transportation planning and development. **Contact:** Yvette E. Conley at yconley@apta.com.

1051 ■ Parsons Brinckerhoff-Jim Lammie Scholarships *(Graduate, Undergraduate/ Scholarship)*

Purpose: To increase and retain the number of young professionals entering the public transportation field as a career in order to sustain growth and improvement throughout the industry. **Focus:** Transportation. **Qualif.:** Applicant must be enrolled in a fully accredited institution; have and maintain at least a 3.0 GPA (B) in course work that is relevant to the industry or required of a degree program; be either employed by or demonstrate a strong interest in entering the public transportation industry; be a college sophomore (30 hours or more satisfactorily completed), junior, senior, or seeking an advanced degree. **Criteria:** Selection is based on demonstrated interest in the public transportation industry as a career, academic achievement, essay content and quality, need for financial assistance and involvement in extracurricular citizenship and leadership activities.

Funds Avail.: No specific amount. **Number Awarded:** 1. **To Apply:** Applicants must submit a completed application form along with a description of internship program or supplemental educational program from nominating/ sponsoring organization for nominee; a typed, double-spaced essay of 1,000 words or less on "In what segment of the public transportation industry will you make a career and why?"; three letters of recommendation; a copy of completed Free Application for Student Aid Form (FAFSA); official college transcript; verification of enrollment; and a copy of the fee schedule from the college/university for the academic year. **Remarks:** The scholarship is awarded to the applicant dedicated to a public transportation engineering career. **Contact:** Yvette E. Conley at yconley@ apta.com.

1052 ■ Florida Public Transportation Association Scholarships (FPTA) *(Graduate, Undergraduate/Scholarship)*

Purpose: To increase and retain the number of young professionals entering the public transportation field as a career in order to sustain growth and improvement throughout the industry. **Focus:** Transportation. **Qualif.:** Applicant must be enrolled in a fully accredited institution; have and maintain at least a 3.0 GPA (B) in course work that is relevant to the industry or required of a degree program; be either employed by or demonstrate a strong interest in entering the public transportation industry; be a college sophomore (30 hours or more satisfactorily completed), junior, senior, or seeking an advanced degree. **Criteria:** Selection is based on demonstrated interest in the public transportation industry as a career, academic achievement, essay content and quality, need for financial assistance and involvement in extracurricular citizenship and leadership activities.

Funds Avail.: No specific amount. **Number Awarded:** 1. **To Apply:** Applicants must submit a completed application form along with a description of internship program or supplemental educational program from nominating/ sponsoring organization for nominee; a typed, double-spaced essay of 1,000 words or less on "In what segment of the public transportation industry will you make a career and why?"; three letters of recommendation; a copy of

Awards are arranged alphabetically below their administering organizations

completed Free Application for Student Aid Form (FAFSA); official college transcript; verification of enrollment; and a copy of the fee schedule from the college/university for the academic year. **Remarks:** The scholarship is awarded to an applicant from the state of Florida, and sponsored by a Florida public transit system or the FPTA. **Contact:** Yvette E. Conley at yconley@apta.com.

1053 ■ Jack R. Gilstrap Scholarships *(Graduate, Undergraduate/Scholarship)*

Purpose: To increase and retain the number of young professionals entering the public transportation field as a career in order to sustain growth and improvement throughout the industry. **Focus:** Transportation. **Qualif.:** Applicant must be enrolled in a fully accredited institution; have and maintain at least a 3.0 GPA (B) in course work that is relevant to the industry or required of a degree program; be either employed by or demonstrate a strong interest in entering the public transportation industry; be a college sophomore (30 hours or more satisfactorily completed), junior, senior, or seeking an advanced degree. **Criteria:** Selection is based on demonstrated interest in the public transportation industry as a career, academic achievement, essay content and quality, need for financial assistance and involvement in extracurricular citizenship and leadership activities.

Funds Avail.: No specific amount. **Number Awarded:** 1. **To Apply:** Applicants must submit a completed application form along with a description of internship program or supplemental educational program from nominating/sponsoring organization for nominee; a typed, double-spaced essay of 1,000 words or less on "In what segment of the public transportation industry will you make a career and why?"; three letters of recommendation; a copy of completed Free Application for Student Aid Form (FAFSA); official college transcript; verification of enrollment; and a copy of the fee schedule from the college/university for the academic year. **Remarks:** The scholarship is awarded to the applicant receiving the highest overall score. **Contact:** Yvette E. Conley at yconley@apta.com.

1054 ■ Louis T. Klauder Scholarships *(Graduate, Undergraduate/Scholarship)*

Purpose: To increase and retain the number of young professionals entering the public transportation field as a career in order to sustain growth and improvement throughout the industry. **Focus:** Transportation; Electrical engineering; Mechanical engineering. **Qualif.:** Applicant must be enrolled in a fully accredited institution; have and maintain at least a 3.0 GPA (B) in course work that is relevant to the industry or required of a degree program; be either employed by or demonstrate a strong interest in entering the public transportation industry; be a college sophomore (30 hours or more satisfactorily completed), junior, senior, or seeking an advanced degrees. **Criteria:** Selection is based on demonstrated interest in the public transportation industry as a career, academic achievement, essay content and quality, need for financial assistance and involvement in extracurricular citizenship and leadership activities.

Funds Avail.: No specific amount. **Number Awarded:** 1. **To Apply:** Applicants must submit a completed application form along with a description of internship program or supplemental educational program from nominating/sponsoring organization for nominee; a typed, double-spaced essay of 1,000 words or less on "In what segment of the public transportation industry will you make a career and why?"; three letters of recommendation; a copy of completed Free Application for Student Aid Form (FAFSA);

official college transcript; verification of enrollment; and a copy of the fee schedule from the college/university for the academic year. **Remarks:** The scholarship is awarded to the applicant dedicated to a career in the rail transit industry as an electrical or mechanical engineer. **Contact:** Yvette E. Conley at yconley@apta.com.

1055 ■ Reba Malone Scholarships *(Graduate, Undergraduate/Scholarship)*

Purpose: To increase and retain the number of young professionals entering the public transportation field as a career in order to sustain growth and improvement throughout the industry. **Focus:** Transportation; Marketing and distribution. **Qualif.:** Applicant must be enrolled in a fully accredited institution; have and maintain at least a 3.0 GPA (B) in course work that is relevant to the industry or required of a degree program; be either employed by or demonstrate a strong interest in entering the public transportation industry; be a college sophomore (30 hours or more satisfactorily completed), junior, senior, or seeking an advanced degree. **Criteria:** Selection is based on demonstrated interest in the public transportation industry as a career, academic achievement, essay content and quality, need for financial assistance and involvement in extracurricular citizenship and leadership activities.

Funds Avail.: No specific amount. **Number Awarded:** 1. **To Apply:** Applicants must submit a completed application form along with a description of internship program or supplemental educational program from nominating/sponsoring organization for nominee; a typed, double-spaced essay of 1,000 words or less on "In what segment of the public transportation industry will you make a career and why?"; three letters of recommendation; a copy of completed Free Application for Student Aid Form (FAFSA); official college transcript; verification of enrollment; and a copy of the fee schedule from the college/university for the academic year. **Remarks:** The scholarship is awarded to the applicant dedicated to a career in marketing/communications. **Contact:** Yvette E. Conley at yconley@apta.com.

1056 ■ Dan M. Reichard, Jr. Scholarships *(Graduate, Undergraduate/Scholarship)*

Purpose: To increase and retain the number of young professionals entering the public transportation field as a career in order to sustain growth and improvement throughout the industry. **Focus:** Transportation; Business administration. **Qualif.:** Applicant must be enrolled in a fully accredited institution; have and maintain at least a 3.0 GPA (B) in course work that is relevant to the industry or required of a degree program; be either employed by or demonstrate a strong interest in entering the public transportation industry; be a college sophomore (30 hours or more satisfactorily completed), junior, senior, or seeking an advanced degree. **Criteria:** Selection is based on demonstrated interest in the public transportation industry as a career, academic achievement, essay content and quality, need for financial assistance and involvement in extracurricular citizenship and leadership activities.

Funds Avail.: No specific amount. **Number Awarded:** 1. **To Apply:** Applicants must submit a completed application form along with a description of internship program or supplemental educational program from nominating/sponsoring organization for nominee; a typed, double-spaced essay of 1,000 words or less on "In what segment of the public transportation industry will you make a career and why?"; three letters of recommendation; a copy of completed Free Application for Student Aid Form (FAFSA);

Awards are arranged alphabetically below their administering organizations

official college transcript; verification of enrollment; and a copy of the fee schedule from the college/university for the academic year. **Remarks:** The scholarship is awarded to the applicant dedicated to a career in the business administration/management area of the transit industry. **Contact:** Yvette E. Conley at yconley@apta.com.

1057 ■ Dr. George M. Smerk Scholarships
(Graduate, Undergraduate/Scholarship)

Purpose: To increase and retain the number of young professionals entering the public transportation field as a career in order to sustain growth and improvement throughout the industry. **Focus:** Transportation. **Qualif.:** Applicant must be enrolled in a fully accredited institution; have and maintain at least a 3.0 GPA (B) in course work that is relevant to the industry or required of a degree program; be either employed by or demonstrate a strong interest in entering the public transportation industry; be a college sophomore (30 hours or more satisfactorily completed), junior, senior, or seeking an advanced degree. **Criteria:** Selection is based on demonstrated interest in the public transportation industry as a career, academic achievement, essay content and quality, need for financial assistance and involvement in extracurricular citizenship and leadership activities.

Funds Avail.: No specific amount. **Number Awarded:** 1. **To Apply:** Applicants must submit a completed application form along with a description of internship program or supplemental educational program from nominating/sponsoring organization for nominee; a typed, double-spaced essay of 1,000 words or less on "In what segment of the public transportation industry will you make a career and why?"; three letters of recommendation; a copy of completed Free Application for Student Aid Form (FAFSA); official college transcript; verification of enrollment; and a copy of the fee schedule from the college/university for the academic year. **Remarks:** The scholarship is awarded to the applicant dedicated to a career in public transit management. **Contact:** Yvette E. Conley at yconley@apta.com.

1058 ■ American Public Works Association (APWA)
2345 Grand Blvd., Ste. 700
Kansas City, MO 64108-2625
Ph: (816) 472-6100
Fax: (816) 472-1610
Free: 800-848-APWA
URL: www.apwa.net

1059 ■ APWA Engineering Scholarships
(Undergraduate/Scholarship)

Purpose: To provide financial assistance for the students taking up civil engineering. **Focus:** Civil engineering. **Qualif.:** Applicants must be students pursuing a career in civil engineering or a related field within the Antelope Valley, Santa Clarita, and Victor Valley areas. **Criteria:** Applicants are evaluated based on their GPA and financial need.

Funds Avail.: $500-$1,500. **To Apply:** Applicants must submit all the required application information. **Deadline:** March 15. **Contact:** Brian Glidden, 42138 10th St. West, Lancaster, CA 93534.

1060 ■ American Public Works Association-Nevada (APWA)
c/o Tom Brady, III, Pres.
2250 Las Vegas Blvd. N
Las Vegas, NV 89030
Ph: (702) 633-1227
E-mail: thomasb@cityofnorthlasvegas.com
URL: nevada.apwa.net

1061 ■ Michael Koizumi APWA Scholarships
(Undergraduate/Scholarship)

Purpose: To promote education in the field of public works, public administration or related field. **Focus:** Public administration. **Qualif.:** Applicant must be a Nevada resident; must plan to enroll in a course of study leading to a career in the field of public works, public administration or a related private enterprise (e.g. business, architecture, science, engineering, etc.); and must be an entering their freshman year or currently enrolled in college. **Criteria:** Awards are given based on nominations by APWA members; financial need-income, family size; desire; achievements; grades. Preference is for students attending a Nevada school.

Funds Avail.: $1000 and $2000. **Number Awarded:** 4. **To Apply:** Applicants must submit completed application form together with copy of transcripts, reference, list of experience, a written statement on financial status, and career objectives. **Deadline:** April 6. **Contact:** Tom Brady, City of North Las Vegas, 2288 Civic Center Drive North Las Vegas, NV 89030, P: 702-633-1227, F: 702-633-2758.

1062 ■ American Quarter Horse Youth Association (AQHYA)
1600 Quarter Horse Dr.
Amarillo, TX 79104-3406
Ph: (806) 376-4811
Fax: (806) 349-6411
URL: www.aqha.com

1063 ■ American Quarter Horse Foundation Scholarships *(Undergraduate/Scholarship)*

Purpose: To develop and educate the future professionals. **Focus:** Education; Nursing; Journalism; Veterinary science and medicine. **Qualif.:** Applicant must be enrolled in college specializing degree programs such as education, nursing, journalism, veterinary and racing. **Criteria:** Applicant will be selected based on financial need, academic merit, equine involvement and civic activities.

Funds Avail.: No specific amount. **To Apply:** Applicant must fill out the application form and submit proof that he/she is currently enrolled in a college or university. **Deadline:** December 1. **Contact:** For more information, contact the Foundation at 806-378-5029 or e-mail at foundation@aqha.org.

1064 ■ American Quilt Study Group (AQSG)
1610 L St.
Lincoln, NE 68508-2509
Ph: (402) 477-1181
Fax: (402) 477-1181
E-mail: aqsg2@americanquiltstudygroup.org
URL: www.americanquiltstudygroup.org

1065 ■ Lucy Hilty Research Grants *(All/Grant)*

Purpose: To provide support for research in the industry of quilting. **Focus:** Art. **Qualif.:** Applicants can be individuals or group affiliated with quilt-related studies. **Criteria:** Grantees will be selected according to the quality and impact of

Awards are arranged alphabetically below their administering organizations

their projects; ability to complete the project; compatibility of the projects for the goal of AQSG; and how the projects will contribute to the quilting industry.

Funds Avail.: $2,000. **To Apply:** Application form is available at the website. Proposal should be limited to a cover letter and the application; include completed proposal description; must state the qualifications of the researcher; include letters of support from cooperating institutions or individuals; and a line-item budget for the amount of funding required. **Deadline:** February 1.

1066 ■ American Radio Relay League Foundation (ARRLF)

225 Main St.
Newington, CT 06111
Ph: (860) 594-0200
Fax: (860) 594-0259
E-mail: foundation@arrl.org
URL: www.arrlf.org

1067 ■ American Radio Relay League Louisiana Memorial Scholarships
(Undergraduate/Scholarship)

Purpose: To support the education of students holding a valid FCC-granted Amateur Radio license for post-secondary education. **Focus:** Radio and television. **Qualif.:** Applicant must hold an FCC amateur radio license, and be a Louisiana resident or attending a four-year college/university in Louisiana; must have a 3.0 GPA. **Criteria:** Award is given based on the submitted materials.

Funds Avail.: $750. **Number Awarded:** 1. **To Apply:** Applicants must submit a completed scholarship application form along with a recent high school (or equivalent) or college transcript. **Deadline:** February 1.

1068 ■ Earl I. Anderson Scholarships
(Undergraduate/Scholarship)

Purpose: To support the education of students holding a valid FCC-granted Amateur Radio license for post-secondary education. **Focus:** Radio and television. **Qualif.:** Applicant must hold an FCC amateur radio license; be a resident of, or attending classes in Illinois, Indiana, Michigan, or Florida; and must be an ARRL member. **Criteria:** Awards are given based on the submitted materials.

Funds Avail.: $1,250. **Number Awarded:** 3. **To Apply:** Applicant must submit a completed scholarship application form along with a recent high school (or equivalent) or college transcript. **Deadline:** February 1.

1069 ■ ARRL Foundation General Fund Scholarships *(Undergraduate/Scholarship)*

Purpose: To support the education of students holding a valid FCC-granted Amateur Radio license for post-secondary education. **Focus:** Radio and television. **Qualif.:** Applicant must hold an FCC amateur radio license. **Criteria:** Awards are given based on the submitted materials.

Funds Avail.: $2,000. **Number Awarded:** Multiple. **To Apply:** Applicants must submit a completed scholarship application form along with a recent high school (or equivalent) or college transcript. **Deadline:** February 1.

1070 ■ ARRLF Mississippi Scholarships
(Undergraduate/Scholarship)

Purpose: To support the education of students holding a valid FCC-granted Amateur Radio license for post-

secondary education. **Focus:** Radio and television; Electronics; Communications. **Qualif.:** Applicant must hold an FCC amateur radio license; be a Mississippi resident; be studying in baccalaureate or higher courses of study in electronics, communications or related fields; and be under 30 years of age. **Criteria:** Award is given based on the submitted materials.

Funds Avail.: $500. **Number Awarded:** 1. **To Apply:** Applicant must submit a completed scholarship application form along with a recent high school (or equivalent) or college transcript. **Deadline:** February 1.

1071 ■ Richard W. Bendicksen Memorial Scholarships *(Undergraduate/Scholarship)*

Purpose: To support the education of students holding a valid FCC-granted Amateur Radio license for post-secondary education. **Focus:** Radio and television. **Qualif.:** Applicant must hold an FCC amateur radio license and attending a four-year college/university. **Criteria:** Award is given based on the submitted materials.

Funds Avail.: $2,000. **Number Awarded:** 1. **To Apply:** Applicant must submit a completed scholarship application form along with a recent high school (or equivalent) or college transcript. **Deadline:** February 1.

1072 ■ William Bennett W7PHO Memorial Scholarships *(Undergraduate/Scholarship)*

Purpose: To support the education of students holding a valid FCC-granted Amateur Radio license for post-secondary education. **Focus:** Radio and television. **Qualif.:** Applicant must hold an FCC amateur radio license; be a Northwest, Pacific or Southwest Division resident; be enrolled in a four-year college/university; and have a GPA of 3.0 or better for an ongoing course of study. **Criteria:** Award is given based on submitted materials.

Funds Avail.: $500. **Number Awarded:** 1. **To Apply:** Applicant must submit a completed scholarship application form along with a recent high school (or equivalent) or college transcript. **Deadline:** February 1.

1073 ■ Henry Broughton, K2AE Memorial Scholarships *(Undergraduate/Scholarship)*

Purpose: To support the education of students holding a valid FCC-granted Amateur Radio license for post-secondary education. **Focus:** Radio and television; Engineering; Science. **Qualif.:** Applicant must hold an FCC amateur radio license; reside within 70 miles of Schenectady NY; studying in baccalaureate or higher courses of study in engineering, sciences or a similar field in an accredited four-year college/university. **Criteria:** Award is given based on the submitted materials.

Funds Avail.: $1,000. **Number Awarded:** 1. **To Apply:** Applicant must submit a completed scholarship application form along with a recent high school (or equivalent) or college transcript. **Deadline:** February 1.

1074 ■ Mary Lou Brown Scholarships
(Undergraduate/Scholarship)

Purpose: To support the education of students holding a valid FCC-granted Amateur Radio license for post-secondary education. **Focus:** Radio and television. **Qualif.:** Applicant must hold an FCC amateur radio license; be a resident of ARRL Northwest Division (AK, ID, MT, OR, WA); studying baccalaureate or higher courses; and have a GPA of 3.0 or higher. **Criteria:** Awards are given based on the submitted materials. Preference will be given to those ap-

Awards are arranged alphabetically below their administering organizations

plicants who have demonstrated an interest in promoting Amateur Radio Service.

Funds Avail.: $2,500. **To Apply:** Applicant must submit a completed scholarship application form along with a recent high school (or equivalent) or college transcript. **Deadline:** February 1.

1075 ■ L.B. Cebik, W4RNL, and Jean Cebik, N4TZP, Memorial Scholarships (Undergraduate/Scholarship)

Purpose: To support the education of students holding a valid FCC-granted Amateur Radio license for post-secondary education. **Focus:** Radio and television. **Qualif.:** Applicant must hold an FCC amateur radio license; and be attending a four-year college/university. **Criteria:** Award is given based on the submitted materials.

Funds Avail.: $1,000. **Number Awarded:** 1. **To Apply:** Applicant must submit a completed scholarship application form along with a recent high school (or equivalent) or college transcript. **Deadline:** February 1.

1076 ■ Central Arizona DX Association Scholarships (Undergraduate/Scholarship)

Purpose: To support the education of students holding a valid FCC-granted Amateur Radio license for post-secondary education. **Focus:** Radio and television. **Qualif.:** Applicant must hold an FCC amateur radio license; be a resident of Arizona; and have a GPA of 3.2 or above. **Criteria:** Graduating high school students will be considered before current college students.

Funds Avail.: $1,000. **Number Awarded:** 1. **To Apply:** Applicant must submit a completed scholarship application form along with a recent high school (or equivalent) or college transcript. **Deadline:** February 1.

1077 ■ Challenge Met Scholarships (Undergraduate/Scholarship)

Purpose: To support the education of students holding a valid FCC-granted Amateur Radio license for post-secondary education. **Focus:** Radio and television. **Qualif.:** Applicant must hold an FCC amateur radio license; and be attending an accredited two or four-year college technical school or university. **Criteria:** Preference is given to application with documented learning disability (by physician or school) and indications that the applicant is putting forth substantial effort regardless of resulting academic grades.

Funds Avail.: $500. **To Apply:** Applicant must submit a completed scholarship application form along with a recent high school (or equivalent) or college transcript. **Deadline:** February 1.

1078 ■ Chicago FM Club Scholarships (Undergraduate/Scholarship)

Purpose: To support the education of students holding a valid FCC-granted Amateur Radio license for post-secondary education. **Focus:** Radio and television. **Qualif.:** Applicant must hold an FCC amateur radio license; residency in FCC Ninth Call district (IN, IL, WI); be attending a post-secondary course of study at an accredited two or four-year college or trade school; and must be a U.S. citizen or within three months of citizenship. **Criteria:** Awards are given based on the submitted materials.

Funds Avail.: $500. **To Apply:** Applicant must submit a completed scholarship application form along with a recent high school (or equivalent) or college transcript. **Deadline:** February 1.

1079 ■ Tom and Judith Comstock Scholarships (Undergraduate/Scholarship)

Purpose: To support the education of students holding a valid FCC-granted Amateur Radio license for post-secondary education. **Focus:** Radio and television. **Qualif.:** Applicant must hold an FCC amateur radio license; be a resident of Texas or Oklahoma; and be a high school senior accepted at a two or four-year college. **Criteria:** Award is given based on the submitted materials.

Funds Avail.: $2,000. **Number Awarded:** 1. **To Apply:** Applicant must submit a completed scholarship application form along with a recent high school (or equivalent) or college transcript. **Deadline:** February 1.

1080 ■ Irvine W. Cook WA0CGS Scholarships (Undergraduate/Scholarship)

Purpose: To support the education of students holding a valid FCC-granted Amateur Radio license for post-secondary education. **Focus:** Radio and television; Electronics; Communications. **Qualif.:** Applicant must hold an FCC amateur radio license; residency in Kansas; and be studying baccalaureate or higher courses in electronics, communications or a related field. **Criteria:** Award is given based on the submitted materials.

Funds Avail.: $1,000. **Number Awarded:** 1. **To Apply:** Applicant must submit a completed scholarship application form along with a recent high school (or equivalent) or college transcript. **Deadline:** February 1.

1081 ■ Charles Clarke Cordle Memorial Scholarships (Undergraduate/Scholarship)

Purpose: To support the education of students holding a valid FCC-granted Amateur Radio license for post-secondary education. **Focus:** Radio and television; Electronics; Communications. **Qualif.:** Applicant must hold an FCC amateur radio license; be a resident of Georgia or Alabama; have a GPA of 2.5 or higher; and be attending an institution in Georgia or Alabama. **Criteria:** Preference is given to applicant studying electronics, communications or related field.

Funds Avail.: $1,000. **Number Awarded:** 1. **To Apply:** Applicants must submit a completed scholarship application form along with a recent high school (or equivalent) or college transcript. **Deadline:** February 1.

1082 ■ Albuquerque ARC/Toby Cross Scholarships (Undergraduate/Scholarship)

Purpose: To support the education of students holding a valid FCC-granted Amateur Radio license for post-secondary education. **Focus:** Radio and television. **Qualif.:** Applicant must hold an FCC amateur radio license; and be a New Mexico resident. **Criteria:** Award is given based on the submitted materials.

Funds Avail.: $500. **Number Awarded:** 1. **To Apply:** Applicant must submit a completed scholarship application form along with a recent high school (or equivalent) or college transcript; and must provide a (one-page) essay stating the role of Amateur Radio to applicant's life. **Deadline:** February 1.

1083 ■ Dayton Amateur Radio Association Scholarships (Undergraduate/Scholarship)

Purpose: To support the education of students holding a valid FCC-granted Amateur Radio license for post-secondary education. **Focus:** Radio and television. **Qualif.:** Applicant must hold an FCC amateur radio license and be

Awards are arranged alphabetically below their administering organizations

attending an accredited four-year college/university. **Criteria:** Awards are given based on the submitted materials.

Funds Avail.: $1,000. **Number Awarded:** 4. **To Apply:** Applicant must submit a completed scholarship application form along with a recent high school (or equivalent) or college transcript. **Deadline:** February 1.

1084 ■ Charles N. Fisher Memorial Scholarships *(Undergraduate/Scholarship)*

Purpose: To support the education of students holding a valid FCC-granted Amateur Radio license for post-secondary education. **Focus:** Radio and television; Electronics; Communications. **Qualif.:** Applicant must hold an FCC amateur radio license; must be a resident of ARRL Southwestern Division (AZ, Los Angeles, Orange, San Diego, Santa Barbara); studying in electronics, communications or related fields. **Criteria:** Award is given based on the submitted materials.

Funds Avail.: $1,000. **Number Awarded:** 1. **To Apply:** Applicant must submit a completed scholarship application form along with a recent high school (or equivalent) or college transcript. **Deadline:** February 1.

1085 ■ William R. Goldfarb Memorial Scholarships *(Undergraduate/Scholarship)*

Purpose: To support the education of students holding a valid FCC-granted Amateur Radio license for post-secondary education. **Focus:** Radio and television; Business; Computer and information sciences; Medicine; Nursing; Engineering; Science. **Qualif.:** Applicant must hold an FCC amateur radio license; must be studying baccalaureate courses in business-related, computers, medical, nursing, engineering or sciences; be a high school senior; and must demonstrate financial need. **Criteria:** Award is given based on the submitted materials.

Funds Avail.: $10,000. **Number Awarded:** 1. **To Apply:** Applicant must submit a completed scholarship application form along with a recent high school (or equivalent) or college transcript and the Free Application for Federal Student Aid (FAFSA) or Student Aid Report (SAR). **Deadline:** February 1.

1086 ■ American Radio Relay League Scholarships Honoring Barry Goldwater, K7UGA *(Undergraduate/Scholarship)*

Purpose: To support the education of students holding a valid FCC-granted Amateur Radio license for post-secondary education. **Focus:** Radio and television. **Qualif.:** Applicant must hold an FCC amateur radio license. **Criteria:** Award is given based on the submitted materials.

Funds Avail.: $5,000. **Number Awarded:** 1. **To Apply:** Applicant must submit a completed scholarship application form along with a recent high school (or equivalent) or college transcript. **Deadline:** February 1.

1087 ■ Paul and Helen L. Grauer Scholarships *(Undergraduate/Scholarship)*

Purpose: To support the education of students holding a valid FCC-granted Amateur Radio license for post secondary-education. **Focus:** Radio and television; Electronics; Communications. **Qualif.:** Applicant must hold an FCC amateur radio license; be a resident of ARRL Midwest Division (IA, KS, MO, NE); be studying in baccalaureate or higher courses in electronics, communications or related field; and be attending school in the Midwest Division. **Criteria:** Award is given based on the submitted materials.

Funds Avail.: $1,000. **Number Awarded:** 1. **To Apply:** Applicant must submit a completed scholarship application form along with a recent high school (or equivalent) or college transcript. **Deadline:** February 1.

1088 ■ K2TEO Martin J. Green, Sr. Memorial Scholarships *(Undergraduate/Scholarship)*

Purpose: To support the education of students holding a valid FCC-granted Amateur Radio license for post-secondary education. **Focus:** Radio and television. **Qualif.:** Applicant must hold an FCC amateur radio license. **Criteria:** Preference is given to a student from a "ham family".

Funds Avail.: $1,000. **Number Awarded:** 1. **To Apply:** Applicant must submit a completed scholarship application form along with a recent high school (or equivalent) or college transcript. **Deadline:** February 1.

1089 ■ Perry F. Hadlock Memorial Scholarships *(Undergraduate/Scholarship)*

Purpose: To support the education of students holding a valid FCC-granted Amateur Radio license for post-secondary education. **Focus:** Radio and television; Technology; Engineering, Electrical. **Qualif.:** Applicant must hold an FCC amateur radio license; must be studying in baccalaureate or higher courses in a technology-related field; preference to electrical and electronics engineering. **Criteria:** Preference is given to applicant studying at Clarkson University, Potsdam NY, or any Atlantic or Hudson Division.

Funds Avail.: $2,000. **Number Awarded:** 1. **To Apply:** Applicant must submit a completed scholarship application form along with a recent high school (or equivalent) or college transcript. **Deadline:** February 1.

1090 ■ Albert H. Hix, W8AH Memorial Scholarships *(Undergraduate/Scholarship)*

Purpose: To support the education of students holding a valid FCC-granted Amateur Radio license for post-secondary education. **Focus:** Radio and television. **Qualif.:** Applicant must hold an FCC amateur radio license; be a resident and attending school in the WV Section; and have a GPA of 3.0 or higher. **Criteria:** Award is given based on the submitted materials.

Funds Avail.: $500. **Number Awarded:** 1. **To Apply:** Applicant must submit a completed scholarship application form along with a recent high school (or equivalent) or college transcript. **Deadline:** February 1.

1091 ■ Seth Horen, K1LOM Memorial Scholarships *(Undergraduate/Scholarship)*

Purpose: To support the education of students holding a valid FCC-granted Amateur Radio license for post-secondary education. **Focus:** Radio and television. **Qualif.:** Applicant must hold an FCC amateur radio license and be attending a four-year college/university. **Criteria:** Award is given based on the submitted materials.

Funds Avail.: $500. **Number Awarded:** 1. **To Apply:** Applicant must submit a completed scholarship application form along with a recent high school (or equivalent) or college transcript. **Deadline:** February 1.

1092 ■ Dr. James L. Lawson Memorial Scholarships *(Undergraduate/Scholarship)*

Purpose: To support the education of students holding a valid FCC-granted Amateur Radio license for post-secondary education. **Focus:** Radio and television;

Awards are arranged alphabetically below their administering organizations

Electronics; Communications. **Qualif.:** Applicant must hold an FCC amateur radio license; be a resident of one of the New England states (ME, NH, VT, CT, RI) or New York State; and be studying in baccalaureate or higher courses in electronics, communications or related fields. **Criteria:** Award is given based on the submitted materials.

Funds Avail.: $500. **Number Awarded:** 1. **To Apply:** Applicant must submit a completed scholarship application form along with a recent high school (or equivalent) or college transcript. **Deadline:** February 1.

1093 ■ Fred R. McDaniel Memorial Scholarships (Undergraduate/Scholarship)

Purpose: To support the education of students holding a valid FCC-granted Amateur Radio license for post-secondary education. **Focus:** Radio and television; Electronics; Communications. **Qualif.:** Applicant must hold an FCC amateur radio license; be a resident of the FCC 5th call district (TX, OK, AR, LA, MS, NM); be studying in baccalaureate or higher courses of study in electronics, communications or related fields. **Criteria:** Preference is given to students with GPA of 3.0 or higher.

Funds Avail.: $500. **Number Awarded:** 1. **To Apply:** Applicant must submit a completed scholarship application form along with a recent high school (or equivalent) or college transcript. **Deadline:** February 1.

1094 ■ Edmond A. Metzger Scholarships (Undergraduate/Scholarship)

Purpose: To support the education of students holding a valid FCC-granted Amateur Radio license for post-secondary education. **Focus:** Radio and television; Electrical engineering. **Qualif.:** Applicant must hold an FCC amateur radio license; be a resident of ARRL Central Division (IL, IN, WI); be studying in baccalaureate or higher courses of study in electrical engineering; be an ARRL member; and attending school in the Central Division. **Criteria:** Award is given based on the submitted materials.

Funds Avail.: $500. **Number Awarded:** 1. **To Apply:** Applicants must submit a completed scholarship application form along with a recent high school (or equivalent) or college transcript. **Deadline:** February 1.

1095 ■ David W. Misek, N8NPX Memorial Scholarships (Undergraduate/Scholarship)

Purpose: To support the education of students holding a valid FCC-granted Amateur Radio license for post-secondary education. **Focus:** Radio and television. **Qualif.:** Applicant must hold an FCC amateur radio license; currently reside in one of nine Ohio counties: Greene, Montgomery, Champaign, Darke, Preble, Miami, Clark, Butler, Warren; and be attending four-year college/university. **Criteria:** Awards are given based on the submitted materials.

Funds Avail.: $1,500. **Number Awarded:** Up to 3. **To Apply:** Applicant must submit a completed scholarship application form along with a recent high school (or equivalent) or college transcript. **Deadline:** February 1.

1096 ■ New England FEMARA Scholarships (Undergraduate/Scholarship)

Purpose: To support the education of students holding a valid FCC-granted Amateur Radio license for post-secondary education. **Focus:** Radio and television. **Qualif.:** Applicant must hold an FCC amateur radio license; and be a resident of one of the New England states (ME, NH, VT, CT, RI). **Criteria:** Awards are given based on the submitted materials.

Funds Avail.: $1,000. **To Apply:** Applicant must submit a completed scholarship application form along with a recent high school (or equivalent) or college transcript. **Deadline:** February 1.

1097 ■ Northern California DX Foundation Scholarships (Undergraduate/Scholarship)

Purpose: To support the education of students holding a valid FCC-granted Amateur Radio license for post-secondary education. **Focus:** Radio and television. **Qualif.:** Applicant must hold an FCC amateur radio license; be attending a junior college, four-year college/university or trade school in the U.S.; and must demonstrate activity and interest in DXing. **Criteria:** Awards are given based on the submitted materials.

Funds Avail.: $1,500. **Number Awarded:** 2. **To Apply:** Applicant must submit a completed scholarship application form along with a recent high school (or equivalent) or college transcript. **Deadline:** February 1.

1098 ■ Ray, NORP and Katie, WOKTE Pautz Scholarships (Undergraduate/Scholarship)

Purpose: To support the education of students holding a valid FCC-granted Amateur Radio license for post-secondary education. **Focus:** Radio and television; Electronics; Computer and information sciences. **Qualif.:** Applicant must hold an FCC amateur radio license; be a resident of the ARRL Midwest Division (IA, KS, MO, NE); be enrolled in electronics, computer science or related field at an accredited 4-year college/university; and be an ARRL member. **Criteria:** Award is given based on the submitted materials.

Funds Avail.: $500-$1,000. **Number Awarded:** 1. **To Apply:** Applicants must submit a completed scholarship application form along with a recent high school (or equivalent) or college transcript. **Deadline:** February 1.

1099 ■ Peoria Area Amateur Radio Club Scholarships (Undergraduate/Scholarship)

Purpose: To support the education of students holding a valid FCC-granted Amateur Radio license for post-secondary education. **Focus:** Radio and television. **Qualif.:** Applicant must hold an FCC amateur radio license; be a resident of Central Illinois in one of these counties: Peoria, Tazewell, Woodford, Knox, McLean, Fulton, Logan, Marshall or Stark; and attending an accredited two or four-year college/university. **Criteria:** Award is given based on the submitted materials.

Funds Avail.: $500. **Number Awarded:** 1. **To Apply:** Applicant must submit a completed scholarship application form along with a recent high school (or equivalent) or college transcript. **Deadline:** February 1.

1100 ■ PHD ARA Scholarships (Doctorate, Undergraduate/Scholarship)

Purpose: To support the education of students holding a valid FCC-granted Amateur Radio license for post-secondary education. **Focus:** Radio and television; Journalism; Computer and information sciences; Electronics. **Qualif.:** Applicant must hold an FCC amateur radio license; be a resident of ARRL Midwest Division (IA, KS, MO, NE); with a course of study in journalism, computer science or electronic engineering; and be the child of a deceased radio amateur. **Criteria:** Award is given based on the submitted materials.

Awards are arranged alphabetically below their administering organizations

Funds Avail.: $1,000. **Number Awarded:** 1. **To Apply:** Applicant must submit a completed scholarship application form along with a recent high school (or equivalent) or college transcript. **Deadline:** February 1.

1101 ■ Thomas W. Porter, W8KYZ Scholarships Honoring Michael Daugherty, W8LSE
(Undergraduate/Scholarship)

Purpose: To support the education of students holding a valid FCC-granted Amateur Radio license for post-secondary education. **Focus:** Radio and television. **Qualif.:** Applicant must hold an FCC amateur radio license and attending an accredited two or four-year college/university or technical school. **Criteria:** Preference is given to the resident of Ohio or West Virginia.

Funds Avail.: $1,000. **Number Awarded:** 1. **To Apply:** Applicant must submit a completed scholarship application form along with a recent high school (or equivalent) or college transcript. **Deadline:** February 1.

1102 ■ Donald Riebhoff Memorial Scholarships
(Undergraduate/Scholarship)

Purpose: To support the education of students holding a valid FCC-granted Amateur Radio license for post-secondary education. **Focus:** Radio and television. **Qualif.:** Applicant must hold an FCC amateur radio license; be studying in baccalaureate or higher courses of study in international studies at an accredited post-secondary school; and be an ARRL member. **Criteria:** Award is given based on the submitted materials.

Funds Avail.: $1,000. **Number Awarded:** 1. **To Apply:** Applicants must submit a completed scholarship application form along with a recent high school (or equivalent) or college transcript. **Deadline:** February 1.

1103 ■ IRARC Memorial Joseph P. Rubino WA4MMD Scholarships *(Undergraduate/Scholarship)*

Purpose: To support the education of students holding a valid FCC-granted Amateur Radio license for post-secondary education. **Focus:** Radio and television; Electronics. **Qualif.:** Applicant must hold an FCC amateur radio license; have a minimum 2.5 GPA on a 4.0 scale; and be enrolled in an undergraduate degree or electronic technician certification program at an accredited institution. **Criteria:** Preference is given to the residents of Florida (Brevard County).

Funds Avail.: $750. **To Apply:** Applicant must submit a completed scholarship application form along with a recent high school (or equivalent) or college transcript. **Deadline:** February 1.

1104 ■ Bill Salerno, W2ONV, Memorial Scholarships *(Undergraduate/Scholarship)*

Purpose: To support the education of students holding a valid FCC-granted Amateur Radio license for post-secondary education. **Focus:** Radio and television. **Qualif.:** Applicant must hold an FCC amateur radio license; have a high school GPA of 3.7 or higher; have an annual family income not exceeding $100,000; and be enrolled at an accredited four-year college/university. **Criteria:** Award is given based on the submitted materials.

Funds Avail.: $1,000. **Number Awarded:** 1. **To Apply:** Applicant must submit a completed scholarship application form along with a recent high school (or equivalent) or college transcript. **Deadline:** February 1.

1105 ■ Eugene Gene Sallee, W4YFR Memorial Scholarships *(Undergraduate/Scholarship)*

Purpose: To support the education of students holding a valid FCC-granted Amateur Radio license for post-secondary education. **Focus:** Radio and television. **Qualif.:** Applicant must hold an FCC amateur radio license; be a resident of the state of Georgia; and have a GPA of 3.0 or higher. **Criteria:** Award is given based on the submitted materials.

Funds Avail.: $500. **Number Awarded:** 1. **To Apply:** Applicant must submit a completed scholarship application form along with a recent high school (or equivalent) or college transcript. **Deadline:** February 1.

1106 ■ Scholarships of the Morris Radio Club of New Jersey *(Undergraduate/Scholarship)*

Purpose: To support the education of students holding a valid FCC-granted Amateur Radio license for post-secondary education. **Focus:** Radio and television. **Qualif.:** Applicant must hold an FCC amateur radio license and be attending a four-year college/university. **Criteria:** Award is given based on the submitted materials.

Funds Avail.: $1,000. **Number Awarded:** 1. **To Apply:** Applicant must submit a completed scholarship application form along with a recent high school (or equivalent) or college transcript. **Deadline:** February 1.

1107 ■ Six Meter Club of Chicago Scholarships
(Undergraduate/Scholarship)

Purpose: To support the education of students holding a valid FCC-granted Amateur Radio license for post-secondary education. **Focus:** Radio and television. **Qualif.:** Applicant must hold an FCC amateur radio license; a resident of Illinois; and be enrolled in a post-secondary course of study leading to undergraduate degree. If no qualified Illinois candidate, award is open to ARRL Central Division (IN, WI). **Criteria:** Award is given based on the submitted materials.

Funds Avail.: $500. **Number Awarded:** 1. **To Apply:** Applicant must submit a completed scholarship application form along with a recent high school (or equivalent) or college transcript. **Deadline:** February 1.

1108 ■ Zachary Taylor Stevens Memorial Scholarships *(Undergraduate/Scholarship)*

Purpose: To support the education of students holding a valid FCC-granted Amateur Radio license for post-secondary education. **Focus:** Radio and television. **Qualif.:** Applicant must hold an FCC amateur radio license and be enrolled in an accredited two or four-year college/university or technical school. **Criteria:** Preference is given to the residents of Amateur radio call areas in MI, OH and WV.

Funds Avail.: $750. **Number Awarded:** 1. **To Apply:** Applicant must submit a completed scholarship application form along with a recent high school (or equivalent) or college transcript. **Deadline:** February 1.

1109 ■ Carole J. Streeter, KB9JBR Scholarships *(Undergraduate/Scholarship)*

Purpose: To support the education of students holding a valid FCC-granted Amateur Radio license for post-secondary education. **Focus:** Radio and television. **Qualif.:** Applicant must hold an FCC amateur radio license and be enrolled in an accredited college/university studying healing arts. **Criteria:** Preference is given to applicants with basic Morse Code proficiency; healing arts study may include

Awards are arranged alphabetically below their administering organizations

courses at teaching hospitals or local colleges.

Funds Avail.: $750. **Number Awarded:** 1. **To Apply:** Applicant must submit a completed scholarship application form along with a recent high school (or equivalent) or college transcript. **Deadline:** February 1.

1110 ■ Norman E. Strohmeier, W2VRS Memorial Scholarships *(Undergraduate/Scholarship)*

Purpose: To support the education of students holding a valid FCC-granted Amateur Radio license for post-secondary education. **Focus:** Radio and television. **Qualif.:** Applicant must hold an FCC amateur radio license; be a resident of Western New York; and have a cumulative GPA of 3.2 or better. **Criteria:** Preference is given to graduating high school seniors.

Funds Avail.: $500. **Number Awarded:** 1. **To Apply:** Applicant must submit a completed scholarship application form along with a recent high school (or equivalent) or college transcript. **Deadline:** February 1.

1111 ■ Gary Wagner, K3OMI Scholarships *(Undergraduate/Scholarship)*

Purpose: To support the education of students holding a valid FCC-granted Amateur Radio license for post-secondary education. **Focus:** Radio and television; Engineering. **Qualif.:** Applicant must hold an FCC amateur radio license; be a resident of NC, VA, WV, MD or TN; enrolled in an accredited four-year college/university (NC, VA, WV, MD, or TN) working towards a Bachelor's of Science in any field of engineering; and have financial need. **Criteria:** Award is given based on the submitted materials.

Funds Avail.: $1,000. **Number Awarded:** 1. **To Apply:** Applicant must submit a completed scholarship application form along with a recent high school (or equivalent) or college transcript. **Deadline:** February 1.

1112 ■ Francis Walton Memorial Scholarships *(Undergraduate/Scholarship)*

Purpose: To support the education of students holding a valid FCC-granted Amateur Radio license for post-secondary education. **Focus:** Radio and television. **Qualif.:** Applicant must hold an FCC amateur radio license; be a resident of Illinois or Central Division (IL, IN, WI); and studying baccalaureate or higher degree. **Criteria:** Awards are given based on the submitted materials.

Funds Avail.: $500. **Number Awarded:** 1 or more. **To Apply:** Applicant must submit a completed scholarship application form along with a recent high school (or equivalent) or college transcript. **Deadline:** February 1.

1113 ■ L. Phil Wicker Scholarships *(Undergraduate/Scholarship)*

Purpose: To support the education of students holding a valid FCC-granted Amateur Radio license for post-secondary education. **Focus:** Radio and television; Electronics; Communications. **Qualif.:** Applicant must hold an FCC amateur radio license; be a resident of, and attending in ARRL Roanoke Division (NC, SC, VA, WV); enrolled in a baccalaureate or higher course in electronics, communications and related fields. **Criteria:** Award is given based on the submitted materials.

Funds Avail.: $1,000. **Number Awarded:** 1. **To Apply:** Applicant must submit a completed scholarship application form along with a recent high school (or equivalent) or college transcript. **Deadline:** February 1.

1114 ■ Yankee Clipper Contest Club, Inc. Youth Scholarships *(Undergraduate/Scholarship)*

Purpose: To support the education of students holding a valid FCC-granted Amateur Radio license for post-secondary education. **Focus:** Radio and television. **Qualif.:** Applicant must hold an FCC amateur radio license; residency or college/university attendance within 175 miles of YCCC Center in Erving MA, including MA, RI, CT, Long Island NY, some of VT, NH, ME, PA, and NJ; and be enrolled in a two or four-year degree program at an accredited college/university. **Criteria:** Award is given based on the submitted materials.

Funds Avail.: $1,000. **Number Awarded:** 1. **To Apply:** Applicant must submit a completed scholarship application form along with a recent high school (or equivalent) or college transcript. **Deadline:** February 1.

1115 ■ Yasme Foundation Scholarships *(Undergraduate/Scholarship)*

Purpose: To support the education of students holding a valid FCC-granted Amateur Radio license for post-secondary education. **Focus:** Radio and television; Science; Engineering. **Qualif.:** Applicant must hold an FCC amateur radio license; and must be enrolled in a science or engineering course at an accredited four-year college/university. **Criteria:** Preference is given to high school applicants ranked in top 5%-10%, or to college students in the top 10%. Participation in local Amateur Radio club and community service is important to selection.

Funds Avail.: $2,000. **Number Awarded:** 5. **To Apply:** Applicant must submit a completed scholarship application form along with a recent high school (or equivalent) or college transcript. **Deadline:** February 1.

1116 ■ American Railway Engineering and Maintenance of Way Association (AREMA)

10003 Derekwood Ln., Ste. 210
Lanham, MD 20706-4875
Ph: (301) 459-3200
Fax: (301) 459-8077
E-mail: bcaruso@arema.org
URL: www.arema.org

1117 ■ American Railway Engineering and Maintenance-of-Way Association Scholarships *(Undergraduate/Scholarship)*

Purpose: To support the education of undergraduate engineering student who has potential interest in railway engineering careers. **Focus:** Engineering. **Qualif.:** Applicant must be enrolled as a full-time undergraduate student in a four or five year program leading to a Bachelor's degree in Engineering or Engineering Technology in a curriculum accredited by the Accreditation Board of Engineering and Technology; have completed at least one quarter or semester prior to the application; interest in railway engineering; and maintaining a minimum GPA of 2.0. **Criteria:** Selection is based on the materials submitted.

Funds Avail.: $1,000. **Number Awarded:** 1. **To Apply:** Applicant must submit a completed AREMA data form together with a cover letter (maximum of 350 words); a resume; two letters of recommendation from a faculty member and another from a present employer, AREMA member or other responsible person; and a transcript from the schools attended and courses currently enrolled in. **Deadline:** March 11. **Remarks:** Staple application materi-

Awards are arranged alphabetically below their administering organizations

als in the upper left hand corner and do not include any photos.

1118 ■ AREMA Committee 18 - Light Density & Short Line Railways Scholarships
(Undergraduate/Scholarship)

Purpose: To support the education of an engineering student who has a potential interest in railway engineering careers. **Focus:** Engineering. **Qualif.:** Applicant must be enrolled full-time in a four or five year program leading to a Bachelor's degree in Engineering or Engineering Technology in a curriculum accredited by the Accreditation Board of Engineering and Technology; have completed at least one quarter or semester in college prior to the application; and have a GPA of 2.00. **Criteria:** Selection is based on the submitted materials.

Funds Avail.: $1,000. **Number Awarded:** 2. **To Apply:** Applicants must submit completed AREMA data form together with a cover letter (maximum of 350 words); a resume; two letters of recommendation, one from a faculty member, and another from a present employer, AREMA member, or other responsible person; and a transcript from the schools attended, and courses currently enrolled in. **Deadline:** March 11. **Remarks:** Staple application materials in the upper left hand corner and do not include any photos.

1119 ■ AREMA Committee 24 - Education and Training Scholarships *(Undergraduate/Scholarship)*

Purpose: To support the education of an engineering student who has a potential interest in railway engineering careers. **Focus:** Engineering. **Qualif.:** Applicant must be enrolled full-time in a four or five year program leading to a Bachelor's degree in Engineering or Engineering Technology in a curriculum accredited by the Accreditation Board of Engineering and Technology; have completed at least one quarter or semester in college prior to the application; have a GPA of 2.00; and a current AREMA student member. **Criteria:** Selection is based on the submitted application materials.

Funds Avail.: $2,500. **Number Awarded:** 1. **To Apply:** Applicants must submit completed AREMA data form together with a cover letter (maximum of 350 words); a resume; two letters of recommendation from a faculty member and another from a present employer, AREMA member or other responsible person; and a transcript from the school(s) attended and courses currently enrolled in. **Deadline:** March 11. **Remarks:** Staple application materials in the upper left hand corner and do not include any photos.

1120 ■ AREMA Committee 33 - Electric Energy Utilization Scholarships *(Undergraduate/Scholarship)*

Purpose: To support the education of an engineering student who has a potential interest in railway engineering careers. **Focus:** Engineering. **Qualif.:** Applicant must be enrolled full-time in a four or five year program leading to a Bachelor's degree in Engineering or Engineering Technology in a curriculum accredited by the Accreditation Board of Engineering and Technology; have completed at least one quarter or semester in college prior to the application; and have a GPA of 2.00. **Criteria:** Selection is based on the submitted materials.

Funds Avail.: $1,000. **Number Awarded:** 1. **To Apply:**

Applicants must submit completed AREMA data form together with a cover letter (maximum of 350 words); a resume; two letters of recommendation, one from a faculty member, and another from a present employer, AREMA member, or other responsible person; and a transcript from the schools attended, and courses currently enrolled in. **Deadline:** March 11. **Remarks:** Staple application materials in the upper left hand corner and do not include any photos.

1121 ■ AREMA Presidential Spouse Scholarships *(Undergraduate/Scholarship)*

Purpose: To support the education of a female engineering student with a potential interest in railway engineering careers. **Focus:** Engineering. **Qualif.:** Applicant must be an enrolled full-time female student in a four or five year program leading to a Bachelor's degree in Engineering or Engineering Technology in a curriculum accredited by the Accreditation Board of Engineering and Technology; have completed at least one quarter or semester prior to the application; and have a minimum GPA of 2.0. **Criteria:** Selection is based on the materials submitted.

Funds Avail.: $1,000. **Number Awarded:** 1. **To Apply:** Applicants must submit completed AREMA data form together with a cover letter (maximum of 350 words); a resume; two letters of recommendation, one from a faculty member, and another from a present employer, AREMA member, or other responsible person; and a transcript from the schools attended, and courses currently enrolled in. **Deadline:** March 11. **Remarks:** Staple application materials in the upper left hand corner and do not include any photos. Submission of additional materials may cause disqualification. **Contact:** For further instructions, e-mail Stacy Spaulding at sspaulding@arema.org.

1122 ■ Committee 12 - Rail Transit Scholarships *(Undergraduate/Scholarship)*

Purpose: To support the education of a student who is also working full-time in the railway industry. **Focus:** Engineering. **Qualif.:** Applicant must be working as full-time in the railway industry; or be enrolled in a four or five year program leading to a Bachelor's degree in Engineering or Engineering Technology in a curriculum accredited by the Accreditation Board of Engineering and Technology; have completed at least one quarter or semester in college prior to the application; and have a GPA of 2.00. **Criteria:** Selection is based on the submitted materials.

Funds Avail.: $1,000. **Number Awarded:** 1. **To Apply:** Applicants must submit completed AREMA data form together with a cover letter (maximum of 350 words); a resume; two letters of recommendation from a faculty member and another from a present employer, AREMA member or other responsible person; and a transcript from the school(s) attended and courses currently enrolled in. **Deadline:** March 11. **Remarks:** Staple application materials in the upper left hand corner and do not include any photos.

1123 ■ Committee 27 - Maintenance-of-Way Work Equipment Scholarships *(Undergraduate/Scholarship)*

Purpose: To support the education of an engineering student. **Focus:** Engineering. **Qualif.:** Applicant must be enrolled full-time student in a four or five year program leading to a Bachelor's degree in Engineering or Engineering Technology in a curriculum accredited by the Accreditation Board of Engineering and Technology; have completed

Awards are arranged alphabetically below their administering organizations

at least one quarter or semester in college prior to the application; and have a GPA of 2.00. **Criteria:** Priority is given to a Committee 27 family member or a family member of someone in the work equipment industry for railroads.

Funds Avail.: $2,500. **Number Awarded:** Two. **To Apply:** Applicant must submit a completed AREMA data form together with a cover letter (maximum of 350 words); a resume; two letters of recommendation from a faculty member and another from a present employer, AREMA member or other responsible person; and a transcript from the school(s) attended and courses currently enrolled in. **Deadline:** March 11. **Remarks:** Staple application materials in the upper left hand corner and do not include any photos.

1124 ■ CSX Scholarships (Undergraduate/ Scholarship)

Purpose: To support the education of an undergraduate engineering student who has potential interest in railway engineering careers. **Focus:** Engineering. **Qualif.:** Applicant must be enrolled full-time as an undergraduate student in a four or five year program leading to a Bachelor's degree in Engineering or Engineering Technology in a curriculum accredited by the Accreditation Board of Engineering and Technology; have completed at least one quarter or semester prior to the application; interest in railway engineering; and maintaining a minimum GPA of 2.0. **Criteria:** Selection is based on the materials submitted.

Funds Avail.: $1,000. **Number Awarded:** 1. **To Apply:** Applicant must submit a completed AREMA data form together with a cover letter (maximum of 350 words); a resume; two letters of recommendation from a faculty member and another from a present employer, AREMA member or other responsible person; and a transcript from the school(s) attended and courses currently enrolled in. **Deadline:** March 11. **Remarks:** Staple application materials in the upper left hand corner and do not include any photos.

1125 ■ John J. Cunningham Memorial Scholarships (Undergraduate/Scholarship)

Purpose: To support the education of student in a professional field that has direct applications in the passenger rail sector. **Focus:** Engineering. **Qualif.:** Applicant must be an enrolled full-time Junior or Senior student in a four or five-year program leading to an undergraduate degree in a professional field that has direct applications in the passenger rail sector; and has a GPA of 2.00. **Criteria:** Selection is based on the submitted materials.

Funds Avail.: $2,000. **To Apply:** Applicant must submit a completed AREMA data form together with a cover letter (maximum of 350 words); a resume; two letters of recommendation from a faculty member and another from a present employer, AREMA member or other responsible person; and a transcript from the school(s) attended and courses currently enrolled in. **Deadline:** March 11. **Remarks:** Staple application materials in the upper left hand corner and do not include any photos. Sponsored jointly by Committees 11 and 17.

1126 ■ Larry L. Etherton Scholarships (Graduate, Undergraduate/Scholarship)

Purpose: To support education of railway engineering students at the University of Illinois in the Engineering Department at Urbana-Champaign. **Focus:** Engineering. **Qualif.:** Applicant must be a student at the University of Illinois at Urbana-Champaign; have at least 2.0 GPA; an

undergraduate or graduate student in the Engineering Department; and interested in railway engineering. **Criteria:** Selection is based on the submitted materials.

Funds Avail.: $1,500. **Number Awarded:** 1. **To Apply:** Applicants must submit completed AREMA data form together with a cover letter (maximum of 350 words); a resume; two letters of recommendation from a faculty member and another from a present employer, AREMA member or other responsible person; and a transcript of records from the school(s) attended and courses currently enrolled in. **Deadline:** March 11. **Remarks:** Staple application materials in the upper left hand corner and do not include any photos.

1127 ■ Michael W. and Jean D. Franke Family Foundation Scholarships (Graduate, Undergraduate/Scholarship)

Purpose: To support education of railway engineering students at the University of Illinois in the Engineering Department at Urbana-Champaign. **Focus:** Engineering. **Qualif.:** Applicant must be a student at the University of Illinois at Urbana-Champaign; have at least 2.0 GPA; an undergraduate or graduate student in the Engineering Department; and interested in railway engineering. **Criteria:** Selection is based on the submitted materials.

Funds Avail.: $6,000. **Number Awarded:** 1. **To Apply:** Applicants must submit completed AREMA data form together with a cover letter (maximum of 350 words); a resume; two letters of recommendation from a faculty member and another from a present employer, AREMA member or other responsible person; and a transcript from the school(s) attended and courses currently enrolled in. **Deadline:** March 11. **Remarks:** Staple application materials in the upper left hand corner and do not include any photos.

1128 ■ Belknap Freeman Carnegie Mellon Scholarships (Undergraduate/Scholarship)

Purpose: To support education of students pursuing a degree in Electrical Engineering at Carnegie Mellon University. **Focus:** Engineering, Electrical. **Qualif.:** Applicant must be a student of Carnegie Mellon University; pursuing an Electrical Engineering degree; and interested in railway engineering and have a goal of obtaining a "Professional Engineering" license. **Criteria:** Selection is based on the submitted materials and result of interview.

Funds Avail.: $10,000. **Number Awarded:** 1. **To Apply:** Applicants must submit completed AREMA data form together with a cover letter (maximum of 350 words); a resume; and a transcript from the school(s) attended and courses currently enrolled in. **Deadline:** March 13. **Remarks:** Staple application materials in the upper left hand corner and do not include any photos.

1129 ■ Michael and Gina Garcia Rail Engineering Scholarships (Undergraduate/Scholarship)

Purpose: To support the education of an engineering student, especially to students already married or supporting a family. **Focus:** Engineering. **Qualif.:** Applicant must be enrolled in a four or five year program leading to a Bachelor's degree in Engineering or Engineering Technology. **Criteria:** Priority is given to a student already married or supporting a family.

Funds Avail.: $2,000. **To Apply:** Applicant must submit a completed AREMA data form together with a cover letter (maximum of 350 words); a resume; two letters of recom-

Awards are arranged alphabetically below their administering organizations

mendation from a faculty member and another from a present employer, AREMA member or other responsible person; and a transcript from the school(s) attended and courses currently enrolled in. **Deadline:** March 11. **Remarks:** Staple application materials in the upper left hand corner and do not include any photos.

1130 ■ Michigan Tech Alumni Scholarships
(Graduate, Undergraduate/Scholarship)

Purpose: To support the education of an engineering student at Michigan Technological University. **Focus:** Engineering. **Qualif.:** Applicant must be an engineering student at Michigan Tech University and interested in railway engineering. **Criteria:** Selection is based on the materials submitted.

Funds Avail.: $1,000 each. **Number Awarded:** Two. **To Apply:** Applicant must submit a completed AREMA data form together with a cover letter (maximum of 350 words); a resume; two letters of recommendation from a faculty member and another from a present employer, AREMA member or other responsible person; and a transcript from the school(s) attended and courses currently enrolled in. **Deadline:** March 11. **Remarks:** Staple application materials in the upper left hand corner and do not include any photos.

1131 ■ Norfolk Southern Foundation Scholarships *(Undergraduate/Scholarship)*

Purpose: To support the education of an engineering student. **Focus:** Engineering. **Qualif.:** Applicant must be enrolled full-time in a four or five year undergraduate program in Engineering or Engineering Technology; institution must be located in Norfolk Southern; service area (22 states, the District of Columbia and Ontario, Canada); have completed at least one quarter or semester in college prior to the application; and have a GPA of 2.00. **Criteria:** Selection is based on the submitted materials.

Funds Avail.: $1,000. **Number Awarded:** 1. **To Apply:** Applicant must submit a completed AREMA data form together with a cover letter (maximum of 350 words); a resume; two letters of recommendation from a faculty member and another from a present employer, AREMA member or other responsible person; and a transcript from the school(s) attended and courses currently enrolled in. **Deadline:** March 11. **Remarks:** Staple application materials in the upper left hand corner and do not include any photos.

1132 ■ PB Rail Engineering Scholarships
(Undergraduate/Scholarship)

Purpose: To support the education of an undergraduate engineering student who has an interest in a railway engineering careers **Focus:** Engineering. **Qualif.:** Applicant must be enrolled full-time as an undergraduate student in a four or five year program leading to a Bachelor's degree in Engineering or Engineering Technology in a curriculum accredited by the Accreditation Board of Engineering and Technology; have completed at least one quarter or semester prior to the application; interest in railway engineering; and maintaining a minimum GPA of 2.0. **Criteria:** Selection is based on the materials submitted.

Funds Avail.: $2,000. **Number Awarded:** 1. **To Apply:** Applicants must submit completed AREMA data form together with a cover letter (maximum of 350 words); a resume; two letters of recommendation, one from a faculty member, and another from a present employer, AREMA member, or other responsible person; and a transcript from

the school(s) attended, and courses currently enrolled in. **Deadline:** March 11. **Remarks:** Staple application materials in the upper left hand corner and do not include any photos.

1133 ■ REMSA Scholarships *(Undergraduate/Scholarship)*

Purpose: To support the education of an undergraduate engineering student who has potential interest in railway engineering careers. **Focus:** Engineering. **Qualif.:** Applicant must be enrolled full-time as an undergraduate student in a four or five year program leading to a Bachelor's degree in Engineering or Engineering Technology in a curriculum accredited by the Accreditation Board of Engineering and Technology; have completed at least one quarter or semester prior to the application; interested in railway engineering; and maintaining a minimum GPA of 2.0. **Criteria:** Selection is based on the materials submitted.

Funds Avail.: $1,000. **Number Awarded:** 1. **To Apply:** Applicants must submit completed AREMA data form together with a cover letter (maximum of 350 words); a resume; two letters of recommendation from a faculty member and another from a present employer, AREMA member or other responsible person; and a transcript from the school(s) attended and courses currently enrolled in. **Deadline:** March 11. **Remarks:** Staple application materials in the upper left hand corner and do not include any photos.

1134 ■ American Red Cross
2025 E St. NW
Washington, DC 20006
Ph: (202) 303-5214
Free: 800-733-2767
E-mail: donorsupport@usa.redcross.org
URL: www.redcross.org

1135 ■ Jane Delano Student Nurse Scholarships *(Undergraduate/Scholarship)*

Purpose: To advance nursing as a career option and to promote the involvement of young nurses in the Red Cross. **Focus:** Nursing. **Qualif.:** Applicants must have contributed volunteer service to a Red Cross unit within the past five years; must have completed the equivalent of at least one year of college/university credits; must be currently enrolled in an accredited United States nursing school; must be currently enrolled as a student in good academic standing. **Criteria:** Selection will be based on Scholarship Selection Committee's criteria.

Funds Avail.: $3,000. **Number Awarded:** 3. **To Apply:** Candidates must submit a completed application form; application Support documents including personal essay (attach to application); endorsement from the Red Cross Unit (attach form to application); endorsement from Nursing School Dean (attach form to application). **Deadline:** July 1. **Remarks:** Established in 2001. **Contact:** Vivian Littlefield, PhD, RN, National Nursing Chair at littlefieldv@usa.redcross.org.

1136 ■ American Rental Association Foundation
1900 19th St.
Moline, IL 61265-4179
Ph: (309) 277-4236
Fax: (309) 764-1533
Free: 800-334-2177

Awards are arranged alphabetically below their administering organizations

E-mail: arafoundation@ararental.org
URL: www.ararental.org/

1137 ■ American Rental Association Foundation Scholarships *(Graduate, Undergraduate, Vocational/Occupational/Scholarship)*

Purpose: To provide scholarships to promising young students looking to enter the rental industry. **Focus:** Industrial education. **Qualif.:** Applicants must be students pursuing a field of study they will use while working in the rental industry or completing a rental-related vocational or certification program. **Criteria:** Selection of applicants will be based on the scholarship application criteria.

Funds Avail.: $1,000-$3,000. **Number Awarded:** 23. **To Apply:** For further information, applicants are advised to contact the ARA Foundation at 1900 19th St., Moline, IL 61265. **Deadline:** March 3.

1138 ■ Ron Marshall Scholarships
(Undergraduate/Scholarship)

Purpose: To provide scholarships to promising young students looking to enter the rental industry. **Focus:** Industrial education. **Qualif.:** Applicants must be pursuing an education applicable to the rental industry. **Criteria:** Selection of applicants will be based on the scholarship application criteria.

Funds Avail.: $500. **Number Awarded:** 2. **To Apply:** Applicants are advised to contact the ARA Foundation at 1900 19th St., Moline, IL 61265. **Remarks:** Ron Marshall was the owner of Reading Rentals in Reading, PA, until his death in October 1995. He was active in the Keystone Rental Association and ARA's Region Two.

1139 ■ Dorothy Wellnitz Canadian Scholarships
(Undergraduate/Scholarship)

Purpose: To provide scholarships to promising young students looking to enter the rental industry. **Focus:** Industrial education. **Qualif.:** Applicants must be pursuing an education program applicable to the rental industry; must be college and technical school students from Canada. **Criteria:** Selection of applicants will be based on the scholarship application criteria.

Funds Avail.: $1,000. **To Apply:** For further information, applicants are advised to contact the ARA Foundation at 1900 19th St., Moline, IL 61265. **Remarks:** Scholarship is named for Dorothy Wellnitz, former executive director of the Canadian Rental Association and is administered by the ARA Foundation.

1140 ■ American Research Center in Egypt (ARCE)

8700 Crownhill Blvd., Ste. 507
San Antonio, TX 78209
Ph: (210) 821-7000
Fax: (210) 821-7007
E-mail: info@arce.org
URL: www.arce.org

1141 ■ William P. McHugh Memorial Fund
Award *(Doctorate, Graduate/Fellowship)*

Purpose: To financially support the students enrolled in a graduate program through education, training and research initiatives. **Focus:** Archeology; Architecture; Art; Economics; History; Literature; Political science; Religious educa-tion; Anthropology. **Qualif.:** Applicants must be U.S. citizens; must be students enrolled in doctoral programs at North America universities, or postdoctoral scholars and professionals affiliated with North American universities and research institutions; must be students of geo-archaeology and prehistory. **Criteria:** Selection of applicants will be based on the criteria given by the Scholarship Committee.

Funds Avail.: $600. **To Apply:** Applicants must complete the application form available on the website; must submit three letters of recommendation and Pre-doctoral students must submit a fourth recommendation attesting to their capacity in ancient or modern languages relating to their proposed research. **Deadline:** January 15.

1142 ■ The National Endowment for the Humanities Fellowships *(Doctorate, Graduate/Fellowship)*

Purpose: To financially support the students enrolled in a graduate program through education, training and research initiatives. **Focus:** Archeology; Architecture; Art; Economics; History; Literature; Political science; Religious educa-tion; Anthropology. **Qualif.:** Applicants must be U.S. citizens; must be students enrolled in doctoral programs at North America universities, or postdoctoral scholars and professionals affiliated with North American universities and research institutions. **Criteria:** Selection of applicants will be based on the criteria given by the Scholarship Committee.

Funds Avail.: No specific amount. **Number Awarded:** 2-4. **To Apply:** Applicants must complete the application form available on the website; must submit three letters of recommendation and Pre-doctoral students must submit a fourth recommendation attesting to their capacity in ancient or modern languages relating to their proposed research. **Deadline:** January 15.

1143 ■ The United States Department of State, Bureau of Educational & Cultural Affairs Fellowships *(Doctorate, Graduate/Fellowship)*

Purpose: To financially support the students enrolled in a graduate program through education, training and research initiatives. **Focus:** Archeology; Architecture; Art; Economics; History; Literature; Political science; Religious educa-tion; Anthropology. **Qualif.:** Applicants must be U.S. citizens; must be students enrolled in doctoral programs at North America universities, or postdoctoral scholars and professionals affiliated with North American universities and research institutions. **Criteria:** Selection of applicants will be based on the criteria given by the Scholarship Committee.

Funds Avail.: No specific amount. **Number Awarded:** 6-7. **To Apply:** Applicants must complete the application form available on the website; must submit three letters of recommendation and Pre-doctoral students must submit a fourth recommendation attesting to their capacity in ancient or modern languages relating to their proposed research. **Deadline:** January 15.

1144 ■ American Research Institute in Turkey (ARIT)

c/o University of Pennsylvania Museum
3260 South St.
Philadelphia, PA 19104-6324
Ph: (215) 898-3474
Fax: (215) 898-0657
E-mail: leinwand@sas.upenn.edu

Awards are arranged alphabetically below their administering organizations

URL: ccat.sas.upenn.edu/ARIT

1145 ■ Critical Language Scholarships for Intensive Summer Institutes *(Graduate, Undergraduate/Scholarship)*

Purpose: To expand the number of Americans studying and mastering critical need foreign languages. **Focus:** Business; Engineering; Science; Social Sciences; Humanities. **Qualif.:** Applicants must be U.S. citizens; must be currently enrolled in a degree-granting program at the undergraduate or graduate level; must have graduated from an undergraduate or graduate program no more than two years ago; undergraduate students must have completed at least one year of general college coursework by program start date (one year is defined as two semesters or three quarters); or students in all disciplines including business, engineering, science, the social sciences and humanities are encouraged to apply. **Criteria:** Recipients are selected based on academic record and potential to succeed in a rigorous academic setting; ability to adapt to a different cultural environment; diversity; plan for continuation of study of the language; and plan to use the language in future career.

Funds Avail.: No stated amount. **To Apply:** Applicants must submit a completed application form along with transcript of records and letters of recommendation. **Deadline:** November 1.

1146 ■ Kenan T. Erim Fellowships for Archaeological Research at Aphrodisias *(Postdoctorate/Fellowship)*

Purpose: To support excavation and/or research about art history and archeology at Aphrodisias in Turkey during the summer. **Focus:** Art History; Architecture; Archeology. **Qualif.:** Applicants must be advanced graduate students engaged in excavation and research at Aphrodisias. **Criteria:** Recipients are selected base on academic records and financial need.

Funds Avail.: $2,375. **To Apply:** Applicants must provide complete application information; three letters of recommendation; a 100-word abstract of the project; letters of reference; and a copy of graduate transcript. **Deadline:** November 1.

1147 ■ Fellowships in the Humanities and Social Sciences in Turkey *(Postdoctorate/Fellowship)*

Purpose: To promote American and Turkish research and exchange related to Turkey. **Focus:** History, Ancient; Medieval Studies; Modern Languages; Humanities; Social Sciences. **Qualif.:** Applicants must be advanced graduate students engaged in research on ancient, medieval, or modern times in Turkey, in any field of humanities and social sciences; must have fulfilled all requirements for the doctorate except the dissertation by June and before beginning any ARIT-sponsored research. (Non-U.S. applicants are expected to maintain an affiliation with an educational institution in the United States or Canada). **Criteria:** Recipients are selected based on academic records and financial need. Preference will be given to applicants with projects of shorter duration.

Funds Avail.: $4,000-$16,000. **To Apply:** Applicants must provide complete application information; three letters of recommendation; a 100-word abstract of the project; letters of reference; and a copy of graduate transcript. **Deadline:** November 1. **Contact:** For further information, applicants may e-mail the ARIT executive director at leinwand@sas.upenn.edu.

1148 ■ Fellowships for Intensive Advanced Turkish Language Study in Turkey *(Graduate, Undergraduate/Fellowship)*

Purpose: To promote American and Turkish research and exchange related to Turkey. **Focus:** Foreign languages; General studies. **Qualif.:** Applicants must be citizens or national/permanent residents of the United States; must be currently enrolled in an undergraduate or graduate level academic program; must have a minimum B average in studies; must perform at the high-intermediate level on a proficiency-based admission examination; and must study an advanced Turkish language at Bogazici University in Istanbul. **Criteria:** Recipients are selected based on academic records and financial need.

Funds Avail.: No specific amount. **Number Awarded:** 15. **To Apply:** Applicants must submit complete application information; three letters of recommendation; letters of reference; and a copy of graduate transcript. **Deadline:** February 4. **Contact:** Erika H. Gilson at 110 Jones Hall, Princeton University, Princeton, NJ 08544-1008; E-mail: ehgilson@princeton.edu.

1149 ■ Getty Research Exchange Fellowship Program for Cultural Heritage Preservation *(Doctorate/Fellowship)*

Purpose: To support advanced regional research and exchanges between research centers in the Mediterranean and Middle East regions. **Focus:** General Studies. **Qualif.:** Applicants must be Turkish citizens who have already obtained PhD; must have professional experience in the study or preservation of cultural heritage; must be willing to undertake specific research project in overseas research centers of another country. **Criteria:** Recipients are selected based on: the significance of the proposal; value of the collaboration proposed; feasibility of the research design; and applicant's research background.

Funds Avail.: $4,000. **To Apply:** Applicants must fill out the application form; submit a project abstract and project description along with a letter of recommendation and 3-page curriculum vitae. **Deadline:** December 31. **Contact:** 212-257-8111; 312-427-2222.

1150 ■ Ilse and George Hanfmann Fellowships *(Doctorate/Fellowship)*

Purpose: To enable nationals of the Republic of Turkey who are graduate students at or recent PhDs from Turkish universities in archaeology and related fields to study abroad (North America or elsewhere). **Focus:** General studies. **Qualif.:** Applicants must be candidates for M.A. or Ph.D. degrees who have finished all course work and passed all qualifying examinations for the degree before entering the tenure of a Hanfmann Fellowship; must be scholars who have received their Ph.D. and have not yet reached 40 years of age. **Criteria:** Recipients are selected based on achievement.

Funds Avail.: $15,000-$45,000. **To Apply:** Applicants must submit a curriculum vitae; one-paragraph summary of the project; statement of purpose (no more than five double-spaced pages, and includes description of the project and its importance, a brief summary of the literature, the reasons for wanting to study or conduct research abroad, what institution this work would be conducted, and why such tenure abroad would be professionally advantageous

Awards are arranged alphabetically below their administering organizations

to the present academic career); official transcript of undergraduate and graduate course work; demonstration of proficiency in the language or languages necessary for conducting research abroad; minimum of three letters of recommendation from scholars familiar with the applicant's work. **Deadline:** February 26. **Contact:** 212-257-8111; 312-427-2222.

1151 ■ Kress Pre-Doctoral Fellowships in the History of Art and Archeology in Turkey (Postdoctorate/Fellowship)

Purpose: To promote American and Turkish research and exchange related to Turkey. **Focus:** Art History; Architecture; Archeology. **Qualif.:** Applicants must be advanced graduate students engaged in research in Turkey; must have fulfilled all preliminary requirements for the doctorate except dissertation by June and before beginning any ARIT-sponsored research; Applicants must be U.S. (Non-U.S. matriculated at U.S. or Canadian institutions). **Criteria:** Recipients are selected based on academic records and financial need.

Funds Avail.: $17,000. **To Apply:** Applicants must provide complete application information; three letters of recommendation; a 100-word abstract of the project; letters of reference; and a copy of graduate transcript. **Deadline:** November 1.

1152 ■ Mellon Advanced Fellowships in Turkey for East European Scholars (Doctorate/Fellowship)

Purpose: To bring the East-Central European scholars into a broader research community. **Focus:** General Studies. **Qualif.:** Applicants must be scholars from Czech Republic, Hungary, Poland, Bulgaria, Romania, Slovakia, Estonia, Latvia and Lithuania who have completed all requirements for the PhD or who hold a PhD degree or its equivalent; must be citizens and permanent residents of one of the nine included countries. **Criteria:** Recipients are selected based on project statement, academic records, and financial need.

Funds Avail.: $20,000. **Number Awarded:** 3. **To Apply:** Applicants must submit three to five-pages project statement outlining the project and its significance; current curriculum vitae; two letters of reference from scholars in the applicant's field commenting on the value and feasibility of the project. **Deadline:** March 3.

1153 ■ National Endowment for the Humanities Advanced Fellowships for Research in Turkey (Postdoctorate/Fellowship)

Purpose: To promote American and Turkish research and exchange related to Turkey. **Focus:** Humanities; Social Sciences; History; Art; Archeology; Literature; Linguistics. **Qualif.:** Applicants must complete formal training and have plans to carry out research in Turkey; must be U.S citizens or three year residents of United States. **Criteria:** Recipients are selected based on academic records and financial need.

Funds Avail.: $16,800 to $50,400. **Number Awarded:** 2 or 3. **To Apply:** Applicants must provide complete application information; three letters of recommendation; a 100-word abstract of the project; letters of reference; and a copy of graduate transcript. **Deadline:** November 1. **Contact:** Application form and supporting documents may sent electronically to leinwand@sas.upenn.edu.

1154 ■ American Respiratory Care Foundation
9425 N MacArthur Blvd., Ste. 100
Irving, TX 75063
Ph: (972) 243-2272
Fax: (972) 484-2720
E-mail: kuykendall@aarc.org
URL: www.arcfoundation.org

1155 ■ Parker B. Francis Respiratory Research Grants (Professional development/Grant)

Purpose: To provide financial assistance for research programs dealing with respiratory care and related topics. **Focus:** General studies. **Qualif.:** Applicants must be physicians or respiratory care practitioners. **Criteria:** Selection will be based on the committee's criteria.

Funds Avail.: $10,000. **To Apply:** Applicants must submit a completed application and research materials to the foundation. Application form is available at the website.

1156 ■ American Road and Transportation Builders Association (ARTBA)
1219 28th St. NW
Washington, DC 20007-3389
Ph: (202) 289-4434
Fax: (202) 289-4435
E-mail: general@artba.org
URL: www.artba.org

1157 ■ The Lanford Family Highway Worker Memorial Scholarship Program (Undergraduate/Scholarship)

Purpose: To provide financial assistance to the children or legally adopted children of highway workers killed or permanently disabled in the line of duty to pursue post-high school education. **Focus:** General studies. **Qualif.:** Applicants must be sons, daughters or legally adopted children of highway workers who died or became permanently disabled in roadway construction zone accidents and their parents have been employed by a transportation construction firm or a transportation public agency at the time of his or her death or disabling injury. **Criteria:** Candidates are evaluated on the basis of their submitted application materials.

Funds Avail.: $5000. **Number Awarded:** 1. **To Apply:** Candidates must submit completed and signed award application form; proof of parent's death in line of duty; if parent is permanently disabled, must submit documentation that shows disability as work-related; proof of guardianship if not living with surviving parent; an official copy of transcript and grade report from the school currently attended or most recently attended; a brief, typewritten statement explaining reasons for wanting to continue education accompanied by recent photo; completed and signed "Free Application for Federal Student Aid" (FAFSA) forms for the current year; federal tax return copy; copy of acceptance letter from the college, university, technical school where the applicants plan to attend; and two letters of recommendation from teachers in support of their application. **Deadline:** March 23. **Contact:** Holly Bolton at 202-289-4434 or hbolton@artba.org.

1158 ■ American Roentgen Ray Society (ARRS)
44211 Slatestone Ct.
Leesburg, VA 20176-5109

Awards are arranged alphabetically below their administering organizations

Ph: (703) 729-3353
Fax: (703) 729-4839
Free: 866-940-2777
E-mail: info@arrs.org
URL: www.arrs.org

1159 ■ American Roentgen Ray Society Scholarships *(Professional development/Scholarship)*

Purpose: To support study in a field selected by the scholars to attain their professional career goals. **Focus:** Radiology. **Qualif.:** Applicants must have earned MD or DO from an accredited institution; completed all the required residency or fellowship training or equivalent; must be full-time faculty appointment as lecturers, instructors, assistant professors or equivalent for no more than five years beyond completion of training; be certified by the American Board of Radiology or equivalent. **Criteria:** Recipients will be selected based on competence and promise of the candidate in research, education or administration related to medical imaging, as indicated by the institution making the nomination and personal qualities of the candidate that indicate that he or she is a true scholar and leader with exceptional potential.

Funds Avail.: $140,000. **Number Awarded:** 2. **To Apply:** Applicants must submit a cover letter stating his or her address, phone and fax numbers and e-mail address, for use by the ARRS administrative office; a curriculum vitae; a three-page summary of the applicant's qualifications, goals and purpose of study; statements from the department and applicant regarding present interests in a specific area related to radiological sciences or education, and long-term scientific and professional objectives or aspirations as they may relate to his or her future career; statement from the Department Chair as to the department's commitment to provide time for the scholar to study, and a commitment ensuring his or her return to the faculty at the completion of the scholarship; and an estimated budget covering the scholar's program over the one or two-year period. **Deadline:** November 19. **Contact:** Materials should be submitted electronically to nianni@arrs.org.

1160 ■ ARRS/Leonard Berlin Scholarships in Medical Professionalism *(Professional development/Scholarship)*

Purpose: To support study and research related to medical ethics, medico-legal principles, patient accountability, sensitivity to patient diversity and/or other topics encompassing medical professionalism. **Focus:** Bioethics. **Qualif.:** Applicants must have an MD or DO from an accredited institution, or equivalent; have completed a radiology residency, and fellowship training where appropriate, or the equivalent; must be certified by the American Board of Radiology or equivalent; must be members of the ARRS at the time the application is submitted and for the duration of the award. **Criteria:** Recipients will be selected based on competence and promise of the candidate in research, education or administration related to medical imaging, as indicated by the institution making the nomination and personal qualities of the candidate that indicate that he or she is a true scholar and leader with exceptional potential.

Funds Avail.: $100,000. **Number Awarded:** 1. **To Apply:** Applicants must submit a cover letter stating his or her address, phone and fax numbers and e-mail address, for use by the ARRS administrative office; a curriculum vitae including details of any other current or pending salary support; a three-page summary of the applicant's qualifications, goals

and purpose of study; a description of course-work that will be undertaken; a listing of mentors, as appropriate to the proposal, and their contributions to the proposal; a letter of nomination from the Department Chair, or when applicable, the Radiology Group Director, and two additional letters of recommendation; and an estimated budget covering the scholar's program over the one or two-year period. **Deadline:** November 19. **Contact:** Candidates must submit all required documents as email attachments to nianni@arrs.org.

1161 ■ American Romanian Orthodox Youth (AROY)

c/o Maranda Tipa, Pres.
2041 Tyler Dr.
Commerce Township, MI 48390
Ph: (734) 395-9707
E-mail: chancery@roea.org
URL: www.roea.org/aroy.html

1162 ■ A.R.F.O.R.A. Undergraduate Scholarships for Women *(Undergraduate/Scholarship)*

Purpose: To support the continuing education of student members. **Focus:** General studies. **Qualif.:** Applicant must be a female voting member of a parish of the Romanian Orthodox Episcopate of America and accepted by a duly accredited university or college. **Criteria:** Selection is based on the application materials.

Funds Avail.: $1,000. **Number Awarded:** 1. **To Apply:** Applicants must send a request for application to ARFORA/Martha Gavrila Scholarship c/o 222 Orchard Park Dr. New Castle, PA 16105. Three letters of recommendation must be mailed sealed with attached photo and must submit a formal letter projecting the plans of the applicant. **Deadline:** May 15.

1163 ■ Pamfil and Maria Bujea Family Orthodox Christian Seminarian Scholarships *(Undergraduate/Scholarship)*

Purpose: To support the education of students seeking ordination into priesthood or wish to serve the Church in a professional manner. **Focus:** Religion; Christian education; Theology **Qualif.:** Applicants must be citizens orpermanent residents of either Canada or the United States of American and show proof thereof. Students must furnish written proof of enrollment in the appropriate higher education program along with a transcripts of the students' grades at the designated institutions. **Criteria:** Award is limited to those who either seek ordination into the priesthood or who wish to serve the Church.

Funds Avail.: $10,000. **Number Awarded:** 1. **To Apply:** Applicants must submit a completed application; a 300-word handwritten essay explaining their mission if they're assigned to Canada; and a posed photograph. Three letters of recommendation obtained sealed, from the authors, must be included with the application. One should be from the applicants' spiritual advisor/priest. **Deadline:** May 31. **Contact:** Application forms must be sent to PO Box 309, Grass Lake, MI 49240-0309.

1164 ■ A.R.F.O.R.A. Martha Gavrila Scholarships for Women *(Postgraduate/Scholarship)*

Purpose: To support the student members in post-graduate studies. **Focus:** General studies. **Qualif.:** Applicant must be a female voting member of a parish of the Romanian

Awards are arranged alphabetically below their administering organizations

Orthodox Episcopate of America; a graduate of a duly accredited university/college; and accepted by a graduate school or a duly accredited university and specify her course of study. **Criteria:** Selection is based on the application materials.

Funds Avail.: $1,000. **Number Awarded:** 1. **To Apply:** Applicants must send a request for application to ARFORA/Martha Gavrila Scholarship c/o 222 Orchard Park Dr New Castle, PA 16105. Three letters of recommendation must be mailed sealed, directly to the attention of the Scholarship Committee. A photo must be included and a formal letter projecting the plans of the applicant. **Deadline:** May 15.

1165 ■ R.O.E.A. Dumitru Golea Goldy-Gemu Scholarships (Undergraduate/Scholarship)

Purpose: To support the continuing education of student members. **Focus:** General studies. **Qualif.:** Applicant must be of Romanian descent and a citizen or permanent resident of the United States or Canada; must be enrolled as a full-time undergraduate student in a recognized four-year educational institution. **Criteria:** Selection is based on the application.

Funds Avail.: $1,500. **Number Awarded:** 2. **To Apply:** Applicant must submit a completed application form; three letters of recommendation; 300 words handwritten essay explaining, "How Romanian heritage makes him/her become a better American/Canadian"; and photo. In addition, applicant must submit written proof of enrollment: 1) For High School applicants: a copy of letter of acceptance from higher education program; 2) Current undergraduate applicants: a transcript of records at the institution; 3) Returning undergraduate applicants: a letter of acceptance from the institution. **Deadline:** May 31. **Contact:** Send application materials to Goldy Scholarship Committee PO Box 309 Grass Lake, MI 49240-0309.

1166 ■ A.R.O.Y. Stanitz Scholarships (Undergraduate/Scholarship)

Purpose: To support the continuing education of student members. **Focus:** General studies. **Qualif.:** Applicant must be an active AROY member; a high school graduate; and a college student or one who intends to enroll in a school or college of university level. **Criteria:** Selection is based on the application.

Funds Avail.: $1,000. **Number Awarded:** 2. **To Apply:** Applicants must submit a biographical history including family; an educational background and grades; list of AROY and church activities; list of extra-curricular interests or achievements; reasons why applying for the scholarship; a photograph; and a letter of recommendation from parish priest or AROY advisors regarding parish and AROY activities. Send all materials to William R. Stanitz/AROY Scholarship The Romanian Orthodox Episcopate of America PO Box 309 Grass Lake, MI 49240-0309. **Deadline:** July 1. **Remarks:** Established in 1971.

1167 ■ American-Scandinavian Foundation
58 Park Ave.
New York, NY 10016
Ph: (212) 779-3587
E-mail: info@amscan.org
URL: www.amscan.org

1168 ■ American-Scandinavian Foundation Fellowships and Grants to Study in America (Graduate/Fellowship, Grant)

Purpose: Promotes international understanding through educational and cultural exchange between the United

States and Denmark, Finland, Iceland, Norway and Sweden. **Focus:** General studies. **Qualif.:** Applicants must be citizens of Denmark, Finland, Iceland, Norway or Sweden who wish to undertake study or research programs (usually at the graduate level) in the United States. **Criteria:** Selection will be based on the committee's criteria.

Funds Avail.: $500,000. **To Apply:** In order to apply, applicants must submit applications to their appropriate cooperative organizations (The Denmark-America Foundation, The League of Finnish-American Societies, The Icelandic-American Society, The Norway-America Association and The Sweden-America Foundation).

1169 ■ American-Scandinavian Foundation Fellowships to Study in Scandinavia (Graduate/Fellowship)

Purpose: Promotes international understanding through educational and cultural exchange between the United States and Denmark, Finland, Iceland, Norway and Sweden. **Focus:** General studies. **Qualif.:** Applicants must have a well-defined research or study project that makes a stay in Scandinavia essential; must be US citizens or permanent residents; must have completed their undergraduate education by the start of their project in Scandinavia. **Criteria:** Priority is given to candidates at the graduate level for dissertation-related study or research.

Funds Avail.: Up to $23,000. **To Apply:** Applicants must submit an official ASF form and supporting documents (letters of reference and academic transcripts) in sealed envelopes. They must also submit one original paper copy and one electronic copy of the following items: signed application form; project summary (not to exceed 200 words); budget form; project statement (not to exceed 1,200 words) and bibliography; curriculum vitae (not to exceed ten pages including publications listing); invitation and other relevant correspondence confirming the availability of overseas resources. Submission via electronic copy must be sent to grants@amscan.org. **Deadline:** November 1.

1170 ■ American-Scandinavian Foundation Grants to Study in Scandinavia (Graduate/Grant)

Purpose: Promotes international understanding through educational and cultural exchange between the United States and Denmark, Finland, Iceland, Norway and Sweden. **Focus:** Arts. **Qualif.:** Applicants must have a well-defined research or study project that makes a stay in Scandinavia essential; must be US citizens or permanent residents; must have completed their undergraduate education by the start of their project in Scandinavia; must be post-graduate scholars, professionals and candidates in the arts to carry out research or study visits of one to three months duration. **Criteria:** Priority is given to candidates at the graduate level for dissertation-related study or research.

Funds Avail.: Amount not specified. **To Apply:** Applicants must submit an official ASF form and supporting documents (letters of reference and academic transcripts) in sealed envelopes. They must also submit one original paper copy and one electronic copy of the following items: signed application form; project summary (not to exceed 200 words); budget form; project statement (not to exceed 1,200 words) and bibliography; curriculum vitae (not to exceed ten pages including publications listing); invitation and other relevant correspondence confirming the availability of overseas resources. Submission via electronic copy must be sent to grants@amscan.org. **Deadline:** November 1.

Awards are arranged alphabetically below their administering organizations

1171 ■ American-Scandinavian Foundation Translation Prize (Professional development/ Prize)

Purpose: To encourage the English translation of Scandinavian literature of the last two centuries. **Focus:** General studies. **Qualif.:** Applicants must be outstanding English translators of poetry, fiction, drama or literary prose originally written in a Nordic language. **Criteria:** Selection will be based on the committee's criteria.

Funds Avail.: $2,000. **To Apply:** An entry must consist of four legible copies of the translation, including a title page and a table of contents for the proposed book of which the manuscript submitted is a part and one copy of the work(s) in the original language. Applicants must also send photocopies of the following pages: a CV containing all contact information including email address for the translator; and a letter or other documents signed by the author, the author's agent or the author's estate granting permission for the translation to be entered in this competition and published in Scandinavian Review. Prose manuscripts must not be longer than 50 pages and must not be longer than 25 pages for poetry. Manuscripts must be typed and double-spaced with numbered pages.

1172 ■ ASF/Annika Teig/Skidmore, Owings and Merril Fellowships (Undergraduate/Fellowship)

Purpose: To support Scandinavian citizens seeking experience in interior design at a leading architecture firm in New York City. **Focus:** Landscape architecture and design; Interior design. **Qualif.:** Applicants must be from Scandinavia who have studied or are currently studying architecture. **Criteria:** Selection will be based on the committee's criteria.

Funds Avail.: No specific amount. **To Apply:** Applicants must submit a curriculum vitae, statement of purpose (no more than two pages describing why the applicant is interested in the award) and digital copies of a work in PDF format. Completed applications must be submitted to teig.fellowship@som.com. **Deadline:** May 28.

1173 ■ Leif and Inger Sjoberg Awards (Professional development/Award)

Purpose: To encourage the English translation of Scandinavian literature of the last two centuries. **Focus:** General studies. **Qualif.:** Applicants must be outstanding English translators of poetry, fiction, drama or literary prose originally written in a Nordic language. **Criteria:** Selection will be based on the committee's criteria.

Funds Avail.: $1,000. **To Apply:** An entry must consist of four legible copies of the translation, including a title page and a table of contents for the proposed book of which the manuscript submitted is a part as well as one copy of the work(s) in the original language. Applicants must also send photocopies of the following pages: a CV containing all contact information, including email address for the translator; and a letter or other document signed by the author, the author's agent or the author's estate granting permission for the translation to be entered in this competition and published in Scandinavian Review. Prose manuscripts must not be longer than 50 pages and must not be longer than 25 pages for poetry. Manuscripts must be typed and double-spaced with numbered pages.

1174 ■ American School Health Association (ASHA)

4340 East West Hwy., Ste. 403
Bethesda, MD 20814

Ph: (301) 652-8072
Fax: (301) 652-8077
Free: 800-445-2742
E-mail: info@ashaweb.org
URL: www.ashaweb.org

1175 ■ ASHA Scholarships (Graduate, Undergraduate/Scholarship)

Purpose: To provide financial assistance for students concentrating on school health education, school nursing and pediatric or adolescent medicine or dentistry. **Focus:** Health education; Nursing; Pediatric medicine; Medicine; Dentistry; Nutrition; Counseling/Guidance. **Qualif.:** Applicants must be juniors, seniors or graduate students enrolled full-time at an institution of higher education; have a 3.0 GPA on a 4.0 scale; have a major related to School Health Education or School Nursing or Pediatric or Adolescent Medicine or Dentistry or other school health specializations (nutrition, counseling, etc.); and must not be previous recipients of this award. **Criteria:** Awards are given based on academic merit and extracurricular activities.

Funds Avail.: $1000 and a complimentary registration to ASHA's annual school health conference and a one-year ASHA membership. **Number Awarded:** 3. **To Apply:** Applicants must send one original and nine copies of the completed application form (application form available online); current resume; transcript; one-page personal statement; and three letters of recommendation. **Deadline:** April 2. **Contact:** For further information, applicants must contact Stephen Conley at the above address; E-mail: sconley@ashaweb.org.

1176 ■ ASHA Student Research Grants (Graduate, Undergraduate/Scholarship)

Purpose: To provide financial assistance for research in areas related to the mission of ASHA. **Focus:** Health education; Nursing; Pediatric medicine; Medicine; Dentistry; Nutrition; Counseling/Guidance. **Qualif.:** Applicants must be student members of ASHA. **Criteria:** Recipients will be selected by the scholarship committee.

Funds Avail.: No specific amount. **To Apply:** Applicants must send one original and five copies of a proposal which includes a cover sheet; a narrative (title-problem, review of related literature, methodology, data analyst, institution IRB protocol documented); and a budget. Proposal should have one inch margins, double-spaced and a font size not smaller than 12. **Deadline:** April 1. **Contact:** For further information, applicants must contact Stephen Conley at the above address; E-mail: sconley@ashaweb.org.

1177 ■ American Schools of Oriental Research (ASOR)

Boston University
656 Beacon St., 5th Fl.
Boston, MA 02215-2010
Ph: (617) 353-6570
Fax: (617) 353-6575
E-mail: asor@bu.edu
URL: www.asor.org

1178 ■ Katherine Barton Platt Excavation Fellowships (Professional development, Undergraduate/Fellowship)

Purpose: To support the participation of ASOR members as volunteers or staff on excavation projects. **Focus:** Gen-

Awards are arranged alphabetically below their administering organizations

eral studies. **Qualif.:** Applicants must be current members of ASOR or students enrolled at an institutional member of ASOR. **Criteria:** Preference will be given to individuals who have not received a support through the heritage programs or other funding sources.

Funds Avail.: $1,000. **Number Awarded:** 10. **To Apply:** Applicants must submit a completed application form and 250-350 words with photo (digital tiff, 300 dpi or higher). Reports and photos should be sent electronically with "Platt Report" in the subject heading. **Deadline:** February.

1179 ■ American Senior Benefits Association (ASBA)

PO Box 300777
Chicago, IL 60630-0777
Ph: (773) 714-7990
Free: 877-906-2722
E-mail: info@asbaonline.org
URL: www.asbaonline.org

1180 ■ ASBA College Scholarship Program
(Undergraduate/Scholarship)

Purpose: To provide educational financial aid to members and their grandchildren. **Focus:** General studies. **Qualif.:** Applicant must be a dependent or grandchild of an ASBA member; enrolled at least one year in college or university. **Criteria:** Awards are given based on academic merit and evaluation of the submitted essay.

Funds Avail.: $1,000. **To Apply:** Applicant must submit an application form (please visit the website); an essay; two letters of recommendation; official copies of high school/college transcript. **Deadline:** May 31.

1181 ■ American Shotcrete Association (ASA)

38800 Country Club Dr.
Farmington Hills, MI 48331
Ph: (248) 848-3780
Fax: (248) 848-3740
E-mail: info@shotcrete.org
URL: www.shotcrete.org

1182 ■ ASA Graduate Scholarships *(Graduate/Scholarship)*

Purpose: To attract, identify and assist outstanding graduate students pursuing careers within the field of concrete with a significant interest in the shotcrete process. **Focus:** Construction. **Qualif.:** Applicant must have been accepted for graduate study in the area of concrete at an accredited college/university within the U.S. or at Laval University in Canada, and be a full-time first or second-year (after bachelor's degree) graduate student during the entire scholarship year. **Criteria:** Selection is based on the essay, submitted data and reference.

Funds Avail.: $3,000. **Number Awarded:** 2. **To Apply:** Applicants must submit a completed typed application form together with one-page resume; essay (1-page limit, 300 words or less, name must be on first page, include all scheduled classes for balance of academic year); two completed online reference forms; and all original undergraduate and graduate transcripts (mailed directly to ASA in sealed envelope with a university stamp). Application materials must be sent together via email in one package. All materials must be in English. **Deadline:** November 2.

1183 ■ American Society of Association Executives (The Center for Association Leadership)

1575 I St. NW Ste 1200
Washington, DC 20005-1103
Ph: (202) 371-0940
Fax: (202) 371-8315
Free: 888-950-2723
E-mail: asaeservice@asaecenter.org
URL: www.asaecenter.org

1184 ■ Diversity Executive Leadership Program Scholarships *(Professional development/Scholarship)*

Purpose: To help individuals from underrepresented segments of the association community advance into the ranks of leadership in the association management profession; to encourage leadership roles in association management; to increase diversity within the field of association management by providing educational and networking opportunities to potential leaders form underrepresented populations; to support scholars by providing opportunities to increase their connections and understanding of association management; to match scholars with mentors to provide career guidance and enhance networking opportunities; to demonstrate the long-term benefit of the program to ASAE and The Center, to the association profession, and to the scholars. **Focus:** Leadership, Institutional and community; Management. **Qualif.:** Member of a racial or ethnic minority group, GLBT, or person with a disability; currently employed as a mid-to-senior level association employee with minimum of three years experience in association management or as an association CEO for a minimum of one year; has a professional, volunteer, civic or community leadership experience. **Criteria:** Preference is given to individuals who are members of ASAE & The Center and/or individuals who work with ASAE & The Center members; Recipients are selected on the basis of commitment to attend the DELP orientation, professional education programs and service on an ASAE and The Center or allied society committee or council.

Funds Avail.: No specific amount. **Number Awarded:** 10. **To Apply:** Application forms for this scholarship are available at the ASAE website. Applicants may also attach their resume; a personal statement that addresses why DELP participation is sought, leadership philosophy and how the applicant has to serve as an agent of change in the association community (one typewritten page in length); and program agreement form signed by the applicant's employer. **Deadline:** March 16. **Contact:** Marilu Morada, DELP Staff Liaison, Phone: 202-326-9527, email: mmorada@asaecenter.org.

1185 ■ American Society of Brewing Chemists (ASBC)

3340 Pilot Knob Rd.
St. Paul, MN 55121-2097
Ph: (651) 454-7250
Fax: (651) 454-0766
E-mail: asbc@scisoc.org
URL: www.asbcnet.org

1186 ■ ASBC Foundation Graduate Scholarships *(Doctorate, Graduate/Scholarship)*

Purpose: To provide financial support to students who are pursuing MS or Ph.D. degrees in brewing science or related

Awards are arranged alphabetically below their administering organizations

areas. **Focus:** Chemistry; Science. **Qualif.:** Candidate must be a current ASBC student member. Candidate must be enrolled in graduate studies by the time the graduate scholarship becomes effective, or be a current graduate student pursuing a course of study leading to an MS or a Ph.D. degree. For full-time graduate study, candidate must be enrolled in an academic schedule that meets the minimum requirements of the university involved. Educational institution in which the recipient is enrolled must be conducting fundamental investigations for the advancement of brewing and malting science. **Criteria:** Scholarship recipients will be selected based on the jury's review of the application materials.

Funds Avail.: Up to $5,000 and certificate. **To Apply:** Applicants must submit a completed application form; copies of transcripts; a letter of application describing career plans; and three letters of recommendation. At least two of which are from deans, department heads and/or professors who have supervised the applicant's most recent academic work. These letters should present essential facts regarding scholastic record, capacity for work, extracurricular activities, career potential, ability to cooperate, character and personality and interest and capability in research. **Deadline:** April 1. **Contact:** Cheryl Kruchten at the above address.

1187 ■ ASBC Foundation Undergraduate Scholarships *(Undergraduate/Scholarship)*

Purpose: To provide financial support to a student who is a daughter or son of an active ASBC member. **Focus:** General studies. **Qualif.:** Candidate must be the daughter or son of an active ASBC member. Candidate must be enrolled as an undergraduate student at a college or university and be actively pursuing a bachelor's degree. For full-time undergraduate students, candidates must be enrolled in an academic schedule that meets the minimum requirements of the attending college or university. **Criteria:** Scholarship recipients will be selected based on the jury's review of the application materials.

Funds Avail.: $1,000. **To Apply:** Applicants must submit a completed application form; copies of transcripts; a letter of application describing career plans; and three letters of recommendation with at least two from the academic adviser and/or faculty members familiar with the applicant's academic record. The confidential letter(s) should include a general appraisal of the scholarship, extracurricular activities and abilities in particular relation to the purposes and eligibility requirements of the scholarships. **Deadline:** April 1. **Contact:** Beth Elliott at the above address.

1188 ■ American Society of Business Publication Editors (ASBPE)

214 N Hale St.
Wheaton, IL 60187
Ph: (630) 510-4588
Fax: (630) 510-4501
E-mail: info@asbpe.org
URL: www.asbpe.org

1189 ■ ASBPE Young Leaders Scholarships
(All/Scholarship)

Purpose: To help young editors in their careers. **Focus:** Business; Editors and editing. **Qualif.:** Applicant must be an editor; 30 years old or younger; worked as an editor in a business magazine for at least two years; must be sponsored by the applicant's chief editor; pursuing career in

business press; and must not be a past winner of the ASBPE Young Leaders Scholarship. **Criteria:** Selection is based on merit.

Funds Avail.: Exact amount is not specified. **Number Awarded:** 5. **To Apply:** Application form is available at the website. **Deadline:** April 1. **Contact:** For further information, applicants may e-mail at asbpe.info@asbpe.org.

1190 ■ American Society of Certified Engineering Technicians

PO Box 1536
Brandon, MS 39043
Ph: (601) 824-8991
Fax: (913) 890-1021
URL: www.ascet.org

1191 ■ Joseph C. Johnson Memorial Grants
(Undergraduate/Scholarship)

Purpose: To diminish the cost of tuition, books, and lab fees for students. **Focus:** Engineering. **Qualif.:** Applicant must be an American citizen or a legal resident, a student, certified, regular, registered or associate member of AS-CET; full or part-time student in an Engineering Technology program (students in a two year program should apply in the first year to receive the grant for their second year. Students in a four year program who apply in the third year may receive the grant for their fourth year); and be qualified for financial aid under the Federal College Work Study Program. Applicant must meet the following grade requirements: 2 points on a 3 point system, 3 points on a 4 point system, 4 points on a 5 point system, or 5 points on a 6 point system. **Criteria:** Priority will be given to applicants who have demonstrated financial need, as verified by the Dean or Registrar of Engineering Technology, or the Financial Aid Office at the institution the applicant attends.

Funds Avail.: $750. **To Apply:** Applicants must submit a fully accomplished printed or typewritten application form available online; a letter of recommendation from a faculty member of the Engineering Technology Department indicating the motivation, progress, achievements, and an evaluation of the applicant's potential in the field of Engineering Technology; letters of recommendation from two personal acquaintances, employers or former employers, outlining association, motivation and potential for success; a copy of transcript of records and be sure to pass all the requirements on time.

1192 ■ Joseph M. Parish Memorial Grants
(Undergraduate/Scholarship)

Purpose: To diminish the cost of tuition, books, and lab fees for students. **Focus:** Engineering. **Qualif.:** Applicants must meet the following minimum grade points average: 2 points on a 3 point system, 3 points on a 4 point system, 4 points on a 5 point system, or 5 points on a 6 point system. must be U.S. citizens or legal residents; be student members of ASCET; be full time students in an Engineering Technology program; qualified for financial aid under the Federal Work Study Program. **Criteria:** Priority will be given to applicants who have demonstrated financial need, as verified by the Dean or Registrar of Engineering Technology, or the Financial Aid Office at the institution the applicant is attending.

Funds Avail.: $500. **Number Awarded:** 1. **To Apply:** Applicants must submit a fully accomplished printed or typewritten application form available online; a letter of

Awards are arranged alphabetically below their administering organizations

recommendation from a faculty member of the Engineering Technology Department indicating the motivation, progress, achievements, and an evaluation of the applicant's potential in the field of Engineering Technology; letters of recommendation from two personal acquaintances, employers or former employers, outlining association, motivation and potential for success; copy of transcript of records and be sure to pass all the requirements on time.

1193 ■ Kurt H. and Donna M. Schuler Cash Grants (Undergraduate/Scholarship)

Purpose: To offset the cost of educational expenses as desired. **Focus:** Engineering. **Qualif.:** Applicants must either be a student, certified, regular, registered, or associate member of ASCET; a high school senior in the last five months of the academic year who will be enrolled in an Engineering Technology curriculum no later than six months following selection for award; achieved passing grades in their present curriculum. **Criteria:** Priority given to applicants who show financial need, as verified by the Dean or Registrar of Engineering Technology, or the Financial Aid Office at the institution the applicant is attending.

Funds Avail.: $400. **To Apply:** Applicants must provide a copy of transcript; a letter of recommendation from a personal acquaintance, faculty member, or employer outlining motivation, progress, outstanding achievements, and an evaluation of the applicant's potential in the field of Engineering Technology.

1194 ■ American Society of Cinematographers

PO Box 2230
Hollywood, CA 90078
Ph: (323) 969-4333
Fax: (323) 882-6391
Free: 800-448-0145
E-mail: office@theasc.com
URL: www.theasc.com

1195 ■ William A. Fraker Student Heritage Awards (Graduate, Undergraduate/Award)

Purpose: To recognize cinematography students who made contributions to advance the art form. **Focus:** Cinema. **Qualif.:** Applicants must be undergraduate, graduate or recently graduated (within one year) cinematography students. **Criteria:** Applicants will be judged based on artful cinematography and effective creation of the images.

Funds Avail.: No specific amount. **To Apply:** Applicants must submit a film entry. **Deadline:** November. **Contact:** For more information, applicants must contact Lisa Muldowney at the above address; Phone: 760-438-5250; E-mail: lisam@cspr.com.

1196 ■ American Society for Clinical Laboratory Science (ASCLS)

1861 International Dr., Ste. 200
Tysons Corner, VA 22102
Ph: (571) 748-3770
E-mail: ascls@ascls.org
URL: www.ascls.org

1197 ■ Alpha Mu Tau Undergraduate Scholarships (Undergraduate/Scholarship)

Purpose: To provide financial assistance for professionals who are involved in advancement of clinical laboratory sciences. **Focus:** Clinical Laboratory sciences. **Qualif.:** Applicants must be United States citizens or permanent residents of the United States; accepted into an NAACLS accredited program in Clinical Laboratory Science, to include Clinical Laboratory Science, Medical Technology, Clinical Laboratory Technician/Medical Laboratory Technician, Cytotechnology or Histotechnology; in or entering their last year of study on September 1st. **Criteria:** Candidates will be evaluated by the Scholarship Committee.

Funds Avail.: $1,500. **To Apply:** Applicants must submit a completed application form including all required documents to Joe Briden, AMTF Scholarship Coordinator, 7809 S 21st Dr., Phoenix, AZ 85041-7736. **Deadline:** April 1.

1198 ■ Ruth M. French Graduate or Undergraduate Scholarships (Doctorate, Graduate, Undergraduate/Scholarship)

Purpose: To provide financial assistance for professionals who are involved in advancement of clinical laboratory sciences. **Focus:** Clinical Laboratory sciences. **Qualif.:** Applicants must be U.S. citizens or permanent residents of the country; must be accepted into or are in an approved Master's or Doctoral program in areas related to Clinical Laboratory Science including Clinical Laboratory Education or Management Programs; or must be accepted into an NAACLS accredited program in Clinical Laboratory Science, to include Clinical Laboratory Science/Medical Technology, Clinical Laboratory Technician/Medical Laboratory Technician, Cytotechnology or Histotechnology; in or entering the last year of study on September 1st. **Criteria:** Candidates will be evaluated by the Scholarship Committee.

Funds Avail.: $3,000. **Number Awarded:** 1. **To Apply:** Applicants must submit a completed application form. **Deadline:** April 1.

1199 ■ Dorothy Morrison Undergraduate Scholarships (Undergraduate/Scholarship)

Purpose: To provide financial assistance to professionals who are involved in advancement of clinical laboratory sciences. **Focus:** Clinical Laboratory sciences. **Qualif.:** Applicants must be United States citizens or permanent residents of the United States; accepted into an NAACLS accredited program in Clinical Laboratory Science, to include Clinical Laboratory Science/Medical Technology, Clinical Laboratory Technician/Medical Laboratory Technician, Cytotechnology or Histotechnology; in or entering their last year of study on September 1st. **Criteria:** Candidates will be evaluated by the Scholarship Committee.

Funds Avail.: $2,000. **Number Awarded:** 1. **To Apply:** Applicants must submit the completed application form; original and four copies of letter of admission; two letters of recommendation; and two performance sheets. Send all application materials to: Joe Briden, Scholarship Coordinator at 7809 S 21st Dr., Phoenix, AZ 85041-7736. **Deadline:** April 1.

1200 ■ American Society of Colon and Rectal Surgeons (ASCRS)

85 W Algonquin Rd., Ste. 550
Arlington Heights, IL 60005
Ph: (847) 290-9184
Fax: (847) 290-9203
E-mail: ascrs@fascrs.org
URL: www.fascrs.org

Awards are arranged alphabetically below their administering organizations

1201 ■ American Society of Colon and Rectal Surgeons International Fellowships (Professional development/Fellowship)

Purpose: To provide opportunities for surgeons to visit clinical, teaching and research activities in North America. **Focus:** Surgery. **Qualif.:** Applicants must have completed their training in colorectal surgery; have manifested interest in colon and rectal surgery as evidenced by practice, teaching, research or writings; have minimum of two years specialty colorectal practice experience; and must have a commitment from a center to host the recipient. **Criteria:** To qualify for the fellowship, candidates should: 1) be proposed in writing by the chair of their department; 2) submit two letters of recommendation from individuals whom they have worked with; and 3) submit other supporting documents, including curriculum vitae.

Funds Avail.: $6,000. **To Apply:** Applicants must submit an application form; two letters of recommendation; completed activity profile; list of publications and presentations made at International meetings. **Deadline:** November 1. **Contact:** Application form and supporting documents must be submitted to Graham Newstead at the above address.

1202 ■ American Society of Colon and Rectal Surgeons Travel Scholarships (Professional development/Scholarship)

Purpose: To help colorectal surgeons further their education. **Focus:** Surgery. **Qualif.:** Applicants must have completed general surgical training and must be currently involved in colorectal surgical training; must demonstrate a commitment to practice colorectal surgery; have a guarantee of one-third funding support within their colorectal society, organization, or group; and be willing to undertake the scholarship at the next meeting. **Criteria:** In order for candidates to qualify, they should: 1) be proposed in writing by the current President or an official nominee of the institution where they are trained; 2) submit references of recommendation from the Chairman of the Department where they are working; 3) submit curriculum vitae; and 4) submit a personal statement.

Funds Avail.: $3,000. **Number Awarded:** 6. **To Apply:** Applicants must submit a filled-out application form; two letters of recommendation (one from any official of the society where they undergo training and one from the Chairman of the Department where they are working); current activity profile; and list of publications, research work and presentations. **Deadline:** November 1. **Contact:** Application form and supporting documents must be sent to: Graham Newstead at the above address.

1203 ■ American Society of Comparative Law (ASCL)

245 Winter St. SE
Salem, OR 97301
Ph: (503) 370-6403
Fax: (503) 370-6375
E-mail: symeon@willamette.edu
URL: www.comparativelaw.org

1204 ■ American Society of Comparative Law TransCoop Programs (All/Fellowship)

Purpose: To provide funds for cooperative research between German, American and/or Canadian scholars in the fields of humanities, social sciences, law and econom-

ics. **Focus:** Humanities; Social Sciences; Law; Economics. **Qualif.:** Applicants must be permanent residents or scholars of United States, Germany and Canada. **Criteria:** Recipients are selected based on originality of the proposed research work; scholarly qualifications of the applicants; and potential to strengthen transatlantic cooperation.

Funds Avail.: No specific amount. **To Apply:** Applicants must submit completed application form; time and expenses schedule indicating when and for what purpose funds will be required; one confidential reference letter; publication list; proof of matching funds. **Deadline:** April 30 and October 31. **Contact:** info@avh.de.

1205 ■ American Society of Composers, Authors and Publishers Foundation (ASCAP)

1 Lincoln Plz.
New York, NY 10023-7142
Ph: (212) 621-6219
Fax: (212) 595-3342
E-mail: info@ascapfoundation.com
URL: www.ascapfoundation.org

1206 ■ Louis Armstrong Scholarships (High School/Scholarship)

Purpose: To award scholarship to students in their junior year. **Focus:** Music. **Qualif.:** Applicant must be a junior-year student and enrolled full-time at Mt. Vernon High School, Mt. Vernon, NY. **Criteria:** Selection will be based on abilities in music performance and composition.

Funds Avail.: No specific amount. **To Apply:** The ASCAP Foundation does not accept applications for this scholarship. Interested students should consult their financial aid office for application information.

1207 ■ Charlotte V. Bergen Scholarships (Undergraduate/Scholarship)

Purpose: To provide scholarship to young composers, aged 18 or under, to be used for music study at an accredited college or music conservatory. **Focus:** Music. **Qualif.:** Applicants must be citizens or permanent residents of the United States or enrolled students with Students Visas. **Criteria:** Selection will be based on the committee's criteria.

Funds Avail.: No specific amount. **To Apply:** Applicants must submit a completed application form, one reproduction of a manuscript or score, biographical information including music studies, background and experience and a list of compositions. Completed Application materials must be postmarked on or before the deadline. **Deadline:** February 12.

1208 ■ Cherry Lane Foundation/Music Alive! Scholarships (Undergraduate/Scholarship)

Purpose: To award scholarships annually to African-American college or university students. **Focus:** Music. **Qualif.:** Applicant must be an African-American college or university student majoring in music. Applicants must demonstrate musical talent and proficiency in the areas of arranging, producing, conducting, performing. **Criteria:** Selection will be based on the committee's criteria.

Funds Avail.: No specific amount. **To Apply:** The ASCAP Foundation does not accept applications for this scholarship. Interested students should consult their school's financial aid office for application information.

1209 ■ Fran Morgenstern Davis Scholarships (Undergraduate/Scholarship)

Purpose: To provide scholarship to the music composition students at the Manhattan School of Music. **Focus:** Music.

Awards are arranged alphabetically below their administering organizations

Qualif.: Applicants must be full-time undergraduate music composition students at the Manhattan School of Music who demonstrate the potential to produce creative and original work and who also demonstrate financial need. **Criteria:** Selection will be based on the Manhattan School of Music faculty's criteria.

Funds Avail.: No specific amount. **Number Awarded:** 2. **To Apply:** Applicants must submit an application together with other required documents to the Manhattan School of Music.

1210 ■ John Denver Music Scholarships
(Undergraduate/Scholarship)

Purpose: To provide young music students with an opportunity to attend a summer music camp which they would otherwise not be able to afford. **Focus:** Music. **Qualif.:** Applicants must be students, aged 10-16, who demonstrate both musical promise and financial need. **Criteria:** Selection will be based on the committee's criteria.

Funds Avail.: No specific amount. **Number Awarded:** 3. **To Apply:** Applicants must submit an application to the Perry-Mansfield School in Steamboat Springs, Colorado. **Contact:** Perry-Mansfield School in Steamboat Springs, Colorado; 800-430-ARTS; p-m@cmn.ne.

1211 ■ Louis Dreyfus Warner-Chappell City College Scholarships *(Undergraduate/Scholarship)*

Purpose: To award scholarships to composition students for scores written for dance, film/video or theater. **Focus:** Music. **Qualif.:** Applicants must be students enrolled in either a B.A. or B.F.A. program at the City College/City University of New York. **Criteria:** Selection will be based on the committee's criteria.

Funds Avail.: No specific amount. **To Apply:** The ASCAP Foundation does not accept applications for this scholarship. Interested students should consult their school's financial aid office for application information.

1212 ■ Steve Kaplan TV and Film Studies Scholarships *(Professional development/Scholarship)*

Purpose: To provide financial assistance for an aspiring television and film composer to attend ASCAP's Film Scoring Workshop in Los Angeles. **Focus:** Filmmaking; Music. **Qualif.:** Applicant must be a television and film composer. **Criteria:** Selection will be based on the committee's criteria.

Funds Avail.: No specific amount. **To Apply:** Interested applicants may contact the Foundation for the application information.

1213 ■ Leiber and Stoller Music Scholarships
(Undergraduate/Scholarship)

Purpose: To provide assistance to young aspiring songwriters, musicians and vocalists. **Focus:** Music. **Qualif.:** Applicants must be incoming freshmen at Berklee College of Music. **Criteria:** Selection will be based on the committee's criteria.

Funds Avail.: No specific amount. **Number Awarded:** 2. **To Apply:** Interested students should consult their financial aid office for application information.

1214 ■ Rudy Perez Songwriting Scholarships
(Undergraduate/Scholarship)

Purpose: To present scholarships to aspiring Latino songwriters. **Focus:** Music. **Qualif.:** Applicant must be an aspir-

ing Latino songwriter who demonstrates potential to produce creative and original work and also demonstrates financial need. **Criteria:** Selection will be based on the committee's criteria.

Funds Avail.: No specific amount. **Number Awarded:** 1. **To Apply:** The ASCAP Foundation does not accept applications for this scholarship. Interested students should consult their school's financial aid office for application information.

1215 ■ David Rose Scholarships
(Undergraduate/Scholarship)

Purpose: To award scholarship to qualified college-level students. **Focus:** Filmmaking; Music. **Qualif.:** Applicant must be a college-level student working toward a career in scoring for film and/or television who is participating in AS-CAP's Film and Television Scoring Workshop. **Criteria:** Selection will be based on the committee's criteria.

Funds Avail.: No specific amount. **To Apply:** The ASCAP Foundation does not accept applications for this scholarship. Interested students should consult their school's financial aid office for application information.

1216 ■ American Society of Crime Laboratory Directors (ASCLD)
139A Technology Dr.
Garner, NC 27529
Ph: (919) 773-2044
Fax: (919) 861-9930
E-mail: office@ascld.org
URL: www.ascld.org

1217 ■ American Society of Crime Laboratory Directors Scholarships *(Graduate, Undergraduate/Scholarship)*

Purpose: To provide opportunities to students intending to enter the forensic field. **Focus:** Science. **Qualif.:** Applicants must be juniors or senior students in a baccalaureate program; or graduate students (master's or doctorate) at an accredited university who are pursuing a degree in forensic science, forensic chemistry, physical or natural science; **Criteria:** Recipients will be selected based on their overall scholastic record especially in forensic science coursework, motivation or commitment to a forensic science career, personal statement and according to faculty or advisor's recommendation. At least three ASCLD members who are not affiliated with institutions from which students are applying will evaluate the pool of applicants. Applicants from FEPAC accredited programs will be given additional consideration.

Funds Avail.: $1,000. **Number Awarded:** 1. **To Apply:** Applicants must submit a completed application form; transcript of records; personal statement; and letter of recommendation of faculty members or a laboratory director. **Deadline:** Initial application will be submitted on April 15; transcripts and recommendations will be on June 30 each year.

1218 ■ American Society of Criminology (ASC)
1314 Kinnear Rd., Ste. 212
Columbus, OH 43212-1156
Ph: (614) 292-9207
Fax: (614) 292-6767
E-mail: asc@asc41.com

Awards are arranged alphabetically below their administering organizations

URL: www.asc41.com

1219 ■ ASC Graduate Fellowships for Ethnic Minorities (Doctorate, Graduate/Fellowship)

Purpose: To promote education in the field of criminology and criminal justice by ethnic minority students. **Focus:** Criminology; Criminal justice. **Qualif.:** Applicant must be an African American, Asian American, Latino, or Native American student entering the field of criminology and criminal justice. **Criteria:** Selection is based on the application materials submitted.

Funds Avail.: $6,000. **Number Awarded:** 3. **To Apply:** Applicants must submit an up-to-date curriculum vitae; an indication of race or ethnicity; copies of undergraduate and graduate transcripts; a statement of need and prospects for financial assistance for graduate study; a letter describing career plans, salient experiences and nature of interest in criminology and criminal justice and three letters of reference. Application package must be sent to Tracey Meares, Yale Law School, 127 Wall St., New Haven, CT 06520. **Deadline:** March 1. **Contact:** Tracey Meares at 203-432-4074, or tracey.meares@yale.edu.

1220 ■ American Society for Eighteenth-Century Studies (ASECS)

Wake Forest University
Winston-Salem, NC 27109
Ph: (336) 727-4694
Fax: (336) 727-4697
E-mail: asecs@wfu.edu
URL: asecs.press.jhu.edu

1221 ■ ASECS Graduate Student Research Paper Awards (Graduate/Award)

Purpose: To recognize pioneering research contributions of the next generation of scholars of eighteenth-century studies. **Focus:** General studies. **Qualif.:** Applicants must be graduate scholars of the eighteenth-century studies. **Criteria:** Recipients will be selected based on submitted paper.

Funds Avail.: $200. **To Apply:** Applicants must submit four copies of a research essay (15-30 pages) that has not been previously published; and must submit a letter of endorsement from a mentoring professor which outlines the originality and contributions in the field of eighteenth-century studies. **Deadline:** January 1.

1222 ■ ASECS Innovative Course Design Competition (Undergraduate/Award)

Purpose: To encourage excellence in undergraduate teaching of the eighteenth century. **Focus:** General studies. **Qualif.:** Applicants must be undergraduate student members in any ASECS constituent disciplines. **Criteria:** Proposals will be evaluated based on relationship to design, readings, pedagogy and/or activities.

Funds Avail.: Amount not specified. **To Apply:** Applicants must submit five copies of a (three to five page) proposal. It should be for a new approach of teaching a unit within a course on the eighteenth century. **Deadline:** October 1. **Contact:** Applicants must submit their proposal to Byron R. Wells at the above address.

1223 ■ ASECS Women's Caucus Editing and Translation Fellowships (Doctorate/Fellowship)

Purpose: To support an editing or a translation work in progress of an eighteenth-century primary text on a feminist or a women's studies subject. **Focus:** Women's studies. **Qualif.:** Applicants must be ASECS members who have received a PhD degree. **Criteria:** Applicants will be evaluated based on submitted proposal.

Funds Avail.: $1,000. **To Apply:** Applicants must submit a project translated or edited by eighteenth-century women writers or works that significantly advance the women's experience in the eighteenth century; must include curriculum vitae, three to five page proposal outlining the project, a two-page bibliography of pertinent works, two letters of recommendation and a budget explaining the candidate's plans for using the funds. Winner will be asked to submit a brief written report on the progress of the project one year after receiving the award. Five copies of the proposal should be submitted to the ASECS office. **Deadline:** January 15.

1224 ■ Paula Backscheider Archival Fellowships (Professional development/Fellowship)

Purpose: To support researchers whose projects necessitate work in archives, repositories and special collections (public and private) in foreign countries and/or in the United States. **Focus:** General studies. **Qualif.:** Applicants must be members of ASECS. **Criteria:** Recipients will be selected based on submitted materials.

Funds Avail.: $750. **To Apply:** Applicants must submit an application form, curriculum vitae, one-page bibliography of major related books and articles, narrative description of the project and two letters of recommendation. **Deadline:** January 1.

1225 ■ Theodore E.D. Braun Research Travel Fellowships (Professional development/Fellowship)

Purpose: To support researchers, regardless of rank, who are working in French literary studies. **Focus:** Area and ethnic studies. **Qualif.:** Applicants must be ASECS members. **Criteria:** Recipients will be selected based on submitted materials.

Funds Avail.: $1,000. **To Apply:** Applicants must submit an application form, curriculum vitae, one-page bibliography of major related books and articles, narrative description of the project and two letters of recommendation. **Deadline:** January 1.

1226 ■ Emilie Du Chatelet Awards (Doctorate/Award)

Purpose: To support research in progress by independent or adjunct scholars on a feminist or women's studies subject. **Focus:** Women's studies. **Qualif.:** Applicants must be ASECS members who have received their PhD and who do not currently hold a tenured, tenure-track or job-secure position in a college or university. **Criteria:** Selection will be based on submitted project.

Funds Avail.: $500. **To Apply:** Applicants must include a curriculum vitae, one to three page research proposal outlining the project and candidate's plans for using the funds. Winner will be asked to submit a brief written report on the progress of the project after one year of receiving the award. **Deadline:** January 15.

1227 ■ James L. Clifford Prize (Professional development/Prize)

Purpose: To recognize authors interested in eighteenth-century studies. **Focus:** General studies. **Qualif.:** Applicants must be author(s) of an article in outstanding study

Awards are arranged alphabetically below their administering organizations

of some aspect of eighteenth-century culture; must be members of the ASECS at the time of submission. Articles must have appeared in print journal, festschrift or other serial publications. **Criteria:** Recipients will be selected based on submitted article.

Funds Avail.: $500. **To Apply:** Applicants must submit an article of no more than 15000 words. Nominations must be submitted in PDF format with one hard copy. **Deadline:** January 1. **Contact:** Applicants must submit their proposal to Byron R. Wells at the above address.

1228 ■ Louis Gottschalk Prize *(Professional development/Prize)*

Purpose: To recognize the book written by the members of the society. **Focus:** General studies. **Qualif.:** Applicants must be authors of a scholarly book including commentaries, biographies, collections of essays by a single author and critical editions or written in any language; authors must be members of the society at the time of application. A book must have a copyright date between November 2010 and October 2011. **Criteria:** Winner will be chosen based on submitted materials.

Funds Avail.: $1,000. **To Apply:** Publishers must submit five copies of a book. **Deadline:** November 15. **Contact:** Submission should be directed to this address: 2598 Reynolda Rd., Ste. C, Winston-Salem, NC 27106.

1229 ■ Hemlow Prize in Burney Studies *(Graduate/Prize)*

Purpose: To recognize the best essay written by students. **Focus:** General studies. **Qualif.:** Applicants must be graduate students. **Criteria:** Applicants will be judged based on essay's originality, coherence, use of source material, awareness of other work in the field and documentation.

Funds Avail.: $250. **To Apply:** Applicants must submit two copies of the essay (one appropriate for blind submission). **Deadline:** September 1. **Contact:** Dr. Lorna Clark at lj_clark@carleton.ca.

1230 ■ Irish-American Research Travel Fellowships *(Professional development/Fellowship)*

Purpose: To support documentary scholarship in Ireland in the period between the Treaty of Limerick (1691) and the Act of Union (1800) to enable North American-based scholars to travel in Ireland and Irish-based scholars to travel in North America for furthering their research. **Focus:** General studies. **Qualif.:** Applicants must be ASECS members who are residents of North America, or members of ASEC's Irish sister organization, Eighteenth-Century Ireland Society who are residents of the Republic of Ireland or Northern Ireland. **Criteria:** Recipients will be selected based on submitted materials.

Funds Avail.: $2,500. **To Apply:** Applicants must submit an application form, curriculum vitae, one-page bibliography of major related books and articles, narrative description of the project and two letters of recommendation. **Deadline:** November 15.

1231 ■ Oscar Kenshur Book Prize *(Professional development/Prize)*

Purpose: To recognize authors working in a range of disciplines. **Focus:** General studies. **Qualif.:** Applicants must be authors of a book. **Criteria:** Award will be given to applicants who best meet the requirements.

Funds Avail.: $1,000. **To Apply:** Authors or publishers must submit three copies of the book. For additional information, applicants must contact the Director of the Center for Eighteenth-Century Studies at Indiana University. **Deadline:** January 31. **Contact:** For further inquiries, applicants must contact Prof. Dror Wahrman at dwahrman@indiana.edu.

1232 ■ Gwin J. and Ruth Kolb Travel Fellowships *(Doctorate, Professional development/Fellowship)*

Purpose: To supplement costs for younger eighteenth-century scholars to travel to distant collections in North America and abroad. **Focus:** General studies. **Qualif.:** Applicants must be members of ASECS who are faculty and independent scholars within the first five years of receipt of their PhD. Advanced doctoral candidates with a demonstrable need for specific collections necessary for their dissertation are also encouraged to apply. **Criteria:** Applicants will be evaluated based on submitted materials.

Funds Avail.: $500. **To Apply:** Applicants must submit an application form, curriculum vitae, one-page bibliography of major related books and articles, narrative description of the project and two letters of recommendation. **Deadline:** January 1.

1233 ■ Catharine Macaulay Prize *(Graduate/Prize)*

Purpose: To recognize student's paper in the field of feminist and gender studies. **Focus:** Women's studies. **Qualif.:** Applicants must be graduate students interested in the field of feminist and gender studies. **Criteria:** Recipients will be selected based on submitted paper.

Funds Avail.: $350. **To Apply:** Applicants must submit a paper. It should advance understanding of gender dynamics, women's experiences and/or women's contributions and offer a feminist analysis of any aspect to eighteenth-century culture and/or society. **Deadline:** September 1.

1234 ■ Robert R. Palmer Research Travel Fellowships *(Professional development/Fellowship)*

Purpose: To support documentary research related primarily to the history and culture of France. **Focus:** General studies. **Qualif.:** Applicants must be members of ASECS. **Criteria:** Recipients will be selected based on submitted materials.

Funds Avail.: $500. **To Apply:** Applicants must submit a completed application form, curriculum vitae, one-page bibliography of major related books and articles, narrative description of the project and two letters of recommendation. **Deadline:** January 1.

1235 ■ Hans Turley Prize in Queer Eighteenth-Century Studies *(Graduate, Professional development/Prize)*

Purpose: To recognize a student's paper on a topic in Lesbian, Gay, Bisexual, Transgender or Queer studies delivered at the ASECS Annual meeting. **Focus:** General studies. **Qualif.:** Applicants must be graduate students, untenured faculty members or independent scholars. **Criteria:** Recipients will be selected based on submitted paper.

Funds Avail.: Amount not specified. **To Apply:** Applicants must submit a paper addressing issues on LGBT or Queer studies. **Deadline:** August 15.

1236 ■ Aubrey L. Williams Research Travel Fellowships *(Professional development/Fellowship)*

Purpose: To support documentary research in eighteenth-century English literature by American-based scholars. **Fo-

Awards are arranged alphabetically below their administering organizations

cus: Literature. **Qualif.:** Applicants must be ASECS members and be residents of North America. **Criteria:** Recipients will be selected based on submitted materials.

Funds Avail.: $1,500. **To Apply:** Applicants must submit an application form, curriculum vitae, one-page bibliography of major related books and articles, narrative description of the project and two letters of recommendation. **Deadline:** January 1.

1237 ■ American Society of Electroneurodiagnostic Technologists (ASET)

402 E Bannister Rd., Ste. A
Kansas City, MO 64131-3019
Ph: (816) 931-1120
Fax: (816) 931-1145
E-mail: info@aset.org
URL: www.aset.org

1238 ■ American Society of Electroneurodiagnostic Technologists Student Education Grants (ASET) *(Undergraduate/Grant)*

Purpose: To assist and encourage students to further or continue their interest in selecting the allied health field of electroneurodiagnostic technology as a pending or continued career. **Focus:** Health sciences. **Qualif.:** Applicant must be a student enrolled full-time in a CAAHEP accredited END school; or an employee of ASET member companies or individuals. Relatives of the Foundation Selection Committee and the Foundation Board of Directors are not qualified for grants. **Criteria:** Selection Committees will review all submitted applications based on applicant's interest in pursuing a career; scholastic achievement including GPA; interest in pursuing a degree; upon references and recommendations by instructors, employers and other pertinent individuals.

Funds Avail.: $1,500. **To Apply:** Applicants must submit an application; copies of transcript; recommendations and reference letters; an outline of the proposed program of study. **Deadline:** July 1. **Contact:** For any questions or additional information, contact Arlen Reimnitz, ASET Executive Director at the above address or e-mail her at arlen@aset.org.

1239 ■ ASET Educational Seminars, Courses and Program Scholarships *(All, Professional development/Scholarship)*

Purpose: To provide conference, seminars, and other educational opportunities to ASET members. **Focus:** Neuroscience. **Qualif.:** Applicant must be an ASET member who wishes to attend an ASET conference, seminar, and other educational opportunities. **Criteria:** Selection is based on financial need and educational needs.

Funds Avail.: No specific amount. **To Apply:** Application form is available at the website. Applicant must include a typed, signed statement and a recommendation letter from a supervisor. **Deadline:** May 4.

1240 ■ American Society for Engineering Education (ASEE)

1818 N St. NW, Ste. 600
Washington, DC 20036-2479
Ph: (202) 331-3500
Fax: (202) 265-8504
E-mail: pubsinfo@asee.org

URL: www.asee.org

1241 ■ NASA Aeronautics Scholarships - Undergraduate Program *(Undergraduate/Scholarship)*

Purpose: To provide financial assistance for rising undergraduate students entering their third year of education at a college or university. **Focus:** Engineering, Mechanical; Engineering, Electrical. **Qualif.:** Applicants must be citizens or nationals of the United States with at least two years of full time study left to complete at an accredited U.S. college or university as of fall. **Criteria:** Applicants are evaluated based on academic performance.

Funds Avail.: $15,000. **To Apply:** Applicants must submit all the required application information electronically at www.asee.org. **Deadline:** January 11.

1242 ■ American Society for Enology and Viticulture (ASEV)

PO Box 1855
Davis, CA 95617-1855
Ph: (530) 753-3142
Fax: (530) 753-3318
E-mail: society@asev.org
URL: asev.org

1243 ■ American Society for Enology and Viticulture Scholarships *(Graduate, Undergraduate/Scholarship)*

Purpose: To define questions in the wine industry and work towards answers based on the relevant and scientifically rigorous information on selected topics. **Focus:** Viticulture. **Qualif.:** Applicants must be undergraduate or graduate students accepted into a full-time accredited four year college or university program; be in their junior status for the upcoming academic year (45/60 quarter units); undergraduate students must have a minimum cumulative grade point average of 3.0; graduate students must have a minimum overall grade point average of 3.2. These averages must be based on a scale maximum of 4.0; have curriculum emphasizing enology, viticulture or science basic to the wine and grape industry. **Criteria:** Undergraduate and graduate students will be rated on a separate basis.

Funds Avail.: Vary from year to year. **To Apply:** Applicants must download the scholarship application form or contact ASEV office; fill out the application form after receiving the packet; must submit an original or copies of transcripts; two original letters of recommendation; (one-page) statement of intent; and list of planned courses for the upcoming academic year. **Deadline:** March 1.

1244 ■ American Society for Environmental History (ASEH)

University of Washington
Interdisciplinary Arts and Sciences Program
1900 Commerce St.
Tacoma, WA 98402
E-mail: director@aseh.net
URL: www.aseh.net

1245 ■ American Society for Environmental History Minority Travel Grants *(Graduate, Professional development/Grant)*

Purpose: To support individuals present their research at ASEH's annual meetings. **Focus:** General studies. **Qualif.:**

Awards are arranged alphabetically below their administering organizations

Applicants must be minority, low income scholars or graduate students. **Criteria:** Recipients will be selected based on qualifications and submitted materials. Special consideration will be given to first time applicants.

Funds Avail.: $500. **To Apply:** Applicants must submit a brief vita or resume (at least two pages); one-page statement outlining their interest/objectives in attending the ASEH conference. Applicants should specify the sources of funding already received and/or applied for. Documents should be e-mailed with the subject line "Madison Travel Grant." **Deadline:** October 14.

1246 ■ Rachel Carson Prize *(Professional development/Prize)*

Purpose: To recognize individuals who work in the field of environmental history. **Focus:** History; Environmental science. **Qualif.:** Applicants must be individuals who made the best dissertation in environmental history. **Criteria:** Applications will be evaluated based on submitted dissertation.

Funds Avail.: Amount not specified. **To Apply:** Applicants must send three copies (hard or paper copies). If dissertation was approved between November 1 of the current year and October 31 of the following year, it should be submitted in PDF format as a single file, less than five megabytes. **Deadline:** November 10. **Contact:** Materials should be submitted electronically to Anne Coleman at acolema3@nd.edu.

1247 ■ Alice Hamilton Prize *(Professional development/Prize)*

Purpose: To recognize individuals who work outside the field of environmental history. **Focus:** General studies. **Qualif.:** Applicants must be authors of an article outside environmental history. **Criteria:** Applications will be evaluated based on submitted articles.

Funds Avail.: Amount not specified. **To Apply:** Applicants must send three copies (hard or paper copies) of an article. **Deadline:** November 10. **Contact:** Materials should be submitted electronically to Anne Coleman at acolema3@nd.edu.

1248 ■ Samuel P. Hays Research Fellowships *(Professional development/Fellowship)*

Purpose: To advance the field of environmental history. **Focus:** History; Environmental science. **Qualif.:** Applicants must be practicing historians (either academic, public, or independent). **Criteria:** Recipients will be judged based on submitted materials.

Funds Avail.: $1,000. **To Apply:** Applicants must submit a two-page (500 words) statement explaining the project and how it is intended for the research funds; must submit a curriculum vitae no more than three pages in length. **Deadline:** September 30. **Contact:** Materials should be submitted electronically to Phil Garone at pgarone@csustan.edu.

1249 ■ George Perkins Marsh Prize *(Professional development/Prize)*

Purpose: To recognize individuals who work in the field of environmental history. **Focus:** History; Environmental science. **Qualif.:** Applicants must be authors of a book in the field of environmental history. **Criteria:** Applications will be evaluated based on submitted books.

Funds Avail.: Amount not specified. **To Apply:** Applicants must send three copies (hard or paper copies) of a book. **Deadline:** November 10. **Contact:** Materials should be

submitted electronically to Anne Coleman at acolema3@nd.edu.

1250 ■ E.V. and Nancy Melosi Travel Grants *(Graduate, Professional development/Grant)*

Purpose: To support individuals present their research at ASEH's annual meetings. **Focus:** General studies. **Qualif.:** Applicants must be graduate students, low income and international scholars. **Criteria:** Recipients will be selected based on qualifications and submitted materials. Special consideration will be given to first time applicants.

Funds Avail.: $500. **To Apply:** Applicants must submit a brief vita or resume (at least two pages); one-page statement outlining their interest/objectives in attending the ASEH conference. Applicants should specify the sources of funding already received and/or applied for. Documents should be e-mailed with the subject line "Madison Travel Grant." **Deadline:** October 14.

1251 ■ Ellen Swallow Richards Travel Grants *(Graduate, Professional development/Grant)*

Purpose: To support individuals present their research at ASEH's annual meetings. **Focus:** General studies. **Qualif.:** Applicants must be graduate students, low income and international scholars. **Criteria:** Recipients will be selected based on qualifications and submitted materials. Special consideration will be given to first time applicants.

Funds Avail.: $500. **To Apply:** Applicants must submit a brief vita or resume (at least two pages); one-page statement outlining their interest/objectives in attending the ASEH conference. Applicants should specify the sources of funding already received and/or applied for. Documents should be e-mailed with the subject line "Madison Travel Grant." **Deadline:** October 14.

1252 ■ Hal Rothman Dissertation Fellowships *(Doctorate/Fellowship)*

Purpose: To recognize graduate students and to support archival research and travel. **Focus:** History; Environmental science. **Qualif.:** Applicants must be PhD students in the field of environmental history. **Criteria:** Recipients will be selected based on qualifications and submitted materials.

Funds Avail.: $1,000. **To Apply:** Applicants must submit a two-page (500 words) statement explaining the project and how it is intended for the research funds, curriculum vitae and a letter of recommendation from graduate advisors. **Deadline:** September 30. **Contact:** Materials should be submitted electronically to Kim Little at klittle@uca.edu.

1253 ■ Morgan and Jeanie Sherwood Travel Grants *(Graduate, Professional development/Grant)*

Purpose: To support individuals present their research at ASEH's annual meetings. **Focus:** General studies. **Qualif.:** Applicants must be graduate students, low income and international scholars. **Criteria:** Recipients will be selected based on qualifications and submitted materials. Special consideration will be given to first time applicants.

Funds Avail.: $500. **To Apply:** Applicants must submit a brief vita or resume (at least two pages); one-page statement outlining their interest/objectives in attending the ASEH conference. Applicants should specify the sources of funding already received and/or applied for. Documents should be e-mailed with the subject line "Madison Travel Grant." **Deadline:** October 14.

Awards are arranged alphabetically below their administering organizations

1254 ■ John D. Wirth Travel Grants for International Scholars *(Graduate, Professional development/Grant)*

Purpose: To help individuals present their research at ASEH's annual meetings. **Focus:** General studies. **Qualif.:** Applicants must be graduate students, low-income and international scholars. **Criteria:** Recipients will be selected based on qualifications and submitted materials. Special consideration will be given to first time applicants.

Funds Avail.: $500. **To Apply:** Applicants must submit a brief vita or resume (at least two pages); one-page statement outlining their interest/objectives in attending the ASEH conference. Applicants should specify the sources of funding already received and/or applied for. Documents should be e-mailed with the subject line "Madison Travel Grant." **Deadline:** October 14.

1255 ■ Donald Worster Travel Grants *(Graduate, Professional development/Grant)*

Purpose: To support individuals present their research at ASEH's annual meetings. **Focus:** General studies. **Qualif.:** Applicants must be graduate students, low income and international scholars. **Criteria:** Recipients will be selected based on qualifications and submitted materials. Special consideration will be given to first time applicants.

Funds Avail.: $500. **To Apply:** Applicants must submit a brief vita or resume (at least two pages); one-page statement outlining their interest/objectives in attending the ASEH conference. Applicants should specify the sources of funding already received and/or applied for. Documents should be e-mailed with the subject line "Madison Travel Grant." **Deadline:** October 14.

1256 ■ American Society of Genealogists (ASG)

PO Box 26836
San Diego, CA 92196
E-mail: asg.sec@gmail.com
URL: www.fasg.org

1257 ■ ASG Scholar Awards *(Professional development/Scholarship)*

Purpose: To provide financial assistance to a scholar to attend an educational training program. **Focus:** Genealogy. **Qualif.:** Applicants must be genealogists, genealogical librarians and researchers working in related fields. **Criteria:** Applicants will be selected by the ASG Scholarship Committee.

Funds Avail.: $500 for tuition expenses. **To Apply:** Applicants must submit three copies of resume; manuscript or published work (maximum of 5000 words); and a 100-150 words statement which (1) identifies the individual's choice of institute program and (2) explanation why individuals may feel that attendance will enhance their growth as geneological scholar. **Deadline:** September 30. **Remarks:** Created in 1996. **Contact:** Melinde Lutz Sanborn, Chair/VP, 84 Rosewell Rd., Bedford, NH 03110.

1258 ■ American Society of Health System Pharmacists (ASHP)

7272 Wisconsin Ave.
Bethesda, MD 20814
Ph: (301) 664-8700
Fax: (301) 657-1251
Free: 866-279-0681
E-mail: custserv@ashp.org
URL: www.ashp.org

1259 ■ ASHP Student Research Awards *(Doctorate/Award)*

Purpose: To recognize pharmacy students for their published or unpublished paper. **Focus:** Pharmacy. **Qualif.:** Applicants must be full-time students enrolled in a Doctor of Pharmacy program at an ACPE-accredited school/college of pharmacy; must be students who are authors of unpublished or published paper that describes a completed research project related to medication use. Article must be written between January 1 and December 31. **Criteria:** Recipients will be selected based on originality, impact, innovation and quality of the paper.

Funds Avail.: $1,500 honorarium plus $1,000 expense allowance. **To Apply:** Applicants must submit an application form and published/unpublished article.

1260 ■ John W. Webb Lecture Awards *(Professional development/Award)*

Purpose: To recognize hospital or health-system pharmacy practitioners and educators who have distinguished themselves with extraordinary dedication to foster excellence in pharmacy management. **Focus:** Pharmacy. **Qualif.:** Applicants must be hospital or health-system practitioners or educators. **Criteria:** Awards will be given to applicants who have demonstrated inspiring leadership that yielded nationally significant innovations in pharmacy practice; have made noteworthy contributions in mentoring new practice leaders; or have inspired a large number of pharmacy students or practitioners to make a commitment to professionalism and innovation in practice management through their teaching, speaking or publications.

Funds Avail.: Amount not specified. **To Apply:** Nominations should be accompanied by a one-to-three page statement about why individuals are qualified for the award along with a copy of the nominee's curriculum vitae. **Contact:** Nominations should be mailed to James G. Stevenson at sections@ashp.org.

1261 ■ American Society of Heating, Refrigerating and Air-Conditioning Engineers (ASHRAE)

1791 Tullie Cir. NE
Atlanta, GA 30329
Ph: (404) 636-8400
Fax: (404) 321-5478
Free: 800-527-4723
E-mail: ashrae@ashrae.org
URL: www.ashrae.org

1262 ■ Henry Adams Scholarships *(Undergraduate/Scholarship)*

Purpose: To help reduce the financial burdens of obtaining an engineering education. **Focus:** Engineering. **Qualif.:** Applicants must be full-time undergraduates in ABET-accredited Engineering Technology program leading to Bachelors of Science or Engineering degree; must have cumulative GPA of at least 3.0 on a scale where 4.0 is the highest. **Criteria:** Recipients are selected based on financial need; leadership ability; and character.

Funds Avail.: $3,000. **To Apply:** Applicants must submit an official transcript of college grades; letter of recommendation; and evaluation form from three references

Awards are arranged alphabetically below their administering organizations

including professor or faculty advisor. **Deadline:** December 1.

1263 ■ American Society of Heating, Refrigerating, and Air-Conditioning Memorial Scholarships *(Undergraduate/Scholarship)*

Purpose: To help reduce the financial burdens of obtaining an engineering education. **Focus:** Engineering. **Qualif.:** Applicants must be full-time undergraduates in an ABET-accredited Engineering Technology program leading to a Bachelor of Science or Engineering Degree and must have cumulative GPA of at least 3.0 on a 4.0 scale. **Criteria:** Recipients are selected based on the need for financial assistance; leadership ability; and character.

Funds Avail.: $3,000. **To Apply:** Applicants must submit an official transcript of college grades; a letter of recommendation; and an evaluation form from three references including professor or faculty advisor. **Deadline:** December 1.

1264 ■ American Society of Heating, Refrigerating, and Air-Conditioning Undergraduate Scholarships *(Undergraduate/Scholarship)*

Purpose: To help reduce the financial burdens of obtaining an engineering education. **Focus:** Engineering. **Qualif.:** Applicants must be full-time undergraduates in an ABET-accredited Engineering Technology program leading to a Bachelor of Science or Engineering Degree and must have cumulative GPA of at least 3.0 on a 4.0 scale. **Criteria:** Recipients are selected based on the need for financial assistance; leadership ability; and character.

Funds Avail.: $3,000. **To Apply:** Applicants must submit an official transcript of college grades; a letter of recommendation; and an evaluation form from three references including professor or faculty advisor. **Deadline:** December 1. **Contact:** Lois Benedict at lbenedict@ashrae.org or 404-636-8400 (ext. 1120).

1265 ■ Willis H. Carrier Scholarships *(Undergraduate/Scholarship)*

Purpose: To help reduce the financial burdens of obtaining an engineering education. **Focus:** Engineering. **Qualif.:** Applicants must be full-time undergraduates in an ABET-accredited Engineering Technology program leading to a Bachelor of Science or Engineering Degree; must have cumulative GPA of at least 3.0 on a 4.0 scale. **Criteria:** Recipients are selected based on need for financial assistance; leadership ability; and character.

Funds Avail.: $10,000. **Number Awarded:** 2. **To Apply:** Applicants must submit an official transcript of college grades; a letter of recommendation; and an evaluation form from three references including professor or faculty advisor. **Deadline:** December 1.

1266 ■ Frank M. Coda Scholarships *(Undergraduate/Scholarship)*

Purpose: To help reduce the financial burdens of obtaining the engineering education. **Focus:** Engineering. **Qualif.:** Applicants must be full-time undergraduates in an ABET-accredited Engineering Technology program leading to a Bachelor of Science or Engineering Degree and must have cumulative GPA of at least 3.0 on a 4.0 scale. **Criteria:** Recipients are selected based on the need for financial assistance; leadership ability; and character.

Funds Avail.: $5,000. **To Apply:** Applicants must submit an official transcript of college grades; a letter of recom-

mendation and an evaluation form from three references including professor or faculty advisor. **Deadline:** December 1.

1267 ■ Duane Hanson Scholarships *(Undergraduate/Scholarship)*

Purpose: To help reduce the financial burdens of obtaining an engineering education. **Focus:** Engineering. **Qualif.:** Applicants must be full-time undergraduates in ABET-accredited Engineering Technology program leading to Bachelors of Science or Engineering degree; must have cumulative GPA of at least 3.0 on a scale where 4.0 is the highest. **Criteria:** Recipients are selected based on financial need; leadership ability; and character.

Funds Avail.: $3,000. **To Apply:** Applicants must submit an official transcript of college grades; letter of recommendation; and evaluation form from three references including professor or faculty advisor. **Deadline:** December 1.

1268 ■ Alwin B. Newton Scholarships *(Undergraduate/Scholarship)*

Purpose: To help reduce the financial burdens of obtaining an engineering education. **Focus:** Engineering. **Qualif.:** Applicants must be full-time undergraduates in an ABET-accredited Engineering Technology program leading to a Bachelors of Science or Engineering degree; must have cumulative GPA of at least 3.0 on a scale of 4.0. **Criteria:** Recipients are selected based on financial need; leadership ability; and character.

Funds Avail.: $3,000. **To Apply:** Applicants must submit official transcripts of college grades; a letter of recommendation; and an evaluation form from three references including a professor or faculty advisor. **Deadline:** December 1.

1269 ■ Donald E. Nichols Scholarships *(Undergraduate/Scholarship)*

Purpose: To help reduce the financial burdens of obtaining an engineering education. **Focus:** Engineering. **Qualif.:** Applicants must be full-time undergraduates in an ABET-accredited Engineering Technology program leading to a Bachelor of Science or Engineering Degree; must have cumulative GPA of at least 3.0 on a 4.0 scale. **Criteria:** Recipients are selected based on the need for financial assistance; leadership ability; and character.

Funds Avail.: $3,000. **To Apply:** Applicants must submit an official transcript of college grades; a letter of recommendation; and an evaluation form from three references including professor or faculty advisor. **Deadline:** December 1.

1270 ■ Reuben Trane Scholarships *(Undergraduate/Scholarship)*

Purpose: To help reduce the financial burdens of obtaining the engineering education. **Focus:** Engineering. **Qualif.:** Applicants must be full-time undergraduates in an ABET-accredited Engineering Technology program leading to a Bachelor of Science or Engineering Degree; must have cumulative GPA of at least 3.0 on a 4.0 scale. **Criteria:** Recipients are selected based on the need for financial assistance; leadership ability; and character.

Funds Avail.: $10,000. **Number Awarded:** 4. **To Apply:** Applicants must submit an official transcript of college grades; a letter of recommendation; and an evaluation form from three references including professor or faculty advisor. **Deadline:** December 1.

Awards are arranged alphabetically below their administering organizations

1271 ■ American Society for Horticultural Science

1018 Duke St.
Alexandria, VA 22314-2851
Ph: (703) 836-4606
Fax: (703) 836-2024
E-mail: webmaster@ashs.org
URL: ashs.org

1272 ■ American Society for Horticultural Science Student Travel Grants *(Graduate, Undergraduate/Grant)*

Purpose: To provide financial assistance to students in the area of horticulture. **Focus:** Horticulture. **Qualif.:** Applicants must be enrolled in horticultural science as a major course of study and must have submitted an abstract title or complete abstract for presentation at the ASHS Annual Conference. **Criteria:** Grants will be awarded on the basis of merit and geographical distribution.

Funds Avail.: $500 (domestic graduate and undergraduate students); $750 (international students). **Number Awarded:** Varies. **To Apply:** Applicants must accomplish application and abstract. Application forms and instructions are available on the website. **Deadline:** April 4. **Contact:** Materials should be submitted to Tecola Forbes at above address or email tforbes@ashs.org.

1273 ■ ASHS Industry Division Student Travel Grants *(Graduate, Undergraduate/Grant)*

Purpose: To provide financial assistance to students in the area of horticulture who are attending the ASHS Annual Conference. **Focus:** Horticulture. **Qualif.:** Award is open to all undergraduate and graduate Horticulture students. **Criteria:** Applicants will be selected based on academic achievement (30 points for 4.0 GPA), recommendation (20 points) and essay (50 points).

Funds Avail.: $1,000. **Number Awarded:** 2. **To Apply:** Applicants must submit transcripts, completed application, letter of recommendation from undergraduate advisor or faculty member and a 500-word essay outlining interest in horticulture and career goals. **Deadline:** March 18.

1274 ■ ASHS Scholars Awards *(Undergraduate/Scholarship)*

Purpose: To recognize and support scholastic achievement and to encourage career development in horticultural science at the undergraduate level. **Focus:** Horticulture. **Qualif.:** Applicant must be an undergraduate student of any class standing at the time of the application; must be registered as a full-time student (minimum 10 credit hours) and actively pursuing a degree in horticulture. **Criteria:** Recipients are chosen based on excellence in academic and scholastic performance in the major (an area of horticulture) and supporting areas of science; participation in extracurricular, leadership and research activities relating to horticulture; participation in university and community service; demonstrated commitment to the horticulture science profession and related career fields; and related horticultural experiences.

Funds Avail.: $1,500. **Number Awarded:** 2. **To Apply:** Applicants must be nominated by the chair/head of the department in which they are majoring; must submit completed application supported by a 250-500 essay, complete resume, three letters of reference and official university/college transcripts. Forms and information are available on the website. **Deadline:** February 4. **Contact:** Tecola Forbes, email: tforbes@ashs.org.

1275 ■ Miklos Faust International Travel Awards *(Doctorate/Fellowship)*

Purpose: To promote international cooperation in fruit crops research and education. **Focus:** Horticulture. **Qualif.:** Applicants must be young scientists (less than 40 yrs. old) who are actively involved in fruit science research; must hold or pursuing a doctoral degree. **Criteria:** Applications are reviewed according to evidence of high originality and strong commitment to research in fruit science.

Funds Avail.: No specific amount. **Number Awarded:** 1. **To Apply:** Applicants must submit a completed application form (available at the website). **Deadline:** May 4. **Contact:** Fatema Gharzai, email: fgharzai@ashs.org.

1276 ■ American Society of Interior Designers (ASID)

608 Massachusetts Ave. NE
Washington, DC 20002-6006
Ph: (202) 546-3480
Fax: (202) 546-3240
E-mail: asid@asid.org
URL: www.interiors.org

1277 ■ Irene Winifred Eno Grants *(All/Grant)*

Purpose: To provide financial assistance to individuals or groups engaged in the creation of an educational program or an interior design research project dedicated to health, safety and welfare. **Focus:** Interior design. **Qualif.:** Applicants must be students, educators, interior design practitioners, institutions or other interior design-related groups. **Criteria:** Selection will be based on the project description, breakdown of potential use of funds and the marketing plan for the use/distribution of the end product of the project.

Funds Avail.: $5,000. **Number Awarded:** 1. **To Apply:** Applicants may apply online and submit a photo (300 dpi in jpeg or gif format) to foundation@asid.org. **Deadline:** March 12.

1278 ■ Legacy Scholarships for Graduate Students *(Graduate/Scholarship)*

Purpose: To encourage talented practicing interior designers to advance their professional development through graduate study and research. **Focus:** Interior design. **Qualif.:** Applicants must be enrolled in or have applied for admission to a graduate-level interior design program at a degree-granting institution. Applicants must have been practicing designers for a period of at least five years prior to graduate school. **Criteria:** Selection will be based on academic/creative accomplishment.

Funds Avail.: $4,000. **To Apply:** Applicants must submit the following requirements: a maximum of 750 words personal statement; official school transcript(s); letter of recommendation; maximum of 100 words biographical statement; headshot picture. **Deadline:** March 12. **Remarks:** Sponsored by: Dora Brahms Fund, Mabelle Wilhelmina Boldt Fund, Yale R. Burge Fund, Raymon Kennedy Fund, Ethel Siegelman Fund and Alan Lucas Fund.

1279 ■ American Society of International Law (ASIL)

2223 Massachusetts Ave. NW
Washington, DC 20008

Awards are arranged alphabetically below their administering organizations

Ph: (202) 939-6000
Fax: (202) 797-7133
E-mail: services@asil.org
URL: www.asil.org

1280 ■ ASIL Arthur C. Helton Fellowship
Program *(All/Fellowship)*

Purpose: To contribute in paying for logistics, housing and living expenses, and other costs related to the fellows fieldwork and research in affiliation with the sponsoring organization. **Focus:** Law. **Qualif.:** Applicants must be students practicing law, human rights professionals, scholars and other individuals seeking assistance in conducting international fieldwork and law-related research. **Criteria:** Recipients are selected based on the performance in conducting research.

Funds Avail.: No specific amount. **To Apply:** Applicants must complete the online application form including description of intended project and career statement; a writing sample; current CV or resume; evidence of law student status and/or date of graduation from a law school; and two letters of recommendation or support. **Deadline:** January 9. **Contact:** Veronica Onorevole, ASIL Senior Programs Associate at fellowship@asil.org.

1281 ■ American Society of Landscape Architects (ASLA)
636 Eye St. NW
Washington, DC 20001-3736
Ph: (202) 898-2444
Fax: (202) 898-1185
Free: 888-999-ASLA
E-mail: info@asla.org
URL: www.asla.org

1282 ■ American Society of Landscape Architects Council of Fellow Scholarships
(Undergraduate/Scholarship)

Purpose: To aid outstanding students who would not otherwise have an opportunity to continue a professional degree program in the area of landscape architecture due to unmet financial need; to increase the interest and participation of economically disadvantaged and underrepresented populations in the study of landscape architecture through a more diverse population; to enrich the profession of landscape architecture through a more diverse population. **Focus:** Landscape architecture and design. **Qualif.:** Applicants must be permanent U.S. citizens or permanent resident aliens who are third, fourth, or fifth-year undergraduates at Landscape Architecture Accreditation Board-accredited programs of landscape architecture. **Criteria:** Recipients are selected based on financial need.

Funds Avail.: $4,000. **Number Awarded:** 2. **To Apply:** Applicants must submit a 300-word essay about how the applicant envisions himself or herself contributing to the profession of landscape architecture; two letters of recommendation specifically addressing the quality of applicant's performance as a student of landscape architecture and promise as a professional (one letter of recommendation must come from a faculty member and the other one must be sent by a non-academic member); and a student aid report. **Deadline:** March 9.

1283 ■ Edith H. Henderson Scholarships
(Undergraduate/Scholarship)

Purpose: To recognize an outstanding architect student. **Focus:** Landscape architecture and design. **Qualif.:** Applicants must be students pursuing a program in landscape architecture. **Criteria:** Recipients are selected based on academic achievement.

Funds Avail.: $1,000. **To Apply:** Applicants must submit a typewritten essay review of Mrs. Henderson's book entitled, "Edith Henderson's Home Landscape Companion" (200-400 words maximum). **Contact:** rfigura@lafoundation.org.

1284 ■ LAF/Class Fund AILA/YAMAGAMI/Hope Fellowships *(Postgraduate/Fellowship)*

Purpose: To provide for the middle ground where the designer, landscape contractor and nursery man, as well as those in formal training could meet and discuss common problems and experiences. **Focus:** Landscape architecture and design. **Qualif.:** Applicants must have earned a bachelor's or a master's degree in landscape architecture; must be landscape architects who have been in practice for a minimum of three years and wish to use the funds for continuing education. **Criteria:** Recipients are selected based on innovative nature of the proposed endeavor; the benefits that may accrue to other members of the profession and the profession in general; the personal goals to be achieved; and qualifications of the applicant.

Funds Avail.: $1,000. **To Apply:** Applicants must submit a 500-word summary of the uniqueness of the proposed activity, skills/knowledge to gain, increased proficiency, and opportunity to exist ; a statement of intent (maximum of 100 words) detailing how the funds would be used and a line item budget if applicable; and two letters of recommendation from licensed landscape architects. **Deadline:** August 1.

1285 ■ William J. Locklin Scholarships
(Undergraduate/Scholarship)

Purpose: To recognize an outstanding architect student and to emphasize the importance of 24-hour lighting in landscape designs. **Focus:** Landscape architecture and design. **Qualif.:** Applicants must be students pursuing a program in lighting design or landscape architectural students focusing on lighting design in studio projects. **Criteria:** Recipients are selected based on quality of the design and its effect.

Funds Avail.: $1,000. **To Apply:** Applicants must submit a typed, double-spaced 300-word essay highlighting the design project, the overall effect to be obtained, rationale for choice of lamp and placement of fixture, and anticipated results; visual samples (schematics/renderings/sketchers or other plans) reduced 81/2"X11"; and one letter of recommendation relevant to the proposed project and applicant, preferably from a current professor. **Deadline:** April 1. **Contact:** rfigura@lafoundation.org.

1286 ■ Raymond E. Page Scholarships
(Undergraduate/Scholarship)

Purpose: To give an undergraduate student the opportunity to follow Mr. Page's example of directing profession in the area of landscape architecture and design by answering the challenges of tomorrow. **Focus:** Landscape architecture and design. **Qualif.:** Applicants must be currently enrolled in an institution or university. **Criteria:** Recipients are selected based on academic standing and financial need.

Funds Avail.: No stated amount. **To Apply:** Applicants must submit a double-spaced, two-page essay describing the applicant's need for financial assistance and how the award is to be used; a letter of recommendation from a cur-

Awards are arranged alphabetically below their administering organizations

rent professor who is familiar with the applicant's character and goals in pursuing an education in landscape architecture; three copies of application; and a cover sheet. **Contact:** rfigura@lafoundation.org.

1287 ■ Rae L. Price Scholarships
(Undergraduate/Scholarship)

Purpose: To bring young creative individuals into careers in the area of landscape architecture and design who may not otherwise have the financial ability to cover all the costs of their educational program. **Focus:** Landscape architecture and design. **Qualif.:** Applicants must be U.S. citizens who are undergraduate students in the final two years of study in LAAB accredited schools; must demonstrate financial need; and must have a minimum "B" GPA. **Criteria:** Recipients are selected based on financial need.

Funds Avail.: $2,000-$5,000. **To Apply:** Applicants must submit a 500-word essay describing the applicant's aspirations, ability to surmount obstacles, high level of drive, and need for financial assistance; two letters of recommendation from current professors familiar with the applicant's character and goals in pursuing an education in landscape architecture. **Deadline:** February 15.

1288 ■ Harriet Barnhart Wimmer Scholarships
(Undergraduate/Scholarship)

Purpose: To recognize an outstanding architect student. **Focus:** Landscape architecture and design. **Qualif.:** Applicants must be females entering their final year of undergraduate landscape studies who have demonstrated excellence in design ability and sensitivity to the environment. **Criteria:** Recipients are selected based on demonstrated excellence in design ability and sensitivity to the environment.

Funds Avail.: $1,000. **To Apply:** Applicant must submit a typed, double-spaced autobiography and statement of personal and professional goals with a maximum of 500-words; one letter of recommendation regarding student's design abilities and attitude from a design instructor; graphic samples of work from three different projects, comprising a total of six 8X10 black and white or color photos; brief written descriptions of design intent for each graphic; and financial aid forms. **Deadline:** April 1. **Contact:** rfigura@lafoundation.org.

1289 ■ David T. Woolsey Scholarships
(Undergraduate/Scholarship)

Purpose: To recognize an outstanding architect student. **Focus:** Landscape architecture and design. **Qualif.:** Applicants must be third, fourth, or fifth year undergraduate or graduate students of landscape architecture who are permanent residents of Hawaii. **Criteria:** Recipients are selected based on academic achievement.

Funds Avail.: $2,000. **To Apply:** Applicants must submit a typed, double-spaced autobiography and statement of personal and professional goals with a maximum of 500 words; a design work; three 81/2X11 .jpg or instructor; and proof of Hawaii residency. **Deadline:** February 15. **Contact:** 203-331-7070; scholarships@lafoundation.org.

1290 ■ American Society for Legal History (ASLH)
New York Law School
185 W Broadway
New York, NY 10013
E-mail: cklafter@ingenia.us

URL: www.legalhistorian.org

1291 ■ Cromwell Fellowships *(Undergraduate/Fellowship)*

Purpose: To support research and writing in American legal history. **Focus:** American History. **Qualif.:** Applicants must be currently enrolled in an institution, college or university. **Criteria:** Recipients are selected based on academic standing. Preference will be given to scholars at the early stage of their careers.

Funds Avail.: $5,000. **Number Awarded:** 3-5. **To Apply:** Applicants must contact the Chair of the Society's Committee for Research Fellowships and Awards for application form and other required documents. **Deadline:** July 13. **Contact:** Michael Grossberg, e-mail: grossber@indiana.edu.

1292 ■ American Society for Mass Spectrometry (ASMS)
2019 Galisteo St., Bldg. I-1
Santa Fe, NM 87505
Ph: (505) 989-4517
Fax: (505) 989-1073
E-mail: office@asms.org
URL: www.asms.org

1293 ■ ASMS Research Awards *(Professional development/Grant)*

Purpose: To promote research done by young scientists in mass spectrometry. **Focus:** Science. **Qualif.:** Applicants must be academic scientists within four years of joining the term track faculty or equivalent in a North American university and who have not yet received awards under this program. **Criteria:** Recipients are selected based on applications and proposals.

Funds Avail.: $35,000. **To Apply:** Applicants must send seven sets of: one-page fiscal proposal and justification; list of current research support; curriculum vitae; and two letters of recommendation. **Deadline:** November 30. **Contact:** ASMS Awards, 2019 Galisteo St., Bldg. 1, Santa Fe, NM 87505.

1294 ■ American Society for Microbiology (ASM)
1752 Inn Main St. NW
Washington, DC 20036
Ph: (202) 942-9207
Fax: (202) 942-9333
E-mail: smaloy@sciences.sdsu.edu
URL: www.asm.org

1295 ■ American Society for Microbiology International Fellowships for Africa
(Postdoctorate/Fellowship)

Purpose: To promote American/Asian collaborations in microbiological research and training. **Focus:** Microbiology. **Qualif.:** Applicants must be members of ASM or any other national microbiological society; must actively involved in research in the microbiological sciences; must have obtained or be in the process of obtaining masters, Ph.D. or other equivalent academic degree within the last five years; must be nationals of non-developed Asian countries; and must be proficient in the use of the English language. **Criteria:** Recipients are selected based on academic excel-

Awards are arranged alphabetically below their administering organizations

lence of the applicant; depth of the applicant's research experience; quality and originality of work proposed during the fellowship; and relevance of the work proposed.

Funds Avail.: $5,000. **To Apply:** Applicants must fill out the application form. **Deadline:** April 15, October 15. **Contact:** international@asmusa.org.

1296 ■ American Society for Microbiology International Fellowships for Asia
(Postdoctorate/Fellowship)

Purpose: To promote American/Asian collaborations in microbiological research and training. **Focus:** Microbiology. **Qualif.:** Applicants must be members of ASM or any other national microbiological society; must be actively involved in research in the microbiological sciences; must have obtained or be in the process of obtaining masters, Ph.D. or other equivalent academic degree within the last five years; must be nationals of non-developed Asian countries; must be proficient in the use of the English language. **Criteria:** Recipients are selected based on the academic excellence; depth of the applicant's research experience; quality and originality of work proposed during the fellowship; and relevance of the work proposed.

Funds Avail.: $5,000. **To Apply:** Applicants must fill out the application form. **Deadline:** April 15, October 15. **Contact:** international@asmusa.org.

1297 ■ American Society for Microbiology International Fellowships for Latin America and the Caribbean *(Postdoctorate/Fellowship)*

Purpose: To promote American/Latin American collaborations in microbiological research and training. **Focus:** Microbiology. **Qualif.:** Applicants must be members of ASM or any other national microbiological society; must be actively involved in research in the microbiological sciences; must have obtained, or be in a process of obtaining masters, Ph.D. or other equivalent academic degree within the last five years; must be nationals of Latin American countries; must be proficient in the use of the English language. **Criteria:** Preference will be given to applicants who can prove three years of membership in ASM or any other national microbiological society; and who have not previously had the opportunity to travel to a facility in another country

Funds Avail.: $4,000. **Number Awarded:** 5. **To Apply:** Applicants must complete the application form; must submit an updated resume; copy honors and awards received; statement of career plans; potential collaborations and proposed research plans; budget; certificates; and letters of reference from academic advisors and/or supervisors. **Deadline:** April 15, October 15. **Contact:** international@asmusa.org.

1298 ■ American Society for Microbiology Undergraduate Research Fellowships (URF)
(Undergraduate/Fellowship)

Purpose: To support programs for education, training, and public information. **Focus:** Microbiology. **Qualif.:** Applicants must be enrolled as full-time matriculating undergraduates in an accredited U.S. institution; must be involved in a research project; must have ASM members in their home institutions willing to serve as a mentor; have not received any financial support for research. **Criteria:** Recipients are selected based on academic achievement; relevant career objectives; potential contribution to overall project outcome; personal motivation to participate in the program; and

achievement in previous research experiences.

Funds Avail.: $1,000-travel support and up to $4,000-student stipend. **To Apply:** Applicants must submit a complete application form. **Deadline:** February 1. **Contact:** fellowships@asmusa.org.

1299 ■ ASM/CCID Program in Infectious Disease and Public Health Microbiology
(Postdoctorate/Fellowship)

Purpose: To support the development of new approaches, methodologies, and knowledge in infectious disease prevention and control in areas within the public health mission of the CDC. **Focus:** Microbiology. **Qualif.:** Applicants must have earned their doctorate degree or completed primary residency within three years from proposed start date; may not have a faculty position or enrolled in a graduate degree program during the fellowship. **Criteria:** Recipients are selected based on scientific merit and training potential of the research proposal; training resources; and have significance with the Centers for Diseases public health mission.

Funds Avail.: $45,243; $3,000-health benefit; $500-$2,000 for professional development. **Number Awarded:** 1. **To Apply:** Applicants must fill out the application form. **Deadline:** January 15. **Contact:** For further information, call 202-942-9295 or e-mail at fellowships@asmusa.org.

1300 ■ ASM Undergraduate Research Capstone Program *(Undergraduate/Fellowship)*

Purpose: To increase the number of underrepresented undergraduate students who have demonstrated the ability to pursue graduate careers in microbiology. **Focus:** Microbiology. **Qualif.:** Applicants must be enrolled as full-time matriculating undergraduates in an accredited U.S. institution; must be either freshmen with college level research experience or sophomores, juniors, or seniors who will not graduate before the completion date of the summer program; must be members of underrepresented group of microbiology; must have taken introductory courses in biology, chemistry and preferably microbiology prior to submission of the application; must have strong interests in obtaining a Ph.D. or M.D/Ph.D. in the microbiological sciences; must have laboratory research experience. **Criteria:** Recipients are selected based on academic achievement and to previous research experiences or independent projects; commitment to research; career goals as a research scientist; motivation to participate in the program; willingness to conduct research with an ASM member at a sponsoring U.S. institution; leadership skills; and involvement in activities that serve the needs of underrepresented groups.

Funds Avail.: $1,000 travel support. **To Apply:** Applicants must submit a complete application form. **Deadline:** December 15. **Contact:** For further information, applicants may call 202-942-9283; Fax: 202-942-9329; E-mail: fellowships-careerinformation@asmusa.org.

1301 ■ ASM Undergraduate Teaching Fellowships (ASM-UTF) *(Undergraduate/Fellowship)*

Purpose: To support students who are interested in a career as an elementary or secondary school science teacher. **Focus:** Education. **Qualif.:** Applicants must be enrolled as full-time matriculating undergraduates in an accredited U.S. institution; must be involved in educational outreach projects; must be a science major interested in education; must have strong faculty ASM members in their home institutions willing to serve as a co-mentor; have not

Awards are arranged alphabetically below their administering organizations

received any financial support for the project during the fellowship. **Criteria:** Recipients are selected based on academic achievement; relevant career objectives; potential contribution to overall project outcome; personal motivation to participate in the program; achievement in previous teaching experience. Preference will be given to applicants whose projects will demonstrate the co-mentor's and institution's financial commitment and have significant impact on their ongoing educational efforts.

Funds Avail.: $2,000-student; $1,000-travel support. **To Apply:** Applicants must submit six copies of complete application form. **Contact:** Applicants may send an e-mail at fellowships-careerinformation@asmusa.org for further information.

1302 ■ Congressional Science Fellowships
(Postdoctorate/Fellowship)

Purpose: To broaden the perspective of both the scientific and governmental communities regarding the value of science-government interaction; to enable more effective use in government of scientific knowledge; and to provide experience to scientists seeking careers involving public use of technical information. **Focus:** Science. **Qualif.:** Applicants must be citizens of the United States; must be members of ASM for at least one year; must have completed their Ph.D. by the time the fellowship begins; must show competence in some aspect of microbiology; must have broad background in science and technology; must have interest and experience in applying scientific knowledge toward the solution of social problems; must be articulate, literate, adaptable, interested in public policy problems; must be able to work with a variety of people from diverse professional backgrounds. **Criteria:** Recipients are selected based on the result of the interview.

Funds Avail.: $60,000. **To Apply:** Applicants must submit a letter indicating a desire to apply; three letters of references; and 1,000-word statement about the qualifications and career goals. **Deadline:** February 22. **Contact:** hgarvey@asmusa.org.

1303 ■ Robert D. Watkins Graduate Research Fellowships *(Postdoctorate/Fellowship)*

Purpose: To increase the number of underrepresented groups completing doctoral degrees in the microbiological sciences. **Focus:** Microbiology. **Qualif.:** Applicants must be formally admitted to a doctoral program in the microbiological sciences in an accredited U.S. institution; have successfully completed the first year of the graduate program; have successfully completed all graduate course work requirements for the doctoral degree by the date of activation of the fellowship; must be student members of ASM; must be mentored by ASM members; must be U.S. citizens or permanent residents. **Criteria:** Recipients are selected based on academic achievement; evidence of successful research plan developed in collaboration with research advisor/mentor; relevant career goals in the microbiological sciences; involvement in activities that serve the needs of underrepresented groups.

Funds Avail.: $63,000. **To Apply:** Applicants must submit three letters of recommendation; and official transcript from all colleges and universities attended. **Deadline:** May 1. **Contact:** fellowships@asmusa.org.

1304 ■ American Society of Military Comptrollers (ASMC)
415 N Alfred St.
Alexandria, VA 22314

Ph: (703) 549-0360
Fax: (703) 549-3181
Free: 800-462-5637
E-mail: asmchq@asmconline.org
URL: www.asmconline.org

1305 ■ American Society of Military Comptrollers National Scholarship Program
(Undergraduate/Scholarship)

Purpose: To provide financial assistance to seniors to accomplish their future financial management baccalaureate educational goals. **Focus:** Business Administration, Economics, Public Administration, Accounting, Finance. **Qualif.:** Applicants must be entering a field of study directly related to financial/resource management. **Criteria:** Recipients are selected based on the selection panel's review of applications. The selection panel will make final recommendations to the ASMC National Executive Committee, who will approve the final award winners.

Funds Avail.: $1,000-$3,000. **Number Awarded:** One. **To Apply:** Applicants must have endorsement letters from ASMC chapters. Applicants must submit completed application form and three letters of recommendation from local ASMC chapter president, high school principal, academic dean, or guidance counselor, and a high school teacher. **Deadline:** March 31. **Contact:** Linda Ryan; 301-227-6341; linda.c.ryan@nga.mil.

1306 ■ American Society of Mining and Reclamation (ASMR)
3134 Montavesta Rd.
Lexington, KY 40502-3548
Ph: (859) 351-9032
Fax: (859) 335-6529
E-mail: asmr@insightbb.com
URL: ces.ca.uky.edu/asmr

1307 ■ American Society of Mining and Reclamation Memorial Scholarships
(Undergraduate/Scholarship)

Purpose: To grant deserving undergraduate students from academic institutions. **Focus:** Mining. **Qualif.:** Applicants must have completed at least sophomore year of curriculum in a science discipline directly relating to and leading to a profession in reclamation; must be full-time students; and must have an adequate grade point of average, carry the curriculum-required hours and participated in other curricular activities. **Criteria:** Recipients are selected based on extracurricular activities; participation; and leadership. Preference will be given to students from schools having an ASMR student chapter.

Funds Avail.: $750-undergraduates; $1,000-Masters; $1,500-Ph.D. **Number Awarded:** 3. **To Apply:** Applicants must complete the application form found at ASMR website; must submit a statement outlining education and career goals; three reference letters from two academic sources, including one from advisor; college transcripts; and resume with list of awards, honors and extracurricular activities listed. **Deadline:** April 8. **Contact:** Application form and other supporting documents should be submitted to Robert W. Naim, UASMR Memorial Scholarship Chair, University of Oklahoma, 202 W. Boyd St., Rm. 334, Norman OK 73019; 405-325-3354; 405-325-4217; naim@ou.edu.

Awards are arranged alphabetically below their administering organizations

1308 ■ American Society of Naval Engineers (ASNE)

1452 Duke St.
Alexandria, VA 22314-3458
Ph: (703) 836-6727
Fax: (703) 836-7491
E-mail: asnehq@navalengineers.org
URL: www.navalengineers.org

1309 ■ American Society of Naval Engineers Scholarships (ASNE) *(Graduate, Undergraduate/ Scholarship)*

Purpose: To improve and promote the profession of naval engineering. **Focus:** Naval engineering. **Qualif.:** Applicant must be a U.S. citizen; undergraduate full-time student in the last year of undergraduate program at an accredited college or university; or graduate student on a full graduate program leading to an engineering or physical science degree at an accredited university; be a member of ASNE. **Criteria:** Selection is based on academic standing (transcript); work history; extracurricular activities; the recommendations and other character references; financial need (many also be considered); and proven interest and commitment to the naval engineering field.

Funds Avail.: $3,000 for undergraduate students; $4,000 for graduate students. **Number Awarded:** 12. **To Apply:** Applicants must submit a completed application form. **Deadline:** February 17. **Remarks:** Inaugurated in 1979. **Contact:** Jared Pierce, 703-836-6727, jpierce@navalengineers.org.

1310 ■ American Society of Nephrology (ASN)

1510 H St. NW, Ste. 800
Washington, DC 20005-1003
Ph: (202) 640-4660
Fax: (202) 637-9793
E-mail: email@asn-online.org
URL: www.asn-online.org

1311 ■ Alaska Kidney Foundation-ASN Research Grants *(Doctorate/Grant)*

Purpose: To provide financial assistance for young faculty to foster evolution towards an independent research career. **Focus:** General studies. **Qualif.:** Applicants must be residents of North America, active members of the ASN and hold an MD or PhD or equivalent degree; must be within seven years of initial faculty appointment and may be in the last two years of a mentored award. **Criteria:** Applicants will be assessed based on their potential and the proposed project for eventual funding by a NIH R01 grant or its equivalent; qualifications with respect to prior training, productivity and independence, as well as the scientific merit of the proposed project; and commitment to the development as independent investigators.

Funds Avail.: $100,000. **To Apply:** Applicants must submit original and three paper copies of the application (including letter from Department Chair or Division Director), and three letters of reference. **Contact:** For more information, applicants must contact Holly Osborne by e-mail at hosborne@asn-online.org.

1312 ■ Carl W. Gottschalk Research Scholar Grants *(Doctorate/Grant)*

Purpose: To provide financial assistance for young faculty to foster evolution towards an independent research career.

Focus: General studies. **Qualif.:** Applicants must be residents of North America, active members of the ASN; must hold an MD or PhD or equivalent degree; and must be within seven years of initial appointment or may be in the last two years of a mentioned award. **Criteria:** Applicants will be assessed based on their potential and the proposed project for eventual funding by a NIH R01 grant or its equivalent; qualifications with respect to prior training, productivity and independence, as well as the scientific merit of the proposed project; and commitment to the development as an independent investigator.

Funds Avail.: $100,000. **To Apply:** Applicants must submit original and three paper copies of the application (including letter from Department Chair or Division Director), and three letters of reference. **Deadline:** January 27. **Contact:** For further information, contact Holly Osborne by e-mail at hosborne@asn-online.org.

1313 ■ Norman Siegel Research Scholar Grants *(Doctorate/Grant)*

Purpose: To provide financial assistance for young faculty to foster evolution towards an independent research career. **Focus:** General studies. **Qualif.:** Applicants must be residents of North America, active members of the ASN and hold an MD or PhD or equivalent degree. **Criteria:** Applicants will be assessed based on their potential and the proposed project for eventual funding by a NIH R01 grant or its equivalent; qualifications with respect to prior training, productivity and independence, as well as the scientific merit of the proposed project; and commitment to the development as independent investigators.

Funds Avail.: $100,000. **To Apply:** Applicants must submit original and three paper copies of the application (including letter from Department Chair or Division Director), and three letters of reference. **Deadline:** January 27. **Contact:** For further information, contact Holly Osborne by e-mail at hosborne@asn-online.org.

1314 ■ American Society for Nondestructive Testing Inc. (The American Industrial Radium and X-ray Society)

1711 Arlingate Ln.
Columbus, OH 43228-0518
Ph: (614) 274-6003
Fax: (614) 274-6899
Free: 800-222-2768
URL: www.asnt.org

1315 ■ ASNT Fellow Awards *(Postdoctorate/ Fellowship)*

Purpose: To honor outstanding and significant contributions of an individual in the advancement of NDT. **Focus:** Engineering. **Qualif.:** Nominees must have 15 years of NDT professional experience and 10 years ASNT membership. **Criteria:** Recipients are selected based on the Selection Committee's review of the application materials.

Funds Avail.: Amount not specified. **Number Awarded:** 15. **To Apply:** Applicants must submit a completed application and nomination forms to ASNT headquarter. **Deadline:** February 1. **Remarks:** Nominations shall be made by the candidate's local section chairman, members of the ASNT Board of Directors, or by ASNT Fellow. **Contact:** For further information, applicants must contact Stephanie Dille at the above address.

Awards are arranged alphabetically below their administering organizations

1316 ■ ASNT Fellowship Awards (Graduate/Fellowship)

Purpose: To fund a specific research in nondestructive testing. **Focus:** Materials research/science; Testing, educational/psychological. **Qualif.:** Program is open to any institution with a graduate educational research program. **Criteria:** Applicant who has the most outstanding proposal about NDT research, investigation or development will be given preference and will be judged based on creativity, content, format, and readability.

Funds Avail.: $15,000. **Number Awarded:** 3. **To Apply:** Applicants must submit an original and eight copies of the research proposal (maximum of 21 pages) consisting of a title page, table of contents, research proposal, program of study, research facilities, budget, research advisor, and background on potential graduate student. An original and eight (8) copies of the proposal shall be forwarded to ASNT. **Deadline:** October 14. **Contact:** For further information, applicants must contact Stephanie Dille at the above address.

1317 ■ Robert B. Oliver ASNT Scholarships (Undergraduate/Scholarship)

Purpose: To assist students who have chosen a career in NDT. **Focus:** Materials research/science; Testing, educational/psychological. **Qualif.:** Applicants must be enrolled in a course work related to nondestructive testing (NDT) leading to an undergraduate degree, an associate degree or a post-secondary certificate. **Criteria:** Applicant who has the most outstanding manuscript about NDT research, investigation or development will be given preference. The manuscript is judge based on creativity, content, format, and readability.

Funds Avail.: $2,500. **To Apply:** Applicants must submit one original and four copies of student manuscript with original illustrations and photos (maximum of ten). Manuscripts must contain the title, author, complete references and must be limited to 5,000 words. International System of Units or SI is preferred for all measurements. Applicants must also submit a completed application form; student's curriculum; transcript; and verification of enrollment letter from an instructor. **Deadline:** February 15. **Contact:** For further information, applicants must contact Stephanie Dille at the above address.

1318 ■ American Society of Podiatric Medical Assistants

c/o Sue Hasenour, PMAC
4472 S Cross St.
Saint Anthony, IN 47575
Ph: (812) 326-2046
Fax: (812) 326-2659
E-mail: suehpmac@gmail.com
URL: www.aspma.org

1319 ■ Zelda Walling Vicha Memorial Scholarships (Undergraduate, Vocational/Occupational/Scholarship)

Purpose: To improve the profession of Podiatric Medical Assisting by providing educational opportunities for ASPMA members. **Focus:** Podiatry. **Qualif.:** Applicant must be a student entering his/her fourth year of school; must have a high scholastic achievement and a definite financial need. **Criteria:** Trustees of the Zelda Walling Vicha Memorial Scholarship Fund will evaluate the application requirements of the candidates.

Funds Avail.: $2,000. **Number Awarded:** 2. **To Apply:** Application forms are available at the website. Applicant must submit the proof of financial need provided by the Financial Aid Office; must prepare an essay which describes the applicant's personal background, career, vocational or academic goals. **Deadline:** May 1. **Contact:** Send completed application form to: Janet B. Grace, PMAC, Zelda Walling Vicha Memorial Scholarship Fund, 3844 Emerson Drive, Schiller Park, IL 60176.

1320 ■ American Society for Quality - Statistic Division

PO Box 3005
Milwaukee, WI 53201-3005
E-mail: contact@asqstatdiv.org
URL: www.asqstatdiv.org

1321 ■ Ellis R. Ott Scholarships (Graduate, Master's/Scholarship)

Purpose: To provide financial assistance to deserving students who are in applied statistics and/or quality management field. **Focus:** Statistics; Quality assurance and control. **Qualif.:** Applicants must be students who are planning to enroll or currently enrolled in a masters degree or higher level in US or Canadian program that has concentration in applied statistics and/or quality management. **Criteria:** Recipients are selected based on the following criteria: demonstrated ability; academic achievement, including honors; career objectives; faculty recommendations; involvement in campus activities, including teaching and tutoring; and industrial exposure including part-time work and internships.

Funds Avail.: No specific amount. **Number Awarded:** 2. **To Apply:** Applicants must submit completed application form; resume; undergraduate transcript; graduate transcript, for students who have graduate school experience; essay of no longer than one page, typewritten, no smaller than 10-point type, stating qualifications, career goals, reasons for seeking the scholarship; two letters of recommendation from professors in the current or intended field of study. **Deadline:** April 1. **Contact:** Dr. Lynne B. Hare, 39 Mile Dr., Chester, NJ 07930, at 908-897-0610 or lynne.hare@comcast.net.

1322 ■ American Society of Radiologic Technologists (ASRT)

15000 Central Ave. SE
Albuquerque, NM 87123-3909
Ph: (505) 298-4500
Fax: (505) 298-5063
Free: 800-444-2778
E-mail: memberservices@asrt.org
URL: www.asrt.org

1323 ■ GE Healthcare Management Scholarship Program (Graduate/Scholarship)

Purpose: To provide resources for healthcare and business administration students. **Focus:** Health services administration. **Qualif.:** Applicants must be students pursuing Master's or Doctoral degrees in the areas of business and healthcare administration. **Criteria:** Recipients are selected based on academic standing and financial need.

Funds Avail.: No specific amount. **To Apply:** Applicants must complete the application form and submit along with

Awards are arranged alphabetically below their administering organizations

an essay, summary of financial need and scholastic information documents. **Contact:** foundation@asrt.org.

1324 ■ Jerman-Cahoon Student Scholarship Program (Undergraduate/Scholarship)

Purpose: To provide resources for radiologic technologists intending to improve patient care and to support education and research in the radiologic sciences. **Focus:** Radiology. **Qualif.:** Applicants must be students attending an entry-level radiologic sciences program. **Criteria:** Recipients are selected based on academic standing and financial need; must be a US citizen, US national or US permanent resident; must have a minimum GPA of 3.0 on a 4.0 scale or B average specifically in radiologic science core curriculum.

Funds Avail.: $2,500. **Number Awarded:** 5. **To Apply:** Applicants must complete the application form and submit along with an essay, summary of financial need and scholastic information documents. Completed application must be submitted electronically as well as printed and included the transcript and evaluation form. Applicants may visit the website for other information and required documents. **Deadline:** February 1. **Contact:** foundation@asrt.org.

1325 ■ Monster Medical Imaging Educators Scholarship Program (Postdoctorate/Scholarship)

Purpose: To provide resources for radiologic technologists intending to improve patient care; to support education and research in the radiologic sciences; and to assist educators who are pursuing their baccalaureate, master's, or doctoral degree to enhance their position as a program director, faculty member, clinical coordinator or clinical instructor. **Focus:** Radiology. **Qualif.:** Applicants must be pursuing their baccalaureate master's or doctoral degree in the area of radiologic technology. **Criteria:** Recipients are selected based on academic standing and financial need.

Funds Avail.: $5,000. **Number Awarded:** 4. **To Apply:** Applicants must complete the application form and submit along an essay, summary of financial need and scholastic information documents. Completed application must be submitted electronically as well as printed and included the transcript and evaluation form. Applicants may visit the website for other information and required documents. **Deadline:** February 1. **Contact:** foundation@asrt.org.

1326 ■ Royce-Osborn Minority Scholarship Program (Undergraduate/Scholarship)

Purpose: To provide resources for radiologic technologists intending to improve patient care and to support education and research in the radiologic sciences. **Focus:** Radiology. **Qualif.:** Applicants must be minority students attending an entry-level radiologic sciences program. **Criteria:** Recipients are selected based on academic standing and financial need.

Funds Avail.: $4,000. **Number Awarded:** 5. **To Apply:** Applicants must complete the application form and submit along with an essay, summary of financial need and scholastic information documents. **Deadline:** February 1. **Contact:** foundation@asrt.org.

1327 ■ Siemens Clinical Advancement Scholarship Program (Postgraduate/Scholarship)

Purpose: To provide resources for radiologic technologists intending to improve patient care; to support education and research in the radiologic sciences; and to advance the ra-

diologic sciences in promoting the professionalism of technologists. **Focus:** Radiology. **Qualif.:** Applicants must be pursuing their baccalaureate master's degree in radiologic sciences. **Criteria:** Recipients are selected based on academic standing and financial need.

Funds Avail.: $5,000. **Number Awarded:** 4. **To Apply:** Applicants must complete the application form and submit along an essay, summary of financial need and scholastic information documents. Completed application must be submitted electronically as well as printed and included the transcript and evaluation form. Applicants may visit the website for other information and required documents. **Deadline:** February 1. **Contact:** foundation@asrt.org.

1328 ■ Varian Radiation Therapy Scholarship Program (Postdoctorate/Scholarship)

Purpose: To provide resources for radiologic technologists intending to improve patient care; to support education and research in the radiologic sciences; and to assist educator therapists pursuing their baccalaureate or doctoral degree to enhance their position as a program director, faculty member, clinical coordinator or clinical instructor. **Focus:** Radiology. **Qualif.:** Applicants must be currently enrolled in an entry-level radiation therapy program; must be a US citizen, US national or US permanent resident; must have a minimum GPA of 3.0 on a 4.0 scale or B average specifically in radiation therapy core curriculum. **Criteria:** Recipients are selected based on academic standing and financial need.

Funds Avail.: $5,000. **Number Awarded:** 19. **To Apply:** Applicants must complete the application form and submit along with an essay, summary of financial need and scholastic information documents. Completed application must be submitted electronically as well as printed and included the transcript and evaluation form. Applicants may visit the website for other information and required documents. **Deadline:** February 1. **Contact:** foundation@asrt.org.

1329 ■ American Society of Safety Engineers (ASSE)

1800 E Oakton St.
Des Plaines, IL 60018
Ph: (847) 699-2929
Fax: (847) 768-3434
E-mail: customerservice@asse.org
URL: www.asse.org

1330 ■ America Responds Memorial Scholarships (Undergraduate/Scholarship)

Purpose: To provide financial support to deserving students. **Focus:** Occupational safety and health. **Qualif.:** Applicant must be a U.S citizen; must be pursuing an undergraduate degree in occupational safety and health. **Criteria:** Selection of applicants will be based on scholarship application criteria. Priority will be given to students who have an experience working as Emergency Responders.

Funds Avail.: $1,000. **Number Awarded:** 1. **To Apply:** Applicant must submit a transcript of records; verification by a safety faculty member; student's narrative; certification; and must attach a letter of recommendation. **Deadline:** December 1. **Contact:** For further information, just contact Adele Gabanski at the above address.

Awards are arranged alphabetically below their administering organizations

1331 ■ American Society of Safety Engineers Construction Safety Scholarships
(Undergraduate/Scholarship)

Purpose: To provide financial support to deserving students. **Focus:** Occupational safety and health; Construction. **Qualif.:** Applicant must be a student pursuing an undergraduate degree in occupational safety and health with an emphasis in construction safety. **Criteria:** Selection of applicants will be based on scholarship application criteria.

Funds Avail.: $1,500. **Number Awarded:** 1. **To Apply:** Applicant must submit a transcript of records; verification by a safety faculty member; student's narrative; certification; and must attach a letter of recommendation. **Deadline:** December 1. **Contact:** For further information, just contact Adele Gabanski at the above address.

1332 ■ ASSE Diversity Committee Scholarships
(Graduate, Undergraduate/Scholarship)

Purpose: To provide financial support to deserving students. **Focus:** Occupational safety and health. **Qualif.:** Applicant must be a student pursuing an undergraduate or graduate degree in occupational safety & health or a closely related field. **Criteria:** Scholarship is open to any individual regardless of race, ethnicity, gender, religion, personal beliefs, age, sexual orientation, physical challenges, geographic location, university or specific area of study.

Funds Avail.: $1,000. **Number Awarded:** 1. **To Apply:** Applicant must submit a transcript of records; verification by a safety faculty member; student's narrative; certification; and must attach a letter of recommendation. **Deadline:** December 1. **Contact:** For further information, just contact Adele Gabanski at the above address.

1333 ■ Bechtel Group Foundation Scholarships for Safety & Health
(Undergraduate/Scholarship)

Purpose: To provide financial support to deserving students. **Focus:** Occupational safety and health; Construction. **Qualif.:** Applicant must be a student pursuing an undergraduate degree in occupational safety and health with an emphasis in construction safety; and must be enrolled or planning to attend at Murray State in Murray, Montana Tech in Butte, of University of Central Missouri. **Criteria:** Selection of applicants will be based on scholarship application criteria. Priority will be given to students with an emphasis in construction safety attending Murray State in Murray, KY, Montana Tech in Butte, MT or Central Washington University in Ellensburg, WA.

Funds Avail.: $4,000. **Number Awarded:** 3. **To Apply:** Applicant must submit a transcript of records; verification by a safety faculty member; student's narrative; certification; and must attach a letter of recommendation. **Deadline:** December 1. **Contact:** For further information, just contact Adele Gabanski at the above address.

1334 ■ Warren K. Brown Scholarships
(Undergraduate/Scholarship)

Purpose: To provide financial support to deserving students. **Focus:** Occupational safety and health. **Qualif.:** Applicant must be a student pursuing an undergraduate degree in occupational safety & health or a closely related field at Murray State University in Murray, KY or Indiana State University in Terre Haute, IN. **Criteria:** Selection of applicants will be based on the scholarship application criteria.

Funds Avail.: $1,000. **Number Awarded:** 1. **To Apply:**

Applicant must submit a transcript of records; verification by a safety faculty member; student's narrative; certification; and must attach a letter of recommendation. **Deadline:** December 1. **Contact:** For further information, just contact Adele Gabanski at the above address or e-mail agabanski@ asse.org.

1335 ■ CNA Foundation Scholarships
(Graduate, Undergraduate/Scholarship)

Purpose: To provide financial support to deserving students. **Focus:** Occupational safety and health. **Qualif.:** Applicant must be a student pursuing an undergraduate or graduate degree in occupational safety & health or a closely related field. **Criteria:** Selection of applicants will be based on the scholarship application criteria.

Funds Avail.: $4,650. **Number Awarded:** 2. **To Apply:** Applicant must submit a transcript of records; verification by a safety faculty member; student's narrative; certification; and must attach a letter of recommendation. **Deadline:** December 1. **Contact:** For further information, just contact Adele Gabanski at the above address.

1336 ■ Scott Dominguez - Craters of the Moon Chapter Scholarships
(Graduate, Undergraduate/ Scholarship)

Purpose: To provide financial support to deserving students. **Focus:** Occupational safety and health. **Qualif.:** Applicant must be a student pursuing an undergraduate or graduate degree in occupational safety & health or a closely related field. Students who are employees or dependents of sponsoring organizations, serving the country through active duty in the armed forces or honorably discharged, members of Boy Scouts, Girl Scouts, FFA, 4H, etc. in previous years, recipients of awards from service organizations or have provided volunteer service to an ASSE chapter are also eligible. Part-time student must have a general or professional ASSE membership. **Criteria:** Priority will be given to students that reside within the Craters of the Moon Chapter, Idaho and the Region II area.

Funds Avail.: $1,000. **Number Awarded:** 1. **To Apply:** Applicant must submit a transcript of records; verification by a safety faculty member; student's narrative; certification; and must attach a letter of recommendation. **Deadline:** December 1. **Contact:** For further information, just contact Adele Gabanski at the above address.

1337 ■ Gold Country Section & Region II Scholarships
(Graduate, Undergraduate/ Scholarship)

Purpose: To provide financial support to deserving students. **Focus:** Occupational safety and health. **Qualif.:** Applicant must be a student pursuing an undergraduate or graduate degree in occupational safety & health or a closely related field; must be a student that resides within the Region II (MT, ID, WY, CO, UT, NV, AZ, NM) area. **Criteria:** Selection of applicants will be based on the scholarship application criteria. Preference will be given to students who reside within the Region II area.

Funds Avail.: $1,000. **Number Awarded:** 1. **To Apply:** Applicants must submit a transcript of records; verification by a safety faculty member; student's narrative; certification; and must attach a letter of recommendation. **Deadline:** December 1. **Contact:** For further information, just contact Adele Gabanski at the above address.

1338 ■ Gulf Coast Past President's Scholarships
(Undergraduate/Scholarship)

Purpose: To provide financial support to deserving students. **Focus:** Occupational safety and health. **Qualif.:**

Awards are arranged alphabetically below their administering organizations

Applicant must be a student pursuing an undergraduate degree in occupational safety and health or a closely related field; and must have a general or professional ASSE membership. **Criteria:** Selection of applicants will be based on scholarship application criteria.

Funds Avail.: $1,000. **Number Awarded:** 2. **To Apply:** Applicant must submit a transcript of records; verification by a safety faculty member; student's narrative; certification; and must attach a letter of recommendation. **Deadline:** December 1. **Contact:** For further information, just contact Adele Gabanski at the above address or e-mail agabanski@ asse.org.

1339 ■ George Gustafson HSE Memorial Scholarships *(Graduate, Undergraduate/ Scholarship)*

Purpose: To provide financial support to deserving students. **Focus:** Occupational safety and health. **Qualif.:** Applicant must be a student pursuing an undergraduate or graduate degree in occupational safety & health or a closely related field; must be a resident of Texas and attending a Texas university. **Criteria:** Priority will be given to students from Texas attending a Texas University.

Funds Avail.: $2,500. **Number Awarded:** 1. **To Apply:** Applicant must submit a transcript of records; verification by a safety faculty member; student's narrative; certification; and must attach a letter of recommendation. **Deadline:** December 1. **Contact:** For further information, just contact Adele Gabanski at the above address.

1340 ■ David Iden Memorial Safety Scholarships *(Undergraduate/Scholarship)*

Purpose: To provide financial support to deserving students. **Focus:** Occupational safety and health. **Qualif.:** Applicant must be a student pursuing an undergraduate degree in occupational safety & health or a closely related field. **Criteria:** Selection of applicants will be based on the scholarship application criteria.

Funds Avail.: $5,250. **Number Awarded:** 4. **To Apply:** Applicant must submit a transcript of records; verification by a safety faculty member; student's narrative; certification; and must attach a letter of recommendation. **Deadline:** December 1. **Contact:** For further information, just contact Adele Gabanski at the above address.

1341 ■ Karl A. Jacobson Scholarships *(Undergraduate/Scholarship)*

Purpose: To provide financial support to deserving students. **Focus:** Occupational safety and health. **Qualif.:** Applicant must be a student pursuing an undergraduate degree in occupational safety & health or a closely related field. **Criteria:** Selection of applicants will be based on the scholarship application criteria.

Funds Avail.: $2,000. **To Apply:** Applicants must submit a transcript of record; for further information about the application form and requirements; applicants are advised to contact the ASSE Foundation at 1800 E Oakton St., Des Plaines, IL 60018.

1342 ■ Greater Baton Rouge Chapter - Don Jones Excellence in Safety Scholarships *(Undergraduate/Scholarship)*

Purpose: To provide financial support to deserving students. **Focus:** Occupational safety and health. **Qualif.:** Applicant must be a student pursuing a degree in occupational safety & health or a closely related field; must

be attending any college or university within Louisiana or within the Southeast U.S. region; must be a student pursuing an associate or bachelor degree. A part-time student must have a general or professional ASSE membership. **Criteria:** Priority will be given to a student attending Southeastern Louisiana University in Hammond, Louisiana, attending any college or university within Louisiana, or any within the Southeast U.S. region.

Funds Avail.: $1,500. **Number Awarded:** 1. **To Apply:** Applicant must submit a transcript of records; verification by a safety faculty member; student's narrative; certification; and must attach a letter of recommendation. **Deadline:** December 1. **Contact:** For further information, just contact Adele Gabanski at the above address.

1343 ■ Southwest Chapter Roy Kinslow Scholarships *(Undergraduate/Scholarship)*

Purpose: To provide financial support to deserving students. **Focus:** Occupational safety and health. **Qualif.:** Applicant must be a student pursuing an undergraduate degree in occupational safety & health or a closely related field at Southeastern Oklahoma State University in Durat, OK or for any student from the Southwest Chapter area attending a school within the Region III boundaries. **Criteria:** Selection of applicants will be based on scholarship application criteria.

Funds Avail.: $1,000. **Number Awarded:** 1. **To Apply:** Applicant must submit a transcript of records; verification by a safety faculty member; student's narrative; certification; and must attach a letter of recommendation. **Deadline:** December 1. **Contact:** For further information, just contact Adele Gabanski at the above address.

1344 ■ James P. Kohn Memorial Scholarships *(Graduate/Scholarship)*

Purpose: To provide financial support to deserving students. **Focus:** Occupational safety and health. **Qualif.:** Applicant must be a student pursuing a graduate degree in occupational safety & health or a closely related field. **Criteria:** Selection of applicants will be based on scholarship application criteria.

Funds Avail.: $1,000. **Number Awarded:** 1. **To Apply:** Applicant must submit a transcript of records; verification by a safety faculty member; student's narrative; certification; and must attach a letter of recommendation. **Deadline:** December 1. **Contact:** For further information, just contact Adele Gabanski at the above address or e-mail agabanski@ asse.org.

1345 ■ Central Indiana ASSE Jim Kriner Memorial Scholarships *(Graduate, Undergraduate/ Scholarship)*

Purpose: To provide financial support to deserving students. **Focus:** Occupational safety and health. **Qualif.:** Applicant must be a student pursuing an undergraduate or graduate degree in occupational safety & health or a closely related field. **Criteria:** Priority will be given to Indiana residents attending school in Indiana or anywhere in the U.S or to non-residents attending an Indiana university.

Funds Avail.: One award is worth $3,000 and two at $1,000 each. **Number Awarded:** 3. **To Apply:** Applicant must submit a transcript of records; verification by a safety faculty member; student's narrative; certification; and must attach a letter of recommendation. **Deadline:** December 1. **Contact:** For further information, just contact Adele Gabanski at the above address.

Awards are arranged alphabetically below their administering organizations

1346 ■ Liberty Mutual Scholarships
(Undergraduate/Scholarship)

Purpose: To provide financial support to deserving students. **Focus:** Occupational safety and health. **Qualif.:** Applicant must be a student pursuing an undergraduate degree in occupational safety & health or a closely related field. **Criteria:** Selection of applicants will be based on scholarship application criteria.

Funds Avail.: $4,500. **Number Awarded:** 2. **To Apply:** Applicant must submit a transcript of records; verification by a safety faculty member; student's narrative; certification; and must attach a letter of recommendation. **Deadline:** December 1. **Remarks:** Students may also be provided the opportunity to attend the conference. **Contact:** For further information, just contact Adele Gabanski at the above address.

1347 ■ Marsh Risk Consulting Scholarships
(Undergraduate/Scholarship)

Purpose: To provide financial support to deserving students. **Focus:** Occupational safety and health. **Qualif.:** Applicant must be a student pursuing an undergraduate degree in occupational safety & health or a closely related field. **Criteria:** Selection of applicants will be based on the scholarship application criteria.

Funds Avail.: $1,000. **Number Awarded:** 1. **To Apply:** Applicant must submit a transcript of records; verification by a safety faculty member; student's narrative; certification; and must attach a letter of recommendation. **Deadline:** December 1. **Contact:** For further information, just contact Adele Gabanski at the above address.

1348 ■ Rixio Medina and Associates Hispanics in Safety Scholarships *(Graduate, Undergraduate/Scholarship)*

Purpose: To provide financial support to deserving students. **Focus:** Occupational safety and health. **Qualif.:** Applicant must be a student pursuing an undergraduate or graduate degree in occupational safety & health or a closely related field; must be a bilingual student. **Criteria:** Selection of applicants will be based on scholarship application criteria.

Funds Avail.: $3,000. **Number Awarded:** 1. **To Apply:** Applicants must submit a transcript of records. For further information about the application form and requirements, applicants are advised to contact the ASSE Foundation at 1800 E Oakton St., Des Plaines, IL 60018. **Deadline:** December 1.

1349 ■ North Florida Chapter Safety Education Scholarships *(Graduate, Undergraduate/Scholarship)*

Purpose: To provide financial support to deserving students. **Focus:** Occupational safety and health. **Qualif.:** Applicant must be a student pursuing an undergraduate or graduate degree in occupational safety & health or a closely related field; must be planning to attend in any Florida College or university. Part-time student must have a general or professional ASSE membership. **Criteria:** Priority will be given to part-time or full-time students who belong to the North Florida chapter, full-time students who attend any Florida college or university or to full-time students attending an ASAC/ABET accredited program nationwide.

Funds Avail.: $1,000. **Number Awarded:** 1. **To Apply:** Applicant must submit a transcript of records; verification by a safety faculty member; student's narrative; certifica-

tion; and must attach a letter of recommendation. **Deadline:** December 1. **Contact:** For further information, just contact Adele Gabanski at the above address or e-mail agabanski@asse.org.

1350 ■ Northeastern Illinois Chapter Scholarships *(Graduate, Undergraduate/Scholarship)*

Purpose: To provide financial support to deserving students. **Focus:** Occupational safety and health. **Qualif.:** Applicant must be a student pursuing an undergraduate or graduate degree in occupational safety & health or a closely related field; must attend Northeastern Illinois University or in any Northeastern Illinois region; must be members or offspring of Northeastern, IL chapter. **Criteria:** Selection of applicants will be based on scholarship application criteria. Preference will be given to students who attend Northern Illinois University in DeKalb, IL or in any Northeastern Illinois region.

Funds Avail.: $2,000. **Number Awarded:** 2. **To Apply:** Applicant must submit a transcript of records; verification by a safety faculty member; student's narrative; certification; and must attach a letter of recommendation. **Deadline:** December 1. **Contact:** For further information, just contact Adele Gabanski at the above address.

1351 ■ PDC Scholarships *(Undergraduate/Scholarship)*

Purpose: To provide financial support to deserving students. **Focus:** Occupational safety and health. **Qualif.:** Applicant must be a student pursuing a degree in occupational safety & health or a closely related field. **Criteria:** Selection of applicants will be based on scholarship application criteria.

Funds Avail.: $1,200. **Number Awarded:** 2. **To Apply:** Applicants must submit a transcript of records; verification by a safety faculty member; student's narrative; certification; and must attach a letter of recommendation. **Deadline:** December 1. **Contact:** For further information, just contact Adele Gabanski at the above address.

1352 ■ Harold F. Polston Scholarships *(Graduate, Undergraduate/Scholarship)*

Purpose: To provide financial support to deserving students. **Focus:** Occupational safety and health. **Qualif.:** Applicant must be a student pursuing an undergraduate or graduate degree in occupational safety & health or a closely related field. **Criteria:** Priority will be given to students that belong to the Middle Tennessee Chapter, those attending Middle Tennessee State University in Murfreesboro, TN or Murray State University in Murray, KY and those who live in the Region VII.

Funds Avail.: $2,000. **Number Awarded:** 1. **To Apply:** Applicants must submit a transcript of records; verification by a safety faculty member; student's narrative; certification; and must attach a letter of recommendation. **Deadline:** December 1. **Contact:** For further information, just contact Adele Gabanski at the above address.

1353 ■ William C. Ray, CIH, CSP Arizona Scholarships *(Graduate, Undergraduate/Scholarship)*

Purpose: To provide financial support to deserving students. **Focus:** Occupational safety and health. **Qualif.:** Applicant must be a student pursuing an undergraduate or graduate degree in occupational safety & health or a closely related field; must reside in Arizona. **Criteria:** Selection will

Awards are arranged alphabetically below their administering organizations

be based on requirements. Priority will be given to students residing in Arizona or within the Region II area.

Funds Avail.: $2,500. **Number Awarded:** 2. **To Apply:** Applicant must submit a transcript of records; verification by a safety faculty member; student's narrative; certification; and must attach a letter of recommendation. **Deadline:** December 1. **Contact:** For further information, just contact Adele Gabanski at the above address.

1354 ■ Harry Taback 9/11 Memorial Scholarships *(Undergraduate/Scholarship)*

Purpose: To provide financial support to deserving students. **Focus:** Occupational safety and health. **Qualif.:** Applicant must be a student pursuing an undergraduate or graduate degree in occupational safety & health or a closely related field; must be a natural born U.S citizen. **Criteria:** Selection of applicants will be based on scholarship application criteria.

Funds Avail.: $1,000. **Number Awarded:** 1. **To Apply:** Applicant must submit a transcript of records; verification by a safety faculty member; student's narrative; certification; and must attach a letter of recommendation. **Deadline:** December 1. **Contact:** For further information, just contact Adele Gabanski at the above address.

1355 ■ Thompson Scholarships for Women in Safety *(Graduate/Scholarship)*

Purpose: To provide financial support to deserving students. **Focus:** Occupational safety and health; Engineering; Medicine; Risk management; Industrial hygiene; Fires and fire prevention; Environmental technology. **Qualif.:** Applicant must be a woman pursuing a degree in safety engineering, safety management, occupational health nursing, occupational medicine, risk management, ergonomics, industrial hygiene, fire safety, environmental safety, environmental health or any other closely related field. **Criteria:** Selection of applicants will be based on scholarship application criteria. Priority will be given to female students.

Funds Avail.: $1,000. **To Apply:** Applicants must submit a transcript of records. For further information about the application form and requirements, applicants are advised to contact the ASSE Foundation at 1800 E Oakton St., Des Plaines, IL 60018. **Deadline:** December 1.

1356 ■ UPS Diversity Scholarships *(Undergraduate/Scholarship)*

Purpose: To provide financial support to deserving students. **Focus:** Occupational safety and health. **Qualif.:** Applicant must be a student pursuing an undergraduate degree in occupational safety & health or a closely relative field; must be of minority ethnic descent or racial group and must be a U.S. citizen. **Criteria:** Selection of applicants will be based on scholarship application criteria.

Funds Avail.: $5,250. **Number Awarded:** 2. **To Apply:** Applicants must submit a transcript of records; for further information about the application form and requirements, applicants are advised to contact the ASSE Foundation at 1800 E Oakton St., Des Plaines, IL 60018. **Deadline:** December 1. **Remarks:** Students will be given the opportunity to attend the conference.

1357 ■ Washington Group International Safety Scholarships *(Undergraduate/Scholarship)*

Purpose: To provide financial support to deserving students. **Focus:** Occupational safety and health; Construc-

tion. **Qualif.:** Applicant must be a student pursuing an undergraduate degree in occupational safety & health with an emphasis in construction safety. **Criteria:** Consideration will be given to students attending an ASAC/ABET accredited program.

Funds Avail.: No specific amount. **To Apply:** Applicants must submit a transcript of record; for further information about the application form and requirements, applicants are advised to contact the ASSE Foundation at 1800 E Oakton St., Des Plaines, IL 60018.

1358 ■ The American Society for Theatre Research (ASTR)

PO Box 1798
Boulder, CO 80306-1798
Ph: (303) 530-1838
Fax: (303) 530-1839
Free: 888-530-1838
E-mail: info@astr.org
URL: www.astr.org

1359 ■ ASTR Research Fellowships *(Professional development/Fellowship)*

Purpose: To underwrite some of the research expenses of scholars undertaking projects significant to the field of theatre and/or performance studies. **Focus:** Theater arts; Performing arts. **Qualif.:** Applicant must be holding a terminal degree and a member of ASTR for at least three years. **Criteria:** Selection is based on the merit of the project within the field of theatre or performance studies.

Funds Avail.: A total of $4,000 which can be divided among multiple winners. **To Apply:** Applicants must submit a 150-word abstract of the project; a longer narrative description of the project indicating its procedures, goals and significance; a budget; a two-page curriculum vitae; and three letters of support from scholars in the proposed or related fields of study. **Deadline:** March 15. **Contact:** Prof. Harley Erdman, Chm. at harley@theater.umass.edu.

1360 ■ Helen Krich Chinoy Dissertation Research Fellowships *(Doctorate/Fellowship)*

Purpose: To financially support PhD candidates with their travel in conducting research projects connected to their dissertations. **Focus:** Theater arts. **Qualif.:** Applicants must be PhD candidates who have passed their qualifying exams within the last two years and have begun working on their dissertations. **Criteria:** Recipients will be selected based on clarity, originality and critical rigor.

Funds Avail.: A total of $3,000 to be divided equally into three awards. **Number Awarded:** 3. **To Apply:** Applicants must submit a project abstract (100 words); description of the proposed project (500 words, including the nature of the project, research strategy, current status of the project and a rationale for the project); a statement on how the award will be used and how will it help the project; a curriculum vitae; and two letters of recommendation (one from the dissertation advisor, and another from a scholar familiar with the applicant's work). Applications must be in **Deadline:** May 7.

1361 ■ American Society of Travel Agents (ASTA)

1101 King St., Ste. 200
Alexandria, VA 22314

Awards are arranged alphabetically below their administering organizations

E-mail: askasta@asta.org
URL: www.astanet.com

1362 ■ Alaska Airlines Scholarships
(Undergraduate/Scholarship)

Purpose: To encourage people to go into the travel and tourism business as their profession. **Focus:** Travel and Tourism. **Qualif.:** Applicants must be travel/tourism students in either a four-year college/university or propriety travel school; must have at least 2.5 GPA on a 4.0 scale; must have relevant training in basic statistics or other social research method courses; must have at least basic computer skills; and must be residents, citizens, or legal aliens of the United States or Canada. **Criteria:** Recipients are selected based on academic standing.

Funds Avail.: $1,000. **Number Awarded:** 1. **To Apply:** Applicants must submit proof of enrollment/acceptance at a travel school, community/junior college, college or university; an official school-printed description or listing of the curriculum where they are enrolled; proof of enrollments in travel and tourism courses, or letter from business colleague that can attest to the applicant's desire to pursue a career in the travel and tourism industry; four identical collated copies of applications and required materials (one original and three photocopies); and a 500-word paper on why the applicant is pursuing a career in the travel and tourism industry, which must include at least two career goals.

1363 ■ American Express Travel Scholarships
(Undergraduate/Scholarship)

Purpose: To encourage the pursuit of education and the growth and development of tomorrow's travel/tourism work force. **Focus:** Travel and Tourism. **Qualif.:** Applicants must be travel/tourism students in either a two or four-year college/university or propriety travel school; must have at least 3.0 GPA on a 4.0 scale; must have relevant training in basic statistics or other social research method courses; must have at least basic computer skills; and must be residents, citizens, or legal aliens of the United States or Canada. **Criteria:** Recipients are selected based on academic standing.

Funds Avail.: $1,000. **Number Awarded:** 1. **To Apply:** Applicants must submit a proof of enrollment/acceptance at a travel school, community/junior college, college or university; an official school-printed description or listing of the curriculum where they enrolled; proof of enrollments in travel and tourism courses, or letter from business colleague that can attest to the applicant's desire to pursue a career in the travel and tourism industry; four identical collated copies of applications and required materials (one original and three photocopies); and a 500-word statement detailing the student's plans in travel and tourism as well as the student's view of the travel industry's future.

1364 ■ American Society of Travel Agents AVIS Scholarships *(Graduate, Professional development, Undergraduate/Scholarship)*

Purpose: To help future travel professionals meet the need for broader business management skills, beyond those dealing solely with travel and tourism issues. **Focus:** Travel and Tourism. **Qualif.:** Applicants must have a minimum of two years of full-time travel industry experience or an undergraduate degree in travel/tourism; may be currently employed in the travel industry; or may be currently enrolled in a minimum of two courses per semester in an accredited undergraduate or graduate level degree program in busi-

ness or equivalent degree program. **Criteria:** Recipients are selected based on merit.

Funds Avail.: $2,000. **Number Awarded:** 1. **To Apply:** Applicants must provide a proof of current employment in the travel industry; transcript from last academic term with proof of a GPA of 3.0 on a 4.0 scale, or if the applicant is returning to school after time spent in the workforce, applicant must submit transcript showing a GPA of 3.0 on 4.0 scale; and a brief essay (500-750 words) explaining how the degree program relates to applicant's future career in the travel industry.

1365 ■ Arizona Chapter Gold Scholarships
(Undergraduate/Scholarship)

Purpose: To encourage serious academic study in the field of travel and tourism. **Focus:** Travel and Tourism. **Qualif.:** Applicants must be travel/tourism students in either a two or four-year college/university or propriety travel school; must have at least 2.5 GPA on a 4.0 scale; must have relevant training in basic statistics or other social research method courses; must have at least basic computer skills; and must be residents, citizens, or legal aliens of the United States or Canada. **Criteria:** Recipients are selected based on academic standing.

Funds Avail.: $3,000. **To Apply:** Applicants must submit a proof of enrollment/acceptance at a travel school, community/junior college, college or university; an official school-printed description or listing of the curriculum where they are enrolled; proof of enrollments in travel and tourism courses, or letter from business colleague that can attest to the applicant's desire to pursue a career in the travel and tourism industry; four identical collated copies of applications and required materials (one original and three photocopies); and a 500-word statement detailing the student's plans in travel and tourism as well as the student's view of the travel industry's future.

1366 ■ David J. Hallissey Memorial Scholarships *(Graduate, Undergraduate/Scholarship)*

Purpose: To encourage academic research in the tourism field. **Focus:** Travel and Tourism. **Qualif.:** Applicants must be travel/tourism students from Washington, DC metro area colleges/universities in undergraduate or graduate travel or tourism programs; must have at least 3.0 GPA on a 4.0 scale; must have relevant training in basic statistics or other social research method courses; must have at least basic computer skills; and must be residents, citizens, or legal aliens of the United States or Canada. **Criteria:** Recipients are selected based on academic standing.

Funds Avail.: $2,000. **To Apply:** Applicants must submit a proof of enrollment/acceptance at a travel school, community/junior college, college or university; an official school-printed description or listing of the curriculum where he/she is enrolled; proof of enrollment in travel and tourism courses, or letter from a business colleague that can attest to the applicant's desire to pursue a career in the travel and tourism industry. Complete application must consist of four identical collated copies of applications and required materials (one original and three photocopies). **Contact:** scholarships@tourismcares.org.

1367 ■ Healy Graduate Scholarships *(Graduate/Scholarship)*

Purpose: To encourage serious academic study in the field of travel and tourism. **Focus:** Travel and Tourism. **Qualif.:** Applicants must be travel/tourism students in either a four-year college/university or propriety travel school; must have

Awards are arranged alphabetically below their administering organizations

at least 2.5 GPA on a 4.0 scale; must have relevant training in basic statistics or other social research method courses; must have at least basic computer skills; and must be residents, citizens, or legal aliens of the United States or Canada. **Criteria:** Recipients are selected based on academic standing.

Funds Avail.: $1,000. **Number Awarded:** 1. **To Apply:** Applicants must submit a proof of enrollment/acceptance at a travel school, community/junior college, college or university; an official school-printed description or listing of the curriculum where they are enrolled; proof of enrollments in travel and tourism courses, or letter from business colleague that can attest to the applicant's desire to pursue a career in the travel and tourism industry; four identical collated copies of applications and required materials (one original and three photocopies); and a 500-word statement suggesting improvements in the travel industry. **Contact:** scholarships@tourismcares.org.

1368 ■ Holland America Line-Westours Research Grants *(Undergraduate/Grant)*

Purpose: To provide funding support for research projects in the travel and tourism field. **Focus:** Travel and Tourism. **Qualif.:** Applicant must be a resident, a citizen, or a legal alien of the United States or Canada and have at least, 2.5 grade point of average on a 4.0 scale. **Criteria:** Recipients are selected based on academic standing.

Funds Avail.: No specific amount. **To Apply:** Applicant must submit a proof of enrollment/acceptance at a travel school, community/junior college, or university; an official school-printed description or listing of the curriculum where he/she is enrolled; a proof of enrollment in travel and tourism courses; and a letter of recommendation from a professor, employer, or business colleague that can attest to the applicant's desire to pursue a career in the travel and tourism industry.

1369 ■ Pleasant Hawaiian Holidays Scholarships *(Undergraduate/Scholarship)*

Purpose: To encourage people to go into the travel and tourism business as their profession. **Focus:** Travel and Tourism. **Qualif.:** Applicants must be travel/tourism students in either a four-year college/university or propriety travel school; must have at least 2.5 GPA on a 4.0 scale; must have relevant training in basic statistics or other social research method courses; must have at least basic computer skills; and must be residents, citizens, or legal aliens of the United States or Canada. **Criteria:** Recipients are selected based on academic standing.

Funds Avail.: $2,500. **To Apply:** Applicants must submit a proof of enrollment/acceptance at a travel school, community/junior college, college or university; an official school-printed description or listing of the curriculum where they are enrolled; proof of enrollments in travel and tourism courses, or letter from business colleague that can attest to the applicant's desire to pursue a career in the travel and tourism industry; four identical collated copies of applications and required materials (one original and three photocopies); and a 500-word paper stating the applicant's career goals.

1370 ■ Stan and Leone Pollard Scholarships *(Undergraduate/Scholarship)*

Purpose: To encourage people to go into the travel and tourism business as their profession. **Focus:** Travel and Tourism. **Qualif.:** Applicants must be travel/tourism students in either a two or four-year college/university or propriety travel school; must have at least 2.5 GPA on a 4.0 scale; must have relevant training in basic statistics or other social research method courses; must have at least basic computer skills; must be residents, citizens, or legal aliens of the United States or Canada. **Criteria:** Recipients are selected based on academic standing.

Funds Avail.: $1,000. **Number Awarded:** 1. **To Apply:** Applicants must submit proof of enrollment/acceptance at a travel school, community/junior college, college or university; an official school-printed description or listing of the curriculum where they are enrolled; proof of enrollments in travel and tourism courses, or letter from business colleague that can attest to the applicant's desire to pursue a career in the travel and tourism industry; four identical collated copies of applications and required materials (one original and three photocopies); and a 500-word paper on the student's objectives in the travel and tourism industry.

1371 ■ George Reinke Scholarships *(Professional development/Scholarship)*

Purpose: To help educate future travel agents. **Focus:** Travel and Tourism. **Qualif.:** Applicants must be travel/tourism students in either a two or four-year college/university or propriety travel school; must have at least 2.5 GPA on a 4.0 scale; must have a relevant training in basic statistics or other social research method courses; must have at least basic computer skills; and must be residents, citizens, or legal aliens of the United States or Canada. **Criteria:** Recipients are selected based on academic standing.

Funds Avail.: $1,500. **Number Awarded:** 2. **To Apply:** Applicants must submit proof of enrollment/acceptance at a travel school, community/junior college, college or university; an official school-printed description or listing of the curriculum where they are enrolled; proof of enrollments in travel and tourism courses, or letter from business colleague that can attest to the applicant's desire to pursue a career in the travel and tourism industry; four identical collated copies of applications and required materials (one original and three photocopies); and a 500-word paper explaining why applicant needs the scholarship. **Contact:** scholarships@tourismcares.org.

1372 ■ Nancy Stewart Scholarships *(Undergraduate/Scholarship)*

Purpose: To fund research projects in the travel and tourism field. **Focus:** Travel and Tourism. **Qualif.:** Applicants must have a minimum of three years of full-time travel industry experience; must be pursuing one of the Travel Institute's four certification program: CTC accreditation, Destination Specialist, Travel Career Development, Professional Management. **Criteria:** Recipients are selected based on the academic standing.

Funds Avail.: $3,000. **To Apply:** Applicants must provide a proof of current employment in the travel industry; transcript from last academic term with proof of a GPA of 3.0 on a 4.0 scale or if the applicant is returning to school after time spent in the workforce, submit a cover letter explaining why applicant is returning to school; a letter of intent to enroll in a Travel Institute course within one year and explaining what benefits they hope to obtain from the Travel Institute program or an application to the ASTA educational program; a letter of recommendation from the official ASTA employer to confirm the employment status; and an original headshot picture. **Deadline:** July 1. **Contact:** scholarships@asta.org.

Awards are arranged alphabetically below their administering organizations

1373 ■ American Society of Women Accountants (ASWA)

1760 Old Meadow Rd., Ste. 500
McLean, VA 22102
Ph: (703) 506-3265
Fax: (703) 506-3266
Free: 800-326-2163
E-mail: aswa@aswa.org
URL: www.aswa.org

1374 ■ ASWA 2-Year College Scholarships
(Undergraduate/Scholarship)

Purpose: To provide financial assistance for students attending Community, State or 2-year Colleges in accounting or finance degree. **Focus:** Accounting; Finance. **Qualif.:** Applicants must be community college students entering their second year of an Associate Degree Program who have completed 15 semester hours or equivalent; must have a minimum cumulative GPA of 3.0 on a 4.0 scale; and must be majoring in accounting or finance. **Criteria:** Scholarship recipients will be selected on the basis of leadership, character and communication skills, scholastic average and financial need.

Funds Avail.: No specific amount. **To Apply:** Applicants must submit a completed application form; 75-word essay about their goals and objectives, what impact they want to have on the accounting world and most likes about accounting; three references (two references must be from accounting faculty); and a copy and the original academic transcript from school.

1375 ■ ASWA Undergraduate Scholarships
(Undergraduate/Scholarship)

Purpose: To provide financial assistance for students attending 3rd, 4th or 5th year in accounting or finance degree. **Focus:** Accounting; Finance. **Qualif.:** Applicants must be students who have completed their sophomore year of college and are majoring in accounting or finance. Applicants must have a minimum cumulative GPA of 3.0 on a 4.0 scale. **Criteria:** Recipients are selected on the basis of leadership, character and communication skills, scholastic average and financial need.

Funds Avail.: Scholarship amount not specified. **To Apply:** Applicant must submit a completed application form; 75-word essay about the his/her goals and objectives, what impact he/she wants to have on the accounting world and most likes about accounting; three references (two references must be from accounting faculty); and a copy and the original academic transcript from school.

1376 ■ American Sociological Association (ASA)

1430 K St. NW, Ste. 600
Washington, DC 20005
Ph: (202) 383-9005
Fax: (202) 638-0882
E-mail: executive.office@asanet.org
URL: www.asanet.org

1377 ■ ASA Minority Fellowship Program
(Doctorate, Master's/Fellowship)

Purpose: To provide financial assistance for students showing interests in studying mental disorder. **Focus:** Drug Abuse; Mental Health. **Qualif.:** Program is open to individuals who are in M.A. programs who have been accepted into sociology Ph.D. programs, or students in the early stages of a doctoral program. **Criteria:** Selection is based on the evidence of: research relevance; trainee skills and ability; supportive institutional environment; and mentor.

Funds Avail.: $15,000. **To Apply:** Applicants must submit a completed Fellowship Application together with the essays (25 a and b); three letters of recommendation (with primary advisor's CV); official transcripts; Curriculum Vitae; and other supporting documents (optional). **Deadline:** January 31. **Contact:** minority.affairs@asanet.org.

1378 ■ American Sokol

9126 Ogden Ave.
Brookfield, IL 60513
Ph: (708) 255-5397
Fax: (708) 255-5398
E-mail: aso@american-sokol.org
URL: www.american-sokol.org

1379 ■ American Sokol Merit Awards
(Undergraduate/Scholarship)

Purpose: To help incoming students pursue their studies in college. **Focus:** Physical education; Physical sciences. **Qualif.:** Applicants must be Sokol Youth or Sokol Adult members who are planning a full-time course or program in an accredited college. Applications must be made in advance of the year of study. **Criteria:** Applicants will be selected based on the following: regular attendance in American Sokol classes for at least three years (juniors may be included but must become American Sokol adult members at age 17); successful completion of Sokol Instructor School(s) - Unit, District, or National; teaching or assisting experience in Sokol gym classes; and service American Sokol Units, Districts, and/or National Organization.

Funds Avail.: $500. **Number Awarded:** 2 students per district. **To Apply:** Successful candidates must submit a recommendation proof of the Unit or District Physical Director; a parent or guardian will be required to sign to the condition that if the candidate cannot submit the needed requirements completely, he or she should repaid the whole amount of the award. **Deadline:** June 1. **Remarks:** The award was instituted by the XIIth American Sokol Convention to be paid from the American Sokol Future Leaders Fund.

1380 ■ American Speech Language Hearing Foundation (ASHF)

2200 Research Blvd.
Rockville, MD 20850-3289
Ph: (301) 296-8700
E-mail: foundation@asha.org
URL: www.ashfoundation.org

1381 ■ American Speech Language Hearing Foundation Clinical Research Grants
(Doctorate/Grant)

Purpose: To support investigations that will advance knowledge of the efficacy of treatment and assessment practices. **Focus:** Disabilities. **Qualif.:** Applicants must have received a Ph.D or equivalent research doctorate within the discipline of communication sciences and disorders or related field and must demonstrate the potential and commitment to conducting independent

Awards are arranged alphabetically below their administering organizations

research with a clear plan for applying for extramural research support. **Criteria:** Recipients are selected based on objectives and significance; experimental design and research method; innovation; facilities and resources; management plan and budget; investigator; mentor and mentoring plan; collaborators and collaboration plan.

Funds Avail.: $50,000-$75,000. **To Apply:** Applicants must submit original application form with all accompanying documents along with a hard copy or electronic version of the proposal. **Deadline:** June 2.

1382 ■ American Speech Language Hearing Foundation Endowed Scholarships
(Postdoctorate/Scholarship)

Purpose: To support the advancement of knowledge in the area of disabilities and to improve the lives of people with speech, language, or hearing disorders. **Focus:** Disabilities. **Qualif.:** Applicants must be enrolled or accepted in a master's or doctoral in communication sciences and disorders program in the United States; and must be enrolled in full-time study for full academic year. **Criteria:** Recipients are selected based on financial need and academic standing.

Funds Avail.: $5,000. **Number Awarded:** 5. **To Apply:** Applicants must complete the Student Information form; Optional Form; letter of application; accompanying documents including statement of good standing, transcript, GPA, Essay, and Confidential Reference form. **Deadline:** June 6. **Contact:** Emily Diaz at the above address.

1383 ■ American Speech Language Hearing Foundation General Scholarships
(Postgraduate/Scholarship)

Purpose: To support the advancement of knowledge in the area of disabilities and to improve the lives of people with speech, language, or hearing disorders. **Focus:** Disabilities. **Qualif.:** Applicants must be enrolled or accepted in a graduate study in communication sciences and disorders program in the United States and must be enrolled in a full-time study for full academic year. **Criteria:** Recipients are selected based on financial need.

Funds Avail.: $5,000. **Number Awarded:** 7. **To Apply:** Applicants must complete the Student Information form; Optional Form; letter of application; accompanying documents including statement of good standing, transcript, GPA, Essay, and Confidential Reference form. **Deadline:** June 6. **Contact:** Emily Diaz at the above address.

1384 ■ American Speech Language Hearing Foundation Scholarships for International Students *(Graduate/Scholarship)*

Purpose: To support the advancement of knowledge in the area of disabilities and to improve the lives of people with speech, language, or hearing disorders. **Focus:** Disabilities. **Qualif.:** Applicants must be full-time international graduate students studying communication sciences and disorders in the United States and demonstrating outstanding achievement. **Criteria:** Recipients are selected based on financial need and academic standing.

Funds Avail.: $5,000. **Number Awarded:** 1. **To Apply:** Applicants must complete the Student Information form and the Optional Form. They must submit letter of application and accompanying documents including statement of good standing, transcript, GPA, Essay and Confidential Reference form. **Deadline:** June 3. **Contact:** Questions should be forwarded to foundationprograms@asha.org or by calling 800-498-2071.

1385 ■ American Speech Language Hearing Foundation Scholarships for Students with Disability *(Graduate/Scholarship)*

Purpose: To support the advancement of knowledge in the area of disabilities and to improve the lives of people with speech, language, or hearing disorders. **Focus:** Disabilities. **Qualif.:** Program is open to individuals who have disorders or disabilities who are enrolled in a communication sciences and disorders program **Criteria:** Recipients are selected based on financial need and academic standing.

Funds Avail.: $5,000. **Number Awarded:** 1. **To Apply:** Applicants must complete the Student Information form; Optional Form; letter of application; accompanying documents including statement of good standing, transcript, GPA, Essay and Confidential Reference form. **Deadline:** June 3. **Contact:** Questions should be forwarded to foundationprograms@asha.org or by calling 800-498-2071.

1386 ■ ASHFA Scholarships for Minority Students *(Graduate/Scholarship)*

Purpose: To support the advancement of knowledge in the area of disabilities and to improve the lives of people with speech, language, or hearing disorders. **Focus:** Disabilities. **Qualif.:** Applicants must be members of a racial or ethnic minority group and must be U.S. citizens; must be graduate students enrolled full-time in a communication sciences and disorders program. **Criteria:** Recipients are selected based on financial need and academic standing.

Funds Avail.: $5,000. **Number Awarded:** 2. **To Apply:** Applicants must complete the Student Information form and Optional Form. They must submit letter of application, accompanying documents including statement of good standing, transcript, GPA, Essay and Confidential Reference form. **Deadline:** June 3. **Contact:** Questions should be forwarded to foundationprograms@asha.org or by calling 800-498-2071.

1387 ■ New Century Scholars Doctoral Scholarships *(Postdoctorate/Scholarship)*

Purpose: To support strong doctoral candidates who are committed to attaining the research doctoral degree and to working in the higher education academic community in the field of communication sciences and disorders in the United States. **Focus:** Disabilities. **Qualif.:** Applicants must be enrolled in a doctorate study in a communication sciences and disorders program in the United States. **Criteria:** Recipients are selected based on academic standing.

Funds Avail.: $10,000. **Number Awarded:** 20. **To Apply:** Applicants must fill out the application form. **Deadline:** May 2.

1388 ■ New Century Scholars Research Grants *(Doctorate/Grant)*

Purpose: To support investigations that will advance knowledge of the efficacy of treatment and assessment practices; to support innovative studies or unmet research. **Focus:** Disabilities. **Qualif.:** Applicants must be scientists with research doctorate within the discipline of communication sciences and disorders or related field; must demonstrate the potential and commitment to conducting independent research with a clear plan for applying for extramural research support. **Criteria:** Recipients are selected based on the objectives and significance; experimental design and research method; innovation; facilities and resources; management plan and budget; investigator; mentor and mentoring plan; collaborators and collaboration plan.

Awards are arranged alphabetically below their administering organizations

Funds Avail.: $10,000. **To Apply:** Applicants must submit original application form with all accompanying documents along with a hard copy or electronic version of the proposal. **Deadline:** April 29.

1389 ■ Research Grants in Speech Science
(Doctorate/Grant)

Purpose: To support investigations that will advance knowledge of the efficacy of treatment and assessment practices; to help further research activities of new investigators that have particular relevance to audiology and/or speech language pathology. **Focus:** Speech and language pathology/audiology. **Qualif.:** Applicants must have received a doctoral degree within the past five years and wish to further research activities in the areas of speech communication. **Criteria:** Recipients are selected based on the clearly stated project aims; significance of the research and its potential impact on the clinical needs relevant to speech-language pathology or audiology; merit of the design for answering the question, including detailed account of the methodology to be used; adequate provision for evaluating the results of the project, explicit statement of how the objectives will be measured; indication of the facilities, resources, personnel and subjects to which the applicant would have access in order to carry out the activities described in the proposal; the perceived ability of the applicant to complete the proposed research within one year period; Management plan that clearly outlines the activities and timeliness.

Funds Avail.: $5,000. **Number Awarded:** 1. **To Apply:** Applicants must submit an original application form and four copies of the completed proposal. **Deadline:** May 6. **Contact:** Questions should be forwarded to foundationprograms@asha.org or by calling 800-498-2071.

1390 ■ Student Research Grants in Audiology
(Doctorate/Grant)

Purpose: To support investigations that will advance knowledge of the efficacy of treatment and assessment practices. To help further the research activities of new investigators whose research have particular relevance to audiology and/or speech language pathology. **Focus:** Audiology. **Qualif.:** Applicants must have received a master's and doctoral degree in communication sciences and disorders and aim to conduct research. **Criteria:** Recipients are selected based on the clearly stated project aims; the significance of the research and its potential impact on the clinical needs relevant to speech-language pathology or audiology; the merit of the design for answering the question, including detailed account of the methodology to be used; adequate provision for evaluating the results of the project, explicit statement of how the objectives will be measured; indication of the facilities, resources, personnel and subjects to which the applicant would have access in order to carry out the activities described in the proposal; the perceived ability of the applicant to complete the proposed research within a one year period; and management plan that clearly outlines the activities and timeliness.

Funds Avail.: $2,000. **To Apply:** Applicants must submit original application form with all accompanying documents and a hard copy or electronic version of the proposal. **Deadline:** May 15.

1391 ■ Student Research Grants in Early Childhood Language Development *(Doctorate/Grant)*

Purpose: To support investigations that will advance knowledge of the efficacy of treatment and assessment practices; to help further research activities of new investigators that have particular relevance to audiology and/or speech language pathology. **Focus:** Speech and language pathology/audiology. **Qualif.:** Applicants must have received a master's and doctoral degree in communication sciences and disorders and aim to conduct research in early childhood language development; and must be enrolled full-time within the academic year. **Criteria:** Recipients are selected based on the clearly stated project aims; the significance of the research and its potential impact on the clinical needs relevant to speech-language pathology or audiology; the merit of the design for answering the question, including detailed account of the methodology to be used; adequate provision for evaluating the results of the project, explicit statement of how the objectives will be measured; indication of the facilities, resources, personnel and subjects to which the applicant would have access in order to carry out the activities described in the proposal; the perceived ability of the applicant to complete the proposed research within one year period; and management plan that clearly outlines the activities and timeliness.

Funds Avail.: $2,000. **Number Awarded:** 2. **To Apply:** Applicants must submit an original application form with all accompanying documents along with four copies of the completed proposal. **Deadline:** May 20. **Contact:** Questions should be forwarded to foundationprograms@asha.org or by calling 800-498-2071.

1392 ■ American Statistical Association (ASA)
732 N Washington St.
Alexandria, VA 22314-1943
Ph: (703) 684-1221
Fax: (703) 684-2037
Free: 888-231-3473
E-mail: asainfo@amstat.org
URL: www.amstat.org

1393 ■ ASA/NSF/BLS Fellowships *(Graduate/Fellowship)*

Purpose: To improve the collaboration between government and academics research. **Focus:** Statistics. **Qualif.:** Applicants should have recognized research records and considerable expertise in their areas of proposed research. **Criteria:** Preference will be given to those who meet the criteria.

Funds Avail.: No specific amount. **To Apply:** Applicants must submit the following information via e-mail: a curriculum vitae; names and addresses of three references; a detailed research proposal that includes background information about research topic, significance of expected results; advantages of conducting research at the BLS; and detailed budget estimate (salary, relocation, travel expenses, research support). **Deadline:** January 27. **Contact:** Jean Fox, 202-691-7370, fox.jean@bls.gov.

1394 ■ Edward C. Bryant Scholarships Trust Fund *(Graduate/Fellowship)*

Purpose: To provide financial assistance for graduate education. **Focus:** Statistics. **Qualif.:** Applicants must have the potential to contribute in survey statistics; must have experience in survey statistics; and must be in a graduate school. **Criteria:** Recipients will be chosen by the ASA Bryant Scholarship Award Committee.

Funds Avail.: $2,500. **To Apply:** Applicants may check the

Awards are arranged alphabetically below their administering organizations

website for the required materials. **Deadline:** April 1. **Remarks:** Westat established the Edward C. Bryant Scholarship Trust Fund in 1995 to honor its co-founder and Chairman Emeritus. Under Dr. Bryant's leadership, Westat, an employee-owned statistical firm established in 1961, has grown into what is now one of the world's leading statistical research corporations serving federal, state, and local governments, as well as businesses and foundations. **Contact:** American Statistical Association at the above address.

1395 ■ Gertrude M. Cox Scholarships *(Doctorate, Graduate/Fellowship)*

Purpose: To encourage more women to enter statistically-oriented professions. **Focus:** Statistics. **Qualif.:** Applicants must be female residents of United States or Canada and must be admitted in a graduate statistical program. **Criteria:** Awards will be given based on merit.

Funds Avail.: $2,000. **To Apply:** Applicants must submit the completed application form, academic reference letter and Cox status form. These forms are available at their website. **Deadline:** April 1. **Contact:** American Statistical Association at the above address.

1396 ■ Samuel S. Wilks Memorial Awards *(Undergraduate/Award)*

Purpose: To provide financial assistance for students who are in need; to honor the memory and distinguished career of Sam by honoring contributions (either recent or past) to the advancement of scientific or technical knowledge, ingenious application of existing knowledge, or successful activity in the fostering of cooperative scientific efforts that have been directly involved in matters of national defense or public interest. **Focus:** Statistics. **Qualif.:** Applicants must demonstrate financial need. **Criteria:** Selection of recipients will be based primarily on contributions (either recent or past) to the advancement of scientific or technical knowledge, ingenious application of existing knowledge, or successful activity in fostering of cooperative scientific efforts that have been directly involved in matters of national defense or public interest.

Funds Avail.: Two ($500) and $1,000 which increases 3% annually. **Number Awarded:** 3. **To Apply:** Applicants may check the website for scholarship instructions and information. **Deadline:** April 1. **Contact:** Copies of documentation must be submitted at pamela@amstat.org.

1397 ■ American Surgical Association (ASA)
500 Cummings Ctr., Ste. 4550
Beverly, MA 01915
Ph: (978) 927-8330
Fax: (978) 524-8890
URL: www.americansurgical.info

1398 ■ ACS/ASA Health Policy and Management Scholarships *(Professional development/Scholarship)*

Purpose: To subsidize attendance and participation in the Executive Leadership Program in Health Policy and Management at Brandeis University. **Focus:** Health education. **Qualif.:** Applicants must be surgeons; must be members in good standing of both the ACS and ASA; must be between 30-60 years old; and planning to attend the Executive Leadership Program in Health Policy and Management at Brandeis University. **Criteria:** Scholarship recipients will be selected based on the Selection Committee's review of the application materials.

Funds Avail.: $8,000. **To Apply:** Applicants must submit a completed application form, a copy of curriculum vitae and one-page essay that discusses why the applicant needs the scholarship to ASA Scholarships Section. **Deadline:** February 1.

1399 ■ American Swedish Institute (ASI)
2600 Park Ave.
Minneapolis, MN 55407-1090
Ph: (612) 871-4907
Fax: (612) 871-8682
E-mail: info@asimn.org
URL: www.asimn.org

1400 ■ Lilly Lorenzen Scholarships *(Undergraduate/Scholarship)*

Purpose: To promote the study of Swedish heritage. **Focus:** Swedish studies. **Qualif.:** Applicants must be Minnesota residents who have knowledge of the Swedish language. **Criteria:** Recipients are selected based on the application materials.

Funds Avail.: $1,000. **To Apply:** Applicants must submit a completed application form and a transcript or a statement of professional and community achievement. **Deadline:** May 1. **Remarks:** Established in memory of Lilly Lorenzen, an instructor in Swedish University of Minnesota and the American Swedish Institute, and author of the book "Of Swedish Ways".

1401 ■ Malmberg Fellowships *(Undergraduate/Fellowship)*

Purpose: To promote study at the American Swedish Institute. **Focus:** Swedish studies. **Qualif.:** Applicants must be students aged 21 years old and above. Residents of Sweden are also qualified. For organizational applicants, the project manager is identified as the applicant. **Criteria:** Recipients are selected based on the submitted documents.

Funds Avail.: No specific amount. **To Apply:** Applicants must send a study proposal.

1402 ■ Malmberg Scholarships *(Undergraduate/Scholarship)*

Purpose: To provide financial assistance for individuals intending to study in Sweden. **Focus:** Swedish studies. **Qualif.:** Applicants must be U.S. citizens; enrolled in a degree-granting program in college/university or in a study or research that requires or can be enhanced by study in Sweden; and must have knowledge in the Swedish language. **Criteria:** Recipients are selected based on submitted application materials.

Funds Avail.: $10,000. **To Apply:** Applicants must submit a completed application form and a letter of invitation or affiliation from the Swedish institution/organization; a project summary (1000 words); transcript (optional if out of school for three years); resume; and two letters of recommendation.

1403 ■ The American University - School of Public Affairs
Ward Cir. Bldg.
4400 Massachusetts Ave. NW
Washington, DC 20016
Ph: (202) 885-2940
Fax: (202) 885-1000

Awards are arranged alphabetically below their administering organizations

E-mail: spagrad@american.edu
URL: www.american.edu/spa

1404 ■ Center for Congressional and Presidential Studies Endowment (CPPS)
(Graduate, Undergraduate/Scholarship)

Purpose: To support students with financial disabilities. **Focus:** Public administration. **Qualif.:** Applicants must be students attending CPPS programs. **Criteria:** Recipients are selected based on merit and financial need.

Funds Avail.: $2,500. **To Apply:** Applicants must submit resume; one-to-two pages letter to the Director of CPPS (the letter should address academic and professional achievements and future aspirations, with detailed financial need). **Remarks:** The support allocated to any student's account will replace a current financial need. The award will not necessarily be available as a cash reimbursement from students account, unless a credit remains on the system after all debts are paid.

1405 ■ Jane R. Glaser Scholarships
(Undergraduate/Scholarship)

Purpose: To provide financial assistance to School of Public Administration students. **Focus:** Public affairs. **Qualif.:** Applicants should be undergraduate students of School of Public Administration. **Criteria:** Recipients are selected based on a review of applications; interviews and consultation with faculty and staff.

Funds Avail.: $2,500. **To Apply:** Applicants must submit one page formal recommendation from advisor; outline of grade point average; activities; reason for studying at Hebrew University; and statement stating interest in receiving the scholarship and studying abroad. **Deadline:** March 15. **Contact:** 202-885-6100; financialaid@american.edu.

1406 ■ American Urological Association Foundation (AUAF)
1000 Corporate Blvd.
Linthicum, MD 21090
Ph: (410) 689-3990
Fax: (410) 689-3998
Free: 866-746-4282
E-mail: auafoundation@auafoundation.org
URL: www.urologyhealth.org

1407 ■ AUA Foundation/Astellas Rising Star in Urology Research Awards *(Postdoctorate, Professional development/Fellowship)*

Purpose: To encourage a young urology faculty to go into, or continue a research career. **Focus:** Urology. **Qualif.:** Applicants must be Board certified or eligible urologists and must have successfully competed for a career development award within the current federal fiscal year. **Criteria:** Applicants will be selected based on scholarship panel's review of the application materials.

Funds Avail.: No specific amount. **To Apply:** Applicants must complete the online application form. They must also prepare a registration summary form; curriculum vitae; application agreement form with all necessary signatures; letter of support from each mentor; letter from urology department chair; current NIH-style biosketch of each mentor; copy of career development grant award letter; copy of career development grant; and copy of career development grant review summary sheets and scores. All materials

must be uploaded and scanned into a single .pdf file. **Deadline:** November 20. **Contact:** Rodney Cotten, Research Manager, grants@auafoundation.org.

1408 ■ AUA Foundation Bridge Awards
(Postgraduate/Fellowship)

Purpose: To support research that will help those who suffer from the effects of urological diseases. **Focus:** Urology. **Qualif.:** Applicant must be a member of AUA; not a previous recipient of the award; must have competed for a peer-reviewed external funding for the project during the current federal fiscal year. **Criteria:** Applicants are selected based on the jury's review of the application materials.

Funds Avail.: $15,000. **To Apply:** Applicants must register online at the AUA Foundation website in order to apply. Applicants must submit the completed application form; a registration summary form; an application agreement form; a NIH-style biosketch; a statement of current other support; letter from the applicant; budget justification worksheet; and letter from the applicant's department chair. The form must be signed by the applicant, department chair and sponsoring institution representative. Scan all materials into one complete .pdf file. **Deadline:** March 31. **Contact:** Rodney Cotten, Research Program Mgr., grants@auafoundation.org.

1409 ■ AUA Foundation - NIDDK/NCI Surgeon-Scientist Awards *(Postgraduate/Fellowship)*

Purpose: To support urology faculty who wish to become independent investigators. **Focus:** Urology. **Qualif.:** Applicants must be Board certified or eligible urologists; must be participating in a training program to obtain a Board Certification in Urology; have successfully competed for NIDDK or NCI career development for the current year. **Criteria:** Priority scores will be given to applicants based on the following criteria: 1) Career development award grant, score and critique; 2) Commitment to applicant's career development by mentor(s) and department chair, including ensured protected time for research; 3) Mentoring plan for the applicants; 4) Resources available to the applicants, including research start-up package, laboratory space and other resources available; 5) Applicant's excellency in urology demonstrated by publication(s) and/or presentation(s); and 6) Balance in the AUA Foundation Surgeon-Scientist Grant portfolio.

Funds Avail.: No specific amount. **To Apply:** Applicants must complete the online application form. Applicants must also prepare a registration summary form; applicant curriculum vitae; application agreement form; letter of support from mentor; letter from urology department chair; current NIH-style biosketch for each mentor; copy of career development grant award letter; copy of career development grant; copy of career development grant review summary sheets and scores. All materials must be uploaded into a single .pdf file. **Deadline:** November 20. **Contact:** Rodney Cotten, grants@auafoundation.org.

1410 ■ AUA Foundation Ph.D. Post-Doctoral Fellowships *(Postdoctorate/Fellowship)*

Purpose: To promote research related to epidemiology of urologic diseases. **Focus:** Urology. **Qualif.:** Applicants must be PhDs with less than five years of post-doctoral experience and with a research interest in urological diseases and conditions and/or any related diseases or dysfunctions. Mentors should be an established basic science academician in either the basic science or clinical department. Mentors must also have experience with funded grants. **Criteria:**

Awards are arranged alphabetically below their administering organizations

Fellowship recipients will be selected based on the scholarship committee's review of the application materials.

Funds Avail.: $30,000. **To Apply:** Applicants must complete the online application form and the application agreement form; two letters of support from individuals other than the mentor; research career goals of the candidate; description of research proposal in layman's terms; research proposal (maximum of 10 pages) which consist of the following: specific aims (1-2 pages), background (2 pages), preliminary data (2-3 pages), methods and procedures (2-4 pages). Applicants must also submit a curriculum vitae (maximum of 5 pages); notification of applications filed to other funding sources. For mentors, requirements are institutional plans; concise statement of reasons that the candidate and mentor should be selected; outline of clinical/research time (M.D. researchers only); mentor's letters of support for applicant; mentor's biosketches; list of mentor's previous fellows and their current positions. **Deadline:** August. **Contact:** Rodney Cotten, Research Coordinator, grants@auafoundation.org.

1411 ■ American Water Resources Association - Colorado Section

PO Box 9382
Denver, CO 80209
Ph: (303) 806-8952
E-mail: lstadjuhar@bbawater.com
URL: awracolorado.havoclite.com

1412 ■ Richard A. Herbert Memorial Scholarships *(Undergraduate/Scholarship)*

Purpose: To enhance the education in water resources. **Focus:** Water Resources. **Qualif.:** Applicant must be enrolled as a student in a degree program at any accredited Colorado public or private college or university; involved in research or independent study pertaining to hydrology, engineering, hydrogeology, aquatic biology, water law, water-resources policy or planning, environmental science or other topics concerning water resources in Colorado. **Criteria:** A standing committee of the AWRA-Colorado Section will review applications and make recommendations to the Board of Directors.

Funds Avail.: $2,000. **Number Awarded:** One. **To Apply:** Applicants must submit a completed application which includes their resume, abstract of current research and letter of recommendation from a faculty advisor. Completed application should be sent electronically to lstadjuhar@bbawater.com. **Deadline:** April 23. **Contact:** Laurel Stadjuhar.

1413 ■ American Water Ski Educational Foundation (AWSEF)

1251 Holy Cow Rd.
Polk City, FL 33868-8200
Ph: (863) 324-2472
Fax: (863) 324-3996
E-mail: info@waterskihalloffame.com
URL: www.waterskihalloffame.com

1414 ■ American Water Ski Educational Foundation Scholarships *(Undergraduate/Scholarship)*

Purpose: To preserve the traditions of one of America's most popular family recreational activities; to encourage and to educate the safe enjoyment of the challenges of water skiing. **Focus:** General studies. **Qualif.:** Applicant must be enrolled with a minimum of two-year course in secondary education; he/she must be a U.S. citizen and a current member of USA Water Ski Foundation. **Criteria:** Applicants will be evaluated based upon the academic qualifications, leadership, extracurricular involvement, recommendations and financial need.

Funds Avail.: No specific amount. **To Apply:** Applicant must fill out the application form; he/she must submit two letters of reference; a 500-word essay on topic, "AWSEF has a beautiful new facility"; an official transcript of grades; or high school transcript (if college freshman). **Deadline:** March 1. **Remarks:** Incomplete applications will not be accepted.

1415 ■ American Water Works Association (AWWA)

6666 W Quincy Ave.
Denver, CO 80235-3098
Ph: (303) 794-7711
Fax: (303) 347-0804
Free: 800-926-7337
E-mail: dlafrance@awwa.org
URL: www.awwa.org

1416 ■ Thomas R. Camp Scholarships *(Graduate/Scholarship)*

Purpose: To support and encourage graduate students conducting applied research in the drinking water field. **Focus:** Water resources; Water supply industry. **Qualif.:** Applicants must be in pursuit of a graduate degree (either masters or doctoral) at an institution of higher education located in Canada, Guam, Puerto Rico, Mexico or the United States. Completion of degree requirements shall be no sooner than December 1 of the application year. **Criteria:** Scholarship recipient will be selected based on academic record and potential to provide leadership in applied research and consulting in the drinking water field.

Funds Avail.: $5,000. **Number Awarded:** 1. **To Apply:** Applicants must submit a completed official application form; a two-page resume that includes educational history; official transcripts of all university education; official GRE Scores (quantitative, verbal and analytical) sent directly from the GRE Testing Center, or a photocopy of the official report; three letters of recommendation (one of which must be from the academic or research advisor); a one-page statement of educational plans and career objectives demonstrating or declaring an interest in the drinking water field; a two to three page proposed plan of research. **Deadline:** January 17. **Remarks:** Camp Dresser and McKee, Inc., created the Thomas R. Camp Scholarship in honor of the contributions of Dr. Camp in the drinking water field. **Contact:** Linda Moody at the above address; Phone: 303-347-6201; E-mail: lmoody@awwa.org.

1417 ■ Holly A. Cornell Scholarships *(Graduate/Scholarship)*

Purpose: To encourage and support outstanding female and/or minority masteral students in pursuit of advanced training in the field of water supply and treatment. **Focus:** Water resources; Water supply industry. **Qualif.:** Applicants must be female and/or minority U.S. citizens, who are currently masters degree students anticipating completion of the requirements for a Masters degree in engineering no

Awards are arranged alphabetically below their administering organizations

sooner than December 1 of the application year. **Criteria:** Recipients are selected based on academic merit and potential to provide leadership in the field of water supply and treatment.

Funds Avail.: $7,500. **To Apply:** Applicants must submit a completed official application form; a two-page resume that includes educational history; official transcripts of all university education; official GRE Scores (quantitative, verbal, and analytical) sent directly from the GRE Testing Center, or a photocopy of the official report; three letters of recommendation (one of which must be from the academic or research advisor); a proposed curriculum of study; a brief (one to two pages) statement describing the student's career objectives. **Deadline:** January 17. **Remarks:** The Holly A. Cornell Scholarship was created by CH2M Hill, Inc. in honor of their co-founder, Holly A. Cornell. **Contact:** Linda Moody at the above address; Phone: 303-347-6201; E-mail: lmoody@awwa.org.

1418 ■ Larson Aquatic Research Support Scholarships (LARS) (Doctorate, Graduate/Scholarship)

Purpose: To support and encourage outstanding graduate students preparing for careers in the fields of science or engineering. **Focus:** Biochemistry; Water resources; Water supply industry; Chemistry. **Qualif.:** Applicants must be students pursuing a masters or doctoral degree at an institution of higher education located in Canada, Guam, Puerto Rico, Mexico, or the United States. Applicants should anticipate completion of their degree requirements no sooner than December 1 of the application year. **Criteria:** Awards are given based on academic record and candidate's potential to provide leadership in the fields served by Dr. Larson.

Funds Avail.: $5,000 for the Masters student recipient; $7,000 for the Ph.D. student recipient. **Number Awarded:** 2. **To Apply:** Applicants must submit a completed application form; a two-page resume that includes educational history; official transcripts of all university education; official GRE Scores (quantitative, verbal and analytical) sent directly from the GRE Testing Center, or a photocopy of the official report; three letters of recommendation (one of which must be from the academic or research advisor); a proposed curriculum of study; a statement of educational plans and career objectives demonstrating or declaring an interest in an appropriate field of endeavor; a research plan, if applicable (required for Masters students conducting research and all Ph.D. students). **Deadline:** January 17. **Remarks:** Larson Aquatic Research Support scholarships honor the memory of Dr. Thurston E. "Lars" Larson. **Contact:** Linda Moody at the above address; Phone: 303-347-6201; E-mail: lmoody@awwa.org.

1419 ■ Abel Wolman Fellowships (Doctorate/Fellowship)

Purpose: To support promising doctoral students in the U.S., Canada and Mexico pursuing advanced training and research in the field of water supply and treatment. **Focus:** Water resources; Water supply industry. **Qualif.:** Candidates must complete the requirements for a Ph.D. within two years of the award and have citizenship or permanent residence in Canada, Mexico or the United States. **Criteria:** Fellowship recipients are selected based on academic record, significance of the proposed research to water supply and treatment and the candidate's potential to do high quality research.

Funds Avail.: Up to $25,000. **To Apply:** Applicants must submit a completed official application form; a two-page resume that includes educational history; official transcripts of all university education; official GRE scores sent directly from the Testing Center or a photocopy of the official report; three letters of recommendation, one of which must be from the dissertation advisor; proposed curriculum of study; a brief description of the dissertation research, including a statement describing how the research will relate specifically to water supply and treatment (two pages of text plus two pages of figures and tables). **Deadline:** January 17. **Remarks:** Created in honor of Dr. Abel Wolman, the "Dean of Water Supply.". **Contact:** Linda Moody at the above address; Phone: 303-347-6201; E-mail: lmoody@awwa.org.

1420 ■ American Watercolor Society (AWS)
47 5th Ave.
New York, NY 10003
Ph: (212) 206-8986
Fax: (212) 206-1960
E-mail: info@americanwatercolorsociety.org
URL: www.americanwatercolorsociety.com

1421 ■ American Watercolor Society Scholarship Program for Art Teachers (Professional development/Scholarship)

Purpose: To enhance and improve the capabilities of teachers in watercolor media. **Focus:** Art; Painting. **Qualif.:** Applicant must be a U.S. citizen and an art teacher at a high school or college level institution in the United States. **Criteria:** Grantees are selected based on the application materials.

Funds Avail.: $500. **To Apply:** Application form is available at the website. Completed application form should be sent at least three months in advance of the start date of the instruction to PO Box 501, Ascutney, VT 05030. **Contact:** scholarship@americanwatercolorsociety.org.

1422 ■ American Welding Society (AWS)
8669 Doral Blvd., Ste. 130
Doral, FL 33166
Ph: (305) 443-9353
Free: 800-443-9353
URL: www.aws.org/w/a

1423 ■ Howard E. and Wilma J. Adkins Memorial Scholarships (Undergraduate/Scholarship)

Purpose: To provide financial assistance to individuals interested in pursuing a career in welding engineering. **Focus:** Welding. **Qualif.:** Applicants must be undergraduate students pursuing a four-year bachelors degree in welding engineering or welding engineering technology; must be 18 years old and above; must have a minimum of 2.8 overall grade point average; must be citizens of the United States; and must plan to attend an accredited engineering school within the United States. **Criteria:** Preference will be given to those individuals residing or attending school in the states of Wisconsin or Kentucky.

Funds Avail.: $2,500. **To Apply:** Applicants must complete the application form and submit it along with a high school diploma and a financial statement. Official transcripts must be sent directly to Registrar's Office. **Deadline:** February 15. **Contact:** found@aws.org.

1424 ■ American Welding Society District Scholarships (Undergraduate/Scholarship)

Purpose: To provide financial assistance to students preparing for a career in the welding and related joining

Awards are arranged alphabetically below their administering organizations

technologies. **Focus:** Welding. **Qualif.:** Applicants must be high school graduates planning to enroll in a welding course program; must attend a school located in United States or its territories. **Criteria:** Recipients are selected based on academic standing.

Funds Avail.: No specific amount. **To Apply:** Applicants must submit a financial statement; transcript of records; personal statement; biography and photo. **Contact:** Mail the package to Nazdhia Prado-Pulido at the above address or e-mail nprado-pulido@aws.org.

1425 ■ American Welding Society International Scholarships *(Undergraduate/Scholarship)*

Purpose: To provide financial assistance to international students who wish to pursue their education in welding and related joining technologies. **Focus:** Welding. **Qualif.:** Applicants must be full-time international students pursuing undergraduates or graduate studies; must have completed at least one year of welding or related fields of study at a Baccalaureate degree-granting institution; and must be in the top 20% of the institution's grading system. Applicants and designated institutions must be members of American Welding Society. Program is not available to students who reside in Canada, United States, or Mexico. **Criteria:** Recipients are selected based on financial need and academic standing.

Funds Avail.: $2,500. **To Apply:** Applicants must submit a copy of the proposed curriculum; verification of enrollment to the institution; two letters of personal reference; two-page professional goal statement with a brief bibliography; transcript of grades or equivalent from each college; proof of country of citizenship; AWS membership number, if member; and financial information regarding tuition fees from the academic institution. **Deadline:** April 1. **Contact:** found@aws.org.

1426 ■ American Welding Society National Scholarships *(Undergraduate/Scholarship)*

Purpose: To advance opportunities for students preparing for a career in the welding and related joining technologies. **Focus:** Welding. **Qualif.:** Applicants must be students pursuing a specific degree at an accredited four-year college or university. **Criteria:** Recipients are selected based on academic standing.

Funds Avail.: $2,500. **To Apply:** Applicants must submit a financial statement; transcript of records; personal statement; biography; and photo. **Deadline:** February 15.

1427 ■ American Welding Society Past Presidents Scholarships *(Undergraduate/Scholarship)*

Purpose: To provide financial assistance to individuals interested in pursuing a bachelor's degree in welding engineering, welding engineering technology, or an engineering program with an emphasis in welding. **Focus:** Welding. **Qualif.:** Applicants must be junior, senior, or graduate level students pursuing a degree in Welding Engineering or Welding Engineering Technology. **Criteria:** Recipients will be selected based on financial need.

Funds Avail.: $2,500. **To Apply:** Applicants must complete the application form and submit it along with one or more recommendation letters from community members, local AWS officers, and/or AWS district directors attesting to the applicant's leadership capability; and (300-500 word) essay on the applicant's objectives and aspirations in the field of welding. **Deadline:** February 15.

1428 ■ American Welding Society Research Fellowships *(Graduate/Scholarship)*

Purpose: To advance opportunities for students preparing for a career in the welding and related joining technologies. **Focus:** Welding. **Qualif.:** Applicants must be graduate students who wish to pursue areas of research related to the welding and joining industry. **Criteria:** Recipients are selected based on academic standing.

Funds Avail.: $25,000. **Number Awarded:** 4. **To Apply:** Applicants must prepare the academic credentials; plans; research history; and proposal. Technical portion of proposal should be: 25-typewritten pages; with two megabytes; 12-point font; and Times New Roman. **Deadline:** February 16. **Contact:** Send application form and supporting documents to: Vicky Pinsky at the above address or e-mail at gricelda@aws.org.

1429 ■ Arsham Amirikian Engineering Scholarships *(Undergraduate/Scholarship)*

Purpose: To provide financial assistance to individuals interested in pursuing a career in either welding engineering or the application of the art of welding in civil and structural engineering. **Focus:** Welding; Civil Engineering. **Qualif.:** Applicants must be undergraduate students pursuing a bachelors degree in civil engineering or welding related degree at an accredited university; must be 18 years of age or above; must have a minimum of 3.0 grade point average; must be citizens of the United States; and have plan to attend an accredited engineering school within the United States. Applicants must have a minimum of 3.0 grade point average throughout the academic year. **Criteria:** Recipients are selected based on financial need.

Funds Avail.: $2,500. **Number Awarded:** 1. **To Apply:** Applicants must submit an application; a high school diploma; and a financial statement. **Deadline:** February 15.

1430 ■ Jerry Baker Scholarships *(Undergraduate/Scholarship)*

Purpose: To provide financial assistance to individuals interested in pursuing a bachelor's degree in welding engineering, welding engineering technology, or an engineering program with an emphasis in welding. **Focus:** Welding. **Qualif.:** Applicants must be undergraduate students pursuing a four-year bachelors degree in welding engineering or welding engineering technology; must be 18 years of age or above; must be full-time students as defined by the academic institution; must have at least a 2.8 overall point average with a 3.0 grade point average in engineering courses; must be citizen of the United States or Canada; and plan to attend an institution located within the United States or Canada. **Criteria:** Recipients are selected based on need. Priority will be given to individuals who demonstrate an interest in pursuing a career with an industrial gas or welding equipment distributor with prior to work experience, clubs, organizations, or extracurricular activities. For individuals residing or attending schools in the states of Alabama, Georgia and Florida are also given preference.

Funds Avail.: $2,500. **Number Awarded:** 1. **To Apply:** Applicants must submit an application form and a high school diploma. **Deadline:** February 15.

1431 ■ Jack R. Barckhoff Welding Management Scholarships *(Undergraduate/Scholarship)*

Purpose: To provide financial assistance to individuals interested in pursuing a career in welding engineering.

Awards are arranged alphabetically below their administering organizations

Focus: Welding. Qualif.: Applicants must be college juniors pursuing a four-year bachelors degree in welding engineering at the Ohio State University; must be 18 years old and above; must have minimum of 2.5 overall grade point average; must be citizens of the United States and plan to attend an accredited engineering school within the United States; must be enrolled and must complete the two-hour credit course in Total Welding Management at the Ohio State University. Criteria: Recipients are selected based on the financial need.

Funds Avail.: $2,500. Number Awarded: 2. To Apply: Applicants must complete the application form and submit it along with a high school diploma, financial statement and a transcript of records. Applicants must also submit (300-500 word) essay on how they see their role once they have graduated in improving the world of welding and its industry in the United States and how they plan to use their education to improve the U.S. competitive position in welding and manufacturing. Deadline: February 15. Contact: found@aws.org.

1432 ■ Edward J. Brady Memorial Scholarships
(Undergraduate/Scholarship)

Purpose: To provide financial assistance to individuals interested in pursuing a career in welding engineering. Focus: Welding. Qualif.: Applicants must be undergraduate students pursuing a four-year bachelors degree in welding engineering or welding engineering technology; must be 18 years old and above; must have a minimum of 2.5 overall grade point average; must be citizens of the United States; and must plan to attend an accredited engineering school within the United States. Criteria: Recipients are selected based on financial need. Priority will be given to welding engineering students.

Funds Avail.: $2,500. Number Awarded: 1. To Apply: Applicants must complete the application form and submit it along with a high school diploma and a financial statement. Official transcripts must be sent directly to the Registrar's Office. Deadline: February 15. Contact: found@aws.org.

1433 ■ William A. and Ann M. Brothers Scholarships (Undergraduate/Scholarship)

Purpose: To provide financial assistance to individuals interested in pursuing a bachelor's degree in welding engineering, welding engineering technology, or an engineering program with an emphasis in welding. Focus: Welding. Qualif.: Applicants must be full-time undergraduate students pursuing a four-year degree in Welding Engineering or Welding Engineering Technology; must have demonstrated leadership abilities; must be 18 years of age or above; must be United States citizens; must have plan to attend an academic institution within the United States or Canada; and must have at least 2.5 overall grade point average. Applicants must be enrolled in a full-time basis. Criteria: Recipients are selected based on financial need. Priority will be given to individuals residing or attending schools in the states of Ohio.

Funds Avail.: $3,500. Number Awarded: 1. To Apply: Applicants must submit an application form; high school diploma; and a financial statement. Deadline: February 15. Contact: found@aws.org.

1434 ■ Donald F. Hastings Scholarships
(Undergraduate/Scholarship)

Purpose: To provide financial assistance to individuals interested in pursuing a career in welding engineering.

Focus: Welding. Qualif.: Applicants must be undergraduate students pursuing a bachelors degree in welding engineering or welding engineering technology; must be 18 years of age or above; must have a minimum of 2.5 overall grade point average; must be United States citizens; and have plan to attend an accredited engineering school within the United States. Applicants may be enrolled full or part time. Criteria: Recipients are selected based on financial need. Priority will be given to students residing or attending schools in the states of Ohio and California.

Funds Avail.: $2,500. Number Awarded: 1. To Apply: Applicants must submit an application; a high school diploma; and a financial statement. Deadline: February 15.

1435 ■ Donald and Shirley Hastings Scholarships (Undergraduate/Scholarship)

Purpose: To provide financial assistance to individuals interested in pursuing a career in welding engineering. Focus: Welding. Qualif.: Applicants must be undergraduate students pursuing a bachelors degree in welding engineering or welding engineering technology; must be 18 years of age or above; must have a minimum of 2.5 overall grade point average; must be United States citizens; and have plan to attend an accredited engineering school within the United States. Applicants may be enrolled full or part time. Criteria: Recipients are selected based on financial need. Priority will be given to students residing or attending schools in the states of Iowa, Ohio, or California.

Funds Avail.: $2,500. To Apply: Applicants must submit an application; a high school diploma; a copy of Free Application Financial Student Aid (FAFSA) and a financial statement. Deadline: February 15. Contact: found@aws.org.

1436 ■ William B. Howell Scholarships
(Undergraduate/Scholarship)

Purpose: To provide financial assistance to individuals interested in pursuing a bachelor's degree in welding engineering, welding engineering technology, or an engineering program with an emphasis in welding. Focus: Welding. Qualif.: Applicants must be full-time undergraduate students pursuing a four-year degree in Welding Engineering or Welding Engineering Technology; must have demonstrated leadership abilities; be 18 years of age or above; must be United States citizens; must have plan to attend an academic institution within the United States or Canada; and must have at least 2.5 overall grade point average. Criteria: Recipients are selected based on financial need. Priority will be given to individuals residing or attending school in the states of Florida, Michigan and Ohio.

Funds Avail.: $2,500. Number Awarded: 1. To Apply: Applicants must submit an application form; high school diploma; and financial statement. Deadline: February 15. Contact: found@aws.org.

1437 ■ Hypertherm International HyTech Leadership Scholarships (Graduate/Scholarship)

Purpose: To provide financial assistance to individuals interested in pursuing a career in welding engineering. Focus: Welding. Qualif.: Applicant must be a graduate student pursuing an advanced degree in engineering management within the welding and cutting industry; has been completed a Bachelor of Science degree or be in the final year and has been accepted for graduate work in engineering management at an accredited graduate school; must graduated with a minimum overall grade point aver-

Awards are arranged alphabetically below their administering organizations

age of 2.8. **Criteria:** Recipients will be selected based on financial need.

Funds Avail.: $2,500. **To Apply:** Applicants must complete the application form and personal statement addressing a proposed advanced academic and post-academic plan. **Deadline:** February 15. **Contact:** found@aws.org.

1438 ■ ITW Welding Companies Scholarships
(Undergraduate/Scholarship)

Purpose: To provide financial assistance to individuals interested in pursuing a career in welding engineering. **Focus:** Welding. **Qualif.:** Applicant must be a senior, full-time undergraduate student working towards a bachelors degree in welding engineering or welding engineering technology; must be 18 years old and above; must have a minimum of 3.0 overall grade point average; must be a citizen of the United States; and must plan to attend an accredited engineering school within the United States. **Criteria:** Recipients are selected based on financial need. Priority will be given to a student who exhibits a strong interest and with more experience in welding equipment.

Funds Avail.: $3,000. **Number Awarded:** 2. **To Apply:** Applicant must complete an application form and submit it along with a high school diploma and a financial statement. **Deadline:** February 15. **Contact:** found@aws.org.

1439 ■ Terry Jarvis Memorial Scholarships
(Undergraduate/Scholarship)

Purpose: To provide financial assistance to individuals interested in pursuing a bachelor's degree in welding engineering, welding engineering technology, or an engineering program with an emphasis in welding. **Focus:** Welding. **Qualif.:** Applicants must be undergraduate students pursuing a four-year bachelors degree in welding engineering or welding engineering technology; must be 18 years of age or above; must be full-time students as defined by the academic institution; must have at least a 2.8 overall point average with a 3.0 grade point average in engineering courses; must be citizens of the United States or Canada; and have plan to attend an institution located within the United States or Canada. **Criteria:** Recipients are selected based on need. Priority will be given to those individuals who demonstrate an interest in pursuing a career with an industrial gas or welding equipment distributor prior to work experience, clubs, organizations, or extracurricular activities. For individuals residing or attending schools in the states of Alabama, Georgia, or Florida are also given preference.

Funds Avail.: $2,500. **Number Awarded:** 1. **To Apply:** Applicants must submit an application form and a high school diploma. **Deadline:** February 15.

1440 ■ John C. Lincoln Memorial Scholarships
(Undergraduate/Scholarship)

Purpose: To provide financial assistance to individuals interested in pursuing a career in welding engineering. **Focus:** Welding. **Qualif.:** Applicants must be undergraduate students pursuing a four-year Bachelors Degree in a welding program at an accredited university; must have 2.5 overall grade point average; must be 18 years old and above; must be citizen of the United States and plan to attend an academic institution located within the United States. **Criteria:** Recipients are selected based on financial need. Priority will be given to those individuals residing or attending school in the States of Ohio and Arizona.

Funds Avail.: $3,500. **To Apply:** Applicants must complete

the application form and submit it along with a high school diploma and a financial statement. **Deadline:** February 15. **Contact:** found@aws.org.

1441 ■ Miller Electric International WorldSkills Competition Scholarships *(Undergraduate/Scholarship)*

Purpose: To provide financial assistance to individuals interested in pursuing a bachelor's degree in welding engineering, welding engineering technology, or an engineering program with an emphasis in welding. **Focus:** Welding. **Qualif.:** Applicants must be undergraduate students pursuing a four-year degree program in an accredited university. **Criteria:** Recipients are selected based on financial need.

Funds Avail.: Maximum of $40,000. **To Apply:** Applicants must complete the National Skills USA Competition and complete the application form.

1442 ■ Robert L. Peaslee-Detroit Brazing and Soldiering Division Scholarships
(Undergraduate/Scholarship)

Purpose: To provide financial assistance to individuals interested in pursuing a bachelor's degree in welding engineering, welding engineering technology, or an engineering program with an emphasis in welding. **Focus:** Welding. **Qualif.:** Applicants must be college junior or senior students pursuing a degree in Welding Engineering or Welding Engineering Technology; must have demonstrated leadership abilities; must be 18 years old and above; must be United States citizens and plan to attend an academic institution within the United States or Canada; must have 3.0 overall grade point average; must express an interest in the resistance welding process; must show emphasis on Brazing and Soldiering application in their coursework. **Criteria:** Recipients are selected based on final decision of Selection Committee.

Funds Avail.: $2,500. **To Apply:** Applicants must submit an application form; two letters of reference; personal statement; an official transcript of records; statement of unmet financial needs; and verification of enrollment. Recipients are required to submit a photograph for publicity purposes. **Deadline:** February 15. **Contact:** found@aws.org.

1443 ■ Ronald C. and Joyce Pierce Scholarships *(Undergraduate/Scholarship)*

Purpose: To provide financial assistance to individuals interested in pursuing a bachelor's degree in welding engineering, welding engineering technology, or an engineering program with an emphasis in welding. **Focus:** Welding. **Qualif.:** Applicants must be college junior or senior students pursuing a degree in Welding Engineering or Welding Engineering Technology; must have demonstrated leadership abilities; must be 18 years of age or above; must be United States citizens; must plan to attend an academic institution within the United States or Canada; must have at least 3.0 overall grade point average; and must express an interest in the resistance welding process and show emphasis on Brazing and Soldiering application in their coursework. **Criteria:** Recipients are selected based on financial need.

Funds Avail.: $2,500. **To Apply:** Applicants must submit an application form; a high school diploma; two letters of reference; personal statement; transcript of records; statement of the unmet financial need; and verification of enrollment. **Contact:** found@aws.org.

Awards are arranged alphabetically below their administering organizations

1444 ■ Praxair International Scholarships
(Undergraduate/Scholarship)

Purpose: To provide financial assistance to individuals interested in pursuing a bachelor's degree in welding engineering, welding engineering technology, or an engineering program with an emphasis in welding. **Focus:** Welding. **Qualif.:** Applicants must be undergraduate students pursuing a degree in Welding Engineering or Welding Engineering Technology; must have demonstrated leadership abilities; must be 18 years old and above; must be citizen of United States and plan to attend an academic institution within the United States or Canada; and must maintain an overall GPA of 2.5. **Criteria:** Preference will be given to welding engineering students.

Funds Avail.: $2,500. **To Apply:** Applicants must an application form. Official transcript of records will be directed to the Office of Registrar. **Deadline:** February 15.

1445 ■ Resistance Welder Manufacturers' Association Scholarships *(Undergraduate/Scholarship)*

Purpose: To provide financial assistance to individuals interested in the resistance of welding process while pursuing a career in welding engineering. **Focus:** Welding. **Qualif.:** Applicants must be college junior students pursuing a degree in Welding Engineering or Welding Engineering Technology; must demonstrate leadership abilities; must be 18 years old and above; must be U.S. citizens and plan to attend an academic institution within the United States or Canada; must at least have a 3.0 overall grade point average; and must be working in a four-year degree in Welding Engineering or Technology. **Criteria:** Recipients are selected based on academic achievements and submitted materials.

Funds Avail.: $2,500. **To Apply:** Applicants must submit an application form along with a high school diploma and an essay of 500 words or less about why the applicant wishes to become involved in the resistance welding industry; two letters of recommendation (one must from advisor and the other one must from employer); personal statement; an official transcript of records; verification of enrollment; and statement of unmet financial needs. **Deadline:** January 15.

1446 ■ Jerry Robinson Inweld Corporation Scholarships *(Undergraduate/Scholarship)*

Purpose: To provide financial assistance to individuals interested in pursuing a career in welding engineering. **Focus:** Welding. **Qualif.:** Applicants must be undergraduate students pursuing a four-year Bachelors Degree in a welding program at an accredited university; must have a 2.5 overall grade point average; must be 18 years old and above; must be a citizen of United States and plan to attend an academic institution located within the United States. **Criteria:** Recipients are selected based on financial need.

Funds Avail.: $2,500. **To Apply:** Applicants must complete the application form and submit it along with a high school diploma and a financial statement; and must provide an essay. **Deadline:** February 15. **Contact:** found@aws.org.

1447 ■ James A. Turner, Jr. Memorial Scholarships *(Undergraduate/Scholarship)*

Purpose: To provide financial assistance to individuals interested in pursuing a career in welding engineering. **Focus:** Welding. **Qualif.:** Applicants must be full-time students pursuing a four-year Bachelor of Business Degree leading to a management career in welding store operations or a welding distributorship; be employed for at least ten hours a week at a welding distributorship; must be 18 years old and above. **Criteria:** Recipients are selected based on financial need.

Funds Avail.: $3,500. **To Apply:** Applicants must complete the application form and submit it along with a high school diploma and a financial statement. Official transcripts will be sent directly to the Registrar's Office. **Deadline:** February 15. **Contact:** found@aws.org.

1448 ■ Amos and Marilyn Winsand-Detroit Section Named Scholarships *(Undergraduate/Scholarship)*

Purpose: To provide financial assistance to individuals interested in pursuing a career in welding engineering. **Focus:** Welding. **Qualif.:** Applicants must be enrolled in a two or four-year program and must be residents of Michigan or attending a Michigan College. **Criteria:** Recipients are selected based on financial.

Funds Avail.: $2,500. **To Apply:** Applicants must submit an application form and a high school diploma. **Deadline:** February 15.

1449 ■ American Wine Society Educational Foundation (AWSEF)
1134 Prospect Ave.
Bethlehem, PA 18018-4914
Ph: (610) 865-2401
Fax: (610) 758-3526
E-mail: lhs0@lehigh.edu
URL: www.awsef.org

1450 ■ American Wine Society Educational Foundation Scholarships *(Graduate/Scholarship)*

Purpose: To support students pursuing an academic program in enology, viticulture, or health aspects of wine. **Focus:** Enology; Viticulture. **Qualif.:** Applicants must be full-time graduate students who have completed at least one semester in a graduate program leading to an MS, PhD, or equivalent in enology, viticulture, or health aspects of wine, and who express intent to work in one of these areas upon completion of the graduate degree (PhD candidates with an MS from another graduate program are eligible); must be North American (U.S., Canada, Mexico, Bahamas and West Indies Islands) citizens or permanent residents, enrolled in a degree located within North American institutions of higher learning. **Criteria:** Applications will be evaluated based on strength of application and accompanied letters of recommendation.

Funds Avail.: $3,000. **Number Awarded:** 9. **To Apply:** Applicants must submit a completed scholarship application form; current official transcripts of all college or university academic records; a written statement which indicates the applicant's intent to pursue a career in a wine or grape related area; a written recommendation from the applicant's academic advisor using the form supplied; three letters of recommendation including the academic advisor's written recommendation. **Deadline:** March 31. **Contact:** Les Sperling at the above address.

1451 ■ American Woman's Society of Certified Public Accountants (AWSCPA)
136 S Keowee St.
Dayton, OH 45402

Awards are arranged alphabetically below their administering organizations

Ph: (973) 222-1872
Fax: (937) 222-5794
Free: 800-297-2721
E-mail: info@awscpa.org
URL: www.awscpa.org

1452 ■ AWSCPA National Scholarships
(Graduate/Scholarship)

Purpose: To support students aspiring to become a Certified Public Accountant. **Focus:** Accounting. **Qualif.:** Applicant must meet the minimum education requirements to sit for the CPA exam within one year of scholarship awarding; must either be an entering Senior, 5th year student, graduate student or a graduate and eligible to take a review course within one year of scholarship awarding; must have a 3.0 GPA in accounting and a 3.0 GPA overall; and must either be a U.S. citizen or a permanent resident of the United States. **Criteria:** Selection is based on the application.

Funds Avail.: Becker CPA Review Course worth $3,065. **To Apply:** Applicants must submit a completed scholarship application form together with a validated transcript and an essay of no longer than 1,000 words. Applicants can also apply online. **Deadline:** May 31. **Remarks:** Sponsored by Becker CPA Review. **Contact:** Laura Riley, CPA of Becker at 646-415-7569 or email at lriley@beckerreview.com.

1453 ■ Americans for Informed Democracy (AID)
1220 L St. NW, Ste. 100-161
Washington, DC 20005
Ph: (202) 544-9662
E-mail: karen@aidemocracy.org
URL: www.aidemocracy.org

1454 ■ Americans for Informed Democracy Global Scholar Tuition *(Undergraduate/ Scholarship)*

Purpose: To provide financial assistance for students from all different fields, backgrounds and interests who have a strong academic records. **Focus:** General studies. **Qualif.:** Applicants must be junior or senior students who have experienced honors or advanced placement-level courses. **Criteria:** Applicants will be evaluated based on academic records, extracurricular achievements and essay writing.

Funds Avail.: $2,395. **To Apply:** Applicants must file online application. Applicants must also submit a short essay explaining "what issue in international affairs he/she has most interest, why and how will it fit into his or her future plans?". **Contact:** info@globalscholar.org.

1455 ■ AmeriGlide
3901A Commerce Park Dr.
Raleigh, NC 27610
Free: 800-790-1635
URL: www.ameriglide.com

1456 ■ AmeriGlide Achiever Scholarships *(All/ Scholarship)*

Purpose: To provide financial assistance for books or other school related supplies to deserving mobility challenged students. **Focus:** General studies. **Qualif.:** Applicant must be enrolled at an accredited two or four year college; must use a manual or electric wheelchair; have a minimum 3.0

GPA; a legal resident of the U.S. or hold a valid student visa. **Criteria:** Selection is based on the submitted application materials.

Funds Avail.: $1,000. **To Apply:** Applicants must submit an application form along with the essay and two character references from a teacher or any other non-related third party. **Contact:** scholarship@ameriglide.com.

1457 ■ AMSUS - The Society of Federal Health Professionals
9320 Old Georgetown Rd.
Bethesda, MD 20814
Ph: (301) 897-8800
Fax: (301) 530-5446
Free: 800-761-9320
E-mail: amsus@amsus.org
URL: www.amsus.org

1458 ■ AMSUS Dentist Awards *(Professional development/Award)*

Purpose: To recognize the accomplishments of federal dentists who have made outstanding contributions as clinicians, researchers, educators or healthcare managers. **Focus:** Dentistry. **Qualif.:** Applicants must be federal dentists. **Criteria:** Recipients will be selected based on submitted narrative.

Funds Avail.: Amount not specified. **To Apply:** Applicants must submit a narrative outlining the following: 1) significant accomplishment(s) warranting AMSUS recognition; 2) evidence of mission support; and 3) demonstrated professional and technical performance.

1459 ■ AMSUS Nursing Awards *(Professional development/Award)*

Purpose: To recognize the accomplishments of federal nurses who have made outstanding contributions as clinicians, researchers, educators or healthcare managers. **Focus:** Nursing. **Qualif.:** Applicants must be federal nurses. **Criteria:** Recipients will be selected based on submitted narrative.

Funds Avail.: Amount not specified. **To Apply:** Applicants must submit a narrative outlining the following: 1) significant accomplishments warranting AMSUS recognition; 2) evidence of mission support; and 3) demonstrated professional and technical performance.

1460 ■ AMSUS Physician Awards *(Professional development/Award)*

Purpose: To recognize the accomplishments of federal physicians who have made outstanding contributions as clinicians, researchers, educators or healthcare managers. **Focus:** Health care services. **Qualif.:** Applicants must be federal physicians. **Criteria:** Recipients will be selected based on submitted narrative.

Funds Avail.: Amount not specified. **To Apply:** Applicants must submit a narrative outlining the following: 1) significant accomplishment(s) warranting AMSUS recognition; 2) evidence of mission support; 3) demonstrated professional and technical performance.

1461 ■ Major General Jerry Sanders Scholarship Program *(High School, Undergraduate/ Scholarship)*

Purpose: To provide financial assistance for those who are pursuing a healthcare related career. **Focus:** Health care

Awards are arranged alphabetically below their administering organizations

services. **Qualif.:** Applicants must be AMSUS members or eligible dependents who are pursuing a healthcare related career; must be high school seniors or graduates who have plans to enroll in a full-time undergraduate or graduate course of study at an accredited four-year college, university, or vocational-technical school for the upcoming academic year. **Criteria:** Applicants will be evaluated based on academic record, demonstrated citizenship, quality and content of submitted essay, letters of recommendation and work experience.

Funds Avail.: $1,000. **To Apply:** Applicants must submit a completed application form; must submit a copy of an official transcript, essay and letter of recommendation.

1462 ■ Lewis L. Seaman Junior Enlisted Awards for Outstanding Operational Support
(Professional development/Award)

Purpose: To recognize junior and senior enlisted medical healthcare professionals who have made a significant impact in the areas of patient care, clinical support or healthcare management and to their service's medical mission. **Focus:** Health care services. **Qualif.:** Applicants must be Active Duty, Reserve or Guard enlisted professionals of the Army, Navy, Air Force or Coast Guard who have exhibited outstanding accomplishments in advancing the healthcare mission of their service. **Criteria:** Recipients will be evaluated based on submitted performance from the previous calendar year.

Funds Avail.: Amount not specified. **To Apply:** Applicants must submit a one-page narrative addressing the following categories: a) professional knowledge, leadership and job performance; b) contingency/deployment and/or humanitarian/community activities; and c) education and other accomplishments.

1463 ■ AMVETS
4647 Forbes Blvd.
Lanham, MD 20706-4380
Ph: (301) 459-9600
Fax: (301) 459-7924
Free: 877-726-8387
E-mail: amvets@amvets.org
URL: www.amvets.org

1464 ■ AMVETS National Scholarships - Entering College Freshmen *(Undergraduate/Scholarship)*

Purpose: To assist deserving children and grandchildren of veterans in attaining post-secondary education. **Focus:** General studies. **Qualif.:** Applicant must be a graduating high school senior entering at the college freshmen level; must have a minimum high school GPA of 3.0; must be the child or grandchild of a United States veteran; must be a U.S. citizen; must have demonstrated academic promise and financial need; and must agree to authorize AMVETS to publicize the scholarship award, if selected. **Criteria:** Selection is based on academic promise, financial need and merit.

Funds Avail.: $1,000 each year. **Number Awarded:** 6. **To Apply:** Applicants must submit a copy of the veteran's honorable discharge (Form DD 214). Dependents of current military personnel must submit a letter from the base commander certifying the active duty status of the parent; an official high school transcript (must be in the 4.0 grade scale or if in a different system, translated to the 4.0 scales);

SAT and/or ACT scores; a complete and signed copy of the parent(s)'/guardian(s)' 1040 tax form (applicant's name must appear on the tax form); a copy of the applicant's Free Application for Federal Student Aid (FAFSA); essay (50-100 words); acceptance letter from the accredited school to be attended; proof of college expenses; and a resume detailing extracurricular activities, volunteer activities, community services and jobs held during the past four years. **Deadline:** April 15. **Contact:** 877-726-8387.

1465 ■ AMVETS National Scholarships - For Veterans *(Undergraduate/Scholarship)*

Purpose: To financially assist veterans who have exhausted government aid or who might not otherwise have the financial means to further their education. **Focus:** General studies. **Qualif.:** Applicant must be a U.S. veteran; a U.S. citizen; must demonstrate financial need; and must agree to authorize AMVETS to publicize the scholarship award, if selected. **Criteria:** Selection is based on academic promise, financial need and merit.

Funds Avail.: $1,000 each year. **Number Awarded:** 3. **To Apply:** Applicants must submit a copy of the veteran's honorable discharge or a letter certifying current service and eligibility for release from active duty prior to attending school; official college transcripts for all courses attempted and any degrees or certificates awarded (must be in the 4.0 grade scale, or if in a different system, translated to the 4.0 scales); a complete and signed copy of the applicant's 1040 tax form; a copy of the Free Application for Federal Student Aid (FAFSA); an essay (50-100 words); acceptance letter or a letter stating current student status from an accredited school; proof of college expenses; and a resume detailing military duty and awards, volunteer activities, community services and jobs held during the past four years. **Deadline:** April 15. **Contact:** 877-726-8387.

1466 ■ AMVETS National Scholarships - JROTC *(Undergraduate/Scholarship)*

Purpose: To support Junior ROTC cadets in pursuing study at an undergraduate college or university. **Focus:** General studies. **Qualif.:** Applicant must be an active JROTC cadet and currently a high school senior; have a minimum high school GPA of 3.0; be the child or grandchild of a U.S. veteran; a U.S. citizen; have demonstrated academic promise and financial need; and agree to authorize AMVETS to publicize the scholarship award, if selected. **Criteria:** Selection is based on academic promise, financial need and merit.

Funds Avail.: $1,000. **Number Awarded:** 1. **To Apply:** Applicant must submit a copy of the veteran's honorable discharge (Form DD 214). Dependents of current military personnel must submit a letter from the base commander certifying the active duty status of the parent; an official transcript including the first grading period of the current school year (must be in the 4.0 grade scale, or if in a different system, translated to the 4.0 scale); SAT and/or ACT scores; a complete and signed copy of the parent(s)'/guardian(s)'s 1040 tax form; a copy of the Free Application for Federal Student Aid (FAFSA); an essay (50-100 words); acceptance letter from the accredited school to attend; proof of college expenses; a letter from program commander verifying participation in ROTC/JROTC activities; and a resume detailing extracurricular activities, volunteer activities, community services and jobs held during the past four years. **Deadline:** April 15. **Contact:** 877-726-8387.

Awards are arranged alphabetically below their administering organizations

1467 ■ Dr. Aurelio M. Caccomo Family Foundation Memorial Scholarships (Undergraduate/Scholarship)

Purpose: To provide financial assistance for veterans/guardsmen/reservists who have exhausted government aid, or who might not otherwise have the financial means to further their education. **Focus:** General studies. **Qualif.:** Applicant must be a U.S. veteran or member of the National Guard or Reserves; a U.S. citizen; have demonstrated financial need; have a high school diploma or GED; agree to authorize AMVETS to publicize the scholarship award, if selected; enrolled or accepted for enrollment to an eligible program; must not be in default on a federal student loan; and not convicted under state or federal law of sale or possession of illegal drugs. **Criteria:** Award is given based on the application materials.

Funds Avail.: $3,000. **Number Awarded:** 1. **To Apply:** Applicants must submit a copy of the veteran's honorable discharge or a letter from the commanding officer certifying current Guard or Reserve status; an official college transcript for all courses attempted and any degrees or certificates awarded (must be in the 4.0 grade scale or if in a different system, translated to the 4.0 scale); a complete and signed copy of the applicant's 1040 tax form; a copy of the Free Application for Federal Student Aid (FAFSA); an essay (50-100 words); acceptance letter or a letter stating current student status from an accredited program; proof of expenses; and a resume detailing military duty and awards, volunteer activities, community services and jobs held during the past four years. **Deadline:** April 15. **Contact:** 877-726-8387.

1468 ■ Anaheim Police Association (APA)
508 N Anaheim Blvd.
Anaheim, CA 92805
Ph: (714) 635-0272
E-mail: office@anaheimpoliceassociation.org
URL: www.anaheimpoliceassociation.org

1469 ■ Anaheim Police Survivors and Scholarship Fund (Undergraduate/Scholarship)

Purpose: To provide financial assistance for education to family and children of any Anaheim Police Officers who could lose his/her life while in the performance of their job through education. **Focus:** General studies. **Qualif.:** Applicants must be entering students or recently high school graduates; continuing students (already enrolled in College Program) or a returning students (entering college after a break in educational experience); children (natural or adopted) of Anaheim Police Officers or Anaheim Reserve Officers enrolled in at least twelve units; must have cumulative GPA of 3.0 or higher. **Criteria:** Recipients are recommended by the American Police Officer's Honorary Association Scholarship Committee and approved by the Board of Trustees of Anaheim Police Survivors and Scholarship Fund.

Funds Avail.: $500 to $1,000. **To Apply:** Applicants must submit completed application form and a short essay of 500 words or less on need for scholarship and goals. **Deadline:** April 1.

1470 ■ Anchor Environmental
720 Olive Way, Ste. 1900
Seattle, WA 98101
Ph: (206) 287-9130
Fax: (206) 287-9131
E-mail: info@anchorqea.com
URL: www.anchorenv.com

1471 ■ Anchor Environmental Scholarships (Graduate/Scholarship)

Purpose: To financially assist graduate students in obtaining their graduate level degree in an aquatic-related field of study. **Focus:** Aquaculture; Fisheries sciences/management; Environmental science; Land management; Landscape architecture and design. **Qualif.:** Applicant must be a full-time graduate student or a person accepted at a U.S. graduate school; must have an undergraduate GPA equivalent of a B average or higher and must major in fisheries; environmental sciences; planning/land use; landscape architecture; or coastal, geotechnical, or environmental engineering (any of which should have an aquatic/waterfront emphasis). **Criteria:** Selection is based on the application materials submitted.

Funds Avail.: $500-$5,000. **To Apply:** Applicants must submit a completed scholarship application form together with the letter(s) of recommendation (professional/academic) from professors, employers, etc.; a certified copy of undergraduate and graduate (if applicable) transcripts; a one-page essay on educational goals, reasons for selecting the major, future plans in the field and how the scholarship will help the student and a resume (optional). **Deadline:** November 12. **Contact:** scholarship@anchorqea.com.

1472 ■ The Anderson Group Summer Institute
PO Box 38334
Los Angeles, CA 90038-0334
Ph: (323) 469-3050
Fax: (323) 469-3050
E-mail: execsecretary@harpsociety.org
URL: www.harpsociety.org

1473 ■ The Anderson Group Summer Institute Scholarships (Professional development/Scholarship)

Purpose: To provide financial assistance for promising individuals for advanced study of harp at a college or university. **Focus:** Music. **Qualif.:** Applicants must be active members of the American Harp Society with maximum age limit of 40 years old by April 15, 2011. **Criteria:** Recipient will be selected based on financial need and musical promise in the study of harp.

Funds Avail.: $1,000. **Number Awarded:** 2. **To Apply:** Applicants must submit biography including applicant's full name, legal residence, present address, telephone number, email address, proof of age, musical and academic education, personal profile, general analysis of financial need and long-range goals for harp-playing, hand-written statement, CD recording, and letter of reference.

1474 ■ Androscoggin County Chamber of Commerce
415 Lisbon St.
Lewiston, ME 04243-0059
Ph: (207) 783-2249
Fax: (207) 783-4481
E-mail: cmorrison@androscoggincounty.com
URL: www.androscoggincounty.com

Awards are arranged alphabetically below their administering organizations

1475 ■ Androscoggin County Chamber of Commerce Adult Scholarships (Undergraduate/Scholarship)

Purpose: To recognize an employee of a Chamber member who has shown effort in advancing his or her education at the college level. **Focus:** General studies. **Qualif.:** Applicants must be employed 20 or more hours by a member of the Androscoggin County Chamber of Commerce; must begin course within 6 months of receiving award; must be matriculated in college-level coursework applicable toward an Associates or Bachelor's degree; must be at least 25 years old. **Criteria:** Selection will be based on the committee's criteria.

Funds Avail.: $1,000. **Number Awarded:** 3. **To Apply:** Applicants must submit a completed application, one-page typewritten essay, completed employer verification form, letter of reference/recommendation from employer. **Deadline:** April 30.

1476 ■ Angus Foundation
3201 Frederick Ave.
St. Joseph, MO 64506
Ph: (816) 383-5100
Fax: (816) 233-9703
E-mail: mjenkins@angusfoundation.org
URL: www.angusfoundation.org

1477 ■ Angus Foundation General Undergraduate Student Scholarships (High School, Undergraduate/Scholarship)

Purpose: To support young men and women who are actively involved in the Angus breed pursuing an undergraduate degree in higher education. **Focus:** General studies. **Qualif.:** Applicants must have been members of National Junior Angus Association and are currently junior, regular or life members of the American Angus Association; must be graduating high school seniors or currently enrolled in a junior college, four-year college/university or other accredited institution of higher education. **Criteria:** Applicants will be chosen based on financial need, personal and/or family hardship, physical handicap, medical disability and other extenuating circumstances.

Funds Avail.: $5,000. **Number Awarded:** 2. **To Apply:** Applicants must complete the application form; must submit a copy of the most recent high school or college transcript; must include three letters of recommendation and member code; and must be U.S. Postal service postmarked by May 1 of the application year. **Deadline:** May 1. **Remarks:** The scholarship must be applied to undergraduate studies and is applicable to any field of study.

1478 ■ Angus Foundation Graduate Student Degree Scholarship Program (Graduate/Scholarship)

Purpose: To support young men and women who are active in Angus breed pursuing an advanced degree in higher education. **Focus:** Animal science and behavior. **Qualif.:** Applicants must have been members of National Angus Association and currently be junior, regular or life members of the American Angus Association; must be currently enrolled in a graduate school pursuing a post-baccalaureate degree; must have a minimum of 3.0 GPA as continuing graduate students; must have not entered their first semester of graduate school; and must have a college/university undergraduate GPA of 2.75. **Criteria:** Preference will be given to applicants who have been extensively involved in Junior Angus activities at the local, state and national levels and those who are pursuing an advanced degree closely related to beef cattle industry.

Number Awarded: 5. **To Apply:** Applicants must submit a signed and dated application form; must be U.S Postal Service postmarked by May 1 of the application year; must include a copy of the most recent college/university transcript, three letters of recommendation and member code. **Deadline:** May 1.

1479 ■ Angus/Talon Youth Educational Learning Program Endowment Fund (Graduate/Scholarship)

Purpose: To support young men and women who are active in Angus breed pursuing an advanced degree in higher education. **Focus:** Animal science and behavior. **Qualif.:** Applicants must be graduate students pursuing an advanced degree related closely to the beef cattle industry. **Criteria:** Preference will be given to applicants who have successfully maintained academic progress.

Funds Avail.: Amount not specified. **To Apply:** Applicants must submit a signed and dated application form; must be U.S Postal Service postmarked by May 1 of the application year; must include a copy of the most recent college/university transcript, three letters of recommendation and member code.

1480 ■ Animals and Society Institute (ASI)
2512 Carpenter Rd., Ste. 202-A
Ann Arbor, MI 48108-1188
Ph: (734) 677-9240
Fax: (734) 677-9242
Free: 800-325-3535
E-mail: info@animalsandsociety.org
URL: www.animalsandsociety.org

1481 ■ ASI Fellowships (Doctorate/Fellowship)

Purpose: To provide financial assistance in order to pursue research at Wesleyan University College of the Environment. **Focus:** Animal science and behavior. **Qualif.:** Applicants must possess a PhD, JD, MSW or equivalent; or be doctoral students at the dissertation stage; must have a commitment to advance research in Human-Animal studies; be actively engaged, during the fellowship program, in a research project that culminates in a journal article, book, or other scholarly presentation. **Criteria:** Recipients will be evaluated based on the contribution from which completed project will make to Human-Animal studies, qualifications of the applicant to complete the research and how well the applicant's project complements the other project.

Funds Avail.: Amount not specified. **To Apply:** Applicants must submit a completed application form.

1482 ■ Anxiety and Depression Association of America (ADAA)
8701 Georgia Ave., Ste. 412
Silver Spring, MD 20910
Ph: (240) 485-1001
Fax: (240) 485-1035
E-mail: sgerfen@adaa.org
URL: www.adaa.org

1483 ■ ADAA Career Development Travel Awards (Professional development/Award)

Purpose: To help young professionals with a career interest in fields related to anxiety disorders; to encourage

Awards are arranged alphabetically below their administering organizations

mental health professionals to advance the field of study of disorders, including the causes, prevention, treatment options and other related issues. **Focus:** Mental health. **Qualif.:** Applicants must have completed their master's degree or are training for Ph.D. or M.D. degrees; must be Ph.D level scientists or clinicians who have received doctorates or completed postdoctoral fellowships within the past three years; must be physician-scientists or clinicians who have completed their residencies or research fellowships within the past three years. **Criteria:** Candidates will be judged based on the following criteria: (1) Evidence of commitment to the field of anxiety disorders; (2) Strength of current program and training; (3) Quality, extent and multidisciplinary nature of research; (4) Professional reference and personal statement.

Funds Avail.: Travel and expenses stipend of up to $1,000 to attend the ADAA Annual Conference. **Number Awarded:** 15. **To Apply:** Applicant must submit the application form with attached curriculum vitae; an abstract following the guidelines; and a letter of recommendation from a mentor, supervisor, department chair or advisor. **Deadline:** November 12. **Contact:** Application materials must be sent to: Career Development Travel Awards, 8701 George Ave., Ste. 412, Silver Spring, MD 20910, e-mail: awards@adaa.org.

1484 ■ ADAA Junior Faculty Research Grants
(Professional development/Grant)

Purpose: To support the junior faculty making the transition to independent investigator. To assist individuals in making the transition from trainee to junior faculty and independent investigator. **Focus:** Mental health. **Qualif.:** Applicant must have completed at least one year of a doctoral fellowship or post-residency research training by the time the research grant is awarded; must have a mentor or senior research collaborator who is an established investigator in anxiety disorders research. Previous ADAA Career Development and Trainee Travel Award winners are eligible to apply. **Criteria:** Special consideration will be given to those applicants whose research with their affiliated institution is dependent on outside funding sources.

Funds Avail.: $1,000 travel grant is awarded to cover expenses. **Number Awarded:** 2. **To Apply:** Applicant must submit a proposal with (250-word) abstract and a statement (three-page maximum, single-spaced) describing research that will accomplished within the grant period; must have the budget outline stating the amount requested with a brief justification; a curriculum vitae; must have a research training or career plans; maximum of two-page description of applicant's current research and a short discussion of the applicant's future career plans; curriculum vitae of the applicant's mentor submitted in the NIMH Biographical Sketch format; collaborator and mentor letter from an on-site or off-site mentor. **Contact:** Geralyn Lederman, Manager of Communications and Public Relations, Phone: 240-485-1030, E-mail: glederman@adaa.org.

1485 ■ Appalachian School of Law (ASL)
PO Box 2825
Grundy, VA 24614
Ph: (276) 935-4349
Fax: (276) 935-8261
Free: 800-895-7411
E-mail: aslinfo@asl.edu
URL: www.asl.edu

1486 ■ Angela D. Dales Merit Scholarship Program *(Undergraduate/Scholarship)*

Purpose: To support students financially in the form of credit against tuition charged. **Focus:** Law. **Qualif.:** Applicants must be at least incoming first year law students. **Criteria:** Recipients are selected based on the Law School Admission Test (LSAT) and Undergraduate Grade Point Average (UGPA). Eligibility for retention of an award during the student's first three years in law school is based on their academic performance. Scholarship will be awarded on a first come, first serve basis.

Funds Avail.: No specific amount. **To Apply:** Applicants must complete and submit an online application available at the website; online certification page; two letters of recommendation; and 500 words or less describing professional goals and qualifications. **Remarks:** Scholarship is awarded on a first-come, first-served basis. **Contact:** financialaid@asl.edu.

1487 ■ Appraisal Institute Education Trust
550 W Van Buren St., Ste. 1000
Chicago, IL 60607
Ph: (312) 335-4100
Fax: (312) 335-4400
Free: 888-756-4624
E-mail: aiservice@appraisalinstitute.org
URL: www.appraisalinstitute.org

1488 ■ Appraisal Institute Education Trust Scholarships *(Graduate, Undergraduate/ Scholarship)*

Purpose: To help finance the education endeavors of individuals concentrating in real estate appraisal, land economics, real estate or allied fields. **Focus:** Real estate; Land economics. **Qualif.:** Applicants must be U.S. citizens, enrolled full-time for the academic year beginning August through June in a University or Community College in the U.S. majoring in real estate appraisal, land economics, real estate or allied fields. **Criteria:** Awarded on the basis of academic excellence.

Funds Avail.: $1,000 Undergraduate; $2,000 Graduate. **To Apply:** Applicants must submit a completed application together with letters of recommendation from the college Dean and two individuals, a signed statement regarding general activities and intellectual interests in college, official copies of all collegiate records and proposed student program. Graduate student applicants must have served, or is about to serve, an internship with an appraiser or the appraisal department of a corporation (letter from employer required). **Deadline:** April 15. **Contact:** Olivia Carreon at the above address.

1489 ■ Arab American Institute (AAI)
1600 K St. NW, Ste. 601
Washington, DC 20006
Ph: (202) 429-9210
Fax: (202) 429-9214
E-mail: webmaster@aaiusa.org
URL: www.aaiusa.org

1490 ■ Al Muammar Scholarships for Journalism *(Undergraduate/Scholarship)*

Purpose: To provide scholarship opportunity to the American students who are Arab descent. **Focus:** Journal-

Awards are arranged alphabetically below their administering organizations

ism. **Qualif.:** Applicants must: be Arab American, college students who are majoring in journalism, as well as college seniors who have been accepted to a graduate journalism school; be a UC citizen or permanent resident of Arab descent; be a full-time student at an accredited college or university in the United States; have current GPA of 3.3 or higher. **Criteria:** Selection will be based on the committee's criteria.

Funds Avail.: $5,000. **To Apply:** Applicant may download an application from the Foundation's website. Applicant must also include an official transcript and letter of recommendation (one letter must be from the professor in the applicant's journalism program and second would be ideally be from a leader in an Arab American community organization with which the applicant has had a relationship). Applicant must send five copies of the following items, collated into five complete packets, each with one copy of each item, in the following order: Completed application form; Unofficial transcript; Resume; Short Essay; Work samples. **Contact:** Al Muammar Scholarship Administrator, Arab American Institute Foundation, 1600 K St. NW Ste. 600 Washington, DC 20006.

1491 ■ Barakat Trust and Barakat Foundation Scholarships *(Graduate/Scholarship)*

Purpose: To provide financial support for students and scholars of Islamic culture. **Focus:** General studies. **Qualif.:** Applicants must have completed at least a B.A. degree and have been accepted for graduate study or an apprenticeship at an accredited university or institution. **Criteria:** Selection will be based on the committee's criteria.

Funds Avail.: No specific amount. **To Apply:** Applicants may contact the Barakat Trust and Barakat Foundation for the application requirements. **Contact:** Barakat Trust and Barakat Foundation, 2665 Kimball Pomona, CA 91767; rc101@earthlink.net.

1492 ■ Ameen Rihani Scholarship Program *(Undergraduate/Scholarship)*

Purpose: To promote academic excellence and to provide an opportunity for outstanding student to reach their fullest potential. **Focus:** Literature; Philosophy; Political science. **Qualif.:** Individual must: be a Lebanese or other Arab Descent; be a citizen or legal permanent residents of the United States; have attained a cumulative GPA of 3.25 on a 4.0 scale; enter a college or university as a full-time, degree-seeking freshman in the fall of the year; have demonstrated leadership abilities through participation in community service, extracurricular or other activities. **Criteria:** Selection will be based on the committee's criteria.

Funds Avail.: $1,500. **To Apply:** Teachers, counselors, and principals are invited to nominate students with outstanding academic qualifications, particularly those who would promote success in the fields of literature, philosophy, or political science. **Contact:** Ameen Rihani Scholarship Program, The Ameen Rihani Organization, 7979 Old Georgetown Rd., Ste. 700 Bethesda, MD 20814.

1493 ■ Arab American Medical Association - Houston Chapter (AAMA)

John P. McGovern Bldg.
1515 Hermann Dr.
Houston, TX 77004
Ph: (713) 524-4267
Fax: (713) 526-1434
E-mail: sandy_king@hcms.org

URL: aama-houston.org

1494 ■ AAMA Houston Chapter - Medical Student Scholarships *(Professional development/ Scholarship)*

Purpose: To support Arab students in their educational pursuit. **Focus:** Medicine; Medical education. **Qualif.:** Applicant must be of Arab heritage; enrolled full-time in an internationally recognized health care related school; accepted to spend one or more of his/her elective months at one of Houston's medical institutions or any affiliated hospitals; willing to provide a written report describing his/her experience during the elective training; and willing to attend AAMA meetings during the training months in Houston. **Criteria:** Priority will be given to applicants residing in Houston.

Funds Avail.: Up to $1,500. **Number Awarded:** Up to four. **To Apply:** Applicants must submit a completed scholarship application form along with an updated CV; a letter verifying enrollment in a medical/health institution/school; a letter of acceptance for elective training at any of the medical institutions in Houston and two letters or recommendation from current instructors. **Remarks:** Established in 2005. **Contact:** Sandy King at the above address.

1495 ■ Archaeological Institute of America (AIA)

Boston University
656 Beacon St., 6th Fl.
Boston, MA 02215-2006
Ph: (617) 353-9361
Fax: (617) 353-6550
E-mail: aia@aia.bu.edu
URL: www.archaeological.org

1496 ■ Jane C. Waldbaum Archaeological Field School Scholarships *(Undergraduate/ Scholarship)*

Purpose: To help students pay their expenses associated with participation on an archaeological excavation or survey project. **Focus:** Archeology. **Qualif.:** Applicants must be juniors and senior undergraduate students who have not yet completed their first year of graduate school and currently enrolled at a college or university in United States or Canada; must be at least 18 years old and have not previously participated in an archaeological excavation. **Criteria:** Applicants will be judged based on academic achievements and financial need.

Funds Avail.: $1,000. **Number Awarded:** 7. **To Apply:** Applicants must complete the online application form; must submit two copies of transcript; a brief cover letter (300 words or less) in the applicant's own words; an outline of anticipated expenses associated with participation on the project and a statement from the applicant indicating any other financial resources available to help cover expenses and two references for letters of recommendation from professors or academic advisors at the applicant's college or university. **Deadline:** March 3. **Contact:** For additional information, just email Deanna Baker at dbaker@aia.bu.edu.

1497 ■ Architectural Precast Association (APA)

6710 Winkler Rd., Ste. 8
Fort Myers, FL 33919-7274
Ph: (239) 454-6989
Fax: (239) 454-6787

Awards are arranged alphabetically below their administering organizations

E-mail: info@archprecast.org
URL: www.archprecast.org

1498 ■ Tom Cory Memorial Scholarships
(Undergraduate/Scholarship)

Purpose: To provide financial assistance for architecture students. **Focus:** Architecture. **Qualif.:** Applicants must have a cumulative GPA of 3.0 or higher; must have at least two semesters of school left to complete from date of award; must be involved in activities related to the architectural field. **Criteria:** Recipients are selected based on academic merit and committee's review of the application.

Funds Avail.: $2,000. **To Apply:** Applicants must send a completed application form; transcript of two years college through the last grading period to the date of application; letter of recommendation from a faculty member of the college; written description of the applicant's career plans after graduation; an essay explaining why the applicant have chosen the architectural field.

1499 ■ Arctic Institute of North America (AINA)
2500 University Dr. NW
Calgary, AB, Canada T2N 1N4
Ph: (403) 220-7515
Fax: (403) 282-4609
E-mail: arctic@ucalgary.ca
URL: www.arctic.ucalgary.ca

1500 ■ Lorraine Allison Scholarships *(Graduate/ Scholarship)*

Purpose: To advance the study of the North American and circumpolar Arctic through the natural and social sciences, the arts and humanities and to acquire, preserve and disseminate information on physical, environmental and social conditions in the North. **Focus:** Natural sciences; Social sciences. **Qualif.:** Applicants must be students enrolled at a Canadian university in a program of graduate study related to northern issues. **Criteria:** Candidates will be selected based on selection committee's review of the application materials.

Funds Avail.: $3,000. **Number Awarded:** 1. **To Apply:** Applicant must provide a two-page description of the northern studies program and relevant project(s) being undertaken; must submit three letters of reference from the applicant's current or past professors; complete curriculum vitae with academic transcript and list of the current source and amounts of research funding, including scholarships, grants and bursaries. Materials should be submitted at above address. **Deadline:** January 10.

1501 ■ Jim Bourque Scholarships *(Postgraduate, Undergraduate/Scholarship)*

Purpose: To support the mature and matriculating students in their studies. **Focus:** Environmental technology; Telecommunications systems. **Qualif.:** Applicants must be Canadian students who are enrolled or intend to take, post-secondary education in environmental studies, traditional knowledge or telecommunications. **Criteria:** Scholarships are given based on financial need, relevance of study, achievements, return on investment and overall presentation of the application.

Funds Avail.: $1,000. **To Apply:** Applicants must submit a description of their intended program of study and the reason for their choice of program (500 words); a copy of

the recent high school or college/university transcript; letter of recommendation from a community leader; a statement of financial need; proof of enrollment to post-secondary institution; and must also provide a proof of Canadian Aboriginal descent. **Deadline:** July 15. **Contact:** Dr. Benoit Beauchamp at the above address; e-mail: bbeaucha@ucalgary.ca.

1502 ■ Arent Fox LLP
1050 Connecticut Ave. NW
Washington, DC 20036-5339
Ph: (202) 857-6000
Fax: (202) 857-6395
E-mail: charyk.william@arentfox.com
URL: www.arentfox.com

1503 ■ Arent Fox Diversity Scholarships
(Undergraduate/Scholarship)

Purpose: To provide financial assistance for qualified individuals intending to pursue their law career. **Focus:** Law. **Qualif.:** Applicants must be U.S citizens or otherwise authorized to work in the United States; must have an excellent academic performance during college and law school; must have excellent oral and written communication skills; must have leadership qualities and community involvement; must be members of a diverse population that historically has been underrepresented in the legal profession; must agree to join the Arent Fox summer program after the first year of law school; and must be first-year law students. **Criteria:** Selection of applicants will be based on their academic performance and financial need.

Funds Avail.: $15,000. **Number Awarded:** 3. **To Apply:** Applicants must submit a resume with cover letter; must provide an undergraduate transcript and law school grades when available; must have three professional or academic references; Arent Fox essay and legal writing sample. **Deadline:** January 15.

1504 ■ Arizona Airport Association (AZAA)
4697 S Golden Arrow Dr.
Green Valley, AZ 85622
Ph: (520) 398-6287
Fax: (520) 398-6287
E-mail: webmaster@azairports.org
URL: www.azairports.org

1505 ■ Marty Rosness Student Scholarships
(Undergraduate/Scholarship)

Purpose: To enhance careers in the aviation industry. **Focus:** Aviation. **Qualif.:** Applicants must be enrolled in bachelor's or master's degree programs in the state of Arizona; and must be enrolled in an accredited aviation management degree program. **Criteria:** Recipients are selected based on academic performance.

Funds Avail.: $1,250-$2,500. **To Apply:** Applicants must submit a completed application form; current copy of college academic transcript of records; resume; and must attach a sheet that includes a reference to the questions or sections from which the applicant is responding to. **Deadline:** Every December 31 of the year. **Contact:** Send applications to: Deena Shaffer, Phoenix-Mesa Gateway Airport located at 5835 S Sossaman Rd., Mesa, AZ 85212, Phone: 480-988-7621, Fax: 480-988-2315, E-mail: dshaffer@phxmesagateway.org.

Awards are arranged alphabetically below their administering organizations

1506 ■ Arizona Artist Blacksmith Association (AABA)

2310 E Melrose St.
Gilbert, AZ 85297
Ph: (480) 988-2070
E-mail: education@az-blacksmiths.org
URL: www.az-blacksmiths.org

1507 ■ AABA Read Carlock Memorial Scholarship Fund *(Professional development/Scholarship)*

Purpose: To provide financial assistance to interested blacksmiths and/or immediate family members of AABA members for skills and abilities development. **Focus:** General studies. **Qualif.:** Applicants must be members of the Arizona Artist Blacksmith Association, as defined by Article 2 sections (a), (b, paragraphs I, II, III, and IV) of the AABA Bylaws, who have been members for at least one year prior to their application, or immediate family of those members. **Criteria:** Applicants are evaluated based on evidence of their strong desire for continued and serious investigation of the craft; quality of work as demonstrated by visual materials submitted with application; level of blacksmithing ability; record of professional activity and achievement; benefit to the Arizona Artist Blacksmith Association and demonstrated involvement with and commitment to AABA.

Funds Avail.: $1,000. **To Apply:** Applicants must submit all the required application information.

1508 ■ Arizona Association of Student Financial Aid Administrators (AASFAA)

c/o Howard Fischer, Vice Pres.
Ottawa University
10020 N 25th Ave.
Phoenix, AZ 85021
Ph: (602) 749-5120
Fax: (602) 371-0035
E-mail: howard.fischer@ottawa.edu
URL: www.aasfaa.org

1509 ■ BIA Higher Education Grants *(Graduate, Postgraduate, Undergraduate/Grant)*

Purpose: To provide quality services to the Hopi people by enhancing a full range of educational opportunities; to maintain efforts to increase the number of employable, degree-holding Hopi professionals; to maintain retention services which will enable students to complete programs. **Focus:** General studies. **Qualif.:** Applicants must be students pursuing an associate, baccalaureate, graduate or post-graduate degree; must be entering freshmen with a GPA of 2.5 for high school course work or a minimum composite of 50% on the GED exam; must have 2.5 GPA for all college work; must be members of Hopi Tribe. **Criteria:** Recipients are selected based on financial need.

Funds Avail.: $2,500. **To Apply:** Applicants must submit an official high school transcript or original GED scores; must submit an official transcript from all post-secondary schools; must submit a Program of Study (POS) or Letter of Acceptance (LOA). **Deadline:** July 1; December 1; April 1. **Contact:** Program Administrator at 928-734-3533.

1510 ■ Educational Enrichment Awards *(Undergraduate/Scholarship)*

Purpose: To develop leadership and personal skills and acquire educational or pre-occupational experiences. **Fo**cus: General studies. **Qualif.:** Applicants must be students in fifth grade through post-secondary level education; must be members of Hopi Tribe; be high school graduates or have earned GED certificate; and must be admitted to a regionally accredited college or university. **Criteria:** Recipients are selected based on financial need.

Funds Avail.: $500. **To Apply:** Applicants must submit an official high school transcript or original GED scores; must submit an official transcript from all post-secondary schools; must submit a Program of Study (POS) or Letter of Acceptance (LOA). **Deadline:** July 1; December 1; April 1. **Contact:** Program Administrator at 928-734-3533.

1511 ■ Hopi Education Awards *(Doctorate, Undergraduate/Award)*

Purpose: To provide quality services to the Hopi people by enhancing a full range of educational opportunities; to maintain efforts to increase the number of employable degree-holding Hopi professionals; to maintain retention services which will enable students to complete programs. **Focus:** General studies. **Qualif.:** Applicants must be students pursuing an AA, BA, BS or PhD from an accredited college or university; entering freshmen students must have a GPA of 2.5 for high school course work or a minimum composite of 50% on the GED exam while continuing students must have an at least 2.5 GPA for all college work; and must be enrolled members of Hopi Tribe. **Criteria:** Recipients are selected based on financial need.

Funds Avail.: $2,500. **To Apply:** Applicants must submit an official high school transcript or original GED scores; must submit an official transcript from all post-secondary schools; must submit a Program of Study (POS) or Letter of Acceptance (LOA). **Deadline:** July 1; December 1; April 1. **Contact:** Program Administrator at 928-734-3533.

1512 ■ Private High School Awards *(Undergraduate/Award)*

Purpose: To encourage Hopi students to achieve and maintain a high level of academic excellence at an accredited private high school. **Focus:** General studies. **Qualif.:** High school applicants must have an eighth grade education with a GPA of 3.50 while continuing students must have a GPA of 3.25. **Criteria:** Recipients are selected based on financial need.

Funds Avail.: $4,000. **Number Awarded:** 10. **To Apply:** Applicants must submit an official high school transcript or original GED scores; must submit an official transcript from all post-secondary schools; must submit a Program of Study (POS) or Letter of Acceptance (LOA) (if applicable). **Deadline:** July 1. **Contact:** Program Administrator at 928-734-3533.

1513 ■ Tribal Priority Scholarships *(Graduate, Professional development, Undergraduate/Scholarship)*

Purpose: To encourage Hopi college students to obtain degrees in subject areas of priority interest to Hopi Tribal Goals and Objectives. **Focus:** General studies. **Qualif.:** Applicants must be junior and senior undergraduate, graduate, post-graduate and professional students in the areas of priority interest to the Hopi Tribe; must have an at least 3.5 GPA. **Criteria:** Recipients are selected based on academic performance.

Funds Avail.: $1,500. **Number Awarded:** 5. **To Apply:** Applicants must submit an official high school transcript or original GED scores; must submit an official transcript from

Awards are arranged alphabetically below their administering organizations

all post-secondary schools; must submit a Program of Study (POS) or Letter of Acceptance (LOA). **Deadline:** July 1; December 1; April 1. **Contact:** Program Administrator, Phone: 928-734-3533, Fax: 928-734-9575.

1514 ■ Arizona Christian School Tuition Organization (ACSTO)

PO Box 6580
Chandler, AZ 85246
Ph: (480) 820-0403
Fax: (480) 820-2027
URL: www.acsto.org

1515 ■ Arizona Christian School Tuition Organization Scholarships *(Undergraduate/ Scholarship)*

Purpose: To support students planning to attend K-12. **Focus:** General studies. **Qualif.:** Applicants must be students planning to attend K-12 in a Christian private school. **Criteria:** Awards are given based on the application.

Funds Avail.: No specific amount. **To Apply:** Applicants must complete the application form available online. **Deadline:** April 15. **Remarks:** All scholarships awarded will be sent directly to the student's school to be applied towards tuition.

1516 ■ Arizona City/County Management Association (ACMA)

1820 W Washington St.
Phoenix, AZ 85007
Ph: (602) 258-5786
Fax: (602) 253-3874
E-mail: info@azmanagement.org
URL: www.azmanagement.org

1517 ■ Marvin A. Andrews Scholarships/ Internships *(Graduate/Internship, Scholarship)*

Purpose: To provide the scholarship recipient the opportunity to intern with a participating Arizona city, town or county. **Focus:** Public Administration. **Qualif.:** Applicants must be full-time students attending either Arizona State University, Northern Arizona University or the University of Arizona who have exhibited strong academic achievement. **Criteria:** Recipients are selected based on interest in local government administration, career plans, academic achievement, school and/or community honors and activities and financial need.

Funds Avail.: $2,000. **To Apply:** Applicants must submit: completed application form; resume; two letters of recommendation; an official graduate-level transcript; a letter addressed to Gayle Mabery, ACMA President addressing their interest in local government management, career goals and financial need or plans for using the scholarship. **Deadline:** December 28. **Contact:** Ian Linssen at 602-258-5786 or ilinssen@azleague.org.

1518 ■ Charles A. Esser Memorial Scholarships *(Graduate/Scholarship)*

Purpose: To honor and financially assist Arizona graduate students in public administration who aspire to a career in local government management. **Focus:** Public administration. **Qualif.:** Applicants must be part-time MPA students

attending either Arizona State University, Northern Arizona University or the University of Arizona who are currently working in local government. **Criteria:** Recipients are selected based on interest in local government administration, career plans, academic achievement, school and/or community honors and activities and financial need.

Funds Avail.: $2,000. **To Apply:** Applicants must submit: completed application form; resume; two letters of recommendation; an official graduate-level transcript; a letter addressed to Gayle Mabery, ACMA President addressing their interest in local government management, career goals and financial needs or plans for using the scholarship. **Deadline:** December 5. **Contact:** Ian Linssen at 602-258-5786 or ilinssen@azleague.org.

1519 ■ Arizona Cowpuncher's Scholarship Organization (ACSO)

PO Box 420
Kirkland, AZ 86332-0420
E-mail: info@allaboutacso.com
URL: www.allaboutacso.com

1520 ■ ACSO Scholarships *(Undergraduate/ Scholarship)*

Purpose: To provide funds for education programs beyond high school. **Focus:** General studies. **Qualif.:** Applicant must be a U.S. citizen, and an Arizona resident; high school graduate or continuing education student attending an accredited college or trade school; taking a minimum of 12 credit hours per semester equivalent and must be involved as owners or employees of ranches. **Criteria:** Selection will be based on the application and the submitted materials.

Funds Avail.: No specific amount. **To Apply:** Applicants must submit the completed scholarship application form in an envelope together with an official birth certificate; two letters of recommendation from persons other than family members; and a letter of intent (which includes a summary of educational attainment, achievements and activities, personal goals, dollar amount for school related expenses, as well as other scholarships applied for and/or granted); and the name of the educational facility that the applicant is planning to attend including the mailing address of the financial aid or registrar office, the email address and contact numbers. **Deadline:** February 10. **Contact:** Valerie Owen.

1521 ■ Arizona Hydrological Society (AHS)

3317 S Higley Rd., Ste. 114-120
Gilbert, AZ 85297
Ph: (480) 270-4937
Free: 866-931-3134
E-mail: azhydrosoc.dir@gmail.com
URL: www.azhydrosoc.org

1522 ■ Arizona Hydrological Society Scholarships *(Graduate, Undergraduate/Scholarship)*

Purpose: To encourage full-time students to excel in the field of hydrology, hydrogeology or any water-resource related fields. **Focus:** Hydrology. **Qualif.:** Applicants must be junior, senior or graduate students at any university or college in Arizona. **Criteria:** Recipients will be select based on GPA; strength of recommendation letter; application letter describing the interest and goals in hydrology and water resources; and degree of need.

Awards are arranged alphabetically below their administering organizations

Funds Avail.: $2,000. **Number Awarded:** 3. **To Apply:** Applicants must submit an application form; official transcripts; and at least one letter of recommendation. **Contact:** For further information, applicants must contact Erin Young 1055 Hano Trail, Flagstaff, AZ 86001; Phone: 928-606-8422; E-mail: eyoung@flusol.com.

1523 ■ Arizona Nursery Association (ANA)
1430 W Broadway Rd., Ste. 110
Tempe, AZ 85282
Ph: (480) 966-1610
Fax: (480) 966-0923
E-mail: info@azna.org
URL: www.azna.org

1524 ■ Arizona Nursery Association Scholarships *(Undergraduate/Scholarship)*
Purpose: To promote and advance the nursery industry for its members and the public they serve. **Focus:** Horticulture. **Qualif.:** Applicants must be residents of Arizona currently or planning to be enrolled in a horticultural-related curriculum at a university, community college or continuing education program; must be currently employed in or have an interest in the nursery industry as a career; must have above-average scholastic achievement or at least two years work experience in the industry; must display involvement in extracurricular activities related to industry. **Criteria:** Recipients are selected based on academic performance.

Funds Avail.: $500-$3,000. **To Apply:** Applicants must complete the online application form. **Deadline:** April 16. **Contact:** scholarship@azna.org.

1525 ■ Arizona Nurses Association (AzNA)
1850 E Southern Ave., Ste. 1
Tempe, AZ 85282-5832
Ph: (480) 831-0404
Fax: (480) 839-4780
E-mail: info@aznurse.org
URL: www.aznurse.org

1526 ■ Arizona Nurses Foundation Scholarships *(Doctorate, Graduate, Undergraduate/ Scholarship)*
Purpose: To enhance the development of Arizona nurses and further the nursing profession in Arizona. **Focus:** Nursing. **Qualif.:** Applicants must be undergraduate and graduate students enrolled in or accepted in an academic education program; must be enrolled part-time or full-time. **Criteria:** Recipients are selected based on potential for leadership in nursing; merit; commitment to professional nursing in Arizona; expressed need for financial assistance; and interest in teaching nursing in Arizona.

Funds Avail.: A.D.N. applicants: $500; BSN, RN-BSN, Masters: $1,000; doctoral applicants: $2,500. **To Apply:** Applicants must submit: completed application form; evidence of admission such as official or unofficial transcript of records; current courses schedule; copy of letter or certificate of admission or a written statement from an appropriate academic official; a brief statement describing the professional's activities; community service and other activities in the last three years that demonstrate the potential for leadership; a statement describing the need for financial assistance; one confidential reference form from an immediate supervisor, student's academic advisor or another

faculty member. **Deadline:** March 1; October 1. **Contact:** carol@aznurse.org.

1527 ■ Arizona Society of Certified Public Accountants (ASCPA)
4801 E Washington St., Ste. 225-B
Phoenix, AZ 85034
Ph: (602) 252-4144
Fax: (602) 252-1511
Free: 888-237-0700
E-mail: chubiak@ascpa.com
URL: www.ascpa.com

1528 ■ ASCPA High School Scholarships *(Undergraduate/Scholarship)*
Purpose: To support students pursuing an accounting degree. **Focus:** Accounting. **Qualif.:** Applicant must be a high school senior enrolling in an Arizona university/community college as a fulltime student majoring in accounting, and a legal U.S. resident and current resident of Arizona. **Criteria:** Selection is based on academic achievement (as documented through GPA, class ranking and standardized test scores) and community involvement and leadership potential (as demonstrated by the student's personal statement and letters of recommendation).

Funds Avail.: $500. **Number Awarded:** 8. **To Apply:** Applicants must submit a completed application form along with a certified high school transcript (contains student's class rank, GPA and test scores); a personal statement on community involvement, career goals and desire to contribute to the community (maximum of 2 pages); and a one-page letter of recommendation from a teacher or a school official. **Deadline:** February 8. **Contact:** Cynthia Figueroa at 602-324-6847/888-237-0700 x-215 or cfigueroa@ascpa.com.

1529 ■ Future CPA Scholarships *(Community College, Graduate, Undergraduate/Scholarship)*
Purpose: To support students pursuing an accounting degree. **Focus:** Accounting. **Qualif.:** Applicant must be an accounting major; a legal U.S. and Arizona resident; a full-time student (12 or more credits per semester or 24 credits per year); has earned at least 12 college/university credits at the time of application; has completed at least one accounting course at a college/university; and has a GPA of 3.0 or better. **Criteria:** Selection is based on academic achievement (as documented through GPA and success in accounting or accounting-related courses), likelihood of becoming a CPA and remaining in Arizona, and community involvement and leadership potential (as demonstrated by the student's personal statement and letter of recommendation).

Funds Avail.: $1,000. **Number Awarded:** 2. **To Apply:** Applicants must submit a completed application form along with the college/university transcripts for all schools attended; resume (includes work experience and information such as extra-curricular activities, public service activities, awards and honors); a one-page essay on future career interests and professional goals (include 2-year and 5-year goals); and letter of recommendation from an instructor or employer. **Deadline:** April 15. **Contact:** Cynthia Figueroa at 602-324-6847/888-237-0700 x-215 or cfigueroa@ascpa.com.

1530 ■ Sam Gallant Memorial Scholarships *(Graduate, Undergraduate/Scholarship)*
Purpose: To support students pursuing an accounting degree. **Focus:** Accounting. **Qualif.:** Applicant must be an

Awards are arranged alphabetically below their administering organizations

accounting major; have a 3.5 minimum GPA; be studying in an Arizona State University Main; an African American; and a legal U.S. resident. **Criteria:** Selection is based on the submitted application materials.

Funds Avail.: $1,000. **Number Awarded:** 1. **To Apply:** Applicants must complete a detailed scholarship application form together with a statement of career goals and a formal resume. Students may contact Arizona State University Main Campus for more information on the scholarship.

1531 ■ University Junior Standing Scholarships
(Undergraduate/Scholarship)

Purpose: To support students pursuing an accounting degree. **Focus:** Accounting. **Qualif.:** Applicant must be an accounting major; have a 3.5 minimum GPA; be studying in an Arizona public university (Arizona State University Main, University of Arizona and Northern Arizona University); have completed the first introductory accounting course and currently enrolled in the second introductory accounting course; and a legal U.S. resident. **Criteria:** Selection is based on the submitted application materials.

Funds Avail.: $1,000. **Number Awarded:** 2. **To Apply:** Applicants must complete a detailed scholarship application form together with a statement of career goals and a formal resume. Students may contact the individual university for applications and to learn more about the process.

1532 ■ University Senior and Master's Program Scholarships *(Graduate/Scholarship)*

Purpose: To support students pursuing an accounting degree. **Focus:** Accounting. **Qualif.:** Applicant must be an accounting major who will begin his/her senior year or master's program; have a 3.5 minimum GPA; be studying in an Arizona public university (Arizona State University Main, University of Arizona and Northern Arizona University); and a legal U.S. resident. **Criteria:** Selection is based on the submitted application materials.

Funds Avail.: $2,000. **Number Awarded:** 2. **To Apply:** Applicants must complete a detailed scholarship application form together with a statement of career goals and a formal resume. Students may contact the individual university for applications and to learn more about the process.

1533 ■ Arkansas Association of Family and Consumer Sciences (ARAFCS)
2301 S University Ave.
Little Rock, AR 72204
E-mail: dfisher@harding.edu
URL: www.arafcs.com

1534 ■ ARAFCS Doctoral Scholarships
(Doctorate/Scholarship)

Purpose: To encourage family and consumer sciences professionals by providing financial assistance for graduate education. **Focus:** General studies. **Qualif.:** Applicant must be a legal resident of Arkansas; must be a family and consumer sciences major at an Arkansas university; must have been admitted to a graduate program; must have at least 3.0 cumulative GPA and maintain a 3.0 GPA on a scale of 4.0 in graduate school; must have demonstrated qualities of leadership in AAFCS; must be a current member of AAFCS; must have been a member of the American and

Arkansas Association of Family and Consumer Sciences for at least two of the last three years. **Criteria:** Applicants will be selected by the scholarship committee, chaired by the AAFCS Scholarship Chairperson, who will review applications and recommend the recipient to the AAFCS Board.

Funds Avail.: No specific amount. **Deadline:** January 31.

1535 ■ ARAFCS Masters Scholarships
(Graduate/Scholarship)

Purpose: To encourage family and consumer sciences professionals by providing financial assistance for graduate education. **Focus:** General studies. **Qualif.:** Applicant must be a legal resident of Arkansas; must be a family and consumer sciences major at an Arkansas university; must have been admitted to a graduate program; must have at least 3.0 cumulative GPA and maintain a 3.0 GPA on a scale of 4.0 in graduate school; must have demonstrated qualities of leadership in AAFCS; must be a current member of AAFCS; must have been a member of the American and Arkansas Association of Family and Consumer Sciences for at least two of the last three years. **Criteria:** Applicants will be selected by the scholarship committee, chaired by the AAFCS Scholarship Chairperson, who will review applications and recommend the recipient to the AAFCS Board.

Funds Avail.: No specific amount. **To Apply:** Applicants must complete the application form available on the website; must submit an official transcript of record. **Deadline:** January 31.

1536 ■ Arkansas Environmental Federation (AEF)
1400 W Markham St., Ste. 302
Little Rock, AR 72201
Ph: (501) 374-0263
Fax: (501) 374-8752
URL: www.environment-protection.org

1537 ■ Randall Matthis for Environmental Studies Scholarships *(Graduate, Undergraduate/Scholarship)*

Purpose: To provide financial assistance for selected students from Arkansas universities. **Focus:** Environmental science; Health education; Natural resources. **Qualif.:** Applicants must be U.S. citizens residing in Arkansas and must be undergraduates or graduate students with at least 2.8 cumulative GPA based on 4.0 system. **Criteria:** Applicants are evaluated based on academic achievement and financial need.

Funds Avail.: $2,500. **To Apply:** Applicants must submit a completed application form; transcript of records; letter of nomination from a faculty member; and two additional letters of recommendation that address candidate's scholastic and personal attributes. **Deadline:** April 9. **Contact:** Application form and other supporting documents should be sent to Jamie Oliver at the above address, or e-mail her at joliver@environmentark.org.

1538 ■ Larry Wilson for Environmental Studies Scholarships *(Graduate, Undergraduate/Scholarship)*

Purpose: To provide financial assistance for selected students from Arkansas universities. **Focus:** Environmental science. **Qualif.:** Applicants must be U.S. citizens residing in Arkansas; must be full-time undergraduates or graduate

Awards are arranged alphabetically below their administering organizations

students at the time of application and in the year scholarship is awarded; must have a minimum of 2.8 cumulative grade point average based of 4.0 scale; must have completed 40 credit hours; and must be nominated by a faculty member. **Criteria:** Applicants are evaluated based on scholastic and personal attributes.

Funds Avail.: $2,500. **To Apply:** Applicants must submit a completed application form; transcript of records; letter of nomination by faculty member; and two letters of recommendation that address the candidate's scholastic and personal attributes. **Deadline:** April 9. **Contact:** Application form and other supporting documents should be sent to Randy Thurman at the above address, or e-mail at rthurman@environmentark.org.

1539 ■ Larry Wilson Scholarships for Undergraduate Civil Engineering Students (Undergraduate/Scholarship)

Purpose: To provide financial assistance for selected students from Arkansas universities. **Focus:** Engineering, Civil. **Qualif.:** Applicants must be U.S. citizens who are residents of Arkansas; must be undergraduate students who have Civil Engineering as a degree goal; must be full-time students at time of application and for year scholarship is awarded; must have a minimum of 2.8 cumulative grade point average based on 4.0 system; and must be nominated by a faculty member. **Criteria:** Applicants are evaluated based on academic achievement and financial need.

Funds Avail.: $2,500. **To Apply:** Applicants must submit a completed application form along with current official transcript(s) and letters. **Deadline:** April 9. **Contact:** For more information, e-mail Communication Director Elyse Geisbauer at egeisbauer@environmentark.org.

1540 ■ Arkansas Library Association (ArLA)
c/o Lynda Hampel, Exec. Admin.
PO Box 958
Benton, AR 72018-0958
Ph: (501) 860-7585
Fax: (501) 778-4014
E-mail: arlib2@sbcglobal.net
URL: www.arlib.org

1541 ■ ArLA Scholarships (Graduate, Master's/Scholarship)

Purpose: To encourage a higher standard of professional training in Arkansas libraries. **Focus:** Library and archival sciences. **Qualif.:** Applicant must be a legal resident of the State of Arkansas; hold or be completing work toward a bachelor's degree from an accredited college or university; have been accepted at an American Library Association accredited program leading to a master's degree in library science or to an NCATE accredited program leading to a master's degree in library media (the course of study should be completed within three academic years after receipt of the award). **Criteria:** Selection is based on applicant's interest in librarianship as a profession, academic record and references.

Funds Avail.: $1,500. **Number Awarded:** 2. **To Apply:** Applicants must submit a completed application form together with an official graduate transcript or proof of enrollment; letter of application; resume; and three letters of reference from individuals qualified to address the academic and professional potential of the applicant. **Dead-**

line: August 10. **Remarks:** Recipient of the scholarship must accept professional employment in an Arkansas library or in a library related position within one year after completing graduate program; continue to work in an Arkansas library or in a library related position for at least one year in a capacity commensurate with his/her training and education after accepting such employment; and maintain membership in the Arkansas Library Association for at least the year of required employment in an Arkansas library or library related position. **Contact:** Barbara Martin at the above address.

1542 ■ Arkansas Nurses Association (ARNA)
1123 S University, Ste. 1015
Little Rock, AR 72204
Ph: (501) 244-2363
Fax: (501) 244-9903
Free: 800-274-4ANA
E-mail: arna@arna.org
URL: www.arna.org

1543 ■ Arkansas Nursing Foundation - Dorothea Fund Scholarships (Professional development/Scholarship)

Purpose: To provide financial assistance to nurses throughout the state of Arkansas. **Focus:** Nursing. **Qualif.:** Applicant must: be a registered nurse; give a statement of commitment to community health nursing; be seeking a degree to become an advanced practice nurse; demonstrate need. **Criteria:** Selection will be based on the committee's criteria.

Funds Avail.: No specific amount. **To Apply:** Applicants must complete the application packet and must include the following: completed application form; cover letter stating desire for the scholarship and intended use of funds (including a statement regarding other financial assistance); statement regarding institutional financial assistance toward the planned degree (tuition waivers or reductions); current resume (one page including education, work experience, achievements and honors, if applicable); two letters of recommendation (with one being from current supervisor or faculty) including information concerning leadership and academic ability of the applicant; official undergraduate and graduate transcript(s) from all nursing programs attended (in sealed envelope with Registrar's signature or stamp on flap); letter of acceptance into degree program accredited by NLNAC or CCNE; and extracurricular activities (achievements, organization memberships, volunteer work). **Deadline:** June 1. **Contact:** Arkansas Nursing Foundation c/o Arkansas Nurses Association at the above address.

1544 ■ Arkansas Nursing Foundation - Mary Gray Scholarships (Professional development/Scholarship)

Purpose: To provide financial assistance to nurses throughout the state of Arkansas. **Focus:** Nursing. **Qualif.:** Applicant must be: a registered nurse; seeking an advanced degree in nursing; interested and/or involved in advanced practice nursing (Advance Nurse Practitioner, Clinical Nurse Specialist, Certified Nurse Midwife, and Certified Nurse Anesthetist). **Criteria:** Selection will be based on the committee's criteria.

Funds Avail.: No specific amount. **To Apply:** Applicants must complete the application packet and must include the following: completed application form; cover letter stating

Awards are arranged alphabetically below their administering organizations

desire for the scholarship and intended use of funds (including a statement regarding other financial assistance); statement regarding institutional financial assistance toward the planned degree (tuition waivers or reductions); current resume (one page including education, work experience, achievements, and honors, if applicable); two letters of recommendation (with one being from current supervisor or faculty) including information concerning leadership and academic ability of the applicant; official undergraduate and graduate transcript(s) from all nursing programs attended (in sealed envelope with Registrar's signature or stamp on flap); letter of acceptance into degree program accredited by NLNAC or CCNE; and extracurricular activities (achievements, organization memberships, volunteer work). **Deadline:** June 1. **Contact:** Arkansas Nursing Foundation c/o Arkansas Nurses Association at the above address.

1545 ■ Arkansas Public Health Association (APHA)

PO Box 250327
Little Rock, AR 72225
Ph: (501) 280-4950
Fax: (501) 280-4999
E-mail: ar_apha@yahoo.com
URL: www.arkpublichealth.org

1546 ■ Arkansas Public Health Association Scholarships *(Undergraduate/Scholarship)*

Purpose: To provide financial support to Arkansas students. **Focus:** Public health. **Qualif.:** Applicants must be Arkansas residents; must be enrolled, or have planned to enroll in a field of public health; must be currently classified as sophomores in college, university or approved Vo-Tech; must have at least 2.5 GPA; must demonstrate financial need. **Criteria:** Applicants will be judged based on the following criteria: (a) GPA; (b) Goals in public health; (c) Honors, organizations, volunteering with health-related organizations; (d) Letter from major professor; (e) Personal reference letter; (f) Present or past public health experience; (f) Full-time student; (g) Part-time student; (h) Financial need.

Funds Avail.: $500-$1,000. **To Apply:** Application forms are available online. Applicants must submit official college, university, or Vo-Tech transcripts; must have a letter of recommendation from major professor; must have a letter of personal reference; must have a statement/explanation of financial need; must have an explanation in 150 words or less concerning their goals and plans with the scholarship, their past and present public health experiences. **Deadline:** March 16. **Contact:** Mail applications to Scholarship Chair, PO Box 250327, Little Rock, AR 72225.

1547 ■ Arkansas Society of Professional Sanitarians Scholarships *(Undergraduate/Scholarship)*

Purpose: To support Arkansas students. **Focus:** Environmental technology. **Qualif.:** Applicant must be an Arkansas resident; must be enrolled, or have plans to enroll, in an environmental field; must be a sophomore student; must have at least a 2.5 GPA; and must demonstrate financial need. **Criteria:** Selection of applicants will be based on the criteria of the ASPS Scholarship Committee.

Funds Avail.: $250-$500. **To Apply:** Application forms are available online; past transcript(s) and short essay about self and career goals. **Deadline:** April 13.

1548 ■ Arkansas Single Parent Scholarship Fund (ASPSF)

614 E Emma Ave., Ste. 119
Springdale, AR 72764
Ph: (479) 927-1402
Fax: (479) 927-0755
E-mail: rnesson@jtlshop.jonesnet.org
URL: www.aspsf.org

1549 ■ Single Parent Scholarships *(Graduate, Undergraduate/Scholarship)*

Purpose: To provide supplemental financial assistance to single parents living in Arkansas who are pursuing a course of instruction that will improve their income-earning potential. **Focus:** General studies. **Qualif.:** Applicant must be a resident of the county in which they are applying; be a single parent with custodial care of at least one minor child; must earn income at or near the poverty level; and have not received a baccalaureate degree, with the exception of candidates for the Master of Arts in Teaching (MAT) degree. **Criteria:** Selection is based on the application materials submitted for review.

Funds Avail.: Varies. **To Apply:** Applicants are encouraged to contact the Single Parent Scholarship Fund in their county (check website for counties with Single Parent Scholarship Fund). **Contact:** Chris Womack at 479-927-1402 x-10, or cwomack@jtlshop.jonesnet.org.

1550 ■ Arkansas State University (Mountain Home, Arkansas) (ASU)

1600 S College St.
Mountain Home, AR 72653
Ph: (870) 508-6100
Fax: (870) 508-6287
E-mail: lfoster@brook.asumh.edu
URL: www.asumh.edu

1551 ■ Arkansas State University Mountain Home Scholarships *(Undergraduate/Scholarship)*

Purpose: To provide financial support to the students enrolled in ASUMH. **Focus:** General studies. **Qualif.:** Applicant must be enrolled at Arkansas State University Mountain Home; must be a resident of Arkansas; must have a GPA average of 2.5-3.0. **Criteria:** Selection of candidates will be based on the application materials and academic criteria.

Funds Avail.: $425 for full-time; $200 for part-time. **Number Awarded:** 4. **To Apply:** Applicant must have three recommendation letters, and for more information regarding the scholarship, applicants are advised to contact the Arkansas State University at the above address. **Contact:** LeQuita Foster, Phone: 870-508-6127; lfoster@brook.asumh.edu.

1552 ■ Armed Forces Communications and Electronics Association (AFCEA)

4400 Fair Lakes Ct.
Fairfax, VA 22033
Ph: (703) 631-6100
Fax: (703) 631-6169
Free: 800-336-4583
E-mail: promo@afcea.org
URL: www.afcea.org

Awards are arranged alphabetically below their administering organizations

1553 ■ AFCEA Math and Science Teachers Scholarships *(Graduate, Undergraduate/ Scholarship)*

Purpose: To promote science, mathematics or information technology education at the US Secondary School. **Focus:** Science; Mathematics and mathematical sciences. **Qualif.:** Applicants must be degree-seeking candidates; must be enrolled full-time in an education curriculum of accredited college or university in the United States; must be U.S. citizens; and must be at least sophomores or juniors at the time of application (only a few second-year students only). For graduating students: at least two classes per semester are required. **Criteria:** Recipients are selected based on committee's review of eligibility and other criteria.

Funds Avail.: 5,000. **Number Awarded:** 50. **To Apply:** Applicants may apply online. Applicants must also submit transcript issued by the school Registrar's Office; and two letters of recommendation from relevant faculty. If currently employed as a teacher, one additional letter from the school principal. Additional documents may be provided (optional). **Deadline:** May 1. **Contact:** Application form and other supporting documents should be sent to Norma Corrales; Phone: 703-631-6149; Toll free: 800-336-6149.

1554 ■ AFCEA Scholarship for Working Professionals *(Graduate/Scholarship)*

Purpose: To provide scholarship to those students pursuing an undergraduate or graduate degree while employed. **Focus:** Engineering; Mathematics; Physics; Communications. **Qualif.:** Applicants must be U.S. citizens attending an accredited college or university in the United States as either a traditional or distance learning students; must be majoring in electrical, chemical, systems or aerospace engineering; mathematics; physics; technical management; computer information systems; computer science or related fields; and must have an overall GPA of 3.0. For graduates, must have completed at least two postgraduate-level courses and are enrolled in an eligible degree-granting master's degree program. undergraduate candidates must be at least second year students attending an accredited college or university in the United States. **Criteria:** Recipients are selected based on committee's review of applications.

Funds Avail.: $2,000. **To Apply:** Applicants may apply online at the AFCEA web site. **Deadline:** September 1. **Contact:** Application form and other supporting documents should be sent to Norma Corrales; Phone: 703-631-6149; Toll free: 800-336-4583.

1555 ■ Armed Forces Communications and Electronics Association Fellowships *(Doctorate, Graduate/Fellowship)*

Purpose: To support the development of engineers and technical personnel. **Focus:** Engineering; Physics; Mathematics; Electronics. **Qualif.:** Candidates must be U.S. citizens with Bachelor of Science and Master of Science degree; must be currently enrolled in a doctoral program at any accredited university in the United States. Majors directly related to the support of U.S. intelligence enterprises with relevance to the mission of AFCEA are also eligible. **Criteria:** Selection will be based on the submitted thesis.

Funds Avail.: $15,000. **To Apply:** Applicants may apply online at AFCEA website; must submit a dissertation title or abstract of the specific area of research; and endorsement by the Dean of the College of Engineering. **Deadline:** February 15. **Contact:** Application form and other supporting documents should be sent to Norma Corrales; Phone: 703-631-6149; Toll free: 800-336-6149.

1556 ■ William E. "Buck" Bragunier Scholarships *(Undergraduate/Scholarship)*

Purpose: To provide scholarship for the general public. **Focus:** Engineering; Mathematics; Physics; Communications; Electronics. **Qualif.:** Applicants must be at least second year college students; must be enrolled full time as sophomores or juniors at the time of application; must have an outstanding record of demonstrated leadership within university or local community. Majors directly related to the support of U.S. intelligence enterprises or national security with relevance to the mission of AFCEA are also eligible. **Criteria:** Primary consideration will be given for academic excellence.

Funds Avail.: $2,000. **To Apply:** Applicants may apply online at AFFECT website. Applicants must also submit two letters of recommendation printed in school stationery and with signature from field-of-study professors. Letters and transcript must be submitted to: Mr. Fred H. Rainbow, VP and Exec. Dir. AFCEA Educational Foundation. **Contact:** Mr. Fred H. Rainbow, VP and Exec. Dir., AFCEA Educational Foundation, 440 Fail Lakes Ct., Fairfax, VA 22033; scholarshipsinfo@afcea.org.

1557 ■ Lt. General Douglas D. Buchholz Memorial Scholarships *(Undergraduate/Scholarship)*

Purpose: To provide scholarships to students connected to the US Military. **Focus:** Engineering; Mathematics; Physics; Communications. **Qualif.:** Applicants must be currently active enlisted soldiers assigned to Fort Gordon, Georgia; must have completed a minimum of 15 semester hours/25 quarter hours; must be currently enrolled either full or part time in an accredited US college; and must have a minimum GPA of 2.5 on a 4.0 scale. **Criteria:** Recipients are selected based on recommendation of Scholarship Board under the guidance of the Fort Gordon Command Sergeant Major.

Funds Avail.: No specific amount. **To Apply:** Students may apply online at the AFCEA web site. **Deadline:** November 15. **Contact:** Mr. Joseph S. Yavorsky, President; president@afcea-augusta.org.

1558 ■ Milton E. Cooper/Young AFCEAN Graduate Scholarships *(Graduate/Scholarship)*

Purpose: To support local chapters and promote education. **Focus:** Electronics; Communication. **Qualif.:** Applicants must be US citizens and young professionals currently employed in a field related to communications, computer science or electronics; must demonstrate strong commitment to the pursuit of advanced college degree (M.S. or Ph.D.) related to communications, computer science, electronics, electrical or systems engineering in preparation for a career in science or engineering; must have GPA of 3.2 or higher; must be currently enrolled in an accredited university or college in the United States. **Criteria:** Recipients are selected based on scholarship committee's review of application materials.

Funds Avail.: $3,000. **To Apply:** Applicants must submit three letters of recommendation with at least one from current employer; and official college transcript reflecting all college-level work. **Deadline:** March 15. **Contact:** Luanne M. Balestrucci; D&S PO Box 7259 Freehold, NJ 07728; lmbalestrucci@dsci-usa.com.

Awards are arranged alphabetically below their administering organizations

1559 ■ Disabled War Veterans Scholarships
(Undergraduate/Scholarship)

Purpose: To provide educational incentives, opportunities and assistance for people engaged in information management, communications and intelligence efforts and fostering excellence in education particularly in the "hard science" disciplines related to C4ISR. **Focus:** Engineering; Mathematics; Physics; Communications. **Qualif.:** Applicants must be currently enrolled and attending either a two-year or four-year in an accredited college or university in the United States; must be enrolled in an accredited distance learning or online degree granting program affiliated with major, accredited two year or four year college or university in the United States. **Criteria:** Recipients are selected based on academic excellence, leadership and financial need.

Funds Avail.: $2,500. **To Apply:** Applicants may apply online at AFFECT website. Applicants must also submit two letters of recommendation printed on school stationery and with signature from field-of-study professors. **Deadline:** April 1. **Contact:** Norma Corrales at 703-631-6149.

1560 ■ Lockheed Martin Graduate Scholarships
(Graduate/Scholarship)

Purpose: To provide scholarships to postgraduate students. **Focus:** Engineering; Mathematics; Physics; Communications. **Qualif.:** Applicants must be U.S. citizens currently enrolled full time in a master's degree program in the following or related fields of electrical, chemical, computer or systems engineering; physics; mathematics; computer science; computer technology; communications technology; communications engineering; technology management; or information management systems. **Criteria:** Recipients will be selected based on demonstrated effort at the master's level of study rather than the potential for such excellence.

Funds Avail.: $3,000. **To Apply:** Applicants may apply online at the AFCEA web site. **Deadline:** June 1. **Contact:** Application form and other supporting documents should be sent to Norma Corrales; Phone: 703-631-6149; Toll free: 800-336-4583.

1561 ■ Lockheed Martin IT Scholarships
(Undergraduate/Scholarship)

Purpose: To provide scholarship to the general public. **Focus:** Engineering; Mathematics; Physics; Communications. **Qualif.:** Applicants must be at least second year college students; and must be enrolled full time as sophomores or juniors at the time of application. Majors directly related to the support of U.S. intelligence enterprises or national security with relevance to the mission of AFCEA are also eligible. **Criteria:** Recipients are selected based from the qualified General Wickham Scholarship applicants.

Funds Avail.: $3,000. **To Apply:** Applicants may apply online. Applicants must also submit two letters of recommendation printed in school stationery and with signature from field-of-study professors; and official transcript of all college level study. **Deadline:** May 1. **Contact:** Mr. Fred H. Rainbow, VP and Exec. Dir., AFCEA Educational Foundation, 4400 Fair Lakes Ct., Fairfax, VA 22033; scholarshipsinfo@afcea.org.

1562 ■ AFCEA General Emmett Paige Scholarships
(Undergraduate/Scholarship)

Purpose: To provide scholarships to students connected to the US Military. **Focus:** Engineering; Mathematics; Physics; Communications. **Qualif.:** Applicants must be on active duty in the uniformed military services, veterans, their spouses or dependents who are currently enrolled full-time in an eligible degree program at an accredited four-year college or university in the United States; must be U.S. citizens; must have a minimum GPA of 3.0 on 4.0 scale. **Criteria:** Recipients are selected based on committee's review of applications.

Funds Avail.: $2,000. **To Apply:** Applicants may apply online at the AFCEA web site. Applicants must also submit a copy of Certificate of Service, Discharge From DD214, or facsimile of current Department of Defense or Coast Guard Identification Card; and two letters of recommendation printed in school stationery and with signature from field-of-study professors. **Deadline:** November 1. **Contact:** Application form and other supporting documents should be sent to Mr. Fred H. Rainbow, 703-631-6138 or 800-336-4583 ext. 6138 or scholarshipsinfo@afcea.org.

1563 ■ Ralph W. Shrader Diversity Scholarships
(Graduate/Scholarship)

Purpose: To provide educational opportunities for talented individuals pursuing advanced degrees at the master's level. **Focus:** Computer and information sciences; Engineering, chemical; Engineering, electrical; Mathematics and mathematical sciences; Physics. **Qualif.:** Applicants must be U.S. citizens currently enrolled full time in a master's degree program in an accredited university in the United States. Scholarships will be awarded to full-time graduate students currently working toward a master's degree in the following or related fields of electrical, electronics, chemical, systems or communications engineering; physics; mathematics; computer science; computer technology; or management information systems. Majors directly related to the support of U.S. intelligence or national security enterprises with relevance to the mission of AFCEA are also eligible. **Criteria:** Recipients are selected based on academic excellence.

Funds Avail.: $3,000. **To Apply:** Applicants may apply online at the AFCEA web site. **Deadline:** September 1. **Contact:** Mr. Fred H. Rainbow at 703-631-6138 or 800-336-4583 ext. 6138 or scholarshipsinfo@afcea.org.

1564 ■ Vice Adm. Jerry O. Tuttle, USN (Ret.) and Mrs. Barbara A. Tuttle Science and Technology Scholarships *(Undergraduate/Scholarship)*

Purpose: To support students working full time. **Focus:** Engineering; Computer and Information Sciences. **Qualif.:** Applicants must be U.S. citizens enrolled full time majoring in technology; and must be sophomores and juniors at the time of application. **Criteria:** Recipients are selected based on the committee's review of application materials. Primary consideration will be given to military enlisted candidates.

Funds Avail.: $2,000. **To Apply:** Applicants may apply online. Applicants must also submit two letters of recommendation printed in school stationery and with signature from field-of-study professors; and official transcript of all college level study. **Deadline:** November 1. **Contact:** Application form and other supporting documents should be sent to Norma Corrales; Phone: 703-631-6149; Toll free: 800-336-4583.

1565 ■ Veterans of Enduring Freedom (Afghanistan) and Iraqi Freedom Scholarships
(Undergraduate/Scholarship)

Purpose: To provide scholarships to students connected to the US military. **Focus:** Engineering; Mathematics; Phys-

Awards are arranged alphabetically below their administering organizations

ics; Communications. **Qualif.:** Applicants must be currently enrolled and attending either a two-year accredited college or university in the United States. **Criteria:** Recipients are selected based on the committee's review of application.

Funds Avail.: $2,500. **To Apply:** Applicants may apply on-line at AFCEA web site. **Deadline:** April 1. **Remarks:** The AFCEA Educational Foundation is pleased to co-sponsor this scholarship opportunity for U.S. War Veterans. **Contact:** Norma Corrales 703-631-6149.

1566 ■ AFCEA General John A. Wickham Scholarships *(Undergraduate/Scholarship)*

Purpose: To provide scholarship to the general public. **Focus:** Engineering; Mathematics; Physics; Communications; Electronics. **Qualif.:** Applicants must be full-time students currently enrolled in an accredited degree granting four-year colleges or universities in the United States; must be at least second year college students enrolled full-time as sophomores or juniors at the time of application; must be U.S. citizens; must have GPA of 3.5 on 4.0 scale. Majors directly related to the support of U.S. intelligence enterprises or national security with relevance to the mission of AFCEA are also eligible. **Criteria:** Recipients are selected based on the committee's criteria.

Funds Avail.: $2,000. **To Apply:** Applicants may apply at AFCEA web site. Applicants must also submit two letters of recommendation printed in school stationery and with signature from field-of-study professors. **Deadline:** May 1. **Contact:** Application form and other supporting documents should be sent to Mr. Fred H. Rainbow, 703-631-6138 or 800-336-4583 ext. 6138 or scholarshipsinfo@afcea.org.

1567 ■ Marine Corps Sgt. Jeannette L. Winters Memorial Scholarships *(Undergraduate/Scholarship)*

Purpose: To provide scholarships to students connected with the U.S. Military. **Focus:** Engineering; Mathematics; Physics; Communications. **Qualif.:** Applicants must be enrolled full time in a Bachelor of Science degree program in accredited colleges or universities in the United States; and must have a minimum GPA of 3.0 on 4.0 scale. Majors directly related to the support of US Intelligence enterprises or national security with relevance to the mission of AFCEA and students who are sophomores, juniors, or seniors who meet the requirements are also eligible to apply. **Criteria:** Recipients are selected based on academic performance.

Funds Avail.: $2,000. **To Apply:** Applicants may apply on-line at the AFCEA web site. Applicants must also submit two letters of recommendation printed in school stationery and with signature from field-of-study professors. **Deadline:** September 1. **Contact:** Application form and other supporting documents should be sent to Norma Corrales; Phone: 703-631-6149; Toll free: 800-336-4583.

1568 ■ Armenian Bar Association

PO Box 29111
Los Angeles, CA 90029
Ph: (323) 666-6288
E-mail: info@armenianbar.org
URL: www.armenianbar.org

1569 ■ Armenian Bar Association Graduate Scholarships in Law *(Graduate/Scholarship)*

Purpose: To support students of Armenian descent attending, or accepted for admission to, an approved law school in the United States, Armenia or elsewhere. **Focus:** Law. **Qualif.:** Applicants must, at the time of submitting the scholarship application: be enrolled in or admitted to, if in the United States, an American Bar Association-accredited or state-accredited law school, or if in Armenia or another country, a law school approved by the Armenia Bar Association; have a strong academic potential as demonstrated by academic performance. **Criteria:** Selection will be based on the committee's criteria.

Funds Avail.: No specific amount. **To Apply:** Applicants must submit a completed application package. Application package must include the following: completed application form; personal essay; two letters of recommendation (from professors, school administrators, Armenian community leaders or others in official capacities who have knowledge of the applicant's academic performance and potential and/or commitment to the Armenian community); official grade transcripts from undergraduate college and law school; and proof of entrance or acceptance into, or continuation in, an approved law school. **Deadline:** April 30.

1570 ■ Armenian Educational Foundation (AEF)

600 W Broadway, Ste. 130
Glendale, CA 91204
Ph: (818) 242-4154
Fax: (818) 242-4913
E-mail: aef@aefweb.org
URL: www.aefweb.org

1571 ■ Richard R. Tufenkian Memorial Scholarships *(Undergraduate/Scholarship)*

Purpose: To provide financial support to qualified students of Armenian parentage. **Focus:** General studies. **Qualif.:** Applicants should have Armenian origin; have a 3.0 GPA; and be undergraduate students. **Criteria:** Awards are given based on academic merit; financial need.

Funds Avail.: $2,000. **Number Awarded:** 5. **To Apply:** Applicants must submit an application form; proof of acceptance to the university or college; first two pages of the most recent income tax returns; sealed official transcript; a letter of reference from university or college and from Armenian community service; an essay; and proof of parent's Armenian origin. **Deadline:** July 31. **Remarks:** Do not use mail which requires a signature upon delivery. **Contact:** For further information, applicants may e-mail hermine@aefweb.org.

1572 ■ Armenian General Benevolent Union

55 E 59th St.
New York, NY 10022-1112
Ph: (212) 319-6383
Fax: (212) 319-6507
E-mail: agbuwb@agbu.org
URL: www.agbu.org

1573 ■ AGBU Scholarships *(Graduate/Loan)*

Purpose: To support the higher education of students of Armenian descent. **Focus:** Communications; Educational administration; Public administration; International affairs and relations; Armenian studies; Law; Medicine. **Qualif.:** Applicant must be a full-time graduate student of Armenian descent; must be a U.S. resident or citizen; and must be enrolled in a competitive college or university in the United

Awards are arranged alphabetically below their administering organizations

States. **Criteria:** Awards are given based on merit.

Funds Avail.: $5,000-$10,000. **To Apply:** Applicants must submit a completed application form with two letters of recommendation; undergraduate/graduate transcript; copy of acceptance letter from the university; copy of Student Aid Report; copy of Financial Awards Letter or a copy of latest filed Federal Tax Return (Form 1040); resume; copies of published work; and a photograph. **Deadline:** April 1. **Remarks:** Students must start repayment of their loans one year after graduating or leaving school.

1574 ■ Armenian Professional Society (APS)

PO Box 10306
Glendale, CA 91209
Ph: (818) 685-9946
E-mail: apsla@apsla.org
URL: www.apsla.org

1575 ■ Armenian Professional Society Scholarship Fund *(Graduate/Scholarship)*

Purpose: To provide financial assistance for the advancement of education. **Focus:** General studies. **Qualif.:** Applicants must be students who have been accepted or enrolled in a graduate school in the United States. **Criteria:** Recipients are selected based on financial need, scholastic achievements, faculty recommendations and involvement in the Armenian Community.

Funds Avail.: No amount mentioned. **To Apply:** Applicants must submit print out of the scholarship application form (in portrait format, neatly typed) along with the official transcripts for the past four years; brief one-page essay about themselves, their involvement in the Armenian community and why they should be scholarship recipients; copies of applicant's and parent's most recent IRS Tax Returns or equivalent financial information; and the obtained two college or university recommendations. **Deadline:** September 1.

1576 ■ Armenian Relief Society - Eastern United States

80 Bigelow Ave., Ste. 200
Watertown, MA 02472
Ph: (617) 926-3801
Fax: (617) 924-7238
E-mail: office@arseastusa.org
URL: www.arseastusa.org

1577 ■ ARS Undergraduate Scholarships *(Undergraduate/Scholarship)*

Purpose: To encourage educational pursuits among undergraduate students of Armenian descent. **Focus:** General studies. **Qualif.:** Applicants must be of Armenian descent; must be undergraduate students who have completed at least one semester at an accredited four-year college or university in the United States or must be enrolled in a two-year college and are transferring to a four-year college or university as full-time students in the Fall. **Criteria:** Grants are made on the basis of financial need, merit and involvement in the Armenian community.

Funds Avail.: No specific amount. **To Apply:** Application must include financial aid forms, recent official transcript, two letters of recommendation and tuition costs. **Deadline:** April 1.

1578 ■ Lazarian Graduate Scholarships *(Graduate/Scholarship)*

Purpose: To encourage educational pursuits among graduate students of Armenian descent. **Focus:** Law; History; Political science; International affairs and relations; Journalism; Business administration; Medicine; Public service. **Qualif.:** Applicants must be of Armenian descent; must pursue their studies at the graduate level (Master's Degree or Doctorate) in the fields of law, history, political science, international relations, journalism, government, economics, business administration, medicine and public service. **Criteria:** Grants are made on the basis of financial need, merit and involvement in the Armenian community.

Funds Avail.: No specific amount. **To Apply:** Application package must include official transcript of college grades with raised seal, tuition costs, applicant's most recent Income Tax Return, three letters of recommendation and proof of acceptance into a graduate program. Application forms and instructions are available on the website. **Deadline:** April 1.

1579 ■ Armenian Students' Association of America (ASA)

333 Atlantic Ave.
Warwick, RI 02888
Ph: (401) 461-6114
E-mail: asa@asainc.org
URL: www.asainc.org/index.php

1580 ■ Armenian American Citizen's League Scholarships *(Undergraduate/Scholarship)*

Purpose: To provide financial assistance to those students who are in need. **Focus:** General Studies. **Qualif.:** Applicants must be permanent residents of the United States who have been living in California for at least two years and are enrolled full-time in an accredited college or university; minimum GPA of 3.0 (B average) is required. **Criteria:** Awards will be based on financial need, academic achievement and involvement in school and community services.

Funds Avail.: $1,000-$2,000. **To Apply:** Applicants must check the available website for the required materials. **Deadline:** March 1. **Contact:** headasa@aol.com.

1581 ■ Armenian American Medical Association Scholarships *(Undergraduate/Scholarship)*

Purpose: To provide financial assistance to those students who are in need. **Focus:** Medicine. **Qualif.:** Applicants must be students enrolled in a U.S. medical school. Award is primarily intended for students residing and studying in a private New England medical school. **Criteria:** Awards granted on the basis of need, merit and involvement in Armenian cultural affairs.

Funds Avail.: $1,000-2,000. **Number Awarded:** 2-3. **To Apply:** Applicants must check the available website for the required materials. **Deadline:** September 15; October 20. **Contact:** For more information, please contact Dr. Edward Karian, Chairperson; 324 Common St. Watertown, MA 02472-4940.

1582 ■ Armenian American Pharmacists' Association Scholarships *(Doctorate, Graduate/Scholarship)*

Purpose: To provide financial support to those students who are pursuing pharmacy. **Focus:** Pharmacy. **Qualif.:**

Awards are arranged alphabetically below their administering organizations

Applicants must be students of Armenian descent, pursuing a baccalaureate of pharmacy, doctor of pharmacy, or graduate degree program at a College of Pharmacy in the commonwealth of Massachusetts, Connecticut or Rhode Island. **Criteria:** Awards will be based on academic excellence and financial need.

Funds Avail.: No specific amount. **To Apply:** Applicants must check the available website for the required materials. **Deadline:** September 15. **Contact:** For inquiries, please contact: Susan A. Krikorian, Chairman of Scholarship Committee; Department of Pharmacy Practice 179 Longwood Avenue, Boston, MA 02115.

1583 ■ Armenian General Athletic Union Scholarships *(Undergraduate/Scholarship)*

Purpose: To provide financial assistance to those students who are in need. **Focus:** General Studies. **Qualif.:** Applicants must be high school students entering college; must be permanent U.S residents. **Criteria:** Awards will be based on academic merit and financial need.

Funds Avail.: $1,000. **To Apply:** Applicants must check the available website for the required materials. **Deadline:** May 15. **Contact:** Mrs. Ann Ajemian at 211 Grand Boulevard, Emerson, NJ 07630-1170.

1584 ■ Armenian Relief Society Scholarships *(Graduate, Undergraduate/Scholarship)*

Purpose: To provide financial assistance to those students who are in need. **Focus:** General Studies. **Qualif.:** Applicants must be undergraduate or graduate students in a four-year college or university. **Criteria:** Awards will be based on academic merit, financial need and involvement in Armenian community.

Funds Avail.: Depends on students' financial conditions. **To Apply:** Applicants must submit three letters of recommendation, transcript and tax returns. **Deadline:** April 1. **Contact:** For more information, please contact: Mr. Sonanz Papazian at 617-926-02472.

1585 ■ Michael M. Assarian Scholarships *(Undergraduate/Scholarship)*

Purpose: To provide financial assistance to those students who are in need. **Focus:** General studies. **Qualif.:** Applicants must be full-time students of Armenian descent enrolled at Wayne State University. **Criteria:** Selection of scholars will be based on scholastic achievement, extracurricular activities and financial need.

Funds Avail.: No specific amount. **To Apply:** Applicants must submit an application, current academic transcript, FAFSA, and two letters of recommendation to the Office of Scholarships and Financial Aid at Wayne State University. **Deadline:** April 29. **Contact:** Private Scholarship Coordinator Office of Scholarships and Financial Aid Detroit, MI 48202; Tel: 313-577-4969.

1586 ■ John M. Azarian Memorial Armenian Youth Scholarship Fund *(Undergraduate/Scholarship)*

Purpose: To provide financial assistance to those students who are in need. **Focus:** General Studies. **Qualif.:** Applicants must be full time enrolled in an accredited college or university; must be permanent residents of the United States. **Criteria:** Awards will be based on financial need, academic merit and involvement in the Armenian community.

Funds Avail.: $500-$3,000. **To Apply:** Applicants must

submit a completed application form and two letters of reference. **Deadline:** May 1. **Contact:** Mr. John M. Azarian, Jr. c/o Azarian Management and Development Company at 6 Prospect Street, Suite 1B, Midland Park, NJ 07432, Tel: 201-444-711, Fax: 214-444-6655.

1587 ■ Hagop Bogigian Scholarship Fund *(Undergraduate/Scholarship)*

Purpose: To provide financial assistance to those students who are in need. **Focus:** Arts. **Qualif.:** Applicants must be students of Armenian descent who are enrolled in a four-year Bachelor of Arts degree program at Mt. Holyoke College; must maintain over a 3.0 GPA, and demonstrate financial need. **Criteria:** Priority will be given to those students with financial need.

Funds Avail.: Award depends on need. **To Apply:** Applicants should apply directly to the financial aid office for financial aid and should indicate on the form that they are of Armenian descent. **Deadline:** March 1. **Contact:** Mt. Holyoke College Financial Aid Office, South Hadley, MA 01075 Tel: 413-538-2457.

1588 ■ Armen H. Bululian Scholarships *(Undergraduate/Scholarship)*

Purpose: To provide financial assistance to those students who are in need. **Focus:** General Studies. **Qualif.:** Applicants must be graduating high school seniors or enrolled full-time undergraduate students in an accredited college or university; must be residents of Monmouth or Ocean Counties in New Jersey. **Criteria:** Awards will be based on academic excellence and involvement in community services.

Funds Avail.: $1,000. **To Apply:** Applicants must check the available website for the required materials. **Deadline:** June 30. **Contact:** For more information, Please contact: Mr. Harout Karakashian at 1184 Ocean Avenue, Elberon, NJ 07740.

1589 ■ Constantinople Armenian Relief Society Scholarships (CARS) *(Undergraduate/Scholarship)*

Purpose: To provide financial assistance to those students who are in need. **Focus:** General studies. **Qualif.:** Applicants must be undergraduate students of Armenian descent; must have a minimum of 3.0 GPA; must be attending college in or residing in the NY/NJ area. **Criteria:** Preference will be based on criteria.

Funds Avail.: $400-$600. **Number Awarded:** 10-20. **To Apply:** Applicants must check the available website for the required materials. **Deadline:** June 30. **Contact:** For inquiries, please contact: Talin Sesetyan CARS Scholarship Committee at PO Box 769 Times Square Station New York, NY 10108 e-mail: talins11@hotmail.com.

1590 ■ Karekin DerAvedision Memorial Endowment Fund *(Undergraduate/Scholarship)*

Purpose: To provide financial assistance to those who are in need. **Focus:** Armenian Studies. **Qualif.:** Applicants must be graduate students in Armenian Studies who has been accepted for admission to UCLA. **Criteria:** Preference will be given to those students who are in need.

Funds Avail.: Maximum of $8,000. **To Apply:** Applicants must check the available website for the required materials. **Deadline:** December 15. **Contact:** UCLA Graduate Division Special; Fellowship Office 1252 Murphy Hall Box 951419 Los Angeles, CA 90095-1419 Tel: 310-825-3521.

Awards are arranged alphabetically below their administering organizations

1591 ■ George & Isabelle Elanjian Scholarships
(Undergraduate/Scholarship)

Purpose: To provide financial assistance to those students who are in need. **Focus:** General Studies. **Qualif.:** Applicants must be incoming freshmen students or enrolled for at least one year at the University of Michigan-Dearborn. **Criteria:** Preference will be given to those who meet the criteria.

Funds Avail.: $700 for tuition to one incoming first year student; $2,000 for one continuing upper-class student. **Number Awarded:** 2. **To Apply:** Applicants must be incoming students and should apply to the UM-D Admissions Office and upperclassmen should apply to the UM-D Financial Aid Office. Applicants must check the available website for the required materials. **Deadline:** February 1. **Contact:** Armenian Students' Association of America at the above address.

1592 ■ Emmanuel Bible College Scholarships
(Undergraduate/Scholarship)

Purpose: To provide financial support to those students who are in need. **Focus:** Religious Education. **Qualif.:** Applicants must be willing to pledge to work as a minister, evangelist, missionary, or youth director after graduation; must study in one of the institutions of Emmanuel Bible College. **Criteria:** Awards will be based on merit and good character.

Funds Avail.: No specific amount. **To Apply:** Applicants must check the contact information for inquiries. **Deadline:** June 30. **Contact:** Dr. Yeghia Babikian, Director; 1605 East Elizabeth Street, Pasadena, CA 91104 Fax: 818-398-2424 Tel: 818-791-2575.

1593 ■ Garikian Scholarship Fund
(Undergraduate/Scholarship)

Purpose: To provide financial assistance to those students who are in need. **Focus:** Armenian Studies; Sociology; Psychology; Political Science; Middle Eastern History; Journalism; Education; Music. **Qualif.:** Applicants must have completed their first academic year in college or university in California; must be pursuing one of the above field of studies. **Criteria:** Preference will be given to those who meet the criteria.

Funds Avail.: $750-$1,000. **To Apply:** Applicants must apply to the Executive Board for application forms and return them, completed, before the deadline. **Deadline:** August 31. **Contact:** Berj S. Baghdoyan c/o Western Prelacy at 4401 Russell Avenue, Los Angeles, CA 90027.

1594 ■ Hai Guin Scholarships Association
(Undergraduate/Scholarship)

Purpose: To provide financial assistance to those students who are in need. **Focus:** General Studies. **Qualif.:** Applicants must be students of Armenian descent, must reside in and attend school in Massachusetts. **Criteria:** Preference will be granted to a college student who has completed the first semester of freshman year; selection based on scholarship achievement and financial need.

Funds Avail.: $1,000. **To Apply:** Applicants must check the available website for the required materials. **Deadline:** October 25. **Contact:** For inquiries, please contact: Hasmig Maserjian (Scholarship Chairperson) at P.O. Box 509, Belmont, MA 02478.

1595 ■ Calouste Gulbenkian Foundation Scholarships *(Graduate, Undergraduate/Scholarship)*

Purpose: To provide financial assistance to those students who are in need. **Focus:** General Studies. **Qualif.:** Ap-

plicants must be sophomores or above who are enrolled full-time in an accredited college or university. **Criteria:** Awards will be based on academic merit and financial need; preference will be given to those applicants whose immediate family has not previously received a scholarship.

Funds Avail.: No specific amount. **To Apply:** Applicants must check the available website for the required materials. **Deadline:** Between February 1 and April 15. **Remarks:** Calouste Sarkis Gulbenkian was an Armenian businessman and philanthropist, he played a major role in making the petroleum reserves of the Middle East available to Western development. By the end of his life he had become one of the world's wealthiest individuals and his art acquisitions are considered one of the greatest private collections. **Contact:** Department of Armenian Communities Avenida de Berna 45-A, P-1067 Lisboa Codex, Portugal; Fax: 351-793-4080.

1596 ■ Sophia Hagopian Memorial Fund
(Undergraduate/Scholarship)

Purpose: To help those students who demonstrate extreme financial need. **Focus:** General Studies. **Qualif.:** Applicants must be students of Armenian descent demonstrating financial need; must provide service to the community by being involved in Armenian organizations and/or activities; and must be full-time students in their junior or senior year of undergraduate studies at an accredited California college or university. **Criteria:** Awards will be given to those who demonstrate financial need.

Funds Avail.: $2,000. **Number Awarded:** 6. **To Apply:** Applicants must check the available website for the required materials. **Deadline:** April 15. **Contact:** 600 West Broadway, Suite 130, Glendale, CA 91204 Tel: 818-242-4154.

1597 ■ Kaspar Hovannisian Memorial Scholarships *(Graduate/Scholarship)*

Purpose: To provide financial assistance to those students who are in need. **Focus:** General Studies. **Qualif.:** Applicants must be graduate students in the field of Armenian Studies. **Criteria:** Preference will be given to those studying Armenian History.

Funds Avail.: Up to $8,000. **To Apply:** Applicants must check the available website for the required materials. **Deadline:** December 15. **Contact:** Armenian Students' Association of America at the above address.

1598 ■ Hirair and Anna Hovnanian Foundation Presidential Scholarships *(Undergraduate/Scholarship)*

Purpose: To provide financial assistance to those students who are in need. **Focus:** General Studies. **Qualif.:** Applicants must be students of Armenian ethnic origin who demonstrate financial need and outstanding academic achievements; must maintain a minimum 2.75 GPA. **Criteria:** Consideration is given to all students of Armenian descent who apply and meet Villanova University's general admissions requirements.

Funds Avail.: No specific amount. **To Apply:** Applicants must check the available website for the required materials. **Deadline:** March 15 for incoming freshman and April 15 all other students. **Contact:** Villanova University; Office of Student Financial Assistance; 800 Lancaster Avenue, Villanova, PA 19085.

1599 ■ Hirair and Anna Hovnanian Foundation Scholarships *(Undergraduate/Scholarship)*

Purpose: To provide financial assistance to those students who are in need. **Focus:** General Studies. **Qualif.:** Ap-

Awards are arranged alphabetically below their administering organizations

plicants must be full-time students enrolled at the Women's College at Georgian Court University, preferably of Armenian descent, who exhibit financial need. **Criteria:** Priority will be given to those who demonstrate financial need and with good academic standing.

Funds Avail.: Full tuition. **To Apply:** Applicants must check the contact information for inquiries. **Contact:** For more information please contact the Financial Aid Office of Georgian Court University at Tel: 908-364-2200, ext. 258.

1600 ■ Rev. and Mrs. A.K. Jizmejian Educational Fund *(Undergraduate/Scholarship)*

Purpose: To provide financial assistance to those students who are in need. **Focus:** Theology. **Qualif.:** Applicants must be full-time theological seminary students and fourth-year undergraduate students who intend to continue their education in a theological seminary. **Criteria:** Preference will be given to those who meet the criteria.

Funds Avail.: $500-$1,500. **To Apply:** Applicants must check the available website for more information. **Deadline:** June 30. **Contact:** Armenian Evangelical Church; Mr. Mihran Jizmejian, Chairman 816-60 Pavane Linkway Don Mills, Ontario, M3C 1A2 Canada.

1601 ■ Knights of Vartan, Fresno Lodge No. 9 Scholarships *(Undergraduate/Scholarship)*

Purpose: To provide financial assistance to those students who are in need. **Focus:** Armenian Studies. **Qualif.:** Applicants must be new or continuing full-time students (12 units per semester) at Fresno State and maintain a 3.0 GPA or higher. **Criteria:** Scholarship will be given to those students who meet the criteria.

Funds Avail.: $750, one for an entering freshman and one for a continuing student at C.S.U.F. **Number Awarded:** 2. **To Apply:** Applicants must check the available website for the required materials. **Deadline:** November 1. **Contact:** Ms. Linda Tamura; Scholarship Coordinator; Tel: 209-278-6572.

1602 ■ Mangasar M. Mangasarian Scholarship Fund *(Graduate/Scholarship)*

Purpose: To provide financial assistance to those students who are in need. **Focus:** General Studies. **Qualif.:** Applicants must be full-time graduate students of Armenian parentage attending the University of California, Berkley. Scholarship is also offered to international students of Armenian descent. **Criteria:** Preference will be given to those who meet the criteria.

Funds Avail.: $500-$3,000. **To Apply:** Applicants must check the available website for the required materials. **Contact:** Mr. Tony Bernez, Scholarship Director or Ms. Diana Bischey 210 Sproul Hall, Berkeley, CA 94720.

1603 ■ National Association for Armenian Studies and Research Scholarships *(Graduate, Postgraduate/Scholarship)*

Purpose: To provide financial assistance to those students who are in need. **Focus:** General Studies. **Qualif.:** Applicants must be graduates or post-graduates doing research about Armenian Studies. **Criteria:** Selection will be based on criteria.

Funds Avail.: No specific amount. **To Apply:** Awards will be given to those who meet the criteria. **Deadline:** Early spring for fall grants; early fall for spring grants; and early winter for summer grants. **Contact:** Mr. Manoog S. Young, Chairman, Board of Directors; 395 Concord Ave., Belmont,

MA 02478 Fax: 617-484-1759 Tel: 617-489-1610.

1604 ■ St. James Armenian Church Memorial Scholarships *(All/Scholarship)*

Purpose: To provide financial assistance to those students who are in need. **Focus:** General Studies. **Qualif.:** Applicants must be affiliated with St. James Armenian Church by being a graduate of the Sunday school, a Sunday school teacher, a church choir member for at least one year, or in some other way acceptable to the scholarship committee. **Criteria:** Scholarships are awarded on the basis of academic achievement, financial need, service to school, community and church and seriousness of purpose.

Funds Avail.: $250-$2,000. **To Apply:** Applicants must check the available website for the required materials. **Deadline:** April 1. **Contact:** Ms. Anita Assarian; 465 Mount Auburn St., Watertown, MA 02172 Tel: 617-923-8860 Fax: 617-926-5503.

1605 ■ Hazaros Tabakoglu Scholarship Fund *(Undergraduate/Scholarship)*

Purpose: To provide financial assistance to those who are in need. **Focus:** General Studies. **Qualif.:** Applicants must be full-time undergraduates of Armenian descent who are or will be enrolled at colleges in the United States. **Criteria:** Preference will be given to those who meet the criteria.

Funds Avail.: $1,000-$5,000. **To Apply:** Applicants must check the available website for the required materials. **Deadline:** May 1. **Contact:** 2 Park Avenue, New York, NY 1016 Tel: 212-686-0010.

1606 ■ Aram Torossian Memorial Scholarships *(Undergraduate/Scholarship)*

Purpose: To provide financial assistance to those students who are in need. **Focus:** General studies. **Qualif.:** Applicant must be a full-time student of Armenian parentage attending the University of California, Berkley. **Criteria:** Preference will be given to those who meet the criteria.

Funds Avail.: $300-$3,000. **To Apply:** Applicants must check the available website for the required materials. **Contact:** Armenian Students' Association of America at the above address.

1607 ■ Union of Marash Armenian Scholarships *(Graduate, Undergraduate/Scholarship)*

Purpose: To provide financial assistance to those students who are in need. **Focus:** General Studies. **Qualif.:** Applicants must be matriculated, full-time undergraduate or graduate students accepted at an accredited institution of higher education. Must demonstrate academic excellence; be of good moral character; be in financial need; and show involvement in community; and must be a descendant of a Marashtsi (a part of Armenia/Asia Minor). **Criteria:** Preference will be given to those who meet the criteria.

Funds Avail.: $500-$1,000. **To Apply:** Applicants must check the available website for the required materials. **Deadline:** July 31. **Contact:** Mrs. Siroon P. Shahinian, PhD, Sec., The Student Fund, One Sussex Rd., Great Neck, NY 11020-1828.

1608 ■ Hurad Van Der Bedrosian Memorial Scholarships *(Graduate/Scholarship)*

Purpose: To provide financial assistance to those students who are in need. **Focus:** General Studies. **Qualif.:** Applicants must be graduate students in Armenian studies at universities with an established chair in the Armenian stud-

Awards are arranged alphabetically below their administering organizations

ies; applicants must be U.S citizens. **Criteria:** Preference will be given to those who meet the criteria.

Funds Avail.: $3,000. **Number Awarded:** 2. **To Apply:** Applicants must submit the following: completed application form; transcript; curriculum vitae; letter from Chairholder. **Deadline:** April 15. **Contact:** 600 West Broadway, Suite 130, Glendale, CA 91204 Tel: 818-242-4154.

1609 ■ Harry and Angel Zerigian Scholarships
(Undergraduate/Scholarship)

Purpose: To provide financial assistance to those students who are in need. **Focus:** Accounting. **Qualif.:** Applicant must be a full-time student with financial need and of Armenian ancestry; must be day-division sophomores majoring in Accounting at Bentley College who have satisfactorily completed all course work through the fall of sophomore year. **Criteria:** Preference is given to those students who attended Haverhill, Lawrence, Waltham or Watertown High Schools.

Funds Avail.: No specific amount. **To Apply:** Applicants must check the available website for the required materials. **Deadline:** March 15. **Contact:** headasa@aol.com.

1610 ■ Army Aviation Association of America (AAAA)
755 Main St., Ste. 4D
Monroe, CT 06468-2830
Ph: (203) 268-2450
Fax: (203) 268-5870
E-mail: aaaa@quad-a.org
URL: www.quad-a.org

1611 ■ AAAA Scholarship Program
(Undergraduate/Scholarship)

Purpose: To provide grants and loans to members who seek further education as well as the member's family who sought college-entry financial aid. **Focus:** General studies. **Qualif.:** Applicant must be a member of AAAA, the spouse of an AAAA member or deceased member, the unmarried son or daughter of an AAAA member or deceased member or the unmarried grandchild of an AAAA member or deceased member. Applicants must be attending an accredited college or university or selected for Fall entry as an undergraduate or graduate. **Criteria:** Scholarship recipients will be selected based on the selection committee's review of the application materials.

Funds Avail.: $1,000 to $10,000. **Number Awarded:** Varies. **To Apply:** Applicants must submit the completed application including the applicant's references made by two individuals; school recommendation; teacher's recommendation; academic reporting form; current transcript of grades; and a photograph. For graduate students, applicants must submit a 250-word essay about the applicant's life experiences, work history and aspirations. **Deadline:** May 1.

1612 ■ Army Nurse Corps Association (ANCA)
PO Box 39235
San Antonio, TX 78218-1235
Ph: (210) 650-3534
Fax: (210) 650-3494
E-mail: membership@e-anca.org
URL: e-anca.org

1613 ■ ANCA Scholarships *(Graduate, Undergraduate/Scholarship)*

Purpose: To provide financial assistance students. **Focus:** Nursing. **Qualif.:** Applicant students in a nursing program approved by an agency acceptable to the United States Secretary of Education; have Internal Revenue Service tax-exempt status; have scholarship fund under the school control; been a supportive of Army Nurse Corps recruitment. **Criteria:** Applicants who are students planning to enter the Army Nurse Corps, Army Reserve or National Guard; previously served in the United States Army, Army Reserve or National Guard; Army Nurse Corps officers enrolled in undergraduate or graduate nursing programs not funded by United States Army, Army Reserve or National Guard; members of Army Medical Department pursuing baccalaureate degree in nursing not funded by United States Army, Army Reserve or National Guard will be given preference.

Funds Avail.: $3,000. **To Apply:** Applicants must submit application template consist of school and location; agency accreditation; internal revenue status; scholarship program; support of army nurse corps recruitment activities; award criteria; application for specific student; and agreement to Education Committee. **Deadline:** March 31.

1614 ■ Army Scholarship Foundation
11700 Preston Rd., Ste. 660-301
Dallas, TX 75230
Fax: (703) 451-1257
E-mail: contactus@armyscholarshipfoundation.org
URL: www.armyscholarshipfoundation.org

1615 ■ First Lieutenant Scott McClean Love Memorial Scholarship - Children of Soldiers
(Undergraduate, Vocational/Occupational/ Scholarship)

Purpose: To financially assist deserving spouses of current or former United States Army personnel in their pursuit of higher education. **Focus:** General studies. **Qualif.:** Applicant must be spouse of a serving enlisted regular active duty, active duty Reserve or active duty National Guard U.S. Army member in good standing; or must be son or daughter of regular duty, active duty Reserve or active duty National Guard U.S. Army members in good standing; or must be son or daughter of former U.S. Army who received an honorable discharge or medical discharge or who were killed while serving in the U.S. Army; must be a high school senior, high school graduate or registered as an undergraduate student at an accredited college or vocational/ technical institution; must have a 2.0 GPA on a 4.0 system; must be a U.S. citizen not reaching 30th birthday by application deadline. **Criteria:** Award is given based on the application materials.

Funds Avail.: No specific amount. **To Apply:** Applicants must submit a completed scholarship application form along with a Free Application for Federal Student Aid (FAFSA); a signed copy of the appropriate income tax return for the previous year; a certificate of good service or the parent's/ spouse's DD 214; a high school transcript and transcripts from all post high school educational institutions (if applicable); an essay; and a photograph. **Deadline:** May 1. **Remarks:** In memory of First Lieutenant Scott McClean Love.

Awards are arranged alphabetically below their administering organizations

1616 ■ First Lieutenant Scott McClean Love Memorial Scholarship - Spouses of Soldiers
(Undergraduate, Vocational/Occupational/ Scholarship)

Purpose: To financially assist deserving spouses of current or former United States Army personnel in their pursuit of higher education. **Focus:** General studies. **Qualif.:** Applicant must be spouse of a serving enlisted regular active duty, active duty Reserve or active duty National Guard U.S. Army member in good standing; or must be son or daughter of regular duty, active duty Reserve or active duty National Guard U.S. Army members in good standing; or must be son or daughter of former U.S. Army who received an honorable discharge or medical discharge or who were killed while serving in the U.S. Army; must be a high school senior, high school graduate or registered as an undergraduate student at an accredited college or vocational/ technical institution; must have a 2.0 GPA on a 4.0 system; must be a U.S. citizen not reaching 30th birthday by application deadline. **Criteria:** Award is given based on the application materials.

Funds Avail.: No specific amount. **To Apply:** Applicants must submit a completed scholarship application form along with a Free Application for Federal Student Aid (FAFSA); a signed copy of the appropriate income tax return for the previous year; a certificate of good service or the parent's/ spouse's DD 214; a high school transcript and transcripts from all post high school educational institutions (if applicable); an essay; and a photograph. **Deadline:** May 1. **Remarks:** In memory of First Lieutenant Scott McClean Love.

1617 ■ Captain Jennifer Shafer Odom Memorial Scholarships - Children of Soldiers
(Undergraduate, Vocational/Occupational/ Scholarship)

Purpose: To financially assist deserving spouses of current or former United States Army personnel in their pursuit of higher education. **Focus:** General studies. **Qualif.:** Applicant must be spouse of a serving enlisted regular active duty, active duty Reserve or active duty National Guard U.S. Army member in good standing; or must be son or daughter of regular duty, active duty Reserve or active duty National Guard U.S. Army members in good standing; or must be son or daughter of former U.S. Army who received an honorable discharge or medical discharge or who were killed while serving in the U.S. Army; must be a high school senior, high school graduate or registered as an undergraduate student at an accredited college or vocational/ technical institution; must have a 2.0 GPA on a 4.0 system; must be a U.S. citizen not reaching 30th birthday by application deadline. **Criteria:** Award is given based on the application materials.

Funds Avail.: No specific amount. **To Apply:** Applicants must submit a completed scholarship application form along with a Free Application for Federal Student Aid (FAFSA); a signed copy of the appropriate income tax return for the previous year; a certificate of good service or the parent's/spouse's DD 214; a high school transcript and transcripts from all post high school educational institutions (if applicable); an essay; and a photograph. **Deadline:** May 1. **Remarks:** In memory of Captain Jennifer Shafer Odom.

1618 ■ Captain Jennifer Shafer Odom Memorial Scholarships - Spouses of Soldiers
(Undergraduate, Vocational/Occupational/ Scholarship)

Purpose: To financially assist deserving spouses of current or former United States Army personnel in their pursuit of higher education. **Focus:** General studies. **Qualif.:** Applicant must be spouse of a serving enlisted regular active duty, active duty Reserve or active duty National Guard U.S. Army member in good standing; or must be son or daughter of regular duty, active duty Reserve or active duty National Guard U.S. Army members in good standing; or must be son or daughter of former U.S. Army who received an honorable discharge or medical discharge or who were killed while serving in the U.S. Army; must be a high school senior, high school graduate or registered as an undergraduate student at an accredited college or vocational/ technical institution; must have a 2.0 GPA on a 4.0 system; must be a U.S. citizen not reaching 30th birthday by application deadline. **Criteria:** Award is given based on the application materials.

Funds Avail.: No specific amount. **To Apply:** Applicants must submit a completed scholarship application form along with a Free Application for Federal Student Aid (FAFSA); a signed copy of the appropriate income tax return for the previous year; a certificate of good service or the parent's/ spouse's DD 214; a high school transcript and transcripts from all post high school educational institutions (if applicable); an essay; and a photograph. **Deadline:** May 1. **Remarks:** In memory of Captain Jennifer Shafer Odom.

1619 ■ Aaron Arnoldsen Memorial Golf Tournament
1325 Airmotive Way, Ste. 220
Reno, NV 89502
Ph: (775) 560-7006
E-mail: info@aamemorial.com
URL: aamemorial.com

1620 ■ Aaron Edward Arnoldsen Memorial Scholarships *(Undergraduate/Scholarship)*

Purpose: To provide financial support to aid students' educational endeavors. **Focus:** General studies. **Qualif.:** Applicants must be junior or senior students; must be graduates of Nevada High School; have 3.0 GPA or below; must be full-time students at the University of Nevada, Reno; and must have a continuing employment through the forthcoming school-year. **Criteria:** Applicants will be evaluated by Scholarship Selection Committee.

Funds Avail.: 2,000. **To Apply:** Applicants must submit completed application form and the other requirements needed.

1621 ■ Art Dealers Association of Canada (ADAC)
511 King St. W, Ste. 302
Toronto, ON, Canada M5V 1K4
Ph: (416) 934-1583
Fax: (416) 934-1584
Free: 866-435-2322
E-mail: info@ad-ac.ca
URL: www.ad-ac.ca

1622 ■ ADAC Foundation Scholarships *(Undergraduate/Scholarship)*

Purpose: To award emerging artists through scholarships given each year. **Focus:** Art. **Qualif.:** Applicants must be

Awards are arranged alphabetically below their administering organizations

Canadian citizens; must be enrolled in a school of Arts degree program in the final year of their undergraduate studies; and must be devoted, committed and show talent and artistic ability. **Criteria:** Recipients will be chosen based on demonstrated academic significance and ongoing commitment to their practice.

Funds Avail.: Amount not specified. **To Apply:** Applicants must submit a statement and curriculum vitae; must submit five examples of their work. Samples should be sent in JPG format and CD should be formatted with compatlbility for both MAC and PC platforms.

1623 ■ Art Institute of Colorado
1200 Lincoln St.
Denver, CO 80203
Ph: (303) 837-0825
Fax: (303) 860-8520
Free: 800-275-2420
E-mail: nderevyanny@aii.edu
URL: www.artinstitutes.edu/denver

1624 ■ Art Institute of Colorado Scholarships
(Undergraduate/Scholarship)

Purpose: To provide higher education programs leading to professional opportunities in the fields of art and design, culinary arts, and technology that prepare graduates for job entry and career advancement. **Focus:** Art. **Qualif.:** Applicants must be high school seniors from the Sixth Congressional District who enter their work in The Artistic Discovery Art Program. **Criteria:** Recipients are selected based on financial need and academic standing.

Funds Avail.: $7,000. **Number Awarded:** 1. **To Apply:** Applicants must complete the application form.

1625 ■ Art Institute's Best Teen Chef in America Culinary Scholarships *(Undergraduate/Prize, Scholarship)*

Purpose: To provide higher education programs leading to professional opportunities in the fields of art and design, culinary arts, and technology which prepare graduates for job entry and career advancement. **Focus:** Art. **Qualif.:** Applicants must be high school seniors. **Criteria:** Recipients are selected based on financial need and academic standing.

Funds Avail.: First, Second and Third Place: full-tuition; Fourth, Fifth and Sixth: half-tuition; Seventh, Eighth and Ninth: quarter-tuition; and $3,000 for the remaining candidate. **Number Awarded:** 10 (Finalist). **To Apply:** Applicants must complete the application form. Applicants must submit a notebook that includes the menu and detailed recipes and directions from each course. Applicants must submit a paragraph stating their reason for wanting to be a culinary professional; and a current high school transcript. **Deadline:** February 5.

1626 ■ James Beard Foundation/Art Institute of Colorado Scholarships *(Undergraduate/Scholarship)*

Purpose: To provide higher education programs leading to professional opportunities in the fields of art and design, culinary arts, and technology which prepare graduates for job entry and career advancement. **Focus:** Art. **Qualif.:** Applicants must be freshmen high school students. Applicants must have a 3.0 GPA. **Criteria:** Recipients are selected based on academic record and financial need.

Funds Avail.: Maximum amount of $1,500. **Number Awarded:** 2. **To Apply:** Applicants must complete the application form and must submit a transcript of records. **Contact:** James Beard Foundation at 212-675-4984.

1627 ■ Colorado PROSTART/Art Institute of Colorado Art Scholarships for High School Seniors *(Undergraduate/Scholarship)*

Purpose: To provide higher education programs leading to professional opportunities in the fields of art and design, culinary arts, and technology which prepare graduates for job entry and career advancement. **Focus:** Art. **Qualif.:** Applicants must be senior high school students. **Criteria:** Recipients are selected based on high school GPA, recommendation, and commitment to pursuing a career in culinary arts.

Funds Avail.: Maximum amount of $25,197. **Number Awarded:** 1. **To Apply:** Applicants must complete the application form and must submit a transcript of records. **Contact:** 303-830-2972.

1628 ■ Arthritis Foundation (AF)
PO Box 7669
Atlanta, GA 30357-0669
Free: 800-283-7800
URL: www.arthritis.org

1629 ■ Arthritis Foundation Doctoral Dissertation Awards for Arthritis Health Professionals *(Professional development/Fellowship)*

Purpose: To advance the research training of arthritis health professionals in their investigative or clinical teaching careers related to the rheumatic diseases. **Focus:** Arthritis. **Qualif.:** Applicants must be health professionals whose research projects are related to arthritis management and/or comprehensive patient care in rheumatology practice, research or education. **Criteria:** Selection will be based on the committee's criteria.

Funds Avail.: $30,000. **To Apply:** Applicants may contact the Foundation for the application process.

1630 ■ Arthritis Foundation Postdoctoral Fellowships *(Doctorate/Fellowship)*

Purpose: To provide salary plus fringe benefits for MDs, DOs, PhDs, or equivalent for a two-year period. **Focus:** Arthritis. **Qualif.:** Applicants must be MDs, DOs, PhDs or equivalent. Ninety percent of the applicant's time must be devoted to arthritis-related research. **Criteria:** Selection will be based on the committee's criteria.

Funds Avail.: $50,000. **To Apply:** Applicants may contact the Foundation for the application process. This award may be combined with other funding sources as long as all awards are concentrated on one research project.

1631 ■ ASCE San Diego Section (ASCE)
PO Box 1028
El Cajon, CA 92022
Ph: (619) 588-0641
Fax: (619) 749-2188
E-mail: cathytriley@cox.net
URL: www.asce-sd.org

1632 ■ Charles McMahon Memorial Construction Management/Engineering Scholarship Awards *(Undergraduate/Scholarship)*

Purpose: To provide financial assistance for students pursuing Construction Management, Construction Engi-

Awards are arranged alphabetically below their administering organizations

neering and/or Construction Practices as a career goal. **Focus:** Construction, Engineering. **Qualif.:** Applicant must be a freshman, sophomore, junior or senior level ASCE student member in good standing at one of the local San Diego universities and must have a minimum 2.5 overall grade point average. **Criteria:** Applicants will be evaluated based on appraisal of applicant's needs, educational plans, academic performance, potential for development, leadership, ASCE activities and other student activities.

Funds Avail.: No specific amount. **To Apply:** Applicants must submit application package that must include a filled-out scholarship application form and proof of ASCE Student Membership. **Deadline:** March 4.

1633 ■ Charles Smith Memorial Scholarship
Awards *(Undergraduate/Scholarship)*

Purpose: To provide financial assistance for student members of ASCE intending to continue their education in college. **Focus:** Engineering, Civil. **Qualif.:** Applicant must be a freshman, sophomore, junior or senior ASCE student member in good standing at one of the local San Diego universities who has a minimum 2.5 overall grade point average. **Criteria:** Applicants will be evaluated based on appraisal of applicant's needs, educational plans, academic performance, potential for development, leadership, ASCE activities and other student activities.

Funds Avail.: No specific amount. **To Apply:** Applicants must submit application package which includes a filled-out scholarship application form and proof of ASCE Student Membership. **Deadline:** March 4.

1634 ■ Ascend
120 Wall St., 3rd Fl.
New York, NY 10005
Ph: (212) 248-4888
Fax: (212) 344-5636
E-mail: info@ascendleadership.org
URL: www.ascendleadership.org

1635 ■ ASCEND/ING Scholarships
(Undergraduate/Scholarship)

Purpose: To recognize and inspire outstanding students. **Focus:** Accounting; Finance. **Qualif.:** Applicants must be current and active Ascend student members who are undergraduates or graduate students; must either be juniors or seniors majoring in accountancy, finance, taxation, management information systems or business-related programs in the academic year; must have strong academic standing and 3.2 GPA or higher and community volunteer experience. **Criteria:** Recipients will be selected based on initial applications; the Ascend Committee will contact the finalists. Recommended finalists will be interviewed and must provide an official college transcript of records.

Funds Avail.: $1,000. **To Apply:** Applicants must submit resume including current GPA; minimum of 500-word personal essay describing career goals; and unofficial college or university transcript of records. **Deadline:** June 30. **Contact:** vanessa.manzano@naasa.org.

1636 ■ Ernst and Young/Ascend Leadership
Scholarship Program *(Undergraduate/ Scholarship)*

Purpose: To enhance the presence and influence of Asian Americans in the accounting and finance profession and to encourage the development of finance professionals and

students while serving as a collective voice for the Asian and Pacific Islander communities in the field of accounting and finance. **Focus:** Accounting; Finance. **Qualif.:** Applicants must be students who demonstrate a desire to pursue a career in accounting and professional services. **Criteria:** Recipients are selected based on academic achievement and financial need.

Funds Avail.: $5,000. **Number Awarded:** 4. **To Apply:** Applicants must complete the application form. **Deadline:** June 15. **Contact:** cat.lam@ascendleadership.org.

1637 ■ Ashburn Institute (AI)
198 Okatie Village Dr., Ste. 103
Bluffton, SC 29909
Ph: (843) 705-7643
Fax: (843) 705-7643
E-mail: info@ashburninstitute.org
URL: www.ashburninstitute.org

1638 ■ Mayme and Herb Frank Scholarship
Program *(Graduate, Undergraduate/Scholarship)*

Purpose: To support the study of international integration and federalism at the graduate level. **Focus:** International affairs and relations. **Qualif.:** Applicants must be graduate students of strong academic standing; must have a thesis or dissertation relating to international integration and/or federalism and coursework that places major weight on international integration and/or federalism; or must have an independent study project relating to international integration and federalism to be conducted as part of a graduate program. **Criteria:** Selection of candidates will be based on the quality of the project and academic standing. Consideration is made by the Frank Education Fund Committee of the Ashburn Institute.

Funds Avail.: $500-$2,000 depending on relevance of the goals of the fund. **To Apply:** Applicants must complete the FEF Application form and must have the description of any course planned to be completed by the applicant during the period of the proposed grant; must submit the copy of the graduate transcripts if currently enrolled in a graduate program or a copy of the applicant's undergraduate transcripts if enrolled in a graduate program but have not yet started it. Application form and other supporting materials must be submitted to: Association to Unite the Democracies c/o The Ashburn Institute, The Frank Educational Fund, PO Box 77164, Washington, DC, 20013-7164, Phone: 202-220-1388, Fax: 202-220-1389. **Deadline:** April 1 for Fall term awards and October 1 for Spring term awards.

1639 ■ Asian American Journalists Association (AAJA)
5 Third St., Ste. 1108
San Francisco, CA 94103
Ph: (415) 346-2051
Fax: (415) 346-6343
E-mail: national@aaja.org
URL: www.aaja.org

1640 ■ AAJA/CNN Scholar Program *(Graduate, Undergraduate/Scholarship)*

Purpose: To provide financial assistance to students majoring in broadcast or online journalism. **Focus:** Journalism; Broadcasting. **Qualif.:** Applicant must be a graduating high school senior, undergraduate or graduate student enrolled

Awards are arranged alphabetically below their administering organizations

full time with at least 12 credit units for each semester and must be currently taking or planning to take journalism courses. **Criteria:** Recipients will be selected on the basis of academic achievement; demonstrated journalistic ability; financial need; commitment to the field of journalism.

Funds Avail.: $25,000. **Number Awarded:** 1. **To Apply:** Applicants must submit the completed application form; a resume; an official transcript; two letters of recommendation; a short essay, not exceeding 500 words, on the topic: "Describe any involvement or interest that you have in the Asian American community. If you were awarded an AAJA scholarship, propose how you would contribute to the field of journalism and/or media issues involving the Asian American and Pacific Islander community." **Deadline:** March. **Contact:** Nao Vang; AAJA Student Programs Coordinator; 415-346-2051; programs@aaja.org.

1641 ■ AAJA/COX Foundation Scholarships
(Graduate, Undergraduate/Scholarship)

Purpose: To assist students who are interested in pursuing a career in print, broadcast, or photojournalism. **Focus:** Journalism; Broadcasting; Photography, Journalistic. **Qualif.:** Applicant must be a graduating high school senior, undergraduate or graduate student enrolled full time with at least 12 credit units for each semester; and must be currently taking or planning to take journalism courses. **Criteria:** Recipients will be selected on the basis of academic achievement; demonstrated journalistic ability; financial need; commitment to the field of journalism.

Funds Avail.: $1,250. **Number Awarded:** 2. **To Apply:** Applicants must submit the completed application form; a resume; an official transcript; two letters of recommendation; a short essay, not exceeding 500 words, on the topic: "Describe any involvement or interest that you have in the Asian American community. If you were awarded an AAJA scholarship, propose how you would contribute to the field of journalism and/or media issues involving the Asian American and Pacific Islander community." **Contact:** Nao Vang; AAJA Student Programs Coordinator; 415-346-2051; programs@aaja.org.

1642 ■ AAJA/S.I. Newhouse Foundation Scholarships *(Graduate, Undergraduate/Scholarship)*

Purpose: To provide educational funds to students pursuing a career in print journalism. **Focus:** Journalism. **Qualif.:** Applicant must be a graduating high school senior, undergraduate or graduate student enrolled full time with at least 12 credit units for each semester; and must be currently taking or planning to take journalism courses. **Criteria:** Recipients will be selected on the basis of academic achievement; demonstrated journalistic ability; financial need; commitment to the field of journalism. This scholarship will also focus on underserved AAPI communities, e.g. Southeast Asians, South Asians and Pacific Islanders.

Funds Avail.: $5,000. **To Apply:** Applicants must submit the completed application form; a resume; an official transcript; two letters of recommendation; a short essay, not exceeding 500 words, on the topic: "Describe any involvement or interest that you have in the Asian American community. If you were awarded an AAJA scholarship, propose how you would contribute to the field of journalism and/or media issues involving the Asian American and Pacific Islander community." **Deadline:** March. **Contact:** Nao Vang; AAJA Student Programs Coordinator; 415-346-2051; programs@aaja.org.

1643 ■ Asian American Lawyers Association of Massachusetts (AALAM)
16 Beacon St.
Boston, MA 02108-3774
E-mail: aalam.info@gmail.com
URL: www.aalam.org

1644 ■ Asian American Lawyers Associations of Massachusetts Scholarships *(Undergraduate/Scholarship)*

Purpose: To promote and enhance the Asian American legal profession by furthering and encouraging professional interaction and the exchange of ideas among its members and with other individuals, groups, and organizations; to improve and facilitate the administration of law and justice through various means. **Focus:** Law. **Qualif.:** Applicants must be enrolled at a law school in the Commonwealth of Massachusetts and must be in good standing. **Criteria:** Recipients are selected based on demonstrated leadership potential, maturity and responsibility, and commitment in making a contribution to the Asian-American community and other indication of excellence whether personal, professional or academic.

Funds Avail.: $2,500. **Number Awarded:** 1. **To Apply:** Applicants must complete the application form; must submit an official transcript of records; resume; one letter of recommendation written by a person who is not related to the candidate; and a signed certification contained at the end of the scholarship application form. **Deadline:** April 15. **Contact:** 111 Huntington Ave., Boston MA 02199.

1645 ■ Asian American Psychological Association (AAPA)
1600 Holloway Ave.
San Francisco, CA 94132
Ph: (415) 338-1690
Fax: (415) 338-0594
E-mail: aalvarez@sfsu.edu
URL: www.aapaonline.org

1646 ■ APA Minority Fellowships Program *(Postdoctorate/Fellowship)*

Purpose: To provide financial support and professional guidance to individuals pursuing predoctoral and postdoctoral training. **Focus:** General Studies. **Qualif.:** Applicants must be individuals who are pursuing predoctoral and postdoctoral training. **Criteria:** Preference will be given to those students who meet the criteria.

Funds Avail.: No specific amount. **To Apply:** Applicants must check the available website for the required materials. **Contact:** Asian American Psychological Association at the above address.

1647 ■ Asian Pacific American Librarians Association (APALA)
PO Box 1669
Goleta, CA 93116
Ph: (805) 893-8067
E-mail: colmenar@library.ucsb.edu
URL: www.apalaweb.org/about/aboutapala.htm

1648 ■ APALA Scholarships *(Doctorate, Graduate/Scholarship)*

Purpose: To provide financial assistance to a student of Asian or Pacific background. **Focus:** Library and archival

Awards are arranged alphabetically below their administering organizations

sciences; Information science and technology. **Qualif.:** Applicant must be of Asian/Pacific Islander heritage; must be a U.S. citizen or permanent resident of the United States or Canada; must be admitted full-time or part-time into a master's degree or doctoral program in library or information science at a library school accredited by ALA. **Criteria:** Recipients are selected based on the Scholarship Committee's review of the application materials.

Funds Avail.: $1,000. **Number Awarded:** 1. **To Apply:** Applicant must submit a completed application form available at the website together with a resume; copy of acceptance letter to an ALA accredited library school or library graduate school transcript; two letters of recommendation; and one page essay on one of the following topics: Your vision of a librarian's role in the twenty-first century and what contributions can I make as an APA Librarian? If applicable, number of hours completed towards degree. **Deadline:** April 30. **Contact:** Heawon Paick, Chm., APALA Scholarship Committee, Junipero Serra Branch, Los Angeles Public Library. Phone: 323-846-5382 Fax: 323-846-5389, heawonpaick@gmail.com.

1649 ■ Asian/Pacific Bar Association of Sacramento (ABAS)

PO Box 2215
Sacramento, CA 95812-2215
Ph: (916) 492-3170
E-mail: abassacramento@yahoo.com
URL: www.abassacramento.com

1650 ■ Asian/Pacific Bar Association of Sacramento Law Foundation Scholarships
(Graduate, Postgraduate/Scholarship)

Purpose: To recognize law students and recent law school graduates who possess extraordinary skills, desire and potential to serve and lead the greater Sacramento Asian-Pacific Islander community. **Focus:** Law. **Qualif.:** Applicants must be either currently enrolled and in good standing at a Sacramento area (including U.C. Davis) law school or currently residing in the Sacramento area; have graduated from law school in Spring/Summer 2011 or winter 2011-12. **Criteria:** Recipients are selected based on potential for community service; leadership in the Asian Pacific Islander community; academic achievement; and financial need.

Funds Avail.: $500-$4,000. **To Apply:** Applicants must submit evidence of scholarship eligibility (a copy of current law school registration or law school diploma will suffice); a personal statement; a current resume; current law school transcripts; financial information; and two references. **Deadline:** February 24. **Contact:** Application form and other supporting documents should be sent to: Darrel Woo, Scholarship Chair; E-mail: abaslawfdnapp@jplawoffice.com.

1651 ■ Asian Pacific Bar Association of Silicon Valley (APBASV)

c/o Bijal V. Vakil
White and Case LLP
3000 El Camino Real 5 Palo Alto Sq., 9th Fl.
Palo Alto, CA 94306
Ph: (650) 213-0303
E-mail: apabasv@gmail.com
URL: www.apabasv.org

1652 ■ APBASV Scholarships *(All/Scholarship)*

Purpose: To support law students in the Bay Area. **Focus:** Law. **Qualif.:** Applicant must be a law student in the Bay Area who has overcome personal hardship or challenges, shown excellence and achievement in law school or demonstrated leadership and service to the Asian Pacific American community. **Criteria:** Preference will be given to law students who will be interning at a non-profit organization that serves the Asian Pacific American community.

Funds Avail.: $3,000. **Number Awarded:** 4. **To Apply:** Applicants must submit a resume (with GPA) and an essay (maximum of 2 pages, double-spaced). Selected finalists are required to undergo an interview in early April. **Deadline:** March 20. **Contact:** apbasv@gmail.com.

1653 ■ Filipino Bar Association of Northern California Scholarships (FBANC) *(All/Scholarship)*

Purpose: To support law students in their educational pursuit. **Focus:** Law. **Qualif.:** Applicant must be a current law student in good academic standing and admitted to a law school. **Criteria:** Selection is based on the applicant's ability to address the essay questions as well as demonstrated interest in serving the Filipino community.

Funds Avail.: $2,500. **Number Awarded:** 2. **To Apply:** Applicants must submit a current law school transcript or admittance letter from a law school; a resume; and the three page essay (double-spaced). Send application materials to: Katie M. Esclamado, Van De Poel, Levy & Allen 1600 S Main Plz., Ste. 325, Walnut Creek, CA 94596, Telephone: 925-934-6102, or E-mail: kmesclamado@gmail.com. **Deadline:** March 24. **Contact:** Katie M. Esclamado at 925-934-6102 or kmesclamado@gmail.com.

1654 ■ Asian and Pacific Islander American Scholarship Fund (APIASF)

1900 L St. NW, Ste. 210
Washington, DC 20036
Ph: (202) 986-6892
Fax: (202) 530-6843
Free: 877-808-7032
E-mail: info@apiasf.org
URL: www.apiasf.org

1655 ■ APIASF Scholarships *(Undergraduate/Scholarship)*

Purpose: To support and encourage all Asian and Pacific Islander American students to pursue higher education by developing future leaders who will contribute back to their communities. **Focus:** General studies. **Qualif.:** Applicant must be of Asian and/or Pacific Islander ethnicity as defined by 2000 census; a U.S. citizen, U.S. National, legal permanent resident or a citizen of the Federated States of Micronesia, Republic of the Marshall Islands or the Republic of Palau; a first-time, incoming college student; enrolled full-time in a two or four-year program at a U.S. accredited college or university in the U.S., Guam, American Samoa, or the Commonwealth of the Northern Mariana Islands for the coming school year. (In the Freely Associated States, this includes the Community Colleges of the Federated States of Micronesia, the Republic of Marshall Islands and the Republic of Palau.) Applicants must have cumulative, unweighted grade point average (GPA) of 2.7 or higher on a 4.0 scale. **Criteria:** Recipient is selected based on academic record and future plans; community service and

Awards are arranged alphabetically below their administering organizations

leadership; and financial need.

Funds Avail.: $2,500-$5,000. **Number Awarded:** 200. **To Apply:** Applicants must complete the application form online, available at the website of APIASF, www.apiasf.org/apply. **Deadline:** January 13.

1656 ■ ASIS International
1625 Prince St.
Alexandria, VA 22314-2818
Ph: (703) 519-6200
Fax: (703) 519-6299
E-mail: asis@asisonline.org
URL: www.asisonline.org

1657 ■ ASIS Foundation Chapter Matching Scholarships *(Undergraduate/Scholarship)*

Purpose: To provide educational assistance to chapter members, student members or student nonmembers pursuing a security career. **Focus:** General studies. **Qualif.:** Applicants must be part- or full-time students who have completed one year of study at an accredited college, university or community college towards a career in security profession; must be undergraduate students (their chapter will set the grade point average required, for them to be qualified for the scholarship) or graduate students who earned at least a 3.0 GPA on a 4.0 scale. **Criteria:** Applicants are evaluated based on their achievements and abilities.

Funds Avail.: $1,000. **To Apply:** Applicants must submit a signed application form, an official transcript, and letter of recommendation from a faculty member to their sponsoring chapter. **Deadline:** November 30. **Contact:** Questions can be addressed to Barbara Buzell; Phone: 703-518-1441; E-mail: bbuzzell@asisonline.org.

1658 ■ ASME International
3 Park Ave.
New York, NY 10016-5990
Ph: (973) 882-1170
Fax: (973) 882-1717
Free: 800-843-2763
E-mail: infocentral@asme.org
URL: www.asme.org

1659 ■ Auxiliary Undergraduate Scholarships *(Graduate, High School, Undergraduate/ Scholarship)*

Purpose: To provide scholarships and new developments in Mechanical Engineering; to honor students who demonstrate outstanding personal and academic characteristics. **Focus:** Mechanical engineering. **Qualif.:** Applicants must be full-time high school, undergraduate, or graduate students pursuing Mechanical Engineering courses or any related field of study in engineering; must be U.S citizens; and be enrolled at an accredited ABET Mechanical Engineering program in United States. **Criteria:** Recipients will be selected based on submitted application, needs, character, and ASME participation.

Funds Avail.: $2,000 cash scholarship used for one academic year. **Number Awarded:** 5. **To Apply:** Applicants must submit letter of recommendation by the Head of The Mechanical Engineering Faculty Advisor; letter from a non-academic reference, instructors or preferably in an Engi-

neering School; an official transcript of records; and should have completed application form. Guidelines and application form is available from the ASME scholarship office or can be downloaded from the ASME website. **Deadline:** March 15. **Contact:** Application form and supporting documents should be sent to Sara Sahay, 170 East Opel Drive, Glastonbury, CT 06033; e-mail at uma.sahay@gmail.com.

1660 ■ Lucy and Charles W.E. Clarke Scholarships *(Undergraduate/Scholarship)*

Purpose: To promote art, science and practice of mechanical and multidisciplinary engineering and allied sciences through educational assistance. **Focus:** Mechanical engineering. **Qualif.:** Scholarship is open to schools accredited by the Accreditation Board for Engineering and Technology or substantially equivalent mechanical engineering technology departments who directly choose incoming freshmen beginning engineering studies in the fall to receive the scholarship. **Criteria:** Recipients are chosen by the departments on the basis of need, academic achievement, community involvement, work experience and recommendations.

Funds Avail.: $2,000 each. **To Apply:** Applications for deserving schools are made by the ASME Student Section as endorsed by the mechanical engineering technology department; Necessary forms are available in the website also indicating other instructions. **Deadline:** October 20. **Contact:** Application form and supporting documents must be mailed to RuthAnn Bigley, 3416 Washington Commons Ave., Kennesaw, GA 30144; Phone: 212-591-7650; Fax: 770-917-8508; E-mail: bigleyr@asme.org.

1661 ■ Elizabeth M. and Winchell M. Parson Scholarships *(Doctorate/Scholarship)*

Purpose: To establish education funds for the purpose of assisting worthy students in the study of mechanical engineering or for graduate work. To promote the advancement of the art and science of mechanical engineering and the dissemination to engineers and the general public of advance and new development in mechanical engineering. **Focus:** Mechanical engineering. **Qualif.:** Applicants must be full-time students seeking doctoral degree in mechanical engineering; must be U.S. citizens; and enrolled in U.S. school at an ABET accredited Mechanical Engineering Department. **Criteria:** Awards are given based on academic merit. Priority is given to students with financial need.

Funds Avail.: No specific amount. **To Apply:** Applicants must submit a letter of recommendation from the Head of the Mechanical Engineering Department or the Faculty Advisor; letter from a non-academic reference; list of scholastic recognition, honors or prizes won, membership in honorary or professional societies; list of extra-curricular college or civic activities in which they have participated and offices held; must submit an official transcript of records; grade and membership number in the American Society of Mechanical Engineers; should have completed application form; Guidelines and application form are available from the ASME scholarship office or can be downloaded from the ASME website. **Deadline:** April 1. **Contact:** Complete application and other information must be returned to Cynthia Pool, 5025 Iroquois Ave., Lakewood, CA 90713; Phone: 562-920-3653; E-mail: cindipool@gmail.com.

1662 ■ Rice-Cullimore Scholarships *(Graduate/ Scholarship)*

Purpose: To honor foreign students demonstrating outstanding personal and academic characteristics and to

Awards are arranged alphabetically below their administering organizations

promote art, science, and practice of mechanical and multidisciplinary engineering and allied sciences. **Focus:** Mechanical Engineering. **Qualif.:** Candidate must be a foreign student intending to do graduate work for a Master's or Doctoral Degree in mechanical engineering in the United States. **Criteria:** Awards are given based on academic record, personal promise, character and financial need; Applicants must demonstrate their commitment to a career in mechanical engineering.

Funds Avail.: $2,000. **To Apply:** Applicant must submit a letter of recommendation from the Head of the Mechanical Engineering Department or the Faculty Advisor; Letter from a non-academic reference; and profile indicating scholastic recognition, honors or prizes won, membership in honorary or professional societies; extra-curricular college or civic activities in which they have participated, and offices held; official transcript; and completed application form. Guidelines and application form can be obtained from the ASME Scholarship Office or can be downloaded from the ASME website. **Contact:** Applicants must submit a copy of the application to Ella Baldwin-Viereck at ellabv@earthlink.net.

1663 ■ Marjorie Roy Rothermel Scholarships
(Graduate/Scholarship)

Purpose: To honor students who demonstrate outstanding personal and academic characteristics and to promote art, science, and practice of mechanical and multidisciplinary engineering and allied sciences. **Focus:** Mechanical engineering. **Qualif.:** Applicants must be U.S. citizens and must be currently enrolled in a Master's degree program in a school at an ABET accredited Mechanical Engineering Department in United States. **Criteria:** Awards are given based on academic merit. Selection of applicants is based on academic performance character, need and ASME participation reviewed and scored by the Scholarship Committee.

Funds Avail.: $2,000. **To Apply:** Applicants must submit letter of recommendation from the Head of The Mechanical Engineering Department or the Faculty Advisor; must file a letter from a non-academic reference; list of scholastic recognition, honors or prizes won; membership in honorary or professional societies; list of extra-curricular college or civic activities in which they have participated, and offices held; an official transcript of records; should have completed application form; Guidelines and application form are available from the ASME scholarship office or can be downloaded from the ASME website. **Deadline:** March 15. **Contact:** Mrs. Otto Prochaska, 332 Valencia St., Gulf Breeze, FL 32561-4032; Phone: 850-932-3698; Email: eprocha340@aol.com.

1664 ■ ASPRS - The Imaging and Geospatial Information Society
5410 Grosvenor Ln., Ste. 210
Bethesda, MD 20814-2160
Ph: (301) 493-0290
Fax: (301) 493-0208
E-mail: asprs@asprs.org
URL: www.asprs.org

1665 ■ Robert E. Altenhofen Memorial Scholarships *(Graduate, Undergraduate/Scholarship)*

Purpose: To promote education in the theoretical aspects of photogrammetry. **Focus:** Photogrammetry. **Qualif.:** Applicants must be undergraduate or graduate student members of ASPRS. **Criteria:** Recipients are selected based on the highest overall ranking.

Funds Avail.: $2,000 and a certificate. **To Apply:** Applicants must submit an application form; a statement (2 pages) regarding plans for continuing studies in theoretical photogrammetry; evidence of capabilities of the applicant in these fields; and academic transcripts. **Deadline:** December 1. **Remarks:** Funded by the estate of Mrs. Helen Altenhofen as a memorial to her husband and the past president of ASPRS, Robert E. Altenhofen. **Contact:** ASPRS Scholarship Administrator at scholarships@asprs.org.

1666 ■ Robert N. Colwell Memorial Fellowships
(Doctorate, Graduate/Fellowship)

Purpose: To promote remote sensing or other related geospatial information technologies to college/university graduate students and to post-doctoral researchers. **Focus:** Remote sensing. **Qualif.:** Applicant must be a graduate student (Masters or PhD level); enrolled or planning to enroll in a college/university in the United States or Canada; or recently graduated post-doctoral researcher pursuing a study in remote sensing or related geospatial information technologies. **Criteria:** Recipients are selected based on the application materials submitted.

Funds Avail.: $5,000 and a certificate. **To Apply:** Applicants must submit completed application form; a listing of courses taken; transcript of all college/university level courses completed; a listing of internships, special projects or work experience; three letters of recommendation; and a statement (maximum of two pages) detailing the applicant's educational or research goals. **Deadline:** December 1. **Remarks:** Established in memory of Robert N. Colwell. **Contact:** ASPRS Scholarship Administrator at scholarships@asprs.org.

1667 ■ ERDAS Internships *(Graduate/Internship)*

Purpose: To fund a research or continue an existing ERDAS project. **Focus:** Photogrammetry; Remote sensing. **Qualif.:** Applicant must be a graduate student of photogrammetry and remote sensing; and a student member of ASPRS. **Criteria:** Applicants are selected based on submitted applications.

Funds Avail.: $2,500. **To Apply:** Applicants must submit an application form; letters of recommendation; official transcripts from each college and university attended; a proposal (maximum of 1000 words) stating the significance of the research, the proposed methodology, the expected results and a schedule. **Deadline:** December 1. **Remarks:** Funded by ERDAS. **Contact:** ASPRS Scholarship Administrator at scholarships@asprs.org.

1668 ■ William A. Fischer Memorial Scholarships *(Graduate/Scholarship)*

Purpose: To facilitate studies and career goals directed towards new and innovative uses of remote sensing data/techniques. **Focus:** Remote sensing. **Qualif.:** Applicants must be current or prospective graduate student members of ASPRS. **Criteria:** Applicants are selected based on the highest overall ranking.

Funds Avail.: $2,000 and a certificate. **To Apply:** Applicant must submit an application form; a statement (2 pages) detailing educational and career plans for continuing studies in remote sensing applications; transcript of grades. **Deadline:** December 1. **Contact:** ASPRS Scholarship Administrator at scholarships@asprs.org.

1669 ■ Ta Liang Memorial Awards *(Graduate/Grant)*

Purpose: To support research-related travel in remote sensing. **Focus:** Remote sensing. **Qualif.:** Applicant must

---

Awards are arranged alphabetically below their administering organizations

be a graduate student member of ASPRS. **Criteria:** Applicants are selected based on scholastic record, research travel plan, letters of recommendation and community service activities.

Funds Avail.: $1,500. **To Apply:** Applicants must submit an application form; a letter of recommendation; a statement (2 pages) detailing the plan for research-related travel; a transcript of all college-level courses completed and grades received; class rank; a description of extracurricular activities (particularly relating to community service). **Deadline:** December 1. **Contact:** ASPRS Scholarship Administrator at scholarships@asprs.org.

1670 ■ Francis H. Moffitt Memorial Scholarships *(Graduate, Undergraduate/Scholarship)*

Purpose: To promote study in surveying and photogrammetry leading to a career in the geospatial mapping profession. **Focus:** Remote sensing; Photogrammetry. **Qualif.:** Program is open to students currently enrolled or planning to enroll in a college/university in the United States or Canada pursuing a program of study in surveying or photogrammetry. **Criteria:** Applicants are selected based on the submitted applications.

Funds Avail.: $4,000. **To Apply:** Applicants must submit an application form; a listing of courses taken and/or those to be taken in surveying and photogrammetry and other related geospatial information technologies; a transcript of all college/university level courses completed; a listing of internships, special projects or work experience; two letters of recommendation or reference form; a statement (maximum of two pages) detailing the applicant's educational and research goals. **Deadline:** December 1. **Remarks:** Established in memory of Frank Moffitt for his lifetime contributions to the photogrammetric surveying profession. **Contact:** ASPRS Scholarship Administrator at scholarships@asprs.org.

1671 ■ The Kenneth J. Osborn Memorial Scholarships *(Undergraduate/Scholarship)*

Purpose: To encourage students to enter the profession of surveying, mapping and photogrammetry or geospatial information and technology. **Focus:** Photogrammetry. **Qualif.:** Applicant must be an undergraduate student enrolled or planning to enroll in a college/university in the United States. **Criteria:** Scholarship will be given to an applicant who has the highest overall ranking.

Funds Avail.: $2,000. **To Apply:** Applicants must submit an application form; a listing of courses taken in surveying; mapping; photogrammetry and geospatial information and technology and the academic grades received; a transcript of all college or university level courses completed; two letters of recommendation from faculty members or professionals; evidence materials of the applicant's capabilities in this field; a statement of work experience; and a personal statement (maximum of 2 pages). **Deadline:** December 1. **Remarks:** Established as a tribute to Kenneth J. Osborn. **Contact:** ASPRS Scholarship Administrator at scholarships@asprs.org.

1672 ■ Paul R. Wolf Memorial Scholarships *(Graduate/Scholarship)*

Purpose: To encourage college students to enter the profession of teaching Surveying, Mapping or Photogrammetry. **Focus:** Photogrammetry, Education. **Qualif.:** Applicant must be a graduate student member of ASPRS; enrolled or planning to enroll in a college/university in the United States; pursuing a program of study in preparation

for entering the teaching profession in the general area of Surveying, Mapping or Photogrammetry. **Criteria:** The committee evaluates each application and will select the applicant who best meets the criteria.

Funds Avail.: $3,000. **To Apply:** Applicants must submit an application form; a listing of courses taken in Surveying, Mapping and Photogrammetry and the academic grades received; a transcript of all college or university level courses; two letters of recommendation from faculty members having knowledge of the applicant's capabilities as an educator in this field; evidence materials of the applicant's capabilities in this field; and a statement of teaching experience. **Deadline:** December 1. **Remarks:** Established in memory of Paul R. Wolf. **Contact:** ASPRS Scholarship Administrator at scholarships@asprs.org.

1673 ■ Z/I Imaging Scholarships *(Graduate/Scholarship)*

Purpose: To support graduate-level studies addressing new and innovative uses of signal processing, image processing techniques and the application of photogrammetry to real-world techniques. **Focus:** Photogrammetry. **Qualif.:** Applicant must be a member of ASPRS; currently pursuing graduate-level studies; or planning to enroll for graduate studies in a college/university in the United States or elsewhere. **Criteria:** Scholarship will be given to an applicant who has the highest overall ranking.

Funds Avail.: $2,000. **To Apply:** Applicants must submit an application form; a statement (2 pages) detailing educational and career plans for continuing studies in photogrammetric applications; two reference forms/letters from faculty members who have knowledge of the applicant's capabilities; and evidence materials of the applicant's capabilities in this field. **Deadline:** December 1. **Contact:** ASPRS Scholarship Administrator at scholarships@asprs.org.

1674 ■ Associated General Contractors of America (AGC)

2300 Wilson Blvd., Ste. 400
Arlington, VA 22201
Ph: (703) 548-3118
Fax: (703) 548-3119
Free: 800-242-1767
E-mail: info@agc.org
URL: www.agc.org

1675 ■ AGC Foundation Outstanding Educator Awards *(Professional development/Award)*

Purpose: To provide recognition and encouragement for university teaching faculty members in construction education. **Focus:** Construction. **Qualif.:** Nominees must be full-time teaching faculty members of a university construction program or a construction-related engineering program or with an institution-approved construction option. Nominees must have at least four years full-time teaching experience. Program must be accredited by either the American Council for Construction Education (ACCE) or the Accreditation Board for Engineering and Technology (ABET). **Criteria:** Award winner is chosen based on the teaching responsibilities and activities with AGC and/or other construction industry organizations.

Funds Avail.: $5,000. **To Apply:** Nominees must submit two copies of nomination form and attachments; the joint letter of nomination; the nomination checklist; a maximum

Awards are arranged alphabetically below their administering organizations

of three letters of reference; and a "Notification of Receipt" Postcard. **Deadline:** November 15. **Contact:** Submit nominations to Melinda Patrician at the above address; Phone: 703-837-5342 Fax: 703-837-5451; E-mail: patricianm@agc.org.

1676 ■ Associated General Contractors of America, New York State Chapter

10 Airline Dr., Ste. 203
Albany, NY 12205
Ph: (518) 456-1134
Fax: (518) 456-1198
E-mail: agcadmin@agcnys.org
URL: www.agcnys.org

1677 ■ AGC New York State Chapter Scholarship Program *(Undergraduate/Scholarship)*

Purpose: To provide financial assistance to college students working toward a degree in Civil Engineering or Construction Technology at a college or university. **Focus:** Civil engineering. **Qualif.:** Applicant must be entering the 2nd, 3rd or 4th year of a two or four-year college; seriously intent upon a career in the highway construction industry. Applicant must pursue a Bachelor or Associate degree in construction or civil engineering and have at least a 2.50 GPA. **Criteria:** Applicants will be evaluated by the Selection Committee of the New York State Chapter, Inc., Associated General Contractors.

Funds Avail.: $2,500. **To Apply:** Applicant must submit a signed, completed five-page application; three evaluation forms: one completed by a college faculty advisor, and two completed by adults not related to the applicant and preferably in the industry; and, official transcript of all college grades. **Deadline:** May 15. **Contact:** bmanning@agcnys.org.

1678 ■ Associated Locksmiths of America (ALOA)

3500 Easy St.
Dallas, TX 75247
Ph: (214) 819-9733
Fax: (214) 819-9736
Free: 800-532-2562
E-mail: president@aloa.org
URL: www.aloa.org

1679 ■ ALOA Scholarship Foundation *(Undergraduate/Scholarship)*

Purpose: To provide financial assistance for educational services, programs and materials concerning locksmithing and security devices and procedures. **Focus:** Technical training. **Qualif.:** Applicants must be individuals desirous of entering the locksmithing field or individuals already in the field of locksmithing who wish to improve their professional skills through education. **Criteria:** Applicants will be evaluated based on their financial needs, character, aptitude for the skills necessary in locksmithing, desire for a career in locksmithing, availability to attend the event for which award is given, demonstrated commitment to the locksmith industry, letters of recommendation from locksmith industry reference, and previous scholarship awards.

Funds Avail.: No amount mentioned. **To Apply:** Applicants must complete the application form provided in the website

of the Foundation and submit it along with the letters of recommendation from locksmith industry references.

1680 ■ Associated Medical Services (AMS)

162 Cumberland St., Ste. 228
Toronto, ON, Canada M5R 3N5
Ph: (416) 924-3368
Fax: (416) 323-3338
E-mail: info@ams-inc.on.ca
URL: php.ams-inc.on.ca

1681 ■ Hannah Junior General Scholarships *(Graduate/Scholarship)*

Purpose: To support excellence in medical history at the graduate level. **Focus:** Medical history. **Qualif.:** Applicant must be a Canadian citizen and permanent resident enrolled at a Canadian university and registered in a full-time program leading to a PhD, or the doctoral portion of a combined MA/PhD or MD/PhD. **Criteria:** Selection is based on merit.

Funds Avail.: $17,700-$35,000 plus a research and travel allowance of $3,000. **Number Awarded:** 2. **To Apply:** Applicants must submit a completed and signed application form together with a letter of nomination submitted by the Chair of the Department supported by letters of recommendation prepared by both the applicant's supervisor and a faculty member; a brief description of the supervisor who will chair the applicant's thesis/dissertation; a full-page statement on career goals and research interests; recent transcript; a statement of other funding sources; curriculum vitae (maximum of 5 pages); and 10 recent writing samples. Ten copies of the complete application including all supporting documents should be forwarded to AMS. In addition, applicants must include an electronic copy of all sections of the application as a PDF file, on diskette or CD-ROM (labeled with name and date). **Deadline:** November 1. **Contact:** amsgrants@ams-inc.on.ca.

1682 ■ Hannah Senior General Scholarships *(Graduate/Scholarship)*

Purpose: To support excellence in medical history at the graduate level. **Focus:** Medical history. **Qualif.:** Applicant must be a Canadian citizen and permanent resident enrolled at a Canadian university and registered in a full-time program leading to a PhD, or the doctoral portion of a combined MA/PhD or MD/PhD. Applicant must have already completed the first year of doctoral studies. **Criteria:** Selection is based on applicant's track record and the scholarly merit of the research program.

Funds Avail.: $17,700-$35,000 plus a research and travel allowance of $3,000. **Number Awarded:** 4. **To Apply:** Applicants must submit a completed, signed application form together with three letters of reference; a brief description of the supervisor who will chair the applicant's thesis/dissertation; a brief description (no more than 75 words) of the proposed research objectives and relevance to the history of medicine; a project proposal (maximum of 6 pages); recent transcripts; statement of other fundings; Ethics certificate; and curriculum vitae. Ten copies of the complete application including all supporting documents should be forwarded to AMS. In addition, applicants must include an electronic copy of all sections of the application as a PDF file, on diskette or CD-ROM (labeled with name and date). **Deadline:** November 1. **Contact:** amsgrants@ams-inc.on.ca.

Awards are arranged alphabetically below their administering organizations

1683 ■ Associated Press Television and Radio Association (APTRA)

1850 N Central Ave., Ste. 640
Phoenix, AZ 85004
URL: www.aptra.com

1684 ■ APTRA Scholarships *(Undergraduate/ Scholarship)*

Purpose: To help students pursue a broadcast journalism course. **Focus:** Broadcasting. **Qualif.:** Applicants must be college students enrolled at a college or university in one of the 13 APTRA states; must be pursuing a career in Broadcast Journalism. (Incoming freshmen and high school seniors are not eligible.) **Criteria:** Judges will evaluate applicants based on academic achievement, financial need and broadcast career goals.

Funds Avail.: $1,500. **Number Awarded:** 2. **To Apply:** Applicants must complete the application form and must attach tapes or writing samples of broadcast-related work. **Deadline:** February 29. **Contact:** Chris Havlik at the above address.

1685 ■ Association for the Advancement of Baltic Studies (AABS)

University of Washington
Box 353420
Seattle, WA 98195-3420
E-mail: aabs@uw.edu
URL: depts.washington.edu/aabs

1686 ■ Association for the Advancement of Baltic Studies Dissertation Grants for Graduate Students *(Doctorate/Grant)*

Purpose: To support doctoral dissertation research and write-up in any field of Baltic Studies. **Focus:** General studies. **Qualif.:** Applicants must be currently enrolled in a PhD program and have completed all requirements for a PhD except the dissertation. **Criteria:** Recipients are selected based on the scholarly potential of the applicant, quality and scholarly importance of the proposed work especially to the development of Baltic studies.

Funds Avail.: $2,000. **To Apply:** Applicants must send three copies of a 500-word proposal, a one-page budget specifying expenses, a CV, evidence of current enrollment in a PhD program and a no more than 25-page writing sample. **Deadline:** December 15. **Contact:** Dr. Daunis Auers, auers@lu.lv.

1687 ■ Association for Africanist Anthropology (AfAA)

c/o American Anthropological Association
220 Wilson Blvd., Ste. 800
Arlington, VA 22201
E-mail: africananthro@gmail.com
URL: www.aaanet.org/sections/afaa

1688 ■ AfAA Graduate Student Paper Awards *(Graduate/Award)*

Purpose: To promote education and research in Africanist anthropology. **Focus:** Anthropology; African studies. **Qualif.:** Candidates must not have completed their PhD at the time of nomination, and all award recipients must be members of the AfAA. **Criteria:** Criteria is based on original-ity of scholarship, creativity of insight and quality of writing. Special consideration will be given to work that incorporates emerging perspectives or interdisciplinary methodologies, which promote further understanding of sub-Saharan Africa and the African diaspora by a broader audience.

Funds Avail.: $500. **To Apply:** Submissions should include a letter of nomination by a scholar other than the author, a copy of the nominated paper and a full CV of the author. **Deadline:** June 1. **Contact:** David Turkon at dturkon@ithaca.edu.

1689 ■ AfAA Undergraduate Student Paper Awards *(Undergraduate/Award)*

Purpose: To promote education and research in Africanist anthropology. **Focus:** Anthropology; African studies. **Qualif.:** Candidates must not have completed their undergraduate studies at the time of nomination, and all award recipients must be members of the AfAA. **Criteria:** Criteria is based on originality of scholarship, creativity of insight and quality of writing. Special consideration will be given to undergraduates planning to pursue a career in anthropology or in service and education on the African continent.

Funds Avail.: $100. **To Apply:** Submissions should include a letter of nomination by an academic mentor and a copy of the student paper. **Deadline:** June 1. **Contact:** J.R. Osborn at w.h.osborn@gmail.com.

1690 ■ Association of American Geographers (AAG)

1710 16th St. NW
Washington, DC 20009-3198
Ph: (202) 234-1450
Fax: (202) 234-2744
E-mail: gaia@aag.org
URL: www.aag.org

1691 ■ Association of American Geographers IGIF Graduate Research Awards *(Graduate, Undergraduate/Scholarship)*

Purpose: To support college and university student career development in the academic areas of applied spatial data analysis or geographic information systems (GIS). **Focus:** Geography. **Qualif.:** Applicants must be full-time students who are currently registered in an undergraduate or graduate degree program providing either a degree or explicit specialization in some area of applied spatial data analysis or GIS study at a duly accredited and recognized college, university or other educational institution located within the United States. **Criteria:** Selection of applicants will be based on the following criteria: (a) The problem statement and context of the proposed research within the literature; (b) Originality and relevance of the research; (c) Validity and effectiveness of the methodology to complete the research; (d) Writing clarity and quality; (e) Faculty endorsement.

Funds Avail.: $500. **To Apply:** Applications for an AAG IGIF Graduate Research Award must consist of the following: (a) Abstract of research intent; (b) Statement of problem and relevancy; (c) Context of proposed research in the literature; (d) Methodology/research design; (e) Anticipated results and significance of such results; (e) Schedule of research; (f) Budget; (g) A letter of recommendation from a faculty member. **Deadline:** November 1. **Contact:** Application form and other supporting materials must be sent to Association of American Geographers,

Awards are arranged alphabetically below their administering organizations

Hess Scholarship, 1710 16th Street NW, Washington, DC 20009-3198.

1692 ■ Association of American Geographers IGIF Student Travel Grants (Graduate, Undergraduate/Grant)

Purpose: To support college and university student career development in the academic areas of applied spatial data analysis or geographic information systems (GIS). **Focus:** Geography. **Qualif.:** Applicants must be full-time students who are currently registered in an undergraduate or graduate degree program providing either a degree or explicit specialization in some area of applied spatial data analysis or GIS study at a duly accredited and recognized college, university or other educational institution located within the United States. **Criteria:** Selection of applicants will be based on academic record; letters of reference by the advisor and chair; and the focus and clarity of the applicant's statement related to his/her career goals as determined by the AAG IGIF Student Travel Grant Committee of Reviewers.

Funds Avail.: $500. **To Apply:** Applicants must submit a letter of not more than three pages in length which may be supplemented by no more than two pages of supporting illustrations (letter should specifically address how the grant funds will be used and should indicate the career goals of the student and how these funds will assist in meeting those goals); must provide a letter from the student's faculty advisor including an endorsement from the chairperson of the applicable program; must have a brief curriculum vita and recent transcript of records. Application form and other supporting materials must be sent to Association of American Geographers, Hess Scholarship, 1710 16th Street NW, Washington, DC 20009-3198. **Deadline:** November 1.

1693 ■ Darrel Hess Community College Geography Scholarships (Undergraduate/Scholarship)

Purpose: To provide financial assistance to qualified individuals who want to pursue their education. **Focus:** Geography. **Qualif.:** Applicants must be students currently enrolled at a US community college, junior college, city college, or similar two-year educational institution; must have completed at least two transfer courses in geography and plan to transfer to a four-year institution as a geography major during the coming academic year. **Criteria:** Selection of applicants will be based on the overall quality of the application, scholastic excellence and academic promise. Consideration will be given to those in need of financial support.

Funds Avail.: $1,000. **Number Awarded:** 2. **To Apply:** Applicants must complete the scholarship application available online at www.aag.org/grantsawards/hessform.rtf; must submit a two-page personal statement describing the applicant's academic and personal background, as well as the applicant's academic goals and interest in pursuing geography as a major at a baccalaureate institution; must have two letters of recommendation from college instructors; must have a copy of the applicant's current unofficial transcript. Application form and other supporting materials must be sent to Association of American Geographers, Hess Scholarship, 1710 16th St. NW, Washington, DC 20009-3198. **Deadline:** December 31.

1694 ■ Association on American Indian Affairs (AAIA)

966 Hungerford Dr., Ste. 12-B
Rockville, MD 20850

Ph: (240) 314-7155
Fax: (240) 314-7159
E-mail: general.aaia@verizon.net
URL: indian-affairs.org

1695 ■ Elizabeth and Sherman Asche Memorial Scholarships (Graduate, Undergraduate/Scholarship)

Purpose: To provide financial assistance to native people aiming for higher education. **Focus:** Public health; Science. **Qualif.:** Applicants must be full-time students from the Continental US or Alaska; must be graduate or undergraduate students pursuing a degree in public health or science. **Criteria:** Applicants will be selected based on the submitted materials.

Funds Avail.: $1,500. **To Apply:** Applicants must submit the completed application form; Financial Need Analysis with FAO signature; certificate of at least 1/4 Indian blood; proof of tribal enrollment; a one-to-three-page essay stating educational goals and life experiences; two letters of recommendation; current Financial Aid Award Letter; copies of official transcript(s); class schedule; and undergraduate class standing. **Deadline:** June 18. **Contact:** Lisa Wyzlic at lw.aaia@verizon.net.

1696 ■ Adolph Van Pelt Special Fund for Indians Scholarships (Undergraduate/Scholarship)

Purpose: To provide financial assistance to native people aiming for higher education. **Focus:** American Indian studies. **Qualif.:** Applicants must be full-time students from the Continental US or Alaska. **Criteria:** Applicants will be selected based on the submitted materials.

Funds Avail.: $1,500. **Number Awarded:** 1. **To Apply:** Applicants must submit the completed application form; Financial Need Analysis with FAO signature; certificate of at least 1/4 Indian blood; proof of tribal enrollment; a one-to-three-page essay stating educational goals and life experiences; two letters of recommendation; current Financial Aid Award Letter; copies of official transcript(s); class schedule; and undergraduate class standing. **Deadline:** June 18. **Contact:** Lisa Wyzlic at lw.aaia@verizon.net.

1697 ■ Allogan Slagle Memorial Scholarships (All/Scholarship)

Purpose: To provide financial assistance to native people aiming for higher education. **Focus:** American Indian studies. **Qualif.:** Applicants must be students who are members of tribes that are not recognized by the Federal Government. **Criteria:** Applicants will be selected based on the submitted materials.

Funds Avail.: $1,500. **To Apply:** Applicants must submit the completed application form; Financial Need Analysis with FAO signature; certificate of at least 1/4 Indian blood; proof of tribal enrollment; a one-to-three-page essay stating educational goals and life experiences; two letters of recommendation; current Financial Aid Award Letter; copies of official transcript(s); class schedule; and undergraduate class standing. **Deadline:** June 18. **Contact:** Lisa Wyzlic at lw.aaia@verizon.net.

1698 ■ Association of American Indian Physicians (AAIP)

1225 Sovereign Row, Ste. 103
Oklahoma City, OK 73108-1854
Ph: (405) 946-7072

Awards are arranged alphabetically below their administering organizations

Fax: (405) 946-7651
E-mail: mknight@aaip.org
URL: www.aaip.org

1699 ■ Association of American Indian Physicians Scholarships *(Graduate, Undergraduate/Scholarship)*

Purpose: To provide a framework for undergraduate and graduate students in the application process to a health professional school. **Focus:** Health Education. **Qualif.:** Applicants must be undergraduate and graduate medical students; must be American Indian and Alaska Native Students. **Criteria:** Preference will be given to those students who meet the criteria.

Funds Avail.: No specific amount. **To Apply:** Applicants must submit the completed application form; AAIP Student Primary Data Sheet Scholarship Application; Recent College and/or University Transcripts; one letter of recommendation from a professor or academic advisor; copy of Certificate of Degree of Indian Blood or Tribal Identification Card; recent photograph for identification and publication purposes; one page personal statement answering: Why they are seeking a professional career in the health professions? What influenced them and the experience(s) they have had to support this decision? Their career goals and where they plan to work. The physician and medical students will use this in their mock interview. **Contact:** For further information, applicants must call at 405-946-7072; E-mail: lmyers@aaip.org.

1700 ■ Association of American Medical Colleges (AAMC)

2450 N St. NW
Washington, DC 20037-1126
Ph: (202) 828-0400
Fax: (202) 828-1125
E-mail: aamcpresident@aamc.org
URL: www.aamc.org

1701 ■ Herbert W. Nickens Medical Student Scholarships *(Undergraduate/Scholarship)*

Purpose: To eliminate inequities in medical education and healthcare and demonstrated leadership efforts in addressing educational, societal, and health care needs of minorities in United States. **Focus:** Medicinal Education. **Qualif.:** Applicants must be US citizens or permanent residents; must be entering third year of study in an accredited US medical school. **Criteria:** Recipients are selected based on academic standing.

Funds Avail.: $5,000. **Number Awarded:** 5. **To Apply:** Applicants must submit one original and nine photocopies of nomination letter from the medical school's dean or the dean's designate discussing the leadership, academic achievement, awards and honors; letters of recommendation from the medical school and faculty member; personal statement (does not exceed 250 words) discussing motivation for pursuing medical career; curriculum vitae; and official medical school academic transcript. **Deadline:** May 4. **Contact:** Angela R. Moses at nickensawards@aamc.org.

1702 ■ Association for Applied and Therapeutic Humor (AATH)

65 Enterprise
Aliso Viejo, CA 92656

Ph: (949) 715-4681
Fax: (949) 715-6931
Free: 888-747-2284
E-mail: info@aath.org
URL: www.aath.org

1703 ■ The Dave Family "Humor Studies" Scholarships *(Undergraduate/Scholarship)*

Purpose: To help cultivate the next generation of AATH members. **Focus:** Recreational Therapy. **Qualif.:** Applicants must be college students pursuing humor/laughter studies with an interest in entering the field of applied or therapeutic humor. **Criteria:** Priority is given to applicants entering colleges and universities in the United States.

Funds Avail.: $500. **To Apply:** Applicants must submit three essays (up to 250 words each) answering these questions: How do you plan to apply your Humor/Laughter education in the field after college?; Why do you feel you are most deserving of this conference scholarship?; How has humor/laughter helped you in a difficult situation? **Deadline:** January 14. **Contact:** Association for Applied Therapeutic Humor; email at staff@aath.org.

1704 ■ Ed Dunkelblau Scholarships *(All/Scholarship)*

Purpose: To honor the work, dedication, commitment and contribution to AATH and the field of therapeutic humor. **Focus:** Recreational Therapy. **Qualif.:** Applicants must be practitioners of color or researchers interested in the cultural applications of therapeutic humor. **Criteria:** Selection will be based on the applicant's awareness of AATH mission.

Funds Avail.: No specific amount. **To Apply:** Applicants are required to submit an application demonstrating interest, statement of work and awareness to the AATH mission. **Deadline:** January 27. **Contact:** E-mail submission should be made to: staff@aath.org.

1705 ■ Margie Klein "Paper Plate" Scholarships *(All/Scholarship)*

Purpose: To honor the work, dedication, commitment and contribution to AATH and in the field of therapeutic humor. **Focus:** Recreational Therapy. **Qualif.:** Applicants must show interest in therapeutic humor. **Criteria:** Recipients are selected based on submitted essay.

Funds Avail.: No specific amount. **To Apply:** Applicants must submit an essay (not to exceed 250 words) describing how humor helped them in work-related situations. **Deadline:** January 27. **Contact:** AATH at the above address.

1706 ■ Lenny Ravich "Shalom" Scholarships *(All/Scholarship)*

Purpose: To help cultivate the next generation of AATH members. **Focus:** Recreational Therapy. **Qualif.:** Program is open to individuals whose works in humor and laughter clearly and tangibly demonstrate commitment to world peace. **Criteria:** Selection will be based on the impact of the applicant's essay.

Funds Avail.: No specific amount. **To Apply:** Applicants must submit three essays (up to 250 words each) answering these questions: How do you presently apply (or plan to apply) your knowledge and experience in humor and laughter to advance world peace?; How has your mission and purpose in life brought you to this moment?; Why do

Awards are arranged alphabetically below their administering organizations

you feel that you are deserving of this scholarship? **Deadline:** January 14. **Contact:** Association for Applied Therapeutic Humor; staff@aath.org.

1707 ■ Patty Wooten Scholarships
(Undergraduate/Scholarship)

Purpose: To honor the work, dedication, commitment and contribution to AATH and the field of therapeutic humor. **Focus:** Recreational Therapy. **Qualif.:** Program is open to nurses (R.N., L.P.N., L.V.N. or C.N.A). **Criteria:** Recipients are selected based on submitted essay.

Funds Avail.: No amount specified. **To Apply:** Applicants must submit an essay (not to exceed 250 words) describing how humor helped them in work-related situations. **Deadline:** January 27.

1708 ■ Association for Asian Studies (AAS)
1021 E Huron St.
Ann Arbor, MI 48104
Ph: (734) 665-2490
Fax: (734) 665-3801
E-mail: mpaschal@asian-studies.org
URL: www.aasianst.org

1709 ■ AAS CIAC Small Grants *(Graduate/Grant)*

Purpose: To support funding requests for indirect costs of research. **Focus:** General studies. **Qualif.:** Applicant must be an AAS member, junior and independent scholar, adjunct faculty, and dissertation-level graduate student. **Criteria:** Applicants must express sincere interest in research, particularly in Chinese or Inner Asia studies.

Funds Avail.: $2,000. **To Apply:** Applicants need not fill out an application form; however, they must submit: a 250-word abstract of the project; a detailed budget of anticipated expenses, including other sources of funding; a two-page (maximum) curriculum vitae In the case of graduate students, a letter of support from their dissertation advisor, without which the application will not be considered. **Deadline:** February 1. **Contact:** David Strand, strand@dickinson.edu.

1710 ■ AAS Korean Studies Scholarship
Program *(Doctorate, Graduate/Scholarship)*

Purpose: To provide scholarship for graduate students majoring in Korean studies in North America for their coursework and/or research. **Focus:** General studies. **Qualif.:** Applicants must be M.A. or Ph.D. students majoring in Korean studies in any university in North America. Applicants must exhibit sufficient ability to use Korean-language sources in their research and study. **Criteria:** Selection will be based on the submitted applications.

Funds Avail.: $10,000-$20,000. **To Apply:** Applicants must complete a Foundation Application Form, a three-page proposal outlining research interests and academic progress of the student, with a separate one-page bibliography; grade transcripts of coursework; and three letters of recommendation, one of which must be from someone able to attest to the applicant's language ability. **Deadline:** January 31.

1711 ■ Association for Behavior Analysis International
550 W Centre Ave., Ste. 1
Portage, MI 49024

Ph: (269) 492-9310
Fax: (269) 492-9316
E-mail: mail@abainternational.org
URL: www.abainternational.org

1712 ■ Behavioral Gerontology SIG Student Research Awards *(Undergraduate/Award)*

Purpose: To promote research and scholarly activity by students in behavioral gerontology. **Focus:** Gerontology. **Qualif.:** All current student presenters are eligible. **Criteria:** Selection will be based on the committee's criteria and the application materials submitted.

Funds Avail.: $50. **To Apply:** There is no formal submission process. Any presentation (e.g., conceptual, review, empirical) that addresses issues relevant to behavioral gerontology is eligible.

1713 ■ Marion Breland-Bailey Awards *(Graduate, Undergraduate/Award)*

Purpose: To promote research and scholarly activity by students in the applied analysis of animal behavior. **Focus:** Zoology. **Qualif.:** All current students and individuals who received degrees in the past year are eligible. Undergraduate submissions will receive special consideration as long as the project was conducted during bachelor's degree training. **Criteria:** Selection will be based on the committee's criteria and the application materials submitted.

Funds Avail.: No specific amount. **To Apply:** Applicants must submit any project (e.g., conceptual, review, empirical) that addresses issues relevant to the applied analysis of animal behavior. The paper should be prepared as if for submission to a journal, and must meet APA publication guidelines. Work project should not exceed 30 pages and should be in Word format. **Deadline:** March 15. **Contact:** Christina Alligood, christina.alligood@disney.com.

1714 ■ Health, Sport, and Fitness SIG Student Research Awards *(Undergraduate/Award)*

Purpose: To promote research and scholarly activity in the area of health, sports or fitness. **Focus:** Health sciences; Sports studies **Qualif.:** All current student presenters are eligible; must be members of ABAI. **Criteria:** Selection will be based on the committee's criteria.

Funds Avail.: No specific amount. **To Apply:** Applicants should send their abstract and summary of data collected so far (plus graph if possible) to majackson@csufresno.edu. **Deadline:** February 28. **Contact:** majackson@csufresno.edu.

1715 ■ Association of Black Law Enforcers (ABLE)
467 Edgeley Blvd., Unit No. 6
Vaughan, ON, Canada L4K 4E9
Ph: (905) 669-3905
Fax: (905) 669-2875
E-mail: info@ablenet.ca
URL: www.ablenet.ca

1716 ■ Peter Butler III - Rose Fortune Scholarship Program *(Undergraduate/Scholarship)*

Purpose: To financially assist black and minority youths in achieving their educational goals. **Focus:** Law enforcement; Criminology; Criminal justice. **Qualif.:** Applicants must be black or minority students who are planning to, or

Awards are arranged alphabetically below their administering organizations

currently attending an accredited college or university in the following programs: a) law enforcement/law and security; b) correctional worker program; c) criminology; d) law or criminal justice studies; or e) police foundation. **Criteria:** Recipients will be selected based on academic achievements, community service and financial need.

Funds Avail.: No specific amount. **To Apply:** Applicants must provide proof of acceptance or present status at an accredited college or university; transcript of current academic standing; letter of support from a community agency or organization where volunteer work is done; and must submit a 500-word essay describing the contributions to the community, reasons of choosing the field, and why they deserve the award. **Deadline:** April.

1717 ■ Association of Black Women Lawyers of New Jersey

PO Box 22524
Trenton, NJ 08607
Ph: (609) 614-7638
E-mail: abwl-nj@yahoogroups.com
URL: abwl-nj.org

1718 ■ Bernadine Johnson-Marshall and Martha Bell Williams Scholarships *(Undergraduate/Award)*

Purpose: To encourage greater participation of African-American women in the field of law. **Focus:** Law. **Qualif.:** Applicants must be either enrolled at an accredited law school in New Jersey or New Jersey permanent residents enrolled at an accredited law school outside of New Jersey. **Criteria:** Scholarships will be awarded on the basis of demonstrated community service/civic involvement, personal financial need, academic achievement and a brief writing sample or essay.

Funds Avail.: No specific amount. **To Apply:** Interested applicants must visit the website to obtain an application. Completed applications can be sent via electronic mail or via US Postal Service mail. **Deadline:** March 9. **Contact:** Sobande F. Afolabi at 2012ABWLScholarship@gmail.com.

1719 ■ Association of Black Women Physicians (ABWP)

4712 Admiralty Way, Ste. No. 175
Marina Del Rey, CA 90292
Ph: (310) 364-1438
URL: www.blackwomenphysicians.org

1720 ■ Rebecca Lee, M.D. Scholarships *(Undergraduate/Scholarship)*

Purpose: To provide educational assistance for female medical students who are permanent residents of Southern California or enrolled in Southern California medical schools. **Focus:** Medicine. **Qualif.:** Applicants must be permanent residents of Southern California at any medical school, or students at a Southern California medical school, who are in good academic standing. **Criteria:** Applicants are evaluated based on academic performance and financial need.

Funds Avail.: $1,000-$5,000. **To Apply:** Applicants must submit academic and financial aid transcripts, medical school acceptance letter or medical school dean's letter of good standing, three letters of recommendation, curriculum vitae and typed personal statement. **Deadline:** September

4. **Contact:** abwpassistant@yahoo.com; 310-364-1438.

1721 ■ Association of California Nurse Leaders (ACNL)

2520 Venture Oaks Way, Ste. 210
Sacramento, CA 95833
Ph: (916) 779-6949
Fax: (916) 779-6945
E-mail: info@acnl.org
URL: www.acnl.org

1722 ■ ACNL Research Scholarships *(Graduate/Scholarship)*

Purpose: To financially support graduate nursing students conducting nursing research study as part of their educational program of study. **Focus:** Nursing. **Qualif.:** Applicants must be enrolled in an accredited academic graduate nursing program and engaged in a research; and has had formal education/preparation in the conduct of nursing research (course work in conducting research). The research must show promise of having relevance to nursing practice, education, or research. **Criteria:** Selection is based on the student's qualifications, application materials, and on the research.

Funds Avail.: $500-$2,500. **To Apply:** Applicants must submit a completed application form along with an ACNL member application form if not a current ACNL member (optional); transcript of program courses to date including GPA; two current recommendation letters; a statement of purpose (no longer than 750 words); and resume and/or curriculum vitae. In addition, applicants must include the research abstract of the project (and status) or proposed project of no more than one page which includes purpose, aims, hypotheses (if applicable), methods, measures, and analysis plan. **Deadline:** October 30. **Contact:** Cathy Novaresi at cathy@acnl.org.

1723 ■ Barbara Brantley Nursing Education Scholarships *(Graduate/Scholarship)*

Purpose: To foster leadership excellence in nursing. **Focus:** Nursing; Nursing administration. **Qualif.:** Applicant must be a student enrolled in a graduate program focused on nursing leadership, management, or administration. **Criteria:** Selection is based on the submitted application materials. Preference will be given to ACNL members.

Funds Avail.: $2,500. **To Apply:** Applicants must submit a completed application form along with an ACNL member application form if not a current ACNL member (optional); transcript of program courses to date including GPA; two current recommendation letters; a statement of purpose (no longer than 750 words); and resume and/or curriculum vitae. **Deadline:** October 30. **Remarks:** Established by the Catalyst Systems, LLC, and administered by the Association of California Nurse Leaders (ACNL). **Contact:** Cathy Novaresi at cathy@acnl.org.

1724 ■ Claire V. Cunningham Masonic Fund for Supporting Leadership in Nursing Scholarships *(Professional development/Scholarship)*

Purpose: To enhance leadership training and development for ACNL members. **Focus:** Nursing. **Qualif.:** Applicant must be an ACNL member in good standing (if not a member, a membership application must be submitted with Scholarship application); and accepted into and present evidence of a leadership program or special study program

Awards are arranged alphabetically below their administering organizations

that supports the advancement of the individual as a nurse leader. **Criteria:** Selection is based on the submitted application materials. Preference will be given to ACNL members.

Funds Avail.: No specific amount. **To Apply:** Applicants must submit a completed application form along with an ACNL member application form if not a current ACNL member (optional); transcript of program courses to date including GPA; two current recommendation letters; a statement of purpose (no longer than 750 words); and resume and/or curriculum vitae. **Remarks:** Established in 1970 by the Masonic Foundation, a charitable trust whose mission is to help further the education of young people from kindergarten through college. **Contact:** Cathy Novaresi at cathy@acnl.org.

1725 ■ Victor E. Schimmel Memorial Nursing Scholarships *(Doctorate, Graduate, Master's/ Scholarship)*

Purpose: To support the advanced educational pursuits of nursing educators and nursing leaders. **Focus:** Nursing; Health care services. **Qualif.:** Applicant must be currently enrolled in a college/university for an advanced degree. **Criteria:** Selection is based on the submitted application materials. Preference will be given to ACNL members.

Funds Avail.: No specific amount. **To Apply:** Applicants must submit a completed application form along with an ACNL member application form if not a current ACNL member (optional); transcript of program courses to date including GPA; two current recommendation letters; a statement of purpose (no longer than 750 words); and resume and/or curriculum vitae. **Remarks:** Established by the Camdem Group in memory of Victor E. Schimmel. **Contact:** Cathy Novaresi at cathy@acnl.org.

1726 ■ Association of California Water Agencies (ACWA)

910 K St., Ste. 100
Sacramento, CA 95814
Ph: (916) 441-4545
Fax: (916) 325-2316
Free: 888-666-2292
E-mail: acwabox@acwa.com
URL: www.acwa.com

1727 ■ Association of California Water Agencies Scholarships *(Undergraduate/Scholarship)*

Purpose: To promote study focusing on water resources. **Focus:** Water resources. **Qualif.:** Applicant must be a resident of California attending one of the selected California schools full-time as a junior or senior during the current academic year. **Criteria:** The award will be based not only on scholastic achievement but also on the individual's commitment and motivation to their chosen vocation. Financial need will be considered.

Funds Avail.: $3,000. **Number Awarded:** 2. **To Apply:** Applicants must submit a completed scholarship application form along with an essay. **Deadline:** April 1. **Contact:** awards@acwa.com.

1728 ■ Stephen K. Hall ACWA Water Law and Policy Scholarships *(Graduate/Scholarship)*

Purpose: To promote study focusing on water resources. **Focus:** Water resources. **Qualif.:** Applicant must be attending a public or private school located in the United

States of America; have completed undergraduate work and at the time of the award be either a part-time or full-time student in graduate studies; and must be carrying at least 8 units per term. **Criteria:** The award will be based not only on scholastic achievement, but also on the individual's commitment and motivation to their chosen vocation. Financial need will be considered.

Funds Avail.: $7,000. **To Apply:** Applicants must submit a completed scholarship application form along with the essay. **Deadline:** April 1. **Contact:** Sarah Langford, sarahl@acwa.com.

1729 ■ Clair A. Hill Scholarships
(Undergraduate/Scholarship)

Purpose: To promote study focusing on water resources. **Focus:** Water resources. **Qualif.:** Applicant must be a resident of California attending one of the selected California schools full-time as a sophomore, junior or senior during the current academic year. **Criteria:** The award will be based not only on scholastic achievement but also on the individual's commitment and motivation to their chosen vocation. Financial need will be considered.

Funds Avail.: $5,000. **To Apply:** Applicants must complete scholarship application available online. Submit completed applications to Solano Irrigation District. **Deadline:** February 1. **Contact:** Solano Irrigation District, c/o Scholarship Committee, 508 Elmira Rd., Vacaville, CA 95687; Phone: 707-448-6847.

1730 ■ Association for Canadian Studies in the United States (ACSUS)

2030 M St. NW, Ste. 350
Washington, DC 20036
Ph: (202) 775-9007
Fax: (202) 775-0061
E-mail: info@acsus.org
URL: www.acsus.org

1731 ■ ACSUS Distinguished Dissertation Awards *(Doctorate/Award)*

Purpose: To honor outstanding doctoral research on Canada at American institutions. **Focus:** General studies. **Qualif.:** Applicants must be nominated by a faculty serving on dissertation committees at universities in the United States; must be members of ACSUS; must have completed their PhD degree in the month of August between 2009 and 2011. **Criteria:** Successful nominees should represent an original work that makes a contribution to the nominee's discipline; must contain at least 50% content on Canada; and the topic must be comparative in nature. The dissertation will be judged on substantive and methodological quality, originality of thought and clarity.

Funds Avail.: $500. **To Apply:** Nomination must be accompanied by a letter of support from the student's dissertation advisor and one from an additional reference who is not a member of ACSUS. Each nomination must be accompanied by a copy of the dissertation (not to exceed 500 words), typed and double-spaced; a one page resume of the nominee; and appendices containing charts, tables and bibliographies. **Deadline:** July 1.

1732 ■ Thomas O. Enders Graduate Fellowships *(Graduate/Fellowship)*

Purpose: To encourage in-depth inclusion of Canadian content in comparative research/projects that have policy

Awards are arranged alphabetically below their administering organizations

relevance for Canada-U.S. relations as well as social, economic, political, security and quality of life issues. **Focus:** General studies. **Qualif.:** Students in any discipline or professional school who are in the process of preparing a graduate thesis or doctoral dissertation related in substantial part to the study of Canada, Canada-U.S. relations or comparative policies in North America; must be U.S. citizens or permanent residents; must be enrolled in full-time masters or doctoral programs at any institution in the United States; and must have obtained, in writing, the support of a faculty member or research scientist at a Canadian university, or the head of an organization or business who agrees to act as the student's academic sponsor during the tenure of their award. **Criteria:** Recipients will be selected based on submitted materials.

Funds Avail.: $3,500. **To Apply:** Applicants must submit a curriculum vitae; one-page proposal outlining the thesis/dissertation project that states why research at the selected university is essential to the project and how such a visit will enhance the quality of the student's research; schedule of the activities; one letter of support from the student's thesis/dissertation chair and another one from the departmental chair or dean of the school; and a letter of invitation from the faculty member or organization head where student will be conducting research. **Deadline:** March 31.

1733 ■ Association of Canadian Universities for Northern Studies (Association universitaire canadienne detudes nordique)

17 York St., Ste. 405
Ottawa, ON, Canada K1N 9J6
Ph: (613) 562-0515
Fax: (613) 562-0533
E-mail: office@acuns.ca
URL: www.acuns.ca

1734 ■ Canadian Polar Commission Scholarships (Doctorate, Graduate/Scholarship)

Purpose: To support Canadian students enrolled in a doctoral program at a Canadian university. **Focus:** General studies. **Qualif.:** Applicant must be a Canadian citizen or permanent resident of Canada presently enrolled in a doctoral program at a Canadian university. **Criteria:** Selection is based on academic record, potential benefit of the research, originality, innovative approach and the applicant's interest in, and commitment to, polar studies.

Funds Avail.: $10,000. **Number Awarded:** 1. **To Apply:** Applicants must submit a completed application form together with two letters of reference; all transcript of grades; and a copy of the research license. **Deadline:** January 30. **Remarks:** Sponsored by the Canadian Polar Commission.

1735 ■ CNST Scholarships (Doctorate, Graduate/Scholarship)

Purpose: To support Canadian students enrolled in a doctoral program at a Canadian university. **Focus:** General studies. **Qualif.:** Applicant must be a citizen or permanent resident of Canada presently enrolled in a doctoral program at a Canadian university. **Criteria:** Selection is based on academic record, the quality of the application, potential benefit of the research, originality, letters of reference and the applicants' interest in, and commitment to, the north and northern scholarship.

Funds Avail.: $5,000. **Number Awarded:** 1. **To Apply:**

Applicants must submit a completed application form together with two letters of reference; all transcript of grades; and copy of the research license. **Deadline:** January 30.

1736 ■ Northern Resident Scholarships (Doctorate, Graduate/Scholarship)

Purpose: To support Canadian students who are long-term residents of Nunavut, Northwest Territories, Yukon or the Provincial North. **Focus:** General studies. **Qualif.:** Applicant must be a Canadian citizen or permanent resident of Canada identified as a long-term resident of Nunavut, Northwest Territories, Yukon or the Provincial North and currently enrolled in a masters or doctoral level program at a Canadian university. **Criteria:** Selection is based on academic record, the quality of the application, potential benefit of the research, letters of reference and the applicant's leadership skills and interest in, and commitment to, northern scholarship.

Funds Avail.: $10,000. **Number Awarded:** 4. **To Apply:** Applicants must submit a completed application form together with two letters of reference; all official transcript of grades; and a copy of the research license. **Deadline:** January 30.

1737 ■ Association of Certified Fraud Examiners (ACFE)

716 W Ave., The Gregor Bldg.
Austin, TX 78701-2727
Ph: (512) 478-9000
Fax: (512) 478-9297
Free: 800-245-3321
E-mail: memberservices@acfe.com
URL: www.acfe.com

1738 ■ Ritchie-Jennings Memorial Scholarships (Graduate, Undergraduate/Scholarship)

Purpose: To support the education of collegiate accounting and criminal justice students around the globe. **Focus:** Accounting; Criminal justice. **Qualif.:** Applicant must be a full-time undergraduate student taking at least 12 semester hours, or a graduate student taking at least 9 semester hours per term at an accredited four-year college/university with a declared major or minor in accounting or criminal justice. **Criteria:** Selection is based on overall academic achievement demonstrated by official transcripts, letters of recommendation, and the essay.

Funds Avail.: Twenty-three $1,000, four $2,500, two $5,000 and one $10,000. **Number Awarded:** 30. **To Apply:** Applicants must submit a completed Ritchie-Jennings Memorial Scholarship Application together with a copy of official transcript(s); three letters of recommendation; and an original 250-500 word essay. **Deadline:** February 3. **Contact:** scholarships@acfe.com.

1739 ■ Association of College Unions International (ACUI)

One City Centre, Ste. 200
120 W 7th St.
Bloomington, IN 47404-3925
Ph: (812) 245-2284
Fax: (812) 245-6710
E-mail: acui@acui.org
URL: www.acui.org

Awards are arranged alphabetically below their administering organizations

1740 ■ Gretchen Laatsch Scholarships
(Graduate/Scholarship)

Purpose: To encourage graduate students to submit professional quality articles in the field of college unions and students activities. **Focus:** General studies. **Qualif.:** Applicants must be recognized by an institution as students in pursuit of graduate degrees in any academic area. **Criteria:** Consideration will be given to students either currently in the field of college union and student activities or those intending to enter the profession.

Funds Avail.: $500. **To Apply:** Applicants must submit an article containing a minimum of 500 words; must have a letter of recommendation from a college union or student activities professional. Application form and requirements must be sent to Association of College Unions International, Gretchen Laatsch Scholarship, One City Center, Ste. 200, 120 W 7th St., Bloomington, IN 47404 or e-mailed to: tarth@acui.org. **Deadline:** January 27. **Remarks:** Scholarship was established by former ACUI President Gretchen Laatsch from the University of Akron and her husband, Jim Switzer.

1741 ■ Association of College and University Auditors (ACUA)
PO Box 14306
Lenexa, KS 66285-4306
Ph: (913) 895-4620
Fax: (913) 895-4652
E-mail: acua-info@goamp.com
URL: www.acua.org

1742 ■ Association of College and University Auditors Scholarships *(Graduate, Undergraduate/Scholarship)*

Purpose: To assist students in their education leading to careers in accounting, auditing, finance, or higher education administration. **Focus:** Accounting; Finance; Educational administration. **Qualif.:** Applicants must be undergraduate or graduate students in a degree program leading to careers in accounting, auditing, finance or higher education administration; have GPA of 2.5 on a 4.0 scale for undergraduates and 3.0 GPA on a 4.0 scale for graduate students. **Criteria:** Selection is based on merits.

Funds Avail.: $500. **Number Awarded:** 2. **To Apply:** Applicants must submit a completed application form together with a (single page) essay; written recommendation; and a copy of transcript. **Deadline:** May 31. **Contact:** Send application to William A. Peters, ACUA Scholarship Chair at The University of Texas Administration Bldg., Ste. 403 El Paso, TX 79968-0586. Phone: 915-747-8921; Email: wpeters@utep.edu. lmandel@calstate.edu.

1743 ■ Association for College and University Clubs (ACUC)
1733 King St.
Alexandria, VA 22314-2720
Ph: (703) 299-2630
Fax: (703) 739-0124
E-mail: acuc@acuclubs.org
URL: www.acuclubs.org

1744 ■ Jack Shrader Memorial Awards *(Professional development/Scholarship)*

Purpose: To promote reciprocal privileges, management education and resource-sharing among university clubs; to assist in furthering the education of a club employee through academic courseworks, seminars or other practicum activities. **Focus:** Writing. **Qualif.:** Any employee of an ACUC member. **Criteria:** Recipients are selected based on the presented ideas evaluated by the sponsors.

Funds Avail.: $1,500. **To Apply:** Applicant must submit a written nomination from the Club's Manager and Board President along with the employee's own statement of career goals; planned use for the scholarship; brief bibliography; and official application form. **Deadline:** December 31.

1745 ■ Association for Compensatory Educators of Texas (ACET)
PO Box 3516
Humble, TX 77347
Ph: (832) 644-5020
Fax: (832) 644-8520
E-mail: kenschrader@acetx.org
URL: acetx.org

1746 ■ Association for Compensatory Educators of Texas Paraprofessionals Scholarships
(Professional development/Scholarship)

Purpose: To provide financial assistance for deserving students. **Focus:** General studies. **Qualif.:** Applicants must be paraprofessionals who wish to return to school to pursue a degree and teacher certification. They must be currently working with a school district in a compensatory program. **Criteria:** Preference will be given to those applicants who meet the criteria.

Funds Avail.: No specific amount. **Number Awarded:** 4. **To Apply:** Applicants must submit proof of a high school diploma or GED and must check the available website to download the scholarship application, information letter, scoring rubric and scoring grid. **Deadline:** January 13. **Contact:** Applications must be submitted in one envelope as one complete document to Sharon Jensen, Scholarship Chairperson.

1747 ■ Association for Compensatory Educators of Texas Scholarships *(Undergraduate/ Scholarship)*

Purpose: To provide remedial assistance and support for students who have failed TAKS or are at-risk of dropping out of school. **Focus:** General studies. **Qualif.:** Applicants must be graduating high school students. **Criteria:** Selection will be made by the committee.

Funds Avail.: $1,000. **Number Awarded:** 20. **To Apply:** Applicants must submit a completed application form. **Deadline:** January 13. **Contact:** Applications must be submitted in one envelope as one complete document to Andrea Hungerford, Scholarship Chairperson.

1748 ■ Association of Desk and Derrick Clubs (ADDC)
5153 E 51st St., Ste. 107
Tulsa, OK 74135
Ph: (918) 622-1749
Fax: (918) 622-1675
E-mail: adotulsa@swbell.net
URL: www.addc.org

Awards are arranged alphabetically below their administering organizations

1749 ■ Association of Desk and Derrick Clubs Education Trust Scholarships *(Undergraduate/ Scholarship)*

Purpose: To provide financial assistance for college students planning a career in the petroleum energy or allied industries. **Focus:** Geology; Geophysics; Engineering, Petroleum; Engineering, Nuclear; Engineering, Mechanical; Energy-related areas. **Qualif.:** Applicant must have completed at least two years or be currently enrolled in the second year of undergraduate study at an accredited college or university; be a U.S. or Canadian citizen; maintain a GPA of 3.2 or above on a 4.0 scale; be pursuing a career in the field of petroleum, energy or allied industry. **Criteria:** Preference will be given to applicants with financial need.

Funds Avail.: No specific amount. **To Apply:** Applicants must submit a completed application form available at the website. **Deadline:** April 1. **Contact:** Jill Coble, jillecoble@yahoo.com.

1750 ■ Association of Donor Recruitment Professionals (ADRP)

c/o Deborah Swift, Executive Director
Austin, TX 78715
Ph: (512) 658-9414
Fax: (866) 498-6527
E-mail: dswift@adrp.org
URL: www.adrp.org

1751 ■ Association of Donor Recruitment Professionals Hughes Scholarships *(Professional development/Scholarship)*

Purpose: To help individuals enhance their professional development. **Focus:** General studies. **Qualif.:** Applicant must be a current member of ADRP; have been involved in donor recruitment/community relations for less than two years. ADRP board members are not eligible to apply. **Criteria:** Recipients will be selected based on submitted application.

Funds Avail.: No stated amount. **To Apply:** Applicant must submit a typewritten 500 words essay describing a creative recruitment idea that he/she has developed or wants to implement; and a typewritten letter of endorsement from his/her immediate supervisor.

1752 ■ Association of Donor Recruitment Professionals Presidential Scholarships *(Professional development/Scholarship)*

Purpose: To provide financial assistance to members who wish to acquire education and networking opportunities. **Focus:** General studies. **Qualif.:** Applicant must be a member of ADRP; have been a donor recruiter for two or more years. ADRP board members are not eligible to apply. **Criteria:** Judging will be based on submitted application.

Funds Avail.: No specific amount. **To Apply:** Applicant must submit a 500 word essay stating why this scholarship would enhance his/her professional development; a letter of endorsement from his/her immediate supervisor; and a letter of endorsement from a blood drive coordinator. Materials must be submitted in a typewritten format.

1753 ■ Nancy J. Chapman Scholarships *(Professional development/Scholarship)*

Purpose: To help individuals enhance their professional development. **Focus:** General studies. **Qualif.:** Applicant must be a current member of ADRP; must be in a management position in donor recruitment. ADRP board members are not eligible to apply. **Criteria:** Recipients will be selected based on submitted application.

Funds Avail.: No stated amount. **To Apply:** Applicant must submit a typewritten 500-word essay stating why this scholarship would enhance his/her professional development and typewritten letter of endorsement from applicant's immediate supervisor.

1754 ■ Charles Drew Scholarships *(Professional development/Scholarship)*

Purpose: To help individuals enhance their professional development. **Focus:** General studies. **Qualif.:** Applicants must be current members of ADRP. Board members are not eligible to apply. **Criteria:** Recipients will be selected based on submitted applications.

Funds Avail.: No specific amount. **To Apply:** Applicants must submit a 500-word essay describing a successful technique they have developed which resulted in an increase in minority donations; and a typewritten letter of endorsement from their immediate supervisor.

1755 ■ Association of Drilled Shaft Contractors

8445 Freeport Pky., Ste. 325
Irving, TX 75063
Ph: (469) 359-6000
Fax: (469) 359-6007
E-mail: adsc@adsc-iafd.com
URL: www.adsc-iafd.com

1756 ■ International Association of Foundation Drilling Scholarships for Civil Engineering Students *(Postgraduate/Scholarship)*

Purpose: To protect, promote, foster and advance the interests of persons, firms or corporations engaged in design, construction, equipment manufacture and distribution for the drilled shaft, anchored earth retention and corresponding industries. **Focus:** Civil Engineering. **Qualif.:** Applicants must be full-time graduate students who are enrolled in less than 12 credit hours; must be willing to work on a full and part-time basis; must be U.S. or Canadian citizens; must be currently enrolled in an ABET or CEAB accredited engineering program or be graduates from such program; must have plans to enter or continue graduate school during the academic year. **Criteria:** Recipients are selected based on academic performance and financial need.

Funds Avail.: $3,000. **To Apply:** Applicants must submit a completed application form; current, official transcript of academic records and two letters of reference from persons familiar with their academic or professional experience. **Deadline:** May 31. **Contact:** Electronic submission of reference letters must be sent to Susan King, ADSC Scholarship Administrator at sking@adsc-iafd.com.

1757 ■ International Association of Foundation Drilling Scholarships for Part-time Civil Engineering Graduate School Students *(Postgraduate/Scholarship)*

Purpose: To protect, promote, foster and advance the interests of persons, firms or corporations engaged in design, construction, equipment manufacture or distribution for the drilled shaft, anchored earth retention and corresponding industries. **Focus:** Civil engineering. **Qualif.:**

Awards are arranged alphabetically below their administering organizations

Applicants must be U.S. or Canadian citizens; must be part-time graduate students majoring in geotechnical or structural engineering; must be currently enrolled in an ABET or CEAB accredited engineering program or be graduates from such program; must have plans to enter or continue graduate school during the academic year and be willing to work on a full or part-time basis. **Criteria:** Recipients are selected based on academic performance and financial need.

Funds Avail.: $3,000. **To Apply:** Applicants must submit a completed application form; current, official transcript of academic record; and two letters of reference from persons familiar with the academic or professional experience. **Deadline:** May 31. **Contact:** Electronic submission of reference letters must be sent to Susan King, ADSC Scholarship Administrator at sking@adsc-iafd.com.

1758 ■ Association for Education and Rehabilitation of the Blind and Visually Impaired (AERBVI)

1703 N Beauregard St., Ste. 440
Alexandria, VA 22311
Ph: (703) 671-4500
Fax: (703) 671-6391
Free: 877-492-2708
E-mail: lou@aerbvi.org
URL: www.aerbvi.org

1759 ■ William and Dorothy Ferrell Scholarship Program *(Undergraduate/Scholarship)*

Purpose: To support the education of selected students who are blind. **Focus:** Visual impairment. **Qualif.:** Applicant must be legally blind; must be studying at the post-secondary level for a career in the field of services to persons who are blind or visually impaired. **Criteria:** Applicants are selected based on submitted applications and supporting materials.

Funds Avail.: $750. **Number Awarded:** 2. **To Apply:** Applicants must submit an application form (available at the website) to scholarships@aerbvi.org; a signed certification of visual status; and original letters of recommendation. **Deadline:** March 15. **Remarks:** Scholarship is awarded biennially. **Contact:** For further information, applicants may e-mail at scholarships@aerbvi.org.

1760 ■ Association for Educational Communications and Technology (AECT)

1800 N Stonelake Dr., Ste. 2
Bloomington, IN 47404
Ph: (812) 335-7675
Fax: (812) 335-7678
Free: 877-677-AECT
E-mail: aect@aect.org
URL: www.aect.org

1761 ■ AECT Foundation Mentor Endowment Scholarships *(Doctorate, Graduate/Scholarship)*

Purpose: To facilitate educational, professional and leadership development in the field of educational communications and technology. **Focus:** Education. **Qualif.:** Applicant must be a graduate student in educational communications and technology pursuing a graduate study during an academic year or a summer session in any accredited college/university in the United States or Canada. **Criteria:**

Selection is based on: scholarship; leadership potential; experience in the field of educational communications and technology (such as employment, field experience, course work, assistantships, presentations, and publications); and letters of recommendation.

Funds Avail.: $3,000. **Number Awarded:** 1. **To Apply:** Applicants must submit a completed application form along with three letters of recommendation to: Addie Kinsinger, 8208 E Voltaire Ave. Scottsdale, AZ 85260-4922, or addkin@msn.com. **Deadline:** June 1. **Contact:** Addie Kinsinger at 480-998-4637 or addkin@msn.com.

1762 ■ AECT Legacy Scholarships *(Graduate, Master's, Professional development/Scholarship)*

Purpose: To improve the teaching/learning process in the library and classroom, and to supplement the recipient's training by extending the use of educational communications and technology. **Focus:** Education; Library and archival sciences. **Qualif.:** Applicant must be a practicing K-12 school teacher or school library/media specialist pursuing a Master's degree or professional certificate in the field. **Criteria:** Selection is based on the submitted application materials.

Funds Avail.: $1,000. **Number Awarded:** 1. **To Apply:** Applicants must submit a completed application along with three letters of recommendation to: Deborah Anthony, President, ECT Foundation, 1017 Pinewood Court, Brighton, MI 48116-2425, Dept. 3374, ED 322 or deborah_anthony@hp.com. **Deadline:** May 15.

1763 ■ ECT Foundation Master Scholarships *(Graduate, Master's/Scholarship)*

Purpose: To support a student currently accepted or enrolled in master's program in the field of educational communications and technology at an accredited college/university. **Focus:** Education. **Qualif.:** Applicant must be a graduate student enrolled in a degree granting program in educational technology at the Master's, (MS) level; must provide evidence of an average of "B" or better; and be a member of AECT. **Criteria:** The winner will be selected by AECT's awards committee.

Funds Avail.: $1,000. **To Apply:** Applicant must submit a completed nomination form. **Deadline:** June 1. **Contact:** Phillip Harris, AECT Awards Chair at pharris@aect.org or 877-677-2328.

1764 ■ McJulien Minority Graduate Scholarships *(Graduate/Scholarship)*

Purpose: To support a minority graduate student pursuing educational communications and technology. **Focus:** Education. **Qualif.:** Applicant must be a full-time graduate student enrolled in a degree granting program in educational technology at the Master's, (MS), Specialist (EdS) or Doctoral (PhD/EdD) level; must provide evidence of an average of "B" or better; and must be a member of AECT. **Criteria:** Selection is based on the submitted applications.

Funds Avail.: No specific amount. **Number Awarded:** 1. **To Apply:** Applicant must submit a completed nomination form. **Deadline:** June 1. **Remarks:** Established by Wes McJulien, past president of AECT and member of the ECT Foundation, in memory of his son, Patrick D. McJulien. **Contact:** Brandon Taylor, MIM President-Elect at bctaylor06@yahoo.com.

1765 ■ Association of Energy Engineers Foundation

4025 Pleasantdale Rd., Ste. 420
Atlanta, GA 30340

Awards are arranged alphabetically below their administering organizations

Ph: (770) 447-5083
Fax: (770) 446-3969
E-mail: info@aeecenter.org
URL: www.aeecenter.org

1766 ■ Association of Energy Engineers Foundation Scholarship Program *(Graduate, Undergraduate/Scholarship)*

Purpose: To encourage qualified practitioners in energy engineering and energy management by awarding scholarships to further education in the field. **Focus:** Energy-related areas. **Qualif.:** Applicants must be undergraduates and graduate degree candidates who are enrolled in engineering or management programs at accredited colleges or universities; and must be nominated by AEE Chapters. **Criteria:** Applicants are evaluated based on the criteria designed by the Scholarship Selection Committee.

Funds Avail.: No specific amount. **To Apply:** Applicants must submit all the required application information. **Deadline:** May 1. **Contact:** James P. Waltz at jpwaltz@eraenergy.com.

1767 ■ Association of Environmental & Engineering Geologists (Association of Engineering Geologists)

3773 Cherry Creek Dr. N, Ste. 575
Denver, CO 80209
Ph: (303) 757-2926
Fax: (720) 230-4846
E-mail: aeg@aegweb.org
URL: www.aegweb.org

1768 ■ Marliave Scholarship Fund *(Undergraduate/Scholarship)*

Purpose: To provide scholarships to those outstanding students in the field of geological engineering. **Focus:** Engineering, Geological. **Qualif.:** Applicants must be outstanding students in geological engineering. **Criteria:** Awards will be given to those students who meet the criteria.

Funds Avail.: No specific amount. **To Apply:** Applicants must submit a completed application form. **Remarks:** The Marliave Scholarship Fund was established in 1968 by the Association of Environmental & Engineering Geologists (AEG). The fund name honors an eminent family of engineering geologists: Chester E. Marliave (1888-1958), and his sons Elmer C. Marliave (1910-1967) and Burton H. Marliave (1917-1991), who were pioneers in the profession. **Contact:** at the above address.

1769 ■ Martin L. Stout Scholarships *(Undergraduate/Scholarship)*

Purpose: To provide financial support to those students who are in need. **Focus:** Engineering, Geological. **Qualif.:** Applicants must be students who are pursuing geological engineering; must be in good academic standing; must have financial need. **Criteria:** Selection will be based on the best response to one of the required essay questions and on appraisals from two professors.

Funds Avail.: No specific amount. **To Apply:** Applicants must submit an original typed and signed application form along with four (4) legible photocopies. **Contact:** at the above address.

1770 ■ Association of Faculties of Pharmacy of Canada (AFPC)

4640 W 7th Ave.
Vancouver, BC, Canada V6R 1X5
Ph: (604) 222-0221
Fax: (604) 222-2574
E-mail: fabbott@telus.net
URL: www.afpc.info

1771 ■ Merck Frosst Canada Ltd. Postgraduate Pharmacy Fellowships *(Doctorate, Postgraduate/Fellowship)*

Purpose: To encourage students to pursue their postgraduate studies in Pharmacy at a Canadian University. **Focus:** Pharmacy. **Qualif.:** Applicants must be in the final year in a pharmacy or pharmaceutical sciences degree program or pharmacy practitioners who are entering postgraduate studies in a faculty, College or School of Pharmacy in Canada or first year graduate students who have a pharmacy or pharmaceutical sciences degree and are enrolled in an M.Sc. or PhD degree in Faculty, College or School of Pharmacy in Canada; must be Canadian citizens or permanent residents of Canada. **Criteria:** Selection of applicants will be based on academic performance, publication activity, and fields of research in need of support.

Funds Avail.: $13,500 stipend and $1,500 for research expenses such as books, travel to symposia and photocopying materials. **To Apply:** Applicants must submit the complete application form together with their official transcript of academic records to Dr. Frank Abbott, Executive Director, 4640 West 7th Ave., Vancouver, BC V6R 1X5. **Deadline:** December 15.

1772 ■ Association of Family Practice Physician Assistants (AFPPA)

1905 Woodstock Rd., Ste. 2150
Roswell, GA 30075
Ph: (770) 640-7605
Fax: (770) 640-1095
Free: 877-890-0181
E-mail: info@afppa.org
URL: www.afppa.org

1773 ■ AFPPA Student Scholarships *(Undergraduate/Scholarship)*

Purpose: To financially assist first and second year physician students. **Focus:** Medicine. **Qualif.:** Applicants must be PA students attending an accredited PA program for more than 12 months or students with 12 months or less of PA education. **Criteria:** Applicants who are AFPPA student members in good academic standing and demonstrate interest in family practice medicine will be given priority.

Funds Avail.: $1,000 for first year students and $1,500 for second year students. **Number Awarded:** 4. **To Apply:** Applicants must submit an essay (maximum of 750 words or less) describing the commitment to family practice medicine and how the current and past community involvement demonstrates this commitment. **Deadline:** September 1. **Contact:** Rene McCarty, PA-C, AFPPA Scholarship Committee Chm., scholarshipchair@afppa.org.

1774 ■ Association for Federal Information Resources Management (AFFIRM)

400 N Washington St., Ste. 300
Alexandria, VA 22314

Awards are arranged alphabetically below their administering organizations

Ph: (703) 778-4646
Fax: (703) 683-5480
E-mail: info@affirm.org
URL: www.affirm.org

1775 ■ AFFIRM University Scholarships
(Undergraduate/Scholarship)

Purpose: To provide scholarships for undergraduate students intending to earn a degree in Information Technology. **Focus:** Information science and technology; Technology. **Qualif.:** Applicant must be a full-time student (12 credits or more); must be a junior or above; must have a minimum of 3.0 cumulative GPA; and must be majoring in some aspect of information technology or related field. **Criteria:** U.S. Citizens are given preference.

Funds Avail.: No specific amount. **To Apply:** Scholarship applications will be provided by the universities. Applicants must prepare a letter of reference from a professor.

1776 ■ Association for Financial Technology (AFT)

34 N High St.
New Albany, OH 43054
Ph: (614) 895-1208
Fax: (614) 895-3466
E-mail: aft@aftweb.com
URL: www.aftweb.com

1777 ■ James E. Stoner Memorial Scholarships
(Undergraduate/Scholarship)

Purpose: To provide educational support for members and members' dependents. **Focus:** General studies. **Qualif.:** Applicants are the employees and their dependents; and must be enrolled full-time at an accredited educational institution. **Criteria:** Selection is based on a scoring point system. Applicant with the most points will receive the award.

Funds Avail.: $3,000 each. **Number Awarded:** 2. **To Apply:** Applicants must submit a completed application form available at the website. **Deadline:** July 1.

1778 ■ Association of Flight Attendants - CWA (AFA) (AFA-CWA)

501 3rd St. NW
Washington, DC 20001
Ph: (202) 434-1300
Fax: (202) 434-1319
Free: 800-424-2401
E-mail: info@afacwa.org
URL: www.afanet.org

1779 ■ Association of Flight Attendants Scholarship Fund *(Undergraduate/Scholarship)*

Purpose: To further the education of promising young men and women who are dependents of AFA members in good standing to have the opportunity for higher education. **Focus:** Aviation. **Qualif.:** Applicants must be dependent of AFA members in good standing seeking to further education at an accredited college or university. **Criteria:** Candidates should: be ranked in the top 15% of their high school class; have excellent scores in SAT or ACT; have demonstrated financial need.

Funds Avail.: $5,000 for the cost of tuition, room, board and book expenses. **Number Awarded:** 1. **To Apply:** Applicants must submit a completed application form (available on the website), 300-word essay, three references and transcript, if applicable. **Deadline:** April 10. **Contact:** PO Box 212, Warrenton, VA 20188.

1780 ■ Association of Food and Drug Officials

2550 Kingston Rd., Ste. 311
York, PA 17402
Ph: (717) 757-2888
Fax: (717) 650-3650
E-mail: afdo@afdo.org
URL: www.afdo.org

1781 ■ George M. Burditt Scholarships
(Undergraduate/Scholarship)

Purpose: To provide financial assistance for students to further their education. **Focus:** General studies. **Qualif.:** Applicants must be juniors preparing to enter their senior year. **Criteria:** Applicants must demonstrate a desire to serve in a career of research, regulatory work, quality control, or teaching in an area related to some aspect of food, drugs or consumer product safety; potential to be a leader; and must have at least 3.0 GPA during the first two years of undergraduate study on a 4.0 scale.

Funds Avail.: $1,500. **To Apply:** Applicants must submit a completed application form; official and complete college transcript, and two letters of recommendation from faculty members. **Deadline:** February 1. **Contact:** Application form and supporting documents must be sent to: Dr. Joanne Brown at the above address; Email: jbrown@afdo.org.

1782 ■ Betsy B. Woodward Scholarships
(Undergraduate/Scholarship)

Purpose: To provide financial assistance for students to further their education. **Focus:** General studies. **Qualif.:** Applicants must be juniors preparing to enter their senior year. **Criteria:** Applicants must demonstrate a desire to serve in a career of research, regulatory work, quality control, or teaching in an area related to some aspect of food, drugs or consumer product safety; potential to be a leader; and must have at least 3.0 GPA during the first two years of undergraduate study on a 4.0 scale.

Funds Avail.: $1,500. **To Apply:** Applicants must submit a completed application form, official and complete college transcript; and two letters of recommendation from faculty members. **Deadline:** February 1. **Contact:** Application form and supporting documents must be sent to: Dr. Joanne Brown at the above address; Email: jbrown@afdo.org.

1783 ■ Association of Former Intelligence Officers (AFIO)

6723 Whittier Ave., Ste. 200
McLean, VA 22101-4533
Ph: (703) 790-0320
Fax: (703) 991-1278
E-mail: afio@afio.com
URL: www.afio.com

1784 ■ David L. Boren Undergraduate Scholarships *(Graduate, Undergraduate/Scholarship)*

Purpose: To provide funding for graduate and undergraduate study in a number of targeted countries and fields.

Awards are arranged alphabetically below their administering organizations

Focus: General studies. **Qualif.:** Applicants must be students currently enrolled in an undergraduate study or graduates planning to attend graduate school; and must have the desire to study foreign languages in addition to any major-related study. **Criteria:** Preferences are given for those students who are interested in studying critical languages or fields related to security interest.

Funds Avail.: $10,000 up to $20,000. **To Apply:** Applicants must complete an official application form which can be obtained from the Loyola College faculty representative. Applicants must also submit application forms online together with the three letters of recommendation, and four semesters' worth of transcripts. **Deadline:** February 10. **Contact:** For further information, applicants may write to Institute of International Education, 1400 K St., NW, Washington, DC 20005-2403; Toll free: 800-618-NSEP; Fax: 202-326-7672; E-mail: nsep@iie.org.

1785 ■ CIA Undergraduate Scholarships
(Undergraduate/Scholarship)

Purpose: To assist minority, disabled and non-disabled deserving students to increase knowledge and academic skills. **Focus:** General studies. **Qualif.:** Applicants must be high school seniors planning to enroll or college sophomores attending a four or five-year college program; must be U.S. citizens; 1,000 SAT (Math or Verbal) or 21 ACT scores or higher (high school students); must have 3.0 on a 4.0 scale high school or college GPA or higher. **Criteria:** Applicants must demonstrate financial need.

Funds Avail.: $18,000. **To Apply:** Applicants must apply online and must successfully complete medical and psychological exam, polygraph interview and extensive background investigation; must attach the following documents: a) SAT or ACT scores (for high school seniors); b) most current FAFSA or SAR; c) school transcripts; and d) two letters of recommendation. **Deadline:** November 1.

1786 ■ Association for Gerontology Education in Social Work (AGESW)
PO Box 198136
Nashville, TN 37219-8136
URL: agesw.org

1787 ■ Aracelis Francis Minority Scholarships in Gerontology *(Master's/Scholarship)*

Purpose: To promote leadership in gerontological social work practice for MSW students. **Focus:** Gerontology. **Qualif.:** Applicants must belong to ethnic minority group which includes American Indian/Alaskan Native, Asian/Pacific Islander, Black and Hispanic; must be enrolled in a Master's of Social Work program in a school accredited or in candidacy by CSWE; must demonstrate a passion and commitment to gerontological social work; must be nominated by one of their professors who know their academic and fieldwork. At least one nominator must be a member of AGESW. **Criteria:** Recipients will be selected based on submitted materials.

Funds Avail.: $1,000. **To Apply:** Nomination packet must include nomination form, letter of recommendation, short resume or curriculum vitae. Awards committee requests that the letter of recommendation provides a brief summary of characteristics, qualities, behaviors and/or activities that exemplify the nominee's scholarship, leadership and dedication to the field of gerontological social work. **Contact:** Holly Dabelko-Schoeny at dabelko-schoeny.1@osu.edu or skolomer@uga.edu.

1788 ■ Association of Government Accountants (AGA)
2208 Mt. Vernon Ave.
Alexandria, VA 22301-1314
Ph: (703) 684-6931
Fax: (703) 548-9367
Free: 800-AGA-7211
E-mail: agamembers@agacgfm.org
URL: www.agacgfm.org

1789 ■ Association of Government Accountants Undergraduate/Graduate Scholarships for Community Service Accomplishments *(Graduate, Undergraduate/Fellowship, Scholarship)*

Purpose: To provide financial assistance to qualified professionals who exemplify and promote excellence in federal, state or local government financial management. **Focus:** Accounting, Economics, Public administration. **Qualif.:** Applicants must be pursuing a degree in a financial management academic discipline; must be actively involved in community service projects. **Criteria:** Applicants will be selected based on community service involvement and accomplishments.

Funds Avail.: $3,000. **Number Awarded:** 1. **To Apply:** Applicants must complete the application form available online; must provide a recommendation letter and transcript of record; must submit an essay (cannot be more than two double-spaced pages). Application forms, essays and any letter of recommendation to: Louise Kapelewski, lkapelewski@agacgfm.org. **Deadline:** March 30.

1790 ■ Association of Government Accountants Undergraduate/Graduate Scholarships for Full-time study *(Graduate, Undergraduate/Fellowship, Scholarship)*

Purpose: To provide financial assistance to qualified professionals who exemplify and promote excellence in federal, state or local government financial management. **Focus:** Accounting, Economics, Public administration. **Qualif.:** Applicant must be an AGA member or family member; must be undertaking full-time undergraduate/graduate study in a financial management academic discipline; must have a minimum GPA of 2.5 on a 4.0 scale. **Criteria:** Applicants will be selected based on community service involvement and accomplishments.

Funds Avail.: $3,000. **Number Awarded:** 4. **To Apply:** Applicants must complete the application form available online; must provide a recommendation letter and transcript of record; must submit an essay (cannot be more than two double-spaced pages). Application forms, essays and any letter of recommendation to: Louise Kapelewski, lkapelewski@agacgfm.org. **Deadline:** March 30.

1791 ■ Association of Government Accountants Undergraduate/Graduate Scholarships for Part-time study *(Graduate, Undergraduate/Fellowship, Scholarship)*

Purpose: To provide financial assistance to qualified professionals who exemplify and promote excellence in federal, state or local government financial management. **Focus:** Accounting, Economics, Public administration. **Qualif.:** Applicants must be an AGA member or family member; must be applied toward full-time undergraduate/graduate study in a financial management academic discipline; must

Awards are arranged alphabetically below their administering organizations

have a minimum GPA of 2.5 on a 4.0 scale. **Criteria:** Applicants will be selected based on community service involvement and accomplishments.

Funds Avail.: $1,000. **To Apply:** Applicants must complete the application form available online; must provide a recommendation letter and transcript of record; must submit an essay (cannot be more than two double-spaced pages). Application forms, essays and any letter of recommendation to: Louise Kapelewski, lkapelewski@agacgfm.org. **Deadline:** March 30.

1792 ■ Association of Independent Colleges and Universities of Pennsylvania (AICUP)

101 N Front St.
Harrisburg, PA 17101
Ph: (717) 232-8649
Fax: (717) 233-8574
E-mail: francis@aicup.org
URL: www.aicup.org

1793 ■ Air Products and Chemicals, Inc. Scholarships *(Undergraduate/Scholarship)*

Purpose: To promote the engineering and information technology profession to individuals from groups historically underrepresented in engineering. **Focus:** Chemical engineering; Mechanical Engineering; Computer and information sciences. **Qualif.:** Applicants must: be full-time undergraduate students majoring only in Chemical engineering, Mechanical engineering, Information technology (computer science, management information systems, IST); be enrolled as a junior in fall; have a minimum GPA of 3.0; be women and/or members of the following minority groups: American Indian or Alaska Native, Asian, Black or African American, Hispanic or Latino, Native Hawaiian or other Pacific Islander. Student must be accepted at, or currently attending, one of 84 member colleges and universities of the Association of Independent Colleges and Universities of Pennsylvania. **Criteria:** Selection will be based on the committee's criteria.

Funds Avail.: $7,500. **Number Awarded:** 3. **To Apply:** Application forms are available at the Financial Aid office; applicant must submit complete application materials to Mary Maronic, Foundation Associate, Association of Independent Colleges and Universities of Pennsylvania. A complete application consists of a completed, signed application form, a copy of the student's transcript, a resume and an essay; the candidate may submit a letter of recommendation. **Deadline:** April 20. **Contact:** Mary Maronic, 717-232-8649 ext. 232; maronic@aicup.org.

1794 ■ Michael Baker Inc. Scholarships for Diversity in Engineering *(Undergraduate/Scholarship)*

Purpose: To promote the engineering and information technology profession to individuals from groups historically underrepresented in engineering. **Focus:** Civil engineering; Architectural engineering. **Qualif.:** Applicants must be: full-time undergraduate students majoring in Civil, Environmental or Architectural Engineering only; enrolled as juniors in the fall; maintaining a minimum GPA of 3.0; women and/or members of the following minority groups: American Indians or Alaska Natives, Asians, Black or African Americans, Hispanics or Latinos, Native Hawaiians or Other Pacific Islanders. Student must be accepted at, or currently attending, one of 84 member colleges and universities of the As-

sociation of Independent Colleges and Universities of Pennsylvania. **Criteria:** Selection will be based on the committee's criteria.

Funds Avail.: No specific amount. **To Apply:** Application forms are available at the Financial Aid office. Applicant must submit complete application to Mary Maronic, Foundation Associate, Association of Independent Colleges and Universities of Pennsylvania. A complete application consists of a completed, signed application form, a copy of the student's transcript, a resume and an essay; the candidate may submit a letter of recommendation. **Contact:** Mary Maronic, 717-232-8649 ext. 232; maronic@aicup.org.

1795 ■ Commonwealth "Good Citizen" Scholarships *(Undergraduate/Scholarship)*

Purpose: To provide scholarship to the students who have shown an extraordinary commitment to community service and who have demonstrated creativity in shaping their volunteer activities. **Focus:** General studies. **Qualif.:** Applicant must be a full-time undergraduate student with an extraordinary commitment to community service and who has demonstrated creativity in shaping his/her volunteer activities; and must attend a school that is a member of the Association of Independent Colleges and Universities of Pennsylvania. **Criteria:** Selection will be based on the Committee's criteria.

Funds Avail.: $1,000. **Number Awarded:** 7. **To Apply:** Applicant must write a brief essay describing their college experience and focusing upon the answers to the following: what volunteer/extracurricular activities do they participate in, either on or off campus; how do their community service activities relate to their major and what leadership roles have they taken; what are their career/academic goals upon graduation; how will they remain involved in their community upon graduation. Applicants should include any additional information that they feel will be helpful in choosing them as a recipients of the Commonwealth "Good Citizen" Scholarship; must limit essay to two double-spaced pages (essay must have 1-inch margins) with a font that is easily readable and set no smaller than 11. Completed applications should be returned to applicants' Financial Aid Office. **Deadline:** April 29. **Contact:** Mary Maronic, 717-232-8649 ext. 232; maronic@aicup.org.

1796 ■ HDR Engineering, Inc. Scholarships for Diversity in Engineering *(Undergraduate/Scholarship)*

Purpose: To promote the engineering and information technology profession to individuals from groups historically underrepresented in engineering. **Focus:** Civil engineering; Architectural engineering; Engineering, Geological. **Qualif.:** Applicants must: be full-time undergraduate students majoring only in civil engineering, structural engineering or geotechnical engineering; be enrolled as juniors in fall; have a minimum GPA of 3.0; be women and/or members of one of the following minority groups: American Indian or Alaska Native, Asian, Black or African American, Hispanic or Latino, Native Hawaiian or Other Pacific Islander. Applicants must be accepted at, or currently attending, one of 84 member colleges and universities of the Association of Independent Colleges and Universities of Pennsylvania. **Criteria:** Selection will be based on the committee's criteria.

Funds Avail.: $2,500. **To Apply:** Application forms are available at the Financial Aid office. Applicant must submit complete application materials to Mary Maronic, Foundation Associate, Association of Independent Colleges and Universities of Pennsylvania. A complete application

Awards are arranged alphabetically below their administering organizations

consists of a completed, signed application form, a copy of the student's transcript, a resume and an essay; the candidate may submit a letter of recommendation. **Deadline:** April 29. **Contact:** Mary Maronic, 717-232-8649 ext. 232; maronic@aicup.org.

1797 ■ McLean Scholarships (Undergraduate/Scholarship)

Purpose: To help full-time undergraduate students who are enrolled in a Nursing or Physician's Assistant program. **Focus:** Nursing. **Qualif.:** Applicant must be a full-time undergraduate student enrolled in a Nursing or Physician Assistant program at one of the Association of Independent Colleges and Universities of Pennsylvania's member institutions; and have at least a 3.0 GPA. Ideal candidates are campus leaders and community volunteers. **Criteria:** Selection will be based on the committee's criteria.

Funds Avail.: $2,500. **Number Awarded:** 7. **To Apply:** Application forms are available at the Financial Aid office. Along with the completed applications, students may submit a copy of their transcript, a letter of recommendation and any other materials that they feel will be helpful to the committee in making their decision. Students must also submit a brief essay describing their college experience, including the following information: why they chose their major; what steps they are taking to ensure that they succeed in their major; what they plan to do upon graduating and their academic/career goals. Applicants should also describe the primary volunteer/extracurricular activities in which they participate; how these activities relate to their major and what leadership roles they have taken. Completed applications should be returned to the applicants' Financial Aid office, which will then select one application to submit to AICUP. **Deadline:** April 19. **Contact:** Mary Maronic, 717-232-8649 ext. 232; maronic@aicup.org.

1798 ■ Association for Iron & Steel Technology
186 Thorn Hill Rd.
Warrendale, PA 15086-7528
Ph: (724) 814-3000
Fax: (724) 814-3001
E-mail: info@aist.org
URL: www.aist.org

1799 ■ AIST Baltimore Chapter Scholarships
(Undergraduate/Scholarship)

Purpose: To enhance education and careers in engineering or metallurgy. **Focus:** Engineering; Metallurgy. **Qualif.:** Applicant must be a dependent or a spouse of a commendable member of the AIST Baltimore Chapter Scholarship; must be attending an eligible, full-time course in the field of engineering at an institution; demonstrate interest towards a career in the field of iron and steel industry. **Criteria:** Recipients are selected by the Scholarship Award Committee.

Funds Avail.: $1,500. **Number Awarded:** 1. **To Apply:** Applicants must submit an application form available at the website; a resume; a copy of SAT/ACT scores; copy of transcripts; two essays (not exceeding 500 words) about the applicant's accomplishments, and the applicant's interest/involvement in the steel and iron industry. Send all documents to: AIST Baltimore Chapter Scholarships, Frank Gasker, Severstal Sparrows Point, 2504 Peck Ave., Sparrows Point, MD 21219. **Deadline:** April 30. **Contact:** Frank Gasker, 2504 Peck Ave., Sparrows Point, MD 21219.

1800 ■ AIST Detroit Chapter Scholarships
(Undergraduate/Scholarship)

Purpose: To enhance education and careers in the iron and steel-related industry. **Focus:** Engineering; Metallurgy. **Qualif.:** Applicant must be a dependent of an AIST Detroit Chapter member in good standing for two or more consecutive years; have a minimum cumulative GPA of 3.0 on a 4.0 scale; must be enrolled full-time as an undergraduate student majoring in engineering, metallurgy or materials science program at an accredited North American university; demonstrate interest towards a career in the field of iron and steel industry. **Criteria:** Recipients are selected by the Scholarship Award Committee.

Funds Avail.: $2,500. **Number Awarded:** 2. **To Apply:** Applicant must submit an application form available at the website; a resume; three letters of recommendation (addressing character, academic status, leadership potential and career commitment) from a high school counselor or college academic advisor, teacher/professor or a previous employer; copy of SAT/ACT scores; copy of current transcripts; an essay (maximum of 2 pages) about the applicant's professional goals, interest in a career in the iron and steel industry, and how the applicant's skills could be applied to enhance the industry. Requirements must be sent to: AIST Detroit Member Chapter Scholarships, c/o Judith A. Quinn, Chapter Secretary 41158 Savage Road Belleville, MI 48111. **Deadline:** April 30. **Contact:** Judith Quinn, 313-319-2815, judieqn@aol.com.

1801 ■ AIST Northwest Chapter Scholarships
(Undergraduate/Scholarship)

Purpose: To enhance education and careers in the field of engineering. **Focus:** Engineering. **Qualif.:** Applicant must be a relative of a member of the AIST Northwest Member Chapter; must be a Pacific Northwest student; must demonstrate great interest in the iron and steel profession. Chemistry, metallurgy, mathematics, engineering and physics students are also qualified for the scholarships. **Criteria:** Priority will be given to engineering students. Academic achievements in chemistry, mathematics and physics are a major basis for the selection. Extra-curricular activities and student statements are also considered.

Funds Avail.: $1,000. **Number Awarded:** 2. **To Apply:** Applicants must submit an application form available at the website; a resume; a recommendation/evaluation from a counselor, teacher or professor; copy of SAT/ACT scores; copy of transcripts; and an essay (maximum of 2 pages) with one of the topics: Purpose in going to college; beneficial experience during the last two summers; most significant experiences and effect on future plans; accomplishments providing the greatest satisfaction; reason why the applicant should be chosen as the recipient of the award. Requirements must be sent to: Gerardo L. Giraldo, 2434 Eyres Pl. W., Seattle, WA 98199. **Deadline:** April 30. **Contact:** Gerardo L. Giraldo at 206-285-7897 or acero9938@comcast.net.

1802 ■ AIST San Francisco Chapter Scholarships (Undergraduate/Scholarship)

Purpose: To provide financial assistance for students who are planning to enter an accredited North American school. **Focus:** General studies. **Qualif.:** Applicant must be related to a San Francisco Chapter member; must be planning to attend or currently enrolled at an accredited university or college (full-time course only). **Criteria:** Recipients are selected by the Scholarship Award Committee.

Funds Avail.: $1,500. **Number Awarded:** 1. **To Apply:**

Awards are arranged alphabetically below their administering organizations

Applicants must submit an application form available at the website; resume; a recommendation/evaluation from a counselor, teacher or professor; copy of SAT/ACT scores; copy of transcripts; an essay (not more than 250 words) that answers the question, "Why are you motivated to attend college and how do you hope to utilize your degree after you graduate?". All requirements must be sent to: Frank Martucci Department Manager - Project Development USS-POSCO Industries 900 Loveridge Rd. Pittsburg, CA 94565. **Deadline:** April 30. **Contact:** Frank Martucci, 925-439-6477, fmartucci@ussposco.com.

1803 ■ AIST Benjamin F. Fairless Scholarships, American Institute of Mining, Metallurgical and Petrolium Engineers (AIME) (Undergraduate/Scholarship)

Purpose: To enhance education and careers in the iron and steel-related industries. **Focus:** Engineering; Metallurgy. **Qualif.:** Applicant must be enrolled full-time in an engineering, metallurgy or materials science program at an accredited North American university; have a minimum GPA of 3.0 on a 4.0 scale; demonstrate interest toward a career in the field of iron and steel industry. **Criteria:** Recipient is selected based on the application and other documents.

Funds Avail.: $2,000. **Number Awarded:** 3. **To Apply:** Applicant must submit an application form available at the website; a resume; an essay (maximum of 2 pages) about the applicant's professional goals, interest in a career in the steel industry, and how the applicant's skills could be applied to enhance the industry; three letters of recommendation (addressing the character, academic status, leadership potential and career commitment) from a college academic advisor, professor and previous employer; and transcripts. **Deadline:** March 4. **Remarks:** Established in 1954. **Contact:** Lori Wharrey at lwharrey@aist.org or 724-816-3044.

1804 ■ Midwest Chapter Scholarships - Jack Gill (Undergraduate/Scholarship)

Purpose: To provide educational assistance for engineering students. **Focus:** Engineering. **Qualif.:** Applicant must be a graduating high school student or a full-time freshman, sophomore or junior student in good academic standing from an accredited institution. **Criteria:** Recipient will be selected according to merit.

Funds Avail.: $3,000. **Number Awarded:** 1. **To Apply:** Applicants must submit an application form available at the website; a resume; a recommendation/evaluation from a counselor, teacher or professor; copy of SAT/ACT scores; copy of transcripts; and an essay (maximum of 2 pages) describing the applicant's objectives for college and career. Requirements should be sent to: AIST Midwest Member Chapter Scholarships c/o Scott Hamilton, Superior Engineering, 2345 167th St., Hammond, IN 46323-1418. **Deadline:** March 15.

1805 ■ Globe-Trotters Chapter Scholarships (Undergraduate/Scholarship)

Purpose: To enhance education and careers in the iron and steel-related industry. **Focus:** Metallurgy. **Qualif.:** Applicant must be a dependent of a member (Globe-Trotters member must also be a current member of AIST); be currently enrolled in an accredited college or university. Postgraduate students are also qualified for the scholarships. **Criteria:** Recipients are selected based on the submitted essay, academic and extracurricular activities.

Funds Avail.: $2,500. **Number Awarded:** 4. **To Apply:**

Applicants must submit an application form available at the website; resume; copy of SAT/ACT scores; a copy of transcripts; an essay (maximum of 300 words) about the reason the applicant has selected the particular field of study, and an explanation on how the scholarship will be applied, such as tuition, books, etc. All required documents, together with the application, must be sent to: Globe-Trotter Scholarships Steve Speth, Charter Steel Company, 1658 Cold Spring Drive, Saukville, WI 53080. **Deadline:** April 30. **Contact:** Steve Speth, speths@chartersteel.com Phone: 262-268-2517, Fax: 262-268-2572.

1806 ■ Northeastern Ohio Chapter Scholarships - Alfred B. Glossbrenner and John Klusch Scholarships (Undergraduate/Scholarship)

Purpose: To provide educational assistance for students who wish to pursue their education and career in engineering and metallurgy. **Focus:** Engineering; Metallurgy. **Qualif.:** Applicant must be a dependent of an at least two-year member of the Association for Iron and Steel Technology, which must be a U.S. citizen or a U.S landed immigrant. Applicant should also be a full-time student from an accredited North American University; pursuing education in the field of engineering or metallurgy. Chemistry, geology, mathematics or physics students are also qualified for the scholarships. **Criteria:** Recipient is selected based on academic achievements in science (i.e. chemistry, mathematics and physics); extra-curricular activities and student statements will also be considered.

Funds Avail.: $1,000. **Number Awarded:** 1. **To Apply:** Applicants must submit an application form available at the website; a resume; a recommendation/evaluation from a counselor, teacher or professor; copy of SAT/ACT scores; copy of transcripts; and an essay (maximum of 2 pages) with one of the topics: Purpose in going to college; beneficial experience during the last two summers; most significant experiences and effect on future plans; accomplishments providing the greatest satisfaction; reason why the applicant should be chosen as the recipient of the award. All documents and application should be sent to: Richard J. Kurz, Chapter Secretary AIST Northeastern Ohio Chapter 22831 East State Street, Rte. 62 Alliance, Ohio 44601. **Deadline:** April 30. **Contact:** Richard J. Kurz at rkurz@eohiomach.com.

1807 ■ AIST Willy Korf Memorial Fund (Undergraduate/Scholarship)

Purpose: To enhance education and careers in iron and steel-related industry. **Focus:** Engineering; Metallurgy. **Qualif.:** Applicants must be enrolled full-time in an engineering, metallurgy or materials science program at an accredited North American university; have a minimum cumulative GPA of 3.0 on a 4.0 scale; demonstrate interest in a career in the iron and steel industry. **Criteria:** Recipients are selected based on the application materials submitted.

Funds Avail.: $3,000. **Number Awarded:** 3. **To Apply:** Applicants must submit an application form available at the website; a resume; three letters of recommendation which address the applicant's character, academic status, leadership potential and career commitment from a college academic advisor, professor and previous employer; transcripts; and an essay (maximum of 2 pages) about the applicant's professional goals, interest in a career in the iron and steel industry, and how the applicant's skills could be applied to enhance the industry. **Deadline:** March 4. **Remarks:** Established by Korf Lurgi Steeltec, Inc. **Contact:**

Awards are arranged alphabetically below their administering organizations

Lori Wharrey lwharrey@aist.org or 724-816-3044.

1808 ■ AIST Ronald E. Lincoln Memorial Scholarships (Undergraduate/Scholarship)

Purpose: To enhance education and careers in the iron and steel-related industries. **Focus:** Engineering; Metallurgy. **Qualif.:** Applicant must be enrolled full-time in an engineering, metallurgy or materials science program at an accredited North American university; have a minimum cumulative GPA of 3.0 on a 4.0 scale; demonstrate interest toward a career in the field of iron and steel industry. **Criteria:** Recipients are selected based on the application materials submitted.

Funds Avail.: $3,000. **Number Awarded:** 2. **To Apply:** Applicants must submit an application form available at the website; a resume; three letters of recommendation (addressing character, academic status, leadership potential and career commitment) from a college academic advisor, professor and previous employer; transcripts; an essay (maximum of 2 pages) about the applicant's professional goals, interest in a career in the iron and steel industry, and how the applicant's skills could be applied to enhance the industry. **Deadline:** March 4. **Remarks:** Established by Chaparral Steel. **Contact:** Lori Wharrey lwharrey@aist.org. or 724-816-3044.

1809 ■ Midwest Chapter Scholarships - Betty McKern (Undergraduate/Scholarship)

Purpose: To provide educational assistance for engineering students. **Focus:** Engineering. **Qualif.:** Applicant must be a graduating female high school student or a full-time freshman, sophomore or junior student in good academic standing from an accredited institution. **Criteria:** Recipient will be selected according to merits.

Funds Avail.: $3,000. **Number Awarded:** 1. **To Apply:** Applicants must submit an application form available at the website; a resume; a recommendation/evaluation from a counselor, teacher or professor; copy of SAT/ACT scores; transcripts; and an essay (maximum of 2 pages) describing the applicant's objectives for college and career. Requirements should be sent to: AIST Midwest Member Chapter Scholarships c/o Scott Hamilton, Superior Engineering, 2345 167th St., Hammond, IN 46323-1418. **Deadline:** March 15.

1810 ■ Midwest Chapter Scholarships - Engineering (Undergraduate/Scholarship)

Purpose: To provide educational assistance for engineering students. **Focus:** Engineering. **Qualif.:** Applicant must be a graduating high school student or a full-time freshman, sophomore or junior student in good academic standing from an accredited institution. **Criteria:** Recipients will be selected according to merit.

Funds Avail.: $1,500. **Number Awarded:** 2. **To Apply:** Applicants must submit an application form available at the website; a resume; a recommendation/evaluation from a counselor, teacher or professor; copy of SAT/ACT scores; a copy of transcripts; and an essay (maximum of 2 pages) describing the applicant's objectives for college and career. Requirements should be sent to: AIST Midwest Member Chapter Scholarships c/o Scott Hamilton, Superior Engineering, 2345 167th St., Hammond, IN 46323-1418. **Deadline:** March 15.

1811 ■ Midwest Chapter Scholarships - Non-Engineering (Undergraduate/Scholarship)

Purpose: To provide educational assistance to non-engineering students. **Focus:** General studies. **Qualif.:** Applicant must be a graduating high school student or a full-time freshman, sophomore or junior student in good academic standing from an accredited institution. **Criteria:** Beneficiary will be selected according to merit.

Funds Avail.: $1,500. **Number Awarded:** 2. **To Apply:** Applicants must submit an application form available at the website; a resume; a recommendation/evaluation from a Counselor, Teacher or Professor; copy of SAT/ACT scores; a copy of transcripts; and an essay (maximum of 2 pages) describing the applicant's objectives for college and career. Requirements should be sent to: AIST Midwest Member Chapter Scholarships c/o Scott Hamilton, Superior Engineering, 2345 167th St., Hammond, IN 46323-1418. **Deadline:** March 15.

1812 ■ Midwest Chapter Scholarships - Western States Awards (Undergraduate/Scholarship)

Purpose: To provide educational assistance for both engineering and non-engineering students. **Focus:** Engineering; General studies. **Qualif.:** Applicant must be a graduating high school student or a full-time freshman, sophomore or junior in good academic standing from an accredited institution. **Criteria:** Recipients will be selected according to merit.

Funds Avail.: $3,000. **Number Awarded:** 1. **To Apply:** Applicants must submit an application form available at the website; a resume; a recommendation/evaluation from a counselor, teacher or professor; copy of SAT/ACT scores; copy of transcripts; and an essay (maximum of 2 pages) describing the applicant's objectives for college and career. Requirements should be sent to: AIST Midwest Member Chapter Scholarships c/o Scott Hamilton, Superior Engineering, 2345 167th St., Hammond, IN 46323-1418. **Deadline:** March 15.

1813 ■ Midwest Chapter Scholarships - Don Nelson (Undergraduate/Scholarship)

Purpose: To provide educational assistance to engineering students. **Focus:** Engineering. **Qualif.:** Applicant must be a graduating high school student or a full-time freshman, sophomore or junior student in good academic standing from an accredited institution. **Criteria:** Grantee will be selected according to merit.

Funds Avail.: $3,000. **Number Awarded:** 1. **To Apply:** Applicants must submit an application form available at the website; a resume; a recommendation/evaluation from a counselor, teacher or professor; copy of SAT/ACT scores; copy of transcripts; and an essay (maximum of 2 pages) describing the applicant's objectives for college and career. Requirements should be sent to: AIST Midwest Member Chapter Scholarships c/o Scott Hamilton, Superior Engineering, 2345 167th St., Hammond, IN 46323-1418. **Deadline:** March 15.

1814 ■ Midwest Chapter Scholarships - Mel Nickel (Undergraduate/Scholarship)

Purpose: To provide educational assistance for engineering students. **Focus:** Engineering. **Qualif.:** Applicant must be a graduating high school student or a full-time freshman, sophomore or junior student in good academic standing from an accredited institution. **Criteria:** Recipients will be selected according to merit.

Funds Avail.: $3,000. **Number Awarded:** 1. **To Apply:** Applicants must submit an application form available at the website; a resume; a recommendation/evaluation from a

Awards are arranged alphabetically below their administering organizations

counselor, teacher or professor; copy of SAT/ACT scores; copy of transcripts; and an essay (maximum of 2 pages) describing the applicant's objectives for college and career. Requirements should be sent to: AIST Midwest Member Chapter Scholarships c/o Scott Hamilton, Superior Engineering, 2345 167th St., Hammond, IN 46323-1418. **Deadline:** March 15.

1815 ■ Ohio Valley Chapter Scholarships
(Undergraduate/Scholarship)

Purpose: To enhance education and careers in engineering, metallurgy, physical science, computer technology or an engineering technology field. **Focus:** Engineering; Metallurgy; Physical sciences. **Qualif.:** Applicant must be a dependent or member of Ohio Valley Chapter of the AIST; planning to attend or currently enrolled full-time curriculum at an accredited university or college; pursuing a degree in Mechanical Engineering, Electrical Engineering, Engineering/Engineering Technology, Environmental Engineering/Sciences, Metallurgy, Physical Sciences, Computer Technology, Computer Programming, Information Systems Technology, Chemistry, Biology/Microbiology, Physics, other engineering-related fields, or other related fields approved by the committee. **Criteria:** Recipient is selected based on academic performance and achievements in mathematics and science, extracurricular activities and essays.

Funds Avail.: $1,000. **Number Awarded:** 2. **To Apply:** Applicants must submit an application form available at the website; a resume; a recommendation/evaluation from a counselor and teacher or professor; copy of SAT/ACT scores; copy of transcripts; an essay (maximum of 2 pages) with either one of the topics: purpose in going to college; beneficial experience during the last two summers; most significant experiences and effect on future plans; accomplishments providing the greatest satisfaction; reasons why he/she should be chosen as the recipient of the award. All requirements must be sent to: Jeff McKain, 11451 Reading Road Cincinnati, OH 45241. Or thru email, Attn: AIST Scholarship, E-mail subject: AIST Scholarship to jeff.mckain@xtek.com. **Deadline:** March 31. **Contact:** Lori Wharrey at lwharrey@aist.org or 724-814-3044.

1816 ■ AIST David H. Samson Scholarships
(Undergraduate/Scholarship)

Purpose: To provide financial support for Canadian students who are pursuing a career in engineering. **Focus:** Engineering. **Qualif.:** Applicant must be a dependent of a Canadian citizen or an immigrant who is a commendable member of the Association for Iron and Steel Technology; must be attending full-time engineering course at an accredited Canadian university or college. Chemistry, geology, mathematics or physics students are also welcome for the scholarships. **Criteria:** Priority will be given to engineering students.

Funds Avail.: $2,000. **Number Awarded:** 1. **To Apply:** Applicant must submit an application form available at the website; a resume; a recommendation/evaluation (from a counselor, teacher or professor); a copy of SAT/ACT scores; a copy of current transcripts; an essay (1-2 pages) with either one of the topics: purpose in going to college; beneficial experience during the last two summers, most significant experiences and effect on future plans; accomplishments providing the greatest satisfaction; reasons why he/she should be chosen as the recipient of the award. All requirements should be sent to: Robert Kneale, AIST Northern Member Chapter, David H. Samson Canadian Scholarship PO Box 1734 Cambridge, ON NIR7G8 Canada.

Deadline: June 30. **Remarks:** Managed by the AIST Northern Member Chapter. **Contact:** Lori Wharrey at lwharrey@aist.org or 724-776-6040, ext. 621.

1817 ■ AIST William E. Schwabe Memorial Scholarships *(Undergraduate/Scholarship)*

Purpose: To enhance education and careers in iron and steel-related industries. **Focus:** Engineering; Metallurgy. **Qualif.:** Applicant must be enrolled full-time in an engineering, metallurgy or materials science program at an accredited North American university; have a minimum cumulative GPA of 3.0 on a 4.0 scale; demonstrate interest in a career in the iron and steel industry. **Criteria:** Recipient will be selected based on the application materials submitted.

Funds Avail.: $3,000. **Number Awarded:** 1. **To Apply:** Applicants must submit an application form available at the website; a resume; three letters of recommendation (addressing character, academic status, leadership potential and career commitment) from a college academic advisor, professor and previous employer; transcripts; an essay (maximum of 2 pages) about the applicant's professional goals, interest in a career in the iron and steel industry, and how the applicant's skills could be applied to enhance the industry. **Deadline:** March 4. **Remarks:** Established in 2005 by the Steel Manufacturers Association (SMA). **Contact:** Lori Wharrey at lwharrey@aist.org or 724-816-3044.

1818 ■ Southeast Member Chapter Scholarships *(Undergraduate/Scholarship)*

Purpose: To provide educational assistance for students who are planning a career in Engineering or the sciences. **Focus:** Engineering. **Qualif.:** Applicant must be a Southeast Chapter student; planning to take up courses in engineering, sciences or other majors related to iron and steel production. **Criteria:** Recipient will be selected based on the SAT or ACT scores for college applicants and on the applicant's GPA from an accredited college or institution (non-first year student). Extra-curricular activities and student's written essays are also considered.

Funds Avail.: $3,000. **Number Awarded:** 1. **To Apply:** Applicants must submit an application form available at the website; a resume; a recommendation/evaluation from a counselor, teacher or professor; copy of SAT/ACT scores; copy of transcripts; and an essay (maximum of 250 words) discussing the applicant's involvement in high school and the reason why the applicant deserves the scholarship. All documents together with the application should be sent to: AIST Southeast Chapter Mike Hutson, Secretary 803 Floyd St., Kings Mountain, NC, 28086. **Deadline:** April 30. **Contact:** Mike Hutson at mike@johnhutsoncompany.com, 704-730-8320.

1819 ■ Association of Jewish Libraries (AJL)
PO Box 1118
Teaneck, NJ 07666
Ph: (212) 725-5359
E-mail: ajlibs@osu.edu
URL: www.jewishlibraries.org

1820 ■ AJL Convention Travel Grants *(All/Grant)*
Purpose: To provide financial assistance to members with financial need. **Focus:** General studies. **Qualif.:** Applicants must be current members of AJL at the time of application. Members in the local area are not eligible to apply. **Criteria:** Applicants are selected based on the committee's review of the application materials.

Awards are arranged alphabetically below their administering organizations

Funds Avail.: No specific amount. **To Apply:** Applicants must complete the application form available online and send it via e-mail, fax, or regular mail. **Remarks:** Grantees must submit an article describing the applicant's convention experience to the AJL Newsletter a year after receiving the award. **Contact:** Application form and supporting documents must be submitted to Ronda Rose at 323-654-3652, 323-650-8414, frose@sbcglobal.net.

1821 ■ AJL Scholarship Program (Graduate/Scholarship)

Purpose: To encourage students to train for, and enter, the field of Judaica librarianship. **Focus:** Library and archival sciences. **Qualif.:** Applicants must be attending or planning to attend an ALA-accredited graduate library school or equivalent; should have an interest in, and demonstrate a potential for, pursuing a career in Judaica librarianship. **Criteria:** Selection is based on the application.

Funds Avail.: $1,000. **To Apply:** Applicants must complete and submit the application form available online; a documentation of acceptance or enrollment; documentation of Jewish studies completed at an academic or less formal level or of experience working in Judaic libraries; and Personal statement as a Word or rtf format. Submit requirements via e-mail, fax, or regular mail to: Shulamith Z. Berger, Curator of Special Collections, Yeshiva University, 500 W, 185th St., New York, NY 10033. **Deadline:** April 1. **Contact:** Shulamith Berger, Phone: 212-960-5451; Fax: 212-960-0066; email: sberger@yu.edu.

1822 ■ Doris Orenstein Memorial Convention Travel Grants (All/Grant)

Purpose: To provide financial assistance to members with financial need. **Focus:** General studies. **Qualif.:** Applicants must be members of the AJL and first time to attend the convention. **Criteria:** Applicants are selected based on the committee's review of the application materials.

Funds Avail.: No specific amount. **To Apply:** Applicants must complete the application form available online and send it via e-mail, fax, or regular mail. **Deadline:** April 30. **Contact:** Yelena Luckert, yluckert@atsumd.edu, Phone: 301-405-9365, Fax: 301-314-2795.

1823 ■ Association of Latino Professionals in Finance and Accounting (ALPFA)

801 S Grand Ave., Ste. 650
Los Angeles, CA 90017
Ph: (213) 243-0004
Fax: (213) 243-0006
E-mail: ceo@national.alpfa.org
URL: www.alpfa.org

1824 ■ ALPFA Scholarship Programs (Postgraduate, Undergraduate/Scholarship)

Purpose: To financially support Hispanic students pursuing studies in accounting, finance, IT or related field. **Focus:** Business; Finance; Accounting. **Qualif.:** Applicants must be full-time Hispanic students or of Hispanic descent; U.S. citizens or permanent residents of the United States or Puerto Rico; attending an accredited university; have a cumulative grade point average of 3.0 and above on a 4.0 scale; must demonstrate financial need; and pursuing an undergraduate or master's degree in business, finance and accounting. **Criteria:** Recipients are selected based on the selection committee's review of all applications.

Funds Avail.: $1,250-$10,000. **To Apply:** Applicants must register first in order to apply online (please visit the website). Applicants must submit an official transcript; proof of family income and citizen status; an essay; letter of recommendation; resume; and The Financial Aid Verification (for semi-finalist only). **Deadline:** December 15. **Contact:** Hispanic College Fund, HCF-info@hispanicfund.org.

1825 ■ Association for Library Service to Children (ALSC)

50 E Huron St.
Chicago, IL 60611-2795
Ph: (312) 280-2162
Fax: (312) 280-5271
Free: 800-545-2433
E-mail: alsc@ala.org
URL: www.ala.org/alsc

1826 ■ Bound to Stay Bound Books Scholarships (BTSB) (Graduate/Scholarship)

Purpose: To provide financial assistance for individuals pursuing a master's or advanced degree in children's librarianship. **Focus:** Library and archival sciences. **Qualif.:** Applicants must be U.S. or Canadian citizens pursuing a master or advanced degree in children's librarianship. **Criteria:** Applicants will be selected on the basis of academic excellence, leadership qualities and the desire to work with children in any type of library.

Funds Avail.: $7,000. **Number Awarded:** 4. **To Apply:** Applicants must submit a completed application form; a personal statement describing career interests and goals; a commitment to library service to children; and three references (must be completed online). **Remarks:** The scholarship is sponsored by the Bound to Stay Bound Books, Inc. **Contact:** Questions regarding applications may be sent by e-mail to Dan Rude at drude@ala.org.

1827 ■ Frederic G. Melcher Scholarships (Graduate/Scholarship)

Purpose: To provide financial assistance for individuals pursuing a master's or advanced degree in children's librarianship. **Focus:** Library and archival sciences. **Qualif.:** Applicants must be U.S. or Canadian citizens pursuing a master or advanced degree in children's librarianship. **Criteria:** Applicants will be selected on the basis of academic excellence, leadership qualities and the desire to work with children in any type of library.

Funds Avail.: $6,000. **Number Awarded:** 2. **To Apply:** Applicants must submit a completed application form; a personal statement describing career interests and goals; a commitment to library service to children; and three references (must be completed online). **Deadline:** March 1. **Remarks:** The scholarship was established as a tribute to Frederic G. Melcher, a great leader in promoting better books for children. **Contact:** Questions regarding applications may be sent by e-mail to Dan Rude at drude@ala.org.

1828 ■ Association of Moving Image Archivists (AMIA)

1313 N Vine St.
Hollywood, CA 90028
Ph: (323) 463-1500
Fax: (323) 463-1506
E-mail: amia@amianet.org

Awards are arranged alphabetically below their administering organizations

URL: www.amianet.org

1829 ■ Rick Chace Foundation Scholarships
(Graduate/Scholarship)

Purpose: To provide financial assistance to deserving students who want to pursue a career in the field of moving image archiving. **Focus:** Library and archival sciences; Museum science. **Qualif.:** Applicants must be enrolled full-time in a graduate-level or other advanced program in moving image studies or production, library or information services, archival administration, museum studies or a related discipline; must have a GPA of at least 3.0. **Criteria:** Candidates will be judged based on their commitment in pursuing a career in the field of moving image archiving, academic records and strength of a student's program of study.

Funds Avail.: $4,000. **To Apply:** Applicant must complete the application form available online; must have the official transcript from the applicant's most recent academic program; must provide an essay of not more than 1,000 words describing their major field of study, interest in moving image archiving, relevant experience and/or education and career goals; must submit two letters of recommendation. **Deadline:** May 21.

1830 ■ Kodak Fellowships in Film Preservation
(Graduate/Fellowship)

Purpose: To provide financial assistance to deserving students who want to pursue a career in the field of moving image archiving. **Focus:** Library and archival sciences; Museum science. **Qualif.:** Applicant must be enrolled full-time in a graduate-level or other advanced program in moving image studies or production, library or information services, archival administration, museum studies or a related discipline; must be accepted into such a program for the next academic year; must have a GPA of at least 3.0; must have strong organizational and interpersonal skills and demonstrate an interest in pursuing a career in the moving image archival field; must be at least 21 years of age and must possess a valid driver's license; must be a US citizen or have a US work visa. **Criteria:** Recipient will be selected based on the following criteria: (1) Commitment to pursuing a career in moving image archiving; (2) Academic record; (3) Program of study as it applies to moving image archiving.

Funds Avail.: $4,000. **To Apply:** Applicant must complete the application form, available online; must submit an official transcript from the applicant's current or most recently completed academic program; must have an essay of not more than 1,000 words describing the applicant's interest and involvement in moving image archiving; must have two letters of recommendation. Application form and other supporting documents must be sent to 1313 North Vine St., Hollywood, CA 90028. **Deadline:** May 1.

1831 ■ Mary Pickford Scholarships *(Graduate/Scholarship)*

Purpose: To provide financial assistance to deserving students who want to pursue a career in the field of moving image archiving. **Focus:** Library and archival sciences; Museum science. **Qualif.:** Applicant must be enrolled full-time in a graduate-level or other advanced program in moving image studies or production, library or information services, archival administration, museum studies or a related discipline; must have a GPA of at least 3.0. **Criteria:** Recipient will be selected based on the scholarship application criteria.

Funds Avail.: $4,000. **To Apply:** Applicant must complete the application form available online; must have the official transcript from the applicant's most recent academic program; must provide an essay of no more than 1,000 words describing applicant's major field of study, interest in moving image archiving, relevant experience and/or education and career goals; must submit two letters of recommendation. **Deadline:** May 1.

1832 ■ CFI Sid Solow Scholarships *(Graduate/Scholarship)*

Purpose: To provide financial assistance to deserving students who want to pursue a career in the field of moving image archiving. **Focus:** Library and archival sciences; Museum science. **Qualif.:** Applicants must be enrolled full time in a graduate-level or other advanced program in moving image studies or production, library or information services, archival administration, museum studies or a related discipline; must have a GPA of at least 3.0 in their current or most recently completed academic program. **Criteria:** Recipient will be selected based on the scholarship application criteria.

Funds Avail.: $4,000. **To Apply:** Applicant must complete the application form available online; must have the official transcript from the applicant's most recent academic program; must provide an essay of no more than 1,000 words describing applicant's major field of study, interest in moving image archiving, relevant experience and/or education and career goals; must submit two letters of recommendation. **Deadline:** May 21.

1833 ■ Sony Pictures Scholarships *(Graduate/Scholarship)*

Purpose: To provide financial assistance to deserving students who want to pursue a career in the field of moving image archiving. **Focus:** Library and archival sciences; Museum science. **Qualif.:** Applicant must be enrolled full-time in a graduate-level or other advanced program in moving image studies or production, library or information services, archival administration, museum studies or a related discipline; must have a GPA of at least 3.0. **Criteria:** Recipient will be selected based on the scholarship application criteria.

Funds Avail.: $4,000. **To Apply:** Applicant must complete the application form available online; must have the official transcript from the applicant's most recent academic program; must provide an essay of no more than 1,000 words describing applicant's major field of study, interest in moving image archiving, relevant experience and/or education and career goals; must submit two letters of recommendation. **Deadline:** May 21.

1834 ■ Universal Studios Preservation Scholarships *(Graduate/Scholarship)*

Purpose: To provide financial assistance to deserving students who want to pursue their career in the field of moving image archiving. **Focus:** Library and archival sciences; Museum science. **Qualif.:** Applicants must be enrolled full-time in a graduate-level or other advanced program in moving image studies or production, library or information services, archival administration, museum studies or a related discipline; must have a GPA of at least 3.0. **Criteria:** Candidates will be judged based on their commitment in pursuing a career in the field of moving image archiving, academic records, and strength of a student's program of study.

Funds Avail.: $4,000. **To Apply:** Applicant must complete

Awards are arranged alphabetically below their administering organizations

the application form available online; must have the official transcript from the applicant's most recent academic program; must provide an essay of not more than 1,000 words describing their major field of study, interest in moving image archiving, relevant experience and/or education and career goals; must submit two letters of recommendation. **Deadline:** May 21.

1835 ■ Association of Occupational Health Professionals in Healthcare (AOHP)

109 VIP Dr., Ste. 220
Wexford, PA 15090
Fax: (724) 935-1560
Free: 800-362-4347
E-mail: info@aohp.org
URL: www.aohp.org

1836 ■ Sandra Bobbitt Continuing Education Scholarships *(Undergraduate/Scholarship)*

Purpose: To provide annual education scholarships to subsidize the educational efforts of members. **Focus:** General studies. **Qualif.:** Applicant must be an AOHP active member in good standing. **Criteria:** Applicants will be evaluated by the Scholarship Selection Committee.

Funds Avail.: $600. **Number Awarded:** 1. **To Apply:** Applicants must submit a typewritten, double-spaced essay limited to 1,000 words. Provide a formal title for the project. State the one category from the following list that best describes the area the research project will address: employment examinations, medical surveillance, immunizations, infectious diseases, employee health records, work injuries, administration, marketing occupational health services, or other healthcare-related topics. Briefly describe the impact/significance of the research project to the occupational health professional in a healthcare setting. List the objectives and goals of the research project. Describe the activities that will be implemented to achieve the goals of the project, e.g., questionnaire. As appropriate, describe the target population, e.g., clinical (nursing, etc.) nonclinical employees. **Deadline:** July 1.

1837 ■ Julie Schmid Research Scholarships *(All/Scholarship)*

Purpose: To encourage, promote and strengthen the knowledge base and expertise of the occupational health professional in healthcare. **Focus:** Occupational safety and health. **Qualif.:** Applicants must have proposals for an original research project on current and/or anticipated issues in healthcare-related occupational health. **Criteria:** Recipient will be selected based on merit in accordance with the evaluation tool; completed proposals shall be submitted according to the format outlined below; must include a cover letter with applicant's name and address; name or any personal identification data must not be included on the proposal itself; address completed proposals and correspondence to the AOHP executive secretary, Research Scholarship Committee chairperson.

Funds Avail.: $2,000. **To Apply:** Applicants must submit a formal title for the project; state the one category from the following list that best describes the area the research project will address: employment examinations, medical surveillance, immunizations, infectious diseases, employee health records, work injuries, administration, marketing occupational health services or other healthcare-related topics; briefly describe the impact/significance of the research

project to the occupational health professional in a healthcare setting; list the objectives and goals of the research project; describe the activities that will be implemented to achieve the goals of the project, e.g., questionnaire. As appropriate, describe the target population, e.g., clinical (nursing, etc.) nonclinical employees. **Deadline:** July 1.

1838 ■ Association of PeriOperative Registered Nurses (AORN)

2170 S Parker Rd., Ste. 400
Denver, CO 80231-5711
Ph: (303) 755-6304
Fax: (303) 755-3212
Free: 800-755-2676
E-mail: custsvc@aorn.org
URL: www.aorn.org

1839 ■ AORN Foundation Scholarship Program *(Undergraduate/Scholarship)*

Purpose: To provide financial assistance to students enrolled in nursing schools and to perioperative nurses pursuing bachelors, masters, or doctoral degrees. **Focus:** Nursing. **Qualif.:** Nursing students must be enrolled in an accredited program as a nursing major for the 2011-2012 academic year; must be a program leading to licensure as a RN. Current nurses must have a commitment to perioperative nursing; must be enrolled in an accredited master's degree program in nursing or in an accredited master's degree program in another discipline for the 2011-2012 academic year. **Criteria:** Recipient is selected based on academics, essay and accurate completion of the scholarship application.

Funds Avail.: Varies. **To Apply:** Applicant must submit all the required application information. **Deadline:** June 15. **Contact:** foundation@aorn.org.

1840 ■ Association of Physician Assistants in Cardiovascular Surgery (APACVS)

7044 S 13th St.
Oak Creek, WI 53134
Fax: (414) 768-8001
Free: 877-221-5651
E-mail: n.short@atstechenterprises.net
URL: www.apacvs.org

1841 ■ APACVS Scholarships *(Postgraduate, Professional development/Scholarship)*

Purpose: To support individuals for the continuous medical education in the field of cardiovascular and thoracic surgery. **Focus:** Cardiology. **Qualif.:** Applicant must be PA surgical resident and a member of the APACVS; must be a physician assistant who is enrolled in a post-graduate residency program who is planning to subspecialty cardiovascular and thoracic surgery. **Criteria:** Candidate will be evaluated by the Scholarship Committee.

Funds Avail.: No amount mentioned. **Deadline:** November 30.

1842 ■ Association for Preservation Technology International (APT)

3085 Stevenson Dr., Ste. 200
Springfield, IL 62703
Ph: (217) 529-9039

Awards are arranged alphabetically below their administering organizations

Fax: (888) 723-4242
E-mail: info@apti.org
URL: www.apti.org

1843 ■ Association for Preservation Technology International Student Scholarships *(Graduate, Undergraduate/Scholarship)*

Purpose: To promote research or projects on preservation technology. **Focus:** Historic preservation. **Qualif.:** Applicants must be enrolled in a trade, undergraduate or graduate program which is affiliated with a trade school, college or university. **Criteria:** Recipients are selected based on the quality of a submitted abstract and a personal statement.

Funds Avail.: No amount specified. **Number Awarded:** 15. **To Apply:** Applicants are required to submit their personal as well as their professor's contact information; a 250-word abstract describing the scope of the project/research and summarizing its relationship to an aspect of preservation technology and/or heritage conservation that relates to the conference theme and/or paper tracks; and 250-word personal statement stating why the conference would be of value to them. Applicants are also required to create an electronic presentation and give an oral presentation during the conference. **Remarks:** Established in 2000. **Contact:** Questions can be addressed to Joan Berkowitz at 646-437-1326, jberkowitz@superstructures.com or Lesley Gilmore at 406-922-7114, lesley@ctagroup.com.

1844 ■ Association for Psychological Science (APS)

1133 15th St. NW, Ste. 1000
Washington, DC 20005
Ph: (202) 293-9300
Fax: (202) 293-9350
URL: www.psychologicalscience.org

1845 ■ Association for Psychological Science Student Grants (APS) *(Graduate, Undergraduate/Grant)*

Purpose: To provide financial support for APS students for their research currently in early development. **Focus:** Psychology. **Qualif.:** Applicant must be an APS undergraduate or graduate student. **Criteria:** Committees will evaluate each research proposal based on its clarity, ability to explain some psychological phenomenon and ability to advance research in a specified area.

Funds Avail.: $500 per graduate student and $300 per undergraduate student. **Number Awarded:** 3 for graduate student and 2 for undergraduate student. **To Apply:** Applicant must submit a cover letter; project summary; and review board approval. Submit through E-mail at apssc.graduate@psychologicalscience.org, with a subject, APSSC Student Grant Submission. The cover letter and Project Summary should be in separate Microsoft Word or Open Format documents and the Review Board Approval should be in a PDF document (or equivalent electronic field type). **Deadline:** November 1.

1846 ■ Association of Public Treasurers of the United States and Canada (APT US & C)

962 Wayne Ave., Ste. 910
Silver Spring, MD 20910
Ph: (301) 495-5560

Fax: (301) 495-5561
E-mail: info@aptusc.org
URL: www.aptusc.org

1847 ■ APT US&C Scholarships *(All/Scholarship)*

Purpose: To encourage continuing of education for all active members. **Focus:** General studies. **Qualif.:** Applicant must be an active member in good standing. **Criteria:** Selection is based on total cost of the conference or institute being attended; the financial condition of the Scholarship Fund; maximum number of awards to a person is two; and on the letter from the applicants' city, town, county, etc.

Funds Avail.: $250-$500. **To Apply:** Applicants must submit a completed APT US & C Scholarship application form together with a letter from the applicants' city, town, county, etc. **Deadline:** May 1.

1848 ■ Association of Registered Nurses of Newfoundland and Labrador (ARNNL)

55 Military Rd.
Saint Johns, NL, Canada A1C 2C5
Ph: (709) 753-6060
Fax: (709) 753-4940
Free: 800-563-3200
E-mail: info@arnnl.nf.ca
URL: www.arnnl.nf.ca

1849 ■ Nancy Llewellyn, RN Pediatric Nursing Bursaries *(Graduate, Professional development/Scholarship)*

Purpose: To provide financial assistance and support to qualified individuals who want to pursue their career in pediatric nursing. **Focus:** Nursing, Pediatric. **Qualif.:** Applicants must exemplify the characteristics of Nancy Llewellyn, RN; must be employed as a nurse in Newfoundland and Labrador; must be a member in good standing with ARNNL; must be a member of the ARNNL education and research trust; must have worked in pediatrics for at least 1 year and intend to pursue a career in pediatric nursing in NL; must be willing to share information obtained through participation in the education program or activity with colleagues; must not have received an ARNNL Trust award in the past 2 years. **Criteria:** Recipient will be selected based on the following criteria: (a) personal statement; (b) reference; and (c) financial need.

Funds Avail.: $500. **To Apply:** Applicant must submit the completed application form available from the website; must complete the reference form. **Deadline:** October 15.

1850 ■ Florrie Penney, RN Rehabilitation Nursing Bursaries *(Graduate, Professional development/Scholarship)*

Purpose: To provide financial assistance to deserving individuals who want to enhance their nursing practice in neurology, neurosurgery, stroke rehabilitation, and/or brain injury. **Focus:** Nursing. **Qualif.:** Applicant must exemplify the characteristics of Mrs. Florrie Penney, RN; must be employed as a nurse in Newfoundland and Labrador; must be a member in good standing with ARNNL; must be a member of the ARNNL education and research trust; must have worked in pediatrics for at least 1 year and intend to pursue a career in pediatric nursing in NL; must be participating in a continuing education program that is relevant to the enhancement of nursing care of clients

Awards are arranged alphabetically below their administering organizations

and/or nursing as a profession. **Criteria:** Recipient will be selected based on the following criteria: (a) personal statement; (b) reference; and (c) financial need.

Funds Avail.: $500. **To Apply:** Applicant must submit the completed application form available from the website; must complete the reference form. **Deadline:** October 15.

1851 ■ Post Basic Course Bursaries (Graduate, Professional development/Scholarship)

Purpose: To provide financial assistance and support to qualified individuals who want to pursue their education and enhance their nursing practice. **Focus:** Nursing. **Qualif.:** Applicant must be employed as a nurse in Newfoundland and Labrador; must be enrolled in an education course/program that is relevant to the enhancement of nursing care of clients and/or nursing as a profession; must be willing to share information obtained through participation in the education course/program with colleagues; must be a member in good standing with ARNNL; must be a member of the ARNNL education and research trust. **Criteria:** Recipients will be selected based on the following criteria: (a) personal statement; (b) reference; and (c) financial need.

Funds Avail.: $1,000. **To Apply:** Applicant must submit a completed application form available from the website; must complete the reference form. **Deadline:** October 15. **Contact:** To request a copy of the application form, applicants may send an email to trust@arnnl.ca.

1852 ■ Violet D. Ruelokke Primary Health Care Awards (Graduate, Professional development/ Scholarship)

Purpose: To provide financial assistance and support to qualified individuals who want to pursue primary health care practice. **Focus:** Health care services. **Qualif.:** Applicant must be employed as a nurse in Newfoundland and Labrador; must be enrolled in an education course/program that is relevant to the enhancement of nursing care of clients and/or nursing as a profession; must be willing to share information obtained through participation in the education course/program with colleagues; must be a member in good standing with ARNNL; must be a member of the ARNNL education and research trust. **Criteria:** Recipients will be selected based on the following criteria: (a) personal statement; (b) reference; and (c) financial need.

Funds Avail.: $500-$1,000. **To Apply:** Applicants must submit a completed application form available from the website; must present PHC research at a conference; must complete a non-credit PHC focused program. **Deadline:** October 15.

1853 ■ St. Clare's Mercy Hospital School of Nursing Alumni Association Scholarships (Graduate/Scholarship)

Purpose: To provide financial assistance to qualified individuals who want to pursue their nursing career. **Focus:** Nursing. **Qualif.:** Applicant must be a graduate of the St. Clare's Mercy Hospital School of nursing, or a son or daughter of a graduate; must be enrolled in a post basic Bachelor of Nursing program at a recognized university; must have completed at least one year of their program; must have achieved a minimum overall average of 70% in completed university courses; must have resided in NL for at least one year prior to commencement of university study; must be a member of the ARNNL Education and Research Trust; must not be a previous recipient of the

scholarship. **Criteria:** Preference will be given to those who have completed at least one year of their graduate program. Recipient will be selected based on the following criteria: (a) academic ability; (b) potential contribution to the nursing profession; (c) personal statement; (d) reference; (e) financial need.

Funds Avail.: $750 for part-time; $1,500 for full-time. **To Apply:** Applicant must submit the completed application form available from the website; must complete the reference form. **Deadline:** October 15.

1854 ■ Association of Rehabilitation Nurses (ARN)
4700 W Lake Ave.
Glenview, IL 60025-1485
Ph: (847) 375-4710
Fax: (847) 375-6481
Free: 800-229-7530
E-mail: info@rehabnurse.org
URL: www.rehabnurse.org

1855 ■ Association of Rehabilitation Nurses Scholarship Program (Undergraduate/ Scholarship)

Purpose: To provide financial assistance to rehabilitation nurses working toward a Bachelor of Science in Nursing (BSN) degree. **Focus:** Nursing. **Qualif.:** Applicant must be a member in good standing of ARN; currently enrolled in a BSN degree program; has completed at least one course and practices rehabilitation nursing at present, a minimum of two years up to present. **Criteria:** The recipient will be selected by ARN based on the application materials provided.

Funds Avail.: $1,500. **To Apply:** Applicants must submit completed form; transcript documenting enrollment in a BSN program; a typed 1-3 page summary of professional and educational goals and achievements which includes: involvement in ARN at the national and local levels, continuing education participation in the past three to five years, professional publications or presentations, community involvement, particularly related to advocating for individuals with disabilities, efforts made to improve rehabilitation nursing practice and the delivery of care in your work setting. **Deadline:** June 1. **Contact:** ARN For additional details, applicants must contact Alice Taylor at the above address; Toll free: 800-229-7530; E-mail: ataylor@connect2amc.com.

1856 ■ Mary Ann Mikulic Scholarships (Professional development/Scholarship)

Purpose: To provide financial assistance covering full tuition of the Professional Rehabilitation Nursing course. **Focus:** Nursing. **Qualif.:** Applicants must be registered nurses with current license practicing in the specialty of rehabilitation nursing and able to meet all the financial responsibilities incurred by participating in the course. **Criteria:** Applicants will be evaluated by the Scholarship committee based on the application provided.

Funds Avail.: Full tuition. **Number Awarded:** One. **To Apply:** Applicants must submit a completed application form along with current curriculum vitae or resume; a letter of support from an employer; and a statement on how the applicants will use the knowledge gained from completing the course and future plans as a rehabilitation nurse. **Deadline:** June 1. **Contact:** Alice Taylor at ataylor@connect2amc.com.

Awards are arranged alphabetically below their administering organizations

1857 ■ Association for Research on Nonprofit Organizations and Voluntary Action (ARNOVA)

550 W N St., Ste. 301
Indianapolis, IN 46202
Ph: (317) 684-2120
Fax: (317) 684-2128
E-mail: tjeavons@arnova.org
URL: www.arnova.org/

1858 ■ ARNOVA Emerging Scholar Awards
(Graduate, Undergraduate/Award)

Purpose: To help and support students and scholars spread their research into practice, and enhance their knowledge. **Focus:** Nonprofit sector. **Qualif.:** Applicants must have a paper accepted for the 2011 ARNOVA Conference. Winners of the past Emerging Scholars Award are not eligible to apply for the Emerging Scholars Award. **Criteria:** Selection of applicants will be based on the following criteria: (1) relevance of research to the field of nonprofit and voluntary action studies; (2) stage of research development; (3) demonstrated interest in nonprofit organization and voluntary action; (4) quality of conference proposal; and (5) letter of recommendation.

Funds Avail.: No specific amount. **To Apply:** Applicants must submit the following requirements: (1) cover letter; (2) copy of ARNOVA conference proposal; (3) letter of acceptance from the Conference Committee Chairs; (4) letter of recommendation from a faculty member or a letter of recommendation from someone who knows the research or work; (5) resume, containing a mailing address, email address, and telephone number; (6) official transcript of record. **Deadline:** September 9.

1859 ■ Association of School Business Officials of Maryland and the District of Columbia (ASBO-MD&DC)

PO Box 6602
Lutherville, MD 21094-6602
Ph: (410) 608-0911
E-mail: asbomddc@comcast.net
URL: www.asbo.org

1860 ■ Dwight P. Jacobus Scholarships
(Undergraduate/Scholarship)

Purpose: To assist individuals who need financial assistance for college education. **Focus:** Business; Education. **Qualif.:** Applicants must be residents of Maryland or District of Columbia for at least one year preceding the date of the award; must be accepted for admission as a full-time student; must demonstrate financial need; and must have a minimum 3.0 overall GPA. **Criteria:** Recipients are selected based on scholastic achievement; financial need; SAT and ACT scores; and quality of extra-curricular achievements.

Funds Avail.: $1,000. **Number Awarded:** 1. **To Apply:** Applicants must file an application and supporting documents with the Chair of the Scholarship Committee for ASBO of Maryland and the District of Columbia. Applications are available from guidance or financial aid offices, or may be requested in writing from the Chair of the Scholarship Committee. **Deadline:** March 1. **Contact:** Mr. Thad Kalmanowicz, ASBDO MD/DC Scholarship Committee Chair, Queen Anne's County Public Schools, 202 Chesterfield Rd., Centerville, MD 21617.

1861 ■ Association of Schools of Public Health Graduate Training Programs (ASPH)

1900 M St. NW, Ste. 710
Washington, DC 20036
Ph: (202) 296-1099
Fax: (202) 296-1252
E-mail: info@asph.org
URL: fellowships.asph.org

1862 ■ ASPH/CDC/PRC Minority Health Fellowships *(Doctorate/Fellowship)*

Purpose: To enhance the preparation of future public health professionals from ethnic and racial minorities by providing training opportunities in prevention research. **Focus:** Public health. **Qualif.:** Applicant must be an underrepresented minority student currently enrolled at the doctoral level, research-based (PhD, DrPH, EdD, ScD) program at an accredited university or school of public health with CDC-funded Prevention Research Centers; must be granted admission to candidacy (completed coursework and passed qualifying exams) prior to the second year of the fellowship program; and must be a U.S. citizen or hold a visa permitting permanent residence in the U.S. **Criteria:** Selection is based on the quality of the essay, strength of credentials, previous professional experience and letters of recommendation.

Funds Avail.: No specific amount. **Number Awarded:** 3. **To Apply:** Applicants must complete the application online. In addition, applicants must submit a hard copy documents of two generic recommendation letters; graduate transcripts (of all ASPH member school(s) of public health attended); and the signature page (available after submitting the online application). **Deadline:** January 10.

1863 ■ ASPH/CDC Public Health Fellowships
(Doctorate, Graduate/Fellowship)

Purpose: To address emerging needs of public health, and to provide leadership and professional opportunities at the Centers for Disease Control and Prevention (CDC) for students and graduate students of ASPH member graduate schools of public health. **Focus:** Public health. **Qualif.:** Applicant must have received an MPH or Doctorate degree prior to the beginning of the fellowship; or an early career professional with MPH or Doctorate degrees (within 5 years of graduation); have received his/her degree(s) from an ASPH-member, CEPH-accredited, graduate school of public health; and be a U.S. citizen or hold a visa permitting permanent residence in the U.S. **Criteria:** All Applications to the program undergo a two-phase review process.

Funds Avail.: No specific amount. **To Apply:** Applicants must complete the application online. In addition, applicants must submit a hard copy documents of two generic recommendation letters; graduate transcripts (of all ASPH member school(s) of public health attended); and the signature page (available after submitting the online application). **Deadline:** December 9. **Remarks:** Established in 1995.

1864 ■ ASPH/CDC Public Health Preparedness Fellowships *(Postdoctorate/Fellowship)*

Purpose: To provide opportunities for a motivated and experienced individual to play a role in helping to shape United States health policy. **Focus:** Public health. **Qualif.:** Applicant must have received an MPH or Doctorate degree prior to the beginning of the fellowship; or an early career professional with MPH or Doctorate degrees (within 5 years

Awards are arranged alphabetically below their administering organizations

of graduation); have received his/her degree(s) from an ASPH-member, CEPH-accredited, graduate school of public health; and a U.S. citizen or hold a visa permitting permanent residence in the U.S. **Criteria:** All Applications to the program undergo a two-phase review process.

Funds Avail.: No specific amount. **To Apply:** Applicants must complete the application online. In addition, applicants must submit a hard copy documents of two generic recommendation letters; graduate transcripts (of all ASPH member school(s) of public health attended); and the signature page (available after submitting the online application).

1865 ■ ASPH/EPA Environmental Health Fellowships *(Doctorate, Postdoctorate/Fellowship)*

Purpose: To provide professional training and opportunities for early career public health professionals by enabling them to work in EPA on current and emerging environmental public health needs. **Focus:** Public health. **Qualif.:** Applicant must have received an MPH or Doctorate degree prior to the beginning of the fellowship (no later than August of the application year); or an early career professional with MPH or Doctorate degree (within 5 years of graduation); must have received his/her degree(s) from an ASPH-member, CEPH-accredited, graduate school of public health; and must be a U.S. citizen or hold a visa permitting permanent residence in the U.S. **Criteria:** All Applications to the program undergo a two-phase review process.

Funds Avail.: No specific amount. **To Apply:** Applicants must complete the application online. In addition, applicants must submit a hard copy documents of two generic recommendation letters; graduate transcripts (of all ASPH member school(s) of public health attended); and the signature page (available after submitting the online application). **Deadline:** December 9.

1866 ■ ASPH/NHTSA Public Health Fellowships *(Postdoctorate/Fellowship)*

Purpose: To provide training opportunities to graduates of accredited schools of public health. **Focus:** Public health. **Qualif.:** Applicant must have received an MPH or Doctorate degree prior to the beginning of the fellowship; or be a career professional with MPH or Doctorate degree (within 5 years of graduation); must have received his/her degree(s) from an ASPH-member, CEPH-accredited, graduate school of public health; and be a U.S. citizen or hold a visa permitting permanent residence in the U.S. **Criteria:** Selection is based on the quality of the essay, strength of credentials, previous professional experience; and letters of recommendation.

Funds Avail.: No specific amount. **To Apply:** Applicants must complete the application online. In addition, applicants must submit a hard copy documents of two generic recommendation letters; graduate transcripts (of all ASPH member school(s) of public health attended); and the signature page (available after submitting the online application). **Deadline:** June 10. **Remarks:** The fellowship program is a collaborative effort between the Association of Schools of Public Health (ASPH) and the U.S. Department of Transportation (DOT), National Highway Traffic Safety Administration (NHTSA).

1867 ■ ASPH Public Health Policy Fellowships *(Doctorate, Postdoctorate/Fellowship)*

Purpose: To provide opportunities for a motivated and experienced individual to play a role in helping to shape United States health policy. **Focus:** Public health. **Qualif.:**

Applicant must have received an MPH or Doctorate degree prior to the beginning of the fellowship; or an early career professional with MPH or Doctorate degree (within 5 years of graduation); have received the degree(s) from an ASPH-member, CEPH-accredited, graduate school of public health; and a U.S. citizen or hold a visa permitting permanent residence in the U.S. **Criteria:** All Applications to the program undergo a two-phase review process.

Funds Avail.: No specific amount. **To Apply:** Applicants must complete the application online. In addition, applicants must submit a hard copy documents of two generic recommendation letters; graduate transcripts (of all ASPH member school(s) of public health attended); and the signature page (available after submitting the online application). **Deadline:** January 10.

1868 ■ ASPH/CDC Allan Rosenfield Global Health Fellowships *(Postdoctorate, Postgraduate/Fellowship)*

Purpose: To enhance the training of graduates of schools of public health with an interest in global health. **Focus:** Public health. **Qualif.:** Applicant must have received his/her Master's or Doctorate degree prior to the beginning of the fellowship or within the last five years (graduate degrees must come from an ASPH member graduate school of public health accredited by the Council on Education for Public Health); and must be a U.S. citizen or hold a visa permitting permanent residence in the U.S. **Criteria:** Selection is based on quality of essay, strength of credentials, previous professional experience; and letters of recommendation.

Funds Avail.: $40,949 to cover all personal living expenses. **To Apply:** Applicants must complete the application online. In addition, applicants must submit a hard copy documents of two generic recommendation letters; graduate transcripts (of all ASPH member school(s) of public health attended); and the signature page (available after submitting the online application). **Deadline:** February 10.

1869 ■ Association of Science-Technology Centers (ASTC)
1025 Vermont Ave. NW, Ste. 500
Washington, DC 20005-6310
Ph: (202) 783-7200
Fax: (202) 783-7207
E-mail: info@astc.org
URL: www.astc.org

1870 ■ Lee Kimche McGrath Worldwide Fellowships *(Professional development/Fellowship)*

Purpose: To foster greater understanding among international colleagues and encourage global participation in ASTC; to support professionals who have genuine need for financial assistance in order to attend conference. **Focus:** Museum science. **Qualif.:** Applicant must be an individual from a science center or museum (open or in development) outside the United States. **Criteria:** Applications are reviewed by the ASTC International Advisory Board. Preference will be given to an applicant whose: (1) institution cannot afford to send a representative to an ASTC conference; (2) participation will benefit other science centers in addition to their own; (3) have limited opportunities to meet professionally with science center colleagues; (4) willing to participate in conference session, writing experiences or institution for an ASTC publication.

Funds Avail.: $1,500 (travel and accommodation). **To Ap-**

Awards are arranged alphabetically below their administering organizations

ply: Application forms are available at the website. **Deadline:** May 31. **Contact:** Laura Huerta Migus at 202-783-7200 x-139 or lhuertamigus@astc.org.

1871 ■ Association of Seventh-Day Adventist Librarians (ASDAL)

c/o Annette Melgosa
Walla Walla University Libraries
104 S College Ave.
College Place, WA 99324
E-mail: annette.melgosa@wallawalla.edu
URL: www.asdal.org

1872 ■ D. Glenn Hilts Scholarships *(Graduate, Undergraduate/Scholarship)*

Purpose: To recognize excellence in scholarship and to encourage individuals with leadership potential to seek employment in a Seventh-day Adventist library. **Focus:** General studies; Library and archival sciences. **Qualif.:** Applicant must be a Seventh-Day Adventist in good standing; be accepted in an American Library Association accredited library school; and must be a full-time student. **Criteria:** Priority is given to applicants with a complete application package.

Funds Avail.: $1,500. **To Apply:** Applicant must submit completed application form available at the website; submit a copy of the acceptance letter from the ALA-accredited library; GRE scores; an essay of 600 words; high school and college transcripts; and three letters of reference (there must be one from the applicant's Seventh-day Adventist pastor). **Deadline:** July 15. **Contact:** Cynthia Mae Helms, at helmsc@andrews.edu.

1873 ■ Association for the Sociology of Religion (ASR)

618 SW 2nd Ave.
Galva, IL 61434-1912
Ph: (309) 932-2727
Fax: (309) 932-2282
E-mail: williamswatos@augustana.edu
URL: www.sociologyofreligion.com

1874 ■ Joseph H. Fichter Research Grants *(Professional development/Grant)*

Purpose: To financially assist scholars involved in promising research in the area of women and religion. **Focus:** Women's studies; Religion. **Qualif.:** Applicants must be ASR members at least during the year prior the submission of their application. **Criteria:** Recipients will be selected based on submitted materials.

Funds Avail.: $24,000. **To Apply:** Applicants must submit a proposal, one-page detailed budget, curriculum vitae and a statement of qualifications that specifically addresses the research project. Proposals should review briefly the previous research and theory that forms the background for the study, describe methods and research timetable and summarize succinctly what this research project aims to discover. Proposals and accompanying documents must be written in English. **Deadline:** May. **Contact:** Materials should be submitted electronically to Barbara J. Denison at bjdeni@ship.edu.

1875 ■ Robert J. McNamara Student Paper Awards *(Graduate/Award)*

Purpose: To recognize outstanding student papers in the sociology of religion. **Focus:** Religion. **Qualif.:** Applicants

must be currently enrolled graduate students who have not defended the PhD when the paper is submitted; membership in the Association for the Sociology of Religion is required either at the time of application or previously. **Criteria:** Applicants will be judged based on submitted paper.

Funds Avail.: $500. **To Apply:** Applicants must submit an abstract from the ASR Program Chair following the guidelines of all standard paper submissions. It should be in the form of articles with a maximum length of 40 double-spaced, single-sided pages inclusive of all materials: text, title, notes, table, figures, etc. The title page should include an abstract of no more than 200 words. Texts should not exceed 12,000 words, approximately 36 double-spaced pages of 12 point font. Applicants should attach their paper as a file, formatted in Microsoft Word. **Deadline:** June. **Contact:** Attached file should be forwarded to Prof. Rachel Kraus at rmkraus@bsu.edu.

1876 ■ Association of State Dam Safety Officials (ASDSO)

450 Old Vine St., Fl. 2
Lexington, KY 40507-1544
Ph: (859) 257-5140
Fax: (859) 323-1958
E-mail: info@damsafety.org
URL: www.damsafety.org

1877 ■ Association of State Dam Safety Officials Undergraduate Scholarships *(Undergraduate/Scholarship)*

Purpose: To promote the study of civil engineering and related fields as a career. **Focus:** Engineering, Civil. **Qualif.:** Applicant must be a U.S. citizen; enrolled in a civil engineering program and in their senior year; pursuing a career in hydraulics, hydrology or geotechnical disciplines or related to design, construction and operation of dams; have 2.5 GPA for the first three years in college and recommended by advisor. **Criteria:** Awards are given based on academic merit; financial need; work experience and essay.

Funds Avail.: A maximum of $10,000. **To Apply:** Applicant must send an application form; transcript; three letters of recommendation; and (500-word) essay describing the proposed study and its importance. **Deadline:** March 31.

1878 ■ Association of Surgical Technologists (AST)

6 W Dry Creek Cir., Ste. 200
Littleton, CO 80120-8031
Ph: (303) 694-9130
Fax: (303) 694-9169
Free: 800-637-7433
E-mail: bteutsch@ast.org
URL: www.ast.org

1879 ■ AST National Honor Society Student Scholarships *(Graduate/Scholarship)*

Purpose: To reward members of the AST National Honor Society who are continuing their education by attending a CAAHEP-accredited surgical assisting program. **Focus:** Surgery. **Qualif.:** Applicant must be a member of the AST National Honor Society; must be in the process of complet-

Awards are arranged alphabetically below their administering organizations

ing a CAAHEP-accredited surgical assisting program or must begin classes within one year of receipt of scholarship; must maintain a 3.0 GPA (based on a 4.0 scale); and must remain in good standing within the institution and must document current AST membership. **Criteria:** Recipients will be selected based on the quality of the application materials submitted.

Funds Avail.: $1,000. **To Apply:** Applicant must submit a completed application form with a professional resume attached. **Deadline:** March 1.

1880 ■ Delmar Cengage Surgical Technology Scholarships *(Graduate/Scholarship)*

Purpose: To reward an individual who is striving to further his/her personal and educational goals by completing a surgical technology program. **Focus:** Surgery. **Qualif.:** Applicants must be enrolled in an CAAHEP-accredited program, or accepted to begin the program. Recipient must maintain a minimum GPA of 2.5. **Criteria:** Recipient will be selected based on academic achievement, progress and writing skills.

Funds Avail.: $1,500. **Number Awarded:** 1. **To Apply:** Applicants must submit a short report of 500 words or less stating the following: professional goals, strengths as a student, and reasons for wanting to enter the surgical technology profession. Applicants must also submit the completed application form. **Deadline:** March 1.

1881 ■ Foundation for Surgical Technology Advanced Education/Medical Mission Scholarships *(Graduate/Scholarship)*

Purpose: To provide financial assistance to current AST members who are pursuing advanced education related to the practice or who are seeking to perform medical mission work. **Focus:** Surgery. **Qualif.:** Applicant must be a current AST member. **Criteria:** Recipients will be selected based on the committee's review of all applications submitted.

Funds Avail.: No specific amount. **To Apply:** Applicants must provide a description of their membership history; an official documentation of the educational program that they are entering; and two letters of recommendation. All educational programs must include an official course outline, program fees and transcript. **Deadline:** December 31.

1882 ■ Foundation for Surgical Technology Scholarships *(Graduate/Scholarship)*

Purpose: To encourage and reward educational excellence as well as to respond to the financial need demonstrated by the surgical technology student and offer assistance to those who seek a career in surgical technology. **Focus:** Surgery. **Qualif.:** Applicants must be currently enrolled in an accredited surgical technology program and eligible to sit for the NBSTSA national surgical technologist certifying examination; must demonstrate superior academic ability; and must have a need for financial assistance. **Criteria:** Recipient selection is based on academic excellence and financial need.

Funds Avail.: No specific amount. **To Apply:** Applicants must complete the four parts of the application form: Student Responsibility; Official Transcript; Instructor Section; and Preceptor Section.

1883 ■ Association of Texas Professional Educators Foundation

305 E Huntland Dr., Ste. 300
Austin, TX 78752

Fax: (512) 302-5884
Free: 800-777-2873
E-mail: admin@atpefoundation.org
URL: www.atpefoundation.org

1884 ■ Barbara Jordan Memorial Scholarships *(Graduate, Undergraduate/Scholarship)*

Purpose: To financially support students enrolled in educator preparation programs at predominantly ethnic-minority institutions. **Focus:** Education. **Qualif.:** Applicant must be a junior, senior or a graduate student enrolled in an accredited college/university educator preparation program. **Criteria:** Selection is based on the application.

Funds Avail.: $1,500. **Number Awarded:** Up to 6. **To Apply:** Applicants must submit a completed application form along with college transcripts with official university imprint (do not fax); a detailed description of participation in any academic, honorary, civic or extracurricular activities in college; an essay (maximum of 2 typed, double-spaced 8 1/2x11 pages) including the applicant's personal educational philosophy, why the applicant wants to become an educator, who influenced the applicant the most in making career decision and why the applicant is applying for the award; and at least two (no more than three) letters of recommendation. **Deadline:** June 3.

1885 ■ Fred Wiesner Educational Excellence Scholarships *(Graduate, Undergraduate/ Scholarship)*

Purpose: To financially support students enrolled in educator preparation programs. **Focus:** Education. **Qualif.:** Applicant must be a college student enrolled in an accredited college/university educator preparation program. **Criteria:** Selection is based on the application.

Funds Avail.: $1,500. **Number Awarded:** 4 (3 undergraduate and 1 graduate student). **To Apply:** Applicants must submit a completed application form along with college transcripts with official university imprint (do not fax); a detailed description of participation in any academic, honorary, civic or extracurricular activities in college; an essay (maximum of 2 typed, double-spaced 8 1/2x11 pages) including the applicant's personal educational philosophy, why the applicant wants to become an educator, who influenced the applicant the most in making career decision and why the applicant is applying for the award; and at least two (no more than three) letters of recommendation. **Deadline:** June 3.

1886 ■ Association of the United States Navy (AUSN)

1619 King St.
Alexandria, VA 22314-2793
Ph: (703) 548-5800
Fax: (866) 683-3647
Free: 866-672-4368
E-mail: admin1@ausn.org
URL: www.navy-reserve.org

1887 ■ Association of the United States Navy Scholarships *(Undergraduate/Scholarship)*

Purpose: To provide educational assistance for the sons and daughters of members of the Association of the United States Navy. **Focus:** General studies. **Qualif.:** Applicants must be children of a AUSN member in good standing; must be U.S. citizens; must be under 24 years of age; and

Awards are arranged alphabetically below their administering organizations

must be enrolled in or accepted for full-time enrollment at an accredited college, university or a fully-accredited technical school. **Criteria:** Selection will be based on financial need, scholastic and leadership ability, potential, character and personal qualities.

Funds Avail.: No specific amount. **To Apply:** Applicants may download an application form available at the AUSN web site. **Deadline:** May 1.

1888 ■ Association of Universities and Colleges of Canada (AUCC)

350 Albert St., Ste. 600
Ottawa, ON, Canada K1R 1B1
Ph: (613) 563-1236
Fax: (613) 563-9745
E-mail: info@aucc.ca
URL: www.aucc.ca

1889 ■ Association of Universities and Colleges of Canada Public Scholarships
(Undergraduate/Scholarship)

Purpose: To foster and promote the interest of higher education. **Focus:** General studies. **Qualif.:** Applicants must be interested in pursuing their postsecondary studies in Canada or abroad and must be Canadian citizens or permanent residents of Canada. **Criteria:** Recipients are selected based on completeness of the application form, requirements and academic performance.

Funds Avail.: No specific amount. **To Apply:** Applicants must complete the application form and submit along with an official, sealed or stamped and signed transcript; letters of reference; essays; and community service. **Contact:** 613-563-9745.

1890 ■ Association of University Programs in Health Administration (AUPHA)

2000 N 14th St., Ste. 780
Arlington, VA 22201-2543
Ph: (703) 894-0940
Fax: (703) 894-0941
E-mail: aupha@aupha.org
URL: www.aupha.org

1891 ■ Corris Boyd Scholarships *(Master's/Scholarship)*

Purpose: To support the education of students of color entering a Master's Degree program. **Focus:** Health care services. **Qualif.:** Applicant must have applied and been accepted to a Master's Degree AUPHA full-member program (but not yet enrolled); a student of color; have a minimum 3.0 GPA (out of 4.0) in undergraduate coursework; and a U.S. citizen. **Criteria:** Selection is based on the applicant's leadership qualities; academic achievements; community involvement; commitment to healthcare; and financial need (may be considered when all other factors are equal).

Funds Avail.: $40,000. **Number Awarded:** 2. **To Apply:** Applicants must complete the application form online. In addition, applicants must submit GRE or GMAT score and score report (uploaded in PDF format or sent by mail or fax); current resume (uploaded in Word or PDF format); a personal statement (maximum of 1,000 words, uploaded in Word or PDF format); three signed letters of recommenda-

tion, one must be from a faculty member, one from an employer/supervisor (uploaded in PDF format or sent by mail or fax); and official transcripts (from all higher education institutions attended). **Deadline:** May 4.

1892 ■ David A. Winston Health Policy Scholarships *(Graduate/Scholarship)*

Purpose: To increase the number and quality of individuals trained in healthcare policy at the state and federal level. **Focus:** Health care services. **Qualif.:** Applicant must be a U.S. citizen and a first year graduate student studying health policy at an AUPHA member program. **Criteria:** Selection is based on the applicant's expressed and demonstrated commitment to health policy, leadership, academic achievement, community involvement and long term career interest.

Funds Avail.: $5,000. **Number Awarded:** 10. **To Apply:** Applicants must complete the application form online. In addition, applicants must submit a letter of nomination for the scholarship from a faculty member; a letter of nomination from a preceptor or employer; a personal statement; a CV detailing both professional and extracurricular activities; undergraduate and first semester graduate transcripts; and GRE or GMAT scores (waived if not required by academic program for admission). **Deadline:** April 13. **Contact:** mhaynes@aupha.org.

1893 ■ Association for Women in Architecture (AWA)

22815 Frampton Ave.
Torrance, CA 90501-5034
Ph: (310) 534-8466
Fax: (310) 257-6885
E-mail: president@awa-la.org
URL: www.awa-la.org

1894 ■ Association for Women in Architecture Scholarships *(Undergraduate/Scholarship)*

Purpose: To advance and support the positions of women in architecture and allied fields. **Focus:** Architecture. **Qualif.:** Applicants must be residents of California or attending a California school; must be enrolled in one of the qualifying majors for the current school term; must have completed a minimum of 18 units in their major by the application due date. **Criteria:** Recipients are selected based on merit as evidenced by grades, personal statement, letter of recommendation and quality of student work.

Funds Avail.: $1,000. **Number Awarded:** 5. **To Apply:** Applicants must complete the application form; must submit an official transcript of records from each college and university attended, two sealed letters of recommendation with signature over the seal from an instructor who has taught in their major; must submit a typewritten personal statement stating the reasons for studying the chosen field and career objectives; must submit a portfolio in "11x17" format showing one-to-three projects from their school work and self-addressed stamped envelope, standard business size. **Deadline:** April 16. **Contact:** Questions can be addressed to Mary Werk at the above address; E-mail: scholarship@awa-la.org.

1895 ■ Association for Women in Computing - Ann Arbor (AWC-AA)

PO Box 1864
Ann Arbor, MI 48106-1864

Awards are arranged alphabetically below their administering organizations

E-mail: awc-president@awc-aa.org
URL: www.awc-aa.org

1896 ■ Ann Arbor AWC Scholarships for Women in Computing *(Professional development, Undergraduate/Scholarship)*

Purpose: To support the education of women pursuing a career in a computer technology-related field. **Focus:** Computer and information sciences. **Qualif.:** Applicant must be a U.S. citizen or a permanent resident; a female student (full or part-time) participating in an institution accredited for higher education in the state of Michigan pursuing a career in a computer or technology-related field; or a female pursuing certification to change a career or to enhance current career in a computer or technology-related field (e.g. PMP Certification, MS Professional certification, and Network Professional certification, among others). **Criteria:** Awards are determined based on the three essay questions.

Funds Avail.: $1,000. **Number Awarded:** One or more. **To Apply:** Applicants must submit a completed scholarship application form along with a resume or CV; essays and two letters of recommendation. **Deadline:** April 1. **Contact:** Susan Gross, students@awc-aa.org.

1897 ■ Association for Women in Computing - Houston Chapter

PO Box 421316
Houston, TX 77242-1316
E-mail: nationalrep@awchouston.org
URL: awchouston.org

1898 ■ Kathi Bowles Scholarships for Women in Technology *(Graduate, Undergraduate/Scholarship)*

Purpose: To recognize women pursuing technology degrees and contributing to their high school, university or community in the areas of service and leadership. **Focus:** Technology; Computer and information sciences; Information science and technology. **Qualif.:** Applicant must reside within the Houston area; be female; a U.S. citizen, or a documented permanent resident of the U.S.; and never at any time has been subject to any disciplinary action by any institution or entity, including, but not limited to, any educational or law enforcement agency. High school students must graduate by June; have a high school GPA of 2.8 on a 4.0 scale; and planning to attend a four-year accredited college/university in the southeastern area of the state of Texas, or a career college to complete an associate degree in technology. Undergraduate students must attend an accredited college/university in the southeastern area of the state of Texas; must be pursuing a graduate degree in a computer-related field; and must currently be in junior status at a college/university. Graduate students must attend an accredited college/university in the southeastern area of the state of Texas pursuing a graduate degree in a computer-related field. **Criteria:** Selection is based on the application materials submitted.

Funds Avail.: No specific amount. **To Apply:** Applicants must submit, in order, a fully completed and signed application/educational data form; resume; recommendation form and letter; transcript (high school students must include SAT/ACT scores); and a one-page written essay. Recommendation form must be sent separately by the recommender with transcript or transcript can be sent under separate cover. **Deadline:** April 30. **Contact:** awchoustonscholarship@yahoo.com.

1899 ■ Association for Women Geoscientists (AWG)

12000 N Washington St., Ste. 285
Thornton, CO 80241
Ph: (303) 412-6219
Fax: (303) 253-9220
E-mail: office@awg.org
URL: www.awg.org

1900 ■ AWG Minority Scholarships *(Undergraduate/Scholarship)*

Purpose: To support students with their educational pursuits. **Focus:** Geosciences. **Qualif.:** Applicant must be a woman who is African-American, Hispanic, or Native American; full-time student pursuing an undergraduate degree in the geosciences at an accredited college or university (high school students who will enter one of these fields during their freshman year may also apply). **Criteria:** Selection is based on merits.

Funds Avail.: $6,000. **Number Awarded:** 1. **To Apply:** Applicants must submit a completed application form together with a statement of academic career goals; two letters of recommendation; transcript; and SAT/ACT scores. **Deadline:** June 30. **Contact:** Questions will be entertained by Christina Tapia at awgscholarship@yahoo.com or minorityscholarship@wg.org.

1901 ■ Chrysalis Scholarships *(Graduate/Grant)*

Purpose: To support a geoscience graduate student with their thesis/ dissertation. **Focus:** Geosciences. **Qualif.:** Applicant must be a female geoscience graduate student. **Criteria:** Selection is based on the application materials.

Funds Avail.: $2,000. **Number Awarded:** 2. **To Apply:** Applicants must submit a letter of application and a reference letter electronically to chrysalis@awg.org, with a subject line: Chrysalis Scholarship. **Deadline:** March 31.

1902 ■ AWG Maria Luisa Crawford Field Camp Scholarships *(Undergraduate/Scholarship)*

Purpose: To support students with their educational pursuits. **Focus:** Geosciences. **Qualif.:** Applicant must be a full-time undergraduate student pursuing a degree in geosciences and must have a GPA of 3.0. **Criteria:** Selection is based on merits.

Funds Avail.: $500. **Number Awarded:** 2. **To Apply:** Applicants must submit a completed application form together with a 250-word essay, two letters of recommendation; and college transcripts. **Deadline:** February 14. **Contact:** For further information, applicants must contact Pranoti Asher, Georgia Southern University, Department of Geology and Geography, Statesboro, GA 30460-814.

1903 ■ Penelope Hanshaw Scholarships *(Graduate, Undergraduate/Scholarship)*

Purpose: To support students with their educational pursuit. **Focus:** Geosciences. **Qualif.:** Applicant must be woman who is enrolled full-time graduate or undergraduate geosciences major; and have a GPA of 3.0. **Criteria:** Selection is based on merit.

Funds Avail.: $500. **To Apply:** Applicant must submit a nomination letter from a geoscience professor; a recommendation letter from a geoscience faculty; a letter of application; and academic transcripts. Send materials to Laurel M. Bybell, US Geological Survey 926 National Center Reston, VA 20192. **Deadline:** April 30. **Remarks:**

Awards are arranged alphabetically below their administering organizations

Sponsored by AWG Potomac Area Chapter. **Contact:** Linda L. Davis.

1904 ■ William Rucker Greenwood Scholarships *(Graduate, Undergraduate/Scholarship)*

Purpose: To support students with educational pursuits. **Focus:** Geosciences. **Qualif.:** Applicant must be a minority woman; enrolled as a full-time graduate or undergraduate geosciences major. **Criteria:** Selection is based on merit.

Funds Avail.: $1,000. **To Apply:** Applicants must submit a letter of recommendation from a geoscience professor or chairperson, and another from a geoscience faculty or employer; and a letter of application. Send materials to Laurel M. Bybell, US Geological Survey 926 National Center Reston, VA 20192. **Deadline:** April 30. **Remarks:** Sponsored by AWG Potomac Area Chapter. **Contact:** Send materials to Linda L. Davis, Geology Department, PAD 118, Grand Valley State University, Allendale, MI 49401.

1905 ■ Janet Cullen Tanaka Scholarships *(Undergraduate/Scholarship)*

Purpose: To encourage women to study geoscience. **Focus:** Geosciences. **Qualif.:** Applicant must be a female undergraduate committed to completing a Bachelor's Degree; pursuing a career or graduate work in the geosciences; a female sophomore, junior, or senior enrolled in a university or two-year college in Washington state west of the Columbia and Okanogan Rivers; have a minimum of 3.2 GPA (or equivalent academic achievement). **Criteria:** Applicants will be judged based on their potential for professional success, academic achievement and financial need.

Funds Avail.: $1,000. **To Apply:** Applicants must submit their name, address, phone number, and email (if available); one paragraph each describing your (1) financial needs, (2) current resources, and (3) academic achievements; one-page essay summarizing your commitment to a career in the geosciences; copies of all college transcripts (photocopies accepted); three letters of reference; provide names, affiliations, phone numbers. **Deadline:** December 6. **Remarks:** Sponsored by AWG Puget Sound Chapter.

1906 ■ Association for Women in Mathematics (AWM)

11240 Waples Mill Rd., Ste. 200
Fairfax, VA 22030-6078
Ph: (703) 934-0163
Fax: (703) 359-7562
E-mail: awm@awm-math.org
URL: www.awm-math.org

1907 ■ Mentoring Travel Grants for Women *(Postdoctorate/Scholarship)*

Purpose: To help young women to develop a long-term working and mentoring relationship with senior mathematicians. **Focus:** Mathematics and mathematical sciences. **Qualif.:** Applicants must be women holding a doctorate degree or equivalent with a work address in the United States; must be in a field supported by the Division of the Mathematical Sciences of the National Science Foundation. **Criteria:** Awards will be determined on a competitive basis by a selection panel consisting of distinguished mathematicians appointed by the AWM.

Funds Avail.: $5,000. **Number Awarded:** 7. **To Apply:** Applicants must have a curriculum vitae; must provide a research proposal which specifies why the proposed travel would be particularly beneficial; must submit a supporting letter from the proposed mentor with the curriculum vitae of the proposed mentor; must have a proposed budget and information about other sources of funding available. **Deadline:** February 1. **Contact:** Jennifer Lewis at the above address.

1908 ■ Travel Grants for Women Researchers *(Postdoctorate/Scholarship)*

Purpose: To enable women to attend research conferences in their fields and to provide valuable opportunities for them to advance their research activities and their visibility in the research community. **Focus:** Mathematics and mathematical sciences. **Qualif.:** Applicants must be women holding a doctorate degree and with a work address in the USA. **Criteria:** Awards will be determined on a competitive basis by a selection panel consisting of distinguished mathematicians appointed by the AWM.

Funds Avail.: $1,500 for domestic travel and $2,000 for foreign travel. **Number Awarded:** 3. **To Apply:** Application requirements and a complete step-by-step process are available online; application must be submitted online. **Deadline:** February 1, May 1 and October 1. **Contact:** Jennifer Lewis at the above address.

1909 ■ Association for Women in Sports Media (AWSM)

161 W Sylvania Ave.
Neptune City, NJ 07753
Ph: (717) 903-3086
E-mail: info@awsmonline.org
URL: awsmonline.org

1910 ■ Association for Women in Sports Media Internship Program *(Graduate, Undergraduate/Internship)*

Purpose: To assist female college students interested in sports media careers through paid internships with employers. **Focus:** Media arts. **Qualif.:** Applicants must be full-time female students seeking an undergraduate or graduate degree. **Criteria:** Applications will be evaluated by the AWSM board members and appropriate media professionals.

Funds Avail.: $1,000. **To Apply:** Applicants must submit the completed application form or a typewritten page containing the information required on the form; a one-page essay of 750 words or less, describing the most memorable experience in sports and sports media; a one-page resume highlighting journalism experience; three references with contact information; one letter of recommendation from a professor, advisor, editor, producer or other supervisor who is familiar with their work; maximum of five samples of their work: clips, editing examples, headlines, layout, press releases, video or audio tapes. Limit recordings to 10 minutes or less. $20 application fee must be paid by check or money order. **Deadline:** October 31. **Contact:** internships@awsmonline.org.

1911 ■ Association for Women Veterinarians Foundation (AWVF)

c/o Lisa C. Freeman, DVM, Chair
Northern Illinois University
Lowden Hall 301
DeKalb, IL 60115
Ph: (815) 753-1883

Awards are arranged alphabetically below their administering organizations

Fax: (815) 753-1631
E-mail: lfreeman1@niu.edu
URL: www.womenveterinarians.org

1912 ■ Association for Women Veterinarians Foundation Student Scholarships *(Graduate/Scholarship)*

Purpose: To provide financial assistance for veterinary medical students. **Focus:** Veterinary science and medicine. **Qualif.:** Applicants must be second or third year veterinary medical students who are attending a college/school of Veterinary Medicine in United States or Canada. **Criteria:** Scholarship recipients will be selected based on the Selection Committee's review of the application materials.

Funds Avail.: $1,500. **Number Awarded:** 8. **To Apply:** Applicants must submit (in a Word or PDF file) full name, address, school's address, present year of attendance in veterinary medical school (2nd or 3rd Year); a resume or curriculum vitae; letter of recommendation from a faculty member; and an essay (maximum of 500 words) on the applicant's purpose for applying for the scholarship and why the association should award the scholarship to the applicant. **Deadline:** January 31. **Contact:** Roberta Robinson, rrobinso@vet.k-state.edu.

1913 ■ Association of Zoo Veterinary Technicians (AZVT)

c/o Marcie Oliva, Exec. Dir.
581705 White Oak Rd.
Yulee, FL 32097-2169
Ph: (312) 742-7211
Fax: (312) 742-7823
E-mail: marcieo@wogilman.com
URL: www.azvt.org

1914 ■ Laurie Page-Peck Scholarship Fund *(Undergraduate/Scholarship)*

Purpose: To provide educational assistance for veterinary or medical technology students. **Focus:** Veterinary science and medicine. **Qualif.:** Applicant must be a veterinary or medical technology student interested in zoo veterinary technology. **Criteria:** Grantees will be selected based on the content, format and grammar of the submitted paper.

Funds Avail.: $1,000. **To Apply:** Applicant must submit a paper about zoo veterinary technology. **Deadline:** Deadline for receipt of abstracts- March 5; Deadline for first- draft paper submission- April 23; Deadline for final draft of paper June 18. **Contact:** Grant Fuhrman, RVT at Houston Zoo, Inc., 1513 N. MacGregor, Houston, TX 77030, gfuhrman@houstonzoo.org.

1915 ■ Astronaut Scholarship Foundation (ASF)

6225 Vectorspace Blvd.
Titusville, FL 32780
Ph: (321) 455-7011
Fax: (321) 264-9176
E-mail: linn@astronautscholarship.org
URL: www.astronautscholarship.org

1916 ■ Astronaut Scholarship Foundation Scholarships *(Undergraduate/Scholarship)*

Purpose: To support the promising students who want to pursue their masters in the fields of science and engineer-

ing. **Focus:** Science; Engineering; Applied mathematics. **Qualif.:** Applicants must be nominated by faculty members; must be U.S citizens; must be engineering or natural or applied science majors or mathematics students intending to pursue research or advance their field upon completion of their final degree; must be junior, senior or master's students; must have shown initiative, creativity and excellence in their chosen field. **Criteria:** Recipients will be selected by the ASF Scholarship Committee.

Funds Avail.: $10,000. **Number Awarded:** 25. **To Apply:** For further information, applicants are advised to contact the Astronaut Scholarship Foundation, 6225 Vectorspace Blvd., Titusville, FL 32780.

1917 ■ Athletic Equipment Managers Association (AEMA)

460 Hunt Hill Rd.
Freeville, NY 13068
Ph: (607) 539-6300
Fax: (607) 539-6340
E-mail: aema@frontiernet.net
URL: www.equipmentmanagers.org

1918 ■ Athletic Equipment Managers Association College Scholarships *(Undergraduate/Scholarship)*

Purpose: To develop further the professional ability of each of its members. **Focus:** General studies. **Qualif.:** Applicant must be full-time college student with one year of collegiate athletic equipment management experience; displays an interest in the field of athletic equipment management. **Criteria:** Selection is based on academic achievement, community involvement, displayed interest in athletic Equipment management, completion of an essay and letters of recommendation.

Funds Avail.: No specific amount. **To Apply:** Applicants must submit a completed application form along with the required materials. **Remarks:** March 15. **Contact:** Application form and supporting documents must be sent to Dorothy Cutting at the above address.

1919 ■ Atkinson Charitable Foundation

One Yonge St., 7th Fl.
Toronto, ON, Canada M5E 1E5
Ph: (416) 368-5152
Fax: (416) 865-3619
E-mail: info@atkinsonfoundation.ca
URL: www.atkinsonfoundation.ca

1920 ■ Atkinson Fellowships in Public Policy *(Professional development/Fellowship)*

Purpose: To financially assist students with undertaking a research project on a topical public policy issue. **Focus:** Journalism. **Qualif.:** Applicants must be full-time Canadian journalists in print or broadcast media. **Criteria:** Preference will be given to those applicants who have already achieved some distinction in reporting on policy issues.

Funds Avail.: $75,000. **Number Awarded:** Varies. **To Apply:** Applicants must submit a three-page maximum letter of intent; curriculum vitae; summary of the topic, brief outline of proposed articles and treatment/approach. **Deadline:** January. **Contact:** Applicants must submit four copies of the letter of intent and curriculum vitae to Elizabeth Chan,

Awards are arranged alphabetically below their administering organizations

Phone: 416-869-4034; E-mail: echan@atkinsonfoundation.ca.

1921 ■ Atlanta Association of Legal Administrators (AALA)

PO Box 79019
Atlanta, GA 30357
Ph: (770) 846-3402
URL: www.atlanta-ala.com

1922 ■ Gene Henson Scholarships (High School, Undergraduate/Scholarship)

Purpose: To provide educational opportunities to well-deserving students in metro Atlanta. **Focus:** General studies. **Qualif.:** Applicants must be senior high school students who are enrolled in one of the local public high schools in Atlanta; must be U.S. citizens; must be interested in attending a four-year college, university or specialized course of instruction within the state of Georgia, including private institutions. **Criteria:** Recipients will be selected based on financial need.

Funds Avail.: Amount not specified. **To Apply:** Applicants must submit a completed application form; must submit a transcript of records; must provide a list of extracurricular activities and enumerated community work; must write an essay (750 words or less) describing the candidate's opinions on current events happening locally, nationally or internationally; must submit a letter of acceptance. Incoming freshmen must include a signed statement from a non-affiliated organization. **Deadline:** March 23. **Contact:** Dina Wolfe.

1923 ■ Atlantic County Bar Association

1201 Bacharach Blvd.
Atlantic City, NJ 08401
Ph: (609) 345-3444
Fax: (609) 345-6279
E-mail: atcobara@aol.com
URL: www.atcobar.org

1924 ■ Vincent S. Haneman-Joseph B. Perskie Memorial Foundation Scholarships (Graduate, Undergraduate/Scholarship)

Purpose: To support law students with their educational pursuit. **Focus:** Law. **Qualif.:** Applicant must be admitted to an American Bar Association accredited law school; a resident of Atlantic County for one year prior to application; and be a law student in any year including the first year. **Criteria:** Selection is based on academic ability, financial need, leadership potential and character.

Funds Avail.: No specific amount. **Number Awarded:** Varies. **To Apply:** Applicants must submit a completed application form. **Deadline:** May 1. **Contact:** Mary Williams Berard at the above address.

1925 ■ Atlantic Provinces Library Association (APLA)

Management Bldg.
6100 University Ave.
Halifax, NS, Canada B3H 3J5
URL: www.apla.ca

1926 ■ Atlantic Provinces Library Association Memorial Awards (Professional development/Scholarship)

Purpose: To provide financial assistance for students who are in need. **Focus:** General studies; Library and archival

sciences. **Qualif.:** Applicants must have a degree and must be currently doing research. **Criteria:** Priority will be given to those students with financial need.

Funds Avail.: No specific amount. **To Apply:** Applicants must send a letter outlining proposed research and estimated costs along with a copy of your curriculum vitae. **Deadline:** March 31. **Contact:** Erin Alcock, Queen Elizabeth II Library, Memorial University, St. John's NL A1B 3Y1, at 709-737-7427/709-737-2153 (fax), or ekalcock@mun.ca.

1927 ■ Carin Alma E. Somers Scholarship Trust (Undergraduate/Scholarship)

Purpose: To support the education of Canadian students with financial need. **Focus:** Library and Information Studies. **Qualif.:** Applicants must be Canadian citizens; must be residents of Atlantic Provinces; and must have demonstrated financial need. **Criteria:** Selection of recipients will be recommended by a committee of the four Provincial Vice Presidents and the President-Elect to the Executive Committee.

Funds Avail.: $2,000. **To Apply:** Applicants must submit a completed application form. **Deadline:** March 31. **Remarks:** Successful applicants will have been accepted in a School of Graduate Studies as candidates for a Master's degree in Library and Information Studies accredited by the American Library Association. The award will normally be announced at the Annual Atlantic Provinces Library Association Spring Conference. **Contact:** Nominations should be submitted to Jocelyne Thompson of University of New Brunswick located at Fredericton NB, E3B 5H5; Phone: 506-458-7053; E-mail: jlt@unb.ca.

1928 ■ Atlantic Salmon Federation (ASF)

15 Rankine Mill Rd.
Chamcook, NB, Canada E5B 3A9
Ph: (506) 529-4581
Fax: (506) 529-1070
Free: 800-565-5666
E-mail: savesalmon@asf.ca
URL: www.asf.ca

1929 ■ Atlantic Salmon Federation Olin Fellowships (All/Fellowship)

Purpose: To improve knowledge or skills in advanced fields while looking for solutions to current problems in Atlantic salmon biology, management and conservation. **Focus:** Marine biology. **Qualif.:** Applicants need not be enrolled in any degree program; must be legal residents of the United States or Canada; and must be enrolled in any accredited university, research laboratory or active management program. **Criteria:** Recipients are selected based on the committee's review of all applications.

Funds Avail.: $1,000-$3,000. **To Apply:** Application forms may be obtained from the Atlantic Salmon Federation Office in Canada or in USA; must attach a statement of qualifications; transcript of grades, if applicable; description of the program or project; and supporting documentation, if required. **Deadline:** March 15.

1930 ■ Audio Engineering Society (AES)

60 E 42nd St., Rm. 2520
New York, NY 10165-2520
Ph: (212) 661-8528
Fax: (212) 682-0477

Awards are arranged alphabetically below their administering organizations

URL: www.aes.org

1931 ■ Audio Engineering Society Educational Foundation Scholarships (Graduate/Grant)

Purpose: To encourage entry of talented students into the profession of audio engineering and related fields. **Focus:** Engineering. **Qualif.:** Applicants must have successfully completed an undergraduate degree program (typically four years) at a recognized college or university; a demonstrated commitment to audio engineering or related fields as a career choice; acceptance or a pending application for graduate studies leading to a masters or higher degree, or an internationally recognized equivalent. **Criteria:** Recipients are selected based on the submitted application requirements.

Funds Avail.: No specific amount. **To Apply:** Applicants must submit two current letters of recommendation (one must be from major professor or academic advisors); a cover page; essays on past achievements and future plans; and list of references. Application forms may be requested from AES Headquarters via email. **Deadline:** May 15.

1932 ■ Austin Business Travel Association (ABTA)

PMB No. 280
4301 W William Cannon Dr., Ste. B-150
Austin, TX 78749
E-mail: info@austinbta.org
URL: www.austinbta.org

1933 ■ Educational and Professional Achievement Scholarships (Undergraduate, Vocational/Occupational/Scholarship)

Purpose: To award scholarship to local high school students applying for higher education support. **Focus:** General studies. **Qualif.:** Applicants must be senior students currently registered and attending classes in the Greater Austin Metropolitan Area, including students in public schools, home-schooled students and students attending private educational institutions; must be planning to further their education or professional development by enrolling in an accredited college or university, a community college, a professional, technical or vocational institute or school. **Criteria:** Selection will be based on the committee's criteria.

Funds Avail.: $1,500. **To Apply:** Applicants may download an application form on-line. Applicants must submit the following requirements: a transcript of grades with a minimum cumulative GPA of 3.0; complete scholarship application form; at least three, but not more than five personal evaluations; a 500-word personal essay titled "Building My Future"; a resume detailing activities at school, work, community service, sports, clubs, etc.; a brief (less than 200 words), creative autobiographical statement. **Deadline:** February 13. **Contact:** Kim Stringer, Chapter Chair; 7301 Burnet Rd., Ste 102, No. 542, Austin, TX 78757; 512-434-1222.

1934 ■ Autism Society of America

4340 East-West Hwy., Ste. 350
Bethesda, MD 20814
Ph: (301) 657-0881
Fax: (301) 657-0869
Free: 800-328-8476
E-mail: conference@autism-society.org

URL: www.autism-society.org/

1935 ■ CVS/All Kids Can Scholars Program (Undergraduate, Vocational/Occupational/Scholarship)

Purpose: To assist individuals with autism intending to pursue education. **Focus:** Mental health. **Qualif.:** Candidate must be an individual with autism completing post-secondary educational or vocational program. **Criteria:** Priority is given to applicants with complete application packages.

Funds Avail.: 1,000. **To Apply:** Applicant must submit the documentation of status as an individual with autism; secondary school transcripts; documentation of acceptance into an accredited, post-secondary educational or vocational program of study; two recommendation letters; and a personal statement (maximum of 500 words) outlining the applicant's qualifications and proposed plan of study. Applicants are required to submit five copies of the application package.

1936 ■ Automotive Hall of Fame (AHF)

21400 Oakwood Blvd.
Dearborn, MI 48124
Ph: (313) 240-4000
Fax: (313) 240-8641
E-mail: ahof@thedrivingspirit.org
URL: www.automotivehalloffame.org

1937 ■ Larry H. Averill Memorial Scholarships (Undergraduate/Scholarship)

Purpose: To financially support students pursuing education in an automotive related career. **Focus:** Automotive technology; Engineering, Automotive. **Qualif.:** Applicant must be an upper level undergraduate; interested in careers in automotive; have a 3.0 GPA; enrolled full-time at an accredited college or university; and have demonstrated financial need. **Criteria:** Applicants are selected based on application and financial need.

Funds Avail.: No specific amount. **To Apply:** Application form is available at the website; or send a letter of request with a self-addressed stamped envelope. Applicants must submit a completed application form; an official transcript; two recommendation letters; and a letter of acceptance for an associate, bachelor or masters program. Send all materials to: Automotive Hall of Fame, Scholarship Programs 21400 Oakwood Blvd. Dearborn, MI 48124. **Deadline:** June 1.

1938 ■ Harold Dieckmann Draper, Sr. Scholarships (Undergraduate/Scholarship)

Purpose: To financially support students pursuing education in an automotive related career. **Focus:** Automotive technology; Engineering, Automotive. **Qualif.:** Applicant must be an upper level undergraduate; interested in careers in automotive; have a 3.4 GPA; enrolled full-time at an accredited college or university; and have demonstrated financial need. **Criteria:** Applicants are selected based on application and financial need.

Funds Avail.: No specific amount. **To Apply:** Application form is available at the website; or send a letter of request with a self-addressed stamped envelope. Applicants must submit a completed application form; an official transcript; two recommendation letters; and a letter of acceptance for an associate, bachelor or masters program. Send all materi-

Awards are arranged alphabetically below their administering organizations

als to: Automotive Hall of Fame, Scholarship Programs 21400 Oakwood Blvd. Dearborn, MI 48124. **Deadline:** June 1.

1939 ■ John E. Echlin Memorial Scholarships
(Undergraduate/Scholarship)

Purpose: To financially support students pursuing education in an automotive related career. **Focus:** Automotive technology; Engineering, Automotive. **Qualif.:** Applicant must be an upper level undergraduate; interested in careers in automotive; have a 3.0 GPA; enrolled full-time at an accredited college or university; and have demonstrated financial need. **Criteria:** Applicants are selected based on application form and financial need.

Funds Avail.: No specific amount. **To Apply:** Application form is available at the website; or send a letter of request with a self-addressed stamped envelope. Applicants must submit a completed application form; an official transcript; two recommendation letters; and a letter of acceptance for an associate, bachelor or masters program. Send all materials to: Automotive Hall of Fame, Scholarship Programs 21400 Oakwood Blvd. Dearborn, MI 48124. **Deadline:** June 1.

1940 ■ Carlyle Fraser/Wilton Looney Scholarships *(Undergraduate/Scholarship)*

Purpose: To financially support students pursuing education in an automotive related career. **Focus:** Automotive technology; Engineering, Automotive. **Qualif.:** Applicant must be an upper level undergraduate; interested in careers in automotive; have a 3.4 GPA; enrolled full-time at an accredited college or university; and have demonstrated financial need. **Criteria:** Preference will be given to applicants attending Northwood University.

Funds Avail.: No specific amount. **To Apply:** Application form is available at the website; or send a letter of request with a self-addressed stamped envelope. Applicants must submit a completed application form; an official transcript; two recommendation letters; and a letter of acceptance for an associate, bachelor or masters program. Send all materials to: Automotive Hall of Fame, Scholarship Programs 21400 Oakwood Blvd. Dearborn, MI 48124. **Deadline:** June 1.

1941 ■ John Goerlich Memorial Scholarships
(Undergraduate/Scholarship)

Purpose: To financially support students pursuing education in an automotive related career. **Focus:** Automotive technology; Engineering, Automotive. **Qualif.:** Applicant must be an upper level undergraduate; interested in careers in automotive; have a 3.4 GPA; enrolled full-time at an accredited college or university; and have demonstrated financial need. **Criteria:** Applicants are selected based on application and financial need.

Funds Avail.: No specific amount. **To Apply:** Application form is available at the website; or send a letter of request with a self-addressed stamped envelope. Applicants must submit a completed application form; an official transcript; two recommendation letters; and a letter of acceptance for an associate, bachelor or masters program. Send all materials to: Automotive Hall of Fame, Scholarship Programs 21400 Oakwood Blvd. Dearborn, MI 48124. **Deadline:** June 1.

1942 ■ Charles V. Hagler Scholarships
(Undergraduate/Scholarship)

Purpose: To financially support students pursuing education in an automotive related career. **Focus:** Automotive

technology; Engineering, Automotive. **Qualif.:** Applicants must be interested in careers in automotive; have a 3.0 GPA; enrolled full-time at an accredited college or university; and have demonstrated financial need. **Criteria:** Applicants are selected based on financial need.

Funds Avail.: No specific amount. **To Apply:** Application form is available at the website or send a letter of request with a self-addressed stamped envelope. Applicants must submit a completed application form; an official transcript; two recommendation letters; and a letter of acceptance for an associate, bachelor or masters program. Send all materials to: Automotive Hall of Fame, Scholarship Programs 21400 Oakwood Blvd. Dearborn, MI 48124. **Deadline:** June 1.

1943 ■ Zenon C.R. Hansen Memorial Scholarships *(Undergraduate/Scholarship)*

Purpose: To financially support students pursuing education in an automotive related career. **Focus:** Automotive technology; Engineering, Automotive. **Qualif.:** Applicant must be an upper level undergraduate; interested in careers in automotive/trucking; have a 3.4 GPA; enrolled full-time at an accredited college or university; and have demonstrated financial need. **Criteria:** Applicants are selected based on application and financial need.

Funds Avail.: No specific amount. **To Apply:** Application form is available at the website; or send a letter of request with a self-addressed stamped envelope. Applicants must submit a completed application form; an official transcript; two recommendation letters; and a letter of acceptance for an associate, bachelor or masters program. Send all materials to: Automotive Hall of Fame, Scholarship Programs 21400 Oakwood Blvd. Dearborn, MI 48124. **Deadline:** June 1.

1944 ■ John W. Koons, Sr. Memorial Scholarships *(Undergraduate/Scholarship)*

Purpose: To financially support students pursuing education in an automotive related career. **Focus:** Automotive technology; Engineering, Automotive. **Qualif.:** Applicant must be an upper level undergraduate; interested in careers in automotive; have a 3.4 GPA; enrolled full-time at an accredited college or university; have demonstrated financial need; must be a U.S. citizen or with student visa. **Criteria:** Applicants are selected based on financial need.

Funds Avail.: No specific amount. **To Apply:** Application form is available at the website or send a letter of request with a self-addressed stamped envelope. Applicant must submit a completed application form; an official transcript; two recommendation letters; and a letter of acceptance for an associate, bachelor or masters program. Send all materials to: Automotive Hall of Fame, Scholarship Programs 21400 Oakwood Blvd. Dearborn, MI 48124. **Deadline:** June 1.

1945 ■ Ken Krum/Bud Kouts Memorial Scholarships *(Undergraduate/Scholarship)*

Purpose: To financially support students pursuing education in an automotive related career. **Focus:** Automotive technology; Engineering, Automotive. **Qualif.:** Applicant must be an upper level undergraduate; interested in careers in automotive; have a 3.0 GPA; enrolled full-time at an accredited college or university; have demonstrated financial need; and must be U.S. citizen. **Criteria:** Applicants are selected based on financial need.

Funds Avail.: No specific amount. **To Apply:** Application

Awards are arranged alphabetically below their administering organizations

form is available at the website; or send a letter of request with a self-addressed stamped envelope. Applicants must submit a completed application form; an official transcript; two recommendation letters; and a letter of acceptance for an associate, bachelor or masters program. Send all materials to: Automotive Hall of Fame, Scholarship Programs 21400 Oakwood Blvd. Dearborn, MI 48124. **Deadline:** June 1.

1946 ■ Brouwer D. McIntyre Memorial Scholarships (Undergraduate/Scholarship)

Purpose: To financially support students pursuing education in an automotive related career. **Focus:** Automotive technology; Engineering, Automotive. **Qualif.:** Applicant must be an upper level undergraduate; interested in careers in automotive replacement parts industry; have a 3.0 GPA; enrolled full-time at Northwood University; and have demonstrated financial need. **Criteria:** Applicants are selected based on application and financial need.

Funds Avail.: No specific amount. **To Apply:** Application form is available at the website; or send a letter of request with a self-addressed stamped envelope. Applicants must submit a completed application form; an official transcript; two recommendation letters; and a letter of acceptance for an associate, bachelor or masters program. Send all materials to: Automotive Hall of Fame, Scholarship Programs 21400 Oakwood Blvd. Dearborn, MI 48124. **Deadline:** June 1.

1947 ■ Jim Moran Scholarships (Undergraduate/Scholarship)

Purpose: To financially support students pursuing education in an automotive related career. **Focus:** Automotive technology; Engineering, Automotive. **Qualif.:** Applicant must have a 2.75 GPA; enrolled full-time at Northwood University majoring in Automotive Marketing or Automotive Aftermarket; and have demonstrated financial need. **Criteria:** Preference will be given to previous winners.

Funds Avail.: No specific amount. **To Apply:** Application form is available at the website or send a letter of request with a self-addressed stamped envelope. Applicants must submit a completed application form; an official transcript; two recommendation letters; and a letter of acceptance for an associate, bachelor or masters program. Send all materials to: Automotive Hall of Fame, Scholarship Programs 21400 Oakwood Blvd. Dearborn, MI 48124. **Deadline:** June 1.

1948 ■ Dorothy M. Ross Memorial Scholarships (Undergraduate/Scholarship)

Purpose: To financially support students pursuing education in an automotive related career. **Focus:** Automotive technology; Engineering, Automotive. **Qualif.:** Applicant must be an undergraduate student; interested in careers in automotive; have a 3.0 GPA; and enrolled full-time at an accredited college or university. **Criteria:** Applicants are selected based on application and financial need.

Funds Avail.: No specific amount. **To Apply:** Application form is available at the website or send a letter of request with a self-addressed stamped envelope. Applicants must submit a completed application form; an official transcript; two recommendation letters; and a letter of acceptance for an associate, bachelor or masters program. Send all materials to: Automotive Hall of Fame, Scholarship Programs 21400 Oakwood Blvd. Dearborn, MI 48124. **Deadline:** June 1.

1949 ■ Stuart H. Snyder Memorial Scholarships (Undergraduate/Scholarship)

Purpose: To financially support students pursuing education in an automotive related career. **Focus:** Automotive technology; Engineering, Automotive. **Qualif.:** Applicant must be an undergraduate student; interested in careers in automotive/trucking; have a 3.0 GPA; enrolled full-time at an accredited college/university; and have demonstrated financial need. **Criteria:** Applicants are selected based on application and financial need.

Funds Avail.: No specific amount. **To Apply:** Application form is available at the website; or send a letter of request with a self-addressed stamped envelope. Applicants must submit a completed application form; an official transcript; two recommendation letters; and a letter of acceptance for an associate, bachelor or masters program. Send all materials to: Automotive Hall of Fame, Scholarship Programs 21400 Oakwood Blvd. Dearborn, MI 48124. **Deadline:** June 1.

1950 ■ Walter W. Stillman Scholarships (Undergraduate/Scholarship)

Purpose: To financially support students pursuing education in an automotive related career. **Focus:** Automotive technology; Engineering, Automotive. **Qualif.:** Applicant must be an upper level undergraduate; interested in careers in automotive; have a 3.0 GPA; enrolled full-time at Northwood University; and have demonstrated financial need. **Criteria:** Preference will be given to applicants from New Jersey.

Funds Avail.: No specific amount. **To Apply:** Application form is available at the website or send a letter of request with a self-addressed stamped envelope. Applicants must submit a completed application form; an official transcript; two recommendation letters; and a letter of acceptance for an associate, bachelor or masters program. Send all materials to: Automotive Hall of Fame, Scholarship Programs 21400 Oakwood Blvd. Dearborn, MI 48124. **Deadline:** June 1.

1951 ■ TRW Foundation Scholarships (Undergraduate/Scholarship)

Purpose: To financially support students pursuing education in an automotive related career. **Focus:** Automotive technology; Engineering, Automotive. **Qualif.:** Applicant must be an undergraduate student; interested in careers in automotive; have a 3.0 GPA; enrolled full-time at an accredited college or university; a U.S. citizen; and have demonstrated financial need. **Criteria:** Preference will be given to applicant attending the University of Michigan.

Funds Avail.: No specific amount. **To Apply:** Application form is available at the website or send a letter of request with a self-addressed stamped envelope. Applicants must submit a completed application form; an official transcript; two recommendation letters; and a letter of acceptance for an associate, bachelor or masters program. Send all materials to: Automotive Hall of Fame, Scholarship Programs 21400 Oakwood Blvd. Dearborn, MI 48124. **Deadline:** June 1.

1952 ■ J. Irving Whalley Memorial Scholarships (Undergraduate/Scholarship)

Purpose: To financially support students pursuing education in an automotive related career. **Focus:** Automotive technology; Engineering, Automotive. **Qualif.:** Applicants must be upper level undergraduates; interested in careers

Awards are arranged alphabetically below their administering organizations

in automotive; have a 3.0 GPA; enrolled full-time North-wood University; and have demonstrated financial need. **Criteria:** Applicants are selected based on application and financial need.

Funds Avail.: No specific amount. **To Apply:** Application form is available at the website or send a letter of request with a self-addressed stamped envelope. Applicants must submit a completed application form; an official transcript; two recommendation letters; and a letter of acceptance for an associate, bachelor or masters program. Send all materials to: Automotive Hall of Fame, Scholarship Programs 21400 Oakwood Blvd. Dearborn, MI 48124. **Deadline:** June 1.

1953 ■ M.H. Yager Memorial Scholarships
(Undergraduate/Scholarship)

Purpose: To financially support students pursuing education in an automotive related career. **Focus:** Automotive technology; Engineering, Automotive. **Qualif.:** Applicant must be an upper level undergraduate; interested in careers in automotive; have a 3.4 GPA; enrolled full-time at an accredited college or university; and have demonstrated financial need. **Criteria:** Applicants are selected based on application and financial need.

Funds Avail.: No specific amount. **To Apply:** Application form is available at the website; or send a letter of request with a self-addressed stamped envelope. Applicants must submit a completed application form; an official transcript; two recommendation letters; and a letter of acceptance for an associate, bachelor or masters program. Send all materials to: Automotive Hall of Fame, Scholarship Programs 21400 Oakwood Blvd. Dearborn, MI 48124. **Deadline:** June 1.

1954 ■ Automotive Industries Association of Canada (AIA)
1272 Wellington St. W
Ottawa, ON, Canada K1Y 3A7
Ph: (800) 808-2920
Fax: (613) 728-6021
E-mail: info.aia@aiacanada.com
URL: www.aiacanada.com

1955 ■ AIA and the Global Automotive After-market Symposium Scholarships
(Undergraduate/Scholarship)

Purpose: To financially support deserving secondary, college and university students intending to pursue a career in automotive aftermarket. **Focus:** Automotive technology. **Qualif.:** Applicants must be graduating high school seniors or have graduated from high school within the past two years; must be enrolled in a college-level program, university or an accredited automotive technical program through either a CAMPE college or a CARS-approved institute; must be attending a full-time program in Canada or the United States. **Criteria:** Applicants will be selected based on their academic merit.

Funds Avail.: $1,000. **To Apply:** Application forms are available at the website. Applicants must prepare a copy of the current school transcript with official school seal; must submit an essay (at least 250 words in length, no longer than one page, double-spaced); letter of recommendation (from a non-family member, preferably an employer, teacher or someone other than a family friend). **Deadline:** June 15.

1956 ■ Hans McCorriston Motive Power Machinist Grant Programs *(Undergraduate, Vocational/Occupational/Scholarship)*

Purpose: To support students pursuing careers as motive power machinists. **Focus:** Automotive technology. **Qualif.:** Applicants must be enrolled in the AIA Motive Power Machinist Training Program or a college-level machinist training program within Canada. **Criteria:** Applications and other supporting documents are reviewed by the Scholarship Committee.

Funds Avail.: $500. **To Apply:** Applicant must fill up the application form available at the website. **Deadline:** October 15. **Remarks:** Grant is named after Hans McCorriston, in honor of his contributions to the motive power industry.

1957 ■ Arthur Paulin Automotive Aftermarket Scholarship Awards *(Postgraduate, Undergraduate/Scholarship)*

Purpose: To provide monetary assistance to deserving students in the automotive field. **Focus:** Automotive technology. **Qualif.:** Applicants must be enrolled in an automotive aftermarket industry-related program or curriculum at a Canadian college or university. **Criteria:** Recipients are selected based on Scholarship Committee's review of applications and other supporting documents.

Funds Avail.: $700. **Number Awarded:** 5. **To Apply:** Application form is available at the website or upon request from the AIA National Office in Ottawa. Applicants must submit a letter stating his/her long-term automotive goals; and a letter from his/her automotive instructor; recent academic achievements, as well as achievements in the automotive sector. **Deadline:** October 31. **Remarks:** Scholarship award was named after long-time AIA volunteer Arthur Paulin, who served on the AIA board of directors for more than nine years.

1958 ■ Marion Roberts Memorial Scholarships
(Undergraduate/Scholarship)

Purpose: To provide financial assistance and encouragement enabling students to further their education at the post-secondary school level. **Focus:** General studies. **Qualif.:** Applicant must be a dependent child or spouse of a full-time employee in an active AIA member company; confirmation of the parent's/spouse employment must be provided by the member company. Applicant must be enrolled in a full-time post-secondary program leading to a degree, certificate or diploma at an accredited university, college, technical school or C.E.G.E.P. **Criteria:** Recipients are selected based on Scholarship Committee's review of applications.

Funds Avail.: $500. **To Apply:** Applicants must fill up the application form available at the website; must prepare a letter that demonstrates leadership ability in school, social or other activities; must have a transcript indicating academic achievement, with an official seal or photocopy of the seal of the school; recent passport-sized photo. **Deadline:** July 15. **Remarks:** Funds established in honor of Marion Roberts, a long-time staff member of the association's head office in Ottawa.

1959 ■ SEMA Memorial Scholarships *(Graduate, Undergraduate, Vocational/Occupational/Scholarship)*

Purpose: To support educational goals for students pursuing careers in the automotive aftermarkets. **Focus:** Automotive technology. **Qualif.:** Applicants must be graduate-level

Awards are arranged alphabetically below their administering organizations

students at an accredited university or college; four-year accredited university or college; three-year accredited university or community college; or vocational/technical school. **Criteria:** Applications are reviewed and scored by an independent panel comprised of business professionals. **Funds Avail.:** $1,000-$4,000, depending on the category. **To Apply:** Applicants must submit an official transcript; two letters of recommendation from a non employer, career counselors or professor on company letterhead; current photographs (head shot) for publication and promotional use; personal essay outlining reasons for pursuing a career in the automotive aftermarker or related field. **Deadline:** April 1.

1960 ■ Automotive Recyclers Association (Automotive Dismantlers & Recyclers Association)

9113 Church St.
Manassas, VA 20110
Ph: (571) 208-0428
Fax: (571) 208-0430
Free: 888-385-1005
E-mail: maria@a-r-a.org
URL: www.a-r-a.org

1961 ■ ARA Scholarship Awards
(Undergraduate/Scholarship)

Purpose: To assist outstanding students to pursue their educational goal. **Focus:** Business; Education, Vocational-technical; Technical training. **Qualif.:** Applicants must be children of an employee of a direct ARA member company; must be a high school senior or pursuing a full-time post high school program in an institution providing trade, business, or technical programs; have at least 3.0 GPA or equivalent. **Criteria:** Applicants will be selected based on their academic achievement.

Funds Avail.: Scholarship amount not specified. **To Apply:** Applicants must submit a completed application form and profile sheet. Transcript of academic records must be sent by the applicant's school/college directly to the ARA Scholarship Advisor. Applicants must obtain a certification and letter of verification from the parents' employer who is a direct member of ARA (should include current employment and the hiring date). Send all requirements to the ARA Scholarship Foundation Advisor. **Deadline:** March 15. **Contact:** ARA Scholarship Advisor, 109 Defiant Way, Grass Valley, CA 95945, arascholar@sbcglobal.net.

1962 ■ Automotive Warehouse Distributors Association

4600 East-West Hwy., Ste. 300
Bethesda, MD 20814
Ph: (301) 654-6664
Fax: (301) 654-3299
E-mail: info@awda.org

1963 ■ AVI Scholarships *(Undergraduate/Scholarship)*

Purpose: To develop quality technicians, managers, and shop owners. **Focus:** Automotive technology. **Qualif.:** Applicants must be 21 years of age; must have a minimum of two years work experience in the mechanical repair industry; must demonstrate an interest in self-improvement through education and training. If an applicant is not a busi-

ness owner, he/she must be recommended by a business owner. **Criteria:** Recipients are selected based on academic performance and demonstrated interest in automotive industry.

Funds Avail.: $1,000. **To Apply:** Applicants must submit a complete application form. **Deadline:** August 17.

1964 ■ Tom Babcox Memorial Scholarships *(All/Scholarship)*

Purpose: To support continuing education tailored specifically for the business needs of the automotive service industry. **Focus:** Automotive technology. **Qualif.:** Applicants must work in mechanical repair industry; must demonstrate an interest in self-improvement through management education; must own or work for a business that as an ASA Collision division member in good standing. If an applicant is not a business owner, he/she must be recommended by a business owner. **Criteria:** Recipients are selected based on academic performance and demonstrated interest in automotive industry.

Funds Avail.: $1,000. **To Apply:** Applicants must submit a complete application form. **Deadline:** August 17.

1965 ■ Richard Cossette/Gale Memorial Scholarships *(All/Scholarship)*

Purpose: To provide and promote practical business management service. **Focus:** Automotive technology. **Qualif.:** Applicants must work in the collision repair industry; must demonstrate an interest in self-improvement through management education; must own or work for a business that as an ASA Collision division member in good standing. If an applicant is not a business owner, he or she must be recommended by a business owner. **Criteria:** Recipients are selected based on academic performance and demonstrated interest in automotive industry.

Funds Avail.: $1,000. **To Apply:** Applicants must submit a complete application form. **Deadline:** August 17.

1966 ■ Florida Automotive Industry Scholarships *(Undergraduate/Scholarship)*

Purpose: To provide and promote practical business management services. **Focus:** Automotive technology. **Qualif.:** Applicants must be high school seniors, or high school graduates, or persons possessing a GED. Individual applicants must be nominated by a member of the association. **Criteria:** Recipients are selected based on academic achievement; merit; and need.

Funds Avail.: No specific amount. **To Apply:** Applicants must submit a complete application form. **Contact:** George Ehrhard, FAIA, 15619 Premiere Dr., Tampa, FL 33624, Phone: 813-962-4445; Fax: 813-962-4741; E-mail: george@faia.org.

1967 ■ APSAIL's Ralph Silverman Memorial Scholarships *(Undergraduate/Scholarship)*

Purpose: To further promote quality and high standards through education within the automotive aftermarket industry. **Focus:** Automotive technology. **Qualif.:** Applicants must be students who intend to pursue a career in the automotive aftermarket industry. Scholarships require Illinois residency and an APSA of Illinois Member Sponsor. **Criteria:** Recipients are selected based on academic performance and demonstrated interest in the automotive industry.

Funds Avail.: $500. **Number Awarded:** 6. **To Apply:** Applicants must submit a complete application form. **Deadline:**

Awards are arranged alphabetically below their administering organizations

June 30. **Contact:** For any questions, just contact Marsha Fogleman, E-mail: marsha@apsail, Toll free: 800-369-2964.

1968 ■ Sloan Northwood University Heavy-Duty Scholarships *(Undergraduate/Scholarship)*

Purpose: To provide and promote practical business management service. **Focus:** Automotive technology. **Qualif.:** Applicants must be enrolled in the university's Automotive Aftermarket Management curriculum, Heavy Duty Management program or the Heavy Duty Vehicle Technology program; must be U.S. citizens and maintain 2.5 cumulative grade point average. **Criteria:** Recipients are selected based on financial need and demonstrated career interest.

Funds Avail.: No specific amount. **To Apply:** Applicants must submit a complete application form. **Contact:** Terry Nyboer at 616-395-5620.

1969 ■ Automotive Women's Alliance Foundation (AWA)

PO Box 4305
Troy, MI 48099
Fax: (248) 239-0291
Free: 877-393-2923
URL: www.awafoundation.org

1970 ■ Automotive Women's Alliance Foundation Scholarships *(Undergraduate/Scholarship)*

Purpose: To support the advancement of automotive professionals and motivate current and future students studying an automotive related field. **Focus:** Automotive technology. **Qualif.:** Candidates must be North American citizens; must be high school seniors or accepted in a college or university; must have and maintain a minimum of 3.0 GPA. **Criteria:** Scholarships are given based on academic merit.

Funds Avail.: $2,500. **To Apply:** Candidates must submit a completed application form; transcript from current educational institution; resume; and one-page cover letter stating the career goals. Freshmen applicants must provide a high school transcript and proof of acceptance from a college, university or class they wish to attend.

1971 ■ Aviation Distributors and Manufacturers Association (ADMA)

100 N 20th St., Ste. 400
Philadelphia, PA 19103-1462
Ph: (215) 320-3872
Fax: (215) 564-2175
E-mail: adma@fernley.com
URL: www.adma.org

1972 ■ Aviation Distributors and Manufacturers Association Scholarship Fund *(All/Scholarship)*

Purpose: To provide assistance for students pursuing careers in the aviation field. **Focus:** Aviation. **Qualif.:** Applicants must be third or fourth year students enrolled in a four-year program at an accredited Aviation institution and possess a minimum of 3.0 grade point average; or a second-year students in an A&P program at a two-year accredited institution. **Criteria:** Recipients are selected based on academic performance, financial need, recommendations, extracurricular activities and leadership contributions.

Funds Avail.: No specific amount. **Number Awarded:** 2.

To Apply: Applicants must submit a filled out application form obtained at www.adma.org. Applicants must submit two letters of reference and a 500-word essay describing their desire to pursue a career in the aviation field. **Deadline:** March 23.

1973 ■ AVS Science and Technology Society (AVS)

125 Maiden Ln., 15th Fl.
New York, NY 10038
Ph: (212) 248-0200
Fax: (212) 248-0245
E-mail: yvonne@avs.org
URL: www.avs.org

1974 ■ AVS Applied Surface Science Division Awards *(Graduate/Award)*

Purpose: To recognize and encourage excellence in continuing graduate studies in the sciences and technologies of interest to American Vacuum Society. **Focus:** Science technologies. **Qualif.:** Applicants must be graduate students that will need to present a poster or talk during any Applied Surface Science Division sessions, plus an additional capsule (3-slide, 5-minute) presentation to the judges. **Criteria:** Selection will be based on the scientific merit and originality of students' work.

Funds Avail.: $1,000. **To Apply:** Students wishing to participate in the competition should contact the ASSD Student Award Chair when submitting an abstract. **Deadline:** May 2. **Contact:** Angela Klink at angela@avs.org.

1975 ■ AVS Biomaterial Interfaces Division Awards *(Graduate/Award)*

Purpose: To recognize and encourage excellence in continuing graduate studies in the sciences and technologies of interest to American Vacuum Society. **Focus:** Science technologies. **Qualif.:** Applicants must be students that will need to present a poster at one of the BI poster session on their thesis research. **Criteria:** Students will be judged on the scientific merit and originality of their research.

Funds Avail.: A total value of $1,500. **Number Awarded:** Three. **To Apply:** Students must submit a copy of their abstract along with a statement of intent to compete for the student prize. **Deadline:** May 2. **Contact:** Angela Klink at angela@avs.org.

1976 ■ AVS Manufacturing Science and Technology Group Awards *(Graduate/Award)*

Purpose: To encourage participation of students in the MSTG program and to acknowledge the valuable contributions they make in advancing state-of-the-art in manufacturing science and technology. **Focus:** Science technologies. **Qualif.:** Applicants must be full-time university graduate students with primary appointments at universities. **Criteria:** Preference will be given to those who give oral presentations of their papers.

Funds Avail.: $500. **Number Awarded:** Two. **To Apply:** Applicants must submit the followig: a 1-page letter of application describing the students research; letter of endorsement by the student's research advisor; copy of submitted abstract; completed application. **Deadline:** May 2. **Contact:** Angela Klink at angela@avs.org.

Awards are arranged alphabetically below their administering organizations

1977 ■ AVS MEMS and NEMS Technical Group Best Paper Awards (Undergraduate, Graduate/Award)

Purpose: To promote outstanding scientific research and technological innovation. **Focus:** Science technologies. **Qualif.:** Candidates must be undergraduate or graduate students. **Criteria:** Candidates will be judged on the quality, originality of their research and their skill in presentation (oral/poster).

Funds Avail.: $500. **To Apply:** Interested candidates should submit a cover letter describing their intent to compete along with a copy of their AVS abstract, current resume and application to Angela Klink. **Deadline:** May 2. **Contact:** Angela Klink at angela@avs.org.

1978 ■ AVS Spectroscopic Ellipsometry Focus Topic Graduate Student Awards (Graduate/Award)

Purpose: To promote outstanding scientific research and technological innovation. **Focus:** Science technologies. **Qualif.:** Interested applicants must be competitive graduate students and young post-doctoral researchers. **Criteria:** Selection will be based on the submitted application materials.

Funds Avail.: No specific amount. **To Apply:** Interested applicants must submit the following: curriculum vitae; a copy of their submitted AVS abstract; and a letter of recommendation from their research advisor. Application materials should be sent by email to Angela Klink. **Deadline:** May 2. **Contact:** Angela Klink at angela@avs.org.

1979 ■ AVS Thin Film Division Harper Awards (Graduate/Award)

Purpose: To promote outstanding scientific research and technological innovation. **Focus:** Science technologies. **Qualif.:** Applicants must be currently registered graduate students. **Criteria:** Selection will be based on the committee's criteria.

Funds Avail.: $600 for the winner; $500 for the two runners-up. **To Apply:** Interested applicants must submit the following: curriculum vitae; a copy of their submitted AVS abstract; and a letter of recommendation from their research advisor. **Deadline:** May 2. **Contact:** Angela Klink at angela@avs.org.

1980 ■ John Coburn and Harold Winters Student Award in Plasma Science and Technology (Graduate/Award)

Purpose: To promote outstanding scientific research and technological innovation. **Focus:** Science technologies. **Qualif.:** Interested candidates must be students. **Criteria:** Winner will be selected from the finalists on the basis of the oral presentation, the quality of research, the clarity of the presentation and the potential for the research to advance the field of plasma science.

Funds Avail.: $500 for each finalist. **Number Awarded:** 6. **To Apply:** Students must submit a curriculum vitae of the nominee; a one-page letter of endorsement from the student's research advisor/mentor; a copy of the nominee's submitted abstract for the AVS International Symposium. **Deadline:** May 2. **Contact:** Angela Klink at angela@avs.org.

1981 ■ Electronic Materials and Processing Division - Postdoctoral Award (Postdoctorate/Award)

Purpose: To promote outstanding scientific research and technological innovation. **Focus:** Science technologies.

Qualif.: Interested applicants must be postdoctoral fellows. **Criteria:** Selection will be based on the submitted materials.

Funds Avail.: No specific amount. **To Apply:** Applicants must submit the following: a copy of the accepted abstract with Program Number; a recommendation letter from their advisor; their curriculum vitae; and a cover letter of request. Application should be sent by email to Dr. Leonard J. Brillson. **Deadline:** September 7. **Contact:** Dr. Leonard J. Brillson at brillson.1@osu.edu.

1982 ■ Dorothy M. and Earl S. Hoffman Awards (Graduate/Award)

Purpose: To recognize and encourage excellence in continuing graduate studies in the sciences and technologies of interest to American Vacuum Society. **Focus:** Science technologies. **Qualif.:** Nominees must be registered graduate students in an accredited academic institution at the time when the applications are due. Applicants are normally expected not to graduate before the award selection. **Criteria:** Selection will be based on the excellence in research and academic record.

Funds Avail.: No specific amount. **To Apply:** Applicants must submit a completed application form, the Report on Candidate Form, abstract to the AVS International Symposium for Division/Group awards and all supporting materials to Angela Klink. **Deadline:** May 2. **Remarks:** Established in 2002. **Contact:** Angela Klink at angela@avs.org.

1983 ■ Magnetic Interfaces and Nanostructures Division - The Leo M. Falicov Student Award (Graduate/Award)

Purpose: To recognize and encourage excellence in continuing graduate studies in the sciences and technologies of interest to American Vacuum Society. **Focus:** Science technologies. **Qualif.:** Interested applicants must be graduate students. **Criteria:** Selection will be based on the oral presentation, considering quality of research and clarity of presentation.

Funds Avail.: $500. **To Apply:** Interested students must submit an abstract and the application to Angela Klink. In addition, a copy of the AVS abstract, reprints/preprints of the work and a letter of recommendation from the advisor should be sent. **Deadline:** May 2. **Contact:** Angela Klink at angela@avs.org.

1984 ■ Nanometer-Scale Science and Technology Division Graduate Award (Graduate/Award)

Purpose: To promote outstanding scientific research and technological innovation. **Focus:** Science technologies. **Qualif.:** Applicants must be graduate students. **Criteria:** Selection is based on the quality of the talk, the responses to questions, and the level of the research.

Funds Avail.: $500 for the finalists; additional $1,000 for the winner. **To Apply:** Applicants must submit a completed application, a copy of the abstract, an extended abstract written by the student of no more than three pages, and a recommendation letter from the student's research advisor, who must be a member of AVS. **Deadline:** May 2. **Remarks:** Established in 1998. **Contact:** Angela Klink at angela@avs.org.

1985 ■ Nellie Yeoh Whetten Award (Graduate/Recognition, Award)

Purpose: To recognize and encourage excellence in continuing graduate studies in the sciences and technolo-

Awards are arranged alphabetically below their administering organizations

gies of interest to American Vacuum Society. **Focus:** Science technologies. **Qualif.:** The nominee must be a registered female graduate student in an accredited academic institution at the time when the applications are due. Applicants are normally expected not to graduate before the award selection. **Criteria:** Selection will be based on the excellence in research and academic record.

Funds Avail.: No specific amount. **To Apply:** Applicants must submit a completed application form, the Report on Candidate Form, abstract to the AVS International Symposium for Division/Group awards and all supporting materials to Angela Klink. **Deadline:** May 2. **Contact:** Angela Klink at angela@avs.org.

1986 ■ Morton M. Traum Surface Science Student Awards *(Graduate, Doctorate/Award)*

Purpose: To promote outstanding scientific research and technological innovation. **Focus:** Science technologies. **Qualif.:** Candidates must be either current graduate students or received the PhD degree in the year of the Symposium. **Criteria:** Selection will be based on the scientific content and presentation skill.

Funds Avail.: $1,000. **To Apply:** Candidates must submit the following: a copy of the abstract that includes the abstract submission number; an extended abstract that does not exceed two pages (including tables, figures and references; and expected graduation date. Electronic submission of all information in a single PDF file, labeled by the applicant's name, ("FirstName_LastName.pdf") is preferred. **Deadline:** May 2. **Contact:** Angela Klink at angela@avs.org.

1987 ■ Russell and Sigurd Varian Award *(Graduate/Award)*

Purpose: To recognize and encourage excellence in continuing graduate studies in the sciences and technologies of interest to American Vacuum Society. **Focus:** Science technologies. **Qualif.:** The nominee must be a registered graudate student in an accredited academic institution at the time when the applications are due. Applicants are normally expected no to graduate before the award selection. **Criteria:** Selection will be based on the excellence in research and academic record.

Funds Avail.: No specific amount. **To Apply:** Applicants must submit a completed application form, the Report on Candidate Form, abstract to the AVS International Symposium for Division/Group awards and all supporting materials to Angela Klink. **Deadline:** May 2. **Remarks:** Extablished in 1982 to commemorate the pioneering work of Russell and Sigurd Varian in the field of vacuum science and technology. The award is supported by Agilent Technologies Vacuum Products Division. **Contact:** Angela Klink at angela@avs.org.

1988 ■ AXA Equitable
1290 Ave. of the Americas
New York, NY 10104
Ph: (212) 314-4600
Free: 877-222-2144
E-mail: service@axaonline.com
URL: www.axa-equitable.com

1989 ■ AXA Achievement Scholarships
(Undergraduate/Scholarship)

Purpose: To provide scholarships to high school seniors and college students who demonstrated outstanding achievement. **Focus:** General studies. **Qualif.:** Applicants must be US citizens or legal residents; be current high school seniors who plan to enroll full-time in an accredited two-year or four-year college or university in the US; demonstrate ambition and self-drive as evidence by outstanding achievement in an activity in school, the community or the workplace; be recommended by an unrelated adult who can attest to the student's achievement. **Criteria:** Primary consideration will be given to the applicant's demonstrated achievement in a non-academic area as reported by the applicant and supported by the appraisal completed by an adult who is not related to the applicant.

Funds Avail.: $10,000. **Number Awarded:** 52. **To Apply:** Application form can be downloaded online. Applicants must submit the completed application form together with complete transcript of grades to: AXA Achievement Scholarship, Scholarship America, One Scholarship Way, PO Box 297, Saint Peter, MN 56082. **Remarks:** The scholarships are sponsored by the AXA Foundation, in association with US News and World Report.

1990 ■ Charles Babbage Institute (CBI)
222-21st Ave. S
Minneapolis, MN 55455
Ph: (612) 624-5050
Fax: (612) 625-8054
E-mail: cbi@umn.edu
URL: www.cbi.umn.edu

1991 ■ Arthur L. Norberg Travel Grants *(All/ Grant)*

Purpose: To provide short-term grants to help scholars offset travel expenses needed to use archival collections at the Charles Babbage Institute. **Focus:** Information Science and Technology. **Qualif.:** Applicants must be scholars intending to use CBI collections for research projects. To be eligible, scholars must reside outside the Twin Cities metropolitan region. **Criteria:** Recipients are selected based on eligibility.

Funds Avail.: $750. **Number Awarded:** 2. **To Apply:** Applicants must submit a two-page CV as well as a 500-word project description that describes the overall research project, identifies the importance of specific CBI collections and discusses the projected outcome (journal article, book chapter, museum exhibit, etc.). Materials must be submitted by email at cbi@umn.edu or mailed at: Charles Babbage Institute: Norberg Travel Fund, 211 Andersen Library, University of Minnesota, 222 - 21st Avenue South, Minneapolis, MN 55455. **Deadline:** January 15. **Contact:** Jeffrey Yost, 612-624-5050, yostx003@umn.edu.

1992 ■ The Adelle and Erwin Tomash Fellowships *(Doctorate/Fellowship)*

Purpose: To administer research projects in the history of information technology and inspire engagement in original research that is disseminated through scholarly publications and conference presentations. **Focus:** Information Science and Technology. **Qualif.:** Applicants must be graduating students of doctoral dissertation research in the history of computing. **Criteria:** Recipients are selected based on the need of the CBI materials, research plans and willingness to make a brief presentation of the research findings.

Funds Avail.: $14,000. **To Apply:** Applicants must submit a curriculum vitae; a five-page, single-spaced statement

Awards are arranged alphabetically below their administering organizations

and justification of the research program including a discussion of methods, research materials, evidence of faculty support for the project, and bibliography. **Deadline:** January 15. **Contact:** Jeffrey Yost, 612-624-5050, yostx003@umn.edu.

1993 ■ The Bailey Family Foundation
912 W Platt St.
Tampa, FL 33606
Ph: (813) 549-6140
Fax: (813) 549-6141
E-mail: contact@bailey-family.org
URL: www.bailey-family.org

1994 ■ The Bailey Family Foundation College Scholarship Program *(Undergraduate/Scholarship)*

Purpose: To financially assist students in continuing their education. **Focus:** General studies. **Qualif.:** Applicants must be U.S. residents; have minimum cumulative GPA of 2.5; must demonstrate financial need; must be enrolled or accepted to one of the participating schools listed on the scholarship application; and must be pursuing an undergraduate degree. **Criteria:** Applicants will be evaluated based on academic achievement and financial need.

Funds Avail.: No specific amount. **To Apply:** Applicants must submit the completed scholarship application form and an essay of no more than 300 words describing any community service or other activities that have influenced the applicant's life or telling the reviewers about the applicant's goals. **Deadline:** September 15.

1995 ■ The Bailey Family Foundation High School Scholarships Program *(Undergraduate/Scholarship)*

Purpose: To provide financial assistance for high school seniors intending to continue their post-secondary education. **Focus:** General studies. **Qualif.:** Applicant must be a U.S. resident; possess a minimum cumulative GPA of 2.5; must demonstrate financial need; must be a graduating senior from a participating high school; and must be pursuing an undergraduate degree. **Criteria:** Applicants will be evaluated based on academic achievement and financial need.

Funds Avail.: No specific amount. **To Apply:** Applicant must submit a completed scholarship application form including an essay of no more than 300 words describing any community service or other activities that have influenced the applicant's life or telling the reviewers about the applicant's goals. **Deadline:** September 15.

1996 ■ Baker, Donelson, Bearman, Caldwell and Berkowitz, P.C. (Memphis, Tennessee)
First Tennessee Bldg., 165 Madison Ave., Ste. 2000
Memphis, TN 38103-2752
Ph: (901) 526-2000
Fax: (901) 577-2303
E-mail: jrhodes@bakerdonelson.com
URL: www.bakerdonelson.com

1997 ■ Baker Donelson Diversity Scholarships *(Undergraduate/Scholarship)*

Purpose: To help law students defray the cost of law school tuition and related expenses. **Focus:** Law. **Qualif.:** Applicants must be diverse law students. **Criteria:** Selection will be based on the committee's criteria.

Funds Avail.: $10,000. **Number Awarded:** Three. **To Apply:** Interested applicants must visit the website for the online application tool. **Deadline:** June 22.

1998 ■ Baker and Hostetler LLP
191 N Wacker Dr., Ste. 3100
Chicago, IL 60606-1901
Ph: (312) 416-6200
Fax: (312) 416-6201
E-mail: rokada@bakerlaw.com
URL: www.bakerlaw.com

1999 ■ Baker and Hostetler Diversity Fellowships *(Undergraduate/Fellowship)*

Purpose: To recruit candidates with diverse backgrounds and perspectives to foster an inclusive workplace. **Focus:** Law. **Qualif.:** Applicants must: be enrolled full-time in an ABA-accredited law school and in good standing as a second-year law student at the time of application; be members of one of the under-represented racial/ethnic groups set forth by the Equal Employment Opportunity Commission or a member of the LGBT community; not a recipient of a similar diversity award from another law firm for the same time period; spend at least eight weeks with the firm. Splitting time between two offices may be permitted based upon approval of the two offices' Hiring Partners; be US citizens or otherwise authorized to work in the United States. **Criteria:** Selection will be based on the demonstrated superior academic performance during college and law school, significant personal achievements and strong community involvement. Law school students will need to possess strong oral and written communication skills, demonstrated leadership achievements and a sincere interest and commitment to join Baker Hostetler.

Funds Avail.: $25,000. **To Apply:** Candidates must provide the following documents: completed application form; current resume; unofficial or official undergraduate and law school transcripts; personal statement; two professional or academic references **Deadline:** October 5. **Contact:** Dee Driscole at ddriscole@bakerlaw.com.

2000 ■ Paul D. White Scholarships *(Undergraduate/Award)*

Purpose: To provide minority law students with valuable experience early in their careers. **Focus:** Law. **Qualif.:** Applicants must be law students of Black or African American, Hispanic or Latino, Native Hawaiian or Pacific Islander, Asian, American Indian or Alaska Native descent. **Criteria:** Selection will be based on the committee's criteria.

Funds Avail.: $7,500. **To Apply:** Application form can be obtained at the website. Applicants must complete and submit completed application and personal statement. **Remarks:** Established in 1997.

2001 ■ Baltimore City Community College (BCCC)
600 E Lombard St., Rm. 206
Baltimore, MD 21202
Ph: (410) 462-8597
Fax: (410) 225-4650
Free: 888-203-1261
E-mail: financialaid@bccc.edu

Awards are arranged alphabetically below their administering organizations

URL: www.bccc.edu

2002 ■ BCCC Foundation Scholarships
(Undergraduate/Scholarship)

Purpose: To provide financial assistance to individuals who have the desire and commitment to pursue their educational goals. **Focus:** General studies. **Qualif.:** Applicants must be graduating high school students with at least 6 credits at BCCC with 2.5 GPA. **Criteria:** Recipients are selected based on academic achievement and financial need.

Funds Avail.: No specific amount. **To Apply:** Applicants must submit completed scholarship application along with a 300-500 word essay and a copy of transcript. **Deadline:** June 15 and November 15.

2003 ■ BCCC Foundation Workforce Scholarships *(Undergraduate/Scholarship)*

Purpose: To provide financial assistance to those who have the desire and commitment to pursue their educational goals. **Focus:** General studies. **Qualif.:** Applicants must be U.S. citizens and residents of Maryland working at least 20 hours a week; must have a 2.5 GPA and enrolled in at least three credits per semester if pursuing credit courses; and must demonstrate financial need through submission of FAFSA. **Criteria:** Recipients are selected based on academic achievement and financial need.

Funds Avail.: No specific amount. **To Apply:** Applicants must submit completed scholarship application along with a 300-500 word essay and a copy of transcript. **Deadline:** June 15 and November 15.

2004 ■ Banff Centre - Leadership Development

Box 1020
Banff, AB, Canada T1L 1H5
Ph: (403) 762-6331
Fax: (403) 762-6422
Free: 800-590-9799
E-mail: leadership@banffcentre.ca
URL: www.banffcentre.ca/departments/leadership

2005 ■ Alliance Pipeline Scholarships *(Professional development/Scholarship)*

Purpose: To support non-profit leaders of Canadian charities in improving their leadership skills. **Focus:** Leadership, Institutional and community. **Qualif.:** Applicant must be an employee of a registered Canadian charity under the Income Tax Act (Canada). **Criteria:** Priority will be given to individuals with organizations operating in a location where Alliance Pipelines has a business interest or association.

Funds Avail.: Full scholarship. No specific amount. **Number Awarded:** 3. **To Apply:** Applicants must submit a completed application form along with a brief outline (on letterhead) of the applicant's organization's history, mission and activities and the role, responsibilities and length of service with the organization; reasons why assistance is required; anticipated benefits from participating in the program; a description of how the applicant will share the learnings from the program with the team, organization and throughout the sector; the name of Supervisor or Board Chair; and the registered charity number with the Canada Revenue Agency (CRA).

2006 ■ Fraser Milner Casgrain Scholarships
(Professional development/Scholarship)

Purpose: To support non-profit leaders of Canadian charities in improving their leadership skills. **Focus:** Leadership, Institutional and community. **Qualif.:** Applicant must be an employee, officer, director or designated agent of a registered Canadian charity under the Income Tax Act (Canada). **Criteria:** Selection is based on the submitted application materials.

Funds Avail.: $2,500. **To Apply:** Applicants must submit a completed application form together with a brief outline (on letterhead, one page) of the applicant's financial contribution to the program and the organization; the names of other agencies applied for funding and the amounts requested; reasons why assistance is required; the anticipated benefits from participating in the program; name of Supervisor of Board Chair; and the registered charity number with the Canada Revenue Agency (CRA).

2007 ■ Investors Group Scholarships for Not-For-Profit Leaders *(Professional development/Scholarship)*

Purpose: To support non-profit leaders of Canadian charities in improving their leadership skills. **Focus:** Leadership, Institutional and community. **Qualif.:** Applicant must be an employee of a registered Canadian charity under the Income Tax Act (Canada) and the organization must be located in Manitoba. **Criteria:** Priority will be given to individuals with organizations in the city of Winnipeg.

Funds Avail.: $4,583. **To Apply:** Applicants must submit a completed application form along with a brief outline (on letterhead) of the applicant's organization's history, mission, activities and the role, responsibilities and length of service with the organization; reasons why assistance is required; anticipated benefits from participating in the program; a description of how the applicant will sharing the learnings from the program with the team, organization and throughout the sector; the name of Supervisor or Board Chair; and the registered charity number with the Canada Revenue Agency (CRA). **Deadline:** June 15.

2008 ■ Lafarge Community Leaders Scholarships *(Professional development/Scholarship)*

Purpose: To support non-profit leaders of Canadian charities in improving their leadership skills. **Focus:** Leadership, institutional and community. **Qualif.:** Applicant must be an employee of a Canadian non-profit organization. **Criteria:** Selection is based on the submitted application materials.

Funds Avail.: $4,000. **Number Awarded:** 3. **To Apply:** Applicants must submit a completed application form along with a brief outline (on letterhead) of the applicant's organization's history, mission, activities and the role, responsibilities and length of service with the organization; reasons why assistance is required; anticipated benefits from participating in the program; a description of how the applicant will sharing the learnings from the program with the team, organization and throughout the sector; and the name of Supervisor or Board Chair.

2009 ■ Youth or the Environment Scholarships
(Professional development/Scholarship)

Purpose: To support non-profit leaders of Canadian charities in improving their leadership skills. **Focus:** Leadership, Institutional and community. **Qualif.:** Applicant must be an employee, officer, director or designated agent of a Canadian registered charity under the Income Tax Act (Canada). The organization must have a substantial focus on either youth or the environment and be at a mid- or upper-level management position. The annual revenue of the organization must be under $3,000,000. **Criteria:** Selection is based on the submitted application materials.

Awards are arranged alphabetically below their administering organizations

Funds Avail.: $5,000. **To Apply:** Applicants must submit a completed application form along with a brief outline (on letterhead) of the applicant's organization's history, mission, activities and role within the areas of focus; the applicant's role and responsibilities and length of service with the organization; the name of Supervisor or Board Chair; a resume; organization's most recent audited financial statements; and registered charity number with CRA.

2010 ■ Bank of Canada

234 Wellington St.
Ottawa, ON, Canada K1A 0G9
Fax: (613) 782-7713
Free: 800-303-1282
E-mail: info@bankofcanada.ca
URL: www.bankofcanada.ca

2011 ■ Bank of Canada Fellowships *(Doctorate, Professional development/Fellowship)*

Purpose: To provide financial support to individuals who have been recognized for their expertise and excellence in bank-related issues. **Focus:** Banking. **Qualif.:** Applicants must be Canadian citizens, permanent residents or legally permitted to work in Canada; must have obtained a PhD degree; and be employed by a Canadian university during the tenure of the fellowship. **Criteria:** Candidates will be chosen based on 1) demonstrated excellence and innovation of their work; 2) applicability to Bank of Canada policy development and/or research; 3) potential to achieve recognition as leaders in the special fields as indicated by consistent high-quality work in publications or presentations; and 4) potential to make contributions in education and development of new researchers.

Funds Avail.: Varies. **To Apply:** Applicants must submit a cover page; letter of nomination from the university; curriculum vitae; current research program and plans (maximum of six, single-sided pages); current research paper and four abstracts; referee information. Materials should appear as a PDF document. Referees are also required to submit two letters of reference (signed and on official letterhead). **Deadline:** November 15. **Contact:** Materials should be submitted to fellowship-bourses@bankofcanada.ca.

2012 ■ Bank of Canada Governor's Awards *(Doctorate, Professional development/Award)*

Purpose: To provide funds to exceptional assistant and associate professors working at Canadian universities who have made contributions in their fields. **Focus:** Business; Finance; Economics. **Qualif.:** Applicants must be Canadian citizens, permanent residents or legally permitted to work in Canada; must have obtained a PhD degree within ten years of application; and be employed by a Canadian university with a program in economics, business/finance as assistants or associate professors during the tenure of the fellowship. **Criteria:** Candidates will be selected based on 1) demonstrated potential to make exemplary research contributions in the specified fields as indicated by publications of refereed and other articles; 2) applicability to Bank of Canada policy development and/or research; and 3) potential to make contributions in education and development of new researchers.

Funds Avail.: $25,000. **To Apply:** Applicants must submit a cover page; letter of nomination from the university; curriculum vitae; current research program and plans (maximum six, single-sided pages); one current research paper and four abstracts (published and unpublished) and referee information. Materials should appear as a PDF document. Referees are also required to submit two letters of reference. **Deadline:** November 15. **Contact:** Materials should be submitted to govaward-boursegouv@bankofcanada.ca.

2013 ■ Banner & Witcoff, Ltd.

10 S Wacker Dr., Ste. 3000
Chicago, IL 60606-7407
Ph: (312) 463-5000
Fax: (312) 463-5001
E-mail: info@bannerwitcoff.com
URL: www.bannerwitcoff.com

2014 ■ Donald W. Banner Diversity Scholarships for Law Students *(Undergraduate/Scholarship)*

Purpose: To foster the development of intellectual property lawyers from diverse backgrounds. **Focus:** Law. **Qualif.:** Applicants must be law students who have entered into a JD program at an ABA-accredited law school in the United States. **Criteria:** Scholarship recipients will be selected by the Donald W. Banner Diversity Scholarship review board based on the following criteria: (1) academic merit (undergraduate, graduate and law school); (2) commitment to the pursuit of a career in IP law; (3) member of a historically underrepresented group in IP law; (3) written communication skills; (4) oral communication skills determined through an interview; and (5) leadership qualities and community involvement.

Funds Avail.: $5,000. **To Apply:** Applicants must complete the Donald W. Banner Diversity Scholarship application form, available online; must submit a resume, academic transcripts (law, undergraduate/graduate school), a writing sample (5-10 pages), three references including contact information, and a one-page statement describing how diversity has impacted the candidate. **Deadline:** January 5. **Contact:** Chris Hummel at chummel@bannerwitcoff.com.

2015 ■ Baptist Communicators Association

c/o Margaret M. Dempsey
1519 Menlo Dr.
Kennesaw, GA 30152
Ph: (770) 425-3728
E-mail: office@baptistcommunicators.org
URL: www.baptistcommunicators.org

2016 ■ Alan Compton and Bob Stanley Professional Scholarships *(Undergraduate/Scholarship)*

Purpose: To provide financial assistance to qualified or prospective members who want to pursue their career. **Focus:** General studies. **Qualif.:** Applicant must not be a member of the scholarship committee or the executive committee. **Criteria:** Selection will be based on the attitude and need of the applicant.

Funds Avail.: $500. **To Apply:** Application materials must include: a) name, address, and phone number of applicant; b) Current position/title, department and agency; c) Number of years worked in public relations/communications and number of years at the applicant's institution; d) Highest level of formal education attained and name of other professional development conferences or workshops attended in the past; e) copy of applicant's job description and resume; f) title and name of person to whom the applicant reports;

Awards are arranged alphabetically below their administering organizations

g) statement of why financial assistance is needed and how much money is required. **Deadline:** February 15.

2017 ■ Al Shackleford and Dan Martin Professional Scholarships *(Undergraduate/Scholarship)*

Purpose: To provide financial assistance to qualified members who want to pursue their career. **Focus:** General studies. **Qualif.:** Applicant must not be a member of the scholarship committee or the executive committee. **Criteria:** Selection will be based on the attitude and need of the applicant.

Funds Avail.: $1,000. **To Apply:** Application materials must include: a) name, address, and phone number of applicant; b) Current position/title, department and agency; c) Number of years worked in public relations/communications and number of years at the applicant's institution; d) Highest level of formal education attained and name of other professional development conferences or workshops attended in the past; e) copy of applicant's job description and resume; f) title and name of person to whom the applicant reports; g) statement of why financial assistance is needed and how much money is required. **Deadline:** February 15.

2018 ■ Bar Association of San Francisco

301 Battery St., 3rd Fl.
San Francisco, CA 94111
Ph: (415) 982-1600
Fax: (415) 477-2388
URL: www.sfbar.org

2019 ■ Bay Area Minority Law Student Scholarships *(Graduate, Undergraduate/Scholarship)*

Purpose: To reaffirm a commitment to diversity in legal education and the legal profession. **Focus:** Law. **Qualif.:** Applicants must be students from minority groups who are underrepresented in Bay Area law schools; and must have received a "letter of admission" from one of the eight Northern California law schools. **Criteria:** Recipients are selected on the submitted application materials.

Funds Avail.: $10,000 yearly. **To Apply:** Applicants must submit a completed application with official undergraduate or graduate transcript; 500-word personal statement; copies of current IRS tax forms; statement of economic need (optional); copies of "letters of admissions" from any ABA accredited law school in Northern California. **Deadline:** May 11. **Contact:** Lauren Luke or email at lluke@sfbar.org.

2020 ■ Barbados Cancer Association (BACA)

PO Box 3094
New York, NY 10163
Ph: (718) 414-3134
E-mail: info@barbadoscancerusa.org
URL: www.barbadoscancerusa.org

2021 ■ Barbados Cancer Association Post-Graduate Scholarships *(Graduate/Scholarship)*

Purpose: To enable graduates to pursue their clinical research and training in cancer prevention. **Focus:** Oncology; Biological and clinical sciences. **Qualif.:** Applicants must be Caribbean community citizens residents in Barbados; must be currently employed as health professionals in Barbados. **Criteria:** Consideration will be given to the facilitating costs of cancer related conferences.

Funds Avail.: April 15. **To Apply:** Applicants must complete

the application form available in the website; must provide a 500-word essay; must have curriculum vitae or resume; must have two recommendation letters and acceptance letter from Institution. **Deadline:** April 15.

2022 ■ Barrientos Scholarship Foundation (BSF)

PO Box 7173
Omaha, NE 68107
Ph: (402) 215-5106
E-mail: info@barrientosscholarship.org
URL: www.barrientosscholarship.org

2023 ■ Artistic Scholarship Awards *(Undergraduate, Vocational/Occupational/Scholarship)*

Purpose: To provide financial assistance to qualified students who want to pursue their studies. **Focus:** Music; Visual arts; Theater arts; Dance. **Qualif.:** Applicants must be students pursuing higher education and career goals that focus on one or more of the arts - music, visual arts, theater, or dance; must be of Latino heritage; must be high school graduating seniors, currently enrolled in college, or adults ready to pursue college; must plan to enroll in at least two classes and attend an accredited community college, university, or technical or vocational school in the state of Nebraska or surrounding greater Omaha Metropolitan area; must have a minimum of 2.5 GPA. **Criteria:** Selection of applicants will be based on the criteria of the Scholarship Selection Committee.

Funds Avail.: $500-$1,000. **To Apply:** Applicants must complete the application form available online; must have a personal essay with a minimum of two pages; must submit letters of recommendation and official high school or college transcript. **Deadline:** May 2.

2024 ■ BSF General Scholarship Awards *(Undergraduate, Vocational/Occupational/Scholarship)*

Purpose: To provide financial assistance to qualified students who want to pursue their studies. **Focus:** Interdisciplinary studies. **Qualif.:** Applicants must be students pursuing higher education and career goals that focus on disciplines other than arts; must be of Latino Heritage; must be high school graduating seniors, currently enrolled in college, or adults ready to pursue college; must plan to enroll in at least two classes and attend an accredited community college, university, or technical or vocational school in the State of Nebraska or surrounding greater Omaha Metropolitan area; must have a minimum of a 2.5 cumulative GPA. **Criteria:** Selection of applicants will be based on the criteria of the Scholarship Selection Committee.

Funds Avail.: $500-$1,000. **Number Awarded:** Multiple. **To Apply:** Applicants must have the application form available online; must have a personal essay with a minimum of two pages; must submit two letters of recommendation and official high school or college transcript. **Deadline:** May 2. **Contact:** Application form and requirements must be sent to Barrientos Scholarship Foundation at the above address.

2025 ■ Barth Syndrome Foundation (BSF)

PO Box 582
Gretna, NE 68028
URL: barthsyndrome.org

2026 ■ BSF Science and Medicine Research Grants *(Professional development/Grant)*

Purpose: To advance the state of knowledge about Barth Syndrome so that progress can be made in finding a

Awards are arranged alphabetically below their administering organizations

specific treatment or cure for this unusual mitochondrial disease. **Focus:** General studies. **Qualif.:** Applicants must be investigators at every professional level. **Criteria:** Selection will be based on the committee's criteria.

Funds Avail.: No specific amount. **To Apply:** Submitted application must be no more than 15 pages (including figures, tables and references) in length; single-sided, using a font size of 12 points and with one-inch margins; must contain the following elements: 1) completed information form; 2) an abstract summarizing the project; 3) a section presenting the specific aims of the project, stating both the objectives and the hypotheses to be tested in the project; 4) discussion of the background and significance of the work proposed, including a critical evaluation of previous research and existing knowledge, specifically identifying the gaps that the project is intended to fill, and explicitly stating the importance of the proposed research; 5) thorough summary of research design and methods, describing the experimental design and methods that will be used to accomplish the specific aims; 6) statement indicating whether human subjects or vertebrate animals will be involved in the research; 7) description of the resources and environment available for the project; 8) a list of project personnel (name, title, institution, and role of the project), including the percentage effort that each person is expected to devote to the project; and 9) detailed budget section for the proposed project, along with a separate narrative fully describing and justifying the expenses. **Deadline:** October 31. **Contact:** Matthew J. Toth, PhD, 132 Creemer Ave., Iselin, NJ 08830; E-mail: matthew.toth@barthsyndrome.org.

2027 ■ Bat Conservation International (BCI)

PO Box 162603
Austin, TX 78716-2603
Ph: (512) 327-9721
Fax: (512) 327-9724
Free: 800-538-2287
E-mail: batinfo@batcon.org
URL: www.batcon.org

2028 ■ Bat Conservation International Student Research Scholarships *(Graduate, Undergraduate/Scholarship)*

Purpose: To help students at universities conduct conservation-relevant research; to support students in research initiatives that is essential in conserving bats and ecosystems. **Focus:** Environmental conservation. **Qualif.:** Applicants must be enrolled in any college or university; must be conducting research that specifically addresses at least one of the specified areas of needs: (1) answering ecological or behavioral questions essential to conservation or management; (2) resolving an economic problem which will further conservation tolerance; (3) documenting key ecological or economic roles of bats; (4) educating people who are directly relevant to conservation success. **Criteria:** Award will be given to those applicants who have completed proposals that clearly address the conservation needs. Reviewers will rank all conservation-relevant proposals and fund those who have received the highest scores.

Funds Avail.: $1,000 to $5,000. **To Apply:** Applicants must apply online or send documents as attachments to grant@batcon.org. **Deadline:** December 15. **Contact:** grant@batcon.org.

2029 ■ John Bayliss Broadcast Foundation

PO Box 51126
Pacific Grove, CA 93950
Ph: (831) 655-5229
E-mail: kmfranke@baylisfoundation.org
URL: www.baylissfoundation.org

2030 ■ John Bayliss Broadcast Foundation Internship Programs *(Undergraduate/Internship)*

Purpose: To enhance students' education at Bayliss Schools across the nation. To provide practical skills that will prepare them for a rewarding future. **Focus:** Broadcasting. **Qualif.:** Applicants must be studying for a career in the radio industry and have taken basic journalism courses as well as specialized courses in the radio communication fields; must have previous radio-related experience; be enrolled in a degree program and entering their junior or senior year in college; must have a GPA of 3.0 or better; and must be at least 18 years of age. **Criteria:** Recipients are selected based on financial need and academic record.

Funds Avail.: No specific amount. **To Apply:** Applicants must submit a resume and complete the application form.

2031 ■ John Bayliss Broadcast Foundation Scholarships *(Undergraduate/Scholarship)*

Purpose: To support broadcasting students. **Focus:** Broadcasting. **Qualif.:** Applicants must be entering their junior or senior year at an institution in the United States; must be preparing for a career in the radio industry, preferably commercial radio; must maintain a 3.0 GPA or better; and must demonstrate a high degree of integrity and a personal sense of responsibility. **Criteria:** Recipients are selected based on financial need, merit, history of radio-related activities, and based the demonstrated degree of integrity and a personal sense of responsibility.

Funds Avail.: $5,000. **Number Awarded:** Varies. **To Apply:** Applicants must provide a typewritten resume; an official transcript; three letters of recommendation written by people other than relatives, a two-page typewritten essay describing their broadcasting goals as they relate to radio and the ways in which they hope to achieve their goals.

2032 ■ BDPA Education Technology Foundation (BETF)

4423 Lehigh Rd., No. 277
College Park, MD 20740
Ph: (513) 284-5968
Fax: (202) 318-2194
E-mail: info@betf.org
URL: www.betf.org

2033 ■ Eli Lilly and Company/Black Data Processing Associates Scholarships *(High School/Scholarship)*

Purpose: To provide outstanding minority students financial assistance in pursuing an information technology-related degree at an accredited two or four-year college or university of their choice. **Focus:** Information science and technology. **Qualif.:** Applicants must be U.S. citizens or permanent residents and graduating high school seniors at the time of their application; must be pursuing an information technology-related degree at an accredited two or four-year college or university; must be student members of BDPA and participate in computer training activities. **Crite-**

Awards are arranged alphabetically below their administering organizations

ria: Applicants are evaluated based on academic excellence; exceptional leadership potential; and impact through service to their communities.

Funds Avail.: $2,500. **To Apply:** Applicants must submit the completed application form; high school transcript; one 500-word essay explaining why information technology is important and the importance of personal commitment in giving back to your community; and two letters of recommendation. **Deadline:** July 1. **Contact:** Application form and supporting documents must be sent to: Jonee' Drake, Lilly Corporate Ctr., Drop Code 6841, Indianapolis, IN 46285; Email: jdrake@lilly.com.

2034 ■ Beacon of Hope Scholarship Foundation

7230 Medical Ctr. Dr., Ste. 300
West Hills, CA 91307
Ph: (818) 716-7003
URL: www.beaconhope.org

2035 ■ Beacon of Hope Scholarships
(Undergraduate/Scholarship)

Purpose: To provide financial assistance to qualified, underprivileged, college-bound African American high school students. **Focus:** General studies. **Qualif.:** Applicants must be graduating African American high school students; must be residents of Mississippi and/or Los Angeles, California; must have at least a "B" average and verification of acceptance and attendance at a four-year college or university in the United States; must participate in any scholarship-related public relations activities. **Criteria:** Recipients are selected based on academic achievement and financial need.

Funds Avail.: $1,000. **To Apply:** Applicants must submit the completed application form along with one certified copy of high school academic transcript; one original photograph; and a hard copy of an essay of at least 1,000 words entitled, "Why I am Deserving of the Beacon of Hope Scholarship".

2036 ■ Beatitudes Society

950 Dena Way
Santa Barbara, CA 93111-1103
E-mail: anne@beatitudessociety.org
URL: www.beatitudessociety.org

2037 ■ Beatitudes Fellowships *(Professional development/Fellowship)*

Purpose: To create new models for church and the pursuit of social justice. **Focus:** Christian education. **Qualif.:** Emerging faith leaders who are: under the age of 40; within seven years of divinity school graduation; based in a community of faith; actively working to engage faith with social justice using a unique approach. **Criteria:** Selection will be based on a proven track record of leadership; a commitment to faith and to social justice; a willingness to take risks; a desire to collaborate with others; a specific project that matches up their deep gladness with the world's great need.

Funds Avail.: $10,000. **To Apply:** Fellows are nominated and then complete an application process that includes an online application and description of their project due, as well as a personal interview.

2038 ■ BECA Foundation

PO Box 936
Escondido, CA 92033
Ph: (760) 741-8246
E-mail: sdbeca@sbcglobal.net
URL: www.becafoundation.org

2039 ■ BECA Foundation-CUSM Scholarships
(Undergraduate/Scholarship)

Purpose: To seek promising students and provide them with the necessary financial assistance, moral support and guidance to complete their education, thereby promoting higher educational and leadership standards within the Hispanic community. **Focus:** General studies. **Qualif.:** Applicants must be Latino students enrolled at CSU San Marcos. **Criteria:** Recipients are selected based on financial need, scholastic determination and community and cultural awareness.

Funds Avail.: No specific amount. **To Apply:** Applicants must complete the application form. **Deadline:** March 2. **Contact:** sdbeca@sbcglobal.net; 760-741-8246.

2040 ■ BECA Foundation General Scholarships Fund *(Undergraduate/Scholarship)*

Purpose: To seek promising students and provide them with the necessary financial assistance, moral support and guidance to complete their education, thereby promoting higher educational and leadership standards within the Hispanic community. **Focus:** General studies. **Qualif.:** Applicant must be a San Diego County High School graduate who is entering college. **Criteria:** Recipients are selected based on financial need and merit; GPA; and community involvement.

Funds Avail.: $500-$1,000. **To Apply:** Applicant must complete an application form; must submit two letters of recommendation; a (one-page) essay; and copy of FAFSA/SAR. **Deadline:** March 2. **Contact:** sdbeca@sbcglobal.net; 760-741-8246.

2041 ■ Alice Newell Joslyn Medical Fund
(Undergraduate/Scholarship)

Purpose: To seek promising students and provide them with the necessary financial assistance, moral support and guidance to complete their education, thereby promoting higher educational and leadership standards within the Hispanic community. **Focus:** Medical Education. **Qualif.:** Applicants must be entering medical/health care professions; must be residents of, or attending a high school or college in San Diego County at the time of application. **Criteria:** Recipients are selected based on financial need, scholastic determination, community and cultural awareness.

Funds Avail.: $500-$2,000. **To Apply:** Applicants must complete the application form. **Deadline:** March 2. **Contact:** sdbeca@sbcglobal.net; 760-741-8246.

2042 ■ Beinecke Rare Book and Manuscript Library

Yale University
PO Box 208240
New Haven, CT 06520
Ph: (203) 432-2972
Fax: (203) 432-4047
E-mail: beinecke.library@yale.edu
URL: www.library.yale.edu/beinecke

2043 ■ Visiting Scholars Fellowships
(Postdoctorate/Fellowship)

Purpose: To support visiting scholars and to provide access to the library for scholars who live outside the greater

Awards are arranged alphabetically below their administering organizations

New Haven area. **Focus:** General studies. **Qualif.:** Applicants must be visiting scholars pursuing post-doctoral or equivalent research in its collections. **Criteria:** Selection will be based on the committee's criteria.

Funds Avail.: No specific amount. **To Apply:** Applicants are asked to submit the following items to the Fellowship Selection Committee: online and printed copy of application form including the materials; curriculum vitae; a maximum of 1,200 words research proposal; detailed list of specific research materials to be consulted at Beinecke during the fellowship; two confidential letters of recommendation sent to the Beinecke Director, specifically addressing the merits of the proposed fellowship project; self-addressed, stamped postcard with the applicants' materials. **Deadline:** December 7.

2044 ■ Yale Graduate and Professional Students Research Fellowships *(Graduate, Professional development/Fellowship)*

Purpose: To support students who wish to use Beinecke collections as a primary resource for their dissertations or culminating projects. **Focus:** General studies. **Qualif.:** Applicants must be graduate students who have completed their course work, passed their qualifying examinations and be prepared to pursue research based upon an approved prospectus; professional school students must be engaged in research for an approved culminating project required for their degree, with the expectation that their project will be undertaken in the final year of their program. **Criteria:** Selection will be based on a competitive basis.

Funds Avail.: $3,000-$13,650. **To Apply:** Applicants must submit the following materials to the Director of the Beinecke Library: an application form; curriculum vitae; a maximum of 1,200 words proposal explaining in detail the specific relationship between the Beinecke Collection and the applicant's research; a detailed list of specific research materials to be consulted at Beinecke during the fellowship; two confidential letters of recommendation sent to the Beinecke Director, one of which must come from the principal director of the applicant's dissertation or culminating project; for graduate students, approved or pending prospectus; for professional school students, a statement explaining how their project fulfills the culminating requirement in their school. **Deadline:** October 19; March 8.

2045 ■ Bel Canto Vocal Scholarship Foundation
55 Tremont St.
Cranston, RI 02920
Ph: (401) 942-6440
E-mail: rjdipanni@cox.net
URL: www.belcantoscholarship.com

2046 ■ Bel Canto Vocal Scholarship Foundation Vocal Competition *(All/Award, Scholarship)*

Purpose: To support the education of young, talented opera singers. **Focus:** Music, Opera. **Qualif.:** Contestants must be U.S. citizens with proof of citizenship, and must be 21 to 36 years old. **Criteria:** Selection is based on the application materials submitted.

Funds Avail.: Over $15,000. **To Apply:** Candidates must audition for the Vocal Competition. **Contact:** Mr. Ronald DiPanni at the above address.

2047 ■ Alexander Graham Bell Association for the Deaf and Hard of Hearing
3417 Volta Pl. NW
Washington, DC 20007
Ph: (202) 337-5220
Fax: (202) 337-8314
E-mail: info@agbell.org
URL: nc.agbell.org

2048 ■ AG BELL College Scholarship Awards *(Undergraduate/Scholarship)*

Purpose: To promote communication for people with hearing loss. **Focus:** Hearing and Deafness. **Qualif.:** Applicants must be enrolled in or applied to a mainstream and accredited college/university as full-time students. **Criteria:** Award will be given to applicant who has been diagnosed with a moderate to profound hearing loss prior to acquiring a spoken language (pre-lingual hearing loss); Applicants hearing loss must be bilateral and in the moderate to profound range; Spoken communication must be the student's primary mode of communication.

Funds Avail.: No specific amount. **Number Awarded:** 2. **To Apply:** Applicants must submit an application, with pages in numbered order; For children who use hearing aids, an unaided Audiogram performed within the last twelve (12) months or for those with cochlear implants, the most recent mapping report (first page only); Verification of the student's application, acceptance or enrollment to a mainstream and accredited university/college; Official transcripts for the most recent two years completed of high school or college; Student essay; Recommendation from a hearing health professional (maximum of two single-sided pages); Recommendation from a current AG Bell member (Maximum of two single-sided pages). If you do not know an AG Bell member, please provide a recommendation from an educational or therapeutic professional; Recommendation from a non-relative who is familiar with the family's financial need (maximum of two single-sided pages). **Deadline:** March. **Contact:** Questions may be directed to financialaid@agbell.org.

2049 ■ George H. Nofer Scholarships for Law and Public Policy *(Doctorate, Graduate/Scholarship)*

Purpose: To promote communication for people with hearing loss. **Focus:** Hearing and Deafness; Public administration. **Qualif.:** Applicants must be accepted at or recently enrolled in an accredited law school or masters/doctoral program in public policy or public administration as a full-time first year rising graduate students. Previous first and second year recipients may re-apply provided that a minimum of nine credit hours was completed. **Criteria:** Award will be given to those applicants who have been diagnosed with a moderate to profound hearing loss prior to acquiring spoken language (pre-lingual hearing loss); Applicants hearing loss must be bilateral and in the moderate to profound range; Must have an unaided Pure-Tone Average of 60dB or greater in the better hearing ear in the speech frequencies of 500, 1000 and 2000 Hz. Applicants with cochlear implants meet this eligibility requirement. Unilateral (one-sided) hearing loss does not qualify; Applicants uses spoken language as the primary mode of communication.

Funds Avail.: No specific amount. **Number Awarded:** 3. **To Apply:** Applicants must submit an application, with pages in numbered order; For students who use hearing aids, an unaided Audiogram performed within the last twelve months or for those with cochlear implants, the most recent mapping report (first page only); Official transcripts for the most recent two completed years of college. For third year applicants, a transcript of your previous year of

Awards are arranged alphabetically below their administering organizations

study will suffice. Verification of the student's application, acceptance or enrollment to a mainstream and accredited university/college (a readable photocopy of a letter, tuition notice, or other correspondence is acceptable); Student essay (as indicated in the application); Recommendation from a hearing health professional (maximum of two single-sided pages); Recommendation from a current AG Bell member (Maximum of two single-sided pages). If you do not know an AG Bell member, please provide a recommendation from an educational or therapeutic professional; Recommendation from a non-relative who is familiar with the family's financial need (maximum of two single-sided pages). **Deadline:** March. **Contact:** Fax: 202-337-8314, E-mail: financialaid@agbell.org.

2050 ■ School Age Financial Aid Program
(Undergraduate/Scholarship)

Purpose: To promote communication for people with hearing loss. **Focus:** Hearing and Deafness. **Qualif.:** Applicant must be a resident of the United States (including territories) or Canada, and must be enrolled or registered for enrollment on a full-time basis in a parochial, independent or private school in which the child participates in a mainstream setting. **Criteria:** Awards will be given to those hearing loss has been diagnosed prior to acquiring spoken language (pre-lingual hearing loss); Hearing loss must be in the moderate to profound range: Spoken communication must be the child's primary mode of communication; The child must be at least six years of age and no older than twenty-one (21) years of age; Parents/guardians must demonstrate financial need. Preference will be given to AG BELL members.

Funds Avail.: No specific amount. **Number Awarded:** Varies. **To Apply:** Applicants must submit an application, with pages in numbered order; For children who use hearing aids, an unaided Audiogram performed within the last twelve months or for those with cochlear implants, the most recent mapping report (first page only); Verification of the child's enrollment, and a narrative from a teacher or principal on the child's progress on school letterhead; Recommendation from a hearing health professional (maximum of two single-sided pages); Recommendation from a current AG Bell member (Maximum of two single-sided pages). If you do not know an AG Bell member, please provide a recommendation from an educational or therapeutic professional; Recommendation from a non-relative who is familiar with the family's financial need (maximum of two single-sided pages). **Deadline:** May 31.

2051 ■ Marc and Ruti Bell Foundation
6800 Broken Sound Pky.
Boca Raton, FL 33487
Ph: (561) 988-1700
Fax: (561) 988-1738
URL: bellfamily.org

2052 ■ Marc and Ruti Bell Foundation Scholarships *(Undergraduate/Scholarship)*

Purpose: To encourage undergraduates in the College of Arts and Science to choose careers in public service. **Focus:** Public service. **Qualif.:** Applicants must be junior and senior high school students who have declared their majors in the field of public service; must have a strong sense of their career goals. **Criteria:** Selection will be based on the following criteria: an excellent academic record; unmet financial need (which would otherwise be

covered by a burdensome loan); commitment to entering a public interest profession, as demonstrated in a personal statement, as well as by a track record of community service and (in some cases) a relevant course of study; an interview (for those who survive a preliminary cut on the basis of the three other criteria mentioned here).

Funds Avail.: No specific amount. **To Apply:** Students may submit an application letter together with the other requirements. **Deadline:** April 1. **Contact:** Matthew S. Santirocco, Dean, College of Arts and Science, New York University, 100 Washington Square E New York, NY 10003-6688; Phone: 212-998-8100; Fax: 212-995-4141.

2053 ■ Ben Meadows Company Inc.
401 S Wright Rd.
Janesville, WI 53546-8729
Ph: (608) 743-8001
Fax: (800) 628-2068
Free: 800-241-6401
E-mail: mail@benmeadows.com
URL: www.benmeadows.com

2054 ■ Ben Meadows Natural Resource Scholarships - Academic Achievement Scholarships *(Undergraduate/Scholarship)*

Purpose: To provide fund for students enrolled in a natural resource program. **Focus:** Forestry; Environmental science; Natural resources; Wildlife conservation, management and science; Fisheries sciences/management. **Qualif.:** Applicant must be a junior or senior student enrolled in a natural resource program working toward a bachelor of arts or science degree, which includes, but not limited to, agro forestry, urban forestry, environmental studies, natural resource management, natural resource recreation, wildlife management, wood science and fisheries management. Student must have a GPA of 3.2 or higher on a 4.0 scale. **Criteria:** Award is given based on the application.

Funds Avail.: $2,500. **Number Awarded:** 1. **To Apply:** Applicant must complete the online scholarship application and must provide a letter of recommendation from educational superior (professor, teacher, advisor); must attach official copies of transcripts reflecting the GPA; must provide a list of clubs, activities and years involved; summary of accomplishments relating to the field of study; and 300 words essay on how these leadership roles help grow and expand interest of the chosen field. **Deadline:** June 30. **Contact:** Application form and supporting documents should be sent to 5400 Grosvenor Ln., Bethesda, MD 20814.

2055 ■ Ben Meadows Natural Resource Scholarships - Leadership Scholarships *(Undergraduate/Scholarship)*

Purpose: To provide fund for students enrolled in a natural resource program. **Focus:** Forestry; Environmental science; Natural resources; Wildlife conservation, management and science; Fisheries sciences/management. **Qualif.:** Applicant must be a junior or senior student enrolled in a natural resource program working toward a bachelor of arts or science degree, which includes, but not limited to, agro forestry, urban forestry, environmental studies, natural resource management, natural resource recreation, wildlife management, wood science and fisheries management. Student must have a GPA of 2.5 or higher on a 4.0 scale. **Criteria:** Award is given based on the application.

Funds Avail.: $2,500. **Number Awarded:** 1. **To Apply:**

Awards are arranged alphabetically below their administering organizations

Applicant must complete the online scholarship application and must provide a letter of recommendation from educational superior (professor, teacher, advisor), and attach official copies of transcripts reflecting the GPA; must provide a list of leadership roles, clubs and years involved; summary of involvement and projects within leadership roles relating to the field of study; and essay of 300 words on how these leadership roles have helped grow and expand interest of chosen field. **Deadline:** June 30. **Contact:** Application form and other supporting documents should be sent to 5400 Grosvenor Ln., Bethesda, MD 20814.

2056 ■ Benign Essential Blepharospasm Research Foundation (BEBRF)

PO Box 12468
Beaumont, TX 77726-2468
Ph: (409) 832-0788
Fax: (409) 832-0890
E-mail: bebrf@blepharospasm.org
URL: www.blepharospasm.org

2057 ■ Benign Essential Blepharospasm Research Foundation Research Grants *(Doctorate, Postdoctorate/Grant)*

Purpose: To encourage researches on cranial dystonia (blepharospasm and Meige's Syndrome) by providing financial support. **Focus:** Medicine. **Qualif.:** Principal investigators must hold M.D. or Ph.D. and intend to conduct researches that relate specifically to benign essential blepharospasm and Meige covering new treatments, pathophysiology and genetics, photophobia and dry eye; non-US citizens working at institutions abroad are eligible to apply. **Criteria:** Recipients are selected based on committee's review of the proposal.

Funds Avail.: $150,000. **To Apply:** Applicants must send curriculum vitae and eight copies of proposals with consent form and necessary signatures. Specific grant guidelines and forms are available on the website. **Deadline:** August 31.

2058 ■ Benton County Foundation (BCF)

PO Box 911
Corvallis, OR 97339
Ph: (541) 753-1603
URL: www.bentoncountyfoundation.org

2059 ■ Margaret Dowell-Gravatt, M.D. Scholarships *(Undergraduate/Scholarship)*

Purpose: To encourage and support ethnic minority undergraduate women enrolled in the College of Science. **Focus:** Zoology; Microbiology; Medical technology; Medicine; Nursing; Physical therapy; Occupational therapy. **Qualif.:** Applicant must: be pursuing a degree in Zoology or Microbiology or one of the following pre-health programs: Medical Technology, Medicine, Nursing, Physical and/or Occupational therapy. Applicant must: be enrolled full-time at the sophomore, junior or senior level; have a GPA of 2.5 overall and 3.0 in science courses required in their major field or pre-health curriculum; qualify for financial assistance as defined by the Financial Aid Office of OSU. **Criteria:** Selection will be based on the committee's criteria.

Funds Avail.: No specific amount. **To Apply:** Applicant may contact the Foundation for application form and other requirements. **Contact:** Benton County Foundation at the above address.

2060 ■ Joel R. Friend Scholarships *(Undergraduate/Scholarship)*

Purpose: To provide scholarship opportunity to the students from OSU. **Focus:** General studies. **Qualif.:** Applicants must be foreign students from Thailand, Taiwan (Republic of China) in attendance at OSU in any field of study; must qualify for financial assistance as defined by the Financial Aid Office of OSU. **Criteria:** Selection will be based on the committee's criteria.

Funds Avail.: No specific amount. **To Apply:** Applicant may contact the Foundation for application form and other requirements. **Deadline:** March 1. **Contact:** Benton County Foundation at the above address.

2061 ■ William Harrison Gill Education Fund *(Undergraduate/Scholarship)*

Purpose: To provide scholarship to the students of Oregon State University. **Focus:** General studies. **Qualif.:** Applicant must: be of Native American descent; be an American citizen with a permanent or guardian residence in one of the following states: Arizona, California, Colorado, Idaho, Montana, Nevada, New Mexico, Oregon, Utah, Washington or Wyoming; and must be students enrolled at Oregon State University. **Criteria:** Selection will be based on the committee's criteria.

Funds Avail.: No specific amount. **To Apply:** Applicant may contact the Foundation for application process and other requirements.

2062 ■ Lucy Hsu Ho Scholarships *(Undergraduate/Scholarship)*

Purpose: To award scholarship to the foreign students of ethnic Chinese descent. **Focus:** General studies. **Qualif.:** Applicants must be foreign students of ethnic Chinese descent; primary preference in awarding the scholarship shall be given to those candidates who have demonstrated leadership in student and/or community activities and organizations, as well as the desire to serve others in the candidate's future chosen field of work. Secondary preference shall be determined by level of financial need; must re-apply for this scholarship each year; must qualify for financial assistance as defined by the Financial Aid Office of OSU. **Criteria:** Selection will be based on the committee's criteria.

Funds Avail.: No specific amount. **To Apply:** Applicant may contact the Foundation for application form and other requirements. **Contact:** Benton County Foundation at the above address.

2063 ■ Kilbuck Family Native American Scholarships *(Undergraduate/Scholarship)*

Purpose: To provide scholarship opportunity to the students enrolled at Oregon State University. **Focus:** General studies. **Qualif.:** Applicant must have a cumulative GPA of 3.0 or above; have at least 1/16 enrolled or documented tribal affiliation; must be a graduate of Oregon or Alaska high schools. Scholarship is renewable for up to 12 terms if a 3.0 cumulative GPA is maintained. **Criteria:** Selection will be based on the committee's criteria.

Funds Avail.: No specific amount. **To Apply:** Applicant may contact the Foundation for application process and other requirements.

2064 ■ David W. Schacht Native American Student Scholarships *(Undergraduate/Scholarship)*

Purpose: To provide scholarship to the students of Oregon State University. **Focus:** General studies. **Qualif.:** Ap-

Awards are arranged alphabetically below their administering organizations

plicants must: be students of Native American descent, defined as self-identified individuals with tribal affiliation; have demonstrated ability and scholarship during high school or during previous college years; must qualify for financial assistance as defined by the Financial Aid Office of OSU. **Criteria:** Selection will be based on the committee's criteria.

Funds Avail.: No specific amount. **To Apply:** Applicant may contact the Foundation for application form and other requirements.

2065 ■ Helen J. and Harold Gilman Smith Scholarships *(Graduate, Undergraduate/ Scholarship)*

Purpose: To provide scholarship to the students pursuing their first baccalaureate or graduate degree in any field of study. **Focus:** General study. **Qualif.:** Applicant must: be a Native American student; have a minimum GPA of 2.75 for their undergraduate freshman year. Graduate students must maintain the minimum GPA level required by their college graduate degree program. Preference is given to students graduating from an American Indian high school. Applicant must qualify for financial assistance as defined by the Financial Aid Office of OSU. **Criteria:** Selection will be based on the committee's criteria.

Funds Avail.: No specific amount. **To Apply:** Applicant may contact the Foundation for application form and other requirements. **Contact:** Benton County Foundation at the above address.

2066 ■ Hugh and Helen Wood Nepales Scholarships *(Undergraduate/Scholarship)*

Purpose: To provide scholarship to the students who are current citizens of Nepal. **Focus:** General studies. **Qualif.:** Applicants must be current students who are citizens of Nepal; primary preference in awarding the scholarship shall be given to those candidates who agree to become a public servant in Nepal for at least five years following graduation. Other requirements include: a 3.5 GPA; a minimum TOEFL score of 550 or other language competency score satisfactory to the university: and all preparatory work completed in Nepal. Secondary consideration will be given to African American students if no Nepalese students meet the requirements. **Criteria:** Selection will be based on the committee's criteria.

Funds Avail.: No specific amount. **To Apply:** Applicant may contact the Foundation for application form and other requirements. **Contact:** Benton County Foundation at the above address.

2067 ■ Berks County Community Foundation (BCCF)
237 Ct. St.
Reading, PA 19601
Ph: (610) 685-2223
Fax: (610) 685-2240
E-mail: info@bccf.org
URL: www.bccf.org

2068 ■ Howard Fox Memorial Law Scholarships *(Undergraduate/Scholarship)*

Purpose: To provide financial assistance for the education of Berks County residents planning to take up law courses. **Focus:** Law. **Qualif.:** Applicants must be Berks County residents entering their second year at an accredited law

school who demonstrate financial need, without discrimination to color, race, national origin or religion. **Criteria:** Recipients are selected based on financial need.

Funds Avail.: $3,000. **To Apply:** Applicant must submit the completed application form with two letters of reference from people who are not related to him or her; copy of law school transcript; and a written recommendation from a professor at the law school he or she is attending. **Deadline:** April 1.

2069 ■ Beta Phi Mu
PO Box 3062100
Tallahassee, FL 32306-2100
Ph: (850) 644-3907
Fax: (850) 644-9763
E-mail: betaphimuinfo@admin.fsu.edu
URL: www.beta-phi-mu.org

2070 ■ Eugene Garfield Doctoral Dissertation Fellowships *(Doctorate, Graduate/Fellowship)*

Purpose: To support library and information science doctoral students working with their dissertation. **Focus:** Library and archival sciences. **Qualif.:** Applicant must be a doctoral student in library and information science; has advanced candidacy with all requirements for degree completed except writing and defense of dissertation. **Criteria:** The Scholarship Committee meets during May and the recipients are announced at the annual meeting in June.

Funds Avail.: $3,000. **Number Awarded:** 6. **To Apply:** Applicant must submit a completed application form together with the abstract of the dissertation (maximum of 300 words); letter of approval from the Dean or Director; personal statement (maximum of 500 words) on post-dissertation plans; and three letters of reference sent to the address on the application. **Deadline:** March 15. **Contact:** Beta Phi Mu, School of Information Studies, Florida State University, Tallahassee, FL 32306-2100.

2071 ■ Sarah Rebecca Reed Scholarships *(Graduate/Scholarship)*

Purpose: To support students with their educational pursuits. **Focus:** Library and archival sciences. **Qualif.:** Applicant must be admitted to a graduate program in library and information studies accredited by the American Library Association and has not completed more than 12 hours by the fall semester following the application deadline. **Criteria:** The Scholarship Committee meets during May and the recipients are announced at the annual meeting in June. Applicants are judged on several factors but the autobiographical note is the prime importance.

Funds Avail.: $2,250. **Number Awarded:** 1. **To Apply:** Applicants must submit the completed application form together with a typed one-page autobiography; current transcripts from all institutions of higher learning; and five letters of recommendation from academic instructors, employers or supervisors of paid volunteer work experience. All applications and documents must be scanned and sent via e-mail. **Deadline:** March 15.

2072 ■ Frank B. Sessa Scholarships for Continuing Professional Education *(Professional development/Scholarship)*

Purpose: To support librarians in increasing their professional skills through additional study or attendance at a formal program or workshop. **Focus:** Library and archival

Awards are arranged alphabetically below their administering organizations

sciences. **Qualif.:** Applicants must be librarians pursuing attendance to a formal program or workshop or activities that will increase their professional skills. **Criteria:** Scholarship will be awarded based on the plan of study; usefulness of the planned study to the applicant's present job; or usefulness of the planned study to the applicant's future professional endeavors. The Scholarship gives low priority to applicants pursuing a formal degree program.

Funds Avail.: $1,500. **To Apply:** Applicant must submit a current vitae; a (1-2 page) typed description of plans for study and their relevance to the present job and plans for the future. All required documents must be submitted electronically. **Deadline:** March 15. **Contact:** betaphimuinfo@admin.fsu.edu.

2073 ■ Blance E. Woolls Scholarships
(Graduate/Scholarship)

Purpose: To support students with their educational pursuits. **Focus:** Library and archival sciences. **Qualif.:** Applicants must be admitted to graduate programs in library and information studies accredited by the American Library Association and have not completed more than 12 hours by the Fall semester following to the application deadline; must have the clear intention in pursuing a career in school library and media service. **Criteria:** Applicants are judged on several factors but the autobiographical note is the prime importance.

Funds Avail.: $2,250. **To Apply:** Applicants must submit the completed application form together with typed one-page autobiography; current transcripts from all institutions of higher learning; and five letters of recommendation from academic instructors, employers or supervisors of paid volunteer work experience. All applications and documents must be scanned and sent via e-mail. **Deadline:** March 15. **Contact:** betaphimuinfo@admin.fsu.edu.

2074 ■ Beta Theta Pi
5134 Bonham Rd.
Oxford, OH 45056
Ph: (513) 523-7591
Fax: (513) 523-2381
Free: 800-800-2382
E-mail: beta@betathetapi.org
URL: www.betathetapi.org

2075 ■ Seth R. and Corrine H. Brooks Memorial Scholarships *(All/Scholarship)*

Purpose: To financially assist students in their pursuit of academic achievement. **Focus:** General Studies. **Qualif.:** Applicants must be any student who will be attending college (including post-graduate students); must be the son or daughter of a Beta alumnus. Previous recipients are not qualified. **Criteria:** Recipients will be selected based on academic achievement and level of involvement on campus or community.

Funds Avail.: $1,250. **Number Awarded:** 2. **To Apply:** Applicants must submit a complete application form; most current transcript of records; and a cover letter stating the reason for desiring a scholarship and academic plans. **Deadline:** April 1. **Contact:** Application form and other supporting documents should be sent to Laura Lednik at the above address or e-mail at laura.lednik@ betathetapi.org.

2076 ■ Bethesda Lutheran Communities
600 Hoffman Dr.
Watertown, WI 53094

Ph: (920) 261-3050
Fax: (920) 261-8441
Free: 800-369-4636
E-mail: john.bauer@mailblc.org
URL: bethesdalutherancommunities.org

2077 ■ Scholarships for Lutheran College Students *(Undergraduate/Scholarship)*

Purpose: To financially support Lutheran students pursuing degrees in any area of service to people with developmental disabilities. **Focus:** Mental health. **Qualif.:** Applicant must be an active communicant member of a Lutheran church; have achieved sophomore status or higher at a college or university; have a 3.0 overall GPA; and have an interest in a career in the field of developmental disabilities. **Criteria:** Selection is based on the application.

Funds Avail.: $3,000. **Number Awarded:** 2. **To Apply:** Applicants must submit a completed application form together with an essay (250 to 300 words) on planned career in the field of developmental disabilities; four letters of recommendations; an official college transcript; an autobiography (one-page, double-spaced); a documentation of service to people who are developmentally disabled (minimum of 100 hrs); and other materials helpful for the application. **Deadline:** April 16. **Contact:** Application form and supporting documents must be sent to Mr. Thomas Heuer at the above address or e-mail at thomas.heuer@ mailblc.org.

2078 ■ Bethune-Cookman University (B-CU)
640 Dr. Mary McLeod Bethune Blvd.
Daytona Beach, FL 32114
Ph: (386) 481-2000
Fax: (386) 481-2621
Free: 800-553-9369
URL: www.cookman.edu

2079 ■ Bethune-Cookman University Excelsior Scholarships *(Undergraduate/Scholarship)*

Purpose: To provide financial assistance for students intending to pursue their education. **Focus:** General studies. **Qualif.:** Applicants must be completing high school in spring; must be incoming freshmen at a university; and must maintain a 3.4 cumulative GPA. **Criteria:** Selection is based on merit.

Funds Avail.: Funds may cover the cost of full-time tuition that is not covered by federal or state financial aid and other non-institutional scholarships. **To Apply:** Applicants must apply for admission to be considered. **Deadline:** February 1.

2080 ■ Bethune-Cookman University Presidential Scholarships *(Undergraduate/ Scholarship)*

Purpose: To provide financial assistance to students intending to pursue their education. **Focus:** General studies. **Qualif.:** Applicants must be completing high school in spring; must be incoming freshmen at any university; and must maintain a 3.5 cumulative GPA. **Criteria:** Selection is based on merit.

Funds Avail.: Fund may be used for full-time tuition, room, boarding fees, and a $500 per semester book voucher only. **To Apply:** Applicants must apply for admission to be considered. **Deadline:** May 1.

Awards are arranged alphabetically below their administering organizations

2081 ■ Noorali Bharwani Professional Corporation

821A 5th St. SW
Medicine Hat, AB, Canada T1A 4H7
Ph: (403) 527-0099
Fax: (403) 529-0711
URL: nbharwani.com

2082 ■ Dr. Noorali & Sabiya Bharwani Endowment *(Undergraduate/Scholarship)*

Purpose: To provide financial assistance to qualified individuals who want to pursue their studies. **Focus:** Nursing. **Qualif.:** Applicants must be first year nursing students with a minimum GPA of B, equivalent of 3.0. **Criteria:** Preference will be given to students with financial need.

Funds Avail.: No specific amount. **To Apply:** For further information about the scholarship and application form, applicants are advice to contact Noorali Bharwani Professional Corporation, 821A 5th St. SW, Medicine Hat, AB T1A 4H7.

2083 ■ Hussein Jina Bharwani Memorial Endowment *(Undergraduate/Scholarship)*

Purpose: To provide financial assistance to qualified individuals who wants to pursue their studies. **Focus:** Nursing. **Qualif.:** Applicants must be nursing students having completed the second year of the nursing program; must have maintained a GPA of 3.0 or better; must have demonstrated a keen interest in the nursing patient; must demonstrate strong clinical skills including good organization and assessment skills and have the ability to establish a positive and constructive rapport with patients, their families and co-workers. **Criteria:** Recipients will be selected based on the committee's review of the application materials.

Funds Avail.: No specific amount. **Number Awarded:** 2. **To Apply:** For further information about the scholarship and application form, applicants are advice to contact Noorali Bharwani Professional Corporation, 821A 5th St. SW Medicine Hat, AB T1A 4H7.

2084 ■ Bibliographical Society of America (BSA)

PO Box 1537
New York, NY 10021
Ph: (212) 452-2710
Fax: (212) 452-2710
E-mail: bsa@bibsocamer.org
URL: www.bibsocamer.org

2085 ■ Katharine Pantzer Fellowships in the British Book Trades *(Professional development/ Fellowship)*

Purpose: To support sustained research in topics relating to book production history in Britain and other related aspects. **Focus:** Library and archival sciences; Printing--History. **Qualif.:** Program is open to individuals conducting research on topics relating to book production and distribution in Britain during the hand-press period as well as studies of authorship, reading and collecting based on the examination of British books published in that period. **Criteria:** Awards are given based on merit.

Funds Avail.: Up to $2,000. **To Apply:** Application instructions and forms are available at the website. **Deadline:** December 1. **Contact:** fellowships@bibsocamer.org.

2086 ■ Bibliographical Society of Canada

Postal Sta. P
Toronto, ON, Canada M5S 2T1
E-mail: gretagolick@rogers.com
URL: www.library.utoronto.ca/bsc/bschomeeng.html

2087 ■ Bernard Amtmann Fellowships *(Postgraduate, Professional development/ Fellowship)*

Purpose: To support the work of a scholar engaged in some area of bibliographical research, including textual studies and publishing history and with a particular emphasis on Canada. **Focus:** General studies. **Qualif.:** Applicants must be members of the Bibliographical Society of Canada. **Criteria:** Scholarship recipient will be selected based on scholastic ability. Preference is given to applicants who display great interest in research work.

Funds Avail.: $1,500. **To Apply:** Application forms are available at the website. Application and attachments must be sent to: Bibliographical Society of Canada PO Box 575, Postal Sta. P, Toronto, ON M5S 2T1. **Deadline:** September 30. **Remarks:** Established in 1992, established in memory of Bernard Amtmann, the bookseller and specialist in Canadiana.

2088 ■ Marie Tremaine Fellowships *(Postgraduate, Professional development/Fellowship)*

Purpose: To support the work of a scholar engaged in some area of bibliographical research, including textual studies and publishing history and with a particular emphasis on Canada. **Focus:** General studies. **Qualif.:** Applicants must be members of the Bibliographical Society of Canada. **Criteria:** Scholarship recipient will be selected based on scholastic ability. Preference is given to applicants who display great interest in research work.

Funds Avail.: $2,000. **To Apply:** Application form will be available at the website. Application should includes the summary and description of the project, budget and must provide references. **Deadline:** February 28. **Remarks:** Established in 1987 in memory of and through the generosity of Marie Tremaine, the doyenne of Canadian bibliographers.

2089 ■ Big Sandy Community and Technical College

1 Bert T. Combs Dr.
Prestonsburg, KY 41653
Ph: (606) 886-3863
Free: 888-641-4132
URL: www.bigsandy.kctcs.edu

2090 ■ Kentucky Educational Excellence Scholarships *(Graduate, Undergraduate/ Scholarship)*

Purpose: To provide financial support for deserving Kentucky high school students and GED recipients intending to pursue their education. **Focus:** General studies. **Qualif.:** Applicants must be high school students; must be U.S. citizens, national or permanent residents; must be residents of Kentucky; must have earned at least a 2.5 GPA in any year of high school while meeting the KEES curriculum requirements; must attend and graduate from a certified Kentucky high school or other approved high school; and must not be a convicted felon. High school graduates applying for a KEES bonus award must have at least an ACT composite score of 15 or a score of 710 or higher on the

Awards are arranged alphabetically below their administering organizations

SAT and must have earned at least a 2.5 GPA in any year of high school while meeting the KEES curriculum requirements. Home school graduates applying for a KEES bonus award must have an ACT composite score of 15 or better on a national exam; must be U.S citizens, national or permanent residents; must be residents of Kentucky; must be enrolled in a participating college; and must not be a convicted felon. GED graduate applicants must have an ACT composite score of 15 or better on a national exam; must have earned a GED in Kentucky within five years of turning 18 years old; must be U.S citizens, national or permanent residents; must be residents of Kentucky; must be enrolled in a participating college within five years of receiving a GED; and must not be a convicted felon. **Criteria:** Selection will be based on merit.

Funds Avail.: Varies. **To Apply:** Applicants are advised to contact KEES for scholarship information and instructions at kees@kheaa.com.

2091 ■ KHEAA Teacher Scholarships
(Undergraduate/Scholarship)

Purpose: To provide financial aid for highly qualified Kentucky students intending to pursue initial teacher certification at participating Kentucky institutions. **Focus:** Teaching. **Qualif.:** Applicants must be residents of Kentucky who are enrolled full-time in a teacher certification program; must demonstrate financial need; and must meet their institution's educational program GPA requirements. **Criteria:** Priority is given to financially incapable applicants.

Funds Avail.: $2,500 for each semester and $1,250 for summer awarded to juniors, seniors, post-baccalaureate or graduate students; $625 each semester and $325 for summer awarded to freshmen and sophomore recipients. **To Apply:** Applicants must complete application package which include the Free Application for Federal Student Aid and a Teacher Scholarship application. Applicants are advised to contact the Federal Student Aid Information Center at 800-433-3243 for further information and instructions. **Deadline:** May 3.

2092 ■ BioCommunications Association (BCA)
220 Southwind Ln.
Hillsborough, NC 27278
Ph: (919) 245-0906
Fax: (919) 245-0906
E-mail: office@bca.org
URL: www.bca.org

2093 ■ Endowment Fund for Education Grants (EFFE) *(Undergraduate/Grant)*

Purpose: To promote and assist study and research in the field of biological communication. **Focus:** Biological and clinical sciences. **Qualif.:** High school students and students currently enrolled in their freshman year at a university or college are not eligible for grant funds. Applicants who are currently enrolled in sophomore, junior and senior years must present documentary evidence to demonstrate that they are in good academic standing for all courses directly related to their major. **Criteria:** Fund Committee will evaluate the complete applications. Selection of applicants will be based on the merit and availability of funds.

Funds Avail.: $500 or less. **To Apply:** Applicants must submit the following documentation: (1) Current curriculum vitae; (2) A full and complete statement of what the applicant/ applicants intend(s) to accomplish within the field of biological photography; (3) Time frame for the project; (4) Details of how the project will benefit biomedical communications and biocommunicators as a whole, and of how this will be measured; (5) An agreement to provide the EFFE Committee with a final report describing the results of the project and its impact on biocommunication; (6) Description of plan to share the resulting educational benefits with the BCA membership; (7) An agreement that the BioCommunications Association, Inc., shall have the right of first publication on any results from project funded wholly or partially from the Endowment Fund for Education. **Deadline:** April 30.

2094 ■ Endowment Fund for Education, Loans
(Undergraduate/Loan)

Purpose: To promote and assist study and research in the field of biological communication. **Focus:** Biological and clinical sciences. **Qualif.:** Applicants must be high school students or students currently enrolled in their freshman year at a university or college; must present documentary evidence to demonstrate that they are in good academic standing for all courses directly related to their major (for sophomore, junior and senior years of high school). **Criteria:** Fund Committees will evaluate the complete applications. Selection of applicants will be based on merit and availability of funds.

Funds Avail.: $500 or less. **To Apply:** Applicants must submit the following documentation: (1) Current curriculum vitae; (2) A financial statement; (3) High school graduates applying for a loan to be used as tuition for the freshman year must present documentation to assure the EFFE Committee that they are in good academic standing for their full senior year. Application forms are available online. **Deadline:** April 30.

2095 ■ Endowment Fund for Education, Loans/ Grants for Educational Materials
(Undergraduate/Grant)

Purpose: To promote and assist study and research in the field of biological communication. **Focus:** Biological and clinical sciences. **Qualif.:** High school students and students currently enrolled in their freshman year at a university or college are not eligible for grant funds. Applicants who are currently enrolled in sophomore, junior and senior years must present documentary evidence to demonstrate that they are in good academic standing for all courses directly related to their major. **Criteria:** Fund Committees will evaluate the complete applications. Selection of applicants will be based on merit and availability of funds.

Funds Avail.: $500 or less. **To Apply:** Applicants must submit the following materials: (1) A complete description of the materials to be purchased; (2) Information about where the materials will be housed and who is to be responsible for their security; (3) Details on how the materials will be made available to the students; (4) The life expectancy of the materials; (5) The relevance of the material to biophotography; (6) The number of students who will use the materials; (7) The total cost and supplier of the materials. **Deadline:** April 30.

2096 ■ Endowment Fund for Education, Loans/ Grants for Equipment *(Undergraduate/Grant)*

Purpose: To promote and assist study and research in the field of biological communication. **Focus:** Biological and clinical sciences. **Qualif.:** High school students and

Awards are arranged alphabetically below their administering organizations

students currently enrolled in their freshman year at a university or college are not eligible for grant funds. Applicants who are currently enrolled in sophomore, junior and senior years must present documentary evidence to demonstrate that they are in good academic standing for all courses directly related to their major. **Criteria:** Fund Committees will evaluate the complete applications. Selection of applicants will be based on merit and availability of funds.

Funds Avail.: $500 or less. **To Apply:** Applicants must submit the following documentation: (1) A complete description of each piece of equipment; (2) The life expectancy of each piece of equipment; (3) The role each piece of equipment will play in the education of biocommunicators; (4) The number of students who can be expected to benefit from the equipment; (5) The total cost of the equipment; (6) The intended supplier of the equipment; (7) An agreement to provide the EFFE Committee with reports at six and twelve months after installation stating how the equipment has been used to benefit the education of biophotography students. **Deadline:** April 30.

2097 ■ Biomagnetic Therapy Association (BTA)
PO Box 394
Lyons, CO 80540
Ph: (303) 823-0307
E-mail: info@biomagnetic.org
URL: www.biomagnetic.org

2098 ■ William Philpott Scholarships *(All/Scholarship)*

Purpose: To encourage educational pursuits among Biomagnetic Therapy Association members who are pursuing certification as a Biomagnetic Specialist at the Biomagnetic Institute. **Focus:** Therapy. **Qualif.:** Applicants must be enrolled at a post-secondary institution and must be pursuing certification as a Biomagnetic Specialist at the Biomagnetic Institute. **Criteria:** Selection is based on ability to complete the program successfully as well as on the applicants' ability to share Biomagnetic Therapy with their communities.

Funds Avail.: Varies. **To Apply:** Applicants must submit a copy of their personal information through e-mail indicating their names, e-mails, addresses and phone numbers and their answers to the question: "Why should you be honored with the scholarship". **Contact:** BTA at the above address.

2099 ■ Biomedical Engineering Society (BMES)
8201 Corporate Dr., Ste. 1125
Landover, MD 20785-2224
Ph: (301) 459-1999
Fax: (301) 459-2444
Free: 877-871-2637
E-mail: info@bmes.org
URL: www.bmes.org

2100 ■ BMES Graduate and Undergraduate Student Awards *(Graduate, Undergraduate/Award)*

Purpose: To promote the future of the biomedical engineering profession. **Focus:** Biomedical sciences. **Qualif.:** Applicants must be graduates or undergraduate students and must be BMES members in good standing. **Criteria:** Selection will be based on the committee's criteria.

Funds Avail.: $500 for graduate students; $400 for undergraduate students. **To Apply:** Applicants must submit an abstract at the time of the official abstract-submission deadline for the Annual Meeting and pay the abstract-submission fee. For the Undergraduate submission: submit two-to-three pages, single spaced, (10-12 font type size) and one inch margins in all sides. A letter of support from the scientific advisor or department chair certifying the originality of the student effort must be uploaded at the time of submission. For the Graduate submission: submit three-to-four pages single spaced, (10-12 font type size) and one inch margins in all sides. A letter of support from the scientific advisor or department chair certifying the originality of the student effort must be uploaded at the time of submission. **Deadline:** June 14. **Contact:** Regina Borkoski, regina@bmes.org.

2101 ■ Birmingham Public School (BPS)
550 W Merrill St.
Birmingham, MI 48009
Ph: (248) 203-3000
Fax: (248) 203-3007
E-mail: webmaster-main@birmingham.k12.mi.us
URL: www.birmingham.k12.mi.us

2102 ■ Birmingham Student Scholarship Fund Association *(Undergraduate/Scholarship)*

Purpose: To provide college financial assistance for students who reside within the boundaries of the Birmingham School District upon high school graduation. **Focus:** General studies. **Qualif.:** Applicants must have their primary residence within the boundaries of the Birmingham Public School or private school district during that year. **Criteria:** Scholarship grants are based on a variety of factors including family financial need, student's academic performance, school or community activities, employment experience, educational goals, and enrollment at a Michigan college, as well as counselor recommendations and other student and family circumstances. In addition, some of the scholarship grants may consider other factors prescribed by a benefactor, including student gender, performance in a particular field of study or a student's school attendance area.

Funds Avail.: $500-$3,000. **Number Awarded:** Varies. **To Apply:** Applicants must submit completed application to the student's high school counselor prior to the filing date set by the Scholar Board each year. The application must be signed by both the student and one parent certifying the truth of the application. The application requires student's and parents' current income tax information, as well as information regarding family housing, unless there is independent written verification of an established pattern of non-support by a parent; scholarship grants will be reduced by 50 percent if information is not received from both parents. The application and instructions can be printed from the webpage. **Deadline:** March 1. **Contact:** BPS at the above address.

2103 ■ Mary E. Bivins Foundation
301 S Polk Ste. 860
Amarillo, TX 79105-1727
Ph: (806) 379-9400
Fax: (806) 379-9404
E-mail: info@bivinsfoundations.org
URL: bivinsfoundations.org

Awards are arranged alphabetically below their administering organizations

2104 ■ Mary E. Bivins Foundation Religious Scholarship Program *(Graduate, Undergraduate/ Scholarship)*

Purpose: To educate ministers to preach the Christian religion. **Focus:** Religious Education. **Qualif.:** Applicants must be dedicated to seeking an undergraduate or graduate education leading to a Bachelors or Masters Degree in a field that prepares the students to preach the Christian religion; must have the intent to serve as pulpit pastors; must be committed to studies and maintain a cumulative undergraduate GPA of 2.75 or above or a cumulative graduate GPA of 3.0 or above; must be permanent residents of one of the 26 counties of the Texas Panhandle; must enroll and pass a minimum of 12 hours each semester at the undergraduate level or 9 hours each semester at the graduate level; must enroll in an accredited college or university. **Criteria:** Preference will be given to those students who meet the criteria.

Funds Avail.: $2,500 per semester for those students classified as a juniors or seniors and $3,500 per semester for graduate students to be used for tuition, books, fees and other expenses as necessary for college/university attendance. **To Apply:** Applicants must check the available website for the required materials. **Remarks:** Scholarships are awarded on an annual basis, and the students are required to continue to meet all award criteria each semester and to complete an application annually. **Contact:** Linda Inks, Scholarship Program Officer, at 806-379-9400 or email: links@bivinsfoundation.org.

2105 ■ Black Alliance for Educational Options (BAEO)
888 16th St. NW, Ste. 800
Washington, DC 20006
Ph: (202) 429-2236
E-mail: info@baeo.org
URL: www.baeo.org

2106 ■ BAEO Children's Scholarship Fund *(High School/Scholarship)*

Purpose: To provide partial tuition assistance for low-income families to send their children to private schools. **Focus:** General Studies. **Qualif.:** Applicants must be: Five years of age or older; from low-income families; students from kindergarten-8th grade. **Criteria:** Preference will be given to those students who meet the criteria.

Funds Avail.: No specific amount. **To Apply:** Applicants must check the available website for the required materials. **Contact:** Black Alliance for Educational Options at the above address.

2107 ■ Black Student Fund *(High School/Scholarship)*

Purpose: To provide financial assistance and support services to Washington DC metropolitan area African-American students. **Focus:** General Studies. **Qualif.:** Applicants must be African American students; must be in grades pre-kindergarten to 12; must be residents in Greater Washington area. **Criteria:** Preference will be given to students who meet the criteria.

Funds Avail.: No specific amount. **To Apply:** Applicants must check the available website for more information. **Contact:** For more information, contact Gwen Thompson, Director, at 202-387-1414 or mail@blackstudentfund.org.

2108 ■ Black Business and Professional Association (BBPA)
675 King St. W, Ste. 210
Toronto, ON, Canada M5V 1M9
Ph: (416) 504-4097
Fax: (416) 504-7343
E-mail: bbpa@bellnet.ca
URL: www.bbpa.org

2109 ■ Hon. Lincoln Alexander Scholarships *(Undergraduate/Scholarship)*

Purpose: To provide support for Black Canadian students. **Focus:** General studies. **Qualif.:** Applicant must be a Canadian citizen or a permanent resident; must be 17 to 30 years of age; and must be enrolled in a full-time degree (graduate or undergraduate), diploma or certificate program at a Canadian college or university for the academic year. **Criteria:** Selection of applicants will be based on academic achievement, financial need, and recognized contribution to the Black community.

Funds Avail.: $2,000. **To Apply:** Applicants must complete the application form and submit along with a letter describing the reasons why they would be worthy recipients of a BBPA National Scholarship; a completed financial information schedule stating their budget for the coming year including information on their expected sources of funding, family income and related information; a letter of reference from the two individuals named in their application (must be a teacher from their high school, college or university, and an individual who is familiar with their community service); and two passport size photos - head shot. Application form and requirements must be sent to The Board of Trustees, BBPA National Scholarship Fund, 675 King St., W, Ste. 210, Toronto, ON M5V 1M9. **Deadline:** May 29.

2110 ■ Louise Bennett-Coverley Scholarships *(Undergraduate/Scholarship)*

Purpose: To provide support to Black Canadian students. **Focus:** General studies. **Qualif.:** Applicant must be a Canadian citizen or a permanent resident; must be 17 to 30 years of age; must be enrolled in a full time degree (graduate or undergraduate), diploma or certificate program at a Canadian college or university for the academic year. **Criteria:** Selection of applicants will be based on academic achievement, financial need, and recognized contribution to the Black community.

Funds Avail.: $2,000. **To Apply:** Applicants must complete the application form and submit along with a letter describing the reasons why they would be worthy recipients of a BBPA National Scholarship; a completed financial information schedule stating their budget for the coming year including information on their expected sources of funding, family income and related information; a letter of reference from the two individuals named in their application (must be a teacher from their high school, college or university, and an individual who is familiar with their community service); and two passport size photos head shot. Application form and requirements must be sent to The Board of Trustees, BBPA National Scholarship Fund, 675 King St., W, Ste. 210, Toronto, ON M5V 1M9. **Deadline:** May 29.

2111 ■ BMO Financial Group Scholarships *(Undergraduate/Scholarship)*

Purpose: To provide support for Black Canadian students. **Focus:** General studies. **Qualif.:** Applicants must be

Awards are arranged alphabetically below their administering organizations

students with academic achievements who have demonstrated social responsibility; must be Canadian citizens or permanent residents; must be 17 to 30 years of age; and must be enrolled in a full-time degree (graduate or undergraduate), diploma or certificate program at a Canadian college or university for the academic year. **Criteria:** Selection of applicants will be based on academic achievement, financial need, and recognized contribution to the Black community.

Funds Avail.: $5,000. **Number Awarded:** 2. **To Apply:** Applicants must complete the application form and submit along with a letter describing the reasons why they would be worthy recipients of a BBPA National Scholarship; a completed financial information schedule stating their budget for the coming year including information on their expected sources of funding, family income and related information; a letter of reference from the two individuals named in their application (must be a teacher from their high school, college or university, and an individual who is familiar with their community service); and two passport size photos - head shot. Application form and requirements must be sent to The Board of Trustees, BBPA National Scholarship Fund, 675 King St., W, Ste. 210, Toronto, ON M5V 1M9. **Deadline:** May 27. **Contact:** bbpascholarships@bellnet.ca.

2112 ■ Tropicana Community Services - Robert K. Brown Scholarships *(Undergraduate/Scholarship)*

Purpose: To provide support for Black Canadian students. **Focus:** Social work. **Qualif.:** Applicant must be enrolled in a course of study in the field of social services; must be a Canadian citizen or a permanent resident; must be 17 to 30 years of age; and must be enrolled in a full-time degree (graduate or undergraduate), diploma or certificate program at a Canadian college or university for the academic year. **Criteria:** Selection of applicants will be based on academic achievement, financial need, and recognized contribution to the Black community.

Funds Avail.: $1,500. **To Apply:** Applicants must complete the application form and submit along with a letter describing the reasons why they would be worthy recipients of a BBPA National Scholarship; a completed financial information schedule stating their budget for the coming year including information on their expected sources of funding, family income and related information; a letter of reference from the two individuals named in their application (must be a teacher from their high school, college or university, and an individual who is familiar with their community service); and two passport size photos - head shot. Application form and requirements must be sent to The Board of Trustees, BBPA National Scholarship Fund, 675 King St., W, Ste. 210, Toronto, ON M5V 1M9. **Deadline:** May 27. **Contact:** bbpascholarships@bellnet.ca.

2113 ■ Herb Carnegie Scholarships *(Undergraduate/Scholarship)*

Purpose: To provide support to Black Canadian students. **Focus:** General studies. **Qualif.:** Applicant must be a Canadian citizen or a permanent resident; must be 17 to 30 years of age; must be enrolled in a full time degree (graduate or undergraduate), diploma or certificate program at a Canadian college or university for the academic year. **Criteria:** Selection of applicants will be based on academic achievement, financial need, and recognized contribution to the Black community.

Funds Avail.: $2,000. **To Apply:** Applicants must complete

the application form and submit along with a letter describing the reasons why they would be worthy recipients of a BBPA National Scholarship; a completed financial information schedule stating their budget for the coming year including information on their expected sources of funding, family income and related information; a letter of reference from the two individuals named in their application (must be a teacher from their high school, college or university, and an individual who is familiar with their community service); and two passport size photos head shot. Application form and requirements must be sent to The Board of Trustees, BBPA National Scholarship Fund, 675 King St., W, Ste. 210, Toronto, ON M5V 1M9. **Deadline:** May 29.

2114 ■ Fraser Milner Casgrain LLP Scholarships *(Undergraduate/Scholarship)*

Purpose: To provide support for Black Canadian students. **Focus:** General studies. **Qualif.:** Applicants must be Canadian citizens or permanent residents; must be 17 to 30 years of age; and must be enrolled in a full-time degree (graduate or undergraduate), diploma or certificate program at a Canadian college or university for the academic year. **Criteria:** Selection of applicants will be based on academic achievement, financial need, and recognized contribution to the Black community.

Funds Avail.: $5,000. **To Apply:** Applicants must complete the application form and submit along with a letter describing the reasons why they would be worthy recipients of a BBPA National Scholarship; a completed financial information schedule stating their budget for the coming year including information on their expected sources of funding, family income and related information; a letter of reference from the two individuals named in their application (must be a teacher from their high school, college or university, and an individual who is familiar with their community service); and two passport size photos - head shot. Application form and requirements must be sent to The Board of Trustees, BBPA National Scholarship Fund, 675 King St., W, Ste. 210, Toronto, ON M5V 1M9. **Deadline:** May 27. **Contact:** bbpascholarships@bellnet.ca.

2115 ■ CIBC Scholarships *(Undergraduate/Scholarship)*

Purpose: To provide support for Black Canadian students. **Focus:** General studies. **Qualif.:** Applicants must be students attending college or university who have shown academic achievement, leadership potential and a commitment to helping in the community; must be Canadian citizens or permanent residents; must be 17 to 30 years of age; and must be enrolled in a full-time degree (graduate or undergraduate), diploma or certificate program at a Canadian college or university for the academic year. **Criteria:** Selection of applicants will be based on academic achievement, financial need, and recognized contribution to the Black community.

Funds Avail.: $5,000. **To Apply:** Applicants must complete the application form and submit along with a letter describing the reasons why they would be worthy recipients of a BBPA National Scholarship; a completed financial information schedule stating their budget for the coming year including information on their expected sources of funding, family income and related information; a letter of reference from the two individuals named in their application (must be a teacher from their high school, college or university, and an individual who is familiar with their community service); and two passport size photos - head shot. Application form and requirements must be sent to The Board of Trustees, BBPA National Scholarship Fund, 675 King

Awards are arranged alphabetically below their administering organizations

St., W, Ste. 210, Toronto, ON M5V 1M9. **Deadline:** May 27. **Contact:** bbpascholarships@bellnet.ca.

2116 ■ Erma Collins Scholarships
(Undergraduate/Scholarship)

Purpose: To provide support for Black Canadian students. **Focus:** General studies. **Qualif.:** Applicants must be students attending community college; must be Canadian citizens or permanent residents; must be 17 to 30 years of age; and must be enrolled in a full time degree (graduate or undergraduate), diploma or certificate program at a Canadian college or university for the academic year. **Criteria:** Selection of applicants will be based on academic achievement, financial need, and recognized contribution to the Black community.

Funds Avail.: $1,000. **Number Awarded:** 1. **To Apply:** Applicants must complete the application form and submit along with a letter describing the reasons why they would be worthy recipients of a BBPA National Scholarship; a completed financial information schedule stating their budget for the coming year including information on their expected sources of funding, family income and related information; a letter of reference from the two individuals named in their application (must be a teacher from their high school, college or university, and an individual who is familiar with their community service); and two passport size photos - head shot. Application form and requirements must be sent to The Board of Trustees, BBPA National Scholarship Fund, 675 King St., W, Ste. 210, Toronto, ON M5V 1M9. **Deadline:** May 28. **Contact:** bbpascholarships@bellnet.ca.

2117 ■ Harry Gairey Scholarships
(Undergraduate/Scholarship)

Purpose: To provide support for Black Canadian students. **Focus:** General studies. **Qualif.:** Applicant must be a Canadian citizen or a permanent resident; must be 17 to 30 years of age; must be enrolled in a full time degree (graduate or undergraduate), diploma or certificate program at a Canadian college or university for the academic year. **Criteria:** Selection of applicants will be based on academic achievement, financial need, and recognized contribution to the Black community.

Funds Avail.: $2,000. **Number Awarded:** 2. **To Apply:** Applicants must complete the application form and submit along with a letter describing the reasons why they would be worthy recipients of a BBPA National Scholarship; a completed financial information schedule stating their budget for the coming year including information on their expected sources of funding, family income and related information; a letter of reference from the two individuals named in their application (must be a teacher from their high school, college or university, and an individual who is familiar with their community service); and two passport size photos - head shot. Application form and requirements must be sent to The Board of Trustees, BBPA National Scholarship Fund, 675 King St., W, Ste. 210, Toronto, ON M5V 1M9. **Deadline:** May 29.

2118 ■ Lucille May Gopie Scholarships
(Undergraduate/Scholarship)

Purpose: To provide support for Black Canadian students. **Focus:** General studies. **Qualif.:** Applicant must be a person who has been encouraged by a single parent to pursue higher education; must be a Canadian citizen or a permanent resident; must be 17 to 30 years of age; and must be enrolled in a full-time degree (graduate or

undergraduate), diploma or certificate program at a Canadian college or university for the academic year. **Criteria:** Selection of applicants will be based on academic achievement, financial need, and recognized contribution to the Black community.

Funds Avail.: $2,000. **To Apply:** Applicants must complete the application form and submit along with a letter describing the reasons why they would be worthy recipients of a BBPA National Scholarship; a completed financial information schedule stating their budget for the coming year including information on their expected sources of funding, family income and related information; a letter of reference from the two individuals named in their application (must be a teacher from their high school, college or university, and an individual who is familiar with their community service); and two passport size photos - head shot. Application form and requirements must be sent to The Board of Trustees, BBPA National Scholarship Fund, 675 King St., W, Ste. 210, Toronto, ON M5V 1M9. **Deadline:** May 27.

2119 ■ Guntley-Lorimer Science and Arts Scholarships *(Undergraduate/Scholarship)*

Purpose: To provide support for Black Canadian students. **Focus:** Science; Art. **Qualif.:** Applicant must be a Canadian citizen or a permanent resident; must be 17 to 30 years of age; and must be enrolled in a full-time degree (graduate or undergraduate), diploma or certificate program at a Canadian college or university for the academic year. **Criteria:** Selection of applicants will be based on academic achievement, financial need, and recognized contribution to the Black community.

Funds Avail.: $2,000-$3,000. **Number Awarded:** 4. **To Apply:** Applicants must complete the application form and submit along with a letter describing the reasons why they would be worthy recipients of a BBPA National Scholarship; a completed financial information schedule stating their budget for the coming year including information on their expected sources of funding, family income and related information; a letter of reference from the two individuals named in their application (must be a teacher from their high school, college or university, and an individual who is familiar with their community service); and two passport size photos - head shot. Application form and requirements must be sent to The Board of Trustees, BBPA National Scholarship Fund, 675 King St., W, Ste. 210, Toronto, ON M5V 1M9. **Deadline:** May 27. **Contact:** bbpascholarships@bellnet.ca.

2120 ■ Al Hamilton Scholarships
(Undergraduate/Scholarship)

Purpose: To provide support for Black Canadian students. **Focus:** General studies. **Qualif.:** Applicant must be a Canadian citizen or a permanent resident; must be 17 to 30 years of age; and must be enrolled in a full time degree (graduate or undergraduate), diploma or certificate program at a Canadian college or university for the academic year. **Criteria:** Selection of applicants will be based on academic achievement, financial need, and recognized contribution to the Black community.

Funds Avail.: $2,000. **To Apply:** Applicants must complete the application form and submit along with a letter describing the reasons why they would be worthy recipients of a BBPA National Scholarship; a completed financial information schedule stating their budget for the coming year including information on their expected sources of funding, family income and related information; a letter of reference

Awards are arranged alphabetically below their administering organizations

from the two individuals named in their application (must be a teacher from their high school, college or university, and an individual who is familiar with their community service); and two passport size photos - head shot. Application form and requirements must be sent to The Board of Trustees, BBPA National Scholarship Fund, 675 King St., W, Ste. 210, Toronto, ON M5V 1M9. **Deadline:** May 29.

2121 ■ William Peyton Hubbard Scholarships
(Undergraduate/Scholarship)

Purpose: To provide support for Black Canadian students. **Focus:** General studies. **Qualif.:** Applicant must be a Canadian citizen or a permanent resident; must be 17 to 30 years of age; and must be enrolled in a full-time degree (graduate or undergraduate), diploma or certificate program at a Canadian college or university for the academic year. **Criteria:** Selection of applicants will be based on academic achievement, financial need, and recognized contribution to the Black community.

Funds Avail.: $2,000. **To Apply:** Applicants must complete the application form and submit along with a letter describing the reasons why they would be worthy recipients of a BBPA National Scholarship; a completed financial information schedule stating their budget for the coming year including information on their expected sources of funding, family income and related information; a letter of reference from the two individuals named in their application (must be a teacher from their high school, college or university, and an individual who is familiar with their community service); and two passport size photos - head shot. Application form and requirements must be sent to The Board of Trustees, BBPA National Scholarship Fund, 675 King St., W, Ste. 210, Toronto, ON M5V 1M9. **Deadline:** May 29.

2122 ■ Right Hon. Michaelle Jean Legacy Scholarships *(Undergraduate/Scholarship)*

Purpose: To provide support for Black Canadian students. **Focus:** General studies. **Qualif.:** Applicant must be a Canadian citizen or a permanent resident; must be 17 to 30 years of age; and must be enrolled in a full-time degree (graduate or undergraduate), diploma or certificate program at a Canadian college or university for the academic year. **Criteria:** Selection of applicants will be based on academic achievement, financial need, and recognized contribution to the Black community.

Funds Avail.: $2,000. **To Apply:** Applicants must complete the application form and submit along with a letter describing the reasons why they would be worthy recipients of a BBPA National Scholarship; a completed financial information schedule stating their budget for the coming year including information on their expected sources of funding, family income and related information; a letter of reference from the two individuals named in their application (must be a teacher from their high school, college or university, and an individual who is familiar with their community service); and two passport size photos - head shot. Application form and requirements must be sent to The Board of Trustees, BBPA National Scholarship Fund, 675 King St., W, Ste. 210, Toronto, ON M5V 1M9. **Deadline:** May 29.

2123 ■ Harry Jerome Scholarships
(Undergraduate/Scholarship)

Purpose: To provide support for Black Canadian students. **Focus:** General studies. **Qualif.:** Applicant must be a

Canadian citizen or a permanent resident; must be 17 to 30 years of age; and must be enrolled in a full-time degree (graduate or undergraduate), diploma or certificate program at a Canadian college or university for the academic year. **Criteria:** Selection of applicants will be based on academic achievement, financial need, and recognized contribution to the Black community.

Funds Avail.: $5,000. **To Apply:** Applicants must complete the application form and submit along with a letter describing the reasons why they would be worthy recipients of a BBPA National Scholarship; a completed financial information schedule stating their budget for the coming year including information on their expected sources of funding, family income and related information; a letter of reference from the two individuals named in their application (must be a teacher from their high school, college or university, and an individual who is familiar with their community service); and two passport size photos - head shot. Application form and requirements must be sent to The Board of Trustees, BBPA National Scholarship Fund, 675 King St., W, Ste. 210, Toronto, ON M5V 1M9. **Deadline:** May 27. **Contact:** bbpascholarships@bellnet.ca.

2124 ■ Beverly Mascoll Scholarships
(Undergraduate/Scholarship)

Purpose: To provide support for Black Canadian students. **Focus:** General studies. **Qualif.:** Applicant must be a Canadian citizen or a permanent resident; must be 17 to 30 years of age; and must be enrolled in a full-time degree (graduate or undergraduate), diploma or certificate program at a Canadian college or university for the academic year. **Criteria:** Selection of applicants will be based on academic achievement, financial need, and recognized contribution to the Black community.

Funds Avail.: $2,000. **To Apply:** Applicants must complete the application form and submit along with a letter describing the reasons why they would be worthy recipients of a BBPA National Scholarship; a completed financial information schedule stating their budget for the coming year including information on their expected sources of funding, family income and related information; a letter of reference from the two individuals named in their application (must be a teacher from their high school, college or university, and an individual who is familiar with their community service); and two passport size photos - head shot. Application form and requirements must be sent to The Board of Trustees, BBPA National Scholarship Fund, 675 King St., W, Ste. 210, Toronto, ON M5V 1M9. **Deadline:** May 29.

2125 ■ Minerva Scholarships *(Undergraduate/Scholarship)*

Purpose: To provide support for Black Canadian students. **Focus:** General studies. **Qualif.:** Applicant must be a Canadian citizen or a permanent resident; must be 17 to 30 years of age; and must be enrolled in a full-time degree (graduate or undergraduate), diploma or certificate program at a Canadian college or university for the academic year. **Criteria:** Selection of applicants will be based on academic achievement, financial need, and recognized contribution to the Black community.

Funds Avail.: $2,000-$4,000. **Number Awarded:** 2-4. **To Apply:** Applicants must complete the application form and submit along with a letter describing the reasons why they would be worthy recipients of a BBPA National Scholarship; a completed financial information schedule stating their budget for the coming year including information on their

Awards are arranged alphabetically below their administering organizations

expected sources of funding, family income and related information; a letter of reference from the two individuals named in their application (must be a teacher from their high school, college or university, and an individual who is familiar with their community service); and two passport size photos - head shot. Application form and requirements must be sent to The Board of Trustees, BBPA National Scholarship Fund, 675 King St., W, Ste. 210, Toronto, ON M5V 1M9. **Deadline:** May 27. **Contact:** bbpascholarships@bellnet.ca.

2126 ■ RBC Financial Group Scholarships
(Graduate/Scholarship)

Purpose: To provide support for Black Canadian students. **Focus:** Business administration. **Qualif.:** Applicants must be students enrolled in a course of study leading to a bachelor's or master's degree in Business Administration or a related program; must be a Canadian citizen or a permanent resident; must be 17 to 30 years of age; and must be enrolled in a full-time degree (graduate or undergraduate), diploma or certificate program at a Canadian college or university for the academic year. **Criteria:** Selection of applicants will be based on academic achievement, financial need, and recognized contribution to the Black community.

Funds Avail.: $4,000. **Number Awarded:** 2. **To Apply:** Applicants must complete the application form and submit along with a letter describing the reasons why they would be worthy recipients of a BBPA National Scholarship; a completed financial information schedule stating their budget for the coming year including information on their expected sources of funding, family income and related information; a letter of reference from the two individuals named in their application (must be a teacher from their high school, college or university, and an individual who is familiar with their community service); and two passport size photos - head shot. Application form and requirements must be sent to The Board of Trustees, BBPA National Scholarship Fund, 675 King St., W, Ste. 210, Toronto, ON M5V 1M9. **Deadline:** May 27.

2127 ■ Scotiabank Scholarship for Business Studies *(Graduate/Scholarship)*

Purpose: To provide support for Black Canadian students. **Focus:** Business. **Qualif.:** Applicant must be a student who has demonstrated high academic achievement as well as leadership skills and a commitment to helping in the community; enrolled in a course of study leading to a business degree; must be a Canadian citizen or a permanent resident; must be 17 to 30 years of age; and must be enrolled in a full-time degree (graduate or undergraduate), diploma or certificate program at a Canadian college or university for the academic year. **Criteria:** Selection of applicants will be based on academic achievement, financial need, and recognized contribution to the Black community.

Funds Avail.: $5,000. **Number Awarded:** 2. **To Apply:** Applicants must complete the application form and submit along with a letter describing the reasons why they would be worthy recipients of a BBPA National Scholarship; a completed financial information schedule stating their budget for the coming year including information on their expected sources of funding, family income and related information; a letter of reference from the two individuals named in their application (must be a teacher from their high school, college or university, and an individual who is familiar with their community service); and two passport size photos - head shot. Application form and requirements must be sent to The Board of Trustees, BBPA National

Scholarship Fund, 675 King St., W, Ste. 210, Toronto, ON M5V 1M9. **Deadline:** May 27. **Contact:** bbpascholarships@bellnet.ca.

2128 ■ Julia Viola Simms Science Scholarships
(Postgraduate/Scholarship)

Purpose: To provide support for Black Canadian students. **Focus:** Mathematics and mathematical sciences; Physics; Chemistry; Biology; Medicine. **Qualif.:** Applicant must be a female student who has been accepted into a postsecondary degree program in one of the sciences such as mathematics, physics, chemistry, biology or medicine; must be a Canadian citizen or a permanent resident; must be 17 to 30 years of age; and must be enrolled in a full-time degree (graduate or undergraduate), diploma or certificate program at a Canadian college or university for the academic year. **Criteria:** Selection of applicants will be based on academic achievement, financial need, and recognized contribution to the Black community.

Funds Avail.: $3,000. **To Apply:** Applicants must complete the application form and submit along with a letter describing the reasons why they would be worthy recipients of a BBPA National Scholarship; a completed financial information schedule stating their budget for the coming year including information on their expected sources of funding, family income and related information; and a letter of reference from the two individuals named in their application (must be a teacher from their high school, college or university, and an individual who is familiar with their community service). Application form and requirements must be sent to The Board of Trustees, BBPA National Scholarship Fund, 675 King St., W, Ste. 210, Toronto, ON M5V 1M9. **Deadline:** May 27. **Contact:** bbpascholarships@bellnet.ca.

2129 ■ Urban Financial Services Coalition Scholarships *(Undergraduate/Scholarship)*

Purpose: To provide support for Black Canadian students. **Focus:** Business, Economics, Finance, Information science and technology. **Qualif.:** Applicant must be a student pursuing studies in business, economics, finance or information technology; must be a Canadian citizen or a permanent resident; must be 17 to 30 years of age; and must be enrolled in a full-time degree (graduate or undergraduate), diploma or certificate program at a Canadian college or university for the academic year. **Criteria:** Selection of applicants will be based on academic achievement, financial need, and recognized contribution to the Black community.

Funds Avail.: $2,000. **Number Awarded:** 2. **To Apply:** Applicants must complete the application form and submit along with a letter describing the reasons why they would be worthy recipients of a BBPA National Scholarship; a completed financial information schedule stating their budget for the coming year including information on their expected sources of funding, family income and related information; a letter of reference from the two individuals named in their application (must be a teacher from their high school, college or university, and an individual who is familiar with their community service); and two passport size photos - head shot. Application form and requirements must be sent to The Board of Trustees, BBPA National Scholarship Fund, 675 King St., W, Ste. 210, Toronto, ON M5V 1M9. **Deadline:** May 29.

2130 ■ Portia White Scholarships
(Undergraduate/Scholarship)

Purpose: To provide support for Black Canadian students. **Focus:** General studies. **Qualif.:** Applicant must be a

Awards are arranged alphabetically below their administering organizations

Canadian citizen or a permanent resident; must be 17 to 30 years of age; and must be enrolled in a full-time degree (graduate or undergraduate), diploma or certificate program at a Canadian college or university for the academic year. **Criteria:** Selection of applicants will be based on academic achievement, financial need, and recognized contribution to the Black community.

Funds Avail.: $2,000. **To Apply:** Applicants must complete the application form and submit along with a letter describing the reasons why they would be worthy recipients of a BBPA National Scholarship; a completed financial information schedule stating their budget for the coming year including information on their expected sources of funding, family income and related information; a letter of reference from the two individuals named in their application (must be a teacher from their high school, college or university, and an individual who is familiar with their community service); and two passport size photos - head shot. Application form and requirements must be sent to The Board of Trustees, BBPA National Scholarship Fund, 675 King St., W, Ste. 210, Toronto, ON M5V 1M9. **Deadline:** May 29.

2131 ■ Dwight Whylie Scholarships
(Undergraduate/Scholarship)

Purpose: To provide support for Black Canadian students. **Focus:** General studies. **Qualif.:** Applicant must be a Canadian citizen or a permanent resident; must be 17 to 30 years of age; and must be enrolled in a full-time degree (graduate or undergraduate), diploma or certificate program at a Canadian college or university for the academic year. **Criteria:** Selection of applicants will be based on academic achievement, financial need, and recognized contribution to the Black community.

Funds Avail.: $2,000. **To Apply:** Applicants must complete the application form and submit along with a letter describing the reasons why they would be worthy recipients of a BBPA National Scholarship; a completed financial information schedule stating their budget for the coming year including information on their expected sources of funding, family income and related information; a letter of reference from the two individuals named in their application (must be a teacher from their high school, college or university, and an individual who is familiar with their community service); and two passport size photos - head shot. Application form and requirements must be sent to The Board of Trustees, BBPA National Scholarship Fund, 675 King St., W, Ste. 210, Toronto, ON M5V 1M9. **Deadline:** May 29.

2132 ■ Black Caucus of the American Library Association (BCALA)

Tippecanoe County Public Library
627 S St.
Lafayette, IN 47901
Ph: (765) 429-0118
Fax: (765) 429-0150
E-mail: jholman@tcpl.lib.in.us
URL: www.bcala.org

2133 ■ E.J. Josey Scholarships *(Graduate/Scholarship)*

Purpose: To support African American students in library and information science. **Focus:** Library and archival sciences. **Qualif.:** Applicant must be an African American Citizen of the U.S. or Canada, and enrolled or accepted by

ALA-accredited graduate program leading to a degree in library and information science at the time of application. **Criteria:** Selection is based on the essay's argument development and critical analysis, clear language, conciseness and creativity.

Funds Avail.: $2,000. **Number Awarded:** 2. **To Apply:** Applicants must write an essay on a given theme. Essays (typed, double-spaced, and in Microsoft word or Corel) must include a cover letter providing the applicant's name, address, phone numbers, graduate program, and name of school and anticipated date of graduation. Only essays submitted via email to bbeal@mcc.cc.ms.us will be considered. **Deadline:** December 15. **Contact:** Billy C. Beal at bbeal@mcc.cc.ms.us.

2134 ■ Black Coaches and Administrators (BCA)

Pan American Plaza
201 S Capitol Ave., Ste. 495
Indianapolis, IN 46225
Ph: (317) 829-5600
Fax: (317) 829-5601
Free: 877-789-1222
E-mail: fkeith@bcasports.org
URL: www.bcasports.org

2135 ■ BCA Ethnic Minority Postgraduate Scholarships for Careers in Athletics
(Postgraduate/Scholarship)

Purpose: To support and encourage minorities who wish to pursue a career in athletics. **Focus:** Sports studies. **Qualif.:** Applicants must be seeking admission or have been accepted into a sports-administration or related program that will assist applicants in obtaining a career in athletics; must be ethnic minorities taking a post graduate study in a full-time status; be U.S. citizens; and must maintain 2.5 GPA. **Criteria:** Selection of recipient is based on merit.

Funds Avail.: $2,500. **Number Awarded:** 10. **To Apply:** Applicants must submit a typed and signed application form; provide an endorsement from an academic and athletic administrator, and one from a faculty member of undergraduate institutions attended; an official transcript; graduate record examination scores or any other professional scores (if available); current resume; and graduate studies acceptance letter. **Contact:** Send application form and supporting documents to Lauren Peterson, Director of Operations and Administration or call 317-829-5619.

2136 ■ Black Nurses Association of Greater Washington

PO Box 55285
Washington, DC 20040
Ph: (202) 291-8866
E-mail: contactus@bnaofgwdca.org
URL: www.bnaofgwdca.org

2137 ■ Dr. Johnella Banks Memorial Scholarships *(Undergraduate/Scholarship)*

Purpose: To empower the community through education, service and caring. **Focus:** Nursing. **Qualif.:** Applicants must be sophomore, junior or first-semester senior nursing students in a registered nursing or practical nursing program; must be currently enrolled in a National League for Nursing accredited program and be in good academic standing with a cumulative grade point average of at least

Awards are arranged alphabetically below their administering organizations

2.8; and must be U.S. citizens. **Criteria:** Recipients are selected based on financial need.

Funds Avail.: No specific amount. **To Apply:** Applicants must submit a current official transcript from their nursing program, two letters of recommendation from which one must come from current faculty member and one must come from the Nursing Faculty Advisor or Designee; must submit a written essay that describes the applicant's objectives and need-based reasons for scholarship application; documented evidence to add support for the applicant's desirability that includes participation in student and nursing activities, community service in the Greater Washington area, awards, letters and certificates; must provide a proof of United States citizenship and evidence of financial need. **Deadline:** January 31. **Contact:** 202-291-8866.

2138 ■ Margaret Pemberton Scholarships
(Undergraduate/Scholarship)

Purpose: To empower the community through education, service and caring. **Focus:** Nursing. **Qualif.:** Applicants must be graduating high school senior students who have been accepted into an accredited National League for Nursing baccalaureate program at a college or university in the United States; must be currently enrolled in a District of Columbia High School in good academic standing with a cumulative GPA of at least 2.8; and must be U.S. citizens. **Criteria:** Recipients are selected based on financial need.

Funds Avail.: No specific amount. **To Apply:** Applicants must submit at least one-page long written essay describing personal and educational goals, contributions to the community and reasons why they should be selected; must submit a documented evidence for support, including participation in activities and organizations, awards, certificates, and/or letters of commendation; must submit an official high school transcript, copy of letter of acceptance to a Baccalaureate Nursing Program in a college or university in the United States of America; must submit two letters of recommendation, from which one must come from a high school counselor or designee and the other one must come from non-related adult who has knowledge of the applicant's potential for success. **Deadline:** April 15. **Contact:** 202-291-8866.

2139 ■ Black Theatre Network
2609 Douglass Rd. SE, Ste. 102
Washington, DC 20020-6540
Ph: (202) 274-5667
E-mail: info@blacktheatrenetwork.org
URL: www.blacktheatrenetwork.org

2140 ■ S. Randolph Edmonds Young Scholars
Competition *(Graduate, Undergraduate/ Scholarship)*

Purpose: To encourage research and scholarship in black theatre. **Focus:** Theatre arts. **Qualif.:** Applicants must be college/university undergraduates or graduates working on a paper concerned with an aspect of the Black Theatre in either the United States or throughout the world. **Criteria:** Selection will be based on the criteria of the panel of judges.

Funds Avail.: 1st Place-$250; 2nd Place-$100. **To Apply:** Applicants must submit their own work. Papers must be typed, double-spaced and in MLA format with a works cited page. If applicable, also include endnotes that demonstrate awareness of formal methods of documentation. Papers should be approximately 10 pages in length, not including

endnotes. **Deadline:** April 30. **Contact:** Artisia V. Green, MFA Young Scholars Competition Coord., Associate Professor of Communications, Media Arts and Theatre, Chicago State University, 9501 S King Drive/DH Rm. 116 Chicago, IL 60628, (Office) 773-995-2502 or youngscholarscoordinator@yahoo.com.

2141 ■ Black Women in Entertainment Law (BWEL)
1841 Broadway, Ste. 713
New York, NY 10023
E-mail: info@bwelfoundation.org
URL: www.bwelfoundation.org

2142 ■ BWEL Law Student Scholarships
(Undergraduate/Scholarship)

Purpose: To support the education of female law students. **Focus:** Law. **Qualif.:** Applicant must be a woman of color enrolled in law school on a full-time or part-time basis; must have completed at least one full semester of law school; have a cumulative GPA of at least 2.5; and be in good academic standing at the time of the application. **Criteria:** Selection is based on the application materials submitted.

Funds Avail.: $5,000. **Number Awarded:** 2. **To Apply:** Applicants must submit a completed application with essay together with a resume and an official copy of law school transcripts. Return the application packet to BWEL, along with all application materials to: Angela M. Rogers, Esq., James E. McMillan, P.C., 19 Fulton St., Ste. 400, New York, NY 10038. **Deadline:** October 22. **Contact:** Angela M. Rogers, Esq., James E. McMillan, P.C., 19 Fulton St., Ste. 400, New York, NY 10038.

2143 ■ Black Women Lawyers' Association of Greater Chicago (BWLA)
321 S Plymouth Ct., Ste. 600
Chicago, IL 60604
Ph: (312) 554-2088
Fax: (312) 962-4645
E-mail: administrator@bwla.org
URL: www.bwla.org

2144 ■ DRI Law Student Diversity Scholarships
(Undergraduate/Scholarship)

Purpose: To provide financial assistance to deserving law students from ABA accredited law schools. **Focus:** Law. **Qualif.:** Applicants must be second-year African American, Hispanic, Asian, Pan Asian or Native American students; or second-year female law students, regardless of race or ethnicity. **Criteria:** Applicants will be evaluated based on demonstrated academic excellence; and service to the profession, community and the cause of diversity.

Funds Avail.: $10,000. **Number Awarded:** 2. **To Apply:** Applicants must submit three recommendations, one each from the following individuals: a) the dean of the student's law school, b) a current or past law professor, and c) an individual who is personally acquainted with the applicant, but who is not related by blood line or adoption; and a cover letter which identifies their academic, personal and/or professional accomplishments and how those accomplishments qualify him or her for DRI's Law Student Diversity Scholarship Award.

Awards are arranged alphabetically below their administering organizations

2145 ■ Black Women in Sisterhood for Action (BISA)

PO Box 1592
Washington, DC 20013
Ph: (301) 460-1565
E-mail: info@bisa-hq.org
URL: feminist.com/bisas1.htm

2146 ■ BISA's Scholarship Assistance Program
(High School/Scholarship)

Purpose: To provide financial assistance to college students who have been accepted for admission to a college or university and need financial assistance. **Focus:** General studies. **Qualif.:** Applicants must be black females; must be graduates or graduating high school seniors. **Criteria:** Recipients are selected based on academic achievement, leadership potential, financial need, honors and potential for academic growth and leadership development.

Funds Avail.: $1,000. **To Apply:** Applicants must submit completed application form; transcript; SAT or ACT scores; parents' income tax submission to IRS (with W-2 Statement); financial aid award letter; and written self-portrait (two typed double spaced pages or one single spaced page) highlighting where they expect to be in their career development in 10 years. **Deadline:** April 6.

2147 ■ Richard Gregory Freeland, II Educational Scholarships *(High School/Scholarship)*

Purpose: To provide financial assistance to offset the cost of education for qualified students who have been accepted by an accredited college or university. **Focus:** Computer and information sciences; Engineering; Telecommunications systems; Business administration. **Qualif.:** Applicants must be graduating high school students of African American ethnicity; reside in Maryland, Washington, DC or the Northern Virginia area; hold a grade point average of 2.5 or above; be pursuing a degree in the areas of computer science, information management, engineering, telecommunications, business management/administration or another technology-related field. **Criteria:** Recipients are selected based on academic achievement, leadership potential, financial need, community service and honors.

Funds Avail.: $500 to $2,500. **To Apply:** Applicants must submit all the required application information. **Deadline:** April 6.

2148 ■ Blair Chiropractic Society

550 E Carson Plaza Dr., Ste. 122
Carson, CA 90746
Ph: (563) 676-6209
E-mail: blairucs@hotmail.com
URL: www.blairchiropractic.com

2149 ■ Beatrice K. Blair Scholarships
(Undergraduate/Scholarship)

Purpose: To enhance the educational opportunities of chiropractic students with an interest in specific upper cervical Blair technique by providing financial assistance to eligible students attending chiropractic schools. **Focus:** Chiropractic. **Qualif.:** The applicant must be a student in good standing at an accredited chiropractic college and a member of a student Blair club if available at their school. **Criteria:** The recipient will be selected based on his or her GPA of at least 2.5 out of 4.0 (C+), and he or she must have

completed at least one Primary Blair Seminar.

Funds Avail.: 1,000. **To Apply:** Applicants must submit a copy of their transcript; two letters of reference; list of Blair seminars they have attended; and an essay (1-2 pages) stating the reasons why they want to practice the Blair technique. **Deadline:** September 1. **Contact:** Dr. Alfred Tomp, Blair Scholarship Committee, 22421 Gilberto No. F, Rancho Santa Margarita, CA 92688.

2150 ■ Blinded Veterans Association (BVA)

477 H St. NW
Washington, DC 20001-2617
Ph: (202) 371-8880
Fax: (202) 371-8258
Free: 800-669-7079
E-mail: snelson@bva.org
URL: www.bva.org

2151 ■ Katherin F. Gruber Scholarship Program
(All/Scholarship)

Purpose: To financially assist the spouses and dependent children of blinded veterans. **Focus:** General studies. **Qualif.:** Applicants must be spouses and dependent children of blinded veterans. **Criteria:** Recipients will be selected based on merit.

Funds Avail.: No specific amount. **To Apply:** Applicants must submit a completed application form along with three letters of reference. **Deadline:** April 20.

2152 ■ Blood Assurance Foundation

705 E 4th St.
Chattanooga, TN 37403-1916
Ph: (423) 756-0966
Fax: (423) 752-8456
Free: 800-962-0628
E-mail: wlf@bloodassurance.org
URL: www.bloodassurance.org

2153 ■ The Crystal Green Blood Assurance Memorial Scholarships *(Undergraduate/Scholarship)*

Purpose: To encourage educational pursuits by providing financial assistance. **Focus:** General studies. **Qualif.:** Applicants must be high school senior students planning to enter an accredited two or four-year college or university; and must have at least "B" average and score of at least 20 on the ACT or 1100 on the SAT cumulative. **Criteria:** Recipients are selected based on the written application, high school transcript, school and community service, letters of recommendation and a marketing plan for a blood drive.

Funds Avail.: $1,500. **Number Awarded:** 12. **To Apply:** Applicants must submit a detailed marketing plan for a new drive promotion; applicants must secure two letters of recommendation and obtain an official high school transcript which includes the first semester senior grades and ACT/SAT test scores. **Contact:** March 31.

2154 ■ Blues Heaven Foundation (BHF)

2120 S Michigan Ave.
Chicago, IL 60616
Ph: (312) 808-1286

Awards are arranged alphabetically below their administering organizations

Fax: (312) 808-0273
E-mail: info@bluesheaven.com
URL: www.bluesheaven.com

2155 ■ Muddy Waters Scholarships
(Undergraduate/Scholarship)

Purpose: To provide financial assistance for students in Chicago. **Focus:** Music education, music, African-American studies, folklore, performing arts, journalism, radio and television. **Qualif.:** Applicant must have a full-time enrollment status in a Chicago area college or university; must be in at least their first year of undergraduate studies or graduate program. **Criteria:** Awards are given based on academic achievement, concentration of studies and financial need.

Funds Avail.: $ 2,000. **To Apply:** Application form is available in website and must be sent to: Blues Heaven Foundation Inc., 2120 S Michigan Ave., Chicago, IL 60616. **Deadline:** April 30.

2156 ■ BMI Foundation
7 World Trade Ctr.
250 Greenwich St.
New York, NY 10007-0030
E-mail: info@bmifoundation.org
URL: bmi.com/foundation

2157 ■ Pete Carpenter Fellowships *(All/Fellowship)*

Purpose: To give aspiring TV and film composers the opportunity to work with the composer Mike Post at his studio in Los Angeles. **Focus:** Music composition. **Qualif.:** Applicant must be an aspiring composer under the age of 35. **Criteria:** Selection is based on the submitted music samples.

Funds Avail.: $3,000. **To Apply:** Applicants must submit a completed, signed and notarized application form along with the original 1-3 minute music sample (should be on CD). **Deadline:** January 29. **Contact:** Ms. Linda Livingston, Dir. carpenterfellowship@bmifoundation.org.

2158 ■ Woody Guthrie Fellowships *(All/Fellowship)*

Purpose: To support students pursuing research topics or themes related to Woody Guthrie which explore his creative work and contribution to American music and culture. **Focus:** American history; Musicology; Humanities; Social sciences. **Qualif.:** Applicant must be pursuing research topics or themes related to Woody Guthrie. **Criteria:** Selection is based on the relevance and value of the project to the Foundation's mission and purposes; quality of the project; evidence of the applicant's potential, motivation and ability to carry out the project successfully; and evidence of the applicant's prior record of achievement in the field covered by the project.

Funds Avail.: $2,500. **To Apply:** Applicants must submit a completed application form together with a curriculum vitae (maximum of 3 pages); a concise description of the proposed research project (maximum of 2 double-spaced pages); and a list of sources with amounts and dates of any other funding (past, present or future) awarded for the present project. **Deadline:** January 31. **Remarks:** In cooperation with the Woody Guthrie Foundation. **Contact:** fellowships@woodyguthrie.org.

2159 ■ John Lennon Scholarships *(All/Prize, Scholarship)*

Purpose: To support songwriters and composers who are current students. **Focus:** Music composition. **Qualif.:** Applicant must be a student at one of the participating colleges/universities or participating through a local National Association for Music Education (MENC) chapter in his/her college; between 15-24 years old; has never had any musical work commercially recorded or distributed; and not a prior BMI Foundation John Lennon Scholarship winner. **Criteria:** Selection is based on the submitted original song in any genre.

Funds Avail.: $10,000 and $5,000. **Number Awarded:** 3. **To Apply:** Applicants must submit a completed application form together with the CD of a song with original words and music (CD should be clearly labeled with the title of the song), and three typed copies of the lyrics (applicant's name must not appear on the CD or on the typed copies of the lyrics). Applicants applying through MENC must contact the Music Department of his/her college to locate the MENC Chapter Advisor at his/her college/university. **Deadline:** April 13. **Remarks:** Established in 1997 by Yoko Ono.

2160 ■ Peermusic Latin Scholarships *(All/Prize, Scholarship)*

Purpose: To support songwriters and composers who are current students. **Focus:** Music composition. **Qualif.:** Applicant must be a student enrolled at a college/university located in the U.S. or Puerto Rico; must be 16-25 years old prior to the application; and has not have had any musical work commercially recorded or distributed. **Criteria:** Selection is based on the submitted original song or instrumental work in a Latin genre.

Funds Avail.: $5,000. **Number Awarded:** 1. **To Apply:** Applicants must submit a completed application form along with the CD of a song or instrumental work with original words and music (CD should be clearly labeled with the title of the song), and three typed copies of the lyrics (applicant's name must not appear on the CD or on the typed copies of the lyric). **Deadline:** February 10. **Remarks:** Established by Ralph Peer II and funded by peermusic in 2003. **Contact:** latinscholarship@bmifoundation.org.

2161 ■ Bohemian Lawyers Association of Chicago
19 Riverside Rd., Ste. 5
Riverside, IL 60546-2606
Ph: (708) 447-5331
E-mail: info@bohemianlawyers.org
URL: www.bohemianlawyers.org

2162 ■ Bohemian Lawyers Association of Chicago Scholarships *(Graduate/Scholarship)*

Purpose: To financially assist the qualified individuals who wish to pursue their law careers in Chicago. **Focus:** Law. **Qualif.:** Applicants must be of Bohemian descent, attending law school in the Chicago area. **Criteria:** Recipient will be selected based on the application materials given.

Funds Avail.: $1,500. **To Apply:** Applicants must complete the application form available in the website; must attach an essay indicating the reasons why they feel they should be awarded the scholarship and any special factors which they believe the committee should consider; must have a current copy of their law school transcript and resume. **Deadline:** March 31.

Awards are arranged alphabetically below their administering organizations

2163 ■ Botanical Society of America (BSA)

PO Box 299
St. Louis, MO 63166
Ph: (314) 577-9566
Fax: (314) 577-9515
E-mail: bsa-manager@botany.org
URL: www.botany.org

2164 ■ J.S. Karling Graduate Student Research Awards *(Graduate/Grant)*

Purpose: To support and promote graduate student research in the field of botanical sciences. **Focus:** Botany. **Qualif.:** Applicants must be BSA members; must be registered full-time graduate students; must have a faculty research advisor who is also a BSA member and has not won the award previously. **Criteria:** Applicants will be selected based on submitted application materials.

Funds Avail.: $500. **To Apply:** The application shall consist the title page, abstract, narrative, budget detailing how the funds would be used, biographical sketch and a (one-page) letter of support from the student's advisor. Materials must be submitted in .pdf format. **Deadline:** March 15.

2165 ■ Bowling Writers Association of America (BWAA)

621 Six Flags Dr.
Arlington, TX 76011
Free: 800-343-1329
E-mail: bwaa@bowlingwriters.com
URL: www.bowlingwriters.com

2166 ■ Chuck Pezzano Scholarships *(Undergraduate, Vocational/Occupational/ Scholarship)*

Purpose: To provide financial support for students pursuing a career in communications that involve the sport of bowling. **Focus:** Communication; Sports writing. **Qualif.:** Applicants must have a minimum of 2.5 GPA; must be high school or vocational school seniors or college students. **Criteria:** Awards are given based on academic merit, civic and bowling participation.

Funds Avail.: $1,500. **Number Awarded:** 3. **To Apply:** Applicants must send an application form (available at the website); transcript; at least one reference letter; maximum of 350 words essay; and any other information to support your application. **Deadline:** May 15. **Remarks:** Established in honor of Chuck Pezzano a BWAA, American Bowling Congress and Professional Bowlers Association Hall of Fame journalist. **Contact:** Completed application form and other supporting documents must be submitted to: Joan Romeo at the above address or e-mail at jromeo@socal.rr.com.

2167 ■ Boys and Girls Club of Ottawa

2825 Dumaurier Ave.
Ottawa, ON, Canada K2B 7W3
Ph: (613) 232-0925
E-mail: sbradford@bgcottawa.org
URL: www.bgcottawa.org

2168 ■ Ottawa Police 150th Anniversary Scholarships *(Undergraduate/Scholarship)*

Purpose: To promote, encourage and sponsor promising individuals who would otherwise experience extreme hardships in pursuing a post-secondary education. **Focus:** Criminal justice. **Qualif.:** Applicants must be students pursuing a career in policing or a related criminal justice field. **Criteria:** Recipients are selected based on financial need, academic achievement and community involvement.

Funds Avail.: No specific amount. **To Apply:** Applicants must submit: a completed application form; completed expenses and income form; up-to-date resume; two letters of recommendation; copy of most recent school transcript; proof of citizenship status; copy of letter of acceptance to an accredited post-secondary school; professional quality color photo; and a 300-1,000 word essay discussing their community involvement, financial need, accomplishment and academics.

2169 ■ Brian Smith Scholarships *(Undergraduate/Scholarship)*

Purpose: To promote, encourage and sponsor promising individuals who would otherwise experience extreme hardships in pursuing a post-secondary education. **Focus:** General studies. **Qualif.:** Applicants must be graduating students from a high school in the Ottawa area planning to attend any university or college in the city of Ottawa. **Criteria:** Recipients are selected based on financial need and demonstrated participation as a community volunteer.

Funds Avail.: $2,500-$5,000. **Number Awarded:** 2. **To Apply:** Applicants must submit: a completed application form; completed expenses and income form; up-to-date resume; two letters of recommendation; copy of most recent school transcript; proof of citizenship status; copy of letter of acceptance to an accredited post-secondary school; professional quality color photo; and a 300-1,000-word essay discussing their community involvement, financial need, accomplishment and academics. **Deadline:** March 31. **Contact:** Asma Shah at ashah@bgcottawa.org.

2170 ■ Brain Tumor Foundation for Children (BTFC)

6065 Roswell Rd. NE, Ste. 505
Atlanta, GA 30328-4015
Ph: (404) 252-4107
Fax: (404) 252-4108
E-mail: info@braintumorkids.org
URL: www.braintumorkids.org

2171 ■ Larry Dean Davis Scholarship Program *(Undergraduate, Vocational/Occupational/ Scholarship)*

Purpose: To encourage educational pursuits among survivors of a pediatric brain or spinal cord tumor by providing financial support. **Focus:** General Studies. **Qualif.:** Candidates must be survivors of pediatric brain or spinal cord tumor who are residents of the state of Georgia; must be entering or currently enrolled in an advanced educational program at a college, university, vocational school, or other setting; and must demonstrate a need for financial assistance. **Criteria:** Recipients are chosen based on combined merit and need.

Funds Avail.: 2,500. **Number Awarded:** 2. **To Apply:** Applicants must submit completed application available on the website; two letters of recommendation; and an essay describing the following: 1) brain or spinal cord tumor experience; 2) brief biographical sketch of themselves and future aspirations; and 3) detailed statement of financial need. Applicants may call the foundation for further informa-

Awards are arranged alphabetically below their administering organizations

tion or to request an application. **Deadline:** April 15. **Contact:** Application form and supporting documents must be forwarded to the BTFC office.

2172 ■ Hilda E. Bretzlaff Foundation (HEBF)

1550 N Milford Rd., Ste. 101
Milford, MI 48381
Ph: (248) 684-3408
Fax: (248) 684-2648
E-mail: klindbeck@hebf.org
URL: www.hebf.org

2173 ■ Hilda E. Bretzlaff Foundation Scholarships *(Undergraduate/Grant)*

Purpose: To provide scholarships that will be a credit to American Society. **Focus:** General studies. **Qualif.:** Applicants must have a 2.0 cumulative grade point average or better. **Criteria:** Recipients will be selected based on financial need.

Funds Avail.: No specific amount. **To Apply:** Applicants may obtain an application by contacting a school, institution or organization having a proposal with the Foundation. Applicants must provide a complete, signed and dated application enclosed with the following items: previous year's tax return for self and parent/guardians; official transcript, (transcripts printed off the internet will not be accepted unless stamped by the school); two letters of recommendation from two different sources; and two essays, "What America Means to Me" and "Goals/Aspirations Essay." **Deadline:** August 4. **Contact:** Kathleen Lindbeck at the above address.

2174 ■ British American Foundation of Texas (BAFTX)

PO Box 421234
Houston, TX 77242
Ph: (713) 587-9900
Fax: (713) 784-7712
E-mail: info@baftx.org
URL: baftx.org

2175 ■ BAFTX Early Starters Awards *(Undergraduate/Scholarship)*

Purpose: To assist the students seeking financial resources for their education. **Focus:** General studies. **Qualif.:** Applicants must be permanent residents of Texas; enrolled in full-time education; between 11 and 14 years old and must maintain a competitive GPA and hold an excellent school attendance record. **Criteria:** Applicants are evaluated based on financial need.

Funds Avail.: $500 up to $1,000. **To Apply:** Applicants must submit the completed application form; essay between 300 and 500 words regarding a British person (past or present) whom they admire; current transcript signed by a member of their teaching staff; letter of recommendation which must come from a teacher in whose class they were enrolled within the past year, or from a guidance counselor at their school (letter must be on school letterhead paper); and a recent photograph.

2176 ■ BAFTX Graduate Awards *(Undergraduate/Scholarship)*

Purpose: To provide financial assistance to aspiring individuals from Great Britain or Texas, USA that are intent on furthering their education in their chosen field. **Focus:** General studies. **Qualif.:** Applicants must be permanent residents of Texas; enrolled in full time education; between 21 and 25 years old; must hold an undergraduate degree with a GPA of 3.5 or above for U.S. applicants and 2.1 (65+) for U.K. applicants. **Criteria:** Applicants are evaluated based on academic achievement and financial need.

Funds Avail.: No specific amount. **To Apply:** Applicants must submit completed application form; essay, not less than 1,000 words, on one of the topics from the application form found at the website of BAFTX; current transcript of academic performance signed by a member of the teaching staff; letter of recommendation from a graduate or undergraduate professor in whose class they were enrolled or from a guidance counselor at their university (letter must be on university letterhead paper); financial statement declaring their eligibility for the program; budget outline stating the sum being requested for tuition fees and other costs associated with graduate tuition; and a recent photograph.

2177 ■ BAFTX Junior Achievers Awards *(Undergraduate/Scholarship)*

Purpose: To provide a summer study program for academically adept students from low-income families in the Houston area. **Focus:** General studies. **Qualif.:** Applicants must be permanent residents of Texas; enrolled in full-time education; between 16 and 17 years old; and must maintain a competitive GPA and excellent school attendance record. **Criteria:** Applicants are evaluated based on financial need.

Funds Avail.: No specific amount. **To Apply:** Applicants must submit completed application form; an essay between 500 and 750 words regarding a British person (past or present) whom they admire; current transcript of academic performance signed by a member of the teaching staff; letter of recommendation which must come from a teacher in whose class they were enrolled within the past year or from a guidance counselor at their school (letter must be on school letterhead); and a recent photograph.

2178 ■ BAFTX Undergraduate Awards *(Undergraduate/Scholarship)*

Purpose: To alleviate the financial burden of college fees. **Focus:** General studies. **Qualif.:** Applicants must be permanent residents of Texas; enrolled in full time education; between 18 and 22 years old; and must maintain a GPA of 3.5. **Criteria:** Applicants are evaluated based on merit and financial need.

Funds Avail.: No specific amount. **To Apply:** Applicants must submit an essay, not less than 1,000 words, on one of the topics given in the application form found at the website of BAFTX; a letter of recommendation which must come from a teacher in whose class they were enrolled within the past year or from a guidance counselor at their university (letter must be on university letterhead paper); current transcript of their academic performance signed by a member of the teaching staff; financial statement declaring their eligibility for the program; budget outline stating the sum being requested for tuition fees and other costs associated with their education for one semester; and a recent photograph.

2179 ■ British Columbia Paraplegic Association (BCPA)

780 SW Marine Dr.
Vancouver, BC, Canada V6P 5Y7
Ph: (604) 324-3611

Awards are arranged alphabetically below their administering organizations

Fax: (604) 326-1229
Free: 877-324-3611
E-mail: vancouver@bcpara.org
URL: www.bcpara.org

2180 ■ BCPA Bursaries *(Undergraduate/Scholarship)*

Purpose: To provide educational funds to deserving students with disabilities. **Focus:** General studies. **Qualif.:** Applicant must be a student with a physical disability; must be a Canadian citizen or landed immigrant, resident of BC and must be attending or planning to attend a post-secondary educational institution in BC. **Criteria:** Recipient will be selected based on merit.

Funds Avail.: Educational fund may vary from year to year according to the availability of funds. **To Apply:** Applicant must submit the completed application form available from the website; must include an official transcript of records, and a letter of reference from either an employer or educator. **Deadline:** June 30.

2181 ■ Broadcast Education Association (BEA)

1771 N St. NW
Washington, DC 20036-2800
Ph: (202) 429-5355
Fax: (202) 775-2981
Free: 888-380-7222
E-mail: hbirks@nab.org
URL: www.beaweb.org

2182 ■ Harold E. Fellows Scholarships *(All/Scholarship)*

Purpose: To provide a broad range of services to academic and professional members to keep them abreast with the latest electronic media developments in radio, television, news technologies, management, sales, news reporting, production, research, communication, law, policy and international systems. **Focus:** Broadcasting. **Qualif.:** Applicants must be professors, industry professionals and students involved in teaching and research related to radio, television and electronic media; must be juniors, seniors and graduate students at BEA Member institutions. **Criteria:** Recipients are selected based on academic performance and potential as professionals.

Funds Avail.: $2,250. **Number Awarded:** 4. **To Apply:** Applicants must submit an official application form from the campus faculty; must submit transcript of records, broadcast and other experiences; written statement of goals and supportive statement from three references. **Deadline:** October 12. **Contact:** beamemberservices@nab.org.

2183 ■ Walter S. Patterson Scholarships *(All/Scholarship)*

Purpose: To provide a broad range of services to academic and professional members to keep them abreast with the latest electronic media developments in radio, television, news technologies, management, sales, news reporting, production, research, communication, law, policy and international systems. **Focus:** Broadcasting. **Qualif.:** Applicants must be professors, industry professionals and students involved in teaching and research related to radio, television and electronic media; must be juniors, seniors and graduate students at BEA Member institutions. **Criteria:** Recipients are selected based on academic performance and potential as professionals.

Funds Avail.: $1,750. **Number Awarded:** 2. **To Apply:** Applicants must submit official application form from the campus faculty; must submit transcript of records, broadcast and other experiences; written statement of goals and supportive statement from three references. **Deadline:** October 11. **Contact:** beamemberservices@nab.org.

2184 ■ Helen J. Sioussat/Fay Wells Scholarships *(All/Scholarship)*

Purpose: To provide a broad range of services to its academic and professional members to keep them abreast with the latest electronic media developments in radio, television, news technologies, management, sales, news reporting, production, research, communication, law, policy and international systems. **Focus:** Broadcasting. **Qualif.:** Applicants must be professors, industry professionals and students involved in teaching and research related to radio, television and electronic media; must be juniors, seniors and graduate students at BEA Member institutions. **Criteria:** Recipients are selected based on academic performance and potential as professionals.

Funds Avail.: $1,250. **Number Awarded:** 2. **To Apply:** Applicants must submit an official application form from the campus faculty; must submit transcript of records, broadcast and other experiences; written statement of goals and supportive statement from three references. **Deadline:** October 12. **Contact:** beamemberservices@nab.org.

2185 ■ Alexander M. Tanger Scholarships *(All/Scholarship)*

Purpose: To provide a broad range of services to academic and professional members to keep them abreast with the latest electronic media developments in radio, television, news technologies, management, sales, news reporting, production, research, communication, law, policy and international systems. **Focus:** Broadcasting. **Qualif.:** Applicants must be professors, industry professionals and students involved in teaching and research related to radio, television and electronic media; must be juniors, seniors and graduate students at BEA Member institutions. **Criteria:** Recipients are selected based on academic performance and potential as professionals.

Funds Avail.: $5,000. **Number Awarded:** 1. **To Apply:** Applicants must submit official application form from the campus faculty; must submit transcript of records, broadcast and other experiences; written statement of goals and supportive statement from three references. **Deadline:** October 11. **Contact:** beamemberservices@nab.org.

2186 ■ Two Year/Community Broadcast Education Association Scholarship Awards *(All/Scholarship)*

Purpose: To provide a broad range of services to academic and professional members to keep them abreast with the latest electronic media developments in radio, television, news technologies, management, sales, news reporting, production, research, communication, law, policy and international systems. **Focus:** Broadcasting. **Qualif.:** Applicants must be professors, industry professionals and students involved in teaching and research related to radio, television and electronic media; must be juniors, seniors and graduate students at BEA Member institutions. **Criteria:** Recipients are selected based on academic performance and potential as professionals.

Funds Avail.: $1,500. **Number Awarded:** 2. **To Apply:** Applicants must submit official application form from the campus faculty; must submit transcript of records, broad-

Awards are arranged alphabetically below their administering organizations

cast and other experiences; written statement of goals and supportive statement from three references. **Deadline:** October 11. **Contact:** beamemberservices@nab.org.

2187 ■ Abe Voron Scholarships *(All/Scholarship)*

Purpose: To provide a broad range of services to academic and professional members to keep them abreast with the latest electronic media developments in radio, television, news technologies, management, sales, news reporting, production, research, communication, law, policy and international systems. **Focus:** Broadcasting. **Qualif.:** Applicants must be professors, industry professionals and students involved in teaching and research related to radio, television and electronic media; must be juniors, seniors and graduate students at BEA Member institutions; must be studying toward a career in radio. **Criteria:** Recipients are selected based on academic performance and potential as professionals.

Funds Avail.: $5,000. **Number Awarded:** 1. **To Apply:** Applicants must submit official application form from the campus faculty; must submit transcript of records, broadcast and other experiences; written statement of goals and supportive statement from three references. **Deadline:** October 11. **Contact:** beamemberservices@nab.org.

2188 ■ Vincent T. Wasilewski Scholarships *(All/Scholarship)*

Purpose: To provide a broad range of services to academic and professional members to keep them abreast with the latest electronic media developments in radio, television, news technologies, management, sales, news reporting, production, research, communication, law, policy and international systems. **Focus:** Broadcasting. **Qualif.:** Applicants must be professors, industry professionals and students involved in teaching and research related to radio, television and electronic media; must be juniors, seniors and graduate students at BEA Member institutions. **Criteria:** Recipients are selected based on academic performance and potential as professionals.

Funds Avail.: $2,500. **Number Awarded:** 1. **To Apply:** Applicants must submit official application forms from the campus faculty; must submit transcript of records, broadcast and other experiences; written statement of goals and supportive statement from three references. **Deadline:** October 11. **Contact:** beamemberservices@nab.org.

2189 ■ Bronx County Bar Association
New York State Supreme Ct. Bldg.
851 Grand Concourse
Bronx, NY 10451-2937
Ph: (718) 293-2227
Fax: (718) 681-0098
E-mail: info@bronxbar.com
URL: www.bronxbar.com

2190 ■ Hon. Peggy Bernheim Memorial Scholarships *(Undergraduate/Scholarship)*

Purpose: To provide financial assistance for the education of law school students who are domiciled in Bronx County. **Focus:** Law. **Qualif.:** Applicants must be first, second or third year law students who are graduating in May or June; must be enrolled at an A.B.A. accredited school; may also be first year students who have completed one semester of study. **Criteria:** Applicants will be evaluated based on academics, financial need, writing sample, personal

interview and law school transcript.

Funds Avail.: $3,000. **Number Awarded:** 2. **To Apply:** Applicants must submit general application. **Deadline:** February 27.

2191 ■ Alexander A. Delle Cese Memorial Scholarships *(Undergraduate/Scholarship)*

Purpose: To provide financial assistance for the education of law school students who are domiciled in Bronx County. **Focus:** Law. **Qualif.:** Applicants must be first, second, or third year law students who are graduating in May or June; must be enrolled at an A.B.A.-accredited school; may also be first year students who have completed one semester of study. **Criteria:** Applicants will be evaluated based on academics, financial need, writing sample, personal interview, and law school transcript.

Funds Avail.: $2,500. **To Apply:** Applicants must submit general application. **Deadline:** February 29.

2192 ■ Craig Lensch Memorial Scholarships *(Undergraduate/Scholarship)*

Purpose: To provide financial assistance for the education of law school students who are domiciled in Bronx County. **Focus:** Law. **Qualif.:** Applicants must be first, second, or third year law students who are graduating in May or June; must be enrolled at an A.B.A. accredited school; may also be first year students who have completed one semester of study. **Criteria:** Applicants will be evaluated based on academics, financial need, writing sample, personal interview, and law school transcript.

Funds Avail.: $3,000. **Number Awarded:** 2. **To Apply:** Applicants must submit general application. **Deadline:** February 27.

2193 ■ Brookdale Foundation Group
950 Third Ave., 19th Fl.
New York, NY 10022
Ph: (212) 308-7355
Fax: (212) 750-0152
E-mail: mpp@brookdalefoundation.org
URL: www.brookdalefoundation.org

2194 ■ Brookdale Leadership in Aging Fellowships *(Professional development/Fellowship)*

Purpose: To foster the development of a new generation of leaders in the field of aging by supporting investigators in the developmental stages of their careers. **Focus:** Aging. **Qualif.:** Applicant must demonstrate leadership potential; provide evidence of an ongoing commitment to a career in aging; have a mentor (or mentors) willing and able to provide professional guidance and to be helpful in the development of the applicant's career and research project; willing to commit at least 75% of his/her time for career development for each of the two years of the Fellowship; propose a project related to the field of aging; have already earned a PhD or MD; and be between the first and tenth years of graduate degree. **Criteria:** Application will be scored as follows: Candidate: 10 points; Project: 5 points; Mentor/Institution: 5 points.

Funds Avail.: No specific amount. **To Apply:** Applicants must submit a completed online application. Materials needed for the application are: statement of Leadership Role in Aging; research project abstract; project description outlining the project's basic theoretical orientation, the goals and objectives of the project and its methodology; state-

Awards are arranged alphabetically below their administering organizations

ment of project's current and future significance to the field; statement of 10 year career plan and action steps with special emphasis on relevance to the field of aging; participation in active grants and/or research projects; candidate's CV; up to three letters of support (one of which should be from the Department Chair or Dean); statement from the mentor(s); mentor's participation in active grants; mentor's CV(s); proposed project budget from the sponsoring institution; sponsoring institution's resource support; verification of Tax Exempt Status; and signed statement of support from sponsoring institution. **Remarks:** Started in 1985. **Contact:** Cara Kenien at 212-308-7355 x-101 or cjk@brookdalefoundation.org.

2195 ■ Brookings Doha Center (BDC)

1775 Massachusetts Ave. NW
Washington, DC 20036
Ph: (202) 797-6000
E-mail: communications@brookings.edu
URL: www.brookings.edu

2196 ■ BDC Visiting Fellowships *(Doctorate/ Fellowship)*

Purpose: To financially assist PhD students in presenting their research at a seminar. **Focus:** General studies. **Qualif.:** Applicants must have PhD degree or broad governmental, civil society or professional experience(s); must be fluent in English. **Criteria:** Recipients will be selected based on submitted materials.

Funds Avail.: Amount not specified. **To Apply:** Applicants must contact BDC office for further information.

2197 ■ John Carter Brown Library

94 George St.
Providence, RI 02912-1894
Ph: (401) 863-2725
Fax: (401) 863-3477
E-mail: jcbl_publications@brown.edu
URL: www.brown.edu

2198 ■ The John Carter Brown Library Long-Term Fellowships *(All/Fellowship)*

Purpose: To give scholars from the U.S. and abroad an opportunity to pursue their work in proximity to a distinguished collection of primary sources. **Focus:** General studies. **Qualif.:** Applicants must be American citizens or have been residents in the United States for three years. **Criteria:** Recipients are selected based on academic standing and financial need.

Funds Avail.: $4,200 per month. **To Apply:** Applicants must complete the application form. **Deadline:** January.

2199 ■ The John Carter Brown Library Short-Term Fellowships *(Doctorate, Postdoctorate/ Fellowship)*

Purpose: To give scholars from the U.S. and abroad an opportunity to pursue their work in proximity to a distinguished collection of primary sources. **Focus:** General studies. **Qualif.:** Applicants must be Americans and foreign nationals who are engaged in pre- or post-doctoral, or independent research. **Criteria:** Recipients are selected based on the academic standing and financial need.

Funds Avail.: $2,100 per month. **To Apply:** Applicants

must complete the application form. **Deadline:** January.

2200 ■ Ron Brown Scholar Program

1160 Pepsi Pl., Ste. 206
Charlottesville, VA 22901
Ph: (434) 964-1588
Fax: (434) 964-1589
E-mail: info@ronbrown.org
URL: www.ronbrown.org

2201 ■ Ron Brown Scholars Program *(Undergraduate/Scholarship)*

Purpose: To identify African-American high school seniors who will make significant contributions to society; to provide financial support to those who are in need. **Focus:** General Studies. **Qualif.:** Applicants must be senior high school students; must excel academically; exhibit exceptional leadership potential; participate in community service activities and demonstrate financial need; must be U.S. citizens or hold a permanent resident visa card. **Criteria:** Scholarship winners are selected based on their submitted applications, interviews and participation on weekend activities.

Funds Avail.: $10,000 annually. **Number Awarded:** 10. **To Apply:** Applicants must mail the application materials in one packet. Transcripts and letters of recommendation should not be sent under separate cover; incomplete, e-mailed or faxed applications will not be considered. **Deadline:** November 1.

2202 ■ Peggy Browning Fund

1528 Walnut St., Ste. 1904
Philadelphia, PA 19103-3648
Ph: (267) 273-7990
Fax: (267) 273-7688
E-mail: mmoffa@peggybrowningfund.org
URL: www.peggybrowningfund.org

2203 ■ Peggy Browning Fund - Chicago School-Year Fellowships *(Graduate, Undergraduate/Fellowship)*

Purpose: To provide assistance for the education of law students about the human rights and needs of workers. **Focus:** Law. **Qualif.:** Applicant must be a student in good standing at a participating law school in proximity to the fellowship location and must have completed at least one year of law school. **Criteria:** Selection is based on submitted application materials.

Funds Avail.: Approximately $4,500. **Number Awarded:** 50. **To Apply:** Applicants must submit a cover letter, a completed application form and resume. **Contact:** Mary Ann Moffa at the above address.

2204 ■ Susan Thompson Buffett Foundation

222 Kiewit Plz.
Omaha, NE 68131
Ph: (402) 943-1383
E-mail: scholarships@stbfoundation.org
URL: www.buffettscholarships.org

2205 ■ Susan Thompson Buffett Foundation Scholarships *(Undergraduate/Scholarship)*

Purpose: To provide financial assistance to qualified individuals. **Focus:** General studies. **Qualif.:** Applicants

Awards are arranged alphabetically below their administering organizations

must be residents of the State of Nebraska; must be graduating high school seniors or undergraduate students who have not already earned a bachelor's degree; must be attending or applying to a Nebraska state public school; must be in need of financial assistance; must have maintained at least a 2.5 GPA throughout high school; must have applied for federal financial aid and have already received back the Student Aid Report that contains their Expected Family Contribution. **Criteria:** Recipients will be selected based on financial need.

Funds Avail.: $3,200 plus a textbook allowance of $400. **To Apply:** Applicants must complete the application form available online; must submit a high school or college transcript; two letters of reference from teachers, employers or clergy members; must have a copy of the Information Summary of their financial aid; must provide one-page handwritten background and personal information. **Deadline:** March 1.

2206 ■ Building Owners and Managers Association of Greater New York (BOMANY)

11 Penn Plz., 22nd Fl., Ste. 2201
New York, NY 10001
Ph: (212) 239-3662
Fax: (212) 268-7441
E-mail: bobbimc@bomany.com
URL: www.bomany.org

2207 ■ BOMA/NY Scholarships *(Undergraduate/ Scholarship)*

Purpose: To financially assist students to further their professional education. **Focus:** General studies. **Qualif.:** Applicants must be currently enrolled RPA, FMA, SMA or SMT students, taking home study, classroom study or accelerated courses; must be employed by a BOMA/NY member firm and working within the 5 Boroughs of New York. **Criteria:** Applicants are evaluated on the basis of merit and demonstrated financial need.

Funds Avail.: No specific amount. **To Apply:** Applicants must submit completed application form along with a one page essay and letter of recommendation from current employer. **Deadline:** June 17.

2208 ■ Bulletin of the Atomic Scientists

1155 E 60th St.
Chicago, IL 60637
Ph: (773) 382-8057
Fax: (773) 980-6932
E-mail: kbenedict@thebulletin.org
URL: www.thebulletin.org

2209 ■ Rieser Fellowships *(Undergraduate/ Fellowship)*

Purpose: To provide financial support for undergraduate students pursuing a project relating to interaction of science, global security, and public policy. **Focus:** Peace studies; National security. **Qualif.:** Applicant must be an undergraduate student at a U.S. college/university. **Criteria:** Awards are given based on academic interests, extracurricular activities and career aspiration.

Funds Avail.: $4,000. **Number Awarded:** 2. **To Apply:** Applicant must send an application form (available at the website); resume; proposal (800-1000 words); official letters confirming internships, acceptance to conference; an essay (one-page, single-spaced) explaining how the fellowship would be benefit the applicant; project budget; and two letters of recommendation. **Deadline:** March 15. **Contact:** kgladish@thebulletin.org.

2210 ■ Burroughs Wellcome Fund

21 T.W. Alexander Dr.
Research Triangle Park, NC 27709
Ph: (919) 991-5100
Fax: (919) 991-5160
E-mail: info@bwfund.org
URL: www.bwfund.org

2211 ■ Burroughs Wellcome Fund Career Awards at the Scientific Interface *(Doctorate, Postdoctorate/Fellowship)*

Purpose: To advance post-doctoral training and to foster the early career development of researchers whose works are dedicated to pursuing a career in academic research. **Focus:** Mathematics and mathematical sciences; Physics; Chemistry; Computer and information sciences; Statistics; Engineering. **Qualif.:** Candidates must hold a PhD degree in one of the fields of mathematics, physics, chemistry, computer science, statistics or engineering; must have completed at least 12 months but not more than 48 months of postdoctoral research by the date of the full invited application deadline; must be committed to full-time careers in research as independent investigators at a North American degree-granting institution; must have at least one first-author publication; a candidate's primary postdoctoral mentor must hold an appointment at an accredited, degree-granting institution in the United States or Canada; must be based at a non-profit institution in the United States or Canada; must not hold nor have accepted a K99 award from the U.S. National Institutes of Health. **Criteria:** Selection will be based on the following: depth and rigor of training in a scientific discipline other than biology; importance of biological questions identified in the proposal and innovation in the approaches chosen to answer them. Candidates should present clear evidence of already beginning to tackle a biological problem; interdisciplinary nature of research plan, the degree to which non-biological methods are integrated and the degree to which the proposed work will open new fields of inquiry; potential of candidate to establish a successful independent research career, evidenced by productivity during the postdoctoral period prior to application; quality of proposed collaborations.

Funds Avail.: $500,000. **To Apply:** Applicants may visit the website to take an eligibility quiz to assist them in determining whether or not they are eligible to apply for this award. Successful completion of the quiz will take them to the next application step. Applicants will be notified upon conclusion of the quiz if they are not eligible to continue. **Deadline:** September 1. **Contact:** Debi Vought, Senior Program Associate; phone: 919-991-5116; email: dvought@bwfund.org.

2212 ■ Burroughs Wellcome Fund Collaborative Research Travel Grants *(Doctorate/Grant)*

Purpose: To support researchers from degree-granting institutions with travel either domestically or internationally to acquire new research techniques, to promote collaborations and to attend courses. **Focus:** Mathematics and mathematical sciences; Physics; Chemistry; Computer and

Awards are arranged alphabetically below their administering organizations

information sciences; Statistics; Engineering. **Qualif.:** Applicants must hold a PhD or are studying for a PhD in mathematics, physics, chemistry, computer science, statistics or engineering who are interested in investigating research opportunities in the biological sciences; or to biologists interested in working with physical scientists to incorporate their ideas and approaches in answering biological questions. **Criteria:** Selection will be made on the basis of scientific quality of the proposed activities and the career development potential of the visit.

Funds Avail.: $15,000. **To Apply:** Applicants may visit the website to take an eligibility quiz that will assist them in determining whether they are eligible to apply for this award. Successful completion of the quiz will take them to the next application step. Applicants will be notified upon conclusion of the quiz if they are not eligible to continue. **Deadline:** December 1.

2213 ■ Career Awards for Science and Mathematics Teachers (Professional development/Award)

Purpose: To recognize teachers who have demonstrated solid knowledge of science and/or mathematics content and have outstanding performance records in educating children. **Focus:** Science; Mathematics and mathematical sciences. **Qualif.:** Candidates in a middle school and high school must hold licensure to teach science and/or mathematics in North Carolina and have completed at least five years of teaching experience at the time of application with at least 70 percent of their time devoted to teaching science and/or mathematics courses. Candidates in elementary schools, who also can be science and/or mathematics specialists, must have completed at least five years of teaching at the time of application; with at least 30 percent of the candidate's time spent teaching science and/or mathematics. At least 20 percent of their time should be spent working with other teachers if they are specialists. Candidates must have superior knowledge of science and/or mathematics, excellent teaching skills, demonstrated leadership and a commitment to continue teaching in the North Carolina Public School system; must be currently licensed North Carolina public school science and/or mathematics teachers who teach in grades K-12 in North Carolina public schools; and must be citizens of the United States. **Criteria:** Selection will be based primarily on the following: candidate's qualifications and potential to conduct high-quality science and/or mathematics teaching; candidate's significant contributions to enhancing students' knowledge of science and/or mathematics; candidate's knowledge of subject content and effectiveness of communications skills; candidate's abilities in the classroom that should demonstrate learner-centered, knowledge-centered, assessment-centered and community-centered learning styles; candidate's support from the principal and superintendent.

Funds Avail.: $175,000. **To Apply:** All applications will require signatures and letters of support from the principal of the candidate's school and the superintendent of the school district. More than one candidate from a school or school district is eligible to apply. In support of the application, the principal and superintendent must demonstrate that the necessary environment for successful science and/or mathematics teaching exists at the school and that there are opportunities for the teacher to be mentored and to mentor other teachers. The principal and superintendent must clearly outline in letters of support how the teaching professional will be supported and developed as a teacher leader in the districts. **Deadline:** January. **Contact:** Mela-

nie Scott, Senior Program Associate, 919-991-5107, mscott@bwfund.org.

2214 ■ Career Fellowship Awards for Medical Scientists (Postdoctorate, Professional development/Fellowship)

Purpose: To support research and other scientific and educational activities. **Focus:** Biomedical sciences. **Qualif.:** Ideal candidate must be two years away from becoming an independent investigator, have at least two years or more of postdoctoral research experience, and have a significant publication record; must hold an MD, DDS, DVM, PharmD or equivalent clinical degree; proposals must be in the area of basic biomedical, disease-oriented, translational, or molecular, genetic, or pharmacological epidemiology research. Proposals that are in the area of epidemiology should contact BWF to determine the eligibility of the proposal; must be a clinical fellow, resident, or a postdoctoral researcher and have at least two years of postdoctoral research experience at the time of application; candidates who hold a junior faculty appointment (Lecturer, Instructor, Assistant Professor-non tenure track, etc.) may be eligible if they have been in a faculty position for two years or less at the time of application; must not be more than 10 years past their most recent doctorate degree; those with a clinical degree not awarded in the United States or Canada must be fully licensed to practice in the United States or Canada; must be committed to a full-time career in research as an independent investigator at a North American degree-granting institution; must be nominated by accredited, degree-granting institutions in the United States or Canada; must be citizens or permanent residents of the United States or Canada at the time of application. Permanent residents of the United States must provide a copy of their Permanent Resident Card with the application. Permanent residents of Canada must provide a copy of their Landed Immigrant Status form with the application. **Criteria:** Selection will be based on the committee's criteria.

Funds Avail.: A total of $700,000. **To Apply:** U.S. or Canadian institutions, including affiliated medical schools, graduate schools and all related hospitals and research institutes may nominate up to five candidates. **Deadline:** October 3. **Remarks:** Award bridges advanced postdoctoral and fellowship training in the early years of faculty service. **Contact:** Debra Holmes, Senior Program Associate; phone: 919-991-5134; email: dholmes@bwfund.org.

2215 ■ Investigators in the Pathogenesis of Infectious Disease Awards (Doctorate, Postdoctorate/Grant)

Purpose: To provide assistant professors the freedom and flexibility to pursue high risk projects and inquiries as multidisciplinary approaches to the study of human infectious diseases. **Focus:** Infectious diseases. **Qualif.:** Candidates will generally have an MD, DVM or PhD degree. The Fund particularly encourages human health-relevant applications from veterinary scientists; must have an established record of independent research and hold a tenure-track position as an assistant professor or equivalent at a degree-granting institution; must be nominated by accredited, degree-granting institutions in the United States or Canada; must be citizens or permanent residents of the United States or Canada at the time of application. Permanent residents of the United States must provide a copy of their Permanent Resident Card with the application. Permanent residents of Canada must provide a copy of their Landed Immigrant Status form with the application. **Criteria:** Selection will be

Awards are arranged alphabetically below their administering organizations

based on candidate's qualifications and potential to conduct innovative research; quality and originality of the proposed research and its potential to advance understanding of fundamental issues of how infectious agents and human hosts interact. Proposals that bring new, solid experimental approaches to under-studied questions will be considered more competitive than proposals that primarily extend work under way; demonstration of an established record of independent research. **Funds Avail.:** $500,000. **To Apply:** Applicants may visit the website to take an eligibility quiz to assist them in determining whether or not they are eligible to apply for this award. Successful completion of the quiz will take them to the next application step. Applicants will be notified upon conclusion of the quiz if they are not eligible to continue. **Deadline:** November 1.

2216 ■ Bush Foundation

332 Minnesota St., Ste. E-900
Saint Paul, MN 55101-1315
Ph: (651) 227-0891
Fax: (651) 297-6485
E-mail: info@bushfoundation.org
URL: www.bushfoundation.org

2217 ■ Bush Artist Fellowships *(All/Fellowship)*

Purpose: To support different artist with significant financial and professional development to further their work and their contributions to their communities. **Focus:** Arts. **Qualif.:** Applicant must be a resident of: Minnesota, North Dakota or South Dakota, and a U.S. citizen or permanent resident; have lived in the listed region at least 24 months immediately prior to the application deadline; and at least 25-years-old on the application deadline. **Criteria:** Selection is based on applicant's strong vision; creative energy; commitment to excellence; and potential to fulfill the purpose of the Bush Artist Program.

Funds Avail.: $48,000. **Number Awarded:** Up to 15. **To Apply:** Applications will be accepted via online submission process. **Deadline:** October 30, November 6. **Remarks:** The Bush Artist Program makes awards in eight categories that rotate on a two-year cycle. **Contact:** Catherine McGuire at artists@bushfoundation.org or cmcguire@bushfoundation.org.

2218 ■ Bush Leadership Fellows Program *(Professional development/Fellowship)*

Purpose: To motivate individuals who are eager to prepare themselves for greater leadership opportunities and to create positive change in their communities. **Focus:** Community leadership. **Qualif.:** Applicant must be a U.S. citizen or permanent resident; be 24 years or older at the application deadline date; have lived or worked for at least one continuous year immediately prior to the application deadline in Minnesota, North Dakota or South Dakota; and not a former Bush Leadership Fellows. **Criteria:** Selection committees review applicants' records with attention to leadership, learning and impact.

Funds Avail.: $25,000-$75,000. **To Apply:** Applications will be accepted via online submission process. **Deadline:** November 20. **Contact:** Martha Lee at mlee@bushfoundation.org.

2219 ■ Business and Professional Women's Foundation (BPWF)

1718 M St. NW, No. 148
Washington, DC 20036

Ph: (202) 293-1100
Fax: (202) 861-0298
E-mail: foundation@bpwfoundation.org
URL: www.bpwfoundation.org

2220 ■ Career Advancement Scholarships *(Undergraduate/Scholarship)*

Purpose: To provide financial assistance to disadvantaged women seeking to further their education. **Focus:** General studies. **Qualif.:** Applicant must be a female at least 25 years of age; must be a U.S citizen or U.S national; must demonstrate critical financial need; must have an expected family contribution (EFC) of $2,500 or less; must be officially accepted into an accredited U.S college or university, including those in American Samoa, Puerto Rico, and the Virgin Islands; must demonstrate clear career plans; must not be earning a doctoral-level or terminal degree. **Criteria:** Applications will be reviewed by the scholarship committee.

Funds Avail.: No specific amount. **To Apply:** Scholarship application and other supporting documents must be sent to BPW foundation. **Remarks:** The Business and Professional Women's Foundation established the Career Advancement Scholarship Program in 1969 to provide scholarships, grants and loans to women seeking to improve their lives.

2221 ■ Business Professionals of America (BPA)

5454 Cleveland Ave.
Columbus, OH 43231-4021
Ph: (614) 895-7277
Fax: (614) 895-1165
Free: 800-334-2007
E-mail: jellis@bpa.org
URL: www.bpanet.org

2222 ■ National Honor Roll Scholarships *(Undergraduate/Scholarship)*

Purpose: To assist outstanding seniors of Business Professionals of America in the Secondary Division. **Focus:** Business. **Qualif.:** Applicants must be members of Business Professionals of America who are graduating high school seniors with minimum grade point average of 3.0. **Criteria:** Applicants are evaluated based on academic success and involvement within the organization.

Funds Avail.: $2,000. **To Apply:** Applicants must submit completed application form along with the school grade transcript or letter from his/her school principal verifying GPA; a one-page, typed resume of activities involving both Business Professionals of America and other school and community activities; three signed recommendation letters on official letterhead from local advisor and two individuals of their choice; a one-page, double-spaced, typed essay on topic, "Where do I see myself professionally in ten years."

2223 ■ Business Solution Association (BSA)

5024-R Campbell Blvd.
Baltimore, MD 21236-5974
Ph: (410) 931-8100
Fax: (410) 931-8111
URL: www.opwa.org

2224 ■ BSA Educational Scholarships *(Undergraduate/Scholarship)*

Purpose: To provide educational assistance to individuals affiliated with the office products industry. **Focus:** General

Awards are arranged alphabetically below their administering organizations

studies. **Qualif.:** Applicant must be an employee, or relative of an employee of an OPWA member company; or a member group or relative of the member group affiliated with the office product industry. **Criteria:** Selection is based on academic success, interest, abilities, and financial need.

Funds Avail.: $500-$2,500. **To Apply:** Application form is available at the website. Applicant must prepare a transcript of grades and credits; a letter of recommendation from a person employed by a firm in the office products industry (must hold an executive or managerial position) and another from a teacher, professor or other educational professional. **Deadline:** March 31.

2225 ■ Calhoun Community College
PO Box 2216
Decatur, AL 35609
Ph: (256) 306-2500
Free: 800-626-3628
E-mail: mcb@calhoun.edu
URL: www.calhoun.edu

2226 ■ Calhoun Scholarships (Undergraduate/ Scholarship)

Purpose: To provide educational assistance for Calhoun students. **Focus:** General studies. **Qualif.:** Applicants must be enrolled at the Calhoun College and must maintain 3.0 cumulative GPA or 2.5 GPA for Fine Arts awardees. **Criteria:** Selection is based on the application materials.

Funds Avail.: $1,500 for full-tuition. **To Apply:** Applicants must complete a FAFSA (Free Application for Federal Student Aid) by March 1 in order to be considered. Applicants must also complete the online scholarship application and submit along with other required materials and information. **Deadline:** March 1. **Contact:** Student Financial Services, 256-306-2624.

2227 ■ California Adolescent Nutrition and Fitness Program (CANFIT)
2140 Shattuck Ave., Ste. 610
Berkeley, CA 94704
Ph: (510) 644-1533
Fax: (510) 644-1535
Free: 800-200-3131
E-mail: info@canfit.org
URL: www.canfit.org

2228 ■ CANFIT Scholarships (Graduate, Undergraduate/Scholarship)

Purpose: to encourage students to consider careers that will improve adolescent nutrition and fitness. **Focus:** Nutrition; Physical education; Public health; Culinary arts. **Qualif.:** Applicant must be a resident of the state of California with African-American, American Indian/Alaska Native, Asian-American, Pacific Islander, or Latino/Hispanic student affiliation expressing financial need; enrolled in an approved masters level or doctoral graduate program in Nutrition, Public Health, or Physical Education, or an American Dietetic Association Pre-Professional Practice Program, and have completed 12-15 units of graduate course work with a 3.0 or better cumulative GPA; or enrolled in an approved bachelor's program in Nutrition, Physical Education, or Culinary Arts, and have completed 50 semester units with a 2.5 or better cumulative GPA (except for Culinary Arts student). **Criteria:** Selection is based on the applica-

tion materials submitted for review.

Funds Avail.: No specific amount. **Number Awarded:** Varies. **To Apply:** Applicants must submit a completed (and signed) Application Cover Sheet together with a completed (and signed) Statement of Financial Status; two recommendations (professors, employers, community leaders); a letter (1-2 typed pages) on academic goals and involvement in community nutrition and/or physical education activities; a 500-1000-word essay on a given topic; a photograph (billfold size or larger) to be published; and a copy of official transcripts of graduate course work to 12-15 units (graduate students) or official transcripts of all college work to accrue 50 units (undergraduate students). Mail original and three additional copies of each document (except transcript and photo) to CANFIT.

2229 ■ California Association of Pest Control Advisers (CAPCA)
2300 River Plaza Dr., Ste. 120
Sacramento, CA 95833
Ph: (916) 928-1625
Fax: (916) 928-0705
E-mail: terry@capca.com
URL: capca.com

2230 ■ Stanley W. Strew Educational Fund Scholarships (Undergraduate/Scholarship)

Purpose: To support and promote agricultural pest control advisers or professional production consultants who serve California agricultural and horticultural producers. **Focus:** Agriculture, Economic aspects. **Qualif.:** Applicants must be junior students currently attending, entering or returning to college in agricultural or horticultural fields; must plan to pursue a career in pest management; must have a 2.5 GPA or better. **Criteria:** Recipients are selected based on academics; financial need; extra curricular activities; pest management experience; professional/career goals; class standing.

Funds Avail.: $3,000; $2,000. **Number Awarded:** 2. **To Apply:** Applicants must submit a completed application form; must include a current official transcript of records; must submit at least two letters of recommendation. **Deadline:** May 11. **Contact:** 916-928-1625.

2231 ■ California Association of Private Postsecondary Schools (CAPPS)
555 Capitol Mall, Ste. 705
Sacramento, CA 95814
Ph: (916) 447-5500
Fax: (916) 440-8970
Free: 888-92-CAPPS
E-mail: info@cappsonline.org
URL: www.cappsonline.org

2232 ■ California Association of Private Postsecondary Schools Scholarships (Undergraduate/Scholarship)

Purpose: To ensure that the needs of the entire sector, from small registered schools to large institutions are met from an educational, policy and business perspective. **Focus:** Cosmetology; Allied health; Nursing. **Qualif.:** Applicants must be enrolled in a cosmetology, massage, aesthetics, nursing or allied health program at a CAPP's

Awards are arranged alphabetically below their administering organizations

member School; must be recommended by the School Director or President. **Criteria:** Recipients are selected based on academic performance.

Funds Avail.: No specific amount. **Number Awarded:** 4. **To Apply:** Applicants must submit one to two-page essay along with the completed application form, transcript and three letters of recommendation. **Contact:** info@cappsonline.com.

2233 ■ California Bar Association
180 Howard St.
San Francisco, CA 94105-1939
Ph: (415) 856-0780
Fax: (415) 856-0788
E-mail: info@calbarfoundation.org
URL: www.calbarfoundation.org

2234 ■ Public Interest Scholarships
(Undergraduate/Scholarship)

Purpose: To help offset high cost of law school education. **Focus:** Law. **Qualif.:** Candidates must be enrolled in a California law school or must have completed at least one year of study at a California law school (the candidates' law school must certify good ethical standing of the candidate while attending law school and must also attest to the candidate's financial need); must maintain at least a 2.5 or equivalent on a 4.0 scale (or provide an explanation of extenuating circumstances if GPA is lower than 2.5). **Criteria:** Selection will be based on the committee's criteria.

Funds Avail.: $7,500. **To Apply:** Applicants must accomplish complete application package which includes: application; certification and authorization form (which includes certification of non-relationship, authorization to use information, name and likeness and consent and authorization to obtain information); resume; personal statement describing the candidate's commitment to and plans for a legal career in public service (not to exceed 400 words); three letters of recommendation; law school transcript; certification of financial need; certification of ethical standing and statement of nomination; and optional statement of financial circumstances. Candidate's name must appear in the upper right-hand corner of each page of every document submitted. **Deadline:** March 16. **Contact:** Jasmine Guillory; 415-856-0780; jquillory@calbarfoundation.org.

2235 ■ Rosenthal Bar Exam Scholarships
(Undergraduate/Scholarship)

Purpose: To provide financial support for outstanding graduating California law students who are embarking on careers in public service law. **Focus:** Law. **Qualif.:** Candidates must be graduating or have graduated from a California law school; must be taking the California Bar Exam for the first time; and must maintain at least a 2.5 GPA or equivalent on a 4.0 scale (or provide an explanation of extenuating circumstances if GPA is lower than 2.5). **Criteria:** Selection will be based on the committee's criteria.

Funds Avail.: $2,000. **To Apply:** Candidates must be nominated by their law school. **Deadline:** February 8. **Contact:** For further information, applicants must contact Jasmine Guillory; E-mail: jguillory@calbarfoundation.org.

2236 ■ California Chicano News Media Association: Latino Journalists of California (CCNMA)
USC Annenberg School of Communication & Journalism
727 W 27th St., Rm. 201
Los Angeles, CA 90007-3212

Ph: (213) 821-0075
Fax: (213) 743-1838
E-mail: ccnmainfo@ccnma.org
URL: www.ccnma.org

2237 ■ Joel Garcia Memorial Scholarships
(Undergraduate/Scholarship)

Purpose: To support qualified Latino students who are planning to pursue a career in journalism. **Focus:** Journalism. **Qualif.:** Applicant must be a Latino college student or graduating high school senior attending a college or university in California (California resident may attend a college or university outside of California). **Criteria:** Selection is based on commitment to the field of journalism, scholastic achievement, community awareness and financial need.

Funds Avail.: $500-$1,000. **To Apply:** Applicants must submit a completed application form together with an autobiographical essay (300-500 words); two reference letters, including at least one from a faculty member (no family members); current official transcripts; and work samples (which include newspaper articles, TV or radio audition tapes, or photographs produced by student applicant). **Deadline:** April 2.

2238 ■ Frank del Olmo Memorial Scholarships
(Undergraduate/Scholarship)

Purpose: To support qualified Latino students who are planning to pursue a career in journalism. **Focus:** Journalism. **Qualif.:** Applicant must be a Latino college student or graduating high school senior attending a college or university in California (California resident may attend a college or university outside of California). **Criteria:** Selection is based on commitment to the field of journalism, scholastic achievement, community awareness and financial need.

Funds Avail.: $500-$1,000. **To Apply:** Applicants must submit a completed application form together with an autobiographical essay (300-500 words); two reference letters, including at least one from a faculty member (no family members); current official transcripts; and work samples (which include newspaper articles, TV or radio audition tapes, or photographs produced by student applicant). **Deadline:** April 2.

2239 ■ California Grocers Association (CGA)
1215 K St., Ste. 700
Sacramento, CA 95814-3946
Ph: (916) 448-3545
Fax: (916) 448-2793
E-mail: rfong@cagrocers.com
URL: www.cagrocers.com

2240 ■ Lou Amen Legacy Scholarships
(Undergraduate/Scholarship)

Purpose: To provide proactive leadership, education, advocacy and information. **Focus:** General studies. **Qualif.:** Applicants must be high school seniors, college freshmen, sophomores and juniors who are dependents of employees or are themselves employees of a CGA member company; must be planning to enroll as full-time college students at an accredited, non-profit college or university in the United States. **Criteria:** Recipients are selected based on academic merit, evidence of outstanding character and leadership potential.

Awards are arranged alphabetically below their administering organizations

Funds Avail.: $1,000. **To Apply:** Applicants must submit a completed application form. **Deadline:** April 1. **Contact:** Brianne Korte, bkorte@cagrocers.com.

2241 ■ Don C. Beaver Memorial Scholarships
(Undergraduate/Scholarship)

Purpose: To provide proactive leadership, education, advocacy and information. **Focus:** General studies. **Qualif.:** Applicants must be high school seniors, college freshmen, sophomores and juniors who are dependents of employees or are themselves employees of a CGA member company; must be planning to enroll as full-time college students at an accredited, non-profit college or university in the United States. **Criteria:** Recipients are selected based on academic merit, evidence of outstanding character and leadership potential.

Funds Avail.: $2,000. **To Apply:** Applicants must submit a completed application form. **Deadline:** April 1. **Contact:** Brianne Korte, bkorte@cagrocers.com.

2242 ■ Jack H. Brown Scholarships
(Undergraduate/Scholarship)

Purpose: To provide proactive leadership, education, advocacy and information. **Focus:** General studies. **Qualif.:** Applicants must be high school seniors, college freshmen, sophomores and juniors who are dependents of employees or are themselves employees of a CGA member company; must be planning to enroll as full-time college students at an accredited, non-profit college or university in the United States. **Criteria:** Recipients are selected based on academic merit, evidence of outstanding character and leadership potential.

Funds Avail.: $1,000. **To Apply:** Applicants must submit a completed application form. **Deadline:** April 1. **Contact:** Brianne Korte, bkorte@cagrocers.com.

2243 ■ California Shopping Cart Retrieval Corporation Inc. Scholarships *(Undergraduate/ Scholarship)*

Purpose: To provide proactive leadership, education, advocacy and information. **Focus:** General studies. **Qualif.:** Applicants must be high school seniors, college freshmen, sophomores and juniors who are dependents of employees or are themselves employees of a CGA member company; must be planning to enroll as full-time college students at an accredited, non-profit college or university in the United States. **Criteria:** Recipients are selected based on academic merit, evidence of outstanding character and leadership potential.

Funds Avail.: No specific amount. **Number Awarded:** 1. **To Apply:** Applicants must submit a completed application form. **Deadline:** April 1. **Contact:** Brianne Korte, bkorte@cagrocers.com.

2244 ■ Classic Wines of California Scholarships *(Undergraduate/Scholarship)*

Purpose: To provide proactive leadership, education, advocacy and information. **Focus:** General studies. **Qualif.:** Applicants must be high school seniors, college freshmen, sophomores and juniors who are dependents of employees or are themselves employees of a CGA member company; must be planning to enroll as full-time college students at an accredited, non-profit college or university in the United States. **Criteria:** Recipients are selected based on academic merit, evidence of outstanding character and leadership potential.

Funds Avail.: $2,000. **Number Awarded:** 2. **To Apply:** Applicants must submit a completed application form. **Deadline:** April 1. **Contact:** Brianne Korte, bkorte@cagrocers.com.

2245 ■ Joey and Florence Franco Legacy Scholarships *(Undergraduate/Scholarship)*

Purpose: To provide proactive leadership, education, advocacy and information. **Focus:** General studies. **Qualif.:** Applicants must be high school seniors, college freshmen, sophomores and juniors who are dependents of employees or are themselves employees of a CGA member company; must be planning to enroll as full-time college students at an accredited, non-profit college or university in the United States. **Criteria:** Recipients are selected based on academic merit, evidence of outstanding character and leadership potential.

Funds Avail.: $1,000. **To Apply:** Applicants must submit a completed application form. **Deadline:** April 1. **Contact:** Brianne Korte, bkorte@cagrocers.com.

2246 ■ Hall of Achievement Scholarships
(Undergraduate/Scholarship)

Purpose: To provide proactive leadership, education, advocacy and information. **Focus:** General studies. **Qualif.:** Applicants must be high school seniors, college freshmen, sophomores and juniors who are dependents of employees or are themselves employees of a CGA member company; must be planning to enroll as full-time college students at an accredited, non-profit college or university in the United States. **Criteria:** Recipients are selected based on academic merit, evidence of outstanding character and leadership potential.

Funds Avail.: $2,000. **To Apply:** Applicants must submit a completed application form. **Deadline:** April 1. **Contact:** Brianne Korte, bkorte@cagrocers.com.

2247 ■ Roger K. Hughes Legacy Scholarships
(Undergraduate/Scholarship)

Purpose: To provide proactive leadership, education, advocacy and information. **Focus:** General studies. **Qualif.:** Applicants must be high school seniors, college freshmen, sophomores and juniors who are dependents of employees or are themselves employees of a CGA member company; must be planning to enroll as full-time college students at an accredited, non-profit college or university in the United States. **Criteria:** Recipients are selected based on academic merit, evidence of outstanding character and leadership potential.

Funds Avail.: $1,000. **To Apply:** Applicants must submit a completed application form. **Deadline:** April 1. **Contact:** Brianne Korte, bkorte@cagrocers.com.

2248 ■ Paul A. Hughes Memorial Scholarships
(Undergraduate/Scholarship)

Purpose: To provide proactive leadership, education, advocacy and information. **Focus:** General studies. **Qualif.:** Applicants must be high school seniors, college freshmen, sophomores and juniors who are dependents of employees or are themselves employees of a CGA member company; must be planning to enroll as full-time college students at an accredited, non-profit college or university in the United States. **Criteria:** Recipients are selected based on academic merit, evidence of outstanding character and leadership potential.

Funds Avail.: $1,000. **Number Awarded:** 1. **To Apply:**

Awards are arranged alphabetically below their administering organizations

Applicants must submit a completed application form. **Deadline:** April 1. **Contact:** Brianne Korte, bkorte@cagrocers.com.

2249 ■ Illuminator Educational Foundation Scholarships *(Undergraduate/Scholarship)*

Purpose: To provide proactive leadership, education, advocacy and information. **Focus:** General studies. **Qualif.:** Applicants must be high school seniors, college freshmen, sophomores and juniors who are dependents of employees or are themselves employees of a CGA member company; must be planning to enroll as full-time college students at an accredited, non-profit college or university in the United States. **Criteria:** Recipients are selected based on academic merit, evidence of outstanding character and leadership potential.

Funds Avail.: $1,000. **Number Awarded:** 10. **To Apply:** Applicants must submit a completed application form. **Deadline:** April 1. **Contact:** Brianne Korte, bkorte@cagrocers.com.

2250 ■ Don Kaplan Legacy Scholarships *(Undergraduate/Scholarship)*

Purpose: To provide proactive leadership, education, advocacy and information. **Focus:** General studies. **Qualif.:** Applicants must be high school seniors, college freshmen, sophomores and juniors who are dependents of employees or are themselves employees of a CGA member company; must be planning to enroll as full-time college students at an accredited, non-profit college or university in the United States. **Criteria:** Recipients are selected based on academic merit, evidence of outstanding character and leadership potential.

Funds Avail.: $1,000. **To Apply:** Applicants must submit a completed application form. **Deadline:** April 1. **Contact:** Brianne Korte, bkorte@cagrocers.com.

2251 ■ Peter and Jody Larkin Legacy Scholarships *(Undergraduate/Scholarship)*

Purpose: To provide proactive leadership, education, advocacy and information. **Focus:** General studies. **Qualif.:** Applicants must be high school seniors, college freshmen, sophomores and juniors who are dependents of employees or are themselves employees of a CGA member company; must be planning to enroll as full-time college students at an accredited, non-profit college or university in the United States. **Criteria:** Recipients are selected based on academic merit, evidence of outstanding character and leadership potential.

Funds Avail.: $1,000. **To Apply:** Applicants must submit a completed application form. **Deadline:** April 1. **Contact:** Brianne Korte, bkorte@cagrocers.com.

2252 ■ Bill MacAloney Legacy Scholarships *(Undergraduate/Scholarship)*

Purpose: To provide proactive leadership, education, advocacy and information. **Focus:** General studies. **Qualif.:** Applicants must be high school seniors, college freshmen, sophomores and juniors who are dependents of employees or are themselves employees of a CGA member company; must be planning to enroll as full-time college students at an accredited, non-profit college or university in the United States. **Criteria:** Recipients are selected based on academic merit, evidence of outstanding character and leadership potential.

Funds Avail.: $1,000. **To Apply:** Applicants must submit a completed application form. **Deadline:** April 1. **Contact:** Brianne Korte, bkorte@cagrocers.com.

2253 ■ Al Plamann Legacy Scholarships *(Undergraduate/Scholarship)*

Purpose: To provide proactive leadership, education, advocacy and information. **Focus:** General studies. **Qualif.:** Applicants must be high school seniors, college freshmen, sophomores and juniors who are dependents of employees or are themselves employees of a CGA member company; must be planning to enroll as full-time college students at an accredited, non-profit college or university in the United States. **Criteria:** Recipients are selected based on academic merit, evidence of outstanding character and leadership potential.

Funds Avail.: $1,000. **To Apply:** Applicants must submit a completed application form. **Deadline:** April 1. **Contact:** Brianne Korte, bkorte@cagrocers.com.

2254 ■ Save Mart Legacy Scholarships *(Undergraduate/Scholarship)*

Purpose: To provide proactive leadership, education, advocacy and information. **Focus:** General studies. **Qualif.:** Applicants must be high school seniors, college freshmen, sophomores and juniors who are dependents of employees or are themselves employees of a CGA member company; must be planning to enroll as full-time college students at an accredited, non-profit college or university in the United States. **Criteria:** Recipients are selected based on academic merit, evidence of outstanding character and leadership potential.

Funds Avail.: $1,000. **To Apply:** Applicants must submit a completed application form. **Deadline:** April 1. **Contact:** Brianne Korte, bkorte@cagrocers.com.

2255 ■ Trelut Family Legacy Scholarships *(Undergraduate/Scholarship)*

Purpose: To provide proactive leadership, education, advocacy and information. **Focus:** General studies. **Qualif.:** Applicants must be high school seniors, college freshmen, sophomores and juniors who are dependents of employees or are themselves employees of a CGA member company; must be planning to enroll as full-time college students at an accredited, non-profit college or university in the United States.

Funds Avail.: $1,000. **To Apply:** Applicants must submit a completed application form. **Deadline:** April 1. **Contact:** Brianne Korte, bkorte@cagrocers.com.

2256 ■ Bob Wilson Legacy Scholarships *(Undergraduate/Scholarship)*

Purpose: To provide proactive leadership, education, advocacy and information. **Focus:** General studies. **Qualif.:** Applicants must be high school seniors, college freshmen, sophomores and juniors who are dependents of employees or are themselves employees of a CGA member company; must be planning to enroll as full-time college students at an accredited, non-profit college or university in the United States. **Criteria:** Recipients are selected based on academic merit, evidence of outstanding character and leadership potential.

Funds Avail.: $1,000. **To Apply:** Applicants must submit a completed application form. **Deadline:** April 1. **Contact:** Brianne Korte, bkorte@cagrocers.com.

2257 ■ California Groundwater Association (CGA)
PO Box 14369
Santa Rosa, CA 95402-6369

Awards are arranged alphabetically below their administering organizations

Ph: (707) 578-4408
Fax: (707) 546-4906
E-mail: wellguy@groundh2o.org
URL: www.groundh2o.org

2258 ■ California Groundwater Association Scholarships *(Undergraduate/Scholarship)*

Purpose: To provide financial assistance to those students who are in need. **Focus:** General Studies. **Qualif.:** Applicants must be California residents; must demonstrate an interest in some facet of groundwater technology. **Criteria:** Preference will be given to those who meet the criteria.

Funds Avail.: $1,000. **To Apply:** Applicants must obtain a CGA sponsor and provide a 500 word essay about their interest in the groundwater field or their chosen field of study. Applicants must check the available website for the additional requirements. **Deadline:** March 15. **Contact:** Please call 707-578-4408 for details.

2259 ■ California-Hawaii Elks Association (CHEA)

5450 E Lamona Ave.
Fresno, CA 93727
Ph: (559) 255-4531
Fax: (559) 456-2659
E-mail: chea@chea-elks.org
URL: www.chea-elks.org

2260 ■ CHEA Undergraduate Scholarship Program for Students with Disabilities *(High School, Undergraduate/Scholarship)*

Purpose: To provide financial assistance to students with disabilities wishing to further their education. **Focus:** General studies. **Qualif.:** Applicants must be U.S. citizens and be residents of California or Hawaii; must have a physical impairment, neurological impairment, visual, hearing and/or speech-language disorder; must be current or graduating high school students; must have passed the General Educational Development (GED) Examination or the California High School Proficiency Examination (CHSPE). **Criteria:** Recipients will be selected based on academic achievement and financial need.

Funds Avail.: $1,000 (community colleges and vocational schools); $2,000 (four-year colleges and universities) per year. **To Apply:** Applicants must submit a completed application form, financial statement, official transcript of records, two letters of recommendation and essay. **Deadline:** March 15.

2261 ■ CHEA Vocational Grants *(High School/ Grant)*

Purpose: To financially assist students planning to pursue an eligible vocational/technical course. **Focus:** General studies. **Qualif.:** Applicants must be high school students; must be residents of California or Hawaii who are American citizens; and must have plans to pursue vocational/ technical courses. **Criteria:** Applicants will be judged based on motivation, need, skills, grades, completeness and neatness of the given directions.

Funds Avail.: $1,000 each. **Number Awarded:** 58. **To Apply:** Applicants must complete the application form; must fill-out the date of application issued; must submit a BPO Elks Lodge endorsement, transcript of grades or work records; must provide a budget for school year projected,

financial information and exhibit.

2262 ■ California Landscape Contractors Association

1491 River Pk. Dr. Ste. 100
Sacramento, CA 95815
Ph: (916) 830-2780
Fax: (916) 830-2788
E-mail: hq@clca.org
URL: www.clca.org

2263 ■ CLCA Landscape Educational Advancement Foundation Scholarships *(Undergraduate/ Scholarship)*

Purpose: To serve and protect the interest of members, promote professionalism and advance public awareness of the landscape industry. **Focus:** Landscape architecture and design. **Qualif.:** Applicants must be students attending an accredited California community college or state university, majoring in ornamental horticulture and taking a minimum of six units. **Criteria:** Recipients are selected based on academic performance and financial need.

Funds Avail.: No specific amount. **To Apply:** Applicants must submit typed, printed and completed application form, personal reference letters and resume. Applicants must also submit a reference letters from most recent employer, ornamental horticulture instructor, counselor, club/activities advisor, or church leader and must provide an official proof of enrollment. **Deadline:** April 16.

2264 ■ California Police Youth Charities (CPYC)

7401 Galilee Rd. Spc. No. 350
Roseville, CA 95678
Ph: (916) 787-4201
Fax: (916) 482-4246
E-mail: calpyc@msn.com
URL: www.calpyc.com/HOME.html

2265 ■ Youth Leadership Scholarships *(Undergraduate/Scholarship)*

Purpose: To recognize twelfth grade students who have engaged in meaningful leadership and citizenship volunteer activities during the past year. **Focus:** General studies. **Qualif.:** Applicants must be high school seniors who wish to pursue their studies in college; must be residents of California, sons, daughters or wards of an active or retired California Peace Officer. **Criteria:** Recipients are selected based on the content, grammar, format creativity and structure of essay, demonstrated importance of good citizenship in their essay, demonstrated leadership, volunteerism, student's work in school and community and number of hours the students volunteered.

Funds Avail.: $1,000. **Number Awarded:** 20. **To Apply:** Applicants must submit a completed application form and essay. **Deadline:** May 1. **Contact:** cbuzzeaton@msn.com.

2266 ■ California Psychological Association (CPA)

1231 I St., Ste. 204
Sacramento, CA 95814-2933
Ph: (916) 286-7979
Fax: (916) 286-7971

Awards are arranged alphabetically below their administering organizations

E-mail: membership@cpapsych.org
URL: www.cpapsych.org

2267 ■ CPA-F Minority Scholarships *(Graduate/Scholarship)*

Purpose: To provide funding for minority students whose interests and talents lie in the field of psychology. **Focus:** Psychology. **Qualif.:** Applicant must be a member of one or more established ethnic minority groups; a graduate from a regionally accredited undergraduate institution, and have been accepted into a doctoral program in psychology at a regionally accredited or approved institution in the State of California; and enrolled as a full-time graduate student. **Criteria:** Applicants will be judged on their potential for pursuing doctoral level work in psychology.

Funds Avail.: $2,000. **Number Awarded:** 3. **To Apply:** Applicants must submit a completed application form which includes an essay along with three letters of recommendation (Applicant Evaluation Form); official copy of most recent transcript (mailed directly from the academic institution to the Foundation); a letter of acceptance directly from the respective graduate program; and financial information. **Deadline:** November 3. **Contact:** Jo Linder-Crow, PhD at 800-995-8606 x-115 or 916-286-7979 x-115, email at jlindercrow@cpapsych.org.

2268 ■ California School Library Association (CSLA)

950 Glenn Dr., Ste. 150
Folsom, CA 95630
Ph: (916) 447-2684
Fax: (916) 447-2695
E-mail: info@csla.net
URL: www.csla.net

2269 ■ Above and Beyond Scholarships *(Graduate/Scholarship)*

Purpose: To encourage practicing Teacher Librarians to pursue either a Master's or Doctorate degree in librarianship or in a related field. **Focus:** Library and archival sciences. **Qualif.:** Applicants must be professional members of the California School Library Association who are enrolled in advanced degree programs; must be residents of California who have planned to continue working in school library profession upon completion of the graduate program. **Criteria:** Selection of applicants will be judged based on criteria settled by scholarship selection committee.

Funds Avail.: $1,000. **To Apply:** Application forms are available online. Applicants must present college transcripts and proof of enrollment in a master's or doctoral program, or proof of pursuing National Board Certification; must submit a 500-word statement describing their professional goals; must provide three letters of recommendation. **Deadline:** May 30.

2270 ■ Jewels Gardiner Scholarships *(Undergraduate/Scholarship)*

Purpose: To assist Northern California students. **Focus:** Library and archival sciences. **Qualif.:** Applicants must be enrolled in a Library Media Teacher Credential program. **Criteria:** Preference will be given to first-time recipients, current CSLA/NS members and with teaching experience.

Funds Avail.: $1,000. **Number Awarded:** 2. **To Apply:**

Application forms are available online. Applicants must submit a letter of recommendation including the following: (a) length of time known and in what capacity; (b) evaluation of applicant's ability as teacher and as fellow worker; (c) evaluation of leadership abilities; (d) description of strengths; and (e) assessment of success as a library media teacher. **Deadline:** August 1 and November 1.

2271 ■ Library Media Teacher Scholarships *(Graduate/Scholarship)*

Purpose: To assist individuals seeking preparation leading toward a degree or certification which will qualify the individual to work as a professional in the library media field in a school setting. **Focus:** Library and archival sciences. **Qualif.:** Applicants must be enrolled in a professional school library media teacher-credentialing program or a master's degree program; must be a resident of the area served by the CSLA Southern Section; must be a member of the California School Library Association. **Criteria:** Selection of applicants will be based on the criteria of the selection committee.

Funds Avail.: $1,000. **To Apply:** Applicants must provide three letters of recommendation: (a) must be from a CSLA member; (b) must be from a professor in the library media; (c) must be from a former or current supervisor or a fellow teacher. **Deadline:** February 15. **Contact:** Janice Gilmore-See, Southern Section President-Elect, 3352 San Carlos Dr., Spring Valley, CA 91918.

2272 ■ Mook & Blanchard Honorary Scholarships *(Graduate/Scholarship)*

Purpose: To assist a school library paraprofessional in obtaining the preparation needed to qualify and serve as a school library media teacher. **Focus:** Library and archival sciences. **Qualif.:** Applicants must be working or have worked within the last three years in a classified position in the library media field either in a school or at a district or county office; must be enrolled in a college or university working towards a BA, BS, or advanced degree in preparation to become a school library media teacher; must be a resident of California; must be a member of the California School Library Association. **Criteria:** Selection of applicants will be based on the criteria of the Scholarship committee.

Funds Avail.: $1,000. **To Apply:** Applicants must provide three letters of recommendation. Application forms are available online. **Deadline:** May 30. **Contact:** Mook and Blanchard Honorary Scholarship, California School Library Association, 950 Glenn Dr., Ste. 150 Folsom, CA 95630.

2273 ■ School Library Paraprofessional Scholarships *(Graduate/Scholarship)*

Purpose: To assist school library paraprofessionals in completing a school library technician/paraprofessional certificate program. **Focus:** Library and archival sciences. **Qualif.:** Applicants must be working in a classified position in the library media field, either in a school, district or County Office of Education; must be enrolled in a two-year paraprofessional program with the goal of becoming a qualified library technician or in a teacher credential program with the ultimate goal of pursuing a Library Media Teacher Services Credential; must be a resident of the area served by the CSLA Southern Section; must be a member of the California School Library Association. **Criteria:** Selection of applicants will be based on the criteria of the selection committee.

Funds Avail.: $500. **To Apply:** Application forms are available online. Applicants must provide three letters of recom-

Awards are arranged alphabetically below their administering organizations

mendation: (a) must be from a professor of the school in which the applicant is enrolled; (b) must be from a CSLA Southern Section member; (c) must be from a former or current supervisor. **Deadline:** January 31 and September 30. **Contact:** anice Gilmore-See, Southern Section President-Elect, 3352 San Carlos Dr., Spring Valley, CA 91978.

2274 ■ California Scottish Rite Foundation

855 Elm Ave.
Long Beach, CA 90813-4491
Ph: (562) 435-6061
Fax: (562) 435-3302
E-mail: foundationsecretary@casr-foundation.org
URL: www.scottishritecalifornia.org

2275 ■ California Scottish Rite Foundation Scholarships *(Undergraduate/Scholarship)*

Purpose: To provide financial assistance to young men and women who want to pursue their education at university and graduate level. **Focus:** General studies. **Qualif.:** Applicants must be undergraduate students who are residents of California state with ages ranging from 17 to 25 years old; must have a grade point average of 3.0 or better. **Criteria:** Applicants are evaluated based on demonstrated high ideals and ability; high grades in school; financial need and part-time employment.

Funds Avail.: $1,500. **To Apply:** Applicants must submit completed application form along with certified transcript of grades for previous semester; typed letter with handwritten signature by student of their employment, planned courses in the coming quarter/semester and current mailing address. **Deadline:** March 13.

2276 ■ California Sea Grant

University of California
9500 Gilman Dr., Dept. 0232
La Jolla, CA 92093-0232
Ph: (858) 534-4440
Fax: (858) 534-2231
E-mail: jeckman@ucsd.edu
URL: www-csgc.ucsd.edu

2277 ■ California Sea Grant State Fellowships *(Graduate/Fellowship)*

Purpose: To provide educational opportunity for graduate students who are interested in marine resources. **Focus:** Water resources. **Qualif.:** Applicants must be graduate students enrolled in the field of marine resources. **Criteria:** Recipients will be evaluated based on submitted application and supporting documents. Host selection will depend on the following categories: a) quality of the fellowship opportunity; b) level of educational benefit for the fellow; c) the host office's previous experience working with interns, fellows or other mentoring/educational programs; and d) level of financial commitment.

Funds Avail.: $3,166 per month. **To Apply:** Applicants must submit a completed application form. Applicants must visit the website for further information.

2278 ■ John A. Knauss Marine Policy Fellowships *(Graduate/Fellowship)*

Purpose: To provide educational experience to students who have interest in marine/ocean/Great Lakes resources and in the national policy decisions affecting those resources. **Focus:** Water resources. **Qualif.:** Applicants must be graduate students with hosts in the legislative branch, executive branch or appropriate associations/institutions located in the Washington, DC area. **Criteria:** Recipients will be selected based on submitted materials.

To Apply: Applicants must submit curriculum vitae, a personal education and career goals statement, two letters of recommendation, copy of all official undergraduate and graduate transcripts, listing of classes and career plan(s). **Deadline:** February 17. **Contact:** Shauna Oh at sgnsgoproposal@ucsd.edu.

2279 ■ West Coast Sea Grant Fellowships *(Graduate/Fellowship)*

Purpose: To financially assist graduate students who have demonstrated skills and experience in marine or aquatic-related science or policy. **Focus:** Water resources; Fisheries sciences/management. **Qualif.:** Applicants must be graduate students in good standing; must be enrolled in a marine-related or professional program at an accredited educational institution in California, Oregon or Washington. **Criteria:** Candidates will be selected based on evaluation scores, academic discipline, expertise and geographic balance.

Funds Avail.: $37,500. **Number Awarded:** 4. **To Apply:** Applicants must submit their personal and academic curriculum vitae; must provide a personal education and career goal statement that emphasizes their abilities and career development; must submit two, signed letters of recommendation and unofficial copies of all undergraduate and graduate student transcripts. Electronic version of the application must be submitted as PDF format using the California Sea Grant submission link available at the website. **Deadline:** October 7. **Contact:** wcgafellow@ucsd.edu.

2280 ■ California Society of Radiologic Technologists (CSRT)

2196 Tanager Ct.
Pleasanton, CA 94566
Ph: (310) 782-0927
Fax: (925) 397-3141
E-mail: csrtwc@thelcgh.com
URL: www.csrt.org

2281 ■ Anna Ames Clinical Excellence Student Grants *(Undergraduate/Grant)*

Purpose: To provide financial assistance to radiologic science students enrolled in JRCERT-approved California schools. **Focus:** Radiology. **Qualif.:** Applicants must be CSRT members or apply for membership at the time of application; must be enrolled full-time in California Department of Health Services approved and Joint Review Committee for Education in Radiologic Technology (JRCERT) accredited education program of Radiologic Sciences; must be enrolled in the program for at least 6 months at the time of receipt of the award; and, must possess exceptional skills in the clinical environment. **Criteria:** Applicants are evaluated based on academic merit.

Funds Avail.: $500. **To Apply:** Applicants must submit the completed application form and all other required materials for the Grant in a sealed envelope to Cecilia Ortiz, CSRT Scholarship Committee Chair, Cal State University Northridge, Health Science Department, 18111 Nordhoff St., Northridge CA 91330-8285. **Deadline:** September 30.

Awards are arranged alphabetically below their administering organizations

2282 ■ Ruth McMillan Student Grants
(Undergraduate/Grant)

Purpose: To provide financial assistance to radiologic science students enrolled in approved California schools. **Focus:** Radiology. **Qualif.:** Applicants must be CSRT members enrolled full-time in a California Department of Health Services approved and CSRT-recognized education program of Radiologic Sciences (at least 6 months enrolled in the program at the time of receipt of the award); must possess a minimum grade point average of 2.5 in all college courses. **Criteria:** Applicants are evaluated based on academic merit.

Funds Avail.: $500. **To Apply:** Applicants must submit a completed application form obtained from the CSRT office and other required materials for the Grant and mail the application in a sealed envelope to Cecilia Ortiz, CSRT Scholarship Committee Chair, Cal State University, Northridge, Health Sciences Department, 18111 Nordhoff St., Northridge CA 91330-8285. **Deadline:** September 30. **Contact:** Lorenza Clausen, CSRT President, 310-782-0927 or e-mail at email@csrt.org.

2283 ■ Superior District Legislative Mentoring Student Grants *(Undergraduate/Grant)*

Purpose: To provide an opportunity to radiologic science students enrolled in approved California schools, through financial assistance, in order for them to participate in the legislative process. **Focus:** Radiology. **Qualif.:** Applicants must be CSRT members enrolled full-time in a California Department of Health Services-approved and CSRT-recognized education program of Radiologic Sciences for at least 6 months at the time of receipt of the award; and, must possess exceptional interest in leadership and the legislative process. **Criteria:** Applicants are evaluated based on personal merit and attributes.

Funds Avail.: $1,500. **Number Awarded:** 4. **To Apply:** Applicants must submit the completed application form obtained from the CSRT office and the all other required application information materials. **Deadline:** December 15.

2284 ■ Superior District Legislative Mentoring Student Grants RT to DC *(Undergraduate/Grant)*

Purpose: To provide an opportunity to radiologic science students enrolled in approved California schools, through financial assistance, in order for them to participate in the legislative process. **Focus:** Radiology. **Qualif.:** Applicants must be CSRT members enrolled full-time in a California Department of Health Services approved and CSRT-recognized education program of Radiologic Sciences for at least 6 months at the time of receipt of the award; must possess exceptional interest in leadership and the legislative process. **Criteria:** Recipients are selected based on academic merit and financial need.

Funds Avail.: $1,500. **Number Awarded:** 2. **To Apply:** Applicants must submit the completed application form obtained from the CSRT office and the other required materials for the award. **Deadline:** December 15.

2285 ■ California State University San Marcos Alumni Association (CSUSM)

Cal State San Macros
333 S Twin Oaks Valley Rd.
San Marcos, CA 92096
Ph: (760) 750-4405
E-mail: alumni@csusm.edu
URL: alumniweb.csusm.edu

2286 ■ Cal State San Macros Alumna Scholarships *(Undergraduate/Scholarship)*

Purpose: To support fellow and future alumni in furthering their education. **Focus:** General studies. **Qualif.:** Applicant must be admitted to a degree or certificate program and enrolled in at least six units. **Criteria:** Selection is based on academic merit, commitment to the community, leadership potential, and diverse interest.

Funds Avail.: No specific amount. **Number Awarded:** 5. **To Apply:** Applicant must submit an application to the Financial Aid and Scholarship Office. **Contact:** Financial Aid and Scholarship Office, 760-750-4850.

2287 ■ California Waterfowl Association (CWA)

4630 Northgate Blvd., Ste. 150
Sacramento, CA 95834
Ph: (916) 648-1406
Fax: (916) 648-1665
E-mail: cwa@calwaterfowl.org
URL: www.calwaterfowl.org

2288 ■ Dennis Raveling Scholarships
(Undergraduate/Scholarship)

Purpose: To provide field experience and training in the tools, methods, concepts of waterfowl, wetlands research and management. **Focus:** Wildlife conservation, management and sciences; Zoology; Botany; Ecology. **Qualif.:** Applicants must be students with a desire to pursue a career in waterfowl or wetlands ecology. **Criteria:** Recipients are selected based on candidates resolve, high academic achievement and project merit.

Funds Avail.: $2,000 for first place; $1,000 for 2nd place. **Number Awarded:** 2. **To Apply:** Applicants must submit a "one-page" proposal summary description on an original research or management project; must submit a detailed proposal if required or "one-page" statement explaining the course of study for which they need to support. Applicants must also submit their resume, letter of support from faculty member and names and phone numbers of two references. **Deadline:** October 31. **Contact:** Nicole Berset at the above address.

2289 ■ Calista Corp.

301 Calista Ct., Ste. A
Anchorage, AK 99518-3000
Ph: (907) 279-5516
Fax: (907) 272-5060
Free: 800-277-5516
E-mail: calista@calistacorp.com
URL: www.calistacorp.com

2290 ■ Calista Scholarships *(Graduate, Undergraduate, Vocational/Occupational/ Scholarship)*

Purpose: To provide financial assistance to Alaska Natives to enable them to participate in continuing educational activities, formal programs of study and programs to improve their status. **Focus:** General studies. **Qualif.:** Applicant must be accepted to an accredited school who is enrolled on a full-time basis; must be a high school graduate or have earned a GED and be in good academic standing with at least 2.0 GPA; must be an Alaska Native shareholder or a lineal descendant of an Alaska Native

Awards are arranged alphabetically below their administering organizations

shareholder with ties to the Calista region. **Criteria:** Recipient will be selected based on scholarship application requirements.

Funds Avail.: $500-$1,500. **To Apply:** Applicants must complete the application form available online; must have the official transcript of records; must have a copy of birth certificate or Certificate of Indian Blood; must have a letter of acceptance from their college, university or vocational school; must provide an essay (up to 500 words) describing their educational and career goals, their reasons for attending school and what they hope to accomplish in the future using the knowledge gained from their educational experience. New applicants must include the Cost Information Sheet from the school they plan to attend, personal statement and complete reference form. Returning applicants are not required to submit a copy of birth certificate and reference form. **Deadline:** June 30. **Contact:** Applicants may e-mail all the requirements to scholarships@calistacorp.com.

2291 ■ Calvin Alumni Association

3201 Burton St. SE
Grand Rapids, MI 49546
Ph: (616) 526-6000
Fax: (616) 526-8551
Free: 800-688-0122
E-mail: info@calvin.edu
URL: www.calvin.edu

2292 ■ Calvin Alumni Association Arizona Central Chapter Scholarships *(Undergraduate/ Scholarship)*

Purpose: To build community among Calvin College alumni and friends; to provide opportunities for service and aspiring alumni to answer God's call in life and vocation. **Focus:** General studies. **Qualif.:** Applicants must be high school seniors who have applied to Calvin and live in central Arizona. **Criteria:** Recipients are selected based on academic performance and financial need.

Funds Avail.: $1,000. **To Apply:** Applicants must answer all questions on the application; must submit a transcript that shows the two most recent years of education; must attach a two written references. **Deadline:** February 2. **Contact:** Ken and Paula Wigboldy, 480-785-9852, fivewigs@cox.net.

2293 ■ Calvin Alumni Association-Black Alumni Chapter Scholarships *(Undergraduate/ Scholarship)*

Purpose: To build community among Calvin College alumni and friends; to provide opportunities for service and aspiring alumni to answer God's call in life and vocation. **Focus:** General studies. **Qualif.:** Applicants must be current Calvin College black students who have completed two semesters; must be in good standing; must be enrolled in a full-time status. **Criteria:** Recipients are selected based on academic performance and financial need.

Funds Avail.: No specific amount. **To Apply:** Applicants must submit a completed application form. **Deadline:** April 14.

2294 ■ Calvin Alumni Association British Columbia Scholarships *(Undergraduate/ Scholarship)*

Purpose: To build community among Calvin College alumni and friends; to provide opportunities for service and aspiring alumni to answer God's call in life and vocation. **Focus:** General studies. **Qualif.:** Applicants must be enrolled as freshmen students. **Criteria:** Recipients are selected based on Christian character and personal involvement in life of their community, desire for a Christian higher education, evidence of leadership, volunteerism and service to the Community.

Funds Avail.: $500. **Number Awarded:** 1. **To Apply:** Applicants must submit a completed application form. **Deadline:** February 2. **Contact:** Elaine Smit, 604-271-0283, elaine_smit@hotmail.com.

2295 ■ Calvin Alumni Association California-Bay Area Scholarships *(Undergraduate/ Scholarship)*

Purpose: To build community among Calvin College alumni and friends; to provide opportunities for service and aspiring alumni to answer God's call in life and vocation. **Focus:** General studies. **Qualif.:** Applicants must be current high school seniors; must live in the LA/Inland Empire Chapter area; must have a minimum GPA of 3.0. **Criteria:** Recipients are selected based on academic performance and financial need.

Funds Avail.: No specific amount. **To Apply:** Applicants must submit a completed application form. **Contact:** 526-461-1489.

2296 ■ Calvin Alumni Association Colorado Chapter Scholarships *(Undergraduate/ Scholarship)*

Purpose: To build community among Calvin College alumni and friends; to provide opportunities for service and aspiring alumni to answer God's call in life and vocation. **Focus:** General studies. **Qualif.:** Applicants must be students who are in good standing, leader in the church community and will continue attributes at Calvin College. **Criteria:** Recipients are selected based on academic standing.

Funds Avail.: $1,000. **Number Awarded:** 7. **To Apply:** Applicants must submit a completed application form; must submit a typed essay, completed evaluation/Letter from Youth Pastor/Minister; completed evaluation/Letter from High School Teacher/Counselor High School Transcript and signature of applicant. **Deadline:** February 2. **Contact:** Ernie Krauth or e-mail at ernie.krauth@gmail.com.

2297 ■ Calvin Alumni Association Florida-Gulf Coast Scholarships *(Undergraduate/Scholarship)*

Purpose: To build community among Calvin College alumni and friends; to provide opportunities for service and inspiring alumni to answer God's call in life and vocation. **Focus:** General studies. **Qualif.:** Applicants must be first year students from the Gulf Coast Florida; must live within the Gulf Coast Chapter area. **Criteria:** Recipients are selected based on academic performance and community involvement.

Funds Avail.: No stated amount. **To Apply:** Applicants must submit a completed application form. **Deadline:** February 2. **Contact:** Max Vreugdenhil, 941-794-3016, vreugdenhil@verizon.net.

2298 ■ Calvin Alumni Association-Illinois Scholarships *(Undergraduate/Scholarship)*

Purpose: To build community among Calvin College alumni and friends; to provide opportunities for service and inspiring alumni to answer God's call in life and vocation. **Focus:** General studies. **Qualif.:** Applicants must be first year

Awards are arranged alphabetically below their administering organizations

students from the Chicagoland Areas. **Criteria:** Recipients are selected based on scholastic achievement, commitment in the areas of leadership, volunteerism and service to the community.

Funds Avail.: $1,000. **To Apply:** Applicants must submit a completed application form; two completed recommendation forms; must submit a completed recommendation from their school Principal or Counselor; must submit an official high school transcript. **Deadline:** February 2. **Contact:** Susan Anderson, 630-462-0406, essengee@juno.com.

2299 ■ Calvin Alumni Association-Iowa/Pella Scholarships *(Undergraduate/Scholarship)*

Purpose: To build community among Calvin College alumni and friends; to provide opportunities for service and inspiring alumni to answer God's call in life and vocation. **Focus:** General studies. **Qualif.:** Applicants must be first year students entering Calvin College and students living within the Pella Chapter area are eligible to apply. **Criteria:** Recipients are selected based on GPA, financial need, recommendations and questions about goals and character.

Funds Avail.: No stated amount. **Number Awarded:** Varies. **To Apply:** Applicants must submit a completed application form, academic recommendation form and character recommendation form. **Deadline:** February 2. **Contact:** Jon Kuyers, jkuy05@iowatelecom.net.

2300 ■ Calvin Alumni Association-Maryland/ Baltimore Scholarships *(Undergraduate/ Scholarship)*

Purpose: To build community among Calvin College alumni and friends; to provide opportunities for service and inspiring alumni to answer God's call in life and vocation. **Focus:** General studies. **Qualif.:** Applicants must be first year students entering Calvin College. **Criteria:** Recipients are selected based on the record of volunteer activity or service in church, community, school or elsewhere.

Funds Avail.: No specific amount. **To Apply:** Applicants must submit a completed application form and three recommendations from non-relatives. **Deadline:** February 2. **Contact:** Brandon Hunt, 209-401-3331, b.l.hunt@gmail.com.

2301 ■ Calvin Alumni Association-Michigan Lakeshore Scholarships *(Undergraduate/ Scholarship)*

Purpose: To build a community among Calvin College alumni and friends; to provide opportunities for service and inspiring alumni to answer God's call in life and vocation. **Focus:** General studies. **Qualif.:** Applicants must be first year students entering Calvin College; must attend a high school on Ottawa, Muskegon or Allegan Counties. **Criteria:** Recipients are selected based on the faith commitment in the areas of leadership, volunteerism and service to the community.

Funds Avail.: $1,000. **To Apply:** Applicants must submit a completed application form, short essay, transcript of records and two reference letters. **Deadline:** February 2. **Contact:** Questions can be addressed to Peter Westra at 616-283-3370 or e-mail peter.j.westra@jci.com.

2302 ■ Calvin Alumni Association-Michigan, Lansing Scholarships *(Undergraduate/ Scholarship)*

Purpose: To build community among Calvin College alumni and friends; to provide opportunities for service; and to inspire alumni to answer God's call in life and vocation.

Focus: General studies. **Qualif.:** Applicants must be first year students entering Calvin College; must have at least 2.5 GPA or better; must live in Mid-Michigan Chapter area. **Criteria:** Recipients are selected based on record of volunteer activities in church, community or school, GPA and written references.

Funds Avail.: $1,000. **Number Awarded:** Varies. **To Apply:** Applicants must submit a completed application form and two written references. **Deadline:** February 2. **Contact:** Submissions should be forwarded to Jane HanderHaagen, 4789 Ardmore Ave., Okemos, MI 48864 or e-mail jvanderh@sbcglobal.net.

2303 ■ Calvin Alumni Association-New Jersey Scholarships *(Undergraduate/Scholarship)*

Purpose: To build a community among Calvin College alumni and friends; to provide opportunities for service and inspiring alumni to answer God's call in life and vocation. **Focus:** General studies. **Qualif.:** Applicants must be students planning to attend Calvin for the first time; must be from local area (New Jersey or New York City metro area). **Criteria:** Recipients are selected based on academic performance and not yet receiving other academic scholarships from Calvin or other sources. Consideration will be given to applicants who have demonstrated a Christian service, personal characters and professional promise.

Funds Avail.: $1,000. **Number Awarded:** Varies. **To Apply:** Applicants must submit a completed application, recommendation form and a high school transcript. **Deadline:** February 2. **Contact:** Jackie Streelman, 7 Coombs Ln., Midland Park, NJ 07432-1200; Phone: 201-444-0844; E-mail: jdstreelman@alumni.calvin.edu.

2304 ■ Calvin Alumni Association-New York, Rochester Scholarships *(Undergraduate/ Scholarship)*

Purpose: To build community among Calvin College alumni and friends; to provide opportunities for service and inspiring alumni to answer God's call in life and vocation. **Focus:** General studies. **Qualif.:** Applicants must be first year Calvin students; must live in Rochester area. **Criteria:** Recipients are selected based on academic performance, Christian character and service and curricular activities.

Funds Avail.: $250-$750. **Number Awarded:** Varies. **To Apply:** Applicants must submit a completed application form, completed references from Pastor/Youth Leader and Teacher/Counselor and transcript of grades. **Deadline:** February 2. **Contact:** Linda Cieminis, 585-671-8735, cieminis@fronntiernet.net.

2305 ■ Calvin Alumni Association-South Florida Scholarships *(Undergraduate/ Scholarship)*

Purpose: To build community among Calvin College alumni and friends; to provide opportunities for service and inspiring alumni to answer God's call in life and vocation. **Focus:** General studies. **Qualif.:** Applicants must be first year students entering Calvin college; students from Palm Beach and surrounding counties are eligible. **Criteria:** Recipients are selected based on GPA, Christian commitment, character, participation in extracurricular school activities, participation in church and community activities.

Funds Avail.: $1,000 to $1,500. **Number Awarded:** Varies. **To Apply:** Applicants must submit a completed application form. **Deadline:** February 2. **Contact:** Applications should be submitted to Phil Wierenga, 10811 Cambay

Awards are arranged alphabetically below their administering organizations

Cir., Boynton Beach, FL 33437; Phone: 561-364-0471; E-mail: wierengap@bellsouth.net.

2306 ■ Calvin Alumni Association-South Florida Sophomore Scholarships
(Undergraduate/Scholarship)

Purpose: To build community among Calvin College alumni and friends; to provide opportunities for service and inspiring alumni to answer God's call in life and vocation. **Focus:** General studies. **Qualif.:** Applicants must be students from Palm Beach and surrounding counties who will be sophomores at Calvin; must have an accumulated GPA of at least 2.0. **Criteria:** Recipients are selected based on academic performance.

Funds Avail.: $500. **To Apply:** Applicants must submit a completed application form; must write a brief letter of application including name, local Florida address, majors and a copy of the most current Calvin transcript. **Deadline:** February 2. **Contact:** Phil Wierenga, wierengap@bellsouth.net.

2307 ■ Calvin Alumni Association-Southeast Michigan Scholarships *(Undergraduate/Scholarship)*

Purpose: To build community among Calvin College alumni and friends; to provide opportunities for service and inspiring alumni to answer God's call in life and vocation. **Focus:** General studies. **Qualif.:** Applicants must be first year students entering Calvin College; must living in Southeast Michigan Chapter area (generally defined as zip codes 48000-48399). **Criteria:** Recipients are selected based on academic performance.

Funds Avail.: $1,000. **Number Awarded:** Varies. **To Apply:** Applicants must submit a completed application form and two written references. **Deadline:** February 2. **Contact:** Materials must be submitted to Ross Weener, 1126 Nielsen Ct., Apt. 2, Ann Arbor, MI 48105; Phone: 734-945-0683; E-mail: rossanddebweener@yahoo.com.

2308 ■ Calvin Alumni Association-Southeastern Wisconsin Scholarships *(Undergraduate/Scholarship)*

Purpose: To build community among Calvin College alumni and friends; to provide opportunities for service and inspiring alumni to answer God's call in life and vocation. **Focus:** General studies. **Qualif.:** Applicants must be undergraduate college students who have completed at least two years of undergraduate education; must be residents of Dodge, Jefferson, Kenosha, Milwaukee, Ozaukee, Racine, Walworth, Washington, or Waukesha County, Wisconsin who attended a church in one of those counties; must intend to attend Calvin College during the next academic year. **Criteria:** Recipients are selected based on cumulative GPA, financial need, Christian commitment and histories of extra-academic church and/or community activities.

Funds Avail.: No stated amount. **To Apply:** Applicants must submit a complete application form, a complete "Statement of Ways and Means" and a certified copy of transcript from each of the colleges attended. **Deadline:** February 2. **Contact:** Questions can be forwarded to Victor Plantinga at vplantinga@gmail.com.

2309 ■ Calvin Alumni Association Southern California Chapter Scholarships
(Undergraduate/Scholarship)

Purpose: To build community among Calvin College alumni and friends; to provide opportunities for service and aspiring alumni to answer God's call in life and vocation. **Focus:** General studies. **Qualif.:** Applicants must be current high school senior students; must live within the Southern California Chapter area; must have a GPA of 3.0. **Criteria:** Recipients are selected based on the consistent pattern of volunteer service, character and scholastic ability.

Funds Avail.: $1,000. **Number Awarded:** 1. **To Apply:** Applicants must submit a completed application form. **Contact:** Christine Koontz, wickersnapper@prodigy.net.

2310 ■ Calvin Alumni Association-Southwest Michigan, Kalamazoo Scholarships
(Undergraduate/Scholarship)

Purpose: To build community among Calvin College alumni and friends; to provide opportunities for service and inspiring alumni to answer God's call in life and vocation. **Focus:** General studies. **Qualif.:** Applicants must be high school senior students who live in Southwest Michigan Chapter area. **Criteria:** Recipients are selected based on answers to application questions and involvement in extra-curricular activities. Preference will be given to students who have not yet received a Calvin National Merit or Presidential Scholarship.

Funds Avail.: No stated amount. **To Apply:** Applicants must submit a completed application form including activities and awards. **Deadline:** February 2. **Contact:** Completed applications must be submitted to Mary Jane Baylor, 1340 Cadet Ln., Kalamazoo, MI 49009; Phone: 269-370-5043; E-mail: rebaylor1@aol.com.

2311 ■ Calvin Alumni Association-Washington, D.C. Scholarships *(Undergraduate/Scholarship)*

Purpose: To build community among Calvin College alumni and friends; to provide opportunities for service and inspiring alumni to answer God's call in life and vocation. **Focus:** General studies. **Qualif.:** Applicants must be incoming first year or transfer Calvin students in the greater D.C./Baltimore area (approximately those living in the following zip code areas: 19900-21899, 22000-22599, 25400-25499 and 26700-26899) who will be entering Calvin. **Criteria:** Recipients are selected based on Christian commitment, scholastic achievement, personal character and professional promise.

Funds Avail.: No stated amount. **To Apply:** Applicants must complete the application form, three copies of recommendation form, high school transcript and a one-page copy of resume. **Deadline:** February 2. **Contact:** Brandon Hunt, 1840 Burke St. SE, Washington, DC 20003; Phone: 209-401-3331; E-mail: b.l.hunt@gmail.com.

2312 ■ Calvin Alumni Association-Washington, Lynden Scholarships *(Undergraduate/Scholarship)*

Purpose: To build community among Calvin College alumni and friends; to provide opportunities for service and inspiring alumni to answer God's call in life and vocation. **Focus:** General studies. **Qualif.:** Applicants must be students living within the Lynden Chapter area; must be high school seniors entering Calvin College with a minimum GPA of 2.50. **Criteria:** Recipients are selected based on demonstrated faith commitment in areas of leadership, volunteerism and service to the church, school and community.

Funds Avail.: $1,00. **Number Awarded:** 2. **To Apply:** Applicants must complete the application form. **Deadline:** February 2. **Contact:** Jacki Matter, 360-354-4315, matterdj@msn.com.

Awards are arranged alphabetically below their administering organizations

2313 ■ Calvin Alumni Association-Washington-Seattle/Tacoma Scholarships *(Undergraduate/Scholarship)*

Purpose: To build community among Calvin College alumni and friends; to provide opportunities for service and inspiring alumni to answer God's call in life and vocation. **Focus:** General studies. **Qualif.:** Applicants must be first year students including transferees entering Calvin and must living within the Seattle/Tacoma Chapter. **Criteria:** Recipients are selected based on academic promise, articulation of educational plans and reasons for attending Calvin College, Christian commitment and personal character and financial need. Preference will be given to students not receiving other academic scholarships from Calvin or other sources.

Funds Avail.: No stated amount. **To Apply:** Applicants must submit a completed application form, high school transcript, two letters of reference submitted in a sealed envelope. **Deadline:** February 2. **Contact:** Application form and supporting documents must be submitted to Brian Wolters, 9516 Palatine Ave. N, Seattle, WA 98103; Phone: 206-850-9031; E-mail: b_wolt@yahoo.com.

2314 ■ Camden County Bar Association (CCBA)
1040 N Kings Hwy., Ste. 201
Cherry Hill, NJ 08034
Ph: (856) 482-0620
Fax: (856) 482-0637
E-mail: info@camdencountybar.org
URL: www.camdencountybar.org

2315 ■ Benjamin Asbell Memorial Scholarships
(Undergraduate/Scholarship)

Purpose: To help law students defray the cost of law school tuition. **Focus:** Law; Law enforcement. **Qualif.:** For the first award, applicants must be day or evening students at the Rutgers-Camden School of Law, who are residents of South Jersey and must not be first-year students. Applicants must also demonstrate genuine financial need, scholastic ability and a history or desire to work in the areas of law enforcement and/or the administration of justice. For the second award, applicants must be students at any of the following law schools: Rutgers-Camden, Rutgers-Newark, Penn, Seton Hall, Temple, Villanova or Widener. **Criteria:** Selection will be based on the committee's criteria.

Funds Avail.: $1,000. **Number Awarded:** Two. **To Apply:** Interested applicants must visit the website to download an application form. **Deadline:** February 28.

2316 ■ Hon. Joseph W. Cowgill Memorial Scholarships *(Undergraduate/Scholarship)*

Purpose: To help law students defray the cost of law school tuition. **Focus:** Law. **Qualif.:** Applicants must be Rutgers-Camden School of Law students who are in the upper half of their class. Applicants must demonstrate genuine financial need as well as be a resident of Camden County. **Criteria:** Selection will be based on the committee's criteria.

Funds Avail.: $1,000. **To Apply:** Interested applicants must visit the website to download an application form. **Deadline:** February 28.

2317 ■ Hon. Ralph W.E. Donges Memorial Scholarships *(Undergraduate/Award)*

Purpose: To help law students defray the cost of law school tuition. **Focus:** Law. **Qualif.:** Applicants must be part-time, evening law students attending the following law schools: Rutgers-Camden, Rutgers-Newark, Penn, Seton, Hall, Temple, Villanova or Widener. Applicants must show a bona fide intention to practice law in Camden County. Applicants should also demonstrate genuine financial need as well as scholastic achievement. **Criteria:** Selection will be based on the committee's criteria.

Funds Avail.: $1,000. **To Apply:** Interested applicants must visit the website to download an application form. **Deadline:** February 28.

2318 ■ DuBois Brothers Scholarships
(Undergraduate/Scholarship)

Purpose: To help law students defray the cost of law school tuition. **Focus:** Law. **Qualif.:** Applicants must be students of any Delaware Valley law school. Applicants must show a bona fide intention to practice law in South Jersey as well as exhibit professionalism and high character in their personal and academic lives. Applicants must also demonstrate genuine financial need. **Criteria:** Selection will be based on the committee's criteria.

Funds Avail.: $1,000. **To Apply:** Interested applicants must visit the website to download an application form. **Deadline:** February 28.

2319 ■ George F. Kugler, Jr. Scholarships
(Undergraduate/Scholarship)

Purpose: To help law students defray the cost of law school tuition. **Focus:** Law. **Qualif.:** Applicants must be second or third-year students attending any New Jersey law school. Applicants must demonstrate genuine financial need as well as a history of and/or desire to work in public service law. **Criteria:** Selection will be based on the committee's criteria.

Funds Avail.: $1,000. **To Apply:** Interested applicants must visit the website to download an application form. **Deadline:** February 28.

2320 ■ Harold and Harriet Plum Memorial Scholarships *(Undergraduate/Scholarship)*

Purpose: To help law students defray the cost of law school tuition. **Focus:** Law. **Qualif.:** Applicants must be students of any accredited law school; must demonstrate scholastic achievement as well as genuine financial need. **Criteria:** Selection will be based on the committee's criteria.

Funds Avail.: $1,000. **To Apply:** Interested applicants must visit the website to download an application form. **Deadline:** February 28.

2321 ■ Louis C. Portella Memorial Scholarships
(Graduate/Scholarship)

Purpose: To help law students defray the cost of law school tuition. **Focus:** Law. **Qualif.:** Applicants must be second or third year full-time students at either Rutgers-Camden or Temple law schools who reside in and intend to practice law in Camden County; must be in good academic standing; must be active in both extracurricular and community activities. **Criteria:** Selection will be based on the committee's criteria.

Funds Avail.: $1,000. **To Apply:** Interested applicants must visit the website to download an application form. **Deadline:** February 28.

2322 ■ Hon. Rudolph J. Rossetti Memorial Scholarships *(Undergraduate/Award)*

Purpose: To help law students defray the cost of law school tuition. **Focus:** Law. **Qualif.:** Applicants must be students

Awards are arranged alphabetically below their administering organizations

attending any Delaware Valley law school. Applicants must demonstrate scholastic achievement and a genuine financial need. **Criteria:** Selection will be based on the committee's criteria.

Funds Avail.: $1,000. **To Apply:** Interested applicants must visit the website to download an application form. **Deadline:** February 28.

2323 ■ Ann S. Salsberg Scholarship Awards
(Undergraduate/Award, Scholarship)

Purpose: To award scholarship to young men and women who qualify for the honor. **Focus:** Paralegal studies. **Qualif.:** Applicants must be high school graduating seniors or high school graduates who are Camden City residents. **Criteria:** Selection will be based on the committee's criteria.

Funds Avail.: $2,000. **To Apply:** Interested applicants must submit the following: a one-page, typed and single spaced brief essay in which the applicants identifies plans they have for the future with regards to their possible pursuit of a legal career; recent transcript with a minimum 3.0 GPA (on a scale of 4.0=A); a provisional letter of acceptance to an accredited 4-year college or university, or any high school graduate currently enrolled in an accredited 4-year college or university; a disclosure of financial information revealing all sources of funding being received or being offered to the applicants including other scholarships, financial awards or other financial assistance. **Deadline:** May 1.

2324 ■ Jay A. Strassberg Memorial Scholarships *(Undergraduate/Scholarship)*

Purpose: To support law students or undergraduate students pursuing degrees in Journalism, Public Relations, Advertising, Communications, or Theater Arts. **Focus:** Law; Journalism; Public relations; Advertising. **Qualif.:** Applicants must be any Temple, Drexel or Rutgers University law students or undergraduate students majoring in the Journalism, Public Relations and Advertising Department of the School of Communications and Theater Arts who demonstrates both financial need and academic achievement. **Criteria:** Preference will be given to candidates from Camden County or the South Jersey area.

Funds Avail.: $1,000. **To Apply:** Interested applicants must submit the following: a brief letter from the applicants detailing their personal and educational background, work history, course of study and plans after graduation; current transcript of undergraduate courses including GPA; letter of recommendation submitted by a member of the Journalism, Public Relations and Advertising Department at Temple University; a disclosure of financial information revealing all sources of funding being received or being offered to the applicants. **Deadline:** March 31.

2325 ■ Daniel B. Toll Memorial Scholarships
(Undergraduate/Scholarship)

Purpose: To help law students defray the cost of law school tuition. **Focus:** Law. **Qualif.:** Applicants must be law students who are not in their final year of study; must be residents of South Jersey, preferably Camden County; must have demonstrated a commitment to the area in charitable, humanitarian and community service activities. **Criteria:** Selection will be based on the committee's criteria.

Funds Avail.: $1,000. **To Apply:** Interested students must visit the website to download an application form. **Deadline:** February 28.

2326 ■ William Tomar Memorial Scholarships
(Undergraduate/Scholarship)

Purpose: To help law students defray the cost of law school tuition. **Focus:** Law. **Qualif.:** Applicants must be incoming, full or part-time law students at Rutgers School of Law - Camden. Applicants should demonstrate genuine financial need and scholastic achievement from previous educational experiences. **Criteria:** Selection will be based on the committee's criteria.

Funds Avail.: $1,000. **To Apply:** Interested students must visit the website to download an application form. An official acceptance letter from Rutgers must be submitted together with the application form. **Deadline:** February 28.

2327 ■ Bruce A. Wallace Memorial Scholarships *(Undergraduate/Scholarship)*

Purpose: To help law students defray the cost of law school tuition. **Focus:** Law. **Qualif.:** Applicants must be third-year students at Rutgers-Camden School of Law; must be from the South Jersey area; must be in the upper half of their class; must demonstrate genuine financial need. **Criteria:** Selection will be based on the committee's criteria.

Funds Avail.: $1,000. **To Apply:** Interested applicants must visit the website to download an application form. **Deadline:** January 31.

2328 ■ Camden County College
200 N Broadway
Camden, NJ 08102-1185
Ph: (856) 338-1817
URL: www.camdencc.edu

2329 ■ Diane Basilone-Engle Memorial Scholarships *(Undergraduate/Scholarship)*

Purpose: To provide opportunity to qualified students to pursue an education at CCC. **Focus:** Theater arts; Secretarial sciences; Veterinary science and medicine; Education. **Qualif.:** Applicants must be students who want to continue their degree or certificate in theater, secretariat science, veterinary science or education. **Criteria:** Recipients are chosen by the College's Scholarship Selection Committee and/or recommendation by department faculty. Preference will be given to applicants who can submit a complete application.

Funds Avail.: No specific amount. **To Apply:** Applicants must submit one recommendation from a faculty member or administrator at Camden County College. Application forms are available online and must be sent to Camden County College Foundation, PO Box 200, College Dr., Blackwood, NJ 08012. **Deadline:** February 16.

2330 ■ Scott Bonners Memorial Scholarships
(Undergraduate/Scholarship)

Purpose: To provide financial assistance to individuals who want to continue their studies at CCC. **Focus:** General studies. **Qualif.:** Applicant must be full time, single parent with financial need; must have a minimum of GPA 3.0. **Criteria:** Recipients are selected based on financial need and academic standing.

Funds Avail.: No specific amount. **To Apply:** Applicant must submit one recommendation from a faculty member or administrator at Camden County College. Application forms are available online. **Deadline:** February 16. **Contact:** Application form and other supporting documents

Awards are arranged alphabetically below their administering organizations

must be sent to Camden County College Foundation, PO Box 200, College Dr., Blackwood, NJ 08012.

2331 ■ Camden County College Employee Memorial Scholarships (Undergraduate/Scholarship)

Purpose: To provide support to qualified individuals who want to pursue an education at CCC. **Focus:** General studies. **Qualif.:** Applicants must have a cumulative GPA of 3.0. **Criteria:** Recipients are chosen by the College's Scholarship Selection Committee and/or recommendation by department faculty.

Funds Avail.: No specific amount. **To Apply:** Applicants must submit one recommendation from a faculty member or administrator at Camden County College. Application forms are available online. **Deadline:** February 16. **Contact:** Application form and other supporting documents must be sent to Camden County College Foundation, PO Box 200, College Dr., Blackwood, NJ 08012.

2332 ■ Camden County College Foundation Scholarships (Undergraduate/Scholarship)

Purpose: To provide support to the outstanding individuals who want to pursue higher education and career goals at CCC. **Focus:** General studies. **Qualif.:** Applicants must be full-time or part-time students returning to CCC; must have a minimum of 3.0 GPA; must have completed 12 college credits. **Criteria:** Recipients are chosen by the College's Scholarship Selection Committee and/ or by recommendation from department faculty.

Funds Avail.: No specific amount. **Number Awarded:** 2. **To Apply:** Applicants must submit one recommendation from a faculty member or administrator at Camden County College. Application forms are available online. **Deadline:** February 16. **Contact:** Application form and other supporting documents must be sent to Camden County College Foundation, PO Box 200, College Dr., Blackwood, NJ 08012.

2333 ■ Camden County Retired Educators Association Scholarships (Undergraduate/Scholarship)

Purpose: To provide financial assistance to qualified individuals who wants to pursue an education at CCC. **Focus:** General studies. **Qualif.:** Applicants must be full time education students returning to CCC; and must have 3.0 GPA. **Criteria:** Recipients are chosen by the College's Scholarship Selection Committee and/or recommendation by department faculty.

Funds Avail.: No specific amount. **Number Awarded:** 2. **To Apply:** Applicants must submit one recommendation from a faculty member or administrator at Camden County College. Application forms are available online. **Deadline:** February 16. **Contact:** Application form and other supporting documents must be sent to Camden County College Foundation, PO Box 200, College Dr., Blackwood, NJ 08012.

2334 ■ James & Maryetta Cook Scholarships (Undergraduate/Scholarship)

Purpose: To encourage a widowed or divorced non-traditional student to continue their studies at CCC. **Focus:** General studies. **Qualif.:** Applicants must be widowed or divorced non-traditional students and returning to CCC; must demonstrate a motivation to succeed despite personal or professional obstacles; must have a minimum GPA of

3.0. **Criteria:** Recipients are chosen by the College's Scholarship Selection Committee and/or recommendation by department faculty and based on completed application.

Funds Avail.: No specific amount. **To Apply:** Applicants must submit one recommendation from a faculty member or administrator at Camden County College. Application forms are available online and must be sent to Camden County College Foundation, PO Box 200, College Dr., Blackwood, NJ 08012. **Deadline:** February 16.

2335 ■ Garden State Rotary Club of Cherry Hill Scholarships (Undergraduate/Scholarship)

Purpose: To provide financial support to qualified individuals who wants to pursue their studies. **Focus:** General studies. **Qualif.:** Applicants must have a minimum GPA of 3.0. **Criteria:** Recipients are chosen by the College's Scholarship Selection Committee and/or recommendation by department faculty. Preference will be given to applicants who can complete the application form and other required materials.

Funds Avail.: No specific amount. **To Apply:** Applicants must submit one recommendation from a faculty member or administrator at Camden County College. Application forms are available online and must be sent to Camden County College Foundation, PO Box 200, College Dr., Blackwood, NJ 08012. **Deadline:** February 16.

2336 ■ Dr. Martin Luther King & Coretta Scott King Student Leadership Scholarships (Undergraduate/Scholarship)

Purpose: To provide financial assistance to qualified individuals who want to pursue their career. **Focus:** General studies. **Qualif.:** Applicants must have completed minimum of 12 college credits; must have a cumulative GPA of 3.0. **Criteria:** Recipients are chosen by the College's Scholarship Selection Committee and/or recommendation by department faculty.

Funds Avail.: No specific amount. **To Apply:** Applicants must submit one recommendation from a faculty member or administrator at Camden County College. Application forms are available online. **Deadline:** February 16. **Contact:** Application form and other supporting documents must be sent to Camden County College Foundation, PO Box 200, College Dr., Blackwood, NJ 08012.

2337 ■ Carolyn Murray Memorial Scholarships (Undergraduate/Scholarship)

Purpose: To encourage individuals to pursue an education at CCC. **Focus:** General studies. **Qualif.:** Applicants must be students returning to CCC; must have a minimum GPA of 3.0. **Criteria:** Recipients are chosen by the College's Scholarship Selection Committee and/or recommendation by department faculty.

Funds Avail.: No specific amount. **To Apply:** Applicants must submit one recommendation from a faculty member or administrator at Camden County College. Application forms are available online and must be sent to Camden County College Foundation, PO Box 200, College Dr., Blackwood, NJ 08012. **Deadline:** February 16.

2338 ■ H.N. Neal Memorial Scholarships (Undergraduate/Scholarship)

Purpose: To provide financial support to male students who wants to pursue an education at CCC. **Focus:** General studies. **Qualif.:** Applicants must be male students with a minimum cumulative GPA of 3.0. **Criteria:** Preference will

Awards are arranged alphabetically below their administering organizations

be given to male students who are attending classes at the Camden Campus, or residents of Camden.

Funds Avail.: No specific amount. **To Apply:** Applicants must submit one recommendation from a faculty member or administrator at Camden County College. Application forms are available online and must be sent to Camden County College Foundation, PO Box 200, College Dr., Blackwood, NJ 08012. **Deadline:** February 16.

2339 ■ Jerrothia Allenfonzo Riggs & Anna & Dorothy Mae Barnes Scholarships
(Undergraduate/Scholarship)

Purpose: To encourage African-American students to pursue their education. **Focus:** General studies. **Qualif.:** Applicants must be an African-American female; must be a first-generation high school graduate and resident of Camden City; must have a minimum GPA of 3.0. **Criteria:** Preference will be given to an adoptee and/or foster child.

Funds Avail.: No specific amount. **To Apply:** Applicants must submit one recommendation from a faculty member or administrator at Camden County College. Application forms are available online and must be sent to Camden County College Foundation, PO Box 200, College Dr., Blackwood, NJ 08012. **Deadline:** February 16.

2340 ■ Madlyn D. Thompson Memorial Scholarships *(Undergraduate/Scholarship)*

Purpose: To provide financial assistance to qualified individuals who want to continue their studies at CCC. **Focus:** General studies. **Qualif.:** Applicants must be a single female parent returning to CCC; must have completed at least 30 credits toward degree and be residents of Camden; must have a minimum GPA of 3.0. **Criteria:** Preference is given to a single, female parent.

Funds Avail.: No specific amount. **To Apply:** Applicants must submit one recommendation from a faculty member or administrator at Camden County College. Application forms are available online and must be sent to Camden County College Foundation, PO Box 200, College Dr., Blackwood, NJ 08012. **Deadline:** February 16.

2341 ■ Mercedes Laurie Wade Scholarships
(Undergraduate/Scholarship)

Purpose: To provide financial assistance to qualified individuals. **Focus:** General studies. **Qualif.:** Applicants must be female athletes, must be currently enrolled full time and with financial need; must have a minimum GPA of 2.5. **Criteria:** Applicants are selected based on application and financial need.

Funds Avail.: No specific amount. **To Apply:** Applicants must submit one recommendation from a faculty member or administrator at Camden County College. Application forms are available online and must be sent to Camden County College Foundation, PO Box 200, College Dr., Blackwood, NJ 08012. **Deadline:** February 16.

2342 ■ Watsontown Volunteer Fire Company Scholarships *(Undergraduate/Scholarship)*

Purpose: To provide financial assistance to individuals who want to pursue an education at CCC. **Focus:** General studies. **Qualif.:** Applicants must be students who want to return to CCC; must have a minimum cumulative GPA 3.0. **Criteria:** Recipients are selected based on financial need and academic standing.

Funds Avail.: No specific amount. **Number Awarded:** 4. **To Apply:** Applicants must submit one recommendation

from a faculty member or administrator at Camden County College. Application forms are available online. **Deadline:** February 16. **Contact:** Application form and other supporting documents must be sent to Camden County College Foundation, PO Box 200, College Dr., Blackwood, NJ 08012.

2343 ■ Cameco Corp.
2121-11th St. W
Saskatoon, SK, Canada S7M 1J3
Ph: (306) 956-6200
Fax: (306) 956-6201
E-mail: info@cameco.com
URL: www.cameco.com

2344 ■ Cameco Corporation Scholarships in the Geological Sciences - Continuing Students
(Undergraduate/Scholarship)

Purpose: To support students who want to pursue their career in geological sciences. **Focus:** Geology. **Qualif.:** Applicants must be full-time students who are Canadian citizens entering their second year of university study and pursuing Bachelor of Science degrees; must have declared majors in the geological sciences; must be registered in 200 level courses related to their majors; must have a sessional weighted average of at least 70% for all credit units attempted in the last regular session. **Criteria:** Recipient will be selected based on scholarship application form and requirements.

Funds Avail.: No specific amount. **Number Awarded:** 2. **To Apply:** Application form can be obtained from: Continuing Students, Student Central, University of Saskatchewan, 105 Administration Place, Saskatoon, SK S7N 5A2. Phone: 306-966-1212. **Deadline:** June 1. **Contact:** askus@usask.ca.

2345 ■ Cameco Corporation Scholarships in the Geological Sciences - Entering Students
(Undergraduate/Scholarship)

Purpose: To support students who want to pursue their career in geological sciences. **Focus:** Geology. **Qualif.:** Applicants must be full-time students who are Canadian citizens pursuing Bachelor of Science degrees and are entering their first year of university study and are registered in specified courses as outlined in guidelines. **Criteria:** Recipient will be selected based on scholarship application form and requirements.

Funds Avail.: No specific amount. **Number Awarded:** 2. **To Apply:** Application form can be obtained from: Entering Students, Recruitment and Admissions, University of Saskatchewan, 105 Administration Place, Saskatoon, SK S7N 5A2. **Deadline:** February 15. **Contact:** Phone: 306-966-5788; Email: admissions@usask.ca.

2346 ■ Cameco Northern Scholarships - Technical Institute *(Undergraduate/Scholarship)*

Purpose: To provide financial assistance to deserving individuals in northern Saskatchewan who want to pursue their education. **Focus:** General studies. **Qualif.:** Applicant must be a resident of northern Saskatchewan or who lived in the north for a minimum of five years; must be enrolled as a full-time student in a program of study leading to certification from a recognized technical institute located in Saskatchewan. **Criteria:** Scholarship application will be reviewed by the selection committee which recommends candidates to Cameco.

Awards are arranged alphabetically below their administering organizations

Funds Avail.: $5,000. **Number Awarded:** 3. **To Apply:** Applicant must complete the scholarship application available online; must submit a letter that includes the following: (1) a statement regarding the applicant's academic plans; (2) a list of the courses the applicant plans to take; (3) the name of the institution at which the applicant plans to enroll (or is enrolled); (4) the applicant's career objectives; (5) reference to the applicant's academic, social and athletic interests; (6) the applicant's goals for the future. Application form and other supporting documents must be sent to Cameco Corporation, Northern Affairs Office, PO Box 1049, La Ronge, SK SOJ 1LO. **Deadline:** June 30. **Contact:** Betty Kopeck, 306-425-4144.

2347 ■ Cameco Northern Scholarships - University *(Undergraduate/Scholarship)*

Purpose: To provide financial assistance to deserving individuals in north Saskatchewan who want to pursue their education. **Focus:** General studies. **Qualif.:** Applicant must be a resident of Northern Saskatchewan or who lived in the north for a minimum of five years; must be enrolled as a full-time student in a program of study leading to a degree from a Saskatchewan university, or from another Canadian university in situations where the student's program of study is not available in Saskatchewan. **Criteria:** Scholarship application will be reviewed by the selection committee which recommends candidates to Cameco.

Funds Avail.: $7,500. **To Apply:** Applicant must complete the scholarship application available online; must submit a letter that includes the following: (1) a statement regarding the applicant's academic plans; (2) a list of the courses the applicant plans to take; (3) the name of the institution at which the applicant plans to enroll (or is enrolled); (4) the applicant's career objectives; (5) reference to the applicant's academic, social and athletic interests; (6) the applicant's goals for the future. Application form and other supporting documents must be sent to Cameco Corporation, Northern Affairs Office, PO Box 1049, La Ronge, SK SOJ 1LO. **Deadline:** June 30. **Contact:** Betty Kopeck, 306-425-4144.

2348 ■ Bernard Michel Scholarships *(Undergraduate/Scholarship)*

Purpose: To provide financial support to a Saskatchewan aboriginal student who wants to pursue their studies. **Focus:** Engineering; Liberal arts. **Qualif.:** Applicants must be Saskatchewan aboriginal students entering their first or second year of study within the Colleges of Engineering, Commerce or Arts and Science at the University of Saskatchewan. **Criteria:** Recipient will be selected based on scholarship application form and requirements.

Funds Avail.: $5,000. **To Apply:** Applicant must complete the application form available online and must be sent to University of Saskatchewan, 105 Administration Place, Saskatoon, SK S7N 5A2. **Deadline:** June 1. **Contact:** 306-966-6748; askus@usask.ca.

2349 ■ Campus Compact
45 Temple Pl.
Boston, MA 02111
Ph: (617) 357-1881
Fax: (617) 357-1889
URL: www.compact.org

2350 ■ Frank Newman Leadership Awards *(Undergraduate/Scholarship)*

Purpose: To provide financial support to students pursuing college. **Focus:** General studies. **Qualif.:** Applicants must

be undergraduate students at Campus Compact member colleges and universities. **Criteria:** Awards are given based on financial need and leadership.

Funds Avail.: $5,000. **Number Awarded:** 2. **To Apply:** Applicants must complete the online application form; prepare a student-written essay; letter of nomination from applicant's president/chancellor; mentoring plan; and a recent head-and-shoulder photo. **Contact:** awards@compact.org.

2351 ■ Campus Discovery
c/o WiseChoice Brands, LLC
Alexandria, VA 22313
URL: www.campusdiscovery.com

2352 ■ Campus Discovery Scholarships *(Graduate, Undergraduate/Scholarship)*

Purpose: To support students in their educational pursuits. **Focus:** General studies. **Qualif.:** Applicant must be a U.S. citizen or legal resident; enrolled full-time at a four-year college/university or a college graduate with a bachelor's degree and has completed at least one full year at one of the listed schools (list available at website). **Criteria:** Selection is based on writing ability (25%), wisdom (25%), originality (25%), and overall excellence (25%).

Funds Avail.: $2,500. **Number Awarded:** 1. **To Apply:** Applicants must submit a complete survey, including an answer to the required open-ended question online. **Deadline:** July 31.

2353 ■ Canada West Equipment Dealers Association
2435 Pegasus Rd. NE
Calgary, AB, Canada T2E 8C3
Ph: (403) 250-7581
Fax: (403) 291-5138

2354 ■ CWEDA Scholarship Program *(Undergraduate/Scholarship)*

Purpose: To help CWEDA employees further their education. **Focus:** General studies. **Qualif.:** Applicants must be current members of CWEDA who are enrolled full-time in an approved course of study. **Criteria:** Applicants will be selected based on submitted materials.

Funds Avail.: $1,000. **To Apply:** Applicants must visit the CWEDA's website for further information. **Deadline:** April 1.

2355 ■ Canadian Anesthesiologists' Society (CAS)
1 Eglinton Ave. E, Ste. 208
Toronto, ON, Canada M4P 3A1
Ph: (416) 480-0602
Fax: (416) 480-0320
E-mail: anesthesia@cas.ca
URL: www.cas.ca

2356 ■ Baxter Corporation Canadian Research Awards in Anesthesia *(Professional development/Award)*

Purpose: To support anesthesia-related research in Canada. **Focus:** Anesthesiology. **Qualif.:** Applicants must

Awards are arranged alphabetically below their administering organizations

be associate/active members of CAS who propose to carry out an original project and are eligible for the New Investigator Awards. **Criteria:** Award winner is chosen based on the scientific merit, importance, and feasibility of the project.

Funds Avail.: $20,000. **To Apply:** Application forms are available online. Applicants must submit documentation of institutional approval of human and/or animal experimentation. **Deadline:** January 8. **Contact:** For further information, applicants may send an e-mail at research@cas.ca.

2357 ■ Canadian Anesthesiologists' Society Research Awards (Professional development/ Award)

Purpose: To support anesthesia-related research in Canada. **Focus:** Anesthesiology. **Qualif.:** Applicants must be associate/active members of CAS who propose to carry out an original project and are eligible for the New Investigator Awards. **Criteria:** Award winner is chosen based on the scientific merit, importance, and feasibility of the project.

Funds Avail.: $30,000. **To Apply:** Application forms are available online. Applicants must submit documentation of institutional approval of human and/or animal experimentation. **Deadline:** January 8. **Contact:** For further information, applicants may send an e-mail at research@cas.ca.

2358 ■ CAS/GE Healthcare Canada Inc. Research Awards (Professional development/ Award)

Purpose: To provide support for infrastructure costs related to a specific research project or program. **Focus:** Medical research. **Qualif.:** Nominees must be associate or active members of the society who are eligible for an award in the field of perioperative imaging related to anesthesia and/or critical care. **Criteria:** Award winner is chosen based on scientific merit, importance, and feasibility of the project.

Funds Avail.: $30,000. **To Apply:** Application forms are available online. Applicants must submit documentation of institutional approval of human and or animal experimentation. **Deadline:** January 8. **Contact:** For further information, applicants may send an e-mail at research@cas.ca.

2359 ■ CAS/Vitaid-LMA Residents' Research Grant Competition (Professional development/ Award)

Purpose: To support anesthesia-related research performed by a resident in Canada. **Focus:** Anesthesiology. **Qualif.:** Nominees must be resident physicians who are in good standing at a Canadian university department of anesthesia. Nominees must be members of the CAS and must propose to carry out an original project within Canada. **Criteria:** Award winner is chosen based on scientific merit, importance, and feasibility of the project.

Funds Avail.: $7,500. **To Apply:** Application forms are available online. Applicants must submit a curriculum vitae; letter from the supervisor that specifies the extent to which the applicant will contribute towards the research project; letter from the residency program director. **Deadline:** January 8. **Contact:** For further information, applicants may send an e-mail at research@cas.ca.

2360 ■ David S. Sheridan Canadian Research Awards (Professional development/Award)

Purpose: To support anesthesia-related research in Canada. **Focus:** Anesthesiology. **Qualif.:** Applicants must

be associate/active members of CAS who propose to carry out an original project and are eligible for the New Investigator Awards. **Criteria:** Award winner is chosen based on the scientific merit, importance, and feasibility of the project.

Funds Avail.: $10,000. **To Apply:** Applicants must fill up the application forms available online. Applicants must submit documentation of institutional approval of human and/or animal experimentation. **Deadline:** January 8.

2361 ■ Smiths Medical Canada Ltd. Research Awards (Professional development/Award)

Purpose: To support pain and regional anesthesia-related research in Canada. **Focus:** Anesthesiology. **Qualif.:** Applicants must be associate or active members of the society who are eligible for a subspecialty award. **Criteria:** Award winner is chosen based on the scientific merit, importance, and feasibility of the research.

Funds Avail.: $10,000. **To Apply:** Applicants must fill out the application forms available online. Applicants must submit documentation of institutional approval of human and/or animal experimentation.

2362 ■ Canadian Association of Black Lawyers (CABL)
20 Toronto St., Ste. 300
Toronto, ON, Canada M5C 2B8
E-mail: info@cabl.ca
URL: www.cabl.ca

2363 ■ Lucie and Thornton Blackburn Scholarships (Undergraduate/Scholarship)

Purpose: To financially assist minority students pursuing education at a Canadian law school. **Focus:** Law. **Qualif.:** Applicants must be minority students entering their second year of study in an LLB or JD program at a Canadian law school. **Criteria:** Applicants will be selected based on financial need.

Funds Avail.: $5,000. **To Apply:** Applicants must submit a completed application form, resume and a two-page essay (approximately 750-1000 words) discussing legal issues. **Deadline:** September.

2364 ■ Canadian Association of Broadcasters (CAB)
PO Box 627, Sta. B
Ottawa, ON, Canada K1P 5S2
Ph: (613) 233-4035
Fax: (613) 233-6961
E-mail: cab@cab-acr.ca
URL: www.cab-acr.ca

2365 ■ BBM Canada Scholarships (Undergraduate/Scholarship)

Purpose: To provide support to qualified individuals who want to pursue their career in broadcasting. **Focus:** Broadcasting. **Qualif.:** Applicant must be enrolled in a graduate studies program, or be in the final year of an honors degree with the intention of entering a graduate program, anywhere in Canada. **Criteria:** Recipient will be selected based on the demonstrated achievement in and knowledge of statistical and/or quantitative research methodology in a course of study at a Canadian university or post-secondary institution.

Awards are arranged alphabetically below their administering organizations

Funds Avail.: $4,000. **To Apply:** Applicant must submit a 250-word essay outlining their interest in and thoughts on audience research; must provide a recommendation from their course director. **Deadline:** June 30.

2366 ■ Ruth Hancock Scholarships
(Undergraduate/Scholarship)

Purpose: To provide support to qualified individuals who want to pursue their career in broadcasting or broadcast sales/marketing. **Focus:** Broadcasting. **Qualif.:** Applicant must be a student enrolled in a recognized communication or marketing course in Canada; must have strong character and leadership qualities; must have a willingness to assist others; must have a genuine interest in pursuing a broadcasting career, as reflected in extracurricular activities related to broadcasting or broadcast sales/marketing, and/or self-initiated undertakings; must have community involvement and/ or volunteer work. **Criteria:** Recipient will be selected based on the criteria of the Scholarship Selection Committee.

Funds Avail.: $1,500. **To Apply:** Applicant must provide 500-word outline and a signed recommendation from their course director. Application forms are available online and must be sent with the other supporting documents to Ruth Hancock Memorial Scholarships, c/o Canadian Association of Broadcasters, PO Box 627 Sta. B, Ottawa, K1P 5S2.

2367 ■ Canadian Association for Business Economics (CABE)
PO Box 828, Station B
Ottawa, ON, Canada K1P 5P9
Ph: (613) 238-4831
Fax: (613) 238-7698
E-mail: info@cabe.ca
URL: www.cabe.ca

2368 ■ Doug Purvis Prize *(Professional development/Prize)*

Purpose: To recognize authors who made contributions to Canadian economic policy. **Focus:** Economics. **Qualif.:** Competition is available to authors working in all print media industries; must have written book(s)in relevance to Canadian economic policy; must have had a series of articles in newspapers or magazines, journals, or government studies including monographs done for Royal Commissions, other official documents and think-tank reports. Materials must be primarily, but not exclusively in the public domain. **Criteria:** Candidates will be chosen based on submitted piece.

Funds Avail.: $10,000. **To Apply:** Electronic submissions must be in PDF format. In case submissions need to be mailed, applicants must submit five copies of the nominated piece including the full details of the nominees, name and address of the nominator and affiliation. **Deadline:** March. **Remarks:** Either mail or electronic submission includes the same information. **Contact:** Electronic submissions can be forwarded to Anne Motte at office@economics.ca.

2369 ■ Canadian Association of Cardiac Rehabilitation
1390 Taylor Ave.
Winnipeg, MB, Canada R3M 3V8
Ph: (204) 488-5854
Fax: (204) 488-4819

E-mail: mthomas@cacr.ca
URL: www.cacr.ca

2370 ■ Canadian Association of Cardiac Rehabilitation Graduate Scholarship Awards
(Graduate/Scholarship)

Purpose: To recognize the research of graduate students in the area of cardiac rehabilitation and to reflect CACR's support of their educational endeavors in this area. **Focus:** Cardiology. **Qualif.:** Students must be a member of the CACR. **Criteria:** Selection will be based on strength of research methodology; feasibility of successfully completing the study; importance and relevance to the field of cardiac rehabilitation; strength of the letter of support; and applicant's potential for continuing to make a valuable contribution to the field of cardiac rehabilitation.

Funds Avail.: $3,000. **Number Awarded:** 4. **To Apply:** Applicants must submit the auto-fill abstract form in English in Word format together with one letter of reference from a current supervisor; and letter of application: a letter outlining the student's current research in the area of cardiac rehabilitation and future directions in this field. The letter should be maximum of two pages in length and must specifically address the rating criteria related to methodology, feasibility, importance and relevance. Completed applications should be emailed to mthomas@cacr.ca. **Deadline:** May 1. **Contact:** Marilyn Thomas, 204-488-5857.

2371 ■ Canadian Association of Chiefs of Police
300 Terry Fox Dr., Unit 100
Kanata, ON, Canada K2K 0E3
Ph: (613) 595-1101
Fax: (613) 383-0372
E-mail: cacp@cacp.ca
URL: www.cacp.ca

2372 ■ Jack Ackroyd Scholarships *(Professional development/Scholarship)*

Purpose: To encourage members of police forces across Canada to further their education with a view of promoting professionalism and excellence throughout the policing community. **Focus:** Law enforcement. **Qualif.:** Applicants must be all uniform and civilian members of police forces, who have completed a degree or certificate program in police studies, criminology, law, or other programs related to law enforcement in an accredited Canadian university or community college. **Criteria:** Applicants who have demonstrated academic excellence in police related studies will be given preference.

Funds Avail.: $100. **Number Awarded:** 5. **To Apply:** Applicants must submit documents pertaining to their personal information, police service of employment, date of graduation, official transcripts of courses and grades, and any other information which may be considered relevant including any letter of support from the police service of which they are members. **Deadline:** October 15.

2373 ■ Canadian Association of Drilling Engineers (CADE)
400 - 5th Ave. SW, Ste. 560
Calgary, AB, Canada T2P 0L2
Ph: (403) 520-0220
Fax: (403) 263-2722
E-mail: info@cadecanada.com.

Awards are arranged alphabetically below their administering organizations

URL: www.cadecanada.com

2374 ■ CADE Bursary *(Undergraduate/ Scholarship)*

Purpose: To financially support the qualified individuals who want to pursue their education in a Petroleum Industry. **Focus:** Petroleum engineering. **Qualif.:** Applicant must be a dependent of a CADE member or must be a CADE member. **Criteria:** Selection process will be based on enrollment in an engineering program as highest priority; financial need; industry experience; overall quality of submission.

Funds Avail.: No specific amount. **To Apply:** Application form and instructions are available at the website. **Deadline:** September 15. **Contact:** Mike Buker at 403-930-9015.

2375 ■ CADE Scholarships *(Undergraduate/ Scholarship)*

Purpose: To financially support the qualified individuals who want to pursue their education in a Petroleum Industry. **Focus:** Petroleum engineering. **Qualif.:** Applicants must be an engineering student at the University of Alberta and the University of Calgary as well as Engineering Technology at the Southern Alberta Institute of Technology and the Northern Alberta Institute of Technology. **Criteria:** Selection process will be based on the criteria of the CADE executive committee.

Funds Avail.: $1,500-$2,000: fourth year; $1000: second year. **Number Awarded:** 4. **To Apply:** Application form and instructions are available at the website.

2376 ■ Canadian Association of Geographers (CAG)

McGill University
Department of Geography
805 Sherbrooke St. W, Rm. 425
Montreal, QC, Canada H3A 0B9
Ph: (514) 398-4946
Fax: (514) 398-7437
E-mail: valerie.shoffey@cag-acg.ca
URL: www.cag-acg.ca

2377 ■ Robin P. Armstrong Memorial Prize for Excellence in Native Studies Awards *(Doctorate, Graduate/Award)*

Purpose: To recognize students and promote excellence in applied research. **Focus:** Geography. **Qualif.:** Applicants must be graduate students pursuing a geography program of study; must have completed a Master's or PhD thesis in native studies on aboriginal topic. **Criteria:** Candidates will be ranked based on the following categories: 1) significance of the problem; 2) conceptualization, design and execution of the study; 3) quality of the results; 4) potential for improving theory; and 5) clarity, insight and originality of the work. Research which involves quantitative data analysis using Statistics Canada and INAC data on aboriginal topics will be given extra points.

Funds Avail.: $1,000. **To Apply:** Applicants must submit a cover letter; curriculum vitae; and 1,000-1,500 words abstract outlining the problem or question studied, review of related literature, design and methodology, statistical results and conclusions, and statement of significance. **Deadline:** December 31. **Contact:** Application form and supporting documents must be sent to Dr. Gail Fondahl, University of British Columbia, 3333 University Way, Prince

George, BC V2N 4Z9; Phone: 250-960-5856; Fax: 250-960-5539; E-mail: fondahlg@unbc.ca.

2378 ■ CAG Health and Health Care Study Group Awards *(Graduate/Award)*

Purpose: To recognize students for excellence in research and presentation skills. **Focus:** General studies. **Qualif.:** Applicants must be members of the Canadian Association of Geographers; must be graduate students or supervisors who are members of the HHCSG at the time of the CAG meeting. **Criteria:** Award will be given to an applicant who conducted the best research.

Funds Avail.: Varies. **To Apply:** Applicants must submit an application form.

2379 ■ Canadian Association of Geographers Historical Geography Study Group Awards *(Doctorate, Graduate, Undergraduate/Award)*

Purpose: To recognize the work of undergraduates, graduates, or Master's students. **Focus:** Geography. **Qualif.:** Applicants must be full-time or part-time undergraduates or Master's students attending a credited Canadian college or university. **Criteria:** Candidates will be judged based on originality, research quality, and style of the submitted essay.

Funds Avail.: $100. **To Apply:** Applicants must submit an essay. It must be a research paper discussing Canadian historical geography and have been written anytime after January 2008. Essay must be submitted in French or English not exceeding 6,000 words including references, footnotes or endnotes. In addition, applicants must also submit the following information: 1) name and contact details; 2) an abstract no longer than 250 words; 3) name of the institution attended at the time of writing the essay; 4) course by which the essay was written; and 5) name of the course instructor. **Remarks:** In the event of a tie, adjudicating committees may issue two awards. **Contact:** Essays must be submitted by electronic mail to Andrew Baldwin at baldwina@queensu.ca.

2380 ■ Canadian Association on Gerontology (CAG)

263 McCaul St., Ste. 328
Toronto, ON, Canada M5T 1W7
Free: 855-224-2240
E-mail: contact@cagacg.ca
URL: www.cagacg.ca

2381 ■ CAG Margery Boyce Bursary Awards *(Postgraduate/Award)*

Purpose: To support post-baccalaureate students who have made a significant contribution to their community through volunteer activities and who are registered in a program of study focused on aging or the aged. **Focus:** Gerontology. **Qualif.:** Applicant must be a CAG member; must be registered, or formally accepted at a recognized Canadian university at the time the application is submitted; must be a Canadian citizen or have permanent resident status. **Criteria:** Recipient will be recommended by the Awards Committee based on his/her contribution to the community through volunteer activities and based on his/her academic performance. Preference will be given to persons returning to university after an absence from formal study.

Funds Avail.: $500. **To Apply:** Applicants must submit an

Awards are arranged alphabetically below their administering organizations

application form with transcripts; proof of registration or acceptance in a university program; letter of support from the faculty supervisor or program Chair which addresses the criteria for the bursary and the letter of support from any community organization that can address the amount and quality of the applicant's volunteer activities as related to the criteria; Applicant must submit a photo and a short biographical profile for the CAG Newsletter. **Deadline:** May 16.

2382 ■ CAG Donald Menzies Bursary Awards
(Postgraduate/Award)

Purpose: To support post-baccalaureate students registered in a program of study focused on aging or the aged. **Focus:** Gerontology. **Qualif.:** Applicant must be a CAG member; must be registered, or formally accepted as a full-time student in a post-baccalaureate program at a recognized Canadian university at the time the application is submitted; must be a Canadian citizen or have permanent resident status. **Criteria:** Recipient will be selected by the Awards Committee based on academic merit among students demonstrating financial need.

Funds Avail.: $1,500. **To Apply:** Applicant must submit the application form with the university transcript; proof of registration, or acceptance in university program; a letter of support from the faculty supervisor; and an approved thesis/research project proposal (if applicable). Applicant must submit a photo and a short biographical profile for the CAG Newsletter. **Deadline:** May 16.

2383 ■ Canadian Association for HIV Research (CAHR)
One Nicholas St., Ste. 1105
Ottawa, ON, Canada K1N 7B7
Ph: (613) 241-5785
E-mail: info@cahr-acrv.ca
URL: www.cahr-acrv.ca

2384 ■ CAHR Master's Level Scholarships
(Master's/Scholarship)

Purpose: To support students who are planning a career in HIV/AIDS research. **Focus:** Medical research. **Qualif.:** Applicants must be enrolled in a Master's degree program and planning to conduct HIV/AIDS research. **Criteria:** Applicants will be evaluated based on achievements, characteristics and abilities of the applicants; quality and potential impact of the proposed research project; strength of the proposed training environment.

Funds Avail.: $17,500. **To Apply:** Applicants must apply online through CIHR's Researchnet. **Deadline:** February 1. **Remarks:** Scholarship is being offered in partnership with the Canadian Institutes of Health Research.

2385 ■ Canadian Association of Insolvency and Restructuring Professionals (CAIRP)
277 Wellington St. W
Toronto, ON, Canada M5V 3H2
Ph: (416) 204-3242
Fax: (416) 204-3410
E-mail: info@cairp.ca
URL: www.cairp.ca

2386 ■ Lloyd Houlden Research Fellowships
(Professional development/Fellowship)

Purpose: To support research that addresses current issues in Canadian insolvency policy and practice. **Focus:**

Law. **Qualif.:** Applicants must be the authors of the paper that addresses those involved in insolvency practice, insolvency law, or in the development and analysis of insolvency policy. Paper should be 7000-10000 words in length. **Criteria:** Recipients will be selected based on submitted paper.

Funds Avail.: $20,000. **To Apply:** Applicants must submit a proposed research, curriculum vitae, publications over the last two years and research in progress. **Deadline:** November 30.

2387 ■ Canadian Association of Law Libraries (CALL)
4 Cataraqui St., Ste. 310
Kingston, ON, Canada K7L 5C8
Ph: (613) 531-9338
Fax: (613) 531-0626
E-mail: office@callacbd.ca
URL: www.callacbd.ca

2388 ■ CALL/ACBD Education Reserve Fund Grants *(Graduate/Grant)*

Purpose: To provide funding support for members of CALL/ACBD intending to further their education in pursuits that do not fit the guidelines of the association's already established scholarships. **Focus:** Law. **Qualif.:** Members of the Canadian Association of Law Libraries/Association canadienne des bibliotheques de droit who have been in good standing for a minimum of 12 months are invited to apply. Applicants' pursuits must be relevant to their career in law libraries or law librarianship. **Criteria:** Selection will be based on merit.

Funds Avail.: No specific amount. **To Apply:** Application form is available online. Applicants must submit completed application form along with a resume and a letter of support from your employer. **Deadline:** April 23. **Contact:** Janet Moss CALL/ACBD Scholarships and Awards Committee, Head Law Librarian, Gerard V. La Forest Law Library, University of New Brunswick, Bag Service 44999 41 Dineen Dr. Fredericton, NB E3B 6C9; jmoss@unb.ca.

2389 ■ Canadian Association of Law Libraries CALL Research Grants *(Graduate/Grant)*

Purpose: To provide financial assistance for members working in law libraries intending to do research in various areas of interest. **Focus:** Law. **Qualif.:** Program is open to members of CALL/ACBD; must be intending to do research projects that promote an understanding of legal information sources or law librarianship. **Criteria:** Selection will be based on the recommendation of the committee to promote proposed research.

Funds Avail.: Up to $3,000. **To Apply:** Applicants may apply individually or in partnership with another member of CALL/ACBD; Applicants must submit completed application available in the website outlining the proposed project, the amount of money requested and a brief budget setting out how funds will be spent. Applicants should be prepared to demonstrate that they have completed a preliminary investigation as to the feasibility of their proposed project. **Deadline:** March 30. **Contact:** Marianne Rogers; 416-736-2100x33934; rogers@yorku.ca.

2390 ■ James D. Lang Memorial Scholarships
(Graduate/Scholarship)

Purpose: To support attendance at a continuing education program, be it a workshop, certificate program or other

Awards are arranged alphabetically below their administering organizations

similar activity deemed appropriate by the CALL/ACBD Scholarships and Awards Committee. **Focus:** Law. **Qualif.:** Members of CALL/ACBD who have been in good standing for a minimum of 12 months are invited to apply. **Criteria:** Scholarship is given based on merit.

Funds Avail.: $2,500. **To Apply:** Application form is available online. Applicants must submit the completed application form along with resume and a letter of support from their employer. **Deadline:** March 15; June 15; September 15. **Contact:** Janet Moss CALL/ACBD Scholarships and Awards Committee, Head Law Librarian, Gerard V. la Forest Law Library, University of New Brunswick, Bag Service 44999 41 Dineen Dr. Fredericton, NB E3B 6C9; Phone: 506-447-3266; E-mail: jmoss@unb.ca.

2391 ■ Diana M. Priestly Memorial Scholarships
(Undergraduate/Scholarship)

Purpose: To encourage and support professional development in the area of law librarianship. **Focus:** Law. **Qualif.:** Program is open to Canadian citizens or landed immigrants; must have previous law library experience and will be enrolled in an accredited Canadian Library School during the next academic term or year; must have a degree from or are currently enrolled in an accredited Canadian Library School and will be enrolled in an approved Canadian Law School during the next academic term or year; or who have a degree from or are currently enrolled in an approved Canadian law School and will be enrolled in an accredited Canadian Library school during the next academic term/year; or who will be concurrently enrolled in an approved Canadian Law School and an accredited Canadian Library School during the next academic term/year. **Criteria:** Recipients are chosen based on applicant's work experience, letter of application and letters of reference. Preference will be given to members of the Canadian Association of Law Libraries/Association canadienne des bibliotheques de droit.

Funds Avail.: $2,500. **Number Awarded:** 1. **To Apply:** Applicants must submit the completed application form available on the website along with resume; written statement from applicant; transcripts; and references. **Deadline:** February 1. **Contact:** Janet Moss, Chair; CALL/ACBD Scholarships and Awards Committee, Head Law Librarian, Gerard V. La Forest Law Library, University of New Brunswick, Bag Service 44999 41 Dineen Dr. Fredericton, NB E3B 6C9; jmoss@unb.ca.

2392 ■ Canadian Association of Law Teachers (CALT)
865 Carling Ave., Ste. 500
Ottawa, ON, Canada K1S 5S8
Ph: (613) 237-2925
E-mail: kiml@cba.org
URL: www.acpd-calt.org

2393 ■ Canadian Association of Law Teachers Award for Academic Excellence *(Professional development/Award)*

Purpose: To honor the exceptional contributions of a Canadian law teacher to research and law teaching. **Focus:** Law. **Qualif.:** Applicants must be Canadian law teachers in mid-career; and must be nominated by one or more colleagues. **Criteria:** Candidates will be evaluated based on the following criteria: (1) quality of teaching; (2) creation of new courses; and (3) research in relation to law reform or other legal matters.

Funds Avail.: No specific amount. **To Apply:** Applicants must submit a complete curriculum vitae; three letters of reference; and representative student's evaluation. Five copies of nomination documents must be submitted. **Contact:** Application materials should be submitted to Anne Saris, C.P. Succursale Centre-ville, Montreal, QC H3C 3P8.

2394 ■ Canadian Association of Neuroscience Nurses (CANN)
c/o Aline Mayer, Membership Chair
30 Chantilly Gate
Stittsville, ON, Canada K2S 2B1
E-mail: membership@cann.ca
URL: www.cann.ca

2395 ■ Lynn Ann Baldwin Scholarships
(Master's/Scholarship)

Purpose: To provide financial support to qualified nurses to pursue master's level education with neuroscience nursing as a focus. **Focus:** Neuroscience. **Qualif.:** Applicants must be registered nurses who have worked in neurosciences and are members of Canadian Association of Neuroscience Nursing in good standing for at least two years; must be in the master's program of study. **Criteria:** Selection will be based on the committee's criteria.

Funds Avail.: No specific amount. **To Apply:** Applicants must submit a completed application form; proof of acceptance into the master's program for which the scholarship is being sought, or proof of registration to write the certification exam; evidence of amount of registration fees; proof of current registration with provincial nursing association; one letter of reference from a person who has had the opportunity to assess your work.

2396 ■ Nueroscience Certification Bursary Awards *(Professional development/Award)*

Purpose: To provide financial support to qualified nurses to pursue additional training in neuroscience nursing. **Focus:** Neuroscience. **Qualif.:** Applicants must be registered nurses who have worked in neurosciences and are members of the Canadian Association of Neuroscience Nurses in good standing. The program or course of study for the Jessie Young Bursary must have a clear Neuroscience focus or component. **Criteria:** Selection will be based on the committee's criteria.

Funds Avail.: No specific amount. **To Apply:** Applicants must submit a completed application form; proof of acceptance into the educational program or course of study which the bursary is being sought, or proof of registration to write the certification exam; evidence of amount of registration fees; proof of current registration with provincial nursing association; and one letter of reference from a person who has had the opportunity to assess the applicant's work. **Deadline:** May 31.

2397 ■ Jessie Young Bursary Awards *(Professional development/Award)*

Purpose: To provide financial support to qualified nurses to pursue additional training in neuroscience nursing. **Focus:** Neuroscience. **Qualif.:** Applicants must be registered nurses who have worked in neurosciences and are members of the Canadian Association of Neuroscience Nurses in good standing. The program or course of study for the Jessie Young Bursary must have a clear Neuroscience focus or component. **Criteria:** Selection will be

Awards are arranged alphabetically below their administering organizations

based on the committee's criteria.

Funds Avail.: No specific amount. **To Apply:** Applicants must submit a completed application form; proof of acceptance into the educational program or course of study which the bursary is being sought, or proof of registration to write the certification exam; evidence of amount of registration fees; proof of current registration with provincial nursing association; one letter of reference from a person who has had the opportunity to assess your work. **Deadline:** April 1.

2398 ■ Canadian Association of Oilwell Drilling Contractors (CAODC)

540 5th Ave. SW, Ste. 800
Calgary, AB, Canada T2P 0M2
Ph: (403) 264-4311
Fax: (403) 263-3796
E-mail: info@caodc.ca
URL: www.caodc.ca

2399 ■ CAODC Occupational Health and Safety Scholarships *(Professional development/ Scholarship)*

Purpose: To help employees of CAODC achieve a higher education. **Focus:** General studies. **Qualif.:** Applicants must be CAODC drilling or service rig member employees with minimum of 12 months on-the-job experience and who are currently employed in one of the following: 1) as motorhands, derrickhands or drillers on a drilling rig; 2) as derrickhands or operators on a service rig; and 3) in a safety related position within the drilling or service rig member company. **Criteria:** Recipients will be selected based on submitted materials.

Funds Avail.: $5,000. **Number Awarded:** 1. **To Apply:** Applicants must complete the application form; must provide a letter of referral and statement of goals. **Deadline:** March 30. **Contact:** Kelli Whitehead at the above address.

2400 ■ CAODC Scholarship Program *(Undergraduate/Scholarship)*

Purpose: To provide educational assistance to employees, children, or legal dependents of an employee of a CAODC drilling or service rig member company to continue their education. **Focus:** General studies. **Qualif.:** Applicants must be legal dependents of an employee or a bonafide employee of the CAODC proper, drilling or service rig member company; must be entering or continuing postsecondary education from an accredited college, university or trade program as full-time students. **Criteria:** Applicants will be evaluated based on submitted materials.

Funds Avail.: $2,000. **Number Awarded:** 5. **To Apply:** Applicants must complete the application form; must submit a transcript of records, statement of goals and a two-page essay. **Deadline:** July 13.

2401 ■ Canadian Association for the Practical Study of Law in Education (CAPSLE)

c/o Lori Pollock
37 Moultrey Crescent
Georgetown, ON, Canada L7G 4N4
Ph: (905) 702-1710
Fax: (905) 873-0662
E-mail: info@capsle.ca
URL: www.capsle.ca

2402 ■ Canadian Association for the Practical Study of Law in Education Fellowships *(Graduate/Fellowship)*

Purpose: To provide an open forum for the practical study of legal issues affecting education. **Focus:** Law. **Qualif.:** Applicants must be Canadian citizens or landed immigrants enrolled in a Faculty of Law, Graduate School of Education or related discipline at a Canadian university. **Criteria:** Recipients will be selected based on submitted proposal.

Funds Avail.: $5,000. **To Apply:** Applicants must submit a one-page proposal for a paper, project, or research that pertains to current practical issues in education law, exhibits academic rigor, is concerned with new or ongoing research or study and not with work that has been done; must be completed by April each year following the award and includes plans for a final paper which will be presented at a CAPSLE Annual Conference; must attach a two-page curriculum vitae and three letters of reference attesting to the applicant's ability. **Deadline:** April 15.

2403 ■ Canadian Association of Radiation Oncology (CARO)

774 Echo Dr.
Ottawa, ON, Canada K1S 5N8
Ph: (613) 260-4188
Fax: (613) 730-1116
E-mail: caro-acro@royalcollege.ca
URL: www.caro-acro.ca

2404 ■ CARO-ELEKTA Research Fellowship Program *(Professional development/Fellowship)*

Purpose: To foster the development of highly qualified clinicians, researchers and future Radiation Oncology leaders. **Focus:** Oncology. **Qualif.:** Applicants must be Canadian citizens or landed immigrants; must hold or intend to sit the Royal College of Physicians and Surgeons of Canada specialist certification examination in Radiation Oncology prior to the beginning of the fellowship; and must be resident members of CARO. **Criteria:** Applicants will be evaluated based on scientific merit; relevance to current or future Radiation Oncology practice in Canada; broad alignment with Elekta's research objectives to treat cancer and brain disorders.

Funds Avail.: $75,000. **To Apply:** Applicants must include a description of the proposed research project and its relevance to Radiation Oncology, identification of the host institution and supervisor, written confirmation from the supervisor that this fellowship will be supported by the host institution, current curriculum vitae and three letters of reference.

2405 ■ Canadian Association of Second Language Teachers (CASLT)

300-950 Gladstone Ave.
Ottawa, ON, Canada K1Y 3E6
Ph: (613) 727-0994
Fax: (613) 727-3831
Free: 877-727-0994
E-mail: admin@caslt.org
URL: www.caslt.org

2406 ■ Robert Roy Awards *(Professional development/Award)*

Purpose: To recognize outstanding contributions by educators and researchers to the second language education

Awards are arranged alphabetically below their administering organizations

field. **Focus:** Education, English as a second language. **Qualif.:** Nominees must have been active members of the CASLT for at least two years; must have distinguished themselves in teaching, research, or writing to the improvement of second language teaching and learning in Canada. **Criteria:** Recipients will be selected based on submitted application.

Funds Avail.: Amount not specified. **To Apply:** Applicants must submit the nominee's information on a single sheet of paper. **Deadline:** March 31. **Contact:** 201-57 Auriga Dr., Ottawa, ON K2E 8B2.

2407 ■ H.H. Stern Grant Awards *(Professional development/Grant)*

Purpose: To support innovative classroom practices in second language learning. **Focus:** Education, English as a second language. **Qualif.:** Applicants must be CASLT members whose proposal expresses the new techniques, strategies and/or approaches to learning; identifies the impact of the project in the classroom, school or community; demonstrates the related improvement and student language learning; has potential for the duplication of classrooms, schools and communities; and includes a brief plan for evaluating the innovation. **Criteria:** Candidates will be chosen based on the submitted application.

Funds Avail.: $200-$500. **To Apply:** Applicants must submit a completed application form; completed project description answering the five focus questions; endorsement by a colleague or supervisor related to the impact of the project. A brief biography (no more than 75 words) and digital passport-style photo should be included in the application. **Contact:** Applications should be sent electronically to rachelgravelle@caslt.org.

2408 ■ Canadian Association of Student Activity Advisors (CASAA)
2460 Tanner Rd.
Victoria, BC, Canada V8Z 5R1
Ph: (250) 652-1634
Fax: (250) 652-4179
E-mail: bconconi@casaaleadership.ca
URL: www.casaaleadership.ca

2409 ■ CASAA Leaders of Distinction Scholarships *(Professional development/Scholarship)*

Purpose: To recognize leadership at the advisor level. **Focus:** General studies. **Qualif.:** Applicants must be active or past members of CASAA or a provincial association; must demonstrate excellence in leadership; must be committed to professional growth; must teach, coach and help others; must foster imagination in bringing about positive change; must show extraordinary commitment to student leadership; must demonstrate service to students, institution and profession; have evidence of impact on and involvement with students. **Criteria:** Recipients will be selected based on demonstrated leadership.

Funds Avail.: Amount not specified. **To Apply:** Applicants must submit a completed application form. **Deadline:** June 30.

2410 ■ CASAA Scholarships *(Undergraduate/Scholarship)*

Purpose: To help high school students pursue their education. **Focus:** General studies. **Qualif.:** Applicants must be enrolled in their senior year in a Canadian high school;

must be currently members of CASAA; must have minimum average of 70% in their graduating year; must have plan to attend an accredited Canadian post-secondary institution; must have superior contribution through membership; and must have made a significant contribution to student leadership initiatives in their community. **Criteria:** Applicants will be selected based on merit.

Funds Avail.: $1,000. **Number Awarded:** 5. **To Apply:** Applicants must submit a completed application form, resume, list of leadership activities completed during high school years, transcript of records and letter of reference from the chairperson or leadership advisor. Applicants must also submit an essay on how they would engage student leaders to make a positive and democratic difference in their school and community. **Deadline:** April 15.

2411 ■ Canadian Association for Theatre Research (CATR)
2507-140 Erskine Ave.
Toronto, ON, Canada M4P 1Z2
Ph: (416) 303-0441
Fax: (647) 344-6198
E-mail: levin@yorku.ca
URL: www.catr-acrt.ca

2412 ■ Robert G. Lawrence Prize *(Doctorate, Graduate, Professional development/Prize)*

Purpose: To recognize research of scholars who have presented an outstanding paper during the CATR annual conference. **Focus:** General studies. **Qualif.:** Award is open to graduate students and scholars who recently completed their PhD (less than five years) and who make a presentation at the annual conference. **Criteria:** Recipients will be selected based on depth and details of the paper and quality of the presentation.

Funds Avail.: $200. **To Apply:** Applicants must forward a copy of their presentation to the president through e-mail attachment. **Contact:** Applicants may e-mail the President, Shelley Scott, at s.scott@uleth.ca.

2413 ■ Heather McCallum Scholarships *(Doctorate, Graduate, Professional development/Scholarship)*

Purpose: To allow researchers to enrich their projects in ways otherwise unaffordable, through travel, access to archives or events, or the purchase of materials. **Focus:** Theater arts. **Qualif.:** Applicants must be graduate students and emerging scholars (within five years upon completion of a PhD) in the fields of theatre, drama and performance studies, with a preference given to topics with a Canadian focus. **Criteria:** Recipients will be chosen based on the following criteria: 1) excellence of the project and its contribution to the discipline; 2) a project which can be completed in a reasonable time; 3) academic records and potential of the applicants; 4) if the request indicates a purchase of anything at an archival value that can be deposited subsequently in the public domain. Preference will be given to those applicants who have not fully established their careers and are not eligible for funds for the particular project applied for from federal, provincial and municipal arts councils or institutions.

Funds Avail.: $1,000. **To Apply:** Applicants must provide a maximum of two pages describing the project for which assistance is required; a detailed breakdown of costs; information concerning applications to other granting agen-

Awards are arranged alphabetically below their administering organizations

cies; up-to-date curriculum vitae; and the name of a person who has been asked to send a letter of reference directly to the Secretary of the Committee.

2414 ■ Canadian Association of University Teachers

2675 Queensview Dr.
Ottawa, ON, Canada K2B 8K2
Ph: (613) 820-2270
Fax: (613) 820-7244
E-mail: acppu@caut.ca
URL: www.caut.ca

2415 ■ J.H. Stewart Reid Memorial Fellowship Trust *(Doctorate/Fellowship)*

Purpose: To support students registered in a doctoral program at a Canadian University. **Focus:** General studies. **Qualif.:** Applicants must be Canadian citizens; must be registered in a doctoral program at a Canadian University who have completed their comprehensive examinations or equivalent; must have their doctoral thesis proposal; must have a first-class academic records in a graduate program; and must not be awardees of scholarships exceeding $25,000. **Criteria:** Recipients will be selected based on submitted applications.

Funds Avail.: $5,000. **To Apply:** Applicants must complete the online application form and must contact the Trustees through postal service, electronic mail and telephone conference call.

2416 ■ Canadian Authors Association-Ottawa Branch

163 Bell St. N
Ottawa, ON, Canada K1R 7E1
E-mail: sherrill_caa@msn.com
URL: www.canauthors-ottawa.org

2417 ■ CAA National Capital Region Writing Contest *(All/Prize)*

Purpose: To recognize and provide funds for written article(s) of an individual. **Focus:** General studies. **Qualif.:** Contest is open to members currently residing in the National Capital Region (Ottawa Branch). Applicant's essay must be original and unpublished work. **Criteria:** Winners will be selected based on submitted essays.

Funds Avail.: Amount not specified. **To Apply:** Applicants must submit an essay or poem. Each entry must be written in English and typed on 8 1/2″ x 11″ paper. **Deadline:** February 4. **Contact:** For further information, applicants must contact Sharyn Heagle at sharyn_40@yahoo.com.

2418 ■ Canadian Bar Association (CBA)

500-865 Carling Ave.
Ottawa, ON, Canada K1S 5S8
Ph: (613) 237-2925
Fax: (613) 237-0185
Free: 800-267-8860
E-mail: info@cba.org
URL: www.cba.org

2419 ■ The Viscount Bennett Fellowships *(Graduate/Fellowship)*

Purpose: To improve the law and it's administration; to promote equal access to justice; to promote the equality in

the legal profession and the justice system; to enhance the knowledge, ethical standards and well-being of members of the legal profession; to safeguard the interest of legal profession; and to encourage the high standards of legal education, training and ethics. **Focus:** Law. **Qualif.:** Applicants must be Canadian citizens who have graduated from an approved law school in Canada; must be members of Canadian Bar Association in good standing. **Criteria:** Recipients are selected based on the result of the conducted interview.

Funds Avail.: $40,000. **To Apply:** Applicants must submit a photocopy of birth certificate; one certified copy of law transcripts; academic distinctions; curriculum vitae; one-page synopsis of the extra-curricular interests as well as activities during the post-secondary studies; one-page statement outlining the course of study to be pursued; and three letters of reference. **Deadline:** November 15. **Contact:** Stephen Hanaon, Email: stephenh@cba.org.

2420 ■ Canadian Blood Services

1800 Alta Vista Dr.
Ottawa, ON, Canada K1G 4J5
Ph: (613) 739-2300
Fax: (613) 731-1411
Free: 888-236-6283
E-mail: feedback@blood.ca
URL: www.bloodservices.ca

2421 ■ Canadian Blood Services Graduate Fellowships *(Graduate/Fellowship)*

Purpose: To attract and support young investigators to initiate or continue training in the field of blood transfusion science. **Focus:** Blood banking. **Qualif.:** Applicant must be engaged in full-time training in research in a Canadian graduate school leading to a PhD or combined health professional Ph.D. program; demonstrate acceptance into a PhD program to receive continued support; in a training program which includes actual involvement in research and not only courses in research methods; and must not hold another award at the same time. **Criteria:** Selection is based on the applicant's academic qualifications, research experience and ability; relevance of the proposed project; and merit of the proposed project and research environment.

Funds Avail.: $21,000/year plus research and travel allowance of $1,000/year. **To Apply:** Applicants must submit a completed application form including all attachments with four complete, collated copies and official, original transcript(s). **Deadline:** May 15. **Contact:** Elaine Konecny at elaine.konecny@blood.ca or 613-739-2230.

2422 ■ Canadian Blood Services Postdoctoral Fellowships *(Postdoctorate/Fellowship)*

Purpose: To foster careers related to transfusion science in Canada. **Focus:** Blood banking. **Qualif.:** Applicant must hold a relevant prerequisite degree (PhD, MD, DDS, or DVM) from a recognized academic institution; be within five years of completing the degree; not holding another award. **Criteria:** Selection is based on the applicant's academic qualifications, research experience and ability; relevance of the proposed project; and merit of the proposed project and research environment.

Funds Avail.: The value of each Fellowship is related to the major degree(s) and experience the applicant holds (with a one time research allowance of $10,000). **To Ap-**

Awards are arranged alphabetically below their administering organizations

ply: Applicants must submit a completed application form including all attachments with four complete, collated copies and official, original transcript(s). **Deadline:** July 5. **Contact:** Elaine Konecny at elaine.konecny@blood.ca or 613-739-2230.

2423 ■ Canadian Cartographic Association (CCA)

615 Booth St., 06Ath Fl.
Ottawa, ON, Canada K1A 0E9
Ph: (613) 992-4339
E-mail: president@cca-acc.org
URL: www.cca-acc.org

2424 ■ Norman Nicholson Scholarships
(Undergraduate/Scholarship)

Purpose: To recognize and encourage exceptional student achievement and ability in any aspect of cartography. **Focus:** Cartography. **Qualif.:** Applicant must be a full-time student in a recognized college or university program; must be a Canadian citizen or landed immigrant. **Criteria:** Applicants are selected based on committee's review of the application materials.

Funds Avail.: $5,000. **To Apply:** Applicants must submit an official transcript of all college or university courses complete with grades received; letters of recommendation from two faculty members who are familiar with the student's works and capabilities; one-page statement from the student regarding plans for continuing education in cartography. **Deadline:** March 15. **Contact:** Elise Pietroniro, 708 Paul Metivier Ave., Nepean, ON, K2J 2T4.

2425 ■ Canadian Centre for Occupational Health and Safety (CCOHS)

135 Hunter St. E
Hamilton, ON, Canada L8N 1M5
Ph: (905) 572-2981
Fax: (905) 572-2206
Free: 800-668-4284
URL: www.ccohs.ca

2426 ■ Dick Martin Scholarships *(Postgraduate/Scholarship)*

Purpose: To encourage students to continue their career in occupational health and safety. **Focus:** Occupational safety and health. **Qualif.:** Applicants must be students who are enrolled, either full-time or part-time, in an occupational health and safety related course or program. **Criteria:** Recipients will be selected based on knowledge of the subject matter, understanding of the principles and values of Dick Martin, and understanding of the role of CCOHS.

Funds Avail.: $3,000. **To Apply:** Applicants must contact CCOHS at 800-668-4284 for further information. **Deadline:** January 31.

2427 ■ Canadian Civil Liberties Association (CCLA)

506-360 Bloor St. W
Toronto, ON, Canada M5S 1X1
Ph: (416) 363-0321
Fax: (416) 861-1291
E-mail: mail@ccla.org
URL: ccla.org

2428 ■ CCLA Summer Legal Internships
(Undergraduate, Graduate/Internship)

Purpose: To help students engage in legal work relating to CCLA's ongoing advocacy efforts in civil liberties and human rights. **Focus:** Law. **Qualif.:** Applicants must be law students, law graduates and graduate students with expertise in Canadian law, public policy, political science, or other relevant fields of study; must have strong writing skills; must have interest in civil liberties, human rights and public policy. **Criteria:** Applicants will be evaluated based on eligibility and submitted materials.

Funds Avail.: Amount not stated. **To Apply:** Applicants must submit a resume, cover letter, transcripts and 800-word unedited writing sample. **Deadline:** February 13.

2429 ■ Chernos Essay Competition *(High School/Prize)*

Purpose: To provide opportunities among high school students. **Focus:** General studies. **Qualif.:** Applicants must be high school students. **Criteria:** Applicants will be selected based on submitted essay.

Funds Avail.: $500. **To Apply:** Applicants must submit an essay addressing one of the questions given by the scholarship committee. **Contact:** education@ccla.org.

2430 ■ Canadian Co-operative Association (CCA)

275 Bank St., Ste. 400
Ottawa, ON, Canada K2P 2L6
Ph: (613) 238-6711
Fax: (613) 567-0658
Free: 866-266-7677
E-mail: info@coopscanada.coop
URL: www.coopscanada.coop

2431 ■ Canadian Association for Studies in Co-operation Scholarships Lemaire Co-operative Studies Awards (CASC) *(Graduate, Undergraduate/Scholarship)*

Purpose: To encourage students to undertake studies which will help them contribute to the development of co-operatives in Canada or elsewhere. **Focus:** Business. **Qualif.:** Applicant must be an undergraduate or graduate taking full or partial credit courses at any university or university-equivalent college, and must take a minimum of one course about co-operatives. **Criteria:** Selection is based on the submitted application materials.

Funds Avail.: $1,000-$3,000. **To Apply:** Applicant must submit a completed application form along with background information; previous degree(s) or official transcripts; academic awards/distinctions/scholarships; two letters of reference (one must be academic); statement of interest in co-operatives; experience with co-operatives (either as volunteer or employee); and a description of the project (3-5 pages for graduate students, 1 page for undergraduates). **Deadline:** March 31. **Contact:** Donna Balkan at donna.balkan@coopscanada.coop.

2432 ■ Canadian Association for Studies in Co-operation Scholarships - Amy and Tim Dauphinee Scholarships (CASC) *(Graduate/Scholarship)*

Purpose: To support studies about co-operative businesses and organizations. **Focus:** Business. **Qualif.:** Applicant must be a graduate student either undertaking stud-

Awards are arranged alphabetically below their administering organizations

ies at a Canadian university or a university-equivalent college (regardless of citizenship) or be a Canadian citizen or landed immigrant studying at such institutions outside Canada. **Criteria:** Selection is based on the applicant's academic record as well as on the importance of the proposed research activities to the development of the co-op movement in Canada or abroad.

Funds Avail.: $3,000. **To Apply:** Applicant must submit a completed application form along with background information; previous degree(s) or official transcripts; academic awards/distinctions/scholarships; two letters of reference (one must be academic); statement of interest in co-operatives; experience with co-operatives (either as volunteer or employee); and 3-5 pages description of project. **Deadline:** March 31. **Contact:** Donna Balkan at donna.balkan@coopscanada.coop.

2433 ■ Canadian Association for Studies in Co-operation Scholarships Alexander Fraser Laidlaw Fellowships (CASC) *(Graduate/Fellowship)*

Purpose: To support studies about co-operative businesses and organizations. **Focus:** Business. **Qualif.:** Applicant must be a graduate student either undertaking studies at a Canadian university or a university-equivalent college (regardless of citizenship) or be a Canadian citizen or landed immigrant studying at such institutions outside Canada. **Criteria:** Selection is based on the applicant's academic record as well as on the importance of the proposed research activities to the development of the co-op movement in Canada or abroad.

Funds Avail.: $1,000. **To Apply:** Applicant must submit a completed application form along with background information; previous degree(s) or official transcripts; academic awards/distinctions/scholarships; two letters of reference (one must be academic); statement of interest in co-operatives; experience with co-operatives (either as volunteer or employee); and 3-5 pages description of project. **Deadline:** March 31. **Contact:** Donna Balkan at donna.balkan@coopscanada.coop.

2434 ■ Canadian Communication Association (CCA)
c/o Daniel Pare, Treas.
University of Ottawa
Department of Communication
554 King Edward Ave.
Ottawa, ON, Canada K1N 6N5
Ph: (613) 562-5800
Fax: (613) 562-5240
E-mail: dpar2@uottawa.ca
URL: www.acc-cca.ca

2435 ■ Beaverbrook Media at McGill Student Paper Prize *(Graduate/Prize)*

Purpose: To recognize the promising scholars in Canadian Communication Studies. **Focus:** Communications. **Qualif.:** Applicants must be students currently enrolled in a graduate program in Communications at a Canadian university; must be fully paid members of the CCA at the time they submit their paper for consideration. **Criteria:** Selection will be based on the following criteria: 1) engagement with communication studies; 2) scholarly insight and originality of research; 3) contribution to communication studies; 4) future research potential; and 5) maturity and sophistication of the argument.

Funds Avail.: $1,000. **To Apply:** Applicants must submit a single-authored essay. Paper must be between 6000-8000 words in Word, RTF, or PDF format. **Deadline:** April 1.

2436 ■ Gertrude J. Robinson Book Prize *(Professional development/Prize)*

Purpose: To recognize Canadian scholars and promote scholarly excellence in Communication fields. **Focus:** Communications. **Qualif.:** Applicants must be Canadian scholars working or living principally in Canada; must be nominated by a CCA member in good standing, publisher, academic dean, chair, or a program director. **Criteria:** Selection will be based on the following categories: 1) engagement with the field of communication studies; 2) scholarly insight and originality of the research; 3) contribution to the field of communication studies; 4) potential to promote or inspire further research by other Canadian scholars; and 5) maturity and sophistication of the argument.

Funds Avail.: Amount not specified. **To Apply:** Applicants must submit a single or multi-authored monograph with publication date the same year as the prize.

2437 ■ Canadian Corporate Counsel Association (CCCA)
410-20 Toronto St.
Toronto, ON, Canada M5C 2B8
Ph: (416) 869-0522
Fax: (416) 869-0946
E-mail: ccca@ccca-cba.org
URL: www.cancorpcounsel.org

2438 ■ Robert V.A. Jones Canadians Corporate Counsel Awards *(Professional development/Award)*

Purpose: To recognize individuals who made contributions to the development or promotion of the Canadian Corporate counsel bar including significant research or writing on related issues. **Focus:** Paralegal studies. **Qualif.:** Applicants must be current or past members of the in-house legal profession in Canada or individuals who made contributions to the Canadian Corporate Counsel. **Criteria:** Recipients will be selected based on submitted materials.

Funds Avail.: Amount not specified. **To Apply:** Applicants must submit a curriculum vitae and supporting letters. To nominate an individual, name, contact information and summary of the reasons for the nominations should be provided. Nominations require the signatures of five CCCA regular members in good standing. **Deadline:** February. **Contact:** For further information, applicants may email johnh@cba.org.

2439 ■ Canadian Council for Aboriginal Business (CCAB)
250 The Esplanade, Ste. 204
Toronto, ON, Canada M5A 1J2
Ph: (416) 961-8663
Fax: (416) 961-3995
E-mail: info@ccab.com
URL: www.ccab.com

2440 ■ Foundation for the Advancement of Aboriginal Youth Bursary Program *(Undergraduate/Scholarship)*

Purpose: To provide scholarship assistance to qualified individuals who want to pursue their post-secondary educa-

Awards are arranged alphabetically below their administering organizations

tion. **Focus:** General studies. **Qualif.:** Applicant must be a Canadian resident, of First Nation, Metis or Inuit heritage and attending either a high school or a post-secondary institute full-time within Canada. **Criteria:** Recipient will be selected based on financial need, academic and career commitment, contribution to family and community and leadership and role model qualities.

Funds Avail.: $750. **To Apply:** Applicant must complete the application form available online; must provide a proof of First Nations, Inuit or Metis ancestry; must have two signed, original letters of support; must provide a copy of the most recent official school transcripts and report card; must include a letter of acceptance; must provide a recent color photo. Application form and other supporting documents must be sent to the Foundation for the Advancement of Aboriginal Youth, c/o Canadian Council for Aboriginal Business, 250 The Esplanade, Ste. 204, Toronto, ON M5A 1J2. **Deadline:** September 30. **Contact:** 866-566-3229, faayinfo@ccab.com.

2441 ■ Foundation for the Advancement of Aboriginal Youth Scholarships (Undergraduate/ Scholarship)

Purpose: To provide scholarship assistance to qualified individuals who want to pursue their post-secondary education. **Focus:** General studies. **Qualif.:** Applicant must be a Canadian resident, of First Nation, Metis or Inuit heritage and attending either high school or a post-secondary institute full-time within Canada. **Criteria:** Recipient will be selected based on financial need, academic and career commitment, contribution to family and community, and leadership and role model qualities.

Funds Avail.: $2,500. **To Apply:** Applicant must complete the application form available online; must provide proof of First Nation, Inuit or Metis ancestry; must have two signed, original letters of support; must provide a copy of the most recent official school transcripts and report card; must include a letter of acceptance; must provide a recent color photo. Application form and other supporting documents must be sent to Foundation for the Advancement of Aboriginal Youth, c/o Canadian Council for Aboriginal Business, 250 The Esplanade, Ste. 204, Toronto, ON M5A 1J2. **Deadline:** September 30. **Contact:** Lori Williams, Phone: 866-566-3229; email: lwilliams@ccab.com.

2442 ■ Canadian Council on International Law (CCIL)

275 Bay St.
Ottawa, ON, Canada K1R 5Z5
Ph: (613) 235-0442
Fax: (613) 232-8228
E-mail: info@ccil-ccdi.ca
URL: www.ccil-ccdi.ca

2443 ■ John Peter Humphrey Student Fellowships (Graduate/Fellowship)

Purpose: To inspire educational achievement by providing support for outstanding students pursuing graduate studies at leading graduate institutions in Canada or worldwide. **Focus:** Political science; Law. **Qualif.:** Applicants must be students of Canadian law and political science (or their equivalent) faculties. **Criteria:** Selection committee appointed by the President of the CCIL will review the applications and base its determination on the applicant's academic accomplishments, proposed program of study, letter of reference, and other information contained in the application.

Funds Avail.: CDN $25,000 for tuition plus a stipend of CDN $10,000 for living expenses. **To Apply:** Applicants must submit the official transcript from each post-secondary academic institution, three letters of reference which speak both of the candidate's academic strengths and weaknesses and his/her likelihood of success in a programme of graduate studies. **Deadline:** November 15.

2444 ■ Canadian Council of Technicians and Technologists (CCTT)

155-955 Green Valley Crescent
Ottawa, ON, Canada K2C 3V4
Ph: (613) 238-8123
Fax: (613) 238-8822
Free: 800-891-1140
E-mail: ccttadm@cctt.ca
URL: www.cctt.ca

2445 ■ Canadian Council of Technicians and Technologists Scholarships for Technology Students (Postgraduate/Scholarship)

Purpose: To assist students with expenses incurred to undertake studies leading to a technician or technologist diploma in a recognized program of study in engineering or applied science technology. **Focus:** Science technologies; Engineering. **Qualif.:** Applicant must be a son or daughter of an individual member of a Constituent member (CM) of CCTT. **Criteria:** Recipients are selected based on the committee's review of the application materials.

Funds Avail.: $1,000. **Number Awarded:** 2. **To Apply:** Applicant must secure a letter from a Constituent member of the council, attesting to the fact that his or her parents are members in good standing; must confirm by official transcripts that he/she is a graduate from grade 12 secondary school program with second-class, or with better standing and has been proven that she/he is enrolled as full-time student in an Engineering or Applied Science Technology Program in Canada. **Deadline:** September 30.

2446 ■ Canadian Cystic Fibrosis Foundation (CCFF)

2221 Yonge St., Ste. 601
Toronto, ON, Canada M4S 2B4
Ph: (416) 485-9149
Fax: (416) 485-0960
Free: 800-378-2233
E-mail: info@cysticfibrosis.ca
URL: www.cysticfibrosis.ca

2447 ■ CCFF Clinical Fellowships (Doctorate, Graduate/Fellowship)

Purpose: To train physicians to become CF specialists so that they can provide ongoing clinical care to individuals with CF in Canada. **Focus:** Cystic fibrosis. **Qualif.:** Applicant must be a Canadian citizen or permanent resident; have an MD degree; have recently completed the clinical training, exam and have obtained medical licensure in Canada. **Criteria:** Selection is based on the applicant's merit and potential.

Funds Avail.: The value will correspond to the applicant's qualifications and experience. **To Apply:** Applicants must submit three letters of recommendation (one from the recent supervisor); description of the proposed clinical train-

Awards are arranged alphabetically below their administering organizations

ing program; and official transcripts. Eleven copies of the application are must be submitted, one of which must contain original signatures. **Deadline:** October 1. **Contact:** amackesy@cysticfibrosis.ca.

2448 ■ CCFF Fellowships *(Doctorate, Graduate/ Fellowship)*

Purpose: To support basic or clinical research training in the areas of biomedical or behavioral sciences pertinent to cystic fibrosis. **Focus:** Cystic fibrosis. **Qualif.:** Applicants must hold an MD or PhD degree or must be graduates who have already completed basic residency training and are eligible for Canadian licensure. **Criteria:** Selection is based on the applicant's merit and potential.

Funds Avail.: Amount will correspond to the applicant's qualifications and experience. **To Apply:** Applicants must submit three letters of recommendation (one from a current supervisor); a description of the proposed research and training program; and official transcripts. Twelve copies of the application are required (1 with original signatures and 11 double-sided photocopies, with each copy stapled in the upper left hand corner). **Deadline:** October 1. **Contact:** amackesy@cysticfibrosis.ca.

2449 ■ CCFF Scholarships *(Doctorate, Graduate/ Scholarship)*

Purpose: To attract investigators to cystic fibrosis research. **Focus:** Cystic fibrosis. **Qualif.:** Applicant must hold an MD or PhD degree; must be sponsored by the chairman of the appropriate department and by the dean of the faculty; and has recently completed the training and wish to devote the majority of the time to cystic fibrosis research. **Criteria:** Selection is based on the caliber of the applicant's research and the potential of the applicant to make an outstanding contribution to cystic fibrosis research.

Funds Avail.: The value will correspond to the applicant's qualifications and experience. **To Apply:** Applicants must submit a completed application form together with the required materials. **Deadline:** October 1. **Contact:** amackesy@cysticfibrosis.ca.

2450 ■ Canadian Diabetes Association (CDA)

1400-522 University Ave.
Toronto, ON, Canada M5G 2R5
Ph: (416) 363-3373
Free: 800-226-8464
E-mail: info@diabetes.ca
URL: www.diabetes.ca

2451 ■ Eli Lilly Graduate Scholarships *(Graduate/Scholarship)*

Purpose: To encourage members to pursue their graduate or post-secondary graduate studies in a diabetes field. **Focus:** Diabetes. **Qualif.:** Applicants must be active DES members for a minimum of one year; must be Canadian citizens or landed immigrants; must not have received another DES or Canadian Diabetes Association scholarships or bursary for the same academic year. **Criteria:** Preference will be given to those who are studying at a Canadian university. Recipient will be selected based on the deliberations of the DES Awards Selection Committee.

Funds Avail.: $5,000. **To Apply:** Applicants must type or submit in electronic format the application form available from the website; must submit two references and one current copy of the applicant's resume or curriculum vitae. **Deadline:** April 1.

2452 ■ Canadian Engineering Memorial Foundation

3-247 Barr St.
Renfrew, ON, Canada K7V 4A6
Fax: (613) 432-6840
Free: 866-883-2363
E-mail: info@cemf.ca
URL: www.cemf.ca

2453 ■ AMEC Aboriginal Undergraduate Scholarships *(Undergraduate/Scholarship)*

Purpose: To provide financial assistance to qualified individuals who want to pursue their studies. **Focus:** Engineering. **Qualif.:** Applicants must be women who are pursuing their studies in an accredited university engineering program. **Criteria:** Selection of applicants will be based on the scholarship application requirements.

Funds Avail.: No specific amount. **Number Awarded:** 1. **To Apply:** Applicants must submit a signed Applicant Declaration together with a completed application form; an informational letter; community activities; reference letter; letter of support; a colored photograph; proof of ancestry; an essay; and a voice sound clip.

2454 ■ AMEC Masters Scholarships *(Graduate, Master's/Scholarship)*

Purpose: To provide financial assistance to qualified individuals who want to pursue their studies. **Focus:** Engineering. **Qualif.:** Applicants must be women in Canada who are pursuing their studies in engineering at the Masters level. **Criteria:** Selection of applicants will be based on the scholarship application requirements.

Funds Avail.: No specific amount. **Number Awarded:** 1. **To Apply:** Applicants must submit a signed Applicant Declaration together with a completed application form; an informational letter; curriculum vitae; reference letter; a colored photograph; proof of citizenship; media coverage; presentation; demonstration video clip; and a voice sound clip.

2455 ■ CEMF Undergraduate Engineering Scholarships *(Undergraduate/Scholarship)*

Purpose: To provide financial assistance to qualified individuals who want to pursue their studies. **Focus:** Engineering. **Qualif.:** Applicants must be Canadian women in engineering in either their 1st, 2nd or 3rd year of study in an accredited program in Canada. **Criteria:** Selection of applicants will be based on the scholarship application requirements.

Funds Avail.: $5,000. **Number Awarded:** 5. **To Apply:** Applicants must submit a signed Applicant Declaration along with the a completed application form; an informational letter; community activities; reference letter; letter of support; proof of citizenship; a colored photograph; and voice sound clip. **Deadline:** January 11.

2456 ■ CEMF Claudette MacKay-Lassonde Graduate Scholarships *(Doctorate, Postdoctorate/Scholarship)*

Purpose: To encourage Canadian women to pursue careers in the field of engineering. **Focus:** Engineering. **Qualif.:** Applicants must be Canadian women who are pursuing studies in engineering at the PhD level; must have an undergraduate engineering degree from an accredited Canadian program; must either be professional engineer or

Awards are arranged alphabetically below their administering organizations

provincially registered as an engineer-in-training/junior engineer. **Criteria:** Applicants will be selected based on: effectiveness of the presentation; community involvement and extra-curricular activities; professional achievements; achievements and leadership potential; overall quality of the electronic and hard copy package.

Funds Avail.: $15,000. **To Apply:** Applicants must submit: an application form; letter of recommendation coming from the Dean's office; applicant declaration; maximum of four pages information letter; curriculum vitae; a colored photo; reference letter; must provide a proof of citizenship; media coverage; PowerPoint presentation; and approximately (20-30 minutes) movie on a CD presenting themselves. The entire application must be type in a (12-point) Times New Roman font, double-spaced, original, signed and in hard copy accompanied by an electronic copy on a Windows XP Platform CD. Reference letters and letter from the Dean can mail directly to CEMF. **Deadline:** January 14. **Contact:** All applications must be submitted directly to: Canadian Engineering Memorial Foundation, PO Box 370, 3-247 Barr St., Renfrew, ON K7V 4 A6.

2457 ■ Vale Inco Limited Masters Scholarships
(Graduate/Scholarship)

Purpose: To provide financial assistance to qualified individuals who want to pursue their studies. **Focus:** Engineering. **Qualif.:** Applicants must be women in Canada who are pursuing their studies in engineering at the Masters level. **Criteria:** Selection of applicants will be based on the scholarship application requirements.

Funds Avail.: $10,000. **Number Awarded:** 1. **To Apply:** Applicants must submit a signed Applicant Declaration along with a completed application form; an informational letter; curriculum vitae; a colored photograph; reference letters; proof of citizenship; presentation; demonstration video clip; voice sound clip; and a letter of recommendation. **Deadline:** January 14.

2458 ■ Canadian Evaluation Society Educational Fund (CESEF)
1485 Laperriere Ave.
Ottawa, ON, Canada K1Z 7S8
Ph: (613) 725-2526
Fax: (613) 729-6206
E-mail: secretariat@evaluation-education.org
URL: cesef.memberlodge.org

2459 ■ Canadian Evaluation Society Educational Fund Scholarships *(Graduate/Scholarship)*

Purpose: To provide scholarship for graduate students wishing to further their knowledge within the field of program evaluation. **Focus:** General studies. **Qualif.:** Program is open to students of program evaluation who are pursuing studies for the purpose of improving the theory and practice of program evaluation. They must be in master's or doctoral level. **Criteria:** Selection will be based on merit and contribution to the field.

Funds Avail.: $5,000; $10,000. **Number Awarded:** 4. **To Apply:** Applicant may contact the society for information about the submission process and deadlines.

2460 ■ Canadian Federation of Independent Grocers (CFIG)
2235 Sheppard Ave. E, Ste. 902
Willowdale, ON, Canada M2J 5B5

Ph: (416) 492-2311
Fax: (416) 492-2347
Free: 800-661-2344
E-mail: info@cfig.ca
URL: www.cfig.ca

2461 ■ Canadian Federation of Independent Grocers National Scholarships *(Undergraduate/Scholarship)*

Purpose: To provide financial assistance to residents and students of Canada for their further educational enrichment. **Focus:** General studies. **Qualif.:** Applicants must be Canadian residents studying in Canada; enrolled or expecting to be enrolled in a post-secondary program of at least two years. High school applicants must be in their last year of secondary studies; college or university applicants must be enrolled in at least one more full year of study as of spring. **Criteria:** Applicants are evaluated based on merit.

Funds Avail.: $6,000. **To Apply:** Applicants must submit (1,000-word) essay on topic given by the Scholarship Committee; list of academic achievements, awards and extracurricular activities; official grade transcript of the last completed year; and the completed application form with all pertinent information properly filled in. **Deadline:** February 15. **Contact:** Kimberly Kwo, Manager Member Services, at 416-492-2311.

2462 ■ Canadian Federation for Sexual Health (CFSH)
2197 Riverside Dr.
Ottawa, ON, Canada K1H 7X3
Ph: (613) 241-4474
Fax: (613) 241-7550
E-mail: admin@cfsh.ca
URL: www.cfsh.ca

2463 ■ Phyllis P. Harris Scholarships
(Postgraduate/Award)

Purpose: To provide educational assistance for a volunteer or individual to pursue studies in the general field of human sexuality, family planning or population. **Focus:** Human relations; Family planning; Population studies. **Qualif.:** Applicant must be a full-time junior or senior at a Canadian university; must be a Canadian citizen or landed immigrant; must have a previous work or volunteer experience in the general field of human sexuality with the intent to pursue a degree in the field of family planning or population issues. **Criteria:** Applicants will be selected based on the evaluation of the submitted essays. Scholarship winners will be selected by a review committee constituted by the Canadian Federation for Sexual Health.

Funds Avail.: $2,600. **To Apply:** Applicants must submit a recent academic transcript and a 500-word typewritten essay outlining their relevant background education, objective and plans for the future. **Deadline:** Jun 30.

2464 ■ John and Lois Lamont Graduate Scholarships *(Postgraduate/Award)*

Purpose: To provide educational assistance for medical students enrolled in full-time graduate studies in a Canadian university. **Focus:** Medical education. **Qualif.:** Applicants must be Canadian citizens or landed immigrants who are graduates of any recognized university; possess an honour degree or its equivalent and intend to pursue a higher

Awards are arranged alphabetically below their administering organizations

degree in the field of sexual and reproductive health. **Criteria:** Applicants will be selected based on the evaluation of the candidate's essay. Scholarship winners will be selected by a review committee constituted by the Canadian Federation for Sexual Health.

Funds Avail.: $2,600. **To Apply:** Applicants must submit a typewritten essay of 500-700 words, outlining their education, background in sex and reproductive health and/or women's issues, aspiration, and plans to access abortion provider training as an elective; must include the curriculum vitae, recent academic transcript and a full list of publications; and must submit a letter of recommendation. **Deadline:** June 30.

2465 ■ Canadian Fertility and Andrology Society (CFAS)
1255 University, Ste. 1107
Montreal, QC, Canada H3B 3W7
Ph: (514) 524-9009
Fax: (514) 524-2163
E-mail: info@cfas.ca
URL: www.cfas.ca

2466 ■ Dr. Biljan Memorial Awards *(Graduate/Award)*

Purpose: To recognize a reproductive endocrinologist or fertility specialist who made a contribution to clinical research. **Focus:** Endocrinology. **Qualif.:** Applicants must be CFAS members; must be clinicians working in the field of reproductive endocrinology and infertility. **Criteria:** Preference will be given to abstracts that address novel approaches to ovulation induction/IVF or that address innovations in patient-focused strategies that improve administrative or clinical care.

Funds Avail.: Amount not specified. **To Apply:** Applicants must submit an application form.

2467 ■ Canadian Fire Safety Association (CFSA)
2175 Sheppard Ave. E, Ste. 310
North York, ON, Canada M2J 1W8
Ph: (416) 492-9417
Fax: (416) 491-1670
E-mail: cfsa@taylorenterprises.com
URL: www.canadianfiresafety.com

2468 ■ Randall Brown and Associates Awards *(Postgraduate/Award)*

Purpose: To inspire pursuits on fire safety awareness by providing financial support for students attending an approved Fire Safety Technology Course in a post-secondary school in Canada. **Focus:** Fires and fire prevention. **Qualif.:** Applicants must be enrolled in a Fire Protection Technology course at a Canadian college or university; must have exceptional overall skills in Codes/Standard Technology; have an academic proficiency of 3.25/4.00; and must be students entering the second and subsequent years of an approved course. **Criteria:** Applicants will be evaluated based on academic achievement and letter of application as required by the association.

Funds Avail.: $850. **To Apply:** Applicants must submit their academic grades accompanied by completed application form. **Deadline:** March 15. **Contact:** Mr. Anthony Van Odyk at the above address.

2469 ■ Fire Safety Awards *(Postgraduate/Award)*

Purpose: To expand fire safety awareness by providing financial assistance for individuals attending an approved Fire Safety Technology Course in a post-secondary school in Canada. **Focus:** Fires and fire prevention. **Qualif.:** Applicants must be enrolled in a Fire Protection Technology course at a Canadian college or university; must have excelled with outstanding leadership, motivation and technical skills and an overall academic proficiency; must be students entering the second and subsequent years of an approved course. **Criteria:** Applicants will be evaluated based on academic achievement and letter of application as required by the association.

Funds Avail.: $850. **To Apply:** Applicants must submit their academic grades together with completed application form. **Contact:** Mr. Anthony Van Odyk at the above address.

2470 ■ Leber Rubes Inc. Awards *(Postgraduate/Award)*

Purpose: To inspire pursuits on fire safety awareness by providing financial support for students attending an approved Fire Safety Technology Course in a post-secondary school in Canada. **Focus:** Fires and fire prevention. **Qualif.:** Applicants must be enrolled in a Fire Protection Technology course at a Canadian college or university; must have exceptional overall skills in Fire Alarm System Technology; have an academic proficiency of 3.25/4.00; and must be students entering the second and subsequent years of an approved course. **Criteria:** Applicants will be evaluated based on academic achievement and letter of application as required by the association.

Funds Avail.: $750. **To Apply:** Applicants must submit their academic grades together with completed application form. **Deadline:** March 15. **Contact:** Mr. Anthony Van Odyk at the above address.

2471 ■ Nadine International Inc. Awards *(Postgraduate/Award)*

Purpose: To expand pursuits on fire safety awareness by providing financial assistance for students enrolled in an approved Fire Safety Technology Course in a post-secondary school in Canada. **Focus:** Fires and fire prevention. **Qualif.:** Applicants must be enrolled in a Fire Protection Technology course at a Canadian college or university; must have exceptional overall skills in Fire Suppression Technology; must have an academic proficiency of 3.25/4.00; must be students entering the second and subsequent years of an approved course. **Criteria:** Applicants will be evaluated based on academic achievement and letter of application as required by the association.

Funds Avail.: $850. **To Apply:** Applicants must submit completed application form accompanied by copy of academic grades. **Deadline:** March 15. **Contact:** Mr. Anthony Van Odyk at the above address.

2472 ■ Underwriters' Laboratories of Canada Awards *(Postgraduate/Award)*

Purpose: To inspire pursuits on fire safety awareness by providing financial assistance for students attending an approved Fire Safety Technology Course in a post-secondary school in Canada. **Focus:** Fires and fire prevention. **Qualif.:** Applicants must be enrolled in a Fire Protection Technology course at a Canadian college or university; must have exceptional academic skills in Codes and Standards; must have an overall proficiency of 3.25/4.00;

Awards are arranged alphabetically below their administering organizations

and must be students entering the second and subsequent years of an approved course. **Criteria:** Applicants will be evaluated based on academic achievement and letter of application as required by the association.

Funds Avail.: $500. **To Apply:** Applicants must submit their academic grades and completed application form. **Deadline:** March 15. **Contact:** Mr. Anthony Van Odyk at the above address.

2473 ■ Canadian Gerontological Nursing Association (CGNA)

c/o Malachite Management Inc.
375 W 5th Ave., Ste. 201
Vancouver, BC, Canada V5Y 1J6
Ph: (604) 484-5698
Fax: (604) 874-4378
E-mail: cgna@malachite-mgmt.com
URL: www.cgna.net

2474 ■ Anne Beckingham Scholarships *(Graduate, Professional development/Scholarship)*

Purpose: To support outstanding registered nurses undertaking further education in a graduate degree program. **Focus:** Nursing; Gerontology. **Qualif.:** Applicant must be a Canadian citizen or landed immigrant at the time of taking up the award; be a member of CGNA for more than two years immediately prior to the application submission; be registered to practice nursing in a Canadian province; have gained acceptance to a suitable program in a recognized educational institution at the time of taking up the award; and must exhibit an interest in, and potential for, a career in gerontological nursing. Applicant must be a registered nurse undertaking further education in: a post-basic undergraduate nursing degree program; a graduate or post graduate degree program relevant to career development, preferably in the field of gerontological nursing - this includes nurse practitioner programs that focus on the care of older adults. **Criteria:** Selection will be based on the committee's criteria.

Funds Avail.: No specific amount. **To Apply:** Applicants must enclose a copy of their certificate to practice nursing in a Canadian province/territory; copy of current national/provincial/territorial gerontological nursing association membership card (or copy of completed CGNA/provincial/territorial association application form); evidence from an academic institution of part-time or full-time student status; academic transcript of most recently completed nursing degree program (please indicate as well those courses with gerontological content); curriculum vitae; and letter of support/recommendation from a current CGNA member. Applicants must complete the application by answering the following questions (in no more than one page for each): Describe your past contributions to gerontological nursing in Canada; Describe why you are interested in furthering your education in gerontological nursing and indicate how this additional education will assist your career plans. **Contact:** Beverly Laurila, Pres. at the above address.

2475 ■ Canadian Evaluation Society Memorial Scholarships *(Graduate, Professional development/Scholarship)*

Purpose: To help students further their education in a graduate degree program. **Focus:** Nursing; Gerontology. **Qualif.:** Applicants must be Canadian citizens or landed immigrants at the time of taking up the award; be member

of CGNA for more than two years immediately prior to the application submission; be registered to practice nursing in a Canadian province; have gained acceptance to a suitable program in a recognized educational institution at the time of taking up the award; and must exhibit an interest in, and potential for, a career in gerontological nursing. **Criteria:** Selection will be based on the committee's criteria.

Funds Avail.: No specific amount. **To Apply:** Applicants must enclose a copy of their certificate to practice nursing in a Canadian province/territory; copy of current national/provincial/territorial gerontological nursing association membership card (or copy of completed CGNA/provincial/territorial association application form); evidence from an academic institution of part-time or full-time student status; academic transcript of most recently completed nursing degree program which should indicate as well those courses with gerontological content; curriculum vitae; and letter of support/recommendation from a current CGNA member. Applicants must complete the application by answering the following questions (in no more than one page for each): Describe your past contributions to gerontological nursing in Canada; Describe why you are interested in furthering your education in gerontological nursing and indicate how this additional education will assist your career plans. **Contact:** Beverly Laurila, Pres.-Elect. at the above address.

2476 ■ SCA Nursing Scholarships *(Graduate, Professional development/Scholarship)*

Purpose: To help students further their education in a graduate degree program. **Focus:** Nursing; Gerontology. **Qualif.:** Applicant must be a Canadian citizen or landed immigrant at the time of taking up the award; must be a member of CGNA for more than two years immediately prior to the application submission; must be registered to practice nursing in a Canadian province; have gained acceptance to a suitable program in a recognized educational institution at the time of taking up the award; and must exhibit an interest in, and potential for, a career in gerontological nursing. **Criteria:** Selection will be based on the committee's criteria.

Funds Avail.: No specific amount. **To Apply:** Applicants must enclose a copy of their certificate to practice nursing in a Canadian province/territory; copy of current national/provincial/territorial gerontological nursing association membership card (or copy of completed CGNA/provincial/territorial association application form); evidence from an academic institution of part-time or full-time student status; and academic transcript of most recently completed nursing degree program (please indicate as well those courses with gerontological content); curriculum vitae; and letter of support/recommendation from a current CGNA member. Applicants must complete the application by answering the following questions (in no more than one page for each): Describe your past contributions to gerontological nursing in Canada; Describe why you are interested in furthering your education in gerontological nursing and indicate how this additional education will assist your career plans. **Contact:** Beverly Laurila, Pres. at the above address.

2477 ■ Canadian Group Psychotherapy Association

c/o Sandy Ramsay
7633 Toombs Dr.
Prince George, BC, Canada V2K 4Z5
URL: cgpa.ca

Awards are arranged alphabetically below their administering organizations

2478 ■ CGPF Endowments Conference Scholarships *(Professional development/ Scholarship)*

Purpose: To financially assist trainees who wish to acquire professional development and to defray the cost of attending the CGPA Annual conference. **Focus:** General studies. **Qualif.:** Applicants must be trainees in group psychotherapy in a GCPA-accredited training program or academic degree program. **Criteria:** Recipients will be evaluated based on training background, work experience, perspective on development of group therapy practice and being associated with the individual's life experience. **Funds Avail.:** Amount not specified. **To Apply:** Applicants must submit a letter of intent, curriculum vitae and letter of support from a mentor. **Contact:** Anthony Joyce at ajoyce@shaw.ca.

2479 ■ Martin Fischer Awards *(All/Award)*

Purpose: To recognize outstanding Canadian trainees or students who are receiving training in group therapy from an established program. **Focus:** General studies. **Qualif.:** Applicants must be students nominated by a training faculty member. **Criteria:** Applicants will be evaluated based on submitted paper, clinical and research achievements. **Funds Avail.:** $500-$1,500. **To Apply:** Applicants must submit three copies of paper accompanying the letter of support and documentation of clinical and research achievements.

2480 ■ Canadian Hard of Hearing Association (CHHA)

2415 Holly Ln., Ste. 205
Ottawa, ON, Canada K1V 7P2
Ph: (613) 526-1584
Fax: (613) 526-4718
Free: 800-263-8068
E-mail: chhanational@chha.ca
URL: www.chha.ca

2481 ■ Canadian Hard of Hearing Association Scholarships *(Undergraduate/Scholarship)*

Purpose: To offer financial assistance and recognition to hard of hearing and deafened students. **Focus:** General studies. **Qualif.:** Applicants must be students registered in a full-time program at a recognized Canadian college or university, with a goal of obtaining a diploma or degree; must be either hard-of-hearing, deafened or orally deaf. **Criteria:** Selection of applicants will be judged by a number of criteria including academic achievement, determination to cope with hearing loss and community involvement. **Funds Avail.:** $1,000. **To Apply:** Application forms are available online. Applicants must submit a copy of the most recent school transcript; must have a personal statement and two letters of reference. **Deadline:** February 28. **Remarks:** Established in 2002. **Contact:** scholarship@chha.ca.

2482 ■ Canadian Hemophilia Society (CHS)

400-1255 University St.
Montreal, QC, Canada H3B 3B6
Ph: (514) 848-0503
Fax: (514) 848-9661
Free: 800-668-2686
E-mail: chs@hemophilia.ca

URL: www.hemophilia.ca

2483 ■ CHS - Bursary Program Scholarships *(Undergraduate/Scholarship)*

Purpose: To bring young volunteers into the CHS while recognizing the importance of education. **Focus:** General studies. **Qualif.:** Applicants must possess academic proficiency; must have experience in community service at volunteer level; and must possess leadership qualities. **Criteria:** Priority is given to those who have financial needs. **Funds Avail.:** $4,000. **To Apply:** Applicant must provide three letters of reference with the application stating the abilities and suitability of the candidate; must provide a letter from his/her physician or any medical authority confirming his/her medical status; must submit an original essay (500 words) to emphasize the logical thinking and adequate writing skills of the applicant; and must submit the original transcript of grades for the last year in secondary school. Application forms are available from the website. **Deadline:** April 30.

2484 ■ CHS - Mature Student Bursary Program Scholarships *(Professional development/ Scholarship)*

Purpose: To encourage educational pursuits of students with hemophilia. **Focus:** General studies. **Qualif.:** Applicant must be at least 30 years of age. **Criteria:** Recipients are selected based on application materials and financial need as reviewed by a committee of academics and lay persons. **Funds Avail.:** $4,000. **To Apply:** Applicants must submit a detailed budget showing their source of income and their projected expenses for a year of study at the institution of their choice; must submit an essay of intent describing past employment and assessment of new career; must provide three letters of reference with their application, none of which may be from a relative (such letters should attest to the abilities and suitability of the candidate for the program being applied for as well as act as a character reference for the candidate); must provide a separate letter from their physician or some medical authority confirming their medical status regarding eligibility to this program. **Deadline:** April 30.

2485 ■ CHS Scholarships *(Undergraduate, Vocational/Occupational/Scholarship)*

Purpose: To bring young volunteers into the CHS while recognizing the importance of education. **Focus:** General studies. **Qualif.:** Applicants must possess academic proficiency (GPA of 3.0 on a 4.0 scale); must have experience in community service at a volunteer level; and must possess leadership qualities. **Criteria:** Priority is given to those who might not be able to succeed in a vocational course requiring strenuous physical labor. **Funds Avail.:** $4,000. **To Apply:** Applicant must provide three letters of reference with the application stating the abilities and suitability of the candidate; must provide a letter from his/her physician or any medical authority confirming his/her medical status; must submit an original 500-word essay to emphasize the logical thinking and adequate writing skills of the applicant; and must submit the original transcript of grades of the last year in secondary school. Application forms are available on the website. **Deadline:** April 30.

2486 ■ Canadian Hospitality Foundation (CHF)

300 Adelaide St. E, No. 399
Toronto, ON, Canada M5A 1N1

Awards are arranged alphabetically below their administering organizations

Ph: (416) 363-3401
Fax: (416) 363-3403
E-mail: chf@theohi.ca
URL: www.thechf.ca

2487 ■ Applied Hospitality Degree Scholarships
(Undergraduate/Scholarship)

Purpose: To provide scholarship to the students enrolled in the first or second year of a community college. **Focus:** Hotel, institutional, and restaurant management; Travel and tourism. **Qualif.:** Applicants must be college students currently enrolled in the first or second year of a community college. Applicants must be Canadian citizens or permanent residents. **Criteria:** Selection will be based on work experience, scholastic record, leadership and ability to get along with others, professional promise, essay and discretionary points.

Funds Avail.: $2,500. **To Apply:** Applicants must complete the application form on-line. In addition, students must submit hard copies of the following documents (please note that missing or incomplete documents may be grounds for elimination): Most current official transcripts of your complete academic history at the college you are enrolled in at this time; one or more letters of recommendation from an instructor and/or administrator form your college; One letters of recommendation from past or present employers; Resume; An essay on one of the topics listed on application form (600 words). Employer and school letters must include telephone numbers and, where possible, e-mail addresses. **Deadline:** May 18. **Contact:** CHF at the above address.

2488 ■ Canadian Hospitality Foundation College Entrance Scholarships *(Undergraduate/Scholarship)*

Purpose: To provide scholarship to the High School students in their final year of school. **Focus:** Culinary arts; Hotel, institutional, and restaurant management; Travel and tourism. **Qualif.:** Applicants must be high school students in their final year of school and who are enrolling in a minimum two-year college program in one of the following areas of training or study: Accommodation; Chef; Cook; Culinary; Events; Food and Beverages; Golf Club; Hospitality; Hotel; Resort; Restaurant; Tourism; Applicants must be Canadian citizens or permanent residents. **Criteria:** Selection will be based on work experience, scholastic record, leadership and ability to get along with others, professional promise and discretionary points.

Funds Avail.: No specific amount. **To Apply:** Applicants must complete the application form on-line. In addition, students must submit hard copies of the following documents (please note that missing or incomplete documents may be grounds for elimination): Final-year official transcripts from your previous academic year and report card from your current academic year (first semester/first term); Letter/s of recommendation from your school principal, teacher or guidance counselor; Letter/s of recommendation from past or present employers. School and employer letters must include telephone numbers and, where possible, e-mail addresses. **Deadline:** May 18. **Contact:** CHF at the above address.

2489 ■ Canadian Hospitality Foundation University Entrance Scholarships
(Undergraduate/Scholarship)

Purpose: To provide scholarships to High School students in their final year of school. **Focus:** Hotel, institutional, and restaurant management; Travel and tourism. **Qualif.:** Applicants must be high school students in their final year of school who are enrolling in a university degree program in one of the following areas of training or study: Hospitality; Hotel; Tourism. Applicants must be Canadian citizens or permanent residents. **Criteria:** Selection will be based on the following criteria: Work experience; Scholastic record; Leadership and ability to get along with others; Professional promise; Discretionary points.

Funds Avail.: No specific amount. **To Apply:** Applicants must complete the application form on-line; in addition, students must submit hard copies of the following documents (please note that missing or incomplete documents may be grounds for elimination): Final-year official transcripts from your previous academic year and report card from your current academic year (first semester/first term); Letter/s of recommendation from your school principal, teacher or guidance counselor; Letter/s of recommendation from past or present employers. School and employer letters must include telephone numbers and, where possible, e-mail addresses.

2490 ■ Culinary (1-Year Program) Scholarships
(Undergraduate/Scholarship)

Purpose: To provide scholarship to the students enrolled in a one-year culinary program. **Focus:** Culinary arts. **Qualif.:** Applicants must: be college students currently enrolled in a one-year (minimum of eight months) culinary certificate program; not have received any other Canadian Hospitality Foundation scholarships; be Canadian citizens or permanent residents. **Criteria:** Selection will be based on work experience, scholastic record, leadership and ability to get along with others, professional promise and discretionary points. Applications selected by the judges are ranked and the scholarships are awarded based on dollar value.

Funds Avail.: No specific amount. **To Apply:** Applicants must complete the application form on-line. In addition, students must submit hard copies of the following documents (please note that missing or incomplete documents may be grounds for elimination): Final-year official transcripts from your previous academic year and report card from your current academic year (first semester/first term); Letter/s of recommendation from your school principal, teacher or guidance counselor; Letter/s of recommendation from past or present employers. School and employer letters must include telephone numbers and e-mail addresses. **Deadline:** May 18.

2491 ■ Canadian Hydrographic Association
6420 Edenwood Dr.
Mississauga, ON, Canada L5N 3H3
Ph: (416) 512-5764
Fax: (416) 512-5830
URL: www.hydrography.ca

2492 ■ Canadian Hydrographic Association Student Awards *(Undergraduate/Award)*

Purpose: To advance the knowledge of hydrography, cartography and associated disciplines. **Focus:** Cartography/Surveying. **Qualif.:** Applicants must be full time students in an accredited post-secondary program in the field of Geomatics in a university or technological college anywhere in Canada. **Criteria:** Selection will be based on the committee's criteria.

Funds Avail.: $2,000. **To Apply:** Applicants will be required to write a short paragraph explaining their financial need in

Awards are arranged alphabetically below their administering organizations

a clear, concise manner on the application form or, if necessary, attached piece of paper. The importance of this aspect of the application is emphasized. Applicants must submit one letter of reference from an official of the university or college where the applicant spent the previous year. Letter of reference must include the address and phone number of this official. **Deadline:** June 30.

2493 ■ Canadian Identification Society (CIS)

c/o Henry Kinsella, Exec. Dir.
19 Candow Crescent
Stittsville, ON, Canada K2S 1K7
Fax: (613) 836-9447
E-mail: admin@cis-sci.ca
URL: www.cis-sci.ca

2494 ■ Canadian Identification Society Essay Scholarship Awards *(Professional development/ Prize)*

Purpose: To help CIS members conduct their research. **Focus:** Law enforcement. **Qualif.:** Applicants must be CIS members or immediate family members employed in law enforcement. **Criteria:** Essays will be evaluated based on originality of the technique, merit as a method of collecting/ processing forensic evidence and the quality of writing.

Funds Avail.: Maximum amount of $300. **To Apply:** Applicants must submit an essay (minimum of 3000 words in either French or English) on forensic identification evidence that describes a successful method of locating, processing or presenting such evidence.

2495 ■ William Donald Dixon Research Grants *(Graduate/Grant)*

Purpose: To provide opportunities to individuals engaged in forensic research. **Focus:** Law enforcement. **Qualif.:** Applicants must be members of CIS who have submitted a relevant research paper in the field of forensic science; must have a bachelor's degree in any discipline; should not be employed in law enforcement. Graduates of three-year programs, undergraduates and part-time applicants are required to be employed in law enforcement. **Criteria:** Recipients will be selected based on submitted research proposals.

Funds Avail.: $500. **Number Awarded:** 2. **To Apply:** Applicants must submit a research proposal, or outline on a topic related to forensic identification. The summary and/or research must be submitted for publishing in the Identification Canada Journal. Letters of recommendation should be obtained from a senior official of their police department, law enforcement official(s), or academic head and employer.

2496 ■ Edward Foster Awards *(All/Award)*

Purpose: To encourage members to conduct research that will benefit the forensic identification profession. **Focus:** Law enforcement. **Qualif.:** Applicants must be nominated by the two CIS members. **Criteria:** Awards will be given to applicants who best meet the qualifications.

Funds Avail.: No specific amount. **To Apply:** Applicants must submit an outline of their contributions to the field of forensic identification.

2497 ■ Canadian Institute for the Administration of Justice (CIAJ)

3101 Chemin de la Tour, Rm. A-3421
Montreal, QC, Canada H3C 3J7

Ph: (514) 343-6157
Fax: (514) 343-6296
E-mail: ciaj@ciaj-icaj.ca
URL: www.ciaj-icaj.ca

2498 ■ Charles D. Gonthier Research Fellowships *(Graduate, Professional development/ Fellowship)*

Purpose: To support research related to justice. **Focus:** Law enforcement. **Qualif.:** Fellowship is open to faculty and graduate students at Canadian universities. **Criteria:** Recipients will be selected based on submitted application and research project.

Funds Avail.: $7,500. **To Apply:** Applicants must submit a completed application form outlining the research project and budget. **Deadline:** November 5. **Contact:** Completed application form and research project must be submitted to Christine Robertson at the above address.

2499 ■ Canadian Institute for Advanced Legal Studies

PO Box 43538
Toronto, ON, Canada M4G 4G8
Ph: (416) 429-3292
Fax: (416) 429-9805
E-mail: info@canadian-institute.com
URL: www.canadian-institute.com

2500 ■ Right Honourable Paul Martin Sr. Scholarships *(Graduate/Scholarship)*

Purpose: To provide financial assistance for students of graduate studies in law at the University of Cambridge, England. **Focus:** Law. **Qualif.:** Applicant must be a graduate of law from a Canadian university; an attendee at a Bar Admission Course in Canada; or an articling student in Canada; and must be accepted into the University of Cambridge and a College of the University of Cambridge for graduate studies in law. **Criteria:** Selection will be based on the committee's criteria.

Funds Avail.: Full scholarship. **Number Awarded:** 2. **To Apply:** Applications must include: curriculum vitae; a personal statement indicating why the applicant wishes to undertake graduate studies in law at the University of Cambridge and why the applicant is suited to undertake such studies; a copy of transcripts for undergraduate and graduate studies, for studies in law and for a Bar Admissions Course, as applicable; and a maximum of three letters of reference. Applications must be submitted by mail, fax or electronic mail no later than the deadline. **Deadline:** December 31. **Contact:** Mr. Randall J. Hofley, VP at the above address.

2501 ■ Canadian Institute of Planners (CIP)

141 Laurier Ave. W, Ste. 1112
Ottawa, ON, Canada K1P 5J3
Ph: (613) 237-7526
Fax: (613) 237-7045
Free: 800-207-2138
E-mail: general@cip-icu.ca
URL: www.cip-icu.ca

2502 ■ CIP Fellow's Travel Scholarships *(Postgraduate/Scholarship)*

Purpose: To inspire future planners by allowing them to travel, observe and study innovative planning projects first

Awards are arranged alphabetically below their administering organizations

hand. **Focus:** General studies. **Qualif.:** Applicant must be a student member who is in the final year of an undergraduate planning program recognized by the Canadian Institute of Planners. **Criteria:** Recipients will be selected based on demonstrated leadership and commitment to their chosen profession and professional association; academic achievement; and a proposal to travel and explore a leading-edge, innovative or new planning initiative or project that will contribute to the depth and breadth of the student's educational experience as reviewed by a jury consisting of three members of the College of Fellows and the Vice President of the Student Scholarship Trust Fund.

Funds Avail.: $4,000. **Number Awarded:** 1. **To Apply:** Applicants must provide their contact information, university and program enrollment information, official transcript, a recommendation letter from the department head and from someone who is familiar with the applicant's commitment to community service, a list of accomplishments and a travel proposal (not more than 4-5 pages in length). Applicants are required to submit six originals and one copy on CD of the submission materials. **Deadline:** February 9. **Contact:** Application form and supporting materials must be submitted to 141 Laurier Ave., Ste. 1112, Ottawa, ON K1P 5J3.

2503 ■ Canadian Institute of Ukrainian Studies (CIUS)

4-30 Pembina Hall
University of Alberta
Edmonton, AB, Canada T6G 2H8
Ph: (780) 492-2972
Fax: (780) 492-4967
E-mail: cius@ualberta.ca
URL: www.ualberta.ca/CIUS

2504 ■ Leo J. Krysa Family Undergraduate Scholarships *(Undergraduate/Scholarship)*

Purpose: To help students pursue their final year of study in the faculty of Arts or Education. **Focus:** Ukrainian studies. **Qualif.:** Candidates must be Canadian citizens or permanent residents of Canada at the time of application; must be students in the faculty of Arts and Education about to enter their final year of study in pursuit of an undergraduate degree; have a program which emphasizes Ukrainian and/or Ukrainian-Canadian studies based on the following areas: Education, History, Humanities and Social Sciences; must have a record of above average grades in their Ukrainian-content courses. **Criteria:** Applications will be judged on a point system that emphasizes academic achievement, performance in Ukrainian-content course, writing sample (paper or essay), and community involvement.

Funds Avail.: Up to $3,500. **To Apply:** Applicants must submit an official transcript of records. Application form is available at the Canadian Institute of Ukrainian Studies, 430 Pembina Hall, University of Alberta, Edmonton, AB, CAN T6G 2H8. **Deadline:** March 1.

2505 ■ Ukrainian Canadian Professional and Business Club Scholarships in Education *(Undergraduate/Scholarship)*

Purpose: To support students who wish to pursue their final year of study in the faculty of Education. **Focus:** Ukrainian studies. **Qualif.:** Applicant must be a full-time undergraduate student completing the third or fourth year in the faculty of Education at the University of Alberta; must

have taken one course in language acquisition or teaching and one senior course in Ukrainian language or literature; must have both academic standing and demonstrated involvement in the Ukrainian community; and have an overall GPA of no less than 7.0. **Criteria:** Application will be judged on a points system that emphasizes academic achievement, performance in Ukrainian-content course, writing sample (paper or essay), and community involvement.

Funds Avail.: $800. **To Apply:** Applicants must submit an official transcript of records. Application form is available from the Canadian Institute of Ukrainian Studies, 430 Pembina Hall, University of Alberta, Edmonton, AB, CAN T6G 2H8. **Deadline:** March 1.

2506 ■ Canadian Institutes of Health Research

160 Elgin St., 9th Fl.
Ottawa, ON, Canada K1A 0W9
Ph: (613) 941-2672
Fax: (613) 954-1800
Free: 888-603-4178
E-mail: info@cihr-irsc.gc.ca
URL: www.cihr-irsc.gc.ca

2507 ■ Institute Community Support Publication Prizes *(Doctorate, Graduate, Undergraduate/ Prize)*

Purpose: To support research that reduces the burden of cancer on individuals and families through prevention strategies, screening, diagnosis, effective treatment, psycho-social support systems and palliation. **Focus:** Oncology. **Qualif.:** Applicants must have a recently published research article as a first author (within 12 months of the application date); must be a student or trainee at any Canadian university, teaching hospital, research center or other health organization (undergraduate, graduate, postgraduate, post-doctoral fellow, resident); must be Canadians or foreigners doing research in Canada. **Criteria:** Individual submissions will be evaluated and ranked according to their individual and collective merit based on the following criteria: relevance to the mandate of ICR; level of the student or trainee's contribution; quality of the journal; impact of the publication; impact on the target audience.

Funds Avail.: $1,000-$6,000. **To Apply:** Applicants must submit a copy of the published article in electronic (PDF format) and hard copy form; and a completed Institute Community Support application form in electronic and hard copy form. Send the completed application package by courier/ registered mail and email to: Publication Prizes - ICS Program, CIHR Institute of Cancer Research, 3655 Promenade Sir-William-Osler, No. 701, Montreal, QC H3G 1Y6. Phone: 514-398-4964. Email: ic.icr@mcgill.ca. **Deadline:** June 30 and December 31. **Contact:** Benoit Lussier, PhD, 3655 Promenade Sir-William-Osler, No. 701, Montreal, QC H3G 1Y6. Phone: 514-398-4964. Email: benoit.lussier@mcgill.ca.

2508 ■ Canadian Iranian Foundation (CIF)

PO Box 91231
West Vancouver, BC, Canada V7V 3N6
Ph: (604) 696-1121
Fax: (604) 922-8584
E-mail: info@cif-bc.com
URL: www.canadianiranianfoundation.com

Awards are arranged alphabetically below their administering organizations

2509 ■ Canadian Iranian Foundation Scholarships (Undergraduate/Scholarship)

Purpose: To assist immigrant students who wish to pursue their academic goals. **Focus:** General studies. **Qualif.:** Applicants must have legal immigrant's status (Canadian Citizen or permanent resident of Canada) and reside in Canada; have shown a great effort in trying to integrate into Canadian Society by volunteering at least 100 hours of community service; have active interest in Iranian and Canadian culture and heritage; must be accepted into a Canadian post-secondary institute in a full degree program by the end of academic year; and must be between 18 to 25 years of age. **Criteria:** Selection will be based on the committee's criteria.

Funds Avail.: $1,000. **To Apply:** Applicants must provide two academic references; letter of reference supporting volunteer services; and sealed official transcript of Grade 12 grades. **Deadline:** April 10.

2510 ■ Canadian IT Law Association (IT.Can)
PO Box 918
Thornhill, ON, Canada L4J 8G7
Ph: (905) 889-0640
E-mail: lisa.ptack@rogers.com
URL: www.it-can.ca

2511 ■ Canadian IT Law Association Student Writing Contest (Doctorate/Prize)

Purpose: To encourage full-time students to have an interest in information technology law. **Focus:** Law. **Qualif.:** Applicants must be full-time students pursuing an LL.B/J.D (including a joint LL.B./J.D.), BCL, LL.L, LL.M or PhD at a Canadian law school, articling or clerking in Canada. **Criteria:** Submissions will be reviewed based on quality, originality and creativity of argument, quality of writing, sophistication and depth of the research.

Funds Avail.: $1,000. **To Apply:** Entries should be between approximately 25 to 50 typed pages, should contain endnotes and not footnotes, should be written in Word format, 12-point font and double-spaced. Submissions may be in English or French. Subject line for the entries should be "IT.Can Student Writing Competition." **Deadline:** June 29. **Contact:** Entries will be accepted by e-mail only to lisa.ptack@rogers.com.

2512 ■ Canadian Journalism Foundation (CJF)
59 Adelaide St. E, Ste. 500
Toronto, ON, Canada M5C 1K6
Ph: (416) 955-0394
Fax: (416) 532-6879
URL: www.cjf-fjc.ca

2513 ■ CJF Canadian Journalism Fellowships (Graduate, Professional development, Undergraduate/Fellowship)

Purpose: To help fellows achieve their future potential as effective and responsible journalists. **Focus:** Journalism. **Qualif.:** Applicants must have at least five years experience and be full-time news or editorial employees with Canadian newspapers, news services, radio, television or magazines. Freelance journalists who have been working consistently in the media over a five-year period will also be considered. Fellows are free to enroll in any graduate or undergraduate courses and use the full facilities of the University of Toronto. **Criteria:** Fellows are selected by a committee appointed by the President of the University of Toronto and the Master of Massey College.

Funds Avail.: $4,900 monthly. **Number Awarded:** Varies. **To Apply:** Applicants must include a proposal for a plan of study; statement of the applicant's experience; samples of work; and supporting letters from an employer or references. **Remarks:** Fellowship is sponsored by University of Toronto and Massey College. **Contact:** Materials should be submitted to Anna Luengo, Massey College, 4 Devonshire Pl., Toronto, ON M5S 2E1; Phone: 416-978-6606; E-mail: annaluengo@masseycollege.ca.

2514 ■ Greg Clerk Awards (Professional development/Award)

Purpose: To recognize and offer a professional development opportunity to working journalists. **Focus:** Journalism. **Qualif.:** Applicants must be Canadian journalists who have been employed for one to five years and are employed by, under contract to, or freelancing on the news and editorial side of regularly published newspapers and periodicals, TV and radio news broadcasters, and online publications. **Criteria:** Applicants will be judged based on submitted materials.

Funds Avail.: Amount not specified. **To Apply:** Applicants must submit a detailed proposal of no more than two pages outlining the use of professional development opportunity; two samples of works; resume; and one letter of recommendation from a relevant employer. TV or radio clips should be no longer than 30 minutes. It should be on disc or available online for download. Original clippings should be accompanied by a printout text (mail), or in PDF format (e-mail). **Deadline:** March. **Contact:** Electronic submissions should be forwarded to programs@cjf-fjc.ca.

2515 ■ Tom Hanson Photojournalism Awards (Professional development/Internship)

Purpose: To give photographers trying to break into photojournalism the chance to perform on the national stage. **Focus:** Photography, Journalistic. **Qualif.:** Applicants must be Canadian photojournalists who have been in the business less than five years (from students to freelancers to photographers) working at regional publications. **Criteria:** Recipients will be selected based on submitted materials.

Funds Avail.: $875 per week. **To Apply:** Applicants must submit a portfolio of their work (at least 12 and no more than 25 photos); detailed proposal of no more than 1000 words explaining how an internship would expand their experience(s) as a photojournalist; resume; and a letter of recommendation (optional) from a current employer or teacher. **Deadline:** January. **Contact:** Questions should be forwarded to Heather McCall at hmccall@cjf-fjc.ca.

2516 ■ Canadian Lawyers Abroad (CLA)
248 Clemow Ave.
Ottawa, ON, Canada K1S 2B6
Ph: (613) 797-1173
Fax: (613) 233-0093
E-mail: info@cla-ace.ca
URL: www.cla-ace.ca

2517 ■ CLA Student Summer Internship Program (Undergraduate/Internship)

Purpose: To help law students defray expenses on their summer working at Non-Governmental Organizations

Awards are arranged alphabetically below their administering organizations

abroad and within Canada. **Focus:** Law. **Qualif.:** Applicants must be law students within CLA-ACE Student Chapter (Dalhousie, Queens, UBC, Calgary, Universite de Montreal, University of New Brunswick, Ottawa, Victoria, Windsor, Osgoode, University of Alberta and Toronto). **Criteria:** Recipients will be selected based on the following criteria; 1) previous volunteer or work experience(s) in Canada or abroad; 2) demonstrated interest in human rights, good governance and the rule of law; 3) relevant educational and work background; 4) strong communication skills; 5) self-sufficiency and self-motivation; 6) problem-solving skills and ability to work with limited resources; 7) and must be respectful, highly adaptable and open to change. Previous overseas experience preferred, but not essential.

Funds Avail.: No stated amount. **To Apply:** Applicants must submit a filled-out application form.

2518 ■ Canadian Library Association (CLA)

1150 Morrison Dr., Ste. 400
Ottawa, ON, Canada K2H 8S9
Ph: (613) 232-9625
Fax: (613) 563-9895
E-mail: info@cla.ca
URL: www.cla.ca

2519 ■ CLA/ACB Dafoe Scholarships *(Graduate/ Scholarship)*

Purpose: To encourage individuals to pursue their masters degree in library and information studies. **Focus:** Library and archival sciences. **Qualif.:** Candidates must be Canadian citizens or landed immigrants; must have professional library/information science degrees at an ALA-accredited institution. **Criteria:** Applicants are selected based on academic achievement, leadership potential and expressed interest in the profession.

Funds Avail.: $5,000. **To Apply:** Application and scholarship reference forms are available at the website. Applicants must submit completed form along transcript of records and proof of admission to library and information studies program. **Deadline:** May 1. **Contact:** CLA/ACB Member Services Department at the above address or email at membership@cla.ca.

2520 ■ H.W. Wilson Scholarships *(Graduate/ Scholarship)*

Purpose: To encourage individuals to pursue their masters degree in library and information studies. **Focus:** Library and archival sciences. **Qualif.:** Candidates must be Canadian citizens or with landed immigrant status; must have professional library degrees at an ALA-accredited institution. **Criteria:** Scholarship applications are reviewed by the Committees of Canadian Library Association. Applications are considered on the basis of academic achievement, leadership potential and demonstrated interest in the profession.

Funds Avail.: $2,000. **To Apply:** Applicants must submit a completed scholarship form and three reference forms available at the website; transcript of records; and proof of admission to a library school. **Deadline:** May 1. **Contact:** Send materials and application forms to CLA/ACB Member Services Department at the above address, Email: membership@cla.ca.

2521 ■ World Book Graduate Scholarships in Library and Information Science *(Graduate/ Scholarship)*

Purpose: To support individuals who wish to pursue a PhD degree in library and information studies. **Focus:** Library

and archival sciences. **Qualif.:** Applicant must be an individual who holds a MLS/MLIS degree and is pursuing a PhD degree in library and information studies in either Canada or the United States; must be a Canadian citizen or landed immigrant. **Criteria:** Recipients are selected based on the application and other supporting documents.

Funds Avail.: $2,500. **To Apply:** Application form is available at the website. **Deadline:** May 1.

2522 ■ Canadian Medical Foundation (CMF)

1870 Alta Vista Dr.
Ottawa, ON, Canada K1G 6R7
Ph: (613) 520-7681
Fax: (613) 520-7692
Free: 866-530-4979
E-mail: info@cmf.ca
URL: www.medicalfoundation.ca

2523 ■ Dr. John Big Canoe Memorial Scholarships *(Undergraduate/Scholarship)*

Purpose: To provide financial support for undergraduate aboriginal medical students. **Focus:** Medicine. **Qualif.:** Applicants must be undergraduate aboriginal students enrolled in the second, third or fourth year of study in a Canadian school of medicine. **Criteria:** Selection is based on academic performance and outstanding contributions to the aboriginal community in Canada.

Funds Avail.: $2,000. **To Apply:** Applicants must submit complete application materials. **Deadline:** September 11.

2524 ■ Canadian Meteorological and Oceanographic Society (CMOS)

PO Box 3211
Sta. D
Ottawa, ON, Canada K1P 6H7
Ph: (613) 990-0300
Fax: (613) 990-1617
E-mail: cmos@cmos.ca
URL: www.cmos.ca

2525 ■ Roger Daley Postdoctoral Publication Awards *(Postdoctorate/Award)*

Purpose: To promote meteorology and oceanography in Canada. **Focus:** Meteorology; Oceanography. **Qualif.:** Candidates must be working in Canada in a non-permanent position as a postdoctoral fellows or research associates and must have received their doctoral degree within five years. **Criteria:** Award is based on the excellence of a publication in the fields of meteorology or oceanography that has appeared or is in press at the time of nomination.

Funds Avail.: $2,000. **To Apply:** Nominating letters should include the current title, full address and phone number of the nominee. An up-to-date CV and a summary of the candidate's work must be included. The nomination should be accompanied by, at least one and at most four, additional letters of support indicating the extent of influence of the candidate's work. Electronic format is preferred; however, hard-copy material will be accepted. **Deadline:** February.

2526 ■ Tertia M.C. Hughes Memorial Graduate Student Prizes *(Graduate/Prize)*

Purpose: To promote meteorology and oceanography in Canada. **Focus:** Meteorology; Oceanography. **Qualif.:** Can-

Awards are arranged alphabetically below their administering organizations

didates must be graduate students registered at a Canadan university or by Canadian graduate students registered at a foreign university. **Criteria:** Selection will be based on the committee's criteria.

Funds Avail.: $500. **To Apply:** Nominating letters should include the current title, full address and phone number of the nominee. An up-to-date CV and a summary of the candidate's work must be included. The nomination should be accompanied by, at least one and at most four, additional letters of support indicating the extent of influence of the candidate's work. Electronic format is preferred; however, hard-copy material will be accepted. **Deadline:** February.

2527 ■ President's Prize (Professional development/Prize)

Purpose: To promote meteorology and oceanography in Canada. **Focus:** Meteorology; Oceanography. **Qualif.:** Candidates must be members of the Society with a recent paper or book of special merit in the fields of meteorology or oceanography. The paper must have been accepted for publication in Atmosphere-Ocean or another refereed journal. **Criteria:** Selection will be based on the committee's criteria.

Funds Avail.: No specific amount. **To Apply:** Nominating letters should include the current title, full address and phone number of the nominee. An up-to-date CV and a summary of the candidate's work must be included. The nomination should be accompanied by, at least one and at most four, additional letters of support indicating the extent of influence of the candidate's work. Electronic format is preferred; however, hard-copy material will be accepted. **Deadline:** February.

2528 ■ Francois J. Saucier Prize in Applied Oceanography (Professional development/Prize)

Purpose: To promote meteorology and oceanography in Canada. **Focus:** Meteorology; Oceanography. **Qualif.:** Candidates must be members of the Society with outstanding contribution to the application of meteorology in Canada. **Criteria:** Selection will be based on the committee's criteria.

Funds Avail.: No specific amount. **To Apply:** Nominating letters should include the current title, full address and phone number of the nominee. An up-to-date CV and a summary of the candidate's work must be included. The nomination should be accompanied by, at least one and at most four, additional letters of support indicating the extent of influence of the candidate's work. Electronic format is preferred; however, hard-copy material will be accepted. **Deadline:** February.

2529 ■ Dr. Andrew Thomson Prize in Applied Meteorology (Professional development/Prize)

Purpose: To promote meteorology and oceanography in Canada. **Focus:** Meteorology; Oceanography. **Qualif.:** Candidates must be members of the Society with outstanding contribution to the application of meteorology in Canada. **Criteria:** Selection will be based on the committee's criteria.

Funds Avail.: No specific amount. **To Apply:** Nominating letters should include the current title, full address and phone number of the nominee. An up-to-date CV and a summary of the candidate's work must be included. The nomination should be accompanied by, at least one and at most four, additional letters of support indicating the extent of influence of the candidate's work. Electronic format is preferred; however, hard-copy material will be accepted. **Deadline:** February.

2530 ■ Canadian National Institute for the Blind (CNIB)

1929 Bayview Ave.
Toronto, ON, Canada M4G 3E8
Ph: (416) 486-2500
Fax: (416) 480-7700
Free: 800-563-2642
E-mail: info@cnib.ca
URL: www.cnib.ca/en

2531 ■ Scholarship Awards of The Aliant Pioneer Volunteers (Postgraduate/Scholarship)

Purpose: To provide financial assistance to a person with vision lost while attending a post-secondary educational program. **Focus:** General studies. **Qualif.:** Candidates must be aged 25 years or under; must have acuity of 20/70 or less with correction; must be Canadian citizens residing in Nova Scotia or Prince Edward Island; must be graduating from grade 12 during the application year (or be a high school graduate) and registered in a post-secondary educational program. Candidates may also be presently employed but returning to an educational program; must have a reasonable level of achievement and a genuine need for financial assistance. **Criteria:** Candidates will be selected based on the Selection Committee's review of the application materials. Priority is given to candidates with financial need.

Funds Avail.: $2,000. **To Apply:** Applicants must submit a completed application form (available on the website); must submit two letters of reference: (1) educational letter of recommendation, and (2) personal or community letter of recommendation including contact information (address, telephone, fax and e-mail); letter of acceptance from post-secondary education institution; must provide a documentation about the candidate's visual acuity. **Deadline:** April 30. **Remarks:** Establshed in 2006. **Contact:** Application form and other supporting documents must be sent to: Selection Committee, Scholarship Award of the Aliant Pioneer Volunteers, c/o Wendy Constable, CNIB, 2717 Gladstone St., Ste. 112, Halifax, NS B3K 0A4; Fax: 902-454-6570; E-mail: wendy.constable@cnib.ca.

2532 ■ Canadian Nurses Foundation (CNF)

50 Driveway St.
Ottawa, ON, Canada K2P 1E2
Ph: (613) 237-2133
Fax: (613) 237-3520
Free: 800-361-8404
E-mail: info@cnf-fiic.ca
URL: www.cnf-fiic.ca

2533 ■ Aplastic Anemia and Myelosdysplasia Scholarships (Graduate/Scholarship)

Purpose: To support students who want to pursue their education. **Focus:** Hematology; Oncology. **Qualif.:** Applicants must be nurses who will be focusing their research in the field of hematology or oncology; must be willing to increase awareness of Aplastic, Anemia and Myelodysplasia issues by presenting to colleagues or sitting on the Board of the Association; must be Canadian citizens or permanent resident status; must be studying in Canada; must be RNs enrolled in a Masters program in a health related field; must be non-nurses who hold a degree in a health-related field or a nursing-related program, which will qualify them as RNs at the Master's level; must be full-time

Awards are arranged alphabetically below their administering organizations

or part-time students, but part-time students must be taking minimum of 2 courses each semester. **Criteria:** Preference will be given to CANO members.

Funds Avail.: $3,000 to $5,000. **To Apply:** Applicants must complete and print the application form available online. For further information, applicants are advised to contact, Jacqueline Solis, Foundation Coordinator at 613-237-2159. **Deadline:** March 31.

2534 ■ AstraZeneca RURAL Scholarships
(Doctorate/Scholarship)

Purpose: To support students who want to pursue their education. **Focus:** Nursing. **Qualif.:** Applicant must be a student doing research that will impact front line nursing care delivery to under serviced or marginalized populations in rural setting; must be a Canadian citizen or permanent resident status; must be studying in Canada; must be a full-time or part-time RN student, but part-time students must be taking a minimum of 2 courses each semester or doing thesis work; must not receive other awards or scholarships during the Scholar Year of the application. **Criteria:** Selection of applicants will be based on the Scholarship application criteria.

Funds Avail.: $1,500 to $6,000. **To Apply:** Applicants must complete and print the application form available online. For further information, applicants are advised to contact, Jacqueline Solis, Foundation Coordinator at 613-237-2159. **Deadline:** March 31.

2535 ■ Dr. Ann C. Beckingham Scholarships
(Doctorate/Scholarship)

Purpose: To support students who want to pursue their education. **Focus:** Nursing. **Qualif.:** Applicant must be a Canadian citizen or with a permanent resident status; must be studying in Canada; must be a full-time or part-time RN student, but part-time students must be taking a minimum of 2 courses each semester or doing thesis work; must not receive other awards or scholarships during the Scholar Year of the application. **Criteria:** Selection of applicants will be based on the Scholarship application criteria.

Funds Avail.: $1,500 to $6,000. **To Apply:** Applicants must complete and print the application form available online; for further information, applicants are advice to contact, Jacqueline Solis, Foundation Coordinator at 613-237-2159. **Deadline:** March 31.

2536 ■ Birks Family Foundation Scholarships
(Undergraduate/Scholarship)

Purpose: To support students who want to pursue their education. **Focus:** Nursing. **Qualif.:** Applicant must be a Canadian citizen or permanent resident status; must be studying in Canada; must be entering at least year 2 as a full-time student of a baccalaureate-nursing program. **Criteria:** Selection of applicants will be based on the Scholarship application criteria.

Funds Avail.: No specific amount. **To Apply:** Applicants must complete and print the application form available online. For further information, applicants are advice to contact, Jacqueline Solis, Foundation Coordinator at 613-237-2159. **Deadline:** March 31. **Remarks:** Scholarship was established by the Birks Family Foundation out of an interest in contributing to a higher standard of living and quality of life by supporting higher education, the hospital sector, and health organizations.

2537 ■ Canadian Nurses Foundation - Baxter Corporation Scholarships *(Graduate/Scholarship)*

Purpose: To support students who want to pursue their education. **Focus:** Nursing. **Qualif.:** Applicants must be students in Nursing Sciences program; must be Canadian citizens or permanent resident status; must be studying in Canada; must be RNs enrolled in a Masters program in a health related field; must be non-nurses who hold a degree in a health-related field and are in a nursing-related program, which will qualify them as RNs at the Master's level; must be full-time or part-time students, but part-time students must be taking a minimum of 2 courses each semester. **Criteria:** Selection of applicants will be based on the Scholarship application criteria.

Funds Avail.: $5,000. **To Apply:** Applicants must complete and print the application form available online. For further information, applicants are advised to contact, Jacqueline Solis, Foundation Coordinator at 613-237-2159. **Deadline:** March 31.

2538 ■ Canadian Nurses Foundation Northern Scholarships *(Undergraduate/Scholarship)*

Purpose: To support students who want to pursue their education. **Focus:** Nursing. **Qualif.:** Applicant must be a student intending to work in Canada's North; must be a Canadian citizen or permanent resident status; must be studying in Canada; must be entering at least year 2 as a full-time student of a baccalaureate-nursing program. **Criteria:** Preference will be given to aboriginal origin or nurses who have worked in the north for at least 2 years.

Funds Avail.: $1, 000 to $3,000. **To Apply:** Applicants must complete and print the application form available online. For further information, applicants are advised to contact, Jacqueline Solis, Foundation Coordinator at 613-237-2159. **Deadline:** March 31.

2539 ■ Canadian Nurses Foundation Scholarships *(Undergraduate/Scholarship)*

Purpose: To support students who want to pursue their education. **Focus:** Nursing. **Qualif.:** Applicants must be Canadian citizens or permanent resident status; must be studying in Canada; must be entering at least year 2 as full-time students of a baccalaureate-nursing program. **Criteria:** Selection of applicants will be based on the Scholarship application criteria.

Funds Avail.: $1,000 to $3,000. **To Apply:** Applicants must complete and print the application form available online. For further information, applicants are advice to contact, Jacqueline Solis, Foundation Coordinator at 613-237-2159. **Deadline:** March 31.

2540 ■ Extendicare Scholarships in Gerontology *(Graduate/Scholarship)*

Purpose: To support students who want to pursue their education. **Focus:** Gerontology. **Qualif.:** Applicants must be nurses who intend to practice, teach or do research in gerontology/long term care; must be Canadian citizens or permanent resident status; must be studying in Canada; must be RNs enrolled in a Masters program in a health related field; must be non-nurses who hold a degree in a health-related field and are in a nursing-related program, which will qualify them as RNs at the Master's level; must be full-time or part-time students, but part-time students must be taking a minimum of 2 courses each semester. **Criteria:** Selection of applicants will be based on the

Awards are arranged alphabetically below their administering organizations

scholarship application criteria.

Funds Avail.: $1,000 to $3,000. **To Apply:** Applicants must complete and print the application form available online; for further information, applicants are advised to contact, Jacqueline Solis, Foundation Coordinator at 613-237-2159. **Deadline:** March 31.

2541 ■ Dr. Helen Preston Glass Fellowships
(Doctorate/Fellowship)

Purpose: To support students who want to pursue their education. **Focus:** Nursing. **Qualif.:** Applicants must be Nurses from Manitoba who are studying in community health nursing, primary health care, health nursing and studies which focus on "at risk population"; must be registered nurses who are undertaking graduate studies in nursing; must be willing to practice in Canada for a period of not less than 6-12 months after the Scholarship has been received; must be Canadian citizens or permanent resident status; must be studying in Canada; must be full-time or part-time RN students, but part-time students must be taking minimum of 2 courses each semester or doing thesis work. **Criteria:** Selection of applicants will be based on the Scholarship application criteria.

Funds Avail.: $3,000 to $5,000. **To Apply:** Applicants must complete and print the application form available online. For further information, applicants are advice to contact, Jacqueline Solis, Foundation Coordinator at 613-237-2159. **Deadline:** March 31.

2542 ■ Judy Hill Scholarships *(Undergraduate/Scholarship)*

Purpose: To support students who want to pursue their education. **Focus:** Nursing. **Qualif.:** Applicant must be a student who has worked in the north and must sign a statement that he/she will practice nursing in the north for a period of 12 months; must be a Canadian citizen or woth a permanent resident status; must be studying in Canada; must be entering at least year 2 as a full-time student of a baccalaureate-nursing program. **Criteria:** Selection of applicants will be based on the Scholarship application criteria.

Funds Avail.: $1,000 to $3,000. **To Apply:** Applicants must complete and print the application form available online; for further information, applicants are advised to contact, Jacqueline Solis, Foundation Coordinator at 613-237-2159. **Deadline:** March 31.

2543 ■ Johnson & Johnson Scholarships
(Undergraduate/Scholarship)

Purpose: To support students who want to pursue their education. **Focus:** Nursing. **Qualif.:** Applicant must be a student who plans to practice nursing in an operating room or a critical care area; must be a Canadian citizen or permanent resident status; must be studying in Canada; must be entering at least year 2 as a full-time student of a baccalaureate-nursing program. **Criteria:** Selection of applicants will be based on the Scholarship application criteria.

Funds Avail.: $1,000 to $3,000. **To Apply:** Applicants must complete and print the application form available online. For further information, applicants are advised to contact, Jacqueline Solis, Foundation Coordinator at 613-237-2159. **Deadline:** March 31.

2544 ■ Dr. Dorothy J. Kergin Scholarships
(Doctorate/Scholarship)

Purpose: To support students who want to pursue their education. **Focus:** Nursing. **Qualif.:** Applicant must be a

Canadian citizen or permanent resident status; must be studying in Canada; must be a full-time or part-time RN student, but part-time students must be taking minimum of 2 courses each semester or doing thesis work; must be a student at the doctoral level. **Criteria:** Selection of applicants will be based on the Scholarship application criteria.

Funds Avail.: $3,000 to $5,000. **To Apply:** Applicants must complete and print the application form available online. For further information, applicants are advised to contact, Jacqueline Solis, Foundation Coordinator at 613-237-2159. **Deadline:** March 31. **Remarks:** Established by Dr. Kergin, a distinguished nurse, who was Professor and Associate Dean of Health Sciences at McMaster University and later Professor and Director of the School of Nursing at the University of Victoria.

2545 ■ Tecla Lin & Nelia Laroza Memorial Scholarships *(Undergraduate/Scholarship)*

Purpose: To support students who want to pursue their education. **Focus:** Nursing. **Qualif.:** Applicant must be a foreign educated nurse working towards baccalaureate degree; must be a Canadian citizen or permanent resident status; must be studying in Canada; must be entering at least year 2 as a full-time student of a baccalaureate-nursing program. **Criteria:** Selection of applicants will be based on the Scholarship application criteria.

Funds Avail.: $1,000 to $3,000. **To Apply:** Applicants must complete and print the application form available online. For further information, applicants are advised to contact, Jacqueline Solis, Foundation Coordinator at 613-237-2159. **Deadline:** March 31.

2546 ■ Eleanor Jean Martin Scholarships
(Graduate/Scholarship)

Purpose: To support students who want to pursue their education. **Focus:** Nursing. **Qualif.:** Applicants must be students interested in studying either Neurosurgical or Cancer nursing fields; must be Canadian citizens or permanent resident status; must be studying in Canada; must be RNs enrolled in a Masters program in a health related field; must be non-nurses who hold a degree in a health-related field and are in a nursing-related program, which will qualify them as RNs at the Master's level; must be full-time or part-time students, but part-time students must be taking a minimum of 2 courses each semester. **Criteria:** Selection of applicants will be based on the Scholarship application criteria.

Funds Avail.: $5,000. **To Apply:** Applicants must complete and print the application form available online. For further information, applicants are advised to contact, Jacqueline Solis, Foundation Coordinator at 613-237-2159. **Deadline:** March 31.

2547 ■ Military Nurses Association Scholarships *(Graduate, Master's/Scholarship)*

Purpose: To support students who want to pursue their education. **Focus:** Nursing. **Qualif.:** Applicants must be students at master level; must be Canadian citizens or permanent residents status; must be studying in Canada; must be RNs enrolled in a Masters program in a health related field; must be non-nurses who hold a degree in a health-related field and are in a nursing-related program, which will qualify them as RNs at the Master's level; must be full-time or part-time students, but part-time students must be taking minimum of 2 courses each semester. **Criteria:** Preference will be given to military nurses, or former military.

Awards are arranged alphabetically below their administering organizations

Funds Avail.: $3,000 to $5,000. **To Apply:** Applicants must complete and print the application form available online. For further information, applicants are advised to contact, Jacqueline Solis, Foundation Coordinator at 613-237-2159. **Deadline:** March 31.

2548 ■ Margaret Munro Scholarships
(Undergraduate/Scholarship)

Purpose: To support students who want to pursue their education. **Focus:** Nursing. **Qualif.:** Applicant must be a student form Prince Edward Island; must be a Canadian citizen or with a permanent resident status; must be studying in Canada; must be entering at least year 2 as a full-time student of a baccalaureate-nursing program. **Criteria:** Selection of applicants will be based on the Scholarship application criteria.

Funds Avail.: $1,000 to $3,000. **To Apply:** Applicants must complete and print the application form available online. For further information, applicants are advised to contact, Jacqueline Solis, Foundation Coordinator at 613-237-2159. **Deadline:** March 31.

2549 ■ Dr. Helen K. Mussallem Fellowships
(Graduate/Scholarship)

Purpose: To support students who want to pursue their education. **Focus:** Nursing. **Qualif.:** Applicants must be students at master level; must be Canadian citizens or permanent residents status; must be studying in Canada; must be RNs enrolled in a Masters program in a health related field; must be non-nurses who hold a degree in a health-related field and are in a nursing-related program, which will qualify them as RNs at the Master's level; must be full-time or part-time students, but part-time students must be taking a minimum of two courses each semester. **Criteria:** Recipients will be evaluated based on academic aptitude, personal strengths and leadership potential. Final decision will be made based on merit, strategic directions of CNF, financial and resources considerations.

Funds Avail.: $5,000. **To Apply:** Applicants must complete and print the application form available online. **Deadline:** March 31. **Remarks:** Established by Dr. Musallen. **Contact:** For further information, applicants are advice to contact, Jacqueline Solis, Foundation Coordinator at 613-237-2159.

2550 ■ New Brunswick Nurses Association Scholarships *(Graduate/Scholarship)*

Purpose: To support students who want to pursue their education. **Focus:** Nursing. **Qualif.:** Applicants must be students from New Brunswick; must be Canadian citizens or permanent resident status; must be studying in Canada; must be RNs enrolled in a Masters program in a health related field; must be non-nurses who hold a degree in a health-related field and are in a nursing-related program, which will qualify them as RNs at the Master's level; must be full-time or part-time students, but part-time students must be taking minimum of 2 courses each semester. **Criteria:** Selection of applicants will be based on the Scholarship application criteria.

Funds Avail.: $3,000 to $5,000. **To Apply:** Applicants must complete and print the application form available online. For further information, applicants are advice to contact, Jacqueline Solis, Foundation Coordinator at 613-237-2159. **Deadline:** March 31.

2551 ■ Sharon Nield Memorial Scholarships
(Undergraduate/Scholarship)

Purpose: To support students who want to pursue their education. **Focus:** Nursing. **Qualif.:** Applicants must be registered nurses returning to school; must be Canadian citizens or have permanent resident status; must be studying in Canada; must be entering at least year 2 as full-time students of a baccalaureate-nursing program. **Criteria:** Selection of applicants will be based on the Scholarship application criteria.

Funds Avail.: $1,000 to $3,000. **To Apply:** Applicants must complete and print the application form available online; for further information, applicants are advised to contact, Jacqueline Solis, Foundation Coordinator at 613-237-2159. **Deadline:** March 31.

2552 ■ Senator Norman Paterson Fellowships
(Doctorate/Fellowship)

Purpose: To support students who want to pursue their education. **Focus:** Nursing. **Qualif.:** Applicant must be a Canadian citizen or permanent resident status; must be studying in Canada; must be a full-time or part-time RN student, but part-time students must be taking a minimum of 2 courses each semester or doing thesis work; must be a student at the doctoral level. **Criteria:** Selection of applicants will be based on the Scholarship application criteria.

Funds Avail.: $1,500 to $6,000. **To Apply:** Applicants must complete and print the application form available online. For further information, applicants are advised to contact, Jacqueline Solis, Foundation Coordinator at 613-237-2159. **Deadline:** March 31. **Remarks:** Established to honour the memory of Mr. Norman M. Paterson, who served as President of the Victorian Order of Nurses in Canada.

2553 ■ Sanofi Pasteur Scholarships *(Graduate/Scholarship)*

Purpose: To support students who want to pursue their education. **Focus:** Nursing. **Qualif.:** Applicants must be Canadian citizens or permanent residents status; must be studying in Canada; must be RNs enrolled in a Masters program in a health related field; must be non-nurses who hold a degree in a health-related field or a nursing-related program, which will qualify them as RNs at the Master's level; must be full-time or part-time students, but part-time students must be taking minimum of 2 courses each semester. **Criteria:** Selection of applicants will be based on the Scholarship application criteria.

Funds Avail.: $3,000 to $5,000. **To Apply:** Applicants must complete and print the application form available online. For further information, applicants are advised to contact, Jacqueline Solis, Foundation Coordinator at 613-237-2159. **Deadline:** March 31. **Remarks:** Established in 1990 by Sanofi Pasteur Ltd. the largest vaccine company in Canada.

2554 ■ Sigma Theta Tau International Scholarships *(Doctorate/Scholarship)*

Purpose: To support students who want to pursue their education. **Focus:** Nursing. **Qualif.:** Applicants must be nurses who are working on their PhD dissertation; must be Canadian citizens or permanent resident status; must be studying in Canada; must be full-time or part-time RN students, but part-time students must be taking a minimum of 2 courses each semester or doing thesis work. **Criteria:** Selection of applicants will be based on the Scholarship application criteria.

Funds Avail.: $1,500 to $6,000. **To Apply:** Applicants must complete and print the application form available online. For further information, applicants are advised to contact, Jacqueline Solis, Foundation Coordinator at 613-237-2159. **Deadline:** March 31.

Awards are arranged alphabetically below their administering organizations

2555 ■ TD Meloche-Monnex Scholarships
(Doctorate/Scholarship)

Purpose: To support students who want to pursue their education. **Focus:** Nursing. **Qualif.:** Applicant must be a Canadian citizen or permanent resident status; must be studying in Canada; must be a full-time or part-time RN student but part-time students must be taking a minimum of two courses each semester or doing thesis work; must be a student at the doctoral level. **Criteria:** Recipients will be evaluated based on academic aptitude, personal strengths and leadership potential. Final decision will be made based on merit, strategic directions of CNF, financial and resources considerations.

Funds Avail.: $5,000. **To Apply:** Applicants must complete and print the application form available online. **Deadline:** March 31. **Remarks:** Established by TD Meloche Monnex, Canada's leading provider of insurance and added-value financial services, known for its exceptional quality of customer service. **Contact:** For further information, applicants are advised to contact, Jacqueline Solis, Foundation Coordinator at 613-237-2159.

2556 ■ John Vanderlee Scholarships
(Undergraduate/Scholarship)

Purpose: To support students who want to pursue their education. **Focus:** Nursing. **Qualif.:** Applicant must be a male student entering at least year 2 as a full-time student of a baccalaureate-nursing program; must be a Canadian citizen or permanent resident status; must be studying in Canada. **Criteria:** Selection of applicants will be based on the Scholarship application criteria.

Funds Avail.: $1,000 to $3,000. **To Apply:** Applicants must complete and print the application form available online; for further information, applicants are advised to contact, Jacqueline Solis, Foundation Coordinator at 613-237-2159. **Deadline:** March 31.

2557 ■ Canadian Occupational Therapy Foundation (COTF)
1125 Colonel By Dr., Ste. No. 3401
Ottawa, ON, Canada K1S 5R1
Ph: (613) 523-2268
Fax: (613) 523-2552
Free: 800-434-2268
E-mail: skamble@cotfcanada.org
URL: www.cotfcanada.org

2558 ■ Canadian Occupational Therapy Foundation Graduate Scholarships *(Graduate/Scholarship)*

Purpose: To support CAOT student members. **Focus:** Occupational therapy. **Qualif.:** Applicants must be life or student members of CAOT enrolled full-time or part-time in a master's or doctoral program related to occupational therapy research. **Criteria:** Selection of applicants will be based on panel's criteria.

Funds Avail.: $3,000 for doctoral and $1,500 for masters. **To Apply:** Applicants must provide ten collated and completed copies of the application form and ten collated and completed copies of all materials listed: (a) Proof of program enrollment for the period of the award; (b) One original and ten copies of post-secondary transcripts; (c) A letter of intent that gives a description of, and rationale for the proposed or ongoing thesis research; must provide a curriculum vitae; must have two references that will provide

statements of support for academic objectives and appraisal of candidate's ability to do graduate work; (d) A photocopy of CAOT membership card. **Deadline:** September 30.

2559 ■ Canadian Occupational Therapy Foundation Invacare Master's Scholarships
(Graduate/Scholarship)

Purpose: To support CAOT student members. **Focus:** Occupational therapy **Qualif.:** Applicants must be individual, life or student members of CAOT enrolled full-time or part-time in a master's program related to occupational therapy. **Criteria:** Selection of applicants will be based on panel's criteria.

Funds Avail.: $2,000. **To Apply:** Applicants must provide ten collated and completed copies of the application form and ten collated and completed copies of all materials listed: (a) Proof of program enrollment for the period of the award; (b) One original and ten copies of post-secondary transcripts; (c) A letter of intent that gives a description of, and rationale for the proposed or ongoing thesis research; must provide curriculum vitae; must have two references that will provide statements of support for academic objectives and appraisal of candidate's ability to do graduate work; (d) A photocopy of CAOT membership card. **Deadline:** September 30.

2560 ■ Thelma Cardwell Scholarships
(Graduate/Scholarship)

Purpose: To support CAOT student members. **Focus:** Occupational therapy. **Qualif.:** Applicants must be individual, life or student members of CAOT enrolled full-time in a master's or doctoral level program who have demonstrated an outstanding contribution to occupational therapy; and must be in good standing. **Criteria:** Selection of applicants will be based on scholarship panel's criteria.

Funds Avail.: $2,000. **To Apply:** Applicants must provide ten collated and completed copies of the application form and ten collated and completed copies of all materials listed: (a) Proof of program enrollment for the period of the award; (b) One original and ten copies of post-secondary transcripts; (c) A letter of intent that gives a description of, and rationale for, the proposed or ongoing thesis research; must provide a curriculum vitae; must have two references that will provide statements of support for academic objectives and appraisal of candidate's ability to do graduate work; (d) A photocopy of CAOT membership card. **Deadline:** September 30.

2561 ■ Goldwin Howland Scholarships
(Graduate/Scholarship)

Purpose: To provide financial support to CAOT students. **Focus:** Occupational therapy. **Qualif.:** Applicants must be enrolled in graduate studies related to occupational therapy in Canada; must be CAOT individual, life or student members in good standing. Applicants enrolled in a university program outside Canada should indicate their intention to return to practice and/or to take up an academic appointment in Canada. **Criteria:** Selection of applicants will be based on scholarship reviewer criteria.

Funds Avail.: $2,000. **To Apply:** Applicants must provide ten collated and completed copies of the application form and ten collated and completed copies of all materials listed: (a) Proof of program enrollment for the period of the award; (b) One original and ten copies of post-secondary transcripts; (c) A letter of intent that gives a description of, and rationale for, the proposed or ongoing thesis research;

Awards are arranged alphabetically below their administering organizations

must provide a curriculum vitae; must have two references that will provide statements of support for academic objectives and appraisal of candidate's ability to do graduate work; (d) A photocopy of CAOT membership card. **Deadline:** September 30.

2562 ■ Canadian Office Products Association (COPA)

402-2800 Skymark Ave.
Mississauga, ON, Canada L4W 5A6
Ph: (905) 624-9462
Fax: (905) 624-0830
E-mail: info@copa.ca
URL: www.copa.ca

2563 ■ COPA Scholarship Fund *(Undergraduate/ Scholarship)*

Purpose: To financially assist undergraduate students further their post-secondary education. **Focus:** General studies. **Qualif.:** Applicants must be entering their first or second post-secondary studies; must be former or current employees, or with parents, guardians, or grandparents who are currently employed by a COPA member company; must be citizens or permanent residents of Canada; must have received a high school diploma within the last five years; must have completed the final two years of high school in not more than two years (this should not be consecutive); must have achieved an overall average of at least 80% in the final two years of high school prior to graduation or a GPA of at least 75% in the first year of college or university; be enrolling the first or second year of study at a university or college recognized by the Association of Universities and Colleges of Canada. **Criteria:** Evaluation will be based on submitted materials.

Funds Avail.: $2,000. **Number Awarded:** 8. **To Apply:** Applicants must complete the online application form; must submit two letters of reference from an academic or community official; a letter of employment verifying the connection to a COPA member company; a 500-word essay on the specified topic; must also submit a copy of the most recent unofficial transcript for the past two academic years. First year student applicants must submit a letter of acceptance and second year student applicants are required to provide a copy of the tuition invoice, if selected as finalists. **Deadline:** June 13.

2564 ■ Canadian Organic Growers

323 Chapel St.
Ottawa, ON, Canada K1N 7Z2
Ph: (613) 216-0741
Fax: (613) 236-0743
Free: 888-375-7383
E-mail: office@cog.ca
URL: www.cog.ca

2565 ■ Mary Perlmutter Scholarships *(Postgraduate/Award)*

Purpose: To encourage researches on the benefits of organic growers through financial assistance. **Focus:** Botany. **Qualif.:** Applicants must be a Canadian citizens or landed immigrants; must have obtained satisfactory results in undergraduate studies in a recognized Canadian college or university; and must have been admitted to the faculty of their choice. **Criteria:** Recipients are selected based on

transcripts, the relevant benefit of the proposed research on organic growers, and reference letters. Selection of winners is made by the COG MPS Committee.

Funds Avail.: $4,000. **To Apply:** Application forms and letter of support forms are available from the website. Applicants must submit academic transcripts and research proposals to the selection committee. **Deadline:** June 30. **Remarks:** The scholarship is named after COG past president and long-time organic grower, Mary Perlmutter. **Contact:** Achim Mohssen-Beyk.

2566 ■ Canadian Pain Society (CPS)

1143 Wentworth St. W, Ste. 202
Oshawa, ON, Canada L1J 8P7
Ph: (905) 404-9545
Fax: (905) 404-3727
E-mail: catherine.bushnell@mcgill.ca
URL: www.canadianpainsociety.ca

2567 ■ Canadian Pain Society Post-Doctoral Fellowship Awards *(Doctorate/Fellowship)*

Purpose: To financially assist PhD students to engage in pain research in and outside Canada. **Focus:** Education, Medical. **Qualif.:** Applicants must have completed their PhD in a pain-related field; must be Canadian citizens or landed immigrants with permanent Canadian residence. **Criteria:** Award will be given to applicants who best meet the requirements.

Funds Avail.: $40,000 per year. **To Apply:** Applicants must submit a cover letter; two-page summary of the proposed research; curriculum vitae; two letters of reference, one of which must come from a PhD supervisor; and a letter of support from the proposed supervisor. **Deadline:** September.

2568 ■ Clinical Pain Management Fellowship Awards *(Postgraduate/Fellowship)*

Purpose: To support graduates of Canadian post-graduate medical education programs who wish to further study in pain management at any institution in and outside Canada. **Focus:** Education, Medical. **Qualif.:** Applicants must have completed an MD; have completed a residency program accredited by the Royal College of Physicians and Surgeons of Canada or the College of Family Physicians of Canada; must be Canadian citizens or landed immigrants with permanent Canadian residence. **Criteria:** Award will be given to applicants who best meet the requirements.

Funds Avail.: $90,000. **To Apply:** Applicants must submit a cover letter; curriculum vitae; two letters of reference, one of which must be from the Director of the residency program. If applicants have already completed specialty training, then a copy of the Royal College of Physicians and Surgeons of Canada or College of Family Physicians of Canada certificate should be submitted along with two letters of reference. A letter of support from the Director of the program the candidate proposes for their fellowship year is also required. **Deadline:** October.

2569 ■ CPS Excellence in Interprofessional Pain Education Awards *(Professional development/Award)*

Purpose: To recognize CPS members who made contributions in interprofessional pain education. **Focus:** Education, Medical. **Qualif.:** Applicants must be CPS members who have demonstrated excellence in interprofessional

Awards are arranged alphabetically below their administering organizations

pain education in an accredited setting with various community healthcare professionals. **Criteria:** Submitted documents will be evaluated based on demonstration of innovation, scholarship, relevance to pain education, and contribution and impact of the work to the field.

Funds Avail.: $2,000 check plus $1,000 for travel expenses. **To Apply:** Each nomination should include a two-page letter submitted to the CPS that documents the nominee's area of educational focus. It should be accompanied by a supporting letter from another CPS member external to the nominee's institution but familiar with the nominee's achievements in IPE; and must submit a curriculum vitae. **Deadline:** October 15.

2570 ■ CPS Interprofessional Nursing Project Awards (Professional development/Award)

Purpose: To recognize CPS members who made contributions in interprofessional pain education. **Focus:** Education, Medical. **Qualif.:** Applicants must be registered nurses who have been members of the Canadian Pain Society (CPS) for at least one year and not been recipients of this award for three years. **Criteria:** This award will be given to applicants who best demonstrate excellence as principal investigators of an interprofessional project on changing pain management practices and improving patient outcomes. All submissions will be ranked according to innovation, feasibility, methodology, ethical considerations and relevance to current practice issues.

Funds Avail.: $2,000 plus $1,000 for travel expenses. **To Apply:** Applicants must submit a brief proposal to the CPS that describes the project including the purpose, objectives, method, evaluation and budget. Proposal should be a maximum of two pages and the project must be completed within one year. Recipients must submit results in an abstract form to be considered for poster presentation at the subsequent scientific meeting; must present five minutes summary of the project at the CPS Special Interest Group-Nursing Issues Luncheon meeting and be present for the award presentation; and must submit receipts for all the travel costs. **Deadline:** October 15. **Contact:** Materials should be submitted to Kathy Reid at nursingsig@canadianpainsociety.ca.

2571 ■ CPS Knowledge Translation Research Awards (Professional development/Grant)

Purpose: To support a pain-related knowledge translation research project. **Focus:** Education, Medical. **Qualif.:** Applicants must be registered nurses who have been members of the Canadian Pain Society (CPS) for at least one year and not been recipients of this grant for three years. **Criteria:** Submissions will be ranked according to feasibility, methodology, ethical considerations and relevance to current practice issues.

Funds Avail.: $2,000. **To Apply:** Applicants must submit a two-page written proposal for the use of the money, purpose, objectives, method, evaluation and budget along with a reference letter from a CPS member; must submit a project which aims to improve patient outcomes using knowledge translation strategies and should be completed within one year; applicants must submit the results in an abstract form to be considered for the presentation at the subsequent CPS Scientific meeting. **Deadline:** October. **Contact:** Materials should be submitted to Kathy Reid at nursingsig@canadianpainsociety.ca.

2572 ■ CPS Nursing Excellence in Pain Management Awards (Professional development/Award)

Purpose: To recognize nurses who consistently exemplify leadership in an area of nursing practice, education, or research in pain management. **Focus:** Education, Medical. **Qualif.:** Applicants must be registered nurses who have been members of the Canadian Pain Society (CPS) for at least the most recent three years and not been previous recipients of this award. Candidates must be nominated by three colleagues, at least one of whom is a CPS member. **Criteria:** Candidates will be ranked based on demonstrated leadership in an area of nursing practice, education, or research in pain management.

Funds Avail.: $1,000 plus $1,000 for travel expenses. **To Apply:** Applicants must submit a completed nomination form made in writing; must include the nominee's curriculum vitae and narrative endorsement describing the qualifications of the candidate. **Deadline:** October. **Contact:** Materials should be submitted to Kathy Reid at nursingsig@canadianpainsociety.ca.

2573 ■ CPS Nursing Research and Education Awards (Professional development/Grant)

Purpose: To support a pain-related research project. **Focus:** Education, Medical. **Qualif.:** Applicants must be registered nurses who have been members of the Canadian Pain Society (CPS) for at least one year and not been recipients of this award for three years. **Criteria:** Submissions will be ranked according to feasibility, methodology, ethical considerations and relevance to current practice issues.

Funds Avail.: $1,000 plus $1,000 for travel expenses. **To Apply:** Applicants must submit a two-page written proposal for the use of money, purpose, objectives, method, evaluation and budget along with a reference letter from a CPS member; must submit the results in an abstract form to be considered for poster presentation at the subsequent CPS Scientific meeting. **Deadline:** October. **Contact:** Materials should be submitted to Kathy Reid at nursingsig@canadianpainsociety.ca.

2574 ■ CPS Outstanding Pain Mentorship Awards (Professional development/Award)

Purpose: To recognize individuals who consistently exemplify outstanding mentorship in training the future pain researchers and/or clinicians. **Focus:** Education, Medical. **Qualif.:** Applicants must be CPS members for at least two years and not been recipients of this award; and must be nominated by at least one colleague. **Criteria:** Award will be given to applicants who best meet the requirements.

Funds Avail.: $1,000 plus $1,500 for travel expenses. **To Apply:** Nominations must be made in writing; must include the nominee's curriculum vitae, narrative endorsement (maximum of 750 words) describing the mentorship qualities of the candidate. Endorsements must be signed by the nominee(s) before submission. **Deadline:** October 15.

2575 ■ CPS Toronto Poly Clinic - ROD Inter-Disciplinary Pain Education Grants (Professional development/Grant)

Purpose: To support education and promote the idea of inter-disciplinary pain medicine. **Focus:** Education, Medical. **Qualif.:** Applicants must be physicians in any discipline; must be Canadian residents and CPS members. **Criteria:** Recipients will be selected based on submitted materials.

Awards are arranged alphabetically below their administering organizations

Funds Avail.: $1,500. **Number Awarded:** 2. **To Apply:** Applicants must e-mail their curriculum vitae along with planned educational activity in pain management. **Deadline:** September.

2576 ■ CPS Trainee Research Awards
(Doctorate/Grant)

Purpose: To support trainees working in any field of pain research. **Focus:** Education, Medical. **Qualif.:** Applicants must be trainees who are in the first three years of a PhD program; must be members of the Canadian Pain Society (CPS); must not hold other sources of external operating funds used to support research. **Criteria:** Judges will evaluate applications according to the trainee's qualifications/ research background, academic excellence and merit of the proposed project.

Funds Avail.: $5,000 plus $1,000 for travel and accommodation expenses. **Number Awarded:** 4. **To Apply:** Applicants must submit curriculum vitae; official (sealed) transcripts from all previous post-secondary institutions; one-page research summary outlining the research and indication of its related category; one-page budget with detailed justification of how funds will be used; and two letters of recommendation that address the trainee's academic and research abilities. Each letter must be sealed and signed across the seal by the writer. **Deadline:** October.

2577 ■ Canadian Paraplegic Association (CPA)
1101 Prince of Wales Dr., Ste. 230
Ottawa, ON, Canada K2C 3W7
Ph: (613) 723-1033
Fax: (613) 723-1060
E-mail: info@canparaplegic.org
URL: www.canparaplegic.org/en

2578 ■ Copnick/Hilliard Scholarships *(Professional development/Scholarship)*

Purpose: To assist and support students with permanent severe mobility impairment such as spinal cord injury to continue their post-secondary education. **Focus:** General studies. **Qualif.:** Applicants must have a spinal cord injury or other physical disability; must be volunteers or staff members of the Canadian Paraplegic Association; must be Canadian citizens or landed immigrants; must demonstrate outstanding initiative and scholastic achievement in a recognized post-secondary institution in Canada. **Criteria:** Recipients will be selected based on academic standing, merit and financial needs.

Funds Avail.: $500. **To Apply:** Applicants may obtain forms at the website. Applicants must submit letters of reference addressing their initiative, scholastic achievement, and contributions as volunteers to persons with spinal cord injury; transcript and medical records. **Deadline:** August 15. **Contact:** Completed application forms and all supporting documents must be mailed to Scholarship Selection Committee at the above address.

2579 ■ Sun Life Financial Peer Support Scholarships *(Professional development/ Scholarship)*

Purpose: To assist peer volunteers and participants with an SCI or other physical disability to advance their post-secondary education in the disability fields. **Focus:** General studies. **Qualif.:** Applicants must have been diagnosed with a spinal cord injury or other physical disability; must be volunteers or staff members of the Canadian Paraplegic Association; must be Canadian citizens or landed immigrants; must be attending or will be attending a recognized post-secondary institution in Canada. **Criteria:** Recipients will be selected based on academic standing, merit and financial needs.

Funds Avail.: $2,500. **To Apply:** Application forms are available at the website. Applicants must provide a copy of their most recent transcript; letters of reference addressing their initiative, scholastic achievement, and contributions as peer volunteers to persons with spinal cord injury. **Deadline:** August 15. **Contact:** Completed application forms and all supporting documents must be mailed to Scholarship Selection Committee at the above address.

2580 ■ Canadian Parking Association (CPA) - Association Canadienne du Stationnement (ACS)
350-2255 St. Laurent Blvd.
Ottawa, ON, Canada K1G 4K3
Ph: (613) 727-0700
Fax: (613) 727-3183
E-mail: info@canadianparking.ca
URL: www.canadianparking.ca

2581 ■ Canadian Parking Association Scholarships *(Undergraduate/Scholarship)*

Purpose: To provide financial assistance to students in their pursuit of academic excellence and to encourage post-secondary study that enhances the parking industry in Canada. **Focus:** General studies. **Qualif.:** Applicants must be registered CPA members whose job function is 50% related to parking, their spouses and dependents, members' employees whose job function is 50% related to parking, their spouses and dependents with a minimum average of 70% in the last three semesters of studies (non-academic courses such as career or personal development-related courses will not be considered). **Criteria:** Applicants will be evaluated based on academic performance; extracurricular activities or volunteer/community involvement, excluding those which are included in the high school curriculum; and quality of reference letters (one from a teacher and one from a person familiar with extracurricular activities or community involvement, excluding family members).

Funds Avail.: $2,000. **Number Awarded:** 10. **To Apply:** Applicants must submit the completed application form; official transcript of the last three semesters; description of extracurricular activities or volunteer/community involvement; two signed letters of reference; and the parental consent form. **Deadline:** May 1.

2582 ■ Canadian Picture Pioneers
250 The E Mall, Ste. 1762
Toronto, ON, Canada M9B 6L3
Ph: (416) 368-1139
Fax: (416) 368-1139
E-mail: cdnpicturepioneers@rogers.com
URL: www.canadianpicturepioneers.ca

2583 ■ Canadian Picture Pioneers Scholarships
(Undergraduate/Scholarship)

Purpose: To assist students who are in need of financial assistance, and who are enrolled in full time studies. **Focus:** Media arts. **Qualif.:** Applicant must be a legal resident of Canada; be 27 years of age and under; currently enrolled

Awards are arranged alphabetically below their administering organizations

in full time studies at a post-secondary institution ; and currently works or have worked in the film industry within the past 6 months, or a child/grandchild of an individual who currently works or who has worked in the film industry in the past 6 months (or has retired from a career in the film industry). **Criteria:** Scholarship will be selected by a panel of judges.

Funds Avail.: $5,000; $2,500; $1,000. **Number Awarded:** 13. **To Apply:** Applicants must complete the online application process. **Deadline:** October 22.

2584 ■ Canadian Political Science Association

No. 204 - 260, rue Dalhousie St.
Ottawa, ON, Canada K1N 7E4
Ph: (613) 562-1202
Fax: (613) 241-0019
E-mail: cpsa@csse.ca
URL: www.cpsa-acsp.ca

2585 ■ Donald Smiley Prize *(Professional development/Prize)*

Purpose: To encourage the ideals of scholarship represented by the great Canadian scientists. **Focus:** Political science. **Qualif.:** Books must be single-authored or multi-authored; authors or co-authors must be citizens or permanent residents of Canada and CPSA members in the year the book was published. **Criteria:** Awards will be given to the best book published in French or English in the field related to the study of government and politics in Canada.

Funds Avail.: Amount not specified. **Number Awarded:** 2. **To Apply:** Authors must submit a book published in France or Canada. **Deadline:** December 10.

2586 ■ Jill Vickers Prize *(Professional development/Prize)*

Purpose: To recognize the authors of papers in the fields of Political Science and related studies. **Focus:** Political science. **Qualif.:** Applicants must be the authors of papers related to the topic of gender and politics presented in English or French. **Criteria:** Recipients will be selected based on the quality of their submissions.

Funds Avail.: $750 and certificate. **To Apply:** An electronic copy of the paper must be e-mailed directly to each member of the Prize jury. **Deadline:** June 15.

2587 ■ Canadian Poultry Research Council

350 Sparks St., Ste. 1007
Ottawa, ON, Canada K1R 7S8
Ph: (613) 566-5916
Fax: (613) 241-5999
E-mail: info@cp-rc.ca
URL: www.cp-rc.ca

2588 ■ Canadian Poultry Research Council Postgraduate Scholarships *(Postgraduate/Scholarship)*

Purpose: To encourage and support graduate students to carry out research in an aspect of poultry science. **Focus:** Poultry science. **Qualif.:** Applicants must be entering the first year of a master's or doctoral program at a Canadian university. **Criteria:** Selection will be based on the committee's criteria.

Funds Avail.: $7,500. **To Apply:** Applicants must complete

and submit the following: a completed CPRC Postgraduate Scholarship application form (available at the website); updated academic transcripts; a two-page resume describing the applicants' goals and academic and extracurricular activities that support their interests in poultry research; a statement of endorsement from applicants' research supervisor describing why they are particularly suitable for this award; outline of proposed research; contributions and statements. **Deadline:** May 1.

2589 ■ Canadian Purchasing Research Foundation

777 Bay St., Ste. 2701
Toronto, ON, Canada M5G 2C8
Fax: (416) 977-8886
Free: 888-799-0877
E-mail: info@purchasingresearch.ca
URL: www.purchasingresearch.ca

2590 ■ Canadian Purchasing Research Foundation Prize *(Doctorate, Graduate/Prize)*

Purpose: To honour research focused on leading-edge developments, best practices or innovation. **Focus:** Purchasing. **Qualif.:** Applicants must be Master's and PhD students at any Canadian university who authored original papers on supply chain management. **Criteria:** Papers will be evaluated by a team of practitioners who will award prizes based on the evaluation criteria.

Funds Avail.: $2,000 - 1st prize; $1,500 - 2nd prize; $1,000 - 3rd prize. **To Apply:** Applicants must submit a research paper which focuses on leading edge developments, best practices or original innovation in the Supply Chain Management field of practice in Canada; and contributes to the knowledge and practice of Supply Management in Canada. The research paper must demonstrate readability and usefulness to SCM Practitioners. Research paper must be 3,000-5,000 words in length, exclusive of tables, appendices, footnotes and bibliography and must be in MS Word or Adobe PDF format. **Deadline:** April 1.

2591 ■ Canadian Sanitation Supply Association (CSSA)

910 Dundas St. W
Whitby, ON, Canada L1P 1P7
Ph: (905) 665-8001
Fax: (905) 430-6418
Free: 866-684-8273
E-mail: tracy@cssa.com
URL: cssa.com

2592 ■ Canadian Sanitation Supply Association Scholarships *(Undergraduate/Scholarship)*

Purpose: To provide scholarship assistance to qualified Canadian students who will be attending college or university in Canada. **Focus:** General studies. **Qualif.:** Applicant must be a student who will be graduating high school; must be an individual who is already enrolled in a college or university in Canada; must be a young Canadian who has achieved a high level of academic and leadership standards. **Criteria:** Applicant will be judged based on the following criteria: (1) Applicant's ability to read and fully comprehend the terms and conditions of the application procedure; (2) Applicant's ability to ensure that all components of the application-the Applicant Information Form, the

Awards are arranged alphabetically below their administering organizations

2″x3″ photo, the essay, the transcripts, the evaluation form and the typed resume-are received by the CSSA Scholarship Foundation office; (3) Applicant's academic achievements as well as school/college activities, volunteerism and social achievements; (4) Quality of the essay - originality, clarity, grammar and presentation.

Funds Avail.: $2,000 offered in each of the five regions: Atlantic Canada, Quebec, Ontario Prairies (Manitoba & Saskatchewan, Alberta), British Columbia. **Number Awarded:** 7. **To Apply:** Applicant must complete the application form available online; must have a photograph, and official high school or college transcript; must provide an essay on: ″What did your school do to make you aware of H1N1 and what precautions were put in place?″; must have a typed resume with name, planned occupation or profession, high school information, college or university information, employment history, activity and leadership record, and applicant evaluation form completed by a counselor or teacher. **Deadline:** June 1.

2593 ■ Sam Tughan Scholarships
(Undergraduate/Scholarship)

Purpose: To provide scholarship assistance to qualified Canadian students who will be attending college or university in Canada. **Focus:** Medicine. **Qualif.:** Applicant must be a student who will be graduating high school; must be an individual who is already enrolled in a college or university in Canada; must be a young Canadian who has achieved a high level of academic and leadership standards. **Criteria:** Applicant will be judged based on the following criteria: (1) Applicant's ability to read and fully comprehend the terms and conditions of the application procedure; (2) Applicant's ability to ensure that all components of the application - the Applicant Information Form, the 2x3 photo, the essay, the transcripts, the evaluation form and the typed resume - are received by the CSSA Scholarship Foundation office; (3) Applicant's academic achievements as well as school/college activities, volunteerism and social achievements; (4) Quality of the essay - originality, clarity, grammar and presentation.

Funds Avail.: $2,000. **Number Awarded:** 1. **To Apply:** Applicant must complete the application form available online; must have a photograph, and official high school or college transcript; must provide an essay on: ″What did your school do to make you aware of H1N1 and what precautions were put in place?″; must have a typed resume with name, planned occupation or profession, high school information, college or university information, employment history, activity and leadership record, and applicant evaluation form completed by a counselor or teacher. **Deadline:** June 1.

2594 ■ Geoffrey H. Wood Scholarships
(Undergraduate/Scholarship)

Purpose: To provide scholarship assistance to qualified Canadian students who will be attending college or university in Canada. **Focus:** Education. **Qualif.:** Applicant must be a student who will be graduating high school; must be an individual who is already enrolled in a college or university in Canada; must be a young Canadian who has achieved a high level of academic and leadership standards. **Criteria:** Applicant will be judged based on the following criteria: (1) Applicant's ability to read and fully comprehend the terms and conditions of the application procedure; (2) Applicant's ability to ensure that all components of the application (the Applicant Information Form, the 2″x3″ photo, the essay, the transcripts, the evaluation form and the typed resume) are received by the CSSA

Scholarship Foundation office; (3) Applicant's academic achievements as well as school/college activities, volunteerism and social achievements; (4) Quality of the essay (originality, clarity, grammar and presentation)

Funds Avail.: $2,000. **Number Awarded:** 1. **To Apply:** Applicant must complete the application form available online; must have a photograph and official high school or college transcript; must provide an essay on: ″What did your school do to make you aware of H1N1 and what precautions were put in place?″; must have a typed resume with name, planned occupation or profession, high school information, college or university information, employment history, activity and leadership record, and applicant evaluation form completed by a counselor or teacher. **Deadline:** June 10. **Contact:** Bob Semenyk, bob@cssa.com.

2595 ■ Canadian Simmental Association (CSA)
No. 13-4101-19th St. NE
Calgary, AB, Canada T2E 7C4
Ph: (403) 250-7979
Fax: (403) 250-5121
Free: 866-860-6051
E-mail: cansim@simmental.com
URL: www.simmental.com

2596 ■ Dr. Allan A. Dixon Memorial Scholarships *(Postgraduate/Scholarship)*

Purpose: To support members of the Canadian Simmental Association and their children. **Focus:** General studies. **Qualif.:** Applicants must be members of the Canadian Simmental Association or children of members, for one year or more by the date of registration; must have past/present involvement with Simmental cattle; must be Canadian citizens; and must be studying at the following qualified educational institutions: a) Canadian universities and colleges recognized by the Association of Canadian Universities and Colleges; b) Canadian Community Colleges or institutions controlled by or under the supervision of provincial departments of education; c) Foreign Universities recommended by the Faculty to pursue the applicant's education and recognized by the Association of Canadian Universities and Colleges. **Criteria:** Preference will be given to applicants who are active members of the Canadian Simmental Association.

Funds Avail.: $1,000. **To Apply:** Application forms will be available from the Garth Sweet Simmental Foundation Office. **Deadline:** October 1. **Remarks:** The scholarship is in the memory of Dr. Allan A. Dixon.

2597 ■ Canadian Society of Biblical Studies (CSBS)
Carleton University
1125 Colonel By Dr.
Ottawa, ON, Canada K1S 5B6
E-mail: zeba.crook@carleton.ca
URL: www.ccsr.ca/csbs/MainPageEnglish.htm

2598 ■ CSBS Student Prize Competition
(Graduate/Prize)

Purpose: To help students demonstrate their research related to Biblical studies. **Focus:** Religion. **Qualif.:** Student essays must be related to the field of Biblical studies; must demonstrate graduate level research ability and show familiarity with the appropriate original and modern

Awards are arranged alphabetically below their administering organizations

languages of scholarly research. Entries must be based on work already completed at the graduate level. **Criteria:** Winners will be selected based on submitted essays. Special attention will be paid to clarity and originality of the paper.

Funds Avail.: $250. **Number Awarded:** 2. **To Apply:** Entries must not be longer than 20 typed pages, should be double-spaced and in 12 point font; should be accompanied by a note from a professor or administrator verifying the candidate's status; must be written in English or French. Applicants are required to submit three copies of their essay. **Contact:** Submissions should be sent to Philip Harland, 4700 Keele St., Toronto, ON, M3J 1P3; Phone: 514-848-2065; E-mail: pharland@yorku.ca.

2599 ■ Canadian Society for Clinical Investigation (CSCI)

114 Cheyenne Way
Ottawa, ON, Canada K2J 0E9
Ph: (613) 730-6240
Fax: (613) 491-0073
Free: 877-968-9449
E-mail: csci@rcpsc.edu
URL: www.csci-scrc.ca

2600 ■ CSCI Distinguished Scientist Lectures and Awards *(Doctorate/Award)*

Purpose: To recognize the contributions made by medical students. **Focus:** Medical research. **Qualif.:** Applicants must be MD or PhD medical students who made significant contributions to medical knowledge. Their research should be generally recognized as expert, innovative and in the forefront of research endeavor; must be proposed by a CSCI member. **Criteria:** Recipients will be selected based on submitted materials.

Funds Avail.: $2,000 with plaque and one-year free membership. **To Apply:** Nomination package should include letters of support from two supporters and a curriculum vitae. **Deadline:** November 28.

2601 ■ Henry Friesen Awards and Lectures *(Doctorate/Award)*

Purpose: To recognize scientists for their contribution to biomedical research and to cover travel and hotel expenses. **Focus:** Biomedical research. **Qualif.:** Applicants must be scientists, MD or PhD students who are notable for their contributions to biomedical research at a Canadian university. The research should be recognizable in the international field as novel, original and of the highest calibre. The body of work should be of significant duration. **Criteria:** Applicants will be selected based on submitted materials.

Funds Avail.: $10,000. **To Apply:** The nomination package should contain letters from two sponsors, the nominee's curriculum vitae and two of the nominee's best publications. **Deadline:** January 30.

2602 ■ Canadian Society of Club Managers (CSCM)

2943-B Bloor St. W
Etobicoke, ON, Canada M8X 1B3
Ph: (416) 979-0640
Fax: (416) 979-1144
Free: 877-376-CSCM

E-mail: national@cscm.org
URL: www.cscm.org

2603 ■ Val Mason Scholarships *(Postgraduate/ Scholarship)*

Purpose: To provide financial assistance to individuals pursuing a career in club management. **Focus:** Management. **Qualif.:** Applicants must be nominated by a member of the society presently enrolled in a school, college or university and must intend to pursue a career in the Private Club Industry; must be employed or have been recently employed at a member club of the society; and must have shown a keen interest in pursuing a career in club management. **Criteria:** Applications and proposals will be reviewed and judged by the society's Scholarship Subcommittee.

Funds Avail.: $2,000. **To Apply:** Applicants must submit a letter of recommendation from the nominating member; transcript of records; a 500-word essay explaining their interests in the Private Club Industry; and must indicate how their education is presently funded. Complete application package must be submitted to: Canadian Society of Club Managers 2943B Bloor St. West, Etobicoke, ON M8X 1B3. **Deadline:** July 16.

2604 ■ Canadian Society for Eighteenth Century Studies (CSECS)

Laurentian University
935 Ramsey Lake Rd.
Sudbury, ON, Canada P3E 2C6
E-mail: sglover@laurentian.ca
URL: www.csecs.ca

2605 ■ David W. Smith Fellowships *(Postdoctorate/Fellowship)*

Purpose: To support students and researchers who do not have access to institutional sources of research funding. **Focus:** General studies. **Qualif.:** Applicants must be doctoral students (from third year onwards), post-doctoral researchers, part-time professors or instructors, non-tenure track professors and independent researchers. **Criteria:** Recipients will be selected based on submitted application materials.

Funds Avail.: $2,000. **To Apply:** Applicants must submit an application form in word format, curriculum vitae and description of the research proposal which includes budget and justification of proposed expenditures. **Deadline:** March. **Contact:** Application form and supporting documents must be submitted to Marc Andre Bernier; Phone: 819-376-5011; Fax: 819-376-5173; E-mail: marc-andre.bernier@uqtr.ca.

2606 ■ Canadian Society of Exploration Geophysicists (CSEG)

Ste. 570, 400-5th Ave. SW
Calgary, AB, Canada T2P 0L6
Ph: (403) 262-0015
Fax: (403) 262-7383
E-mail: cseg.office@shaw.ca
URL: www.cseg.ca

2607 ■ CSEG Scholarship Trust Fund *(Graduate, Undergraduate/Scholarship)*

Purpose: To provide financial support for promising graduate students pursuing careers in the field of exploration

Awards are arranged alphabetically below their administering organizations

geophysics. **Focus:** Geophysics. **Qualif.:** Applicants must be undergraduates with above average standing or graduate students enrolled in an academic program directed toward an exploration geophysics career at any Canadian university. **Criteria:** Applicants are selected based on academic performance, financial need, interest in geophysics and extra-curricular activities.

Funds Avail.: No specific amount. **To Apply:** Applicants must provide a transcript of post-secondary education accompanied by a list of courses currently in progress and recommendation letters from two faculty members or a past or current employer mailed directly to the Committee by the author. **Deadline:** June 15.

2608 ■ Canadian Society for Medical Laboratory Science (CSMLS)

PO Box 2830, LCD 1
Hamilton, ON, Canada L8N 3N8
Ph: (905) 528-8642
Fax: (905) 528-4968
Free: 800-263-8277
E-mail: info@csmls.org
URL: www.csmls.org

2609 ■ CSMLS Student Scholarship Awards
(Postgraduate/Scholarship)

Purpose: To cultivate and nurture future leaders in the field of medical laboratory science. **Focus:** Medical laboratory technology. **Qualif.:** Applicants must be current members of CSMLS and enrolled in the final year of a full-time Canadian training program in general medical laboratory technology, diagnostic cytology, and clinical genetics; must be Canadian citizens or permanent residents. **Criteria:** Applicants will be evaluated based on academic achievement, leadership and volunteer service and financial need. Scholarship applications will be reviewed by the CSMLS Grants and Scholarships Committee.

Funds Avail.: No specific amount. **To Apply:** Applicants must submit the application forms together with the official transcript of records; two letters of recommendation, one should be from a faculty member or college official and one should be from a community leader or other person. **Deadline:** October 1.

2610 ■ Canadian Society for Otolaryngology Head and Neck Surgery (CSOHNS)

221 Millford Cres.
Elora, ON, Canada N0B 1S0
Ph: (519) 846-0630
Fax: (519) 846-9529
Free: 800-655-9533
E-mail: cso.hns@sympatico.ca
URL: www.entcanada.org

2611 ■ CSOHNS Fellowships *(Graduate/ Fellowship)*

Purpose: To help students pursue advanced training in Canada. **Focus:** General studies. **Qualif.:** Applicants must be MD or equivalent in good standing and must be permanent residents or in an accredited otolaryngology training program in Canada. Otolaryngologists who wish to undergo advanced training may also apply. Host institutions must be affiliated with a Canadian medical school or an ac-

credited medical school abroad. Eligible supervisors must demonstrate competence in the field of further study, must be prepared to supervise fellows for a period not less than a year, and must not be supervising a CSOHNS funded fellow in the concurrent year as the applicant. **Criteria:** Applications will be ranked based on demonstrated academic and clinical productivity of the applicants and supervisors, interest in subspecialty area, clinical and academic exposure at host institution, need for advanced training, letters of reference and evaluations of supervisor from the Society and Fund sponsored fellows.

Funds Avail.: $25,000. **Number Awarded:** 2. **To Apply:** Application forms must be completed by the applicants and supervisors. Candidates must submit the supporting documents which include curriculum vitae, four letters of recommendation and supporting documentation from a Canadian institution outlining any clinical position that the institution might offer. **Deadline:** February. **Contact:** Application forms and supporting documents can be mailed to Dr. Jeffrey Harris 1E4.29 MacKenzie Centre, 8440-112 St., Edmonton, AB T6G 2B7; Phone: 780-407-7958; Fax: 780-407-3885; E-mail: jeffreyharris@cha.ab.ca.

2612 ■ Canadian Society of Petroleum Geologists (CSPG)

110-333 5th Ave. SW, 110-333 5th Ave. SW
Calgary, AB, Canada T2P 3B6
Ph: (403) 264-5610
Fax: (403) 264-5898
E-mail: lis.bjeld@cspg.org
URL: www.cspg.org

2613 ■ Glen Ruby Memorial Scholarships
(Undergraduate/Scholarship)

Purpose: To promote excellence in petroleum geology and geophysics by assisting in the development of future geoscientists. **Focus:** Geoscience. **Qualif.:** Applicants must be students in their second, third or fourth year of studies in areas related to petroleum geology and geophysics. **Criteria:** Selection will be based on merit.

Funds Avail.: $2,000-$5,000. **To Apply:** Applicants must submit the completed application form together with copy of transcripts. Application forms are available online. **Deadline:** October 31. **Remarks:** Scholarships will be administered through the CSPG Trust Fund. **Contact:** June Hamm, Conoco Philips Canada; PO Box 130, 401-9th Avenue SW, Calgary, AB, T2P 2H7.

2614 ■ Canadian Society for the Study of Education (CSSE)

260 Dalhousie St., Ste. 204
Ottawa, ON, Canada K1N 7E4
Ph: (613) 241-0018
Fax: (613) 241-0019
E-mail: csse-scee@csse.ca
URL: www.csse-scee.ca/csse

2615 ■ Canadian Society for the Study of Education Mentorship Awards *(Professional development/Award)*

Purpose: To recognize a faculty member who has provided outstanding support and encouragement for graduate students. **Focus:** General studies. **Qualif.:** Applicant must be a faculty member mentoring graduate students which

Awards are arranged alphabetically below their administering organizations

include, but is not limited to: 1) encouraging contributions to the knowledge base of graduate students; 2) providing opportunities for student's professional growth as teachers and researchers; and 3) modeling active membership in professional societies and encouraging students to do the same. **Criteria:** Award will be given to applicants who can provide evidence of recognition from graduate students.

Funds Avail.: No stated amount. **To Apply:** Applicant must submit a cover letter; a blind letter of nomination describing why the nominee deserves to be recognized for mentoring graduate students; and three to five letters of support from other mentees and colleagues. **Deadline:** March 26. **Contact:** CCGSE Mentorship Award Committee Chair, Lori Friesen at lfriesen@ualberta.ca.

2616 ■ Canadian Society for the Study of Education New Scholar Fellowships (CSSE)
(Professional development/Fellowship)

Purpose: To recognize and support the work of Assistant Professors in Education. **Focus:** Education. **Qualif.:** Applicant must be a full-time, tenure-track assistant professor in Education in an academic unit in Canada. **Criteria:** Selection will be made based on submitted application and project.

Funds Avail.: No stated amount. **To Apply:** Applicant must mark the appropriate box on the Proposal Presentation Cover Sheet and must submit a copy of his/her full paper in advance.

2617 ■ CSSE ARTS Graduate Research Awards
(Graduate/Award)

Purpose: To recognize the thesis, projects, or dissertation of graduate students. **Focus:** Education. **Qualif.:** Applicants must be Canadians who are graduates of Canadian universities; must have studied abroad, and work must have been accepted within two years prior to the year of conference. **Criteria:** Recipients will be selected based on submitted materials.

Funds Avail.: $500. **To Apply:** Applicants must submit a cover letter; a copy of the signed committee acceptance of the dissertation, thesis, or project; 1,000-1,500 words outlining the following: 1) problem; 2) questions addressed in the study; 3) brief review of the major literature; 4) design methodology; 5) conclusions; and 6) statement of significance. **Deadline:** March 1. **Contact:** Application form and supporting documents must be sent to: Kathryn Ricketts at krickett@sfu.ca.

2618 ■ Canadian Society for the Study of Higher Education (CSSHE)
260 Dalhousie St., Ste. 204
Ottawa, ON, Canada K1N 7E4
Ph: (613) 241-0018
Fax: (613) 241-0019
E-mail: csshe-scees@csse.ca
URL: www.csshe-scees.ca

2619 ■ CSSHE Masters Thesis/Project Awards
(Master's/Award)

Purpose: To recognize outstanding Master's thesis or project in Canadian universities in the area of higher education. **Focus:** Education; Educational administration. **Qualif.:** Applicants must have completed the requirements for a Master's degree at a Canadian university; must be nominated by a faculty member. **Criteria:** Applicants will be

chosen based on submitted project or thesis.

Funds Avail.: No specific amount. **To Apply:** Faculty members must submit two nominations. Each submission must include five copies of an expanded abstract (1000-1500 words). It should contain the problem statement, significance of the study, methodology, major findings and recommendations. A separate file with the full text of the thesis or project should also be submitted. **Deadline:** February 29. **Contact:** Dr. Walter Archer, University of Alberta, 2-367 Enterprise Sq., 10230 Jasper Ave., Edmonton, AB T5J 4P6; E-mail: walter.archer@ualberta.ca.

2620 ■ CSSHE Research Awards *(Professional development/Award)*

Purpose: To recognize practicing scholars in mid-career for publishing outstanding research on any aspect of Canadian post-secondary education. **Focus:** Education; Educational administration. **Qualif.:** Applicants must be scholars with demonstrated contributions in research focusing on Canadian post-secondary education. **Criteria:** Award will be made on the basis of published research with particular emphasis given to work published in the last five years.

Funds Avail.: Amount not specified. **To Apply:** Applicants must submit a letter of nomination describing the candidate and stating the reason(s) why he/she has been chosen for a research award; must also submit a curriculum vitae or example(s) of the published scholarship. **Deadline:** February 29.

2621 ■ Canadian Society for Unconventional Gas (CSUG)
237-8th Ave. SE, Ste. 420
Calgary, AB, Canada T2G 5C3
Ph: (403) 233-9298
E-mail: info@csug.ca
URL: www.csug.ca

2622 ■ Charles F. Brandenburg Memorial Scholarships *(Undergraduate/Scholarship)*

Purpose: To help students pursue their education for the growth and interest of the unconventional gas industry in Canada. **Focus:** Geology; Physics. **Qualif.:** Applicants must be third year students at a recognized post-secondary institution; must be enrolled in a full-time status at an accredited Canadian university. **Criteria:** Scholarship will be awarded to an applicant who best meets the qualifications.

Funds Avail.: $2,500. **To Apply:** Applicants must submit an application form. **Deadline:** August 31. **Contact:** David Marchioni, cbm-geology@shaw.ca.

2623 ■ Canadian Technical Asphalt Association (CTAA)
895 Fort St., Ste. 300
Victoria, BC, Canada V8W 1H7
Ph: (250) 361-9187
Fax: (250) 361-9187
E-mail: admin@ctaa.ca
URL: www.ctaa.ca

2624 ■ Canadian Technical Asphalt Association Scholarships *(Undergraduate/Scholarship)*

Purpose: To support students preparing for careers related to asphalt paving technology. **Focus:** Engineering, Chemi-

Awards are arranged alphabetically below their administering organizations

cal; Engineering, Civil. **Qualif.:** Applicants must have been admitted or currently enrolled in a technical college or a university leading to either a diploma or degree. **Criteria:** Recipients will be chosen based on their submitted application form and supporting documents.

Funds Avail.: $1,000-$2,000. **To Apply:** Applicants must submit a completed application form; resume; current academic transcripts; maximum of 500 words statement explaining why they deserve to receive the scholarship; and three letters of reference (one from advisor and two from individuals knowledgeable in technical or academic qualifications of the applicant). **Deadline:** July 1. **Remarks:** Selected applicants must send a letter of acknowledgement to the CTAA Head Office with a description stating how this award will support their studies.

2625 ■ Canadian Transportation Research Forum (CTRF)

PO Box 23033
Woodstock, ON, Canada N4T 1R9
Ph: (519) 421-9701
Fax: (519) 421-9319
E-mail: cawoudsma@ctrf.ca
URL: www.ctrf.ca

2626 ■ CTRF Scholarships for Graduate Study in Transportation *(Graduate/Scholarship)*

Purpose: To financially support students in their educational pursuit. **Focus:** Business administration; Civil engineering; Economics; Geography; Law. **Qualif.:** Applicant must be a Canadian citizen or a land immigrant. **Criteria:** Selection is based on academic ability, relevant work experience, stated career objectives and supporting letters of reference. Preference will be given to applicants who are enrolled in policy and business oriented studies at any Canadian institutions.

Funds Avail.: $4,000. **Number Awarded:** 7. **To Apply:** Applicants must submit a covering letter (including name, address, telephone/fax numbers and e-mail address); official transcript(s) (scanned as a .pdf file); description of work experience or resume (optional); a 300-word summary outlining graduate research project or field of study; and two letters of reference. Submit all documentation (including transcripts) on a CD via mail. Reference letters must be submitted to cawoudsma@ctrf.ca. **Deadline:** December 31. **Contact:** Carole Ann Woudsma at the above address. Referees may send their letters by email to cawoudsma@ctrf.ca.

2627 ■ Canadian Urological Association (CUA)

1155 University, Ste. 1303
Montreal, QC, Canada H3B 3A7
Ph: (514) 395-0376
Fax: (514) 395-1664
E-mail: corporate.office@cua.org
URL: www.cua.org

2628 ■ Canadian Urological Association Community-based Research Awards *(Doctorate/ Award)*

Purpose: To support faculty members at an approved medical school in Canada within two years of initial appointment. **Focus:** Urology. **Qualif.:** Candidates must have an MD degree and have completed clinical training in urol-

ogy; and must hold an active staff appointment for the practice of urology in a Canadian center. **Criteria:** Recipients will be selected based on scientific merit as determined by the members of the CUASF council. Preference will be given to first time applicants.

Funds Avail.: $15,000. **To Apply:** Applicants must submit an original application form and must provide five copies of the following documents: a) letter of support from the Chair of their university, department, or division; b) two letters of recommendation from an individual who is not at the candidate's current institution or department. Applicants may include up to three published reprints of their research. Research proposal is suggested to be in this format: 1) statement of the objective(s); 2) recent relevant research by an applicant; 3) brief review of literature and background information; 4) hypothesis; 5) design and methodology; 6) analysis of data; and 7) summary page. **Deadline:** March 1. **Contact:** Application form and supporting documents must be sent to: Martin Gleave, Chairman of the Scholarship Foundation, Department of Urological Sciences, 2775 Laurel St., 6th Fl., Vancouver, BC V5Z 1M9; Phone: 604-875-5006; Fax: 604-875-5604.

2629 ■ Canadian Urological Association Fellowships *(Graduate/Fellowship)*

Purpose: To support faculty members at an approved medical school in Canada within two years of initial appointment. **Focus:** Urology. **Qualif.:** Candidates must have an MD degree and have completed a clinical training in urology. **Criteria:** Recipients will be selected based on submitted application form and supporting documents.

Funds Avail.: No stated amount. **To Apply:** Applicants must submit an original application form and must provide five copies of the following documents: a) letter of support from the Chair of their university, department, or division; b) two letters of recommendation from an individual who is not at the candidate's current institution or department. Applicants may include up to three published reprints of their research. Research proposal is suggested to be in this format: 1) statement of the objective(s); 2) recent relevant research by the applicant; 3) brief review of literature and background information; 4) hypothesis; 5) design and methodology; 6) analysis of data; and 7) summary page. **Deadline:** March 1. **Contact:** Application form and supporting documents must be sent to: Martin Gleave, Chairman of the Scholarship Foundation, Department of Urological Sciences, 2775 Laurel St., 6th Fl., Vancouver, BC V5Z 1M9; Phone: 604-875-5006; Fax: 604-875-5604.

2630 ■ Canadian Water Resources Association (CWRA)

9 Corvus Ct.
Ottawa, ON, Canada K2E 7Z4
Ph: (613) 237-9363
Fax: (613) 594-5190
E-mail: services@aic.ca
URL: www.cwra.org

2631 ■ Canadian Water Resources Association Scholarships *(All/Scholarship)*

Purpose: To raise awareness of the value of water; to promote responsible and effective water resource management in Canada. **Focus:** Water resources. **Qualif.:** Applicants must be members of the Canada Water Resources Association. **Criteria:** Recipients are selected based on academic excellence and project relevance to water management.

Awards are arranged alphabetically below their administering organizations

Funds Avail.: $1,500. **Number Awarded:** 2. **To Apply:** Applicants must provide a statement from the chairman/director of the department which verifies that the application is reflective of the project; a 500-word statement which outlines the applicant's research project and its relevance to sustainable water resources; official transcript of records; two references to be sent directly to the Scholarship Committee by the referees or appropriate official of the university or college; a statement from the program chairman or director endorsing the application from that program, including confirmation of the applicant's full-time registration; and completed application form. **Deadline:** February 28.

2632 ■ Ken Thomson Scholarships
(Undergraduate/Scholarship)

Purpose: To raise awareness of the value of water; to promote responsible and effective water resource management in Canada. **Focus:** Water resources. **Qualif.:** Applicant must be the second-highest ranked graduate student whose program of study focuses upon applied, natural or social science aspects of water resources; must be Canadian citizen or landed immigrant attending a Canadian University or college; must be enrolled in full-time graduate studies in any discipline. **Criteria:** Recipients are selected based on academic excellence and project relevance to water management and development.

Funds Avail.: $2,000. **To Apply:** Applicants must provide a statement from the chairman/director of the department which verifies that the application is reflective of the project; a 500-word statement which outlines the applicant's research project and its relevance to sustainable water resources; official transcript of records; two references to be sent directly to the Scholarship Committee by the referees or appropriate official of the university or college; a statement from the program chairman or director endorsing the application from that program, including confirmation of the applicant's full-time registration; and completed application form. **Deadline:** February 28.

2633 ■ Canadian Water and Wastewater Association (CWWA)
1010 Polytek St., Unit 11
Ottawa, ON, Canada K1J 9H9
Ph: (613) 747-0524
Fax: (613) 747-0523
E-mail: admin@cwwa.ca
URL: www.cwwa.ca

2634 ■ Steve Bonk Scholarships *(Postgraduate/Scholarship)*

Purpose: To provide educational assistance to those embarking on careers associated with municipal water supply or wastewater. **Focus:** General studies. **Qualif.:** Applicants must be Canadian citizens or permanent residents of Canada; must be residents of current CWWA municipal members, or attend college or university in a municipal or CWWA Academic members; must have completed successfully one year of post-secondary education; must be registered as full-time students in further studies; must intend to pursue a career related to the municipal water or wastewater industry. **Criteria:** Candidates will be selected based on the academic achievement, statement/essay, and work experience/extracurricular activities.

Funds Avail.: $500. **To Apply:** Applicants must have a copy of the post-secondary course transcripts completed to date; must have a description/list of planned further stud-

ies; must provide a statement or essay (500 words) of the applicant's interest, knowledge and future goals in the water/wastewater industry together with applicable work experience or extracurricular activities. Application and other supporting documents must be sent to: CWWA - Steve Bonk Scholarship, 11-1010 Polytek Rd., Ottawa, ON K1J 9H9. **Deadline:** June 1.

2635 ■ Cancer for College (CFC)
1345 Specialty Dr., Ste. E
Vista, CA 92081
Ph: (760) 599-5096
E-mail: info@cancerforcollege.org
URL: www.cancerforcollege.org

2636 ■ Cancer for College Scholarships *(Graduate, Undergraduate/Scholarship)*

Purpose: To support current and former cancer patients in their educational pursuits. **Focus:** General studies. **Qualif.:** Applicant must be a U.S. resident enrolled in an accredited university, community college or trade school; and must be a cancer patient, cancer survivor and/or amputee. **Criteria:** Selection is based on the submitted application materials.

Funds Avail.: $500-$4,000. **Number Awarded:** Varies. **To Apply:** Applicants must submit a completed application form together with a summary of cancer treatments including date of diagnosis, place of treatment, doctor's contact information and health status; a personal statement (minimum of one page double-spaced, type written page); a description of how the applicant's college education is being financed with a copy of all financial aid being received; a copy of an acceptance letter or a letter of good standing from the registrar's office; two letters of recommendation (doctor, nurse, teacher, counsellor, mentor, etc.), one letter must be from the treating physician/nurse. Applicants applying from a junior college only need to complete the application form and supply a single letter from the treating doctor.

2637 ■ Cancer Research Institute (CRI)
One Exchange Plz.
55 Broadway, Ste. 1802
New York, NY 10006
Ph: (212) 688-7515
Fax: (212) 832-9376
Free: 800-992-2623
E-mail: bbrewer@cancerresearch.org
URL: www.cancerresearch.org

2638 ■ Irvington Institute Fellowships of the Cancer Research Institute *(Postdoctorate/Fellowship)*

Purpose: To support and train young scientists who wish to receive training in cancer immunology or general immunology. **Focus:** Immunology. **Qualif.:** Applicant must have a doctoral degree prior to the award activation. **Criteria:** A panel of 23 scientists drawn from our Scientific Advisory Council rigorously evaluates each candidate, the intended sponsor and training environment, and the nature and feasibility of the proposed project.

Funds Avail.: $50,000 for the first year, $53,000 for the second year and $57,000 for the third year. **To Apply:** Applicants must submit completed application and materials in electronic format. Documents to be uploaded are: brief

Awards are arranged alphabetically below their administering organizations

description of the applicants' background and research accomplishments; list of other funding sources with due dates; curriculum vitae and bibliography; abstract of research in non-technical English; concise research proposal (maximum of 10 pages); letter from the sponsor introducing the applicant and describing the sponsor's qualifications to direct the proposed research; sponsor's curriculum vitae; and two letters of recommendation. **Deadline:** April 1 and October 1. **Remarks:** Established in 1971. **Contact:** Lynne A. Harmer at grants@cancerresearch.org.

2639 ■ Cancer Survivors' Fund
PO Box 792
Missouri City, TX 77459
Ph: (281) 437-7142
Fax: (281) 437-9568
E-mail: csf@cancersurvivorsfund.org
URL: www.cancersurvivorsfund.org

2640 ■ Cancer Survivors' Fund Scholarships
(Undergraduate/Scholarship)

Purpose: To augment the expenses associated with the college education of young cancer survivors. **Focus:** General Studies. **Qualif.:** Applicants must be cancer survivors or currently diagnosed with cancer; must be enrolled in or accepted for enrollment in an undergraduate school. **Criteria:** Recipients are selected by a Committee based on applicant's personal hardship, financial and emotional needs and academic qualifications.

Funds Avail.: No specific amount. **To Apply:** Applicants must complete the online scholarship application; must submit two letters of recommendation from two different academic teachers addressing why they should receive the scholarship; a letter from an attending physician verifying their medical history and current medical situation; must agree to do volunteer work to use their cancer experience to help other young cancer patients and survivors coping with a life threatening or life-altering event; must submit an essay discussing the following question: How has my experience with cancer impacted my life values and career goals? Essays must be minimum of 500 words and a maximum of 1200 words. **Remarks:** The applicants and their parents if they are minors, must sign a release, that they agree to have their name and photo published in the news media or any CSF publication as a recipient of Cancer Survivors' Fund scholarship and that they agree to have their name, photo and success story to be published on the website or in any CSF publication.

2641 ■ Cancer Treatment Centers of America (CTCA)
1336 Basswood Rd.
Schaumburg, IL 60173
Ph: (847) 342-7458
E-mail: christopher.hamrick@ctca-hope.com
URL: www.cancercenter.com

2642 ■ Cancer Treatment Centers of America Post-Graduate Management Fellowships
(Postgraduate/Fellowship)

Purpose: To provide an opportunity to post-graduate students to work directly with hospital leadership teams on strategic and operational objectives. **Focus:** Health care services. **Qualif.:** Applicant must be a graduate of MHA,

MBA (with healthcare concentration), MPH or MSN programs, with at least two years of professional work experience. **Criteria:** Selection is based on the submitted application materials.

Funds Avail.: No specific amount. **To Apply:** Applicants must submit a Cover letter along with a resume; official graduate school transcripts; three sealed letters of recommendation, one from each of the following: program director, professor and employer; letter of intent, expressing short- and long-term goals, applicant's expectations from the fellowship and how CTCA fits to his/her career plan. **Deadline:** October 31. **Remarks:** Founded by Mr. Roger C. Cary, who is the Chief Operating Officer of CTCA and the former President and CEO of CTCA at Midwestern Regional Medical Center. **Contact:** recruitment@ctca-hope.com.

2643 ■ Cape Coral Community Foundation (CCCF)
4729 Vincennes Blvd.
Cape Coral, FL 33904
Ph: (239) 542-5594
E-mail: cccf@capecoralcf.org
URL: capecoralcf.planyourlegacy.org

2644 ■ The Helen and Edward Brancati Teacher Development Scholarships *(Professional development/Scholarship)*

Purpose: To assist teachers employed by an accredited school in the United States who wish to continue their education. **Focus:** General studies. **Qualif.:** Applicants must be teachers employed by an accredited school in the United States who are seeking post-graduate education or need funds to continue their education classes, workshops, conferences or certification courses; must be U.S. citizens. **Criteria:** Recipients are selected based on demonstrated ability to create an atmosphere of learning for students across the broad spectrum of a mainstream classroom, complete application, letter of recommendation, essay and other materials.

Funds Avail.: $750. **To Apply:** Applicants must show proof of employment; must provide a copy of teaching certificate, written evaluations from their school principal; must outline a plan for how these funds will be used to increase their professional development or enhance their classroom; must provide a 500-word original essay discussing their reasons for becoming a teacher and how this scholarship will be beneficial; must submit a proof of enrollment or most recent transcript. **Deadline:** October 31. **Contact:** For further information, applicants must contact Beth Sanger at the above address; E-mail: beth@capecoralcf.org.

2645 ■ The Rotary Club of Cape Coral Goldcoast Scholarship Fund *(Undergraduate/ Scholarship)*

Purpose: To assist eligible high school seniors to further their education by attending college. **Focus:** General Studies. **Qualif.:** Applicants must be graduating seniors of any high school in Lee County; must have a 3.2 GPA or better; must be accepted to at least one accredited junior college, college or university; must be residents of Cape Coral; must be U.S. citizens and active in school and community. **Criteria:** Recipients are selected based on academic standing, academic history, school and community involvement, career and academic goals and three letters of recommendation.

Awards are arranged alphabetically below their administering organizations

Funds Avail.: $4,000. **Number Awarded:** 3. **To Apply:** Applicants must submit a completed application form. **Deadline:** April 1.

2646 ■ Cape Fear Community College Foundation
411 N Front St.
Wilmington, NC 28401
Ph: (910) 362-7207
URL: cfcc.edu/foundation

2647 ■ Cape Fear Community College Merit Scholarships *(Undergraduate, Vocational/Occupational/Scholarship)*

Purpose: To assist the local high school students of North Carolina throughout the course of their studies. **Focus:** General studies. **Qualif.:** Applicants must be U.S. citizens; must be high school senior students who have applied for or been approved to enroll in Cape Fear Community College in a curriculum program and possess academic potential as shown by high school grades, rank in class; must maintain 3.0 GPA and have completed 12 credit hours during their fall semester. **Criteria:** Applicants are judged based on academic achievement and financial need. Consideration will be given to non-school activities, work record, community service and association with the applicant's vocational field of interest.

Funds Avail.: $1,800. **Number Awarded:** 10. **To Apply:** Applicants must submit all required application information including the letter of recommendation from high school principal, guidance counselor or high school teacher. **Deadline:** March 30. **Contact:** Kay Warren at kwarren@cfcc.edu.

2648 ■ Capital City AIDS Fund (CCAF)
PO Box 160636
Sacramento, CA 95816
Ph: (916) 448-1110
E-mail: capcityaidsfund@yahoo.com
URL: www.capcityaidsfund.org

2649 ■ Helen Veress-Mitchell Scholarship Fund *(Graduate, Undergraduate/Scholarship)*

Purpose: To help people living with HIV/AIDS attend college and pursue a two-year, four-year, or graduate degree. **Focus:** General studies. **Qualif.:** Applicants must be enrolled in a college or technical school with a minimum nine hours of class work; must remain in good standing with a minimum GPA of 2.0 or higher. **Criteria:** Selection will be based on evaluation of submitted documents and specific criteria.

Funds Avail.: $1,500. **To Apply:** Applicants should submit a completed application form; transcripts from the last two academic years including GPA; proof of enrollment for current academic year; two recommendation letters from a medical provider and/or educator. **Deadline:** June. **Remarks:** All information submitted is confidential. **Contact:** For further information, applicants must contact Stuart Eldridge at 916-455-2777 or e-mail scholarship@capcityaidsfund.org.

2650 ■ CareerFitter.com
Box 134
Pisgah Forest, NC 28768-0134
Ph: (918) 477-2280
E-mail: 2008@careerfitter.com
URL: www.careerfitter.com

2651 ■ CareerFitter Scholarships *(Graduate, Undergraduate/Scholarship)*

Purpose: To support students in their educational pursuits. **Focus:** General studies. **Qualif.:** Applicant must be a student enrolled or planning to enroll in a college, university or graduate school program during the spring/summer/fall term; a U.S. citizen or permanent resident; and with a minimum of 2.5 GPA. **Criteria:** Selection is based on the essay.

Funds Avail.: $500. **Number Awarded:** Varies. **To Apply:** Applicants are required to complete the application form online. In addition, students must write an essay on the topic: What is the perfect career for you, and why? **Deadline:** September 15. **Contact:** admin3@careerfitter.com.

2652 ■ Caribbean Hotel and Tourism Association (CHTA)
2655 Le Jeune Rd., Ste. 910
Coral Gables, FL 33134
Ph: (305) 443-3040
Fax: (305) 443-3005
E-mail: alec@caribbeanhotelandtourism.com
URL: www.caribbeanhotelassociation.com

2653 ■ Caribbean Hotel and Tourism Association Academic Scholarships *(Graduate, Undergraduate/Scholarship)*

Purpose: To provide people throughout the Caribbean region with an awareness of the industry's varied career opportunities a well as technical and professional development. **Focus:** Hotel, Institutional and Restaurant Management. **Qualif.:** Applicants must be full-time or must be secondary school graduates pursuing a diploma or degree in hotel and restaurant management or culinary arts in a two-year or four-year program at an affiliated CHA institution; or either be full-time students who are currently pursuing a diploma or degree in hotel and restaurant management, culinary arts in a two-year, four-year, or a graduate program at an affiliated CHA institution and who have completed first semester of the program; must be born in Caribbean and registered as Caribbean National. **Criteria:** Recipients are selected based on potential for success in the hotel industry and financial need.

Funds Avail.: $500-$5,000. **To Apply:** Applicants must complete the application form; must submit a copy of certificates or awards; must include a current photo; must submit references or recommendations. **Contact:** Applicants may send their applications with all attachments and endorsements to CHTA Office or via e-mail at foundation@caribbeanhotelandtourism.com.

2654 ■ Carnegie Institution for Science
1530 P St. NW
Washington, DC 20005
Ph: (202) 387-6400
Fax: (202) 387-8092
E-mail: president@ciw.edu
URL: carnegiescience.edu

Awards are arranged alphabetically below their administering organizations

2655 ■ Carnegie Observatories Graduate Research Fellowships *(Doctorate, Graduate/Fellowship)*

Purpose: To support graduate students interested in carrying out all or part of their thesis research under the supervision of a Carnegie Staff member. **Focus:** General studies. **Qualif.:** Applicants must have completed all requisite coursework and examinations at their home institution, and be ready to conduct full-time research toward their PhD dissertation, at the start of the appointment. Since a PhD degree will be awarded by the home institution, applicants must obtain written approval from the department chair or head granting permission for the applicant to participate in the program. **Criteria:** Selection will be based on the committee's criteria.

Funds Avail.: No specific amount. **To Apply:** Applicants must submit a brief cover letter summarizing the application and its contents; department head/chair approval letter; a list of potential advisors and projects; title of research project to be conducted with the Carnegie advisor; letters of recommendation sent by the three individuals familiar with the academic qualifications and scientific potential of the applicant. If English is not the native language, letters should assess their English proficiency. letters should be submitted by email; an official transcript of the Applicants' courses and grades to be mailed by the university Registrar; curriculum vitae and publication record; a four page maximum statement of previous and current research; a four page maximum summary of the research project. All application materials, except for the transcript of grades should be submitted online. Documents should be uploaded in PDF format. **Deadline:** April 15. **Contact:** Carnegie Observatories, 813 Santa Barbara St., Pasadena, CA 91101; Phone: 626-304-0248; Fax: 626-795-8136; Email: gradfellowships@obs.carnegiescience.edu.

2656 ■ Carpenters' Company (CC)

320 Chestnut St.
Carpenters Hall
Philadelphia, PA 19106
Ph: (215) 925-0167
E-mail: carphall@carpentershall.com
URL: www.carpentershall.org

2657 ■ Carpenters' Company Scholarships *(Undergraduate/Scholarship)*

Purpose: To promote the study of architecture, structural engineering, or construction engineering/management. **Focus:** Architecture; Engineering, Architectural; Construction. **Qualif.:** Applicant must be a full-time third or fourth year student at an accredited degree program in architecture, structural engineering, or construction engineering/management and must be certified as having financial need by the financial aid advisor at the attended school. **Criteria:** Award is given based on the application materials submitted.

Funds Avail.: No specific amount. **To Apply:** Applicants must submit a completed scholarship application form. **Deadline:** April 16.

2658 ■ Cascade Blues Association (CBA)

PO Box 14493
Portland, OR 97293-0493
Ph: (503) 223-1850
Fax: (503) 223-1850
E-mail: cbastaff@cascadeblues.org
URL: www.cascadeblues.org

2659 ■ Christopher Mesi Memorial Music Scholarships *(Undergraduate/Scholarship)*

Purpose: To encourage anyone to pursue an undergraduate degree at a local college. **Focus:** Music. **Qualif.:** Applicants must be high school seniors or college music students; must have GPA of 2.75 or better. **Criteria:** Recipients are selected based on demonstrated achievement through their involvement in school or community activities.

Funds Avail.: $500. **To Apply:** Applicants must submit their transcript of records; two letters of recommendation from which one must come from a music teacher and one must come from a counselor, employer or teacher; and a proof of college enrollment. **Deadline:** July 1. **Remarks:** This award can be used at any Oregon and Washington college for continued education in the field of music.

2660 ■ Catching the Dream (Native American Scholarship Fund)

8200 Mountain Rd. NE, Ste. 203
Albuquerque, NM 87110-7856
Ph: (505) 262-2351
Fax: (505) 262-0534
E-mail: nscholarsh@aol.com
URL: www.catchingthedream.org

2661 ■ Sergeant Douglas and Charlotte De-Horse Scholarships *(Graduate, Undergraduate/Scholarship)*

Purpose: To support American Indian students in their education. **Focus:** Military science and education. **Qualif.:** Applicants must be American Indian students who have completed one year of any Army, Navy, or Air Force Junior Reserve Officer Training program; enrolled in an Army, Navy, or Air Force Reserve Officer Training Program; must be veterans of the U.S. Army, Navy, Air Force, Merchant Marine or Coast Guard; and enrolled in undergraduate or graduate program of study. **Criteria:** Applicants are selected based submitted application.

Funds Avail.: No specific amount. **To Apply:** Applicants must submit a completed application; letters of recommendation; personal essay; and high school transcripts. **Deadline:** April 15 and September 15. **Remarks:** The First Sergeant Douglas and Charlotte DeHorse Scholarship was established in 2007 to honor the American Indian veterans.

2662 ■ MESBEC Scholarships *(Undergraduate/Scholarship)*

Purpose: To support the education of Native Schools. **Focus:** Mathematics and mathematical sciences; Engineering; Science; Business; Education; Computer and information sciences. **Qualif.:** Applicants must be 1/4 or more degree Native American; be enrolled members of a "U.S. tribe"; attending or planning to attend a college/university within the United States on a full-time basis that is fully accredited; studying in the field of business, finance, management, economics, banking, hotel management, and related field; have excellent grades; high ACT or SAT scores; and have a strong commitment to their Native American community. **Criteria:** Scholarships are awarded based on merit.

Funds Avail.: $500-$5000. **To Apply:** Applicants must submit a completed application form (available at the web-

Awards are arranged alphabetically below their administering organizations

site); financial need analysis; a copy of the IRS 1040 Federal Tax Return for the previous year; Certificate of Native American Blood; an essay explaining career goals; three letters of recommendation; official transcripts; a copy of standardized test scores; copy of letter of admission from an accredited college or university or graduate school and degree program in the United States; and a photograph (2X3) of head and shoulders. **Deadline:** March 15, April 15, and September 15. **Contact:** Application form and supporting documents may send electronically to nscholarsh@aol.com.

2663 ■ Native American Leadership Education Scholarships (NALE) *(Postdoctorate, Undergraduate/Scholarship)*

Purpose: To support paraprofessionals native students in Native American Schools planning to complete their degree in education, counseling, or school administration. **Focus:** Education; Counseling/Guidance; Educational administration. **Qualif.:** Applicants must be 1/4 or more degree Native American; be enrolled members of a "U.S. tribe"; attending or planning to attend a college/university within the United States on a full-time basis that is fully accredited (college level and can range from bachelor's degrees to postdoctoral study); have excellent grades; high ACT or SAT scores; and have a strong commitment to their Native American community. **Criteria:** Scholarships are awarded based on merit.

Funds Avail.: $500-$5000. **To Apply:** Applicants must submit a completed application form (available at the website); financial need analysis; a copy of the IRS 1040 Federal Tax Return for the previous year; Certificate of Native American Blood; an essay explaining career goals; three letters of recommendation; official transcripts; a copy of standardized test scores; copy of letter of admission from an accredited college/university or graduate school and degree program in the United States; and a photograph (2X3) of head and shoulders. **Deadline:** March 15, April 15 and September 15. **Contact:** Application form and supporting documents may send electronically to nscholarsh@aol.com.

2664 ■ Tribal Business Management Program Scholarships (TBM) *(Undergraduate/Scholarship)*

Purpose: To support students planning to work in economic development for tribes. **Focus:** Business; Finance; Management; Economics; Banking; Hotel, institutional, and restaurant management. **Qualif.:** Applicants must be 1/4 or more degree Native American; be enrolled members of "U.S. tribes"; attending or planning to attend a college/university within the United States on a full-time basis that is fully accredited; studying in the field of business, finance, management, economics, banking, hotel management and related fields; have excellent grades; high ACT or SAT scores; and have a strong commitment to their Native American community. **Criteria:** Scholarships are awarded based on merit.

Funds Avail.: $500-$5000. **To Apply:** Applicants must submit a completed application form (available at the website); financial need analysis; a copy of the IRS 1040 Federal Tax Return for the previous year; Certificate of Native American Blood; an essay explaining career goals; three letters of recommendation; official transcripts; a copy of standardized test scores; copy of letter of admission from an accredited college or university or graduate school and degree program in the United States; and a photograph (2X3) of head and shoulders. **Deadline:** March 15, April 15 and September 15. **Contact:** Application form and support-

ing documents must be submitted electronically to nscholarsh@aol.com.

2665 ■ Catholic Biblical Association of America (CBA)
Catholic University of America
433 Caldwell Hall
Washington, DC 20064
Ph: (202) 319-5519
Fax: (202) 319-4799
E-mail: cua-cathbib@cua.edu
URL: catholicbiblical.org

2666 ■ Catholic Biblical Association of America Scholarships *(Undergraduate/Scholarship)*

Purpose: To provide support to students who want to pursue their biblical studies. **Focus:** Bible studies. **Qualif.:** Applicant must be a full-time student in doctoral programs on biblical studies at four institutions: (a) Catholic University of America; (b) Graduate Theological Union at Berkeley; (c) University of Notre Dame. **Criteria:** Applicants will be selected based on the following criteria: (1) Doctoral programs in both Old Testament and New Testament, which include a theological component; (2) Quality programs, as judge on faculty and on course requirements, including biblical language requirements resembling those of the Pontifical Biblical Institute for the S.S.L., including both Hebrew and Greek.

Funds Avail.: Full tuition fee and a stipend of $15,500. **To Apply:** For further information, applicants are advised to contact the Association at Catholic University of America, 433 Caldwell Hall, Washington, DC 20064.

2667 ■ Catholic Library Association (CLA)
205 W Monroe St., Ste. 314
Chicago, IL 60606-5061
Ph: (312) 739-1776
Fax: (312) 739-1778
E-mail: mmccarthy@cathla.org
URL: www.cathla.org

2668 ■ Rev. Andrew L. Bouwhuis Memorial Scholarship Program *(Graduate/Scholarship)*

Purpose: To foster advanced studies in the field of Library Science. **Focus:** Library and archival sciences; Science. **Qualif.:** Applicant must be attending a graduate library school and in need of financial assistance. **Criteria:** Recipient is selected based on collegiate records, evidence of need for financial help and acceptance in a graduate school program.

Funds Avail.: $1,500. **To Apply:** Applicant must prepare a copy of an acceptance letter at a graduate library school; resume; personal statement on the applicant's interest in librarianship; statement of financial need; reference letter (from a librarian, employer or college instructor); and official transcript. Application materials must be forwarded to the Scholarship Committee. **Deadline:** February 1. **Remarks:** In memory of Reverend Andrew L. Bouwhuis.

2669 ■ Catholic United Financial
3499 Lexington Ave. N
St. Paul, MN 55126-7055
Ph: (651) 490-0170

Awards are arranged alphabetically below their administering organizations

Free: 800-568-6670
E-mail: info@catholicunited.org
URL: www.catholicaid.com

2670 ■ Catholic Aid Association's Post-High School Tuition Scholarships *(Undergraduate/Scholarship)*

Purpose: To provide financial assistance to students to pursue their education. **Focus:** General studies. **Qualif.:** Applicants must be members of Catholic Aid for at least two years (prior to application deadline and at the time the award is given); must be entering their first or second year of post-high school education. **Criteria:** Recipients will be selected based on submitted application.

Funds Avail.: $500 for students attending a Catholic college or university; $300 for those attending a non-Catholic educational institution. **Number Awarded: 2. To Apply:** Applicants must submit a filled out application form; an insurance certificate or annuity; and GPA for the last year of school attended either high school, college, or trade school. **Deadline:** February 15. **Remarks:** Previous applicants are ineligible to apply. **Contact:** If have questions, feel free to contact the Fraternal Department via e-mail: fraternal@catholicaid.org.

2671 ■ Cave Conservancy of the Virginias (CCV)
13131 Overhill Lake Ln.
Glen Allen, VA 23059
Ph: (804) 798-4893
URL: www.caveconservancyofvirginia.org

2672 ■ CCV Foundation Graduate and Undergraduate Fellowships *(Doctorate, Graduate, Undergraduate/Fellowship)*

Purpose: To promote study and research on caves and karst in any field. **Focus:** Cave studies; Archeology; Biology; Engineering, Geological; Geography; Geology; Social sciences. **Qualif.:** Applicant must be a full-time graduate or undergraduate student at a U.S. college/university studying caves and karst in any field, including but not limited to archeology, biology, engineering, geography, geology and social sciences. **Criteria:** Selection is based on the application materials submitted for review.

Funds Avail.: $5,000 (undergraduate and graduate students) and $15,000 (PhD Students). **To Apply:** Undergraduate applicants must submit a letter of intent, a proposal of the research (maximum of 500 words), a letter of support and undergraduate transcripts. Graduate applicants (MS and PhD) must submit a letter of intent, a curriculum vitae, a thesis proposal, graduate transcript and two letters of recommendation (one from the thesis advisor). Application materials must be submitted to Cave Conservancy Foundation. **Deadline:** May 1 (undergraduate) and June 1 (graduate). **Contact:** For undergraduate students: Dr. Horton H. Hobbs III, Department of Biology, Wittenberg University, PO Box 720, Springfield OH 45501-0720, hhobbs@wittenberg.edu. For graduate students: Dr. David C. Culver, Department of Environmental Sciences, American University, 4400 Massachusetts Ave. NW, Washington, DC 20016-8007, dculver@american.edu.

2673 ■ CDA Foundation
1201 K St., Ste. 1511
Sacramento, CA 95814
Ph: (916) 554-4905

Free: 800-232-7645
E-mail: foundationinfo@cda.org
URL: www.cdafoundation.org

2674 ■ CDA Foundation Allied Dental Student Scholarships *(All/Scholarship)*

Purpose: To support individuals interested in becoming a dental hygienist, dental assistant, registered dental assistant or dental lab tech who are enrolled in a national or state-approved program. **Focus:** Dentistry; Dental laboratory technology; Dental hygiene. **Qualif.:** Applicant must be interested in becoming or already enrolled in a California dental hygienist, dental assistant, or a dental laboratory technician program; must demonstrate responsibility/leadership, community organization involvement or any outstanding achievements; and possess a positive desire to have a career in the dental field. **Criteria:** Selection is based on the submitted application and materials.

Funds Avail.: Up to $1,000. **To Apply:** Applicants must contact the local dental society to retrieve an application form, criteria and application submission deadline date.

2675 ■ CDA Foundation Dental Student Scholarships *(All/Scholarship)*

Purpose: To support dental students working towards completing their education. **Focus:** Dentistry; Dental laboratory technology; Dental hygiene. **Qualif.:** Applicant must be enrolled full-time in a California dental school; must demonstrate financial need, responsibility/leadership, volunteer community/organization involvement; and must be in good academic and ethical standing with the dental school. **Criteria:** Selection is based on: Financial need (34%); Community leadership (66%); and Proven good academic and ethical standing.

Funds Avail.: Up to $5,000. **Number Awarded:** One recipient from each of the California dental schools. **To Apply:** Applicants must complete the online application along with all requested and applicable attachments (scan into file format). **Contact:** Jolene Murray at jolene.murray@cda.org or 800-232-7645 x-4929.

2676 ■ Latinos for Dental Careers Scholarships *(All/Scholarship)*

Purpose: To increase the number of Latinos in the dental profession. **Focus:** Dentistry; Dental laboratory technology; Dental hygiene. **Qualif.:** Applicants must be a dental student, dental hygiene student (accepted to or in a DH program based in a California dental school) or an international student dentist accepted to or enrolled at a California dental school; must be of Latino descent, and currently enrolled or accepted in a California dental school program; and must be enrolled full time. **Criteria:** Selection is based on the submitted application and materials.

Funds Avail.: $1,000. **To Apply:** Applicants must complete the online application along with all requested and applicable attachments (scan into file format). **Deadline:** May 30. **Contact:** Jolene Murray at jolene.murray@cda.org or 800-232-7645 x-4929.

2677 ■ Bettie Underwood Dental Assisting Scholarships *(All/Scholarship)*

Purpose: To support dental assisting students in pursuit of their educational goals. **Focus:** Dentistry; Dental laboratory technology; Dental hygiene. **Qualif.:** Applicant must be interested in becoming a dental assistant and is currently enrolled in a state-approved program; must demonstrate

Awards are arranged alphabetically below their administering organizations

financial need, responsibility/leadership, volunteer community/organization involvement and any outstanding academic achievements; and must possess a strong desire for a career in the dental field. **Criteria:** Selection is based on financial need, community service/leadership and achievement.

Funds Avail.: $1,000. **Number Awarded:** 1. **To Apply:** Applicants must complete the online application along with all requested and applicable attachments (scan into file format). Applicants are required to provide a proof/certification of hours in any volunteer community services or involvement. **Deadline:** March 31. **Remarks:** In memory of Bettie Underwood, an outstanding leader in dental assisting in California and the nation. **Contact:** Jolene Murray at jolene.murray@cda.org or 800-232-7645 x-4929.

2678 ■ CEDAM International

2 Fox Rd.
Croton-on-Hudson, NY 10520
Ph: (914) 271-5365
E-mail: cedam@bestweb.net
URL: www.cedam.org

2679 ■ Lloyd Bridges Scholarships *(Graduate, Professional development/Scholarship)*

Purpose: To enable a qualified educator to participate at no cost in a CEDAM sponsored or sanctioned expedition. **Focus:** Aquaculture. **Qualif.:** Applicant must be a certified scuba diver, a teacher (elementary or secondary level), or actively engaged in an education program at an institution or environmental organization, such as an aquarium, science center or relevant non-profit organization. **Criteria:** Scholarship will be awarded based on the applicant's merit and financial need.

Funds Avail.: No specific amount. **To Apply:** Applicant must complete the application form available on the website; must submit a 500-word essay and two recommendation letters. **Deadline:** May 1.

2680 ■ Center for Advanced Study in the Behavioral Sciences (CASBS)

75 Alta Rd.
Stanford, CA 94305
Ph: (650) 321-2052
Fax: (650) 321-1192
E-mail: info@casbs.stanford.edu
URL: www.casbs.org

2681 ■ CASBS Residential Fellowships *(Doctorate, Professional development/Fellowship)*

Purpose: To extend knowledge of the principles governing human behavior to help solve the critical problems of contemporary society. **Focus:** Behavioral sciences. **Qualif.:** Applicants must have a PhD, professional degree (e.g., J.D., M.D.) or equivalent foreign degree; have achieved an equivalent level of professional reputation. Faculty at all academic levels or independent scholars may apply, provided they exhibit a high level of achievement (adjusted for rank) including a strong record of research publications. Ethnic minorities, women, international scholars and scholars from less research-oriented colleges and universities are also encouraged to apply. **Criteria:** Selection will be based on the criteria of several external reviewers, including experts in the applicant's field(s).

Funds Avail.: No specific amount. **To Apply:** Applicants may visit the website for the online application. **Deadline:** April. **Contact:** For further information, applicants must contact Cynthia Pilch at secretary@casbs.stanford.edu.

2682 ■ Center for Craft, Creativity and Design

1181 Broyles Rd.
Hendersonville, NC 28793
Ph: (828) 890-2050
Fax: (828) 890-2060
E-mail: info@craftcreativitydesign.org
URL: www.craftcreativitydesign.org

2683 ■ Craft Research Fund *(Professional development/Grant)*

Purpose: To support innovative research on artistic and critical issues in craft theory and history. **Focus:** Crafts. **Qualif.:** Applicants must be researchers, scholars or museum curators. **Criteria:** Peer panel of readers will evaluate applications based on the following criteria: 1) if completed properly, the proposal will advance scholarship and knowledge in U.S. Craft; 2) the plan for dissemination identifies the audience and have supporting documents; 3) project must be feasible based on timeline, expertise and budget reflected in the application; 4) addresses the goals of Craft Research Fund.

Funds Avail.: $15,000. **To Apply:** Applicants must submit five copies of the proposal in the following order by page: 1) cover sheet; 2) one-page summary of the proposal; 3) three other scholars/colleagues who have written the three most significant works of the chosen topic; 4) timeline and schedule for completing the project; 5) budget page; 6-7) curriculum vitae; 8-12) no more than five pages project description; 13-14) letter of support from a field scholar and from an institution, publication, organization, participant or anyone who is affiliated with the project; 15) image(s) that would compliment or may add to the clarity of the proposal (optional). **Deadline:** July 1.

2684 ■ Center for Cultural Judaism

80 8th Ave., Ste. 206
New York, NY 10011
Ph: (212) 564-6711
Fax: (212) 564-6721
E-mail: jesse@culturaljudaism.org
URL: culturaljudaism.org

2685 ■ Israeli Fellowships *(Doctorate, Postdoctorate/Fellowship)*

Purpose: To promote the Jewish traditions, histories, philosophies, languages, literature and culture. **Focus:** Jewish studies. **Qualif.:** Applicants must be students and scholars in Israel at doctoral and post-doctoral levels from the humanities, social sciences, education or arts, who are fully engaged with well-established university departments able to research themes drawn from the following fields: (1) Modernization and secularization in Jewish life during the past 250 years, including secularization of Jewish thought, historiography, Biblical scholarship; the secularization of daily life, Jewish politics, the emergence of modern national and social movements; (2) Intellectual, political and social underpinning of secularism and secularization in Jewish history, culture and way of life; linkages between secularization and other related processes, such as modernization,

Awards are arranged alphabetically below their administering organizations

democratization, liberalization, pluralism and globalization; (3) Aspects and manifestations of Jewish secularism in the arts, literature, lifestyle and practices; The renewal of Hebrew as a lay language and of secular Hebrew literature; the rise and decline of the secular Yiddish culture in Europe and in USA; aspects of secular cultural experience in the pre-state Yishuv and in Israeli society; readings in Jewish traditional culture and in a secular approach. **Criteria:** Selection will be based on the committee's criteria.

Funds Avail.: $15,000. **Number Awarded:** Ten. **To Apply:** Interested applicants must contact the center for the application process. **Contact:** lamda@netvision.net.il.

2686 ■ Center for the Education of Women (CEW)
330 E Liberty St.
Ann Arbor, MI 48104
Ph: (734) 764-6005
Fax: (734) 998-6203
E-mail: contactcew@umich.edu
URL: www.cew.umich.edu

2687 ■ Center for the Education of Women Scholarships *(Graduate, Undergraduate/ Scholarship)*

Purpose: To honor the academic performance of women students at the University of Michigan. **Focus:** General studies. **Qualif.:** Applicants must be undergraduates, graduates and full-time or part-time students attending the University of Michigan (Ann Arbor, Flint, Dearborn Campuses); must have experienced a lapse in education of at least 48 consecutive months and 48 non-consecutive; and must have not yet received a scholarship. **Criteria:** Recipients are selected based on strength of motivation; impact on the chosen field; academic record and potential; creativity; and contributions.

Funds Avail.: No specific amount. **Number Awarded:** 40. **To Apply:** Applicants must submit a filled-out application form; transcript of records from all previous educational institutions attended; three letters of recommendation from either professors or supervisors; and completed financial statement. Provide the needed materials with five completed copies (original and four copies). **Contact:** Questions should be directed to Jackie Johnson at jmjhsnon@umich.edu.

2688 ■ Center for the Education of Women Student Research Grants *(Graduate, Undergraduate/Grant)*

Purpose: To promote every woman's career, leadership, education, growth and development, healing and wellbeing. **Focus:** Women's studies. **Qualif.:** Applicants must be graduates and upper division undergraduate students attending University of Michigan-Ann Arbor who are doing dissertation, thesis, or research. **Criteria:** Recipients are selected based on submitted proposals.

Funds Avail.: Up to $1,000. **To Apply:** Applicants must submit a filled-out application form with student ID number; two-page proposal accompanied by project budget; a letter of support from an advisor; a curriculum vitae; and proof of IRB approval for the project (if relevant). **Contact:** Submit application packets to: Susan Kaufmann at the above address; Email: kaufmann@umich.edu; Call at 734-764-7640.

2689 ■ Center for Global Initiatives
University of North Carolina at Chapel Hill
FedEx Global Education Ctr.

301 Pittsboro St., Ste. 3002
Campus Box 5145
Chapel Hill, NC 27599-5145
Ph: (919) 962-3094
Fax: (919) 962-5375
E-mail: cgi@unc.edu
URL: cgi.unc.edu

2690 ■ C.V. Starr Scholarships *(Undergraduate, Graduate/Scholarship)*

Purpose: To support University of North Carolina students who demonstrate financial need to undertake an independent internationally-oriented experience. **Focus:** General studies. **Qualif.:** Applicants must be undergraduate and graduate students. Undergraduate applicants should be "Pell-eligible" based on demonstrated financial need; must have at least 2.8 GPA. Graduate applicants must not be U.S. citizens or permanent residents (green card holders). Applicants must have plan of returning to UNC for at least one semester upon completing their internationally-oriented experience. **Criteria:** Applications will be evaluated based on feasibility and planning, need, impact and budget.

Funds Avail.: $3,000-$5,000. **Number Awarded:** 6. **To Apply:** Applicants must complete an online application form and must include the following: a) basic biography; b) project title and summary; c) short answer questions; d) letter of affiliation; e) list of three references; f) detailed budget; g) list of additional funding sources; h) unofficial transcript; and i) international student need analysis worksheet. **Deadline:** March 6.

2691 ■ Center for International Environmental Law (CIEL)
1350 Connecticut Ave. NW, Ste. 1100
Washington, DC 20036
Ph: (202) 785-8700
Fax: (202) 785-8701
E-mail: info@ciel.org
URL: www.ciel.org

2692 ■ Louis B. Sohn Fellowships in Human Rights and Environment *(Graduate/Fellowship)*

Purpose: To offer fellowship positions to recent law school graduates and members of the bar who wish to develop or increase their knowledge of the practice of public interest, international environmental law. **Focus:** Law. **Qualif.:** Applicant must be a recent law school graduate or a member of the bar. **Criteria:** Selection is based on the submitted application materials.

Funds Avail.: No specific amount. **To Apply:** Applicants must submit a letter, resume, writing sample, and an additional essay that describes applicant's interest and background in human rights and the environment and how these legal instruments can or should be used to protect human rights and the environment (maximum of 500 words). The applicant must indicate in the cover letter that he/she would like to be considered for the fellowship. **Contact:** Sofia Plagakis at splagakis@ciel.org.

2693 ■ Center for Jewish History (CJH)
15 W 16th St.
New York, NY 10011
Ph: (212) 294-8301
E-mail: inquiries@cjh.org

Awards are arranged alphabetically below their administering organizations

URL: www.cjh.org

2694 ■ Graduate Research Fellowships
(Doctorate/Fellowship)

Purpose: To support original research at the Center for Jewish History in the field of Jewish Studies. **Focus:** Jewish studies. **Qualif.:** Open to all qualified doctoral candidates in accredited institutions. Applicants must have the appropriate visa for acceptance of the stipend and for the required duration of the award. **Criteria:** Preference will be given to those candidates who draw on the library and archival resources of more than one partner.

Funds Avail.: A stipend of up to $15,000. **To Apply:** Applicants must complete the following requirements: cover letter stating area of interest, knowledge of relevant languages, and how the project relates to the mission of the Center for Jewish History; curriculum vitae, including contact information, education, publications, scholarly and/or museum activities, teaching experience and any other relevant work experience; specific research proposal of no more than five pages, including specific reference to the collections at the Center and clearly stated goals for research during the period of the fellowship; official graduate school transcript; three letters of recommendation, including from the students' academic advisors, which address the significance of the candidate's work for the field as well as the candidate's ability to fulfill the proposed work. Send all application materials together electronically as one PDF continuous document. Letters of recommendation may arrive under separate cover. **Deadline:** February 1. **Contact:** Judith C. Siegel, Director of Academic and Public Programs; fellowships@cjh.org.

2695 ■ NEH Fellowships for Senior Scholars
(Doctorate/Fellowship)

Purpose: To support college and university faculty as they worked to complete their dissertations using the partner collections. **Focus:** Humanities; Jewish studies; Russian studies; European studies; German studies. **Qualif.:** Open to all college and university faculty who received a PhD more than six years prior to the start of the fellowship; must be US citizens as well as foreigners who have lived in the US for at least three years prior to the application deadline; must have the appropriate visa for acceptance of the stipend for the duration of the award. **Criteria:** Selection will be based on the committee's criteria.

Funds Avail.: A stipend of up to $50,400. **To Apply:** Applicants must complete the following requirements: cover letter stating area of interest, knowledge of relevant languages, and how the project relates to the mission of the Center for Jewish History; curriculum vitae, including contact information, education, publications, scholarly and/or museum activities, teaching experience and any other relevant work experience; specific research proposal of no more than five pages, including specific reference to the collections at the Center and clearly stated goals for research during the period of the fellowship; three letters of recommendation, which address the significance of the candidates' work for their field as well as the candidates' ability to fulfill the proposed work. Send all application materials together electronically as one continuous PDF document. Letters of recommendation may arrive under separate cover. **Deadline:** December 1. **Contact:** Judith C. Siegel, Director of Academic and Public Programs; fellowships@cjh.org.

2696 ■ Prins Foundation Fellowship for Senior Scholars *(Doctorate/Fellowship)*

Purpose: To support international senior scholars as they worked to complete their dissertations using the partner collections. **Focus:** Humanities; Jewish studies; Russian studies; European studies; German studies. **Qualif.:** Applicants must be foreign senior scholars in any field who have completed a PhD more than six years prior to the start of the fellowship and whose research will benefit substantially from consultation of materials housed at the Center. **Criteria:** Selection will be based on the committee's criteria. Preference will be given to candidates from Eastern Europe and the former Soviet Union.

Funds Avail.: A stipend of $75,000 as well as a relocation stipend of up to $15,000. **To Apply:** Applicants must complete the following requirements: curriculum vitae, including information, education, publications, scholarly and/or museum activities, teaching experience and any other relevant work experience; detailed research proposal consisting of four to five pages, including specific reference to the collections at the Center and clearly stated goals for research during the period of the fellowship; three letters of recommendation that address the significance of the candidate's work for their field as well as the candidate's ability to fulfill the proposed research project; two recent publications consisting of either an article published in a scholarly journal, a chapter in an edited collection, or the introduction and a subsequent chapter from a recently published book; 1- to 2-page essay articulating why they wish to emigrate and what they hope to accomplish after concluding the fellowship. Send all application materials together electronically as one PDF continuous document. Applicants are responsible for ensuring that letters of recommendation are submitted electronically by recommenders by the deadline. **Deadline:** February 1. **Contact:** Judith C. Siegel, Director of Academic and Public Programs; fellowships@cjh.org.

2697 ■ Prins Foundation Post-Doctoral and Early Career Fellowship for Emigrating Scholars *(Professional development, Postdoctorate/Fellowship)*

Purpose: To support international scholars as they worked to complete their dissertations using the partner collections. **Focus:** Humanities; Jewish studies; Russian studies; European studies; German studies. **Qualif.:** Applicants must be scholars from outside the United States who seek permanent teaching and research positions who are at the beginning of their career; must have the appropriate visa for acceptance of the stipend for the duration of the award. **Criteria:** Selection will be based on the committee's criteria. Preference will be given to candidates from Eastern Europe and the former Soviet Union.

Funds Avail.: $35,000. **To Apply:** Applicants must complete the following materials: cover letter stating area of interest, knowledge of relevant languages, and how the project relates to the mission of the Center for Jewish History; curriculum vitae, including contact information, education, publications, scholarly and/or museum activities, teaching experience and any other relevant work experience; specific research proposal of no more than five pages, including specific reference to the collections at the Center and clearly stated goals for research during the period of the fellowship; three letters of recommendation, which address the significance of the candidates' work for their field as well as the candidates' ability to fulfill the proposed work. Send all application materials together

Awards are arranged alphabetically below their administering organizations

electronically as one PDF continuous document. Letters of recommendation may arrive under separate cover. **Deadline:** December 15. **Contact:** Judith C. Siegel, Director of Academic and Public Programs; fellowships@cjh.org.

2698 ■ Joseph S. Steinberg Emerging Jewish Filmmaker Fellowships (Undergraduate, Graduate/Fellowship)

Purpose: To help further existing projects, or to start new projects, whose subject matter is in line with the collections housed at the Center. **Focus:** Jewish studies. **Qualif.:** Applicants must be undergraduate and graduate emerging filmmakers working on their own original projects on topics related to modern Jewish history. **Criteria:** Students are selected for one academic year of research through a rigorous and competitive process.

Funds Avail.: Up to $5,000. **To Apply:** Applicants must visit the website to obtain an application form. Applicants must also submit at least one but no more than two letter of reference from instructors or professional contacts. Send all application materials together electronically on one PDF document. **Deadline:** October 15. **Contact:** Judith C. Siegel at fellowships@cjh.org.

2699 ■ Visiting Scholars Program (Doctorate/ Fellowship)

Purpose: To support visiting scholars as they worked to complete their dissertations using the partner collections. **Focus:** Jewish studies. **Qualif.:** Applicants must be scholars who have their PhD or equivalent terminal degree; must be scholars working on projects that make use of the Center partner collections. **Criteria:** Selection will be based on the committee's criteria.

Funds Avail.: No specific amount. **To Apply:** Applicants must complete the following requirements: a complete curriculum vitae; a description of the proposed research, maximum of three pages in length, including an explanation of which of the Center partners' collections will be used; the names and contact information of two references. Send all application materials together electronically as one continuous PDF document. **Contact:** Judith C. Siegel, Director of Academic and Public Programs; fellowships@cjh.org.

2700 ■ Center for Lesbian and Gay Studies (CLAGS)

City University of New York
365 Fifth Ave.
New York, NY 10016
Ph: (212) 817-1955
Fax: (212) 817-1567
E-mail: clags@gc.cuny.edu
URL: web.gc.cuny.edu/clags

2701 ■ Center for Lesbian and Gay Studies Fellowships (Graduate/Fellowship)

Purpose: To provide fund to support research, travel or writing. **Focus:** Homosexuality. **Qualif.:** Applicants must be graduate students, academic or independent scholars who work on dissertation. **Criteria:** Applicants will be selected by the fellowships committee of the Center for Lesbian and Gay Studies based on the review of the application materials.

Funds Avail.: $6,250-$7,500. **To Apply:** Applicants must submit a cover letter with contact information; a 5-10-page proposal; a curriculum vitae; and two letters of recommendation. **Deadline:** November 15. **Contact:** Letters of recommendation should be sent by e-mail directly from recommenders to clagsfellowships@gmail.com.

2702 ■ Martin Duberman Fellowships (Professional development/Fellowship)

Purpose: To award a senior scholar from any country doing scholarly research on the lesbian, gay, bisexual, transgender, and queer experience. **Focus:** Homosexuality. **Qualif.:** Applicant must be a tenured university professor; advanced independent scholar; must be able to show a prior contribution to the field of LGBTQ. **Criteria:** Applicants will be selected based on the fellowships committee's review of the application materials.

Funds Avail.: $7,500. **To Apply:** Applicants must submit a completed application form; a cover letter with contact information; a proposal of 5-10 pages; curriculum vitae; an evidence of contribution to the field of LGTBQ studies; and two letters of recommendation. **Deadline:** November 15. **Contact:** clagsfellowships@gmail.com.

2703 ■ Joan Heller-Diane Bernard Fellowships (Graduate, Undergraduate/Fellowship)

Purpose: To supports research into the impact of lesbians and/or gay men on U.S. society and culture. **Focus:** Homosexuality. **Qualif.:** Applicants must be junior scholars, graduate students, untenured professors, independent researchers, or senior scholars. Applicants conducting a research on lesbians are encouraged to apply. **Criteria:** Applicants will be selected based on the fellowships committee's review of the application materials.

Funds Avail.: $6,250. **Number Awarded:** 2. **To Apply:** Applicants must submit a cover letter with contact information; a proposal of 5-10 pages; evidence of contribution to the field of LGTBQ studies; curriculum vitae; and two letters of recommendation. **Deadline:** November 15. **Contact:** For further information, applicants may contact the Fellowship Coordinator by phone: 212-817-1958 or by e-mail: clagsfellowships@gmail.com.

2704 ■ Center for Plant Conservation (CPC)

PO Box 299
St. Louis, MO 63166-0299
Ph: (314) 577-9450
Fax: (314) 577-9465
E-mail: cpc@mobot.org
URL: www.centerforplantconservation.org

2705 ■ Catherine H. Beattie Fellowships (Graduate/Fellowship)

Purpose: To enable a graduate student in biology, horticulture or a related field to conduct research on a rare or endangered U.S. plant. **Focus:** Biology, Horticulture. **Qualif.:** Applicants must be graduate students in biology or horticulture. **Criteria:** Preference will be given to students focusing on endangered flora of the Carolinas or the southeastern United States.

Funds Avail.: $1,000-$4,000 and will serve as compensation for work done by a graduate student. **To Apply:** Applications should be submitted to the Center for Plant Conservation and must include the following: (a) a 2-3 page proposal which includes a description of the research project and how it relates to the student's academic and professional development; (b) an itemized budget for the

Awards are arranged alphabetically below their administering organizations

funds requested; (c) a current resume; (d) a letter of endorsement by an academic advisor from the institution where the student is pursuing graduate studies; (e) the names of three additional persons qualified to describe the student's character and ability; (f) official transcripts for both undergraduate and graduate academic records. **Deadline:** November 30.

2706 ■ Center for Reintegration

347 W 37th St.
New York, NY 10018
Ph: (212) 957-5090
Fax: (212) 974-0228
E-mail: reintegration@reintegration.com
URL: www.reintegration.com

2707 ■ Lilly Reintegration Scholarships *(All, Vocational/Occupational/Scholarship)*

Purpose: To help people with schizophrenia and related disorders acquire the educational and vocational skills they need to reintegrate into society, secure meaningful work and reclaim their lives. **Focus:** General studies. **Qualif.:** Applicant must be diagnosed with schizophrenia, schizophreniform, schizoaffective disorder, or bipolar disorder; be currently receiving medical treatment for the disease including medications and psychiatric follow-up; be actively involved in rehabilitative or reintegrative efforts such as clubhouse membership, part-time work, volunteer efforts or school enrollment; and must be a U.S. citizen and plan to attend a school in the U.S. **Criteria:** Selection is based on academic success; references from three individuals; quality of essay; thoughtfulness and appropriateness of academic and vocational/career goals; rehabilitation involvement; success in dealing with the disease; recent volunteer and/or vocational experience and completion of application requirements.

Funds Avail.: Support on tuition, books, laboratory supplies, and mandatory fees. **Number Awarded:** Varies. **To Apply:** Applicants must submit a completed scholarship application form together with the essay (maximum of 3 double-spaced typed pages); 3 unopened, postmarked recommendation forms; official transcripts; copy of desired school's statement of standard education costs from the school's manual or financial aid office; and a signed consent and release form. **Deadline:** January 31. **Remarks:** Sponsored by Eli Lilly and Company. **Contact:** Lilly Secretariat, PMB 327 310 Busse Hwy Park Ridge, IL 60068-3251, Phone: 800-809-8202, or lillyscholarships@reintegration.com.

2708 ■ Center for Women in Government and Civil Society (CWGCS)

University at Albany
135 Western Ave.
Draper Hall, Rm. 302
Albany, NY 12222
Ph: (518) 442-3900
Fax: (518) 442-3877
E-mail: cwgcs@uamail.albany.edu
URL: www.albany.edu/womeningov

2709 ■ Center for Women in Government and Civil Society Fellowships *(Graduate/Fellowship)*

Purpose: To encourage graduate students to pursue careers in public policy while increasing the capacity of the

New York State Government. **Focus:** Government. **Qualif.:** Applicants must be graduate students at any accredited college or university in New York State; have completed 12 graduate credits before applying with degree completion scheduled after fellowships; and must have demonstrated interest in studies, research, employment or voluntary activities designed to improve the status of women and underrepresented populations. **Criteria:** Recipients will be selected based on result of the interview. Preference will be given to those applicants who are bright and motivated women who have demonstrated an interest in public policy and issues of underrepresented populations.

Funds Avail.: $9,000. **To Apply:** Applicants must submit curriculum vitae; transcript of record; letters of reference. **Deadline:** September 1.

2710 ■ Centers for Disease Control and Prevention (CDC)

1600 Clifton Rd.
Atlanta, GA 30333
Ph: (404) 639-7405
Fax: (800) 311-3435
Free: 800-232-4636
E-mail: cdcinfo@cdc.gov
URL: www.cdc.gov

2711 ■ CDC Presidential Management Fellows Program *(Graduate/Fellowship)*

Purpose: To provide experience and training to prepare fellows for a career in the federal government. **Focus:** Management. **Qualif.:** Applicants must be recent graduates with a MA, JD or PhD degree; must be U.S. citizens or permanent residents. **Criteria:** Selection will be based on the committee's criteria.

Funds Avail.: No specific amount. **To Apply:** Applicants must be nominated by their schools. After their nomination, applicants will take an assessment at the nearest Office of Personnel Management, Presidential Management Fellows (OPM PMF). **Deadline:** October 15 for the application; October 31 for nomination.

2712 ■ CDC Preventive Medicine Residency and Fellowships *(Professional development/Fellowship)*

Purpose: To provide hands-on experiences in public health agencies at the federal, state and local levels. **Focus:** Medicine. **Qualif.:** Applicants must commit to a one or two-year full-time training period (depending on the program); be willing to relocate throughout the duration of the training; meet the professional and licensing requirements for hiring by the U.S. government according to the U.S. Office of Personnel Management; be U.S. citizens or permanent residents; have trained in the Epidemic Intelligence Service (EIS) program or have comparable applied epidemiology experience; have completed at least 12 months of ACGME-accredited postgraduate clinical training involving at least 11 months of direct patient care; have a current, full and unrestricted medical license from a U.S. licensing jurisdiction; have a Master of Public Health or equivalent accredited degree, per ACGME requirement. **Criteria:** Selection will be based on the committees's criteria.

Funds Avail.: No specific amount. **To Apply:** Applicants must visit the website for the online application and must submit the following supporting documents: three letters of recommendation; a copy of certificated or letters from

Awards are arranged alphabetically below their administering organizations

sponsoring institutions verifying completion of ACGME-accredited postgraduate clinical training; official transcripts for all degrees earned since high school; proof of a current, full and unrestricted license to practice their qualifying clinical specialty in a US licensing jurisdiction. Submit supporting documents via mail or courier that provides tracking services to PMR/F. **Deadline:** September 15. **Contact:** Phone: 404-498-6140; Fax: 404-498-6105; Email: prevmed@cdc.gov.

2713 ■ CDC Public Health Informatics Fellowships *(Graduate, Postdoctorate/Fellowship)*

Purpose: To provide training and experience in applying computer and information science and technology to real public health problems. **Focus:** Computer and information sciences. **Qualif.:** Applicants must meet both the educational and professional requirements; must have a doctoral or masteral degree; willing to commit a two-year, full-time program; be willing to be relocated in Atlanta, GA. Qualifying degree must be from an accredited academic institution in one of the following: public health, medicine, healthcare, health-services research, computer science, information systems, statistics, epidemiology, public health informatics or related discipline. Documented one-year experience for doctoral level candidates and three-year experience for masters level candidates is required in one of the following fields: public health informatics, health informatics or related field, information systems, information science, computer science and information technology. Additionally, documented one-year experience for doctoral level candidates and three-year experience for masters level candidates is required in one of the following areas: Public health, related healthcare profession (medicine, nursing, veterinary medicine, dentistry, allied health professions). **Criteria:** Selection will be based on the committee's criteria.

Funds Avail.: No specific amount. **To Apply:** Applicants must visit the website for the online application; must submit three letters of recommendation, one letter must be from a faculty member or supervisor and official transcripts for all degrees earned must be mailed as one package. **Deadline:** November 14 for the online application; November 28 for the supporting documents. **Contact:** Phone: 404-498-6219; Fax: 404-498-6135; Email: phifp@cdc.gov.

2714 ■ National Center for Health Statistics Postdoctoral Research Awards *(Postdoctorate/Fellowship)*

Purpose: To provide opportunities for postdoctoral candidates of unusual promise and ability to conduct research which is compatible with the interests of NCHS. **Focus:** General studies. **Qualif.:** Applicants must be citizens of the United States or legal permanent residents with a work authorization. Applicants are responsible for obtaining the necessary authorization. Permanent residency status does not qualify as citizenship; must have held doctorates for less than three years or are in the process of receiving doctorate degrees at the time of application; must hold the PhD or other earned research degree recognized by the United States as equivalent to the PhD; must present acceptable evidences of having completed all the formal academic requirements for the degree before appointment; must have demonstrated ability for creative research; applicant's training and research experiences may be in any appropriate discipline or combination required for the proposed research. **Criteria:** Proposals will be evaluated with respect to the following criteria: project's relevance to NCHS's mission and contribution to the field; strength of the approach, design and methodology; feasibility of the

project; applicant's personal and professional qualification. **Funds Avail.:** $70,000-$89,000. **To Apply:** Applicants must submit a curriculum vitae, official transcripts of all graduate and undergraduate credits, three reference letters and statement of research interest. **Contact:** Cynthia Link, Office of Management and Operations, National Center for Health Statistics, 3311 Toledo Rd., Rm. 5115, Hyattsville, MD 20782; Fax: 301-458-4018.

2715 ■ Steven M. Teutsch Prevention Effectiveness Fellowships *(Doctorate/Fellowship)*

Purpose: To establish a cadre of quantitative policy analysts who provide information for health policy decision-makers regarding allocation and use of resources to maximize health impact. **Focus:** Economics; Engineering, Industrial; Health sciences; Health services administration; Operations research. **Qualif.:** Applicants must hold a doctoral degree in economics or applied economics, decision sciences, health services research or related health sciences, industrial engineering or operations research, public policy or policy analysis or related quantitatively-oriented field; non-US citizens must be legal permanent residents or eligible for J-1 status. **Criteria:** Selection will be based on the committee's criteria.

Funds Avail.: No specific amount. **To Apply:** Applicants must visit the website for the online application; must submit three signed letters of recommendation, signed letter from the Department Chair and official transcripts for degrees earned. Supporting documents can be e-mailed; however, original documents are required prior to final selection. **Deadline:** January 21 for the online application; January 19 for the supporting documents. **Contact:** Steven M. Teutsch, 404-498-6324 or e-mail pef@cdc.gov.

2716 ■ Central Florida Jazz Society

PO Box 540133
Orlando, FL 32854
Ph: (407) 539-2357
E-mail: cfjsjazz@yahoo.com
URL: www.centralfloridajazzsociety.com

2717 ■ Central Florida Jazz Society Scholarships *(Undergraduate/Award, Scholarship)*

Purpose: To support amateur jazz musicians in furthering their education. **Focus:** Music, Jazz. **Qualif.:** Applicants must be amateur jazz musicians who are high school seniors or students in the first 3 years of college; be interested in furthering their studies in jazz music; and be residents of, or attend/plan to attend a college in, Central Florida: Orange, Seminole, Osceola, Brevard or Volusia counties. There is no age restriction. **Criteria:** Applicants will be judged based on: technique, expression, style (interpretation), performance presence (showmanship) and overall performance.

Funds Avail.: First place award is $1,500; second place, $1000; third place, $500. **To Apply:** An initial screening of all applicants will require an audition cassette tape, CD or DVD containing 1 or 2 improvised choruses of two selections of different tempos (labeled with the student's name on the recording). In addition to the musical recording, a letter of recommendation, from an individual familiar with the applicant's musicianship, character and commitment to jazz study, must be submitted. **Deadline:** March 31. **Contact:** "Moe" Lowe at 407-644-3506 or lowem@juno.com.

2718 ■ Central Ohio Diabetes Association

1100 Dennison Ave.
Columbus, OH 43201

Awards are arranged alphabetically below their administering organizations

Ph: (614) 884-4400
Fax: (614) 884-4484
E-mail: coda@diabetesohio.org
URL: www.diabetesohio.org

2719 ■ The Youth Scholarship Program
(Undergraduate/Scholarship)

Purpose: To provide scholarships to those students with diabetes. **Focus:** Diabetes. **Qualif.:** Applicants must be full-time undergraduate students with diabetes in the Central Ohio area; must demonstrate exemplary adjustment to living with diabetes; show financial need; and demonstrate involvement in extracurricular activities which help others and foster personal growth. **Criteria:** Preference will be given to those students who will meet the criteria.

Funds Avail.: No specific amount. **To Apply:** Applicants must submit a completed application form. **Deadline:** February. **Contact:** Central Ohio Diabetes Association at the above address.

2720 ■ Central Texas Bluegrass Association (CTBA)
PO Box 9816
Austin, TX 78766-9816
Ph: (512) 415-3177
E-mail: ctba@centraltexasbluegrass.org
URL: www.centraltexasbluegrass.org

2721 ■ Willa Beach-Porter Music Scholarships
(Undergraduate/Scholarship)

Purpose: To further the enjoyment of bluegrass music through teaching, sharing and playing; to promote bluegrass music in Central Texas. **Focus:** Music. **Qualif.:** Applicants must be 12 years of age or over and must be Texas residents. **Criteria:** Recipients are selected based on financial need.

Funds Avail.: No specific amount. **To Apply:** Applicants must complete an application form. **Deadline:** May 15. **Contact:** 512-261-9440.

2722 ■ CentraState Healthcare Foundation
916 Rte. 33, Ste. 6
Freehold, NJ 07728
Ph: (732) 294-7030
URL: www.centrastatefoundation.org

2723 ■ CentraState Associated Auxiliaries Scholarships *(Undergraduate/Scholarship)*

Purpose: To provide scholarship assistance to a deserving student who wants to pursue the health care field. **Focus:** Health care services. **Qualif.:** Applicant must be a student or adult who lives and volunteers in the CentraState service area; must be pursuing a career in the health care field. **Criteria:** Recipient will be selected based on the criteria of the Scholarship Selection Committee.

Funds Avail.: $500. **Number Awarded:** 3. **To Apply:** Applicant must submit the application form along with transcript, two letters of recommendation and complete essay requirements to Mrs. Valerie MacPhee. **Deadline:** April 29. **Contact:** Mrs. Valerie MacPhee, PO Box 32, Perrineville, NJ 08535.

2724 ■ CentraState Band Aid Open Committee Scholarships *(Undergraduate/Scholarship)*

Purpose: To provide scholarship assistance to a graduating high school senior who attends the Freehold Regional High School District's Medical Science Program. **Focus:** Health sciences. **Qualif.:** Applicants must be planning to pursue a career in the health profession; must be students enrolled in the Medical Sciences Program in the Freehold Regional High School District. **Criteria:** Recipient will be selected based on the criteria of the CentraState Healthcare Foundation Scholarship Committee.

Funds Avail.: $2,000. **To Apply:** Applicants must submit a current transcript, letters of recommendation from two teachers and/or counselors and the completed essay requirements. Scholarship application form may be obtained from Ms. Marybeth Ruddy at the school or from CentraState Healthcare Foundation Office. **Deadline:** April 6.

2725 ■ CentraState Healthcare Foundation Health Professional Scholarships
(Undergraduate/Scholarship)

Purpose: To provide scholarship assistance to a deserving student who wants to pursue the healthcare field. **Focus:** Health care services. **Qualif.:** Applicant must be a graduating student who has chosen to pursue a career in the health profession. **Criteria:** The Scholarship Selection Committee will review scholarship application.

Funds Avail.: $1,000. **Number Awarded:** 3. **To Apply:** Applicant must submit the appropriate form along with transcript, two letters of recommendation, and the complete essay requirements. **Deadline:** April 30. **Contact:** Lynn Cannon at the above address.

2726 ■ DCH Freehold Toyota Scholarships
(Undergraduate/Scholarship)

Purpose: To provide scholarship assistance to a graduating high school senior who attends the Freehold Regional High School District's Medical Science Program. **Focus:** Health sciences. **Qualif.:** Applicants must be planning to pursue a career in the health profession; must be students enrolled in the Medical Sciences Program in the Freehold Regional High School District. **Criteria:** Recipient will be selected based on the criteria of the CentraState Healthcare Foundation Scholarship Committee.

Funds Avail.: $1,000. **Number Awarded:** 2. **To Apply:** Applicants must submit a current transcript, letters of recommendation from two teachers and/or counselors and the completed essay requirements. Scholarship application form may be obtained from Ms. Marybeth Ruddy at the school or from CentraState Healthcare Foundation Office. **Deadline:** April 6.

2727 ■ Norkus Charitable Foundation Scholarships *(Undergraduate/Scholarship)*

Purpose: To provide scholarship assistance to a graduating high school senior who attends the Freehold Regional High School District's Medical Science Program. **Focus:** Health sciences. **Qualif.:** Applicants must be planning to pursue a career in the health profession; must be students enrolled in the Medical Sciences Program in the Freehold Regional High School District. **Criteria:** Recipient will be selected based on the criteria of the CentraState Healthcare Foundation Scholarship Committee.

Funds Avail.: $1,000. **To Apply:** Applicants must submit a current transcript, letters of recommendation from two teachers and/or counselors and the completed essay requirements. Scholarship application form may be obtained from Ms. Marybeth Ruddy at the school or from CentraState Healthcare Foundation Office. **Deadline:** April 6.

Awards are arranged alphabetically below their administering organizations

2728 ■ Star and Barry Tobias Scholarships
(Undergraduate/Scholarship)

Purpose: To provide scholarship assistance to a graduating high school senior who attends the Freehold Regional High School District's Medical Science Program. **Focus:** Health sciences. **Qualif.:** Applicants must be planning to pursue a career in the health profession; must be students enrolled in the Medical Sciences Program in the Freehold Regional High School District. **Criteria:** Recipient will be selected based on the criteria of the CentraState Healthcare Foundation Scholarship Committee.

Funds Avail.: $2,500. **To Apply:** Applicant must submit a current transcript, letters of recommendation from two teachers and/or counselors and the completed essay requirements. Scholarship application form may be obtained from Ms. Marybeth Ruddy at the school or from CentraState Healthcare Foundation Office. **Deadline:** April 6.

2729 ■ Centre for International Sustainable Development Law (CISDL)
Chancellor Day Hall
3644 Peel St.
Montreal, QC, Canada H3A 1W9
Ph: (514) 398-8918
Fax: (514) 398-4659
E-mail: secretariat@cisdl.org
URL: www.cisdl.org

2730 ■ CISDL Associate Fellows *(Graduate/Fellowship)*

Purpose: To promote sustainable societies and the protection of ecosystems by advancing understanding, development and implementation of international sustainable development law. **Focus:** Law. **Qualif.:** Applicant may be a law or legal graduate student from a developing country or from one of the leading international law programmes of university law faculties around the world. **Criteria:** Selection is based on CISDL research priorities, the candidate's academic and professional qualifications and indication from a Lead Counsel that they will work with the candidate on a particular project. Preference is given to research fellows presently based in Montreal or in the country of a CISDL Lead Counsel.

Funds Avail.: No specific amount. **To Apply:** Applicants must submit a completed application form along with a cover letter and current CV. **Deadline:** September 1 or October 1. **Contact:** Marie-Claire Cordonier Segger at mcsegger@cisdl.org or Ashfaq Khalfan at akhalfan@cisdl.org.

2731 ■ CISDL Legal Research Fellows
(Graduate/Fellowship)

Purpose: To promote sustainable societies and the protection of ecosystems by advancing understanding, development and implementation of international sustainable development law. **Focus:** Law. **Qualif.:** Applicant must hold a law degree or graduate degree in law; must have more than 5 years of legal experience in his/her field; must hold an excellent academic and professional credentials; and can demonstrate a specific interest in international law related to sustainable development, particularly in the areas of current research and undertaking within the CISDL. **Criteria:** Selection is based on academic and professional qualifications. Preference is given to applications from research fellows presently based in Montreal or in the country of a CISDL Lead Counsel.

Funds Avail.: No specific amount. **To Apply:** Applicants must submit a completed application form together with a curriculum vitae and a cover letter. **Deadline:** October 1; February 1. **Contact:** Marie-Claire Cordonier Segger at mcsegger@cisdl.org or Ashfaq Khalfan at akhalfan@cisdl.org.

2732 ■ CISDL Senior Research Fellows *(Professional development/Fellowship)*

Purpose: To promote sustainable societies and the protection of ecosystems by advancing understanding, development and implementation of international sustainable development law. **Focus:** Law. **Qualif.:** Applicant may be a professor of international law or hold an equivalent professional experience in the field of international expertise; must have an internationally recognized level of expertise and must be backed by superb academic and professional credentials; must have years of experience in international law related to sustainable development. **Criteria:** Preference is given to CISDL fellows from developing countries, and those who are based in universities or international law institutions affiliated with CISDL.

Funds Avail.: No specific amount. **To Apply:** Applicants must submit a completed application form together with a current resume. **Deadline:** October 1 and February 1. **Contact:** Marie-Claire Cordonier Segger at mcsegger@cisdl.org or Ashfaq Khalfan at akhalfan@cisdl.org.

2733 ■ Centre de Recherches Mathematiques (CRM)
Universite de Montreal
Pavillon Andre-Aisenstadt
2920 Chemin de la tour, Rm. 5357
Montreal, QC, Canada H3T 1J4
Ph: (514) 343-7501
Fax: (514) 343-2254
E-mail: crm@crm.umontreal.ca
URL: www.crm.umontreal.ca

2734 ■ CRM-ISM Postdoctoral Fellowships
(Postdoctorate/Fellowship)

Purpose: To support promising researchers who have recently obtained or are expected to obtain a PhD in the mathematical science. **Focus:** Mathematics and mathematical sciences. **Qualif.:** Applicants must have obtained a PhD within three years. **Criteria:** Selection is based on merit. Preference will be given to applicants who are not currently registered at one of the ISM member universities.

Funds Avail.: $40,000 per year. **To Apply:** Applicants must complete the application online. In addition, applicants must submit a curriculum vitae in PDF format; research project (PDF format); and the names of 2-5 people who will write the letters of recommendation in support of the application. **Deadline:** December 1.

2735 ■ Chattanooga Bar Association (CBA)
The Pioneer Bldg.
801 Broad St., Ste. 420
Chattanooga, TN 37402
Ph: (423) 756-3222
Fax: (423) 265-6602
E-mail: lhood@chattbar.org
URL: www.chattbar.org

Awards are arranged alphabetically below their administering organizations

2736 ■ Liberty Bell Award Law Scholarships
(Graduate/Scholarship)

Purpose: To support law students with their educational pursuit. **Focus:** Law. **Qualif.:** Applicant must be recent (within three years) University of Tennessee at Chattanooga graduate who is enrolled for the year beginning in the Fall, of his/her graduation date from UTC, in the College of Law at the University of Tennessee at Knoxville, the University of Memphis Cecil C. Humphreys School of Law, Vanderbilt University Law School, or the Nashville School of Law. **Criteria:** Selection is based on the application and materials.

Funds Avail.: $2,500. **To Apply:** Applicants must submit a completed application form along with a certified college transcript that contains the student's undergraduate class rank and test scores; a personal statement that provides a brief biographical sketch, and a description of the applicant's goals for the future; a personal or financial statement/circumstances comparable to the applicant's submission to the law school; and a letter of recommendation from applicant's undergraduate teacher or advisor. **Deadline:** June 30. **Contact:** Lynda M. Hood at the above address.

2737 ■ Chelsea Publishing Company Inc.
201 Charles St.
Providence, RI 02904-2294
Ph: (401) 455-4000
Fax: (401) 331-3842
Free: 800-321-4267
E-mail: cust-serv@ams.org
URL: www.ams.org

2738 ■ AMS Centennial Fellowships
(Postdoctorate/Fellowship)

Purpose: To promote study and research in mathematics. **Focus:** Mathematics and mathematical sciences. **Qualif.:** Applicant must have held his/her doctoral degree for at least three years and not more than twelve years at the inception of the award. **Criteria:** Selection is based on the excellence of the applicant's research.

Funds Avail.: $80,000, plus allowance or $8,000. **Number Awarded:** Varies. **To Apply:** Applicants must submit a completed application form along with the required materials. **Deadline:** December 1. **Contact:** prof-serv@ams.org.

2739 ■ Chemical Heritage Foundation (CHF)
315 Chestnut St.
Philadelphia, PA 19106-2702
Ph: (215) 925-2222
Fax: (215) 925-1954
E-mail: info@chemheritage.org
URL: www.chemheritage.org

2740 ■ Chemical Heritage Foundation Travel Grants (CHF) *(All/Grant)*

Purpose: To promote research about history of chemical and molecular sciences, technologies and industries. **Focus:** Chemistry. **Qualif.:** Applicants must be researchers residing more than 75 miles from Philadelphia. **Criteria:** Recipients are selected based on committee's review of the research.

Funds Avail.: $750 per week. **Number Awarded:** 1. **To**

Apply: Applicants must send a one-page statement of research project; curriculum vitae less than three pages; budget estimate; and a letter of reference which must be submitted to travelgrants@chemheritage.org.

2741 ■ Cherokee Nation
PO Box 948
Tahlequah, OK 74465
Ph: (918) 453-5000
Free: 800-256-0671
URL: www.cherokee.org

2742 ■ Cherokee Nation Graduate Scholarships
(Graduate/Scholarship)

Purpose: To support Cherokee Nation Tribal Citizens pursuing degrees at a college or university. **Focus:** General studies. **Qualif.:** Applicant must be a Cherokee Nation Tribal citizen seeking graduate degrees; permanent resident in the Cherokee Nation area, which is defined as counties within the Cherokee boundaries; or permanent resident in the contiguous counties to the Cherokee Nation boundaries, (including contiguous counties in Arkansas, Kansas, Missouri, and Oklahoma). **Criteria:** Selection is based on the following preferences: First: Continuing students; Second: Classification order of new applicants (Senior, Junior, Sophomore, Freshman); Third: Academic performance.

Funds Avail.: $1,000. **To Apply:** Applicants must submit a completed application form together with a copy of Social Security card; copy of Tribal Citizenship card (blue); official undergraduate transcript with Bachelor's Degree conferment; and a letter of acceptance to graduate program. **Deadline:** June 11.

2743 ■ Cherokee Nation Pell Scholarships
(Undergraduate/Scholarship)

Purpose: To support Cherokee Nation Tribal Citizens pursuing degrees at a college or university. **Focus:** General studies. **Qualif.:** Applicant must be a Cherokee Nation tribal citizen who qualified for Federal Pell Grant funding regardless of permanent residence. **Criteria:** Selection is based on the following preferences: First: Continuing students; Second: Classification order of new applicants (Senior, Junior, Sophomore, Freshman); Third: Academic performance.

Funds Avail.: No specific amount. **To Apply:** Applicants must submit a completed application form together with Student Aid Report (all pages); copy of Social Security card; copy of Tribal Citizenship card (blue); official high school transcript (7 semester) or GED scores (Freshmen only); copy of ACT/SAT or College Placement Test Scores (Freshmen only); and official Undergraduate Transcript with most recent semester grades (if applicable). **Deadline:** June 11.

2744 ■ Cherokee Nation Scholarships
(Undergraduate/Scholarship)

Purpose: To support Cherokee Nation Tribal Citizens pursuing degrees at a college or university. **Focus:** General studies. **Qualif.:** Applicant must be a Cherokee Nation tribal citizen who does not qualify for Federal Pell Grant funding; a permanent resident in the Cherokee Nation area, which is defined as counties within the Cherokee Nation boundaries; or permanent resident in the contiguous counties to the Cherokee Nation boundaries (including contiguous

Awards are arranged alphabetically below their administering organizations

counties in Arkansas, Kansas, Missouri, and Oklahoma). **Criteria:** Selection is based on the following preferences: First: Continuing students; Second: Classification order of new applicants (Senior, Junior, Sophomore, Freshman); Third: Academic performance.

Funds Avail.: $1,000. **To Apply:** Applicants must submit a completed application form together with Student Aid Report (all pages); copy of Social Security card; copy of Tribal Citizenship card (blue); official high school transcript (7 semester) or GED scores (Freshmen only); copy of ACT/SAT or College Placement Test Scores (Freshmen only); and official Undergraduate Transcript with most recent semester grades (if applicable). **Deadline:** June 11.

2745 ■ Chicago Bar Foundation (CBF)
321 S Plymouth Ct., Ste. 3B
Chicago, IL 60604
Ph: (312) 554-1204
Fax: (312) 554-1203
E-mail: proos@chicagobar.org
URL: www.chicagobarfoundation.org

2746 ■ Abraham Lincoln Marovitz Public Interest Law Scholarships *(Undergraduate/Scholarship)*

Purpose: To support a needy law student pursuing a public interest legal career. **Focus:** Law. **Qualif.:** Applicants must be first-year students attending one of the nine Illinois law schools (Chicago-Kent College of Law, University of Chicago Law School, DePaul University College of Law, University of Illinois College of Law, John Marshall Law School, Loyola University School of Law, Northern Illinois University Law School, Northwestern University School of Law and Southern Illinois University School of Law). **Criteria:** Recipients will be selected on the basis of the following: (1) solid commitment to public interest issues, as demonstrated by past and present activities; (2) desire to practice public interest law; (3) commitment to pursue a career in public interest law, as demonstrated by an application essay and personal interview; (4) ability to achieve success as a lawyer; (5) demonstrated financial need; and (6) demonstrated commitment to live and work in Chicago area after law school graduation.

Funds Avail.: $10,000 in the first year. **To Apply:** Applicants must submit a cover letter with attached application form; resume; official transcript from undergraduate institution and graduate institution; two letters of reference about commitment to public interest work; brief essay (no more than three pages, explaining commitment to pursue a career in public interest law). **Deadline:** May 11. **Contact:** Application form and other supporting documents should be sent to Barbara A. Chasnoff at the above address.

2747 ■ Chicago Railroad Mechanical Association (CRMA)
c/o Ken Denby, Sec.-Treas.
2303 Flemming Rd.
Valparaiso, IN 46383
Ph: (219) 464-9470
E-mail: k.denby@comcast.net
URL: www.thecrma.org

2748 ■ CRMA Scholarships *(Graduate, Undergraduate/Scholarship)*

Purpose: To provide financial assistance to eligible college or university students. **Focus:** General studies. **Qualif.:**

Applicants must be either sons, daughters, adopted children, grandchildren or stepchildren of CRMA members who have maintained current membership in the association; must be enrolled at the time of application as full-time undergraduate or graduate students at an accredited junior college offering associate degree, a college or university offering bachelor or graduate degrees; must demonstrate successful completion of the previous year of study by maintaining at least a 2.75 accumulated GPA on a scale of 1 to 4 with an "A" equal to 4; must have accumulated enough credits from accredited school(s) in time for the fall semester to have obtained at least a sophomore level standing at the college or university of enrollment. **Criteria:** Selection will be based on the evaluation of narrative; transcript; recommendations; activities; honors and overall abilities.

Funds Avail.: Up to $2,000. **Number Awarded:** 3. **To Apply:** Applicants must submit a completed application form including the narrative requested in Section E of the application; official transcript from learning institute's Bursar office including work completed; two recommendation letters. The application, narrative statement, transcript and recommendation letters must be submitted in one envelope. **Deadline:** July 15. **Contact:** Jerry Gruender, Chairman of the Scholarship Committee at 13107 Vicky St., Planfield, IL 60585.

2749 ■ Chicana/Latina Foundation (CLF)
1419 Burlingame Ave. Ste. N
Burlingame, CA 94010
Ph: (650) 373-1083
Fax: (650) 373-1090
E-mail: clfinfo@chicanalatina.org
URL: www.chicanalatina.org

2750 ■ Chicana Latina Scholarship Fund *(Graduate, Undergraduate/Scholarship)*

Purpose: To assist Latina students in completing their undergraduate and graduate college education. **Focus:** General Studies. **Qualif.:** Applicants must be Chicana/Latina women of the Northern California counties; must be enrolled in accredited colleges, universities and community colleges in one of the listed Northern California counties; must have been residents for at least two years in one of the listed Northern California counties; must be enrolled as full-time college students, have completed a minimum of 15 college semester units after high school graduation, and have at least a 2.5 GPA; must have demonstrated leadership and civic/community involvement. **Criteria:** Preference will be given to those who meet the criteria.

Funds Avail.: $1,500. **To Apply:** Applicants must check the available website to download the application form. **Contact:** Chicana Latina Foundation at the above address.

2751 ■ Childhood Cancer Canada Foundation
21 St. Clair Ave. E Ste. 801
Toronto, ON, Canada M4T 1L9
Ph: (416) 489-6440
Fax: (416) 489-9812
Free: 800-363-1062
E-mail: info@childhoodcancer.ca
URL: www.candlelighters.ca

2752 ■ Childhood Cancer Foundation Scholarships *(Undergraduate/Scholarship)*

Purpose: To provide scholarships to young Canadians who are in treatment or who have survived childhood care.

Awards are arranged alphabetically below their administering organizations

Focus: Cancer. **Qualif.:** Applicant must be a Canadian citizen or landed immigrant; must be between the ages of 17-25 years and be either treated for some form of childhood cancer or still be on treatment. **Criteria:** Scholarship is based on financial need.

Funds Avail.: $1,500-$5,000. **To Apply:** Applicant must write a 300-500 word letter describing their future academic goals and reasons for applying for the scholarship; must provide a letter of acceptance; a statement from their doctor, pediatrician or oncologist stating that they have had some form of childhood cancer; must print and complete the application form available online. Application form and requirements must be sent to Scholarship Program, Childhood Cancer Foundation, 21 St. Clair Ave. E, Ste. 801, Toronto, ON M4T 1L9. **Deadline:** June 13. **Contact:** gillian@childhoodcancer.ca.

2753 ■ Childhood Cancer Survivor Scholarships (All/Scholarship)

Purpose: To support young Canadians and assist them financially with their first year of post-secondary school education. **Focus:** Cancer. **Qualif.:** Applicants must be young Canadians who are childhood cancer survivors; must be Canadian citizens or landed immigrants between the ages of 17-25 years. **Criteria:** Recipients are selected based on financial need.

Funds Avail.: $1,500. **To Apply:** Applicants must write a 300-500 word letter describing their future academic goals and highlighting their reasons for applying for this scholarship; must provide a copy of the letter of acceptance to a university, college or any post-secondary educational program and a copy of their most recent transcript, if not first year students; must provide a statement from a doctor/pediatrician and oncologist stating that they had some form of childhood cancer; must complete the application form. **Deadline:** June 30. **Contact:** 416-489-9812.

2754 ■ Children's Hospital of Philadelphia
3400 Civic Center Blvd.
Philadelphia, PA 19104-5127
Ph: (215) 590-1000
Free: 800-879-2467
E-mail: fordg@email.edu
URL: www.chop.edu

2755 ■ Eagles Fly for Leukemia Scholarships (Undergraduate/Scholarship)

Purpose: To abolish childhood cancers and enhance the lives of children and families in their communities. **Focus:** Health care services. **Qualif.:** Applicants must be survivors of childhood cancer. **Criteria:** Recipients are selected based on the financial need.

Funds Avail.: $1,500. **To Apply:** Applicants must submit a complete application form. **Contact:** Trish Fluvio, pafulvio@aol.com.

2756 ■ Barbara Palo Foster Memorial Scholarships (Graduate, Undergraduate/Scholarship)

Purpose: To support the financial needs of young adults who have lost a parent/guardian to cancer or have a parent/guardian with cancer and are seeking higher education in the field of nursing. **Focus:** Nursing. **Qualif.:** Applicant must be 35 years or younger at the time of the application; must be a young adult who has lost a parent/guardian to cancer or has a parent/guardian with cancer; must be cur-

rently attending, or planning to attend a two to four-year college or university or training program and seeking a degree in the field of nursing (including graduate and professional schools); and must demonstrate an interest in furthering patient education, focusing on persons from medically underserved communities and/or women's health issues. **Criteria:** Selection is based on merit and income criteria.

Funds Avail.: Varies. **To Apply:** Applicant must complete an application. **Contact:** Claire Carlson at carlsoncl@email.chop.edu.

2757 ■ Michael A. Hunter Memorial Scholarships (Undergraduate/Scholarship)

Purpose: To help improve the quality of life of people afflicted with leukemia. **Focus:** Healthcare services. **Qualif.:** Applicants must be graduating high school seniors, community college and four-year university students who are leukemia patients and/or children of non-surviving leukemia patients; must be enrolled full-time; and must have a minimum GPA of 3.0 or "B" average. **Criteria:** Recipients are selected based on financial need.

Funds Avail.: $1,000-$2,500. **Number Awarded:** 7. **To Apply:** Applicants must submit a complete application form.

2758 ■ Matt Stauffer Memorial Scholarships (Undergraduate, Vocational/Occupational/Scholarship)

Purpose: To support the financial needs of young adults who have been affected by cancer and intend to pursue higher education. **Focus:** Health care services. **Qualif.:** Applicants must be 35 years or younger at the time of application; must be young adult cancer survivor/patients diagnosed between the ages of 15 and 35; must be currently attending or accepted at a two to four-year college, university or vocational program including graduate and professional schools; and must be degree-seeking. **Criteria:** Recipients are selected based on demonstrated leadership abilities and commitment to their community.

Funds Avail.: varies. **To Apply:** Applicants must submit a complete application form.

2759 ■ Marilyn Yetso Memorial Scholarships (Undergraduate, Vocational/Occupational/Scholarship)

Purpose: To support the financial needs of young adults who have lost a parent/guardian to cancer or have a parent/guardian with cancer and are seeking higher education. **Focus:** Health care services. **Qualif.:** Applicants must be 35 years at younger time of application; must be young adults who have lost a parent/guardian to cancer or have a parent/guardian with cancer or the parent/guardian experienced a cancer diagnosis between the ages of 15 and 35; must be currently attending or accepted to a two- to four-year college, university or vocational program including graduate and professional schools; and must be degree-seeking. **Criteria:** Recipients are selected based on their demonstrated leadership abilities and commitment to their community.

Funds Avail.: Varies. **To Apply:** Applicants must submit a completed application form.

2760 ■ Vera Yip Memorial Scholarships (Undergraduate, Vocational/Occupational/Scholarship)

Purpose: To support the financial needs of young adults who are impacted by cancer and seeking higher education.

Awards are arranged alphabetically below their administering organizations

Focus: General Studies. **Qualif.:** Applicant must be 35 years or younger at the time of application; must be young adult who has lost a parent/guardian to cancer or has a parent/guardian with cancer or the parent/guardian has been experienced a cancer diagnosis between the ages of 15 and 35; must be currently attending or planning to attend a four-year college, university or vocational program and seeking a bachelor's degree or higher; and must have demonstrated leadership abilities and commitment to their community. **Criteria:** Recipients are selected based on merit.

Funds Avail.: Varies. **To Apply:** Applicants must accomplish complete application.

2761 ■ Children's Literature Association (ChLA)
PO Box 138
Battle Creek, MI 49016-0138
Ph: (269) 965-8180
Fax: (269) 965-3568
E-mail: kkiessling@childlitassn.org
URL: www.childlitassn.org

2762 ■ Hannah Beiter Graduate Student Research Grants *(Doctorate, Graduate/Grant)*

Purpose: To encourage young individuals to pursue their research that may be related to the dissertation or Master's thesis. **Focus:** Literature, Children's. **Qualif.:** Applicants must be a member of the Children's Literature Association. **Criteria:** Applicants will be selected based on their proposal and reference letter.

Funds Avail.: $500-$1,500. **To Apply:** Applicants must provide a cover letter including the name, telephone number, mailing address and email address, academic institution and status; must submit curriculum vitae and two reference letter. Email complete proposal as attachment to: Kathy Kiessling, ChLA Administrator at kkiessling@childlitassn.org. **Deadline:** February 1.

2763 ■ Jane Coffin Childs Memorial Fund
PO Box 208000
New Haven, CT 06520-8000
Ph: (203) 785-4612
E-mail: jccfund@yale.edu
URL: www.jccfund.org

2764 ■ Jane Coffin Childs Memorial Fund - Medical Research Fellowships *(Doctorate/Fellowship)*

Purpose: To award fellowships to suitably qualified individuals for full-time postdoctoral studies in the medical and related sciences bearing on cancer. **Focus:** Cancer. **Qualif.:** Applicants in general should not have more than one year of postdoctoral experience; must hold either the MD degree or the PhD degree in the field in which they propose to study or furnish evidence of equivalent training and experience; must be citizens of any country but for foreign nationals awards will be made only for study in the US. American citizens may hold a fellowship either in the US or in a foreign country. **Criteria:** Selection will be based on the committee's criteria.

Funds Avail.: The basic stipend at present is $45,000 the first year, $46,000 the second year, and $48,000 the third year, with an additional $1,000 for each dependent child. **To Apply:** An Applicant in addition to submitting evidence

as to pre- and postdoctoral training must supply (a) the names and addresses of three individuals personally acquainted both with the applicant and with the applicant's professional work, one of whom should be the principal pre-doctoral advisor, (b) a suitably documented outline of the research problem proposed, and (c) the written consent of the chief of laboratory and a responsible fiscal officer of the host institution indicating their willingness to accept and provide necessary facilities for the Fellow. **Deadline:** February 1. **Contact:** Kim Roberts at the above address.

2765 ■ Chinese American Medical Society (CAMS)
41 Elizabeth St., Ste. 600
New York, NY 10013
Ph: (212) 334-4760
Fax: (212) 965-1876
E-mail: jlove@camsociety.org
URL: www.camsociety.org

2766 ■ Chinese American Medical Society Summer Research Fellowships Program *(Undergraduate/Fellowship)*

Purpose: To support clinical and basic science research among Chinese American, medical and dental students. **Focus:** Medical technology; Dental laboratory technology. **Qualif.:** Applicant must be a current student in an accredited medical or dental school in the United States; working on a project in the basic science or clinical research. **Criteria:** Special consideration will be given to projects involving Chinese American health issues.

Funds Avail.: $400 per week. **To Apply:** Applicants must submit completed CAMS Summer Research Fellowship Application; project description; personal statement; curriculum vitae; a two letters from a supervising investigator supporting the research project and from the Dean verifying good standing. **Deadline:** April 30. **Contact:** Mail application form and supporting documents to Dr. Jerry Huo at the above address or e-mail jerryhuomd@gmail.com for further information.

2767 ■ Esther Lim Memorial Scholarships *(Undergraduate/Scholarship)*

Purpose: To provide educational assistance to medical, dental students, and scientists. **Focus:** Medical technology; Dental laboratory technology. **Qualif.:** Applicant must be a medical or dental student or scientist matriculated in a medical or dental school. **Criteria:** Selection is based on merit.

Funds Avail.: No specific amount. **Number Awarded:** 3-5. **To Apply:** Application form is available at the website. Applicants must submit completed application form along with a letter from the Dean of Students verifying good standing; two letters of recommendation; a personal statement; and a current vitae. **Deadline:** April 30. **Remarks:** Established as a result of a bequest by Dr. Lim, a late member of the society, and her family. **Contact:** Mail application form and supporting documents to Dr. Jerry Huo MD at the above address or jerryhuomd@gmail.com for further information.

2768 ■ Ruth Liu Memorial Scholarships *(Undergraduate/Scholarship)*

Purpose: To provide educational assistance for medical, dental students, and scientists. **Focus:** Medical technology; Dental laboratory technology. **Qualif.:** Applicant must be a

Awards are arranged alphabetically below their administering organizations

medical or dental student or scientist matriculated in a medical or dental school. **Criteria:** Selection is based on merit.

Funds Avail.: No specific amount. **Number Awarded:** 3-5. **To Apply:** Application form is available at the website. Applicants must submit completed application form along with a letter from the Dean of Students verifying good standing; two letters of recommendation; a personal statement; and a current vitae. Send all materials to: Jerry Huo MD, Chairman, CAMS Scholarship Committee 32 Aspen Road, Scarsdale NY 10583, jerryhuomd@gmail.com. **Deadline:** April 30. **Remarks:** Established in 1996 by her husband Dr. George Liu and friends. **Contact:** Application form and supporting documents must be submitted by mail to Dr. Jerry Huo at the above address or e-mail jerryhuomd@gmail.com for further information.

2769 ■ Chinese Professionals Association of Canada (CPAC)

4150 Finch Ave. E
Scarborough, ON, Canada M1S 3T9
Ph: (416) 298-7885
Fax: (416) 298-0068
E-mail: office@chineseprofessionals.ca
URL: www.chineseprofessionals.ca

2770 ■ CC Times Scholarships *(Undergraduate/ Scholarship)*

Purpose: To help needy students further their education. **Focus:** General studies. **Qualif.:** Applicants must be secondary or post-secondary students or either be CPAC members and/or children with financial difficulties; must be enrolled in a degree program and have completed at least two semesters in a recognized university. **Criteria:** Recipients will be selected based on demonstrated leadership and academic achievements.

Funds Avail.: No specific amount. **To Apply:** Applicants must contact Howard Shen, President of the Education Foundation of CPAC, for further information.

2771 ■ Chinese Professionals Association of Canada BMO Diversity Scholarships *(Undergraduate/Scholarship)*

Purpose: To help needy students further their education. **Focus:** General studies. **Qualif.:** Applicants must be secondary or post-secondary students or either be CPAC members and/or children with financial difficulties; must be enrolled in a degree program and have completed at least two semesters in a recognized university. **Criteria:** Recipients will be selected based on demonstrated leadership and academic achievements.

Funds Avail.: No specific amount. **To Apply:** Applicants must contact Howard Shen, President of the Education Foundation of CPAC, for further information.

2772 ■ Chinese Professionals Association of Canada Education Foundation Awards *(High School/Award)*

Purpose: To encourage high school students to pursue higher education. **Focus:** General studies. **Qualif.:** Applicants must have completed grade 10, 11 or 12. **Criteria:** Recipients will be selected based on academic excellence and community involvement.

Funds Avail.: No specific amount. **To Apply:** Applicants

must contact Howard Shen, President of the Education Foundation of CPAC, for further information.

2773 ■ Chinese Professionals Association of Canada Journalism Scholarships *(Undergraduate/Scholarship)*

Purpose: To help needy students further their education. **Focus:** General studies. **Qualif.:** Applicants must be secondary or post-secondary students or either be CPAC members and/or children with financial difficulties; must be enrolled in a degree program and have completed at least two semesters in a recognized university. **Criteria:** Recipients will be selected based on demonstrated leadership and academic achievements.

Funds Avail.: No specific amount. **To Apply:** Applicants must contact Howard Shen, President of the Education Foundation of CPAC, for further information.

2774 ■ Chinese Professionals Association of Canada Professional Achievement Awards *(Professional development/Award)*

Purpose: To award professional immigrants. **Focus:** General studies. **Qualif.:** Applicants must have achieved an outstanding stature in their profession in Canada; must have used CPAC's services (including bridging program) for them to land new jobs; and must have achieved a successful accomplishment on a different profession other than the training they had before. **Criteria:** Award will be given to those who best meet the qualifications.

Funds Avail.: No specific amount. **To Apply:** Applicants must contact Howard Shen, President of the Education Foundation of CPAC, for further information.

2775 ■ Pang Xiaoyan Scholarships *(Undergraduate/Scholarship)*

Purpose: To help needy students further their education. **Focus:** General studies. **Qualif.:** Applicants must be secondary or post-secondary students or either be CPAC members and/or children with financial difficulties; must be enrolled in a degree program and have completed at least two semesters in a recognized university. **Criteria:** Recipients will be selected based on demonstrated leadership and academic achievements.

Funds Avail.: No specific amount. **To Apply:** Applicants must contact Howard Shen, President of the Education Foundation of CPAC, for further information.

2776 ■ Chopin Foundation of the United States

1440 79th St. Causeway, Ste. 117
Miami, FL 33141
Ph: (305) 868-0624
Fax: (305) 865-5150
E-mail: info@chopin.org
URL: www.chopin.org

2777 ■ Chopin Foundation of the United States Scholarships *(Undergraduate/Scholarship)*

Purpose: To support pianists studying music. **Focus:** Music, Piano. **Qualif.:** Applicants must be American pianists (citizens or legal residents); not younger than 14 and not older than 17 years; studying in the field of music, majoring in piano, and enrolled at the secondary or undergraduate school level as a full-time student. **Criteria:** Applicants are selected based on merit.

Awards are arranged alphabetically below their administering organizations

Funds Avail.: $1,000. **Number Awarded:** 10. **To Apply:** Applicants must submit a statement of career goals; minimum of two references from piano teachers or performers; a video tape of 20-30 minutes of Chopin's works, registration fee of $25 and proof of enrollment. **Deadline:** April 15.

2778 ■ Choristers Guild (CG)

12404 Park Central Dr., Ste. 100
Dallas, TX 75251-1802
Ph: (469) 398-3606
Fax: (469) 398-3611
Free: 800-246-7478
E-mail: jrindelaub@mailcg.org
URL: www.choristersguild.org

2779 ■ Ruth K. Jacobs Memorial Scholarships
(Graduate, Undergraduate/Scholarship)

Purpose: To provide financial aid to full-time students preparing for church music ministry. **Focus:** Music. **Qualif.:** Applicant must be a junior, senior or graduate student majoring in music who holds choral music with children and youth as a primary interest; has an official transcript sent from all past and current institutions in which enrolled; demonstrate talent, leadership ability and promise of future usefulness in church music; and shows the need for financial aid. **Criteria:** Recipient is selected on the basis of academic merit, interest in church music, ministry of church music as a vocation and financial need.

Funds Avail.: $1,500. **To Apply:** Applicant must submit an application form; transcript of records; and give four references who are acquainted with the applicant's qualifications. **Deadline:** February 1.

2780 ■ Christian Missionary Scholarship Foundation (CMSF)

3230 Lake Dr. SE
Grand Rapids, MI 49546
Ph: (616) 526-7731
Fax: (616) 526-6777
E-mail: info@christianmissionaryscholarship.org
URL: www.christianmissionaryscholarship.org

2781 ■ CMSF Scholarships *(Graduate, Undergraduate/Scholarship)*

Purpose: To provide financial support for the education of the children of missionaries. **Focus:** General studies. **Qualif.:** Applicant must be the child of a missionary currently on or recently returned from the mission field in a country other than his own passport country. **Criteria:** Selection is based on the application materials submitted for review.

Funds Avail.: No specific amount. **Number Awarded:** Over 200. **To Apply:** Applicants must submit a completed Scholarship application form. **Deadline:** February 15. **Remarks:** Recipients must attend at least one among the six colleges: Calvin College-Grand Rapids, MI; Dordt College-Sioux Center, IA; Hope College-Holland, MI; Kuyper College-Grand Rapids, MI; Trinity Christian College-Palos Heights, IL; Wheaton College-Wheaton, IL.

2782 ■ Christian Pharmacists Fellowship International (CPFI)

PO Box 24708
West Palm Beach, FL 33416-4708
Ph: (561) 803-2737
Fax: (561) 803-2738
Free: 888-253-6885
E-mail: office@cpfi.org
URL: www.cpfi.org

2783 ■ Christian Pharmacist Fellowship International *(All/Fellowship)*

Purpose: To assist Christian students in pursuing a career on pharmacy. **Focus:** Pharmacy. **Qualif.:** Applicant must be a national CPFI member; enrolled in an accredited pharmacy college/university or training program. **Criteria:** Awards are given based on the merit of the application and the Christian relevance of the project. Preference will be given to applicants whose plans or projects are experiential in nature or become the component of the curriculum.

Funds Avail.: $250-$1,000. **To Apply:** Applicant must send completed application form; description of the plan or project; an email support from the Dean and from an instructor/mentor; and a resume. **Deadline:** October 1, March 1 and June 1. **Contact:** Scholarship Committee Chairman, Daniel Sparado, 501-686-6491 or sparadodanielc@uams.edu.

2784 ■ Christian Record Services for the Blind (CRSB)

PO Box 6097
Lincoln, NE 68506-0097
Ph: (402) 488-0981
Fax: (402) 488-7582
E-mail: info@christianrecord.org
URL: www.christianrecord.org

2785 ■ CRS Scholarships *(Undergraduate/Scholarship)*

Purpose: To assist blind young people who wish to pursue their college education. **Focus:** General studies. **Qualif.:** Applicants must be legally blind; planning to attend college as a full-time student on the undergraduate level. **Criteria:** Scholarship recipients will be selected based on the Selection Committee's review of the application materials.

Funds Avail.: No specific amount. **Number Awarded:** 10. **To Apply:** Applicants must submit a completed Scholarship application and character reference forms. Application form includes: personal background; financial budget; and recent photo. **Deadline:** April 1. **Contact:** Shelly Kittleson at 4444 S 52nd St., Lincoln, NE 68516.

2786 ■ Christian Scholarship Foundation (CSF)

Yale Divinity School
409 Prospect St.
New Haven, CT 06511
URL: csfinc.org

2787 ■ CSF Graduate Fellowships *(Graduate/Fellowship)*

Purpose: To provide financial assistance to ministers enrolled in doctoral programs in religion and related fields. **Focus:** Religion; Bible studies; Theology. **Qualif.:** Applicant must be a Christian teaching or planning to teach religion and related subjects in universities, colleges, schools of theology and Bible chairs; and have completed at least one full year of study as a candidate for the PhD or equivalent

Awards are arranged alphabetically below their administering organizations

post-graduate degree prior to the year of application. **Criteria:** Selection is based on the application materials submitted for review.

Funds Avail.: $2,000-$10,000. **Number Awarded:** 3-5. **To Apply:** Applicants must submit a completed application form together with transcripts of all previous academic works (graduate and undergraduate); letters of recommendation; a research paper or other example of most scholarly written work; a summary statement of plans for the academic year; and an estimated budget showing the income and expenditures. **Deadline:** January 15.

2788 ■ Winston Churchill Foundation

600 Madison Ave., Ste. 1601
New York, NY 10022-1737
Ph: (212) 752-3200
Fax: (212) 246-8330
E-mail: info@winstonchurchillfoundation.org
URL: www.winstonchurchillfoundation.org

2789 ■ The Churchill Scholarships
(Postgraduate/Scholarship)

Purpose: To pursue graduate studies in engineering, mathematics, or the sciences at the Cambridge. **Focus:** Engineering; Mathematics and mathematical science. **Qualif.:** Applicants must be citizens of the United States and must be enrolled in one of the institutions participating in the scholarship program competition or students who have recently graduated from one of those institutions. Applicants must be between the ages of 19 and 26. **Criteria:** Recipients are selected based on the academic achievement in all disciplines; the capacity to contribute to the advancement of knowledge in the sciences, engineering or mathematics by pursuing original, creative work at advanced levels as demonstrated by awards and prizes as reference.

Funds Avail.: $45,000-$50,000. **To Apply:** Applicants must complete the application form; four letters of reference; proposed program of the study; personal statement. **Deadline:** November. **Contact:** 212-984-5442.

2790 ■ CIHR Training Program in Health Law and Policy

University of Toronto
Faculty of Law
84 Queen's Park
Toronto, ON, Canada M5S 2C5
Ph: (416) 978-3724
Fax: (416) 978-2648
E-mail: info@healthlawtraining.ca
URL: www.healthlawtraining.ca

2791 ■ CIHR Health Law and Policy Fellowships *(Graduate/Fellowship)*

Purpose: To increase research capacity in the area of health law and policy. **Focus:** Law. **Qualif.:** Applicants must be admitted into the Faculty of Law graduate program at one of the three participating institutions (Dalhousie University, University of Alberta, and University of Toronto). **Criteria:** Selection is based on the submitted application and materials.

Funds Avail.: Minimum of $17,850/year. **Number Awarded:** 10. **To Apply:** Applicants must submit a completed application form together with the transcripts from all

universities attended (certified copies); two academic letters of reference; and a one-page statement of interest in health law and policy. **Deadline:** March 15. **Contact:** Chrystal Gray at chrystal.gray@dal.ca.

2792 ■ Cincinnati Scholarship Foundation (CSF)

602 Main St., Ste. 1000
Cincinnati, OH 45202
Ph: (513) 345-6701
Fax: (513) 345-6705
URL: www.cincinnatischolarshipfoundation.org

2793 ■ CSF Michael Bany Memorial Scholarships *(Undergraduate/Scholarship)*

Purpose: To help students of Greater Cincinnati area achieve a college education. **Focus:** General studies. **Qualif.:** Applicant must be a resident of Greater Cincinnati and attending college as a full-time student. **Criteria:** Awards are given based on need.

Funds Avail.: No specific amount. **To Apply:** Applicant must submit a completed scholarship application form along with a copy of recent transcript; expected Family Contribution (EFC) from Student Aid Report (SAR), which comes as a result of filing the FAFSA; and a copy of Financial Aid Award Letter from the chosen college to be attended. **Deadline:** April 30. **Remarks:** Faxed applications will not be considered.

2794 ■ CSF Walter and Marilyn Bartlett Scholarships *(Undergraduate/Scholarship)*

Purpose: To help students from Greater Cincinnati area to achieve the dream of a college education. **Focus:** General studies. **Qualif.:** Applicant must be a resident of Greater Cincinnati and attending college as a full-time student. **Criteria:** Awards are given based on need.

Funds Avail.: No specific amount. **To Apply:** Applicant must submit a completed scholarship application form along with a copy of recent transcript; expected Family Contribution (EFC) from Student Aid Report (SAR), which comes as a result of filing the FAFSA; and a copy of Financial Aid Award Letter from the chosen college to be attended. **Deadline:** April 30. **Remarks:** Faxed applications will not be considered.

2795 ■ CSF Johnny Bench Scholarships *(Undergraduate/Scholarship)*

Purpose: To help students from Greater Cincinnati area to achieve the dream of a college education. **Focus:** General studies. **Qualif.:** Applicant must be a resident of Greater Cincinnati and attending college as a full-time student. **Criteria:** Awards are given based on need.

Funds Avail.: No specific amount. **To Apply:** Applicant must submit a completed scholarship application form along with a copy of recent transcript; expected Family Contribution (EFC) from Student Aid Report (SAR), which comes as a result of filing the FAFSA; and a copy of Financial Aid Award Letter from the chosen college to be attended. **Deadline:** April 30. **Remarks:** Faxed applications will not be considered.

2796 ■ CSF M. and E. Brown Scholarships *(Undergraduate/Scholarship)*

Purpose: To help students of Greater Cincinnati area achieve a college education. **Focus:** General studies. **Qualif.:** Applicant must be a resident of Greater Cincinnati and

Awards are arranged alphabetically below their administering organizations

attending college as a full-time student. **Criteria:** Awards are given based on need.

Funds Avail.: No specific amount. **To Apply:** Applicant must submit a completed scholarship application form along with a copy of recent transcript; expected Family Contribution (EFC) from Student Aid Report (SAR), which comes as a result of filing the FAFSA; and a copy of Financial Aid Award Letter from the chosen college to be attended. **Deadline:** April 30. **Remarks:** Faxed applications will not be considered.

2797 ■ CSF Eugene Carroll Scholarships
(Undergraduate/Scholarship)

Purpose: To help students from Greater Cincinnati area to achieve the dream of a college education. **Focus:** General studies. **Qualif.:** Applicant must be a resident of Greater Cincinnati and attending college as a full-time student. **Criteria:** Awards are given based on need.

Funds Avail.: No specific amount. **To Apply:** Applicant must submit a completed scholarship application form along with a copy of recent transcript; expected Family Contribution (EFC) from Student Aid Report (SAR), which comes as a result of filing the FAFSA; and a copy of Financial Aid Award Letter from the chosen college to be attended. **Deadline:** April 30. **Remarks:** Faxed applications will not be considered. **Contact:** scholarship@fuse.net.

2798 ■ CFT/ACPSOP Scholarships
(Undergraduate/Scholarship)

Purpose: To help students from Greater Cincinnati area to achieve their dream of a college education. **Focus:** General studies. **Qualif.:** Applicant must be a resident of Greater Cincinnati and attending college as a full-time student. **Criteria:** Awards are given based on need.

Funds Avail.: No specific amount. **To Apply:** Applicant must submit a completed scholarship application form along with a copy of recent transcript; expected Family Contribution (EFC) from Student Aid Report (SAR), which comes as a result of filing the FAFSA; and a copy of Financial Aid Award Letter from the chosen college to be attended. **Deadline:** April 30. **Remarks:** Faxed applications will not be considered. **Contact:** scholarship@fuse.net.

2799 ■ Cincinnati High School Scholarships
(High School/Scholarship)

Purpose: To encourage students to achieve their highest academic potential. **Focus:** General studies. **Qualif.:** Applicant must attend a Cincinnati Public School in grades 7-12; meet the Federal Poverty Income Guidelines; maintains a minimum 2.50 GPA with no "Fs", "Xs" or "Is" in any subject; and be referred by a designated counselor or school representative. **Criteria:** Award is given based on the application.

Funds Avail.: A monthly stipend based on GPA. **To Apply:** Applications are only available from the representative at the student's school. The CSF representatives provide applications to students they recommend for the program. **Remarks:** Started in 1918. The program works only for students attending Cincinnati Public Schools. **Contact:** scholarship@fuse.net.

2800 ■ CSF T.L. Conlan Memorial Scholarships
(Undergraduate/Scholarship)

Purpose: To help students from Greater Cincinnati area to achieve the dream of a college education. **Focus:** General studies. **Qualif.:** Applicant must be a resident of Greater

Cincinnati and attending college as a full-time student. **Criteria:** Awards are given based on need.

Funds Avail.: No specific amount. **To Apply:** Applicant must submit a completed scholarship application form along with a copy of recent transcript; expected Family Contribution (EFC) from Student Aid Report (SAR), which comes as a result of filing the FAFSA; and a copy of Financial Aid Award Letter from the chosen college to be attended. **Deadline:** April 30. **Remarks:** Faxed applications will not be considered.

2801 ■ CSF Ach Family Scholarships
(Undergraduate/Scholarship)

Purpose: To help students from Greater Cincinnati area to achieve the dream of a college education. **Focus:** General studies. **Qualif.:** Applicant must be a resident of Greater Cincinnati and attending college as a full-time student. **Criteria:** Awards are given based on need.

Funds Avail.: No specific amount. **To Apply:** Applicant must submit a completed scholarship application form along with a copy of recent transcript; expected Family Contribution (EFC) from Student Aid Report (SAR), which comes as a result of filing the FAFSA; and a copy of Financial Aid Award Letter from the chosen college to be attended. **Deadline:** April 30. **Remarks:** Faxed applications will not be considered. **Contact:** scholarship@fuse.net.

2802 ■ CSF Barr Foundation Scholarships
(Undergraduate/Scholarship)

Purpose: To help students from Greater Cincinnati area to achieve the dream of a college education. **Focus:** General studies. **Qualif.:** Applicant must be a resident of Greater Cincinnati and attending college as a full-time student. **Criteria:** Awards are given based on need.

Funds Avail.: No specific amount. **To Apply:** Applicant must submit a completed scholarship application form along with a copy of recent transcript; expected Family Contribution (EFC) from Student Aid Report (SAR), which comes as a result of filing the FAFSA; and a copy of Financial Aid Award Letter from the chosen college to be attended. **Deadline:** April 30. **Remarks:** Faxed applications will not be considered. **Contact:** scholarship@fuse.net.

2803 ■ CSF Barrett Family Scholarships
(Undergraduate/Scholarship)

Purpose: To help students from Greater Cincinnati area to achieve the dream of a college education. **Focus:** General studies. **Qualif.:** Applicant must be a resident of Greater Cincinnati and attending college as a full-time student. **Criteria:** Awards are given based on need.

Funds Avail.: No specific amount. **To Apply:** Applicant must submit a completed scholarship application form along with a copy of recent transcript; expected Family Contribution (EFC) from Student Aid Report (SAR), which comes as a result of filing the FAFSA; and a copy of Financial Aid Award Letter from the chosen college to be attended. **Deadline:** April 30. **Remarks:** Faxed applications will not be considered. **Contact:** scholarship@fuse.net.

2804 ■ CSF Bigg's/Curtis Breeden Scholarships
(Undergraduate/Scholarship)

Purpose: To help students of Greater Cincinnati area achieve a college education. **Focus:** General studies. **Qualif.:** Applicant must be a resident of Greater Cincinnati and attending college as a full-time student. **Criteria:** Awards are given based on need.

Awards are arranged alphabetically below their administering organizations

Funds Avail.: No specific amount. **To Apply:** Applicant must submit a completed scholarship application form along with a copy of recent transcript; expected Family Contribution (EFC) from Student Aid Report (SAR), which comes as a result of filing the FAFSA; and a copy of Financial Aid Award Letter from the chosen college to be attended. **Deadline:** April 30. **Remarks:** Faxed applications will not be considered.

2805 ■ CSF Borden Inc. Scholarships
(Undergraduate/Scholarship)

Purpose: To help students from Greater Cincinnati area to achieve the dream of a college education. **Focus:** General studies. **Qualif.:** Applicant must be a resident of Greater Cincinnati and attending college as a full-time student. **Criteria:** Awards are given based on need.

Funds Avail.: No specific amount. **To Apply:** Applicant must submit a completed scholarship application form along with a copy of recent transcript; expected Family Contribution (EFC) from Student Aid Report (SAR), which comes as a result of filing the FAFSA; and a copy of Financial Aid Award Letter from the chosen college to be attended. **Deadline:** April 30. **Remarks:** Faxed applications will not be considered.

2806 ■ CSF Castellini Foundation Scholarships
(Undergraduate/Scholarship)

Purpose: To help students from Greater Cincinnati area to achieve the dream of a college education. **Focus:** General studies. **Qualif.:** Applicant must be a resident of Greater Cincinnati and attending college as a full-time student. **Criteria:** Awards are given based on need.

Funds Avail.: No specific amount. **To Apply:** Applicant must submit a completed scholarship application form along with a copy of recent transcript; expected Family Contribution (EFC) from Student Aid Report (SAR), which comes as a result of filing the FAFSA; and a copy of Financial Aid Award Letter from the chosen college to be attended. **Deadline:** April 30. **Remarks:** Faxed applications will not be considered.

2807 ■ CSF Cincinnati Bell Scholarships
(Undergraduate/Scholarship)

Purpose: To help students from Greater Cincinnati area to achieve the dream of a college education. **Focus:** General studies. **Qualif.:** Applicant must be a resident of Greater Cincinnati and attending college as a full-time student. **Criteria:** Awards are given based on need.

Funds Avail.: No specific amount. **To Apply:** Applicant must submit a completed scholarship application form along with a copy of recent transcript; expected Family Contribution (EFC) from Student Aid Report (SAR), which comes as a result of filing the FAFSA; and a copy of Financial Aid Award Letter from the chosen college to be attended. **Deadline:** April 30. **Remarks:** Faxed applications will not be considered. **Contact:** scholarship@fuse.net.

2808 ■ CSF Cincinnati Financial Corporation Scholarships *(Undergraduate/Scholarship)*

Purpose: To help students from Greater Cincinnati area to achieve the dream of a college education. **Focus:** General studies. **Qualif.:** Applicant must be a resident of Greater Cincinnati and attending college as a full-time student. **Criteria:** Awards are given based on need.

Funds Avail.: No specific amount. **To Apply:** Applicant must submit a completed scholarship application form along

with a copy of recent transcript; expected Family Contribution (EFC) from Student Aid Report (SAR), which comes as a result of filing the FAFSA; and a copy of Financial Aid Award Letter from the chosen college to be attended. **Deadline:** April 30. **Remarks:** Faxed applications will not be considered. **Contact:** scholarship@fuse.net.

2809 ■ CSF Cincinnati Milacron Scholarships
(Undergraduate/Scholarship)

Purpose: To help students from Greater Cincinnati area to achieve the dream of a college education. **Focus:** General studies. **Qualif.:** Applicant must be a resident of Greater Cincinnati and attending college as a full-time student. **Criteria:** Awards are given based on need.

Funds Avail.: No specific amount. **To Apply:** Applicant must submit a completed scholarship application form along with a copy of recent transcript; expected Family Contribution (EFC) from Student Aid Report (SAR), which comes as a result of filing the FAFSA; and a copy of Financial Aid Award Letter from the chosen college to be attended. **Deadline:** April 30. **Remarks:** Faxed applications will not be considered.

2810 ■ CSF Crosset Family Scholarships
(Undergraduate/Scholarship)

Purpose: To help students from Greater Cincinnati area to achieve the dream of a college education. **Focus:** General studies. **Qualif.:** Applicant must be a resident of Greater Cincinnati and attending college as a full-time student. **Criteria:** Awards are given based on need.

Funds Avail.: No specific amount. **To Apply:** Applicant must submit a completed scholarship application form along with a copy of recent transcript; expected Family Contribution (EFC) from Student Aid Report (SAR), which comes as a result of filing the FAFSA; and a copy of Financial Aid Award Letter from the chosen college to be attended. **Deadline:** April 30. **Remarks:** Faxed applications will not be considered. **Contact:** scholarship@fuse.net.

2811 ■ CSF Dater Foundation Scholarships
(Undergraduate/Scholarship)

Purpose: To help students from Greater Cincinnati area to achieve the dream of a college education. **Focus:** General studies. **Qualif.:** Applicant must be a resident of Greater Cincinnati and attending college as a full-time student. **Criteria:** Awards are given based on need.

Funds Avail.: No specific amount. **To Apply:** Applicant must submit a completed scholarship application form along with a copy of recent transcript; expected Family Contribution (EFC) from Student Aid Report (SAR), which comes as a result of filing the FAFSA; and a copy of Financial Aid Award Letter from the chosen college to be attended. **Deadline:** April 30. **Remarks:** Faxed applications will not be considered. **Contact:** scholarship@fuse.net.

2812 ■ CSF Duke Energy Scholarships
(Undergraduate/Scholarship)

Purpose: To help students from Greater Cincinnati area to achieve the dream of a college education. **Focus:** General studies. **Qualif.:** Applicant must be a resident of Greater Cincinnati and attending college as a full-time student. **Criteria:** Awards are given based on need.

Funds Avail.: No specific amount. **To Apply:** Applicant must submit a completed scholarship application form along with a copy of recent transcript; expected Family Contribution (EFC) from Student Aid Report (SAR), which comes as

Awards are arranged alphabetically below their administering organizations

a result of filing the FAFSA; and a copy of Financial Aid Award Letter from the chosen college to be attended. **Deadline:** April 30. **Remarks:** Faxed applications will not be considered. **Contact:** scholarship@fuse.net.

2813 ■ CSF Farmer Family Foundation Scholarships *(Undergraduate/Scholarship)*

Purpose: To help students from Greater Cincinnati area to achieve the dream of a college education. **Focus:** General studies. **Qualif.:** Applicant must be a resident of Greater Cincinnati and attending college as a full-time student. **Criteria:** Awards are given based on need.

Funds Avail.: No specific amount. **To Apply:** Applicant must submit a completed scholarship application form along with a copy of recent transcript; expected Family Contribution (EFC) from Student Aid Report (SAR), which comes as a result of filing the FAFSA; and a copy of Financial Aid Award Letter from the chosen college to be attended. **Deadline:** April 30. **Remarks:** Faxed applications will not be considered. **Contact:** scholarship@fuse.net.

2814 ■ CSF Fifth Third Bank Combined Scholarships *(Undergraduate/Scholarship)*

Purpose: To help students from Greater Cincinnati area to achieve the dream of a college education. **Focus:** General studies. **Qualif.:** Applicant must be a resident of Greater Cincinnati and attending college as a full-time student. **Criteria:** Awards are given based on need.

Funds Avail.: No specific amount. **To Apply:** Applicant must submit a completed scholarship application form along with a copy of recent transcript; expected Family Contribution (EFC) from Student Aid Report (SAR), which comes as a result of filing the FAFSA; and a copy of Financial Aid Award Letter from the chosen college to be attended. **Deadline:** April 30. **Remarks:** Faxed applications will not be considered. **Contact:** scholarship@fuse.net.

2815 ■ CSF Fletemeyer Family Scholarships *(Undergraduate/Scholarship)*

Purpose: To help students from Greater Cincinnati area to achieve the dream of a college education. **Focus:** General studies. **Qualif.:** Applicant must be a resident of Greater Cincinnati and attending college as a full-time student. **Criteria:** Awards are given based on need.

Funds Avail.: No specific amount. **To Apply:** Applicant must submit a completed scholarship application form along with a copy of recent transcript; expected Family Contribution (EFC) from Student Aid Report (SAR), which comes as a result of filing the FAFSA; and a copy of Financial Aid Award Letter from the chosen college to be attended. **Deadline:** April 30. **Remarks:** Faxed applications will not be considered. **Contact:** scholarship@fuse.net.

2816 ■ CSF Gardner Foundation Scholarships *(Undergraduate/Scholarship)*

Purpose: To help students from Greater Cincinnati area to achieve the dream of a college education. **Focus:** General studies. **Qualif.:** Applicant must be a resident of Greater Cincinnati and attending college as a full-time student. **Criteria:** Awards are given based on need.

Funds Avail.: No specific amount. **To Apply:** Applicant must submit a completed scholarship application form along with a copy of recent transcript; expected Family Contribution (EFC) from Student Aid Report (SAR), which comes as a result of filing the FAFSA; and a copy of Financial Aid Award Letter from the chosen college to be attended.

Deadline: April 30. **Remarks:** Faxed applications will not be considered. **Contact:** scholarship@fuse.net.

2817 ■ CSF G.E. Aircraft Engines Scholarships *(Undergraduate/Scholarship)*

Purpose: To help students from Greater Cincinnati area to achieve the dream of a college education. **Focus:** General studies. **Qualif.:** Applicant must be a resident of Greater Cincinnati, and attending college as a full-time student. **Criteria:** Awards are given based on need.

Funds Avail.: No specific amount. **To Apply:** Applicants must submit a completed scholarship application form along with a copy of recent transcript; expected Family Contribution (EFC) from Student Aid Report (SAR), which comes as a result of filing the FAFSA; and a copy of Financial Aid Award Letter from the chosen college to be attended. **Deadline:** April 30. **Remarks:** Faxed applications will not be considered.

2818 ■ CSF Goldman, Sachs and Company Scholarships *(Undergraduate/Scholarship)*

Purpose: To help students from Greater Cincinnati area to achieve the dream of a college education. **Focus:** General studies. **Qualif.:** Applicant must be a resident of Greater Cincinnati and attending college as a full-time student. **Criteria:** Awards are given based on need.

Funds Avail.: No specific amount. **To Apply:** Applicant must submit a completed scholarship application form along with a copy of recent transcript; expected Family Contribution (EFC) from Student Aid Report (SAR), which comes as a result of filing the FAFSA; and a copy of Financial Aid Award Letter from the chosen college to be attended. **Deadline:** April 30. **Remarks:** Faxed applications will not be considered. **Contact:** scholarship@fuse.net.

2819 ■ CSF Greater Cincinnati Scholarships Association *(Undergraduate/Scholarship)*

Purpose: To help students from Greater Cincinnati area to achieve the dream of a college education. **Focus:** General studies. **Qualif.:** Applicant must be a resident of Greater Cincinnati and attending college as a full-time student. **Criteria:** Awards are given based on need.

Funds Avail.: No specific amount. **To Apply:** Applicant must submit a completed scholarship application form along with a copy of recent transcript; expected Family Contribution (EFC) from Student Aid Report (SAR), which comes as a result of filing the FAFSA; and a copy of Financial Aid Award Letter from the chosen college to be attended. **Deadline:** April 30. **Remarks:** Faxed applications will not be considered. **Contact:** scholarship@fuse.net.

2820 ■ CSF Heidelberg Distributing Co. Scholarships *(Undergraduate/Scholarship)*

Purpose: To help students from Greater Cincinnati area to achieve the dream of a college education. **Focus:** General studies. **Qualif.:** Applicant must be a resident of Greater Cincinnati and attending college as a full-time student. **Criteria:** Awards are given based on need.

Funds Avail.: No specific amount. **To Apply:** Applicant must submit a completed scholarship application form along with a copy of recent transcript; expected Family Contribution (EFC) from Student Aid Report (SAR), which comes as a result of filing the FAFSA; and a copy of Financial Aid Award Letter from the chosen college to be attended. **Deadline:** April 30. **Remarks:** Faxed applications will not be considered. **Contact:** scholarship@fuse.net.

Awards are arranged alphabetically below their administering organizations

2821 ■ CSF Heinz Pet Products Scholarships
(Undergraduate/Scholarship)

Purpose: To help students from Greater Cincinnati area to achieve the dream of a college education. **Focus:** General studies. **Qualif.:** Applicant must be a resident of Greater Cincinnati and attending college as a full-time student. **Criteria:** Awards are given based on need.

Funds Avail.: No specific amount. **To Apply:** Applicant must submit a completed scholarship application form along with a copy of recent transcript; expected Family Contribution (EFC) from Student Aid Report (SAR), which comes as a result of filing the FAFSA; and a copy of Financial Aid Award Letter from the chosen college to be attended. **Deadline:** April 30. **Remarks:** Faxed applications will not be considered. **Contact:** scholarship@fuse.net.

2822 ■ CSF Juilfs Foundation Scholarships
(Undergraduate/Scholarship)

Purpose: To help students from Greater Cincinnati area to achieve the dream of a college education. **Focus:** General studies. **Qualif.:** Applicant must be a resident of Greater Cincinnati and attending college as a full-time student. **Criteria:** Awards are given based on need.

Funds Avail.: No specific amount. **To Apply:** Applicant must submit a completed scholarship application form along with a copy of recent transcript; expected Family Contribution (EFC) from Student Aid Report (SAR), which comes as a result of filing the FAFSA; and a copy of Financial Aid Award Letter from the chosen college to be attended. **Deadline:** April 30. **Remarks:** Faxed applications will not be considered.

2823 ■ CSF Kroger Cincinnati/Dayton Scholarships *(Undergraduate/Scholarship)*

Purpose: To help students from Greater Cincinnati area to achieve the dream of a college education. **Focus:** General studies. **Qualif.:** Applicant must be a resident of Greater Cincinnati and attending college as a full-time student. **Criteria:** Awards are given based on need.

Funds Avail.: No specific amount. **To Apply:** Applicant must submit a completed scholarship application form along with a copy of recent transcript; expected Family Contribution (EFC) from Student Aid Report (SAR), which comes as a result of filing the FAFSA; and a copy of Financial Aid Award Letter from the chosen college to be attended. **Deadline:** April 30. **Remarks:** Faxed applications will not be considered.

2824 ■ CSF Lazarus/Federated Scholarships
(Undergraduate/Scholarship)

Purpose: To help students of Greater Cincinnati area achieve a college education. **Focus:** General studies. **Qualif.:** Applicant must be a resident of Greater Cincinnati and attending college as a full-time student. **Criteria:** Awards are given based on need.

Funds Avail.: No specific amount. **To Apply:** Applicant must submit a completed scholarship application form along with a copy of recent transcript; expected Family Contribution (EFC) from Student Aid Report (SAR), which comes as a result of filing the FAFSA; and a copy of Financial Aid Award Letter from the chosen college to be attended. **Deadline:** April 30. **Remarks:** Faxed applications will not be considered.

2825 ■ CSF McCall Educational Scholarships
(Undergraduate/Scholarship)

Purpose: To help students of Greater Cincinnati area achieve a college education. **Focus:** General studies. **Qua-**

lif.: Applicant must be a resident of Greater Cincinnati and attending college as a full-time student. **Criteria:** Awards are given based on need.

Funds Avail.: No specific amount. **To Apply:** Applicant must submit a completed scholarship application form along with a copy of recent transcript; expected Family Contribution (EFC) from Student Aid Report (SAR), which comes as a result of filing the FAFSA; and a copy of Financial Aid Award Letter from the chosen college to be attended. **Deadline:** April 30. **Remarks:** Faxed applications will not be considered.

2826 ■ CSF Midland Company Scholarships
(Undergraduate/Scholarship)

Purpose: To help students from Greater Cincinnati area to achieve the dream of a college education. **Focus:** General studies. **Qualif.:** Applicant must be a resident of Greater Cincinnati and attending college as a full-time student. **Criteria:** Awards are given based on need.

Funds Avail.: No specific amount. **To Apply:** Applicant must submit a completed scholarship application form along with a copy of recent transcript; expected Family Contribution (EFC) from Student Aid Report (SAR), which comes as a result of filing the FAFSA; and a copy of Financial Aid Award Letter from the chosen college to be attended. **Deadline:** April 30. **Remarks:** Faxed applications will not be considered.

2827 ■ CSF Nethercott Family Scholarships
(Undergraduate/Scholarship)

Purpose: To help students from Greater Cincinnati area to achieve the dream of a college education. **Focus:** General studies. **Qualif.:** Applicant must be a resident of Greater Cincinnati and attending college as a full-time student. **Criteria:** Awards are given based on need.

Funds Avail.: No specific amount. **To Apply:** Applicant must submit a completed scholarship application form along with a copy of recent transcript; expected Family Contribution (EFC) from Student Aid Report (SAR), which comes as a result of filing the FAFSA; and a copy of Financial Aid Award Letter from the chosen college to be attended. **Deadline:** April 30. **Remarks:** Faxed applications will not be considered.

2828 ■ CSF Ohio National Foundation Scholarships *(Undergraduate/Scholarship)*

Purpose: To help students from Greater Cincinnati area to achieve the dream of a college education. **Focus:** General studies. **Qualif.:** Applicant must be a resident of Greater Cincinnati and attending college as a full-time student. **Criteria:** Awards are given based on need.

Funds Avail.: No specific amount. **To Apply:** Applicant must submit a completed scholarship application form along with a copy of recent transcript; expected Family Contribution (EFC) from Student Aid Report (SAR), which comes as a result of filing the FAFSA; and a copy of Financial Aid Award Letter from the chosen college to be attended. **Deadline:** April 30. **Remarks:** Faxed applications will not be considered.

2829 ■ CSF Pepper Family Scholarships
(Undergraduate/Scholarship)

Purpose: To help students from Greater Cincinnati area to achieve the dream of a college education. **Focus:** General studies. **Qualif.:** Applicant must be a resident of Greater Cincinnati and attending college as a full-time student.

Awards are arranged alphabetically below their administering organizations

Criteria: Awards are given based on need.

Funds Avail.: No specific amount. **To Apply:** Applicant must submit a completed scholarship application form along with a copy of recent transcript; expected Family Contribution (EFC) from Student Aid Report (SAR), which comes as a result of filing the FAFSA; and a copy of Financial Aid Award Letter from the chosen college to be attended. **Deadline:** April 30. **Remarks:** Faxed applications will not be considered.

2830 ■ CSF Pichler Family Scholarships
(Undergraduate/Scholarship)

Purpose: To help students from Greater Cincinnati area to achieve the dream of a college education. **Focus:** General studies. **Qualif.:** Applicant must be a resident of Greater Cincinnati and attending college as a full-time student. **Criteria:** Awards are given based on need.

Funds Avail.: No specific amount. **To Apply:** Applicant must submit a completed scholarship application form along with a copy of recent transcript; expected Family Contribution (EFC) from Student Aid Report (SAR), which comes as a result of filing the FAFSA; and a copy of Financial Aid Award Letter from the chosen college to be attended. **Deadline:** April 30. **Remarks:** Faxed applications will not be considered.

2831 ■ CSF PNC Bank Scholarships
(Undergraduate/Scholarship)

Purpose: To help students from Greater Cincinnati area to achieve the dream of a college education. **Focus:** General studies. **Qualif.:** Applicant must be a resident of Greater Cincinnati and attending college as a full-time student. **Criteria:** Awards are given based on need.

Funds Avail.: No specific amount. **To Apply:** Applicant must submit a completed scholarship application form along with a copy of recent transcript; expected Family Contribution (EFC) from Student Aid Report (SAR), which comes as a result of filing the FAFSA; and a copy of Financial Aid Award Letter from the chosen college to be attended. **Deadline:** April 30. **Remarks:** Faxed applications will not be considered.

2832 ■ CSF Procter and Gamble Scholarships
(Undergraduate/Scholarship)

Purpose: To help students from Greater Cincinnati area to achieve the dream of a college education. **Focus:** General studies. **Qualif.:** Applicant must be a resident of Greater Cincinnati and attending college as a full-time student. **Criteria:** Awards are given based on need.

Funds Avail.: No specific amount. **To Apply:** Applicant must submit a completed scholarship application form along with a copy of recent transcript; expected Family Contribution (EFC) from Student Aid Report (SAR), which comes as a result of filing the FAFSA; and a copy of Financial Aid Award Letter from the chosen college to be attended. **Deadline:** April 30. **Remarks:** Faxed applications will not be considered.

2833 ■ CSF SC Johnson, A Family Company Scholarships *(Undergraduate/Scholarship)*

Purpose: To help students from Greater Cincinnati area to achieve the dream of a college education. **Focus:** General studies. **Qualif.:** Applicant must be a resident of Greater Cincinnati and attending college as a full-time student. **Criteria:** Awards are given based on need.

Funds Avail.: No specific amount. **To Apply:** Applicant

must submit a completed scholarship application form along with a copy of recent transcript; expected Family Contribution (EFC) from Student Aid Report (SAR), which comes as a result of filing the FAFSA; and a copy of Financial Aid Award Letter from the chosen college to be attended. **Deadline:** April 30. **Remarks:** Faxed applications will not be considered.

2834 ■ CSF Scripps Headliners Scholarships
(Undergraduate/Scholarship)

Purpose: To help students from Greater Cincinnati area to achieve the dream of a college education. **Focus:** General studies. **Qualif.:** Applicant must be a resident of Greater Cincinnati and attending college as a full-time student. **Criteria:** Awards are given based on need.

Funds Avail.: No specific amount. **To Apply:** Applicant must submit a completed scholarship application form along with a copy of recent transcript; expected Family Contribution (EFC) from Student Aid Report (SAR), which comes as a result of filing the FAFSA; and a copy of Financial Aid Award Letter from the chosen college to be attended. **Deadline:** April 30. **Remarks:** Faxed applications will not be considered.

2835 ■ CSF Semple Foundation Scholarships
(Undergraduate/Scholarship)

Purpose: To help students from Greater Cincinnati area to achieve the dream of a college education. **Focus:** General studies. **Qualif.:** Applicant must be a resident of Greater Cincinnati and attending college as a full-time student. **Criteria:** Awards are given based on need.

Funds Avail.: No specific amount. **To Apply:** Applicant must submit a completed scholarship application form along with a copy of recent transcript; expected Family Contribution (EFC) from Student Aid Report (SAR), which comes as a result of filing the FAFSA; and a copy of Financial Aid Award Letter from the chosen college to be attended. **Deadline:** April 30. **Remarks:** Faxed applications will not be considered.

2836 ■ CSF Union Central 135th Anniversary Scholarships *(Undergraduate/Scholarship)*

Purpose: To help students from Greater Cincinnati area to achieve the dream of a college education. **Focus:** General studies. **Qualif.:** Applicant must be a resident of Greater Cincinnati and attending college as a full-time student. **Criteria:** Awards are given based on need.

Funds Avail.: No specific amount. **To Apply:** Applicant must submit a completed scholarship application form along with a copy of recent transcript; expected Family Contribution (EFC) from Student Aid Report (SAR), which comes as a result of filing the FAFSA; and a copy of Financial Aid Award Letter from the chosen college to be attended. **Deadline:** April 30. **Remarks:** Faxed applications will not be considered.

2837 ■ CSF U.S. Bank N.A. Scholarships
(Undergraduate/Scholarship)

Purpose: To help students from Greater Cincinnati area to achieve the dream of a college education. **Focus:** General studies. **Qualif.:** Applicant must be a resident of Greater Cincinnati and attending college as a full-time student. **Criteria:** Awards are given based on need.

Funds Avail.: No specific amount. **To Apply:** Applicant must submit a completed scholarship application form along with a copy of recent transcript; expected Family Contribu-

Awards are arranged alphabetically below their administering organizations

tion (EFC) from Student Aid Report (SAR), which comes as a result of filing the FAFSA; and a copy of Financial Aid Award Letter from the chosen college to be attended. **Deadline:** April 30. **Remarks:** Faxed applications will not be considered.

2838 ■ CSF Western-Southern Foundation Scholarships (Undergraduate/Scholarship)

Purpose: To help students from Greater Cincinnati area to achieve the dream of a college education. **Focus:** General studies. **Qualif.:** Applicant must be a resident of Greater Cincinnati and attending college as a full-time student. **Criteria:** Awards are given based on need.

Funds Avail.: No specific amount. **To Apply:** Applicant must submit a completed scholarship application form along with a copy of recent transcript; expected Family Contribution (EFC) from Student Aid Report (SAR), which comes as a result of filing the FAFSA; and a copy of Financial Aid Award Letter from the chosen college to be attended. **Deadline:** April 30. **Remarks:** Faxed applications will not be considered.

2839 ■ CSF Woodward Trustees Scholarships (Undergraduate/Scholarship)

Purpose: To help students from Greater Cincinnati area to achieve the dream of a college education. **Focus:** General studies. **Qualif.:** Applicant must be a resident of Greater Cincinnati and attending college as a full-time student. **Criteria:** Awards are given based on need.

Funds Avail.: No specific amount. **To Apply:** Applicant must submit a completed scholarship application form along with a copy of recent transcript; expected Family Contribution (EFC) from Student Aid Report (SAR), which comes as a result of filing the FAFSA; and a copy of Financial Aid Award Letter from the chosen college to be attended. **Deadline:** April 30. **Remarks:** Faxed applications will not be considered.

2840 ■ CSF Wynne Family Memorial Scholarships (Undergraduate/Scholarship)

Purpose: To help students from Greater Cincinnati area to achieve the dream of a college education. **Focus:** General studies. **Qualif.:** Applicant must be a resident of Greater Cincinnati and attending college as a full-time student. **Criteria:** Awards are given based on need.

Funds Avail.: No specific amount. **To Apply:** Applicant must submit a completed scholarship application form along with a copy of recent transcript; expected Family Contribution (EFC) from Student Aid Report (SAR), which comes as a result of filing the FAFSA; and a copy of Financial Aid Award Letter from the chosen college to be attended. **Deadline:** April 30. **Remarks:** Faxed applications will not be considered.

2841 ■ CSF Estelle Davis Memorial Scholarships (Undergraduate/Scholarship)

Purpose: To help students from Greater Cincinnati area to achieve the dream of a college education. **Focus:** General studies. **Qualif.:** Applicant must be a resident of Greater Cincinnati and attending college as a full-time student. **Criteria:** Awards are given based on need.

Funds Avail.: No specific amount. **To Apply:** Applicant must submit a completed scholarship application form along with a copy of recent transcript; expected Family Contribution (EFC) from Student Aid Report (SAR), which comes as a result of filing the FAFSA; and a copy of Financial Aid

Award Letter from the chosen college to be attended. **Deadline:** April 30. **Remarks:** Faxed applications will not be considered. **Contact:** scholarship@fuse.net.

2842 ■ CSF Thomas J. Emery Memorial Scholarships (Undergraduate/Scholarship)

Purpose: To help students from Greater Cincinnati area to achieve the dream of a college education. **Focus:** General studies. **Qualif.:** Applicant must be a resident of Greater Cincinnati and attending college as a full-time student. **Criteria:** Awards are given based on need.

Funds Avail.: No specific amount. **To Apply:** Applicant must submit a completed scholarship application form along with a copy of recent transcript; expected Family Contribution (EFC) from Student Aid Report (SAR), which comes as a result of filing the FAFSA; and a copy of Financial Aid Award Letter from the chosen college to be attended. **Deadline:** April 30. **Remarks:** Faxed applications will not be considered.

2843 ■ CSF Lyle Everingham Scholarships (Undergraduate/Scholarship)

Purpose: To help students of Greater Cincinnati area achieve a college education. **Focus:** General studies. **Qualif.:** Applicant must be a resident of Greater Cincinnati and attending college as a full-time student. **Criteria:** Awards are given based on need.

Funds Avail.: No specific amount. **To Apply:** Applicant must submit a completed scholarship application form along with a copy of recent transcript; expected Family Contribution (EFC) from Student Aid Report (SAR), which comes as a result of filing the FAFSA; and a copy of Financial Aid Award Letter from the chosen college to be attended. **Deadline:** April 30. **Remarks:** Faxed applications will not be considered.

2844 ■ CSF Lyle and Arlene Everingham Scholarships (Undergraduate/Scholarship)

Purpose: To help students of Greater Cincinnati area achieve a college education. **Focus:** General studies. **Qualif.:** Applicant must be a resident of Greater Cincinnati and attending college as a full-time student. **Criteria:** Awards are given based on need.

Funds Avail.: No specific amount. **To Apply:** Applicant must submit a completed scholarship application form along with a copy of recent transcript; expected Family Contribution (EFC) from Student Aid Report (SAR), which comes as a result of filing the FAFSA; and a copy of Financial Aid Award Letter from the chosen college to be attended. **Deadline:** April 30. **Remarks:** Faxed applications will not be considered.

2845 ■ CSF William A. Friedlander Scholarships (Undergraduate/Scholarship)

Purpose: To help students from Greater Cincinnati area to achieve the dream of a college education. **Focus:** General studies. **Qualif.:** Applicant must be a resident of Greater Cincinnati and attending college as a full-time student. **Criteria:** Awards are given based on need.

Funds Avail.: No specific amount. **To Apply:** Applicant must submit a completed scholarship application form along with a copy of recent transcript; expected Family Contribution (EFC) from Student Aid Report (SAR), which comes as a result of filing the FAFSA; and a copy of Financial Aid Award Letter from the chosen college to be attended. **Deadline:** April 30. **Remarks:** Faxed applications will not be considered.

Awards are arranged alphabetically below their administering organizations

2846 ■ CSF Priscilla Gamble Scholarships
(Undergraduate/Scholarship)

Purpose: To help students from Greater Cincinnati area to achieve the dream of a college education. **Focus:** General studies. **Qualif.:** Applicant must be a resident of Greater Cincinnati and attending college as a full-time student. **Criteria:** Awards are given based on need.

Funds Avail.: No specific amount. **To Apply:** Applicant must submit a completed scholarship application form along with a copy of recent transcript; expected Family Contribution (EFC) from Student Aid Report (SAR), which comes as a result of filing the FAFSA; and a copy of Financial Aid Award Letter from the chosen college to be attended. **Deadline:** April 30. **Remarks:** Faxed applications will not be considered.

2847 ■ CSF Richard Heekin Scholarships
(Undergraduate/Scholarship)

Purpose: To help students from Greater Cincinnati area to achieve the dream of a college education. **Focus:** General studies. **Qualif.:** Applicant must be a resident of Greater Cincinnati and attending college as a full-time student. **Criteria:** Awards are given based on need.

Funds Avail.: No specific amount. **To Apply:** Applicant must submit a completed scholarship application form along with a copy of recent transcript; expected Family Contribution (EFC) from Student Aid Report (SAR), which comes as a result of filing the FAFSA; and a copy of Financial Aid Award Letter from the chosen college to be attended. **Deadline:** April 30. **Remarks:** Faxed applications will not be considered.

2848 ■ CSF Dwight Hibbard Scholarships
(Undergraduate/Scholarship)

Purpose: To help students from Greater Cincinnati area to achieve the dream of a college education. **Focus:** General studies. **Qualif.:** Applicant must be a resident of Greater Cincinnati and attending college as a full-time student. **Criteria:** Awards are given based on need.

Funds Avail.: No specific amount. **To Apply:** Applicant must submit a completed scholarship application form along with a copy of recent transcript; expected Family Contribution (EFC) from Student Aid Report (SAR), which comes as a result of filing the FAFSA; and a copy of Financial Aid Award Letter from the chosen college to be attended. **Deadline:** April 30. **Remarks:** Faxed applications will not be considered. **Contact:** Student Aid Report (SAR) and Financial Aid Award Notification must be e-mailed to scholarship@fuse.net.

2849 ■ CSF Florette B. Hoffheimer Scholarships
(Undergraduate/Scholarship)

Purpose: To help students from Greater Cincinnati area to achieve the dream of a college education. **Focus:** General studies. **Qualif.:** Applicant must be a resident of Greater Cincinnati and attending college as a full-time student. **Criteria:** Awards are given based on need.

Funds Avail.: No specific amount. **To Apply:** Applicant must submit a completed scholarship application form along with a copy of recent transcript; expected Family Contribution (EFC) from Student Aid Report (SAR), which comes as a result of filing the FAFSA; and a copy of Financial Aid Award Letter from the chosen college to be attended. **Deadline:** April 30. **Remarks:** Faxed applications will not be considered. **Contact:** scholarship@fuse.net.

2850 ■ CSF Roger and Joyce Howe Family Scholarships
(Undergraduate/Scholarship)

Purpose: To help students from Greater Cincinnati area to achieve the dream of a college education. **Focus:** General studies. **Qualif.:** Applicant must be a resident of Greater Cincinnati and attending college as a full-time student. **Criteria:** Awards are given based on need.

Funds Avail.: No specific amount. **To Apply:** Applicant must submit a completed scholarship application form along with a copy of recent transcript; expected Family Contribution (EFC) from Student Aid Report (SAR), which comes as a result of filing the FAFSA; and a copy of Financial Aid Award Letter from the chosen college to be attended. **Deadline:** April 30. **Remarks:** Faxed applications will not be considered.

2851 ■ CSF Ella Wilson Johnson Scholarships
(Undergraduate/Scholarship)

Purpose: To help students from Greater Cincinnati area to achieve the dream of a college education. **Focus:** General studies. **Qualif.:** Applicant must be a resident of Greater Cincinnati and attending college as a full-time student. **Criteria:** Awards are given based on need.

Funds Avail.: No specific amount. **To Apply:** Applicant must submit a completed scholarship application form along with a copy of recent transcript; expected Family Contribution (EFC) from Student Aid Report (SAR), which comes as a result of filing the FAFSA; and a copy of Financial Aid Award Letter from the chosen college to be attended. **Deadline:** April 30. **Remarks:** Faxed applications will not be considered. **Contact:** scholarship@fuse.net.

2852 ■ CSF David J. Joseph Company Scholarships
(Undergraduate/Scholarship)

Purpose: To help students from Greater Cincinnati area to achieve the dream of a college education. **Focus:** General studies. **Qualif.:** Applicant must be a resident of Greater Cincinnati and attending college as a full-time student. **Criteria:** Awards are given based on need.

Funds Avail.: No specific amount. **To Apply:** Applicant must submit a completed scholarship application form along with a copy of recent transcript; expected Family Contribution (EFC) from Student Aid Report (SAR), which comes as a result of filing the FAFSA; and a copy of Financial Aid Award Letter from the chosen college to be attended. **Deadline:** April 30. **Remarks:** Faxed applications will not be considered. **Contact:** scholarship@fuse.net.

2853 ■ CSF M. Kantor and Brothers Scholarships
(Undergraduate/Scholarship)

Purpose: To help students from Greater Cincinnati area to achieve the dream of a college education. **Focus:** General studies. **Qualif.:** Applicant must be a resident of Greater Cincinnati, and attending college as a full-time student. **Criteria:** Awards are given based on need.

Funds Avail.: No specific amount. **To Apply:** Applicants must submit a completed scholarship application form along with a copy of recent transcript; expected Family Contribution (EFC) from Student Aid Report (SAR), which comes as a result of filing the FAFSA; and a copy of Financial Aid Award Letter from the chosen college to be attended. **Deadline:** April 30. **Remarks:** Faxed applications will not be considered.

2854 ■ CSF Raymond and Augusta Klink Scholarships
(Undergraduate/Scholarship)

Purpose: To help students from Greater Cincinnati area to achieve the dream of a college education. **Focus:** General

Awards are arranged alphabetically below their administering organizations

studies. **Qualif.:** Applicant must be a resident of Greater Cincinnati and attending college as a full-time student. **Criteria:** Awards are given based on need.

Funds Avail.: No specific amount. **To Apply:** Applicant must submit a completed scholarship application form along with a copy of recent transcript; expected Family Contribution (EFC) from Student Aid Report (SAR), which comes as a result of filing the FAFSA; and a copy of Financial Aid Award Letter from the chosen college to be attended. **Deadline:** April 30. **Remarks:** Faxed applications will not be considered.

2855 ■ CSF Bob and Linda Kohlhepp Scholarships *(Undergraduate/Scholarship)*

Purpose: To help students from Greater Cincinnati area to achieve the dream of a college education. **Focus:** General studies. **Qualif.:** Applicant must be a resident of Greater Cincinnati and attending college as a full-time student. **Criteria:** Awards are given based on need.

Funds Avail.: No specific amount. **To Apply:** Applicant must submit a completed scholarship application form along with a copy of recent transcript; expected Family Contribution (EFC) from Student Aid Report (SAR), which comes as a result of filing the FAFSA; and a copy of Financial Aid Award Letter from the chosen college to be attended. **Deadline:** April 30. **Remarks:** Faxed applications will not be considered.

2856 ■ CSF Carl H. Lindner Family Scholarships *(Undergraduate/Scholarship)*

Purpose: To help students from Greater Cincinnati area to achieve the dream of a college education. **Focus:** General studies. **Qualif.:** Applicant must be a resident of Greater Cincinnati and attending college as a full-time student. **Criteria:** Awards are given based on need.

Funds Avail.: No specific amount. **To Apply:** Applicant must submit a completed scholarship application form along with a copy of recent transcript; expected Family Contribution (EFC) from Student Aid Report (SAR), which comes as a result of filing the FAFSA; and a copy of Financial Aid Award Letter from the chosen college to be attended. **Deadline:** April 30. **Remarks:** Faxed applications will not be considered.

2857 ■ CSF Corwin Nixon Scholarships *(Undergraduate/Scholarship)*

Purpose: To help students from Greater Cincinnati area to achieve the dream of a college education. **Focus:** General studies. **Qualif.:** Applicant must be a resident of Greater Cincinnati and attending college as a full-time student. **Criteria:** Awards are given based on need.

Funds Avail.: No specific amount. **To Apply:** Applicant must submit a completed scholarship application form along with a copy of recent transcript; expected Family Contribution (EFC) from Student Aid Report (SAR), which comes as a result of filing the FAFSA; and a copy of Financial Aid Award Letter from the chosen college to be attended. **Deadline:** April 30. **Remarks:** Faxed applications will not be considered.

2858 ■ CSF Charles and Claire Phillips Scholarships *(Undergraduate/Scholarship)*

Purpose: To help students from Greater Cincinnati area to achieve their dream of a college education. **Focus:** General studies. **Qualif.:** Applicant must be a resident of Greater Cincinnati and attending college as a full-time student.

Criteria: Awards are given based on need.

Funds Avail.: No specific amount. **To Apply:** Applicant must submit a completed scholarship application form along with a copy of recent transcript; expected Family Contribution (EFC) from Student Aid Report (SAR), which comes as a result of filing the FAFSA; and a copy of Financial Aid Award Letter from the chosen college to be attended. **Deadline:** April 30. **Remarks:** Faxed applications will not be considered. **Contact:** scholarship@fuse.net.

2859 ■ CSF George and Amy Polley Scholarships *(Undergraduate/Scholarship)*

Purpose: To help students from Greater Cincinnati area to achieve the dream of a college education. **Focus:** General studies. **Qualif.:** Applicant must be a resident of Greater Cincinnati, and attending college as a full-time student. **Criteria:** Awards are given based on need.

Funds Avail.: No specific amount. **To Apply:** Applicants must submit a completed scholarship application form along with a copy of recent transcript; expected Family Contribution (EFC) from Student Aid Report (SAR), which comes as a result of filing the FAFSA; and a copy of Financial Aid Award Letter from the chosen college to be attended. **Deadline:** April 30. **Remarks:** Faxed applications will not be considered.

2860 ■ CSF Marvin Rammelsberg Memorial Scholarships *(Undergraduate/Scholarship)*

Purpose: To help students of Greater Cincinnati area achieve a college education. **Focus:** General studies. **Qualif.:** Applicant must be a resident of Greater Cincinnati and attending college as a full-time student. **Criteria:** Awards are given based on need.

Funds Avail.: No specific amount. **To Apply:** Applicant must submit a completed scholarship application form along with a copy of recent transcript; expected Family Contribution (EFC) from Student Aid Report (SAR), which comes as a result of filing the FAFSA; and a copy of Financial Aid Award Letter from the chosen college to be attended. **Deadline:** April 30. **Remarks:** Faxed applications will not be considered.

2861 ■ CSF Robert H. Reakirt Foundation Scholarships *(Undergraduate/Scholarship)*

Purpose: To help students from Greater Cincinnati area to achieve the dream of a college education. **Focus:** General studies. **Qualif.:** Applicant must be a resident of Greater Cincinnati and attending college as a full-time student. **Criteria:** Awards are given based on need.

Funds Avail.: No specific amount. **To Apply:** Applicant must submit a completed scholarship application form along with a copy of recent transcript; expected Family Contribution (EFC) from Student Aid Report (SAR), which comes as a result of filing the FAFSA; and a copy of Financial Aid Award Letter from the chosen college to be attended. **Deadline:** April 30. **Remarks:** Faxed applications will not be considered.

2862 ■ CSF William J. Rielly/MCURC Scholarships *(Undergraduate/Scholarship)*

Purpose: To help students from Greater Cincinnati area to achieve the dream of a college education. **Focus:** General studies. **Qualif.:** Applicant must be a resident of Greater Cincinnati and attending college as a full-time student. **Criteria:** Awards are given based on need.

Funds Avail.: No specific amount. **To Apply:** Applicant

Awards are arranged alphabetically below their administering organizations

must submit a completed scholarship application form along with a copy of recent transcript; expected Family Contribution (EFC) from Student Aid Report (SAR), which comes as a result of filing the FAFSA; and a copy of Financial Aid Award Letter from the chosen college to be attended. **Deadline:** April 30. **Remarks:** Faxed applications will not be considered.

2863 ■ CSF Mary Roberts Scholarships
(Undergraduate/Scholarship)

Purpose: To help students of Greater Cincinnati area achieve a college education. **Focus:** General studies. **Qualif.:** Applicant must be a resident of Greater Cincinnati and attending college as a full-time student. **Criteria:** Awards are given based on need.

Funds Avail.: No specific amount. **To Apply:** Applicant must submit a completed scholarship application form along with a copy of recent transcript; expected Family Contribution (EFC) from Student Aid Report (SAR), which comes as a result of filing the FAFSA; and a copy of Financial Aid Award Letter from the chosen college to be attended. **Deadline:** April 30. **Remarks:** Faxed applications will not be considered.

2864 ■ CSF Charlotte R. Schmidlapp Scholarships *(Undergraduate/Scholarship)*

Purpose: To help students from Greater Cincinnati area to achieve their dream of a college education. **Focus:** General studies. **Qualif.:** Applicant must be a resident of Greater Cincinnati and attending college as a full-time student. **Criteria:** Awards are given based on need.

Funds Avail.: No specific amount. **To Apply:** Applicant must submit a completed scholarship application form along with a copy of recent transcript; expected Family Contribution (EFC) from Student Aid Report (SAR), which comes as a result of filing the FAFSA; and a copy of Financial Aid Award Letter from the chosen college to be attended. **Deadline:** April 30. **Remarks:** Faxed applications will not be considered. **Contact:** scholarship@fuse.net.

2865 ■ CSF H.C. Schott Foundation Scholarships *(Undergraduate/Scholarship)*

Purpose: To help students from Greater Cincinnati area to achieve the dream of a college education. **Focus:** General studies. **Qualif.:** Applicant must be a resident of Greater Cincinnati and attending college as a full-time student. **Criteria:** Awards are given based on need.

Funds Avail.: No specific amount. **To Apply:** Applicant must submit a completed scholarship application form along with a copy of recent transcript; expected Family Contribution (EFC) from Student Aid Report (SAR), which comes as a result of filing the FAFSA; and a copy of Financial Aid Award Letter from the chosen college to be attended. **Deadline:** April 30. **Remarks:** Faxed applications will not be considered. **Contact:** Student Aid Report (SAR) and Financial Aid Award Notification must be e-mailed to scholarship@fuse.net.

2866 ■ CSF Nelson Schwab Jr. Family Scholarships *(Undergraduate/Scholarship)*

Purpose: To help students from Greater Cincinnati area to achieve the dream of a college education. **Focus:** General studies. **Qualif.:** Applicant must be a resident of Greater Cincinnati and attending college as a full-time student. **Criteria:** Awards are given based on need.

Funds Avail.: No specific amount. **To Apply:** Applicant

must submit a completed scholarship application form along with a copy of recent transcript; expected Family Contribution (EFC) from Student Aid Report (SAR), which comes as a result of filing the FAFSA; and a copy of Financial Aid Award Letter from the chosen college to be attended. **Deadline:** April 30. **Remarks:** Faxed applications will not be considered.

2867 ■ CSF Judge Benjamin Schwartz Scholarships *(Undergraduate/Scholarship)*

Purpose: To help students from Greater Cincinnati area to achieve the dream of a college education. **Focus:** General studies. **Qualif.:** Applicant must be a resident of Greater Cincinnati and attending college as a full-time student. **Criteria:** Awards are given based on need.

Funds Avail.: No specific amount. **To Apply:** Applicant must submit a completed scholarship application form along with a copy of recent transcript; expected Family Contribution (EFC) from Student Aid Report (SAR), which comes as a result of filing the FAFSA; and a copy of Financial Aid Award Letter from the chosen college to be attended. **Deadline:** April 30. **Remarks:** Faxed applications will not be considered.

2868 ■ CSF E.W. Scripps Scholarships
(Undergraduate/Scholarship)

Purpose: To help students from Greater Cincinnati area to achieve the dream of a college education. **Focus:** General studies. **Qualif.:** Applicant must be a resident of Greater Cincinnati and attending college as a full-time student. **Criteria:** Awards are given based on need.

Funds Avail.: No specific amount. **To Apply:** Applicant must submit a completed scholarship application form along with a copy of recent transcript; expected Family Contribution (EFC) from Student Aid Report (SAR), which comes as a result of filing the FAFSA; and a copy of Financial Aid Award Letter from the chosen college to be attended. **Deadline:** April 30. **Remarks:** Faxed applications will not be considered. **Contact:** scholarship@fuse.net.

2869 ■ CSF S. David Shor Scholarships
(Undergraduate/Scholarship)

Purpose: To help students from Greater Cincinnati area to achieve the dream of a college education. **Focus:** General studies. **Qualif.:** Applicant must be a resident of Greater Cincinnati and attending college as a full-time student. **Criteria:** Awards are given based on need.

Funds Avail.: No specific amount. **To Apply:** Applicant must submit a completed scholarship application form along with a copy of recent transcript; expected Family Contribution (EFC) from Student Aid Report (SAR), which comes as a result of filing the FAFSA; and a copy of Financial Aid Award Letter from the chosen college to be attended. **Deadline:** April 30. **Remarks:** Faxed applications will not be considered.

2870 ■ CSF Lowe Simpson Scholarships
(Undergraduate/Scholarship)

Purpose: To help students of Greater Cincinnati area achieve a college education. **Focus:** General studies. **Qualif.:** Applicant must be a resident of Greater Cincinnati and attending college as a full-time student. **Criteria:** Awards are given based on need.

Funds Avail.: No specific amount. **To Apply:** Applicant must submit a completed scholarship application form along with a copy of recent transcript; expected Family Contribu-

Awards are arranged alphabetically below their administering organizations

tion (EFC) from Student Aid Report (SAR), which comes as a result of filing the FAFSA; and a copy of Financial Aid Award Letter from the chosen college to be attended. **Deadline:** April 30. **Remarks:** Faxed applications will not be considered.

2871 ■ CSF Frank Foster Skillman Scholarships *(Undergraduate/Scholarship)*

Purpose: To help students from Greater Cincinnati area to achieve the dream of a college education. **Focus:** General studies. **Qualif.:** Applicant must be a resident of Greater Cincinnati and attending college as a full-time student. **Criteria:** Awards are given based on need.

Funds Avail.: No specific amount. **To Apply:** Applicant must submit a completed scholarship application form along with a copy of recent transcript; expected Family Contribution (EFC) from Student Aid Report (SAR), which comes as a result of filing the FAFSA; and a copy of Financial Aid Award Letter from the chosen college to be attended. **Deadline:** April 30. **Remarks:** Faxed applications will not be considered. **Contact:** scholarship@fuse.net.

2872 ■ CSF Helen Steiner Rice Scholarships *(Undergraduate/Scholarship)*

Purpose: To help students from Greater Cincinnati area to achieve the dream of a college education. **Focus:** General studies. **Qualif.:** Applicant must be a resident of Greater Cincinnati and attending college as a full-time student. **Criteria:** Awards are given based on need.

Funds Avail.: No specific amount. **To Apply:** Applicant must submit a completed scholarship application form along with a copy of recent transcript; expected Family Contribution (EFC) from Student Aid Report (SAR), which comes as a result of filing the FAFSA; and a copy of Financial Aid Award Letter from the chosen college to be attended. **Deadline:** April 30. **Remarks:** Faxed applications will not be considered. **Contact:** Student Aid Report (SAR) and Financial Aid Award Notification must be e-mailed to scholarship@fuse.net.

2873 ■ CSF Joseph S. Stern, Jr. Scholarships *(Undergraduate/Scholarship)*

Purpose: To help students from Greater Cincinnati area to achieve the dream of a college education. **Focus:** General studies. **Qualif.:** Applicant must be a resident of Greater Cincinnati and attending college as a full-time student. **Criteria:** Awards are given based on need.

Funds Avail.: No specific amount. **To Apply:** Applicant must submit a completed scholarship application form along with a copy of recent transcript; expected Family Contribution (EFC) from Student Aid Report (SAR), which comes as a result of filing the FAFSA; and a copy of Financial Aid Award Letter from the chosen college to be attended. **Deadline:** April 30. **Remarks:** Faxed applications will not be considered.

2874 ■ CSF Martha W. Tanner Memorial Scholarships *(Undergraduate/Scholarship)*

Purpose: To help students of Greater Cincinnati area achieve a college education. **Focus:** General studies. **Qualif.:** Applicant must be a resident of Greater Cincinnati and attending college as a full-time student. **Criteria:** Awards are given based on need.

Funds Avail.: No specific amount. **To Apply:** Applicant must submit a completed scholarship application form along with a copy of recent transcript; expected Family Contribu-

tion (EFC) from Student Aid Report (SAR), which comes as a result of filing the FAFSA; and a copy of Financial Aid Award Letter from the chosen college to be attended. **Deadline:** April 30. **Remarks:** Faxed applications will not be considered.

2875 ■ CSF Christopher Todd Grant Memorial Scholarships *(Undergraduate/Scholarship)*

Purpose: To help students from Greater Cincinnati area to achieve the dream of a college education. **Focus:** General studies. **Qualif.:** Applicant must be a resident of Greater Cincinnati and attending college as a full-time student. **Criteria:** Awards are given based on need.

Funds Avail.: No specific amount. **To Apply:** Applicant must submit a completed scholarship application form along with a copy of recent transcript; expected Family Contribution (EFC) from Student Aid Report (SAR), which comes as a result of filing the FAFSA; and a copy of Financial Aid Award Letter from the chosen college to be attended. **Deadline:** April 30. **Remarks:** Faxed applications will not be considered.

2876 ■ CSF Dee Wacksman Memorial Scholarships *(Undergraduate/Scholarship)*

Purpose: To help students from Greater Cincinnati area to achieve the dream of a college education. **Focus:** General studies. **Qualif.:** Applicant must be a resident of Greater Cincinnati and attending college as a full-time student. **Criteria:** Awards are given based on need.

Funds Avail.: No specific amount. **To Apply:** Applicant must submit a completed scholarship application form along with a copy of recent transcript; expected Family Contribution (EFC) from Student Aid Report (SAR), which comes as a result of filing the FAFSA; and a copy of Financial Aid Award Letter from the chosen college to be attended. **Deadline:** April 30. **Remarks:** Faxed applications will not be considered. **Contact:** Student Aid Report (SAR) and Financial Aid Award Notification must be e-mailed to scholarship@fuse.net.

2877 ■ CSF HCRTA/Glen O. and Wyllabeth Wise Scholarships *(Undergraduate/Scholarship)*

Purpose: To help students from Greater Cincinnati area to achieve the dream of a college education. **Focus:** General studies. **Qualif.:** Applicant must be a resident of Greater Cincinnati and attending college as a full-time student. **Criteria:** Awards are given based on need.

Funds Avail.: No specific amount. **To Apply:** Applicant must submit a completed scholarship application form along with a copy of recent transcript; expected Family Contribution (EFC) from Student Aid Report (SAR), which comes as a result of filing the FAFSA; and a copy of Financial Aid Award Letter from the chosen college to be attended. **Deadline:** April 30. **Remarks:** Faxed applications will not be considered. **Contact:** scholarship@fuse.net.

2878 ■ CSF L and T Woolfolk Memorial Scholarships *(Undergraduate/Scholarship)*

Purpose: To help students of Greater Cincinnati area achieve a college education. **Focus:** General studies. **Qualif.:** Applicant must be a resident of Greater Cincinnati and attending college as a full-time student. **Criteria:** Awards are given based on need.

Funds Avail.: No specific amount. **To Apply:** Applicant must submit a completed scholarship application form along with a copy of recent transcript; expected Family Contribu-

Awards are arranged alphabetically below their administering organizations

tion (EFC) from Student Aid Report (SAR), which comes as a result of filing the FAFSA; and a copy of Financial Aid Award Letter from the chosen college to be attended. **Deadline:** April 30. **Remarks:** Faxed applications will not be considered.

2879 ■ CSF L.B. Zapoleon Scholarships
(Undergraduate/Scholarship)

Purpose: To help students of Greater Cincinnati area achieve a college education. **Focus:** General studies. **Qualif.:** Applicant must be a resident of Greater Cincinnati and attending college as a full-time student. **Criteria:** Awards are given based on need.

Funds Avail.: No specific amount. **To Apply:** Applicant must submit a completed scholarship application form along with a copy of recent transcript; expected Family Contribution (EFC) from Student Aid Report (SAR), which comes as a result of filing the FAFSA; and a copy of Financial Aid Award Letter from the chosen college to be attended. **Deadline:** April 30. **Remarks:** Faxed applications will not be considered.

2880 ■ Cintas Foundation
c/o Nancy Reisman, Esq., Sec.
Morris & McVeigh
767 3rd Ave., 4th Fl.
New York, NY 10017
URL: www.cintasfoundation.org

2881 ■ Cintas Foundation Fellowships in Architecture *(Professional development/ Fellowship)*

Purpose: To encourage the development of artists in architecture. **Focus:** Architecture. **Qualif.:** Applicants must be artists living outside of Cuba; must be Cuban citizens or with direct lineage (having a Cuban parent or grandparent). **Criteria:** Applicants will be evaluated based on submitted materials.

Funds Avail.: Amount not specified. **To Apply:** Applicants must submit a completed, original application (completed either in English or Spanish); must prepare two narrative statements, two letters of recommendation and work samples. Acceptable formats are DVDs and CDs accompanied by a corresponding image list. Materials must be accompanied by the work sample form. Limit submission to ten samples. **Deadline:** August 1. **Contact:** Jessica Brodsky, 300 NE 2nd Ave., Miami, FL 33132; Phone: 305-237-7722; Fax: 305-237-7711; Email: jbrodsky@mdc.edu.

2882 ■ Cintas Foundation Fellowships in Visual Arts *(Professional development/Fellowship)*

Purpose: To encourage the development of artists in visual arts. **Focus:** Visual arts. **Qualif.:** Applicants must be artists living outside of Cuba; must be Cuban citizens or with direct lineage (having a Cuban parent or grandparent). **Criteria:** Applicants will be evaluated based on submitted materials.

Funds Avail.: Amount not specified. **To Apply:** Applicants must submit an original application (completed either in English or Spanish); must prepare two narrative statements, two letters of recommendation and work samples. Applicants may submit maximum of 10 digital images. Acceptable formats are DVDs and CDs accompanied by a corresponding image list. **Deadline:** August 1. **Contact:** Jessica Brodsky, 300 NE 2nd Ave., Miami, FL 33132; Phone: 305-237-7722; Fax: 305-237-7711; Email: jbrodsky@mdc.edu.

2883 ■ Brandon Fradd Fellowships in Music Competition *(Professional development/ Fellowship)*

Purpose: To encourage the development of artists in music composition. **Focus:** Music. **Qualif.:** Applicants must be artists living outside of Cuba; must be Cuban citizens or with direct lineage (having a Cuban parent or grandparent). **Criteria:** Recipients will be evaluated based on submitted materials.

Funds Avail.: Amount not specified. **To Apply:** Applicants must submit an original application (completed either in English or Spanish); must submit two narrative statements, two letters of recommendation and work samples (three to five recordings). Samples should be in DVDs or CDs in MP3 format. **Deadline:** August 1. **Contact:** Jessica Brodsky, 300 NE 2nd Ave., Miami, FL 33132; Phone: 305-237-7722; Fax: 305-237-7711; Email: jbrodsky@mdc.edu.

2884 ■ Citizens' Scholarship Foundation of Wakefield
PO Box 321
Wakefield, MA 01880
Ph: (781) 245-4890
Fax: (781) 245-6761
E-mail: csfofwakefield@earthlink.net
URL: www.csfofwakefield.org

2885 ■ Citizens' Scholarship Foundation of Wakefield Scholarships *(All/Scholarship)*

Purpose: To financially support the education of Wakefield, MA students. **Focus:** General studies. **Qualif.:** Applicant must be a resident of Wakefield who will be attending school in a full-time basis and must demonstrate financial need. **Criteria:** Selection is based on financial need and merit.

Funds Avail.: Varies. **Number Awarded:** Varies. **To Apply:** Applicants must submit a completed Financial Aid Questionaire (FAQ) along with a $5.00 processing fee to: Scholarship America, PO Box 297, St. Peter, MN 56082. In addition, applicants must submit a completed Application form to the foundation. **Deadline:** March 31.

2886 ■ Civic Music Association of Milwaukee
3195 S Superior St., Ste. 209
Milwaukee, WI 53207
Ph: (414) 483-3223
Fax: (414) 483-3356
E-mail: info@civicmusicmilwaukee.org
URL: www.civicmusicmilwaukee.org

2887 ■ John D. Anello Sr. and Albert A. Silverman Memorial Scholarships *(Undergraduate/ Scholarship)*

Purpose: To provide music education and performance opportunities with an emphasis on youth in the greater Milwaukee area. **Focus:** Music, vocal. **Qualif.:** Applicants must be full-time high school or college Wisconsin music students, ages 14-22 and must have one Italian parent or grandparent. **Criteria:** Recipients are selected based on the performance.

Funds Avail.: $1,000; $500. **Number Awarded:** 3. **To Apply:** Applicants must submit a complete application form; must pass the audition process; must attach a 250-word

Awards are arranged alphabetically below their administering organizations

brief description including the musical study they plan to focus on and why and a brief biography that includes school involvement, honors, awards and any other accomplishments. **Deadline:** December 15. **Contact:** 3195 S. Superior St., Ste. 209 Milwaukee, WI 53207.

2888 ■ Norbert J. Beihoff Scholarships
(Undergraduate/Scholarship)

Purpose: To encourage one or more students who have demonstrated exceptional musical potential but are not presently taking private lessons. **Focus:** Music. **Qualif.:** Applicants must be fourth to seventh grade band and orchestra students who have not yet had the opportunity for private study. **Criteria:** Recipients are selected based on the quality of the audition, musical ability, potential, attitude and reliability, parent's statement describing their commitment and support for the lessons and home practice and student's essay about his/her musical experiences and participation in school music activities.

Funds Avail.: No specific amount. **To Apply:** Applicants must undergo an audition and must prepare an essay about his or her experiences in school music activities. **Deadline:** December 15. **Contact:** civicmusiccma@aol.com.

2889 ■ Elizabeth W. Boyce Scholarships
(Undergraduate/Scholarship)

Purpose: To provide music education and performance opportunities with an emphasis on youth in the greater Milwaukee area. **Focus:** Music, vocal. **Qualif.:** Applicants must be high school sophomores, juniors and seniors in Milwaukee Metropolitan Area High School in Milwaukee. **Criteria:** Recipients are selected based on the performance.

Funds Avail.: $2,000. **To Apply:** Applicants must submit a completed application form; 250-words or less about your future plans for study and performance and how you would use the scholarship monies. Applicants must also submit a high quality CD or cassette tape. The recording should contain approximately 15 minutes of music performed by the applicant, including at least two contrasting periods and styles. **Deadline:** December 15. **Contact:** 3195 S. Superior St., Ste. 209 Milwaukee, WI 53207.

2890 ■ Harold A. Levin Scholarships
(Undergraduate/Scholarship)

Purpose: To provide music education and performance opportunities with an emphasis on youth in the greater Milwaukee area. **Focus:** Music. **Qualif.:** Applicants must be college students majoring in music who graduated from a Milwaukee area high school or who currently attend a Milwaukee area college, who are under 30 years of age. **Criteria:** Recipients are selected based on the quality of the taped performances.

Funds Avail.: $5,000. **To Apply:** Applicants must submit three copies of a CD or high quality cassette tape containing not more than 15 minutes of music, including at least two contrasting periods and styles and recorded within the last 12 months. **Deadline:** October 1. **Contact:** civicmusiccma@aol.com.

2891 ■ Donald and Idabelle Mohr Scholarships
(Undergraduate/Scholarship)

Purpose: To provide music education and performance opportunities with an emphasis on youth in the greater Milwaukee area. **Focus:** Music education. **Qualif.:** Applicants must be graduating seniors pursuing further educa-

tion in a musical field, including music education, music therapy, theory-composition, performance and musicology. **Criteria:** Recipients are selected based on the performance.

Funds Avail.: $500. **To Apply:** Applicants must submit a completed application form; must pass the audition process; must attach a 250-word brief description including the musical study they plan to focus on and why and a brief biography that includes school involvement, honors, awards and any other accomplishments. **Deadline:** December 15. **Contact:** 3195 S. Superior St., Ste. 209 Milwaukee, WI 53207.

2892 ■ Civil Air Patrol (CAP)
105 S Hansell St., Bldg. 714
Maxwell AFB, AL 36112
Free: 877-227-9142
URL: www.gocivilairpatrol.com

2893 ■ Civil Air Patrol Scholarships for School and Flying *(Undergraduate/Scholarship)*

Purpose: To provide academic and flight scholarships to deserving cadets and seniors. **Focus:** Aeronautics; Aviation. **Qualif.:** Applicant must be a current CAP member; have earned the Billy Mitchell Award (Cadets only); have earned a Senior Rating in any specialty track (Seniors only); Possess and maintain an academic and discipline standard acceptable to the school; be enrolled in a full-time course of study during the academic year for which the scholarship is awarded; have not received the scholarship in the past that you are applying for. **Criteria:** Selection will be based on submitted application.

Funds Avail.: No specific amount. **To Apply:** Applicants may apply online. Selected applicants for scholarships must provide official school transcripts and other supporting documents to validate the information that is provided in the application. **Deadline:** January 15. **Contact:** Questions can be addressed to cadets@capnhq.gov.

2894 ■ Civitan International (CI)
PO Box 130744
Birmingham, AL 35213-0744
Ph: (205) 591-8910
Fax: (205) 592-6307
Free: 800-CIV-ITAN
E-mail: civitan@civitan.org
URL: www.civitan.org

2895 ■ Civitan Shropshire Scholarships
(Undergraduate, Vocational/Occupational/ Scholarship)

Purpose: To provide financial assistance to students enrolled in undergraduate or graduate studies. **Focus:** General studies. **Qualif.:** Applicants must be Civitans (or Civitans' children or grandchildren) and must have been Civitan for at least two years and/or must be or have been Junior Civitans for no less than two years; must be students pursuing careers which help further the ideals and purposes of Civitan International as embodied in its Creed; must be enrolled in a degree or certificate program at an accredited community college, vocational school, four-year college or graduate school. **Criteria:** Recipients are selected based on academic record; professional objectives; civitan involvement; community-service activities; and financial need.

Awards are arranged alphabetically below their administering organizations

Funds Avail.: $1,000. **To Apply:** Applicants must submit all required application materials. Junior Civitan candidates must submit a letter of endorsement coming from an advisor or school principal. Applicants must call the Foundation if unable to access their website. **Deadline:** January 31. **Contact:** Applicants may e-mail all the required materials to rosemarysmith@civitan.org.

2896 ■ Clan Ross Association of the United States
5044 Via Donaldo
Yorba Linda, CA 92886
Ph: (714) 779-8425
E-mail: thetartan@aol.com
URL: clanross.org

2897 ■ Clan Ross Foundation Scholarships
(Undergraduate/Scholarship)

Purpose: To enhance the knowledge of the youth about Scottish culture. **Focus:** Scottish studies. **Qualif.:** Applicants must be current members of Clan Ross Association of the United States, Inc. for at least a year. Applicants who are also related with the current members of the Association are also welcome to apply. Families or members of the Clan Ross Scholarship Committee are disqualified for the scholarships. **Criteria:** Recipients will be selected based on their keen interests and dedications in studying Scottish culture, accomplishments in the chosen area of study, and academic capability.

Funds Avail.: $1,000 each. **Number Awarded:** 2. **To Apply:** Applicants must write or call the Clan Ross Association for complete information and application form. **Contact:** Virgil Bumann, 1867 Via Acorde, Camarillo, CA 93010.

2898 ■ Willis W. and Ethel M. Clark Foundation
PO Box 89
Pebble Beach, CA 93953-0089
Ph: (831) 625-1175
Fax: (831) 625-1175
E-mail: clarkfoundation@redshift.com
URL: www.theclarkfoundation.org

2899 ■ Willis W. and Ethel M. Clark Foundation Fellowships *(Graduate/Fellowship)*

Purpose: To provide financial assistance to deserving students who are attending graduate school or who have been accepted to a graduate school. **Focus:** Public service. **Qualif.:** Applicant must have been born, raised and/or have lived in one of the coastal communities of the Monterey Peninsula (Marina, Sand City, Seaside, Del Rey Oaks, Monterey, Pacific Grove, Pebble Beach, Carmel, Carmel Valley Village, and Big Sur); enrolled in an advanced program of study in a field of significant public interest benefit; have an above average academic achievement; have potential to make a significant contribution to society in general and, in particular, the coastal communities of the Monterey Peninsula; have proven commitment to volunteerism and public service; have demonstrated passion for community betterment and able to document a continuing philosophy toward community service for the area; and have responsible career goals for advancement in the chosen field. **Criteria:** Selection is based on submitted application materials and oral interview.

Funds Avail.: Up to $10,000. **Number Awarded:** One or

more. **To Apply:** Applicants must submit a completed, typed original plus one copy of the application form together with a resume/curriculum vitae (original plus one copy); a narrative autobiography (original plus one copy, maximum of two pages, double-spaced); statement of community service (original plus one copy, maximum of two pages, double-spaced); career goals (original plus one copy, maximum of one page, double-spaced); official transcripts (original plus one copy); proof of enrollment; and two letters of recommendation. **Deadline:** January 31 and October 15.

2900 ■ Classical Association of Canada
c/o Jonathan Edmondson
York University
Department of History
4700 Keele St., 2178 Vari Hall
Toronto, ON, Canada M3J 1P3
Ph: (416) 736-2100
E-mail: president@cac-scec.ca
URL: cac-scec.ca

2901 ■ Desmond Conacher Scholarships
(Graduate/Scholarship)

Purpose: To assist and encourage young scholars entering graduate study in classics. **Focus:** Classical studies. **Qualif.:** Applicants must be Canadian citizens or permanent residents; must be entering the first year of graduate studies in classics or similar program in a Canadian university; and must be less than 28 years of age on January 1st of the year of application. **Criteria:** Awards will be given to applicants who have demonstrated academic achievement, professional promise, and an appropriate undergraduate preparation.

Funds Avail.: $2,500. **To Apply:** Applicants must submit a completed application form; personal statement (maximum of 1,000 words) describing the applicant's previous academic career, employment experience, academic and career objectives; list of academic awards and honors received at the post-secondary level; transcript of records; two letters of recommendation from university teachers. **Deadline:** April 10. **Contact:** Questions should be addressed to the Awards Committee Chair, Prof. Alison Keith at akeith@chass.utoronto.ca.

2902 ■ Cleveland Leadership Center
One Cleveland Ctr.
1375 E Ninth St., Ste. 2430
Cleveland, OH 44115
Ph: (216) 592-2400
Fax: (216) 621-7733
URL: www.cleveleads.org

2903 ■ Cleveland Executive Fellowships (CEF)
(Professional development/Fellowship)

Purpose: To prepare individuals for effective and ethical leadership in the public-affairs arena. **Focus:** Public affairs. **Qualif.:** Applicant must have significant professional achievements and substantial organizational responsibilities; must have an average of 5-10 years of experience; have a minimum of five years of experience and/or a master's degree. **Criteria:** Selection is based on submitted applications.

Funds Avail.: $40,000 annual stipend. **Number Awarded:**

Awards are arranged alphabetically below their administering organizations

25. **To Apply:** Applicants must submit a completed application electronically. Application requires: two copies of completed application form, including written essays; two copies of a professional-quality resume (maximum of 2 pages); three letters of recommendation; and official academic transcripts for all higher education institutions attended. **Deadline:** April 4. **Contact:** Hannah Belsito at hbelsito@cleveleads.org.

2904 ■ Clinic for the Rehabilitation of Wildlife (CROW)

PO Box 150
Sanibel, FL 33957
Ph: (239) 472-3644
Fax: (239) 472-8544
E-mail: info@crowclinic.org
URL: www.crowclinic.org

2905 ■ CROW Fellowships *(All/Fellowship)*

Purpose: To provide individuals with a thorough understanding of the rehabilitation process for injured and orphaned wildlife on the Gulf Coast of Southwest Florida. **Focus:** Wildlife conservation, management, and science. **Qualif.:** Applicant must be interested in wildlife rehabilitation and medicine, and must have the pre-exposure rabies vaccine prior to beginning employment. **Criteria:** Selection is based on the applicant's promptness, positive attitude, willingness to work long hours, and good communication skills.

Funds Avail.: Shared housing and a stipend of $250/month. **Number Awarded:** 3. **To Apply:** Applicants must contact the clinic for the application information. **Contact:** Dr. PJ Deitschel at the above address.

2906 ■ Clinical Laboratory Management Association (CLMA)

401 N Michigan Ave. Ste. 2200
Chicago, IL 60611
Ph: (312) 321-5111
Fax: (312) 673-6927
E-mail: info@clma.org
URL: www.meclma.com

2907 ■ Clinical Laboratory Management Association High School Senior Scholarships
(High School/Scholarship)

Purpose: To financially assist talented people pursuing education in the field of laboratory medicine. **Focus:** Medicine. **Qualif.:** Applicants must be undergraduate students who are Maine residents and who wish to become Medical Technologists (Clinical Laboratory Scientists), Medical Laboratory Technicians, Histotechnologists, or Cytologists. **Criteria:** Recipients are selected based on academic performance, character, commitment to laboratory medicine and financial need.

Funds Avail.: $500. **To Apply:** Applicants must submit a completed application form; printed essay; transcript of high school grades; two letters of recommendation (at least one must come from an academic source, e.g. teacher, guidance counselor, or principal). **Deadline:** May 17. **Contact:** Sonia E. Russell MT (ASCP); DCPA; 417 State St., Webber W, Ste. 541, Bangor, ME 04401; 207-561-2413.

2908 ■ Clinical Laboratory Management Association Undergraduate Scholarships
(Undergraduate/Scholarship)

Purpose: To financially assist talented people pursuing education in the field of laboratory medicine. **Focus:** Medicine. **Qualif.:** Applicant must be a clinical laboratory scientist working towards an advanced degree or a student who is a Maine resident and wishes to become a medical technologist, a medical laboratory technician, a histotechnologist or a cytologist **Criteria:** Recipient will be selected based on academic performance, character, commitment to laboratory medicine and financial need.

Funds Avail.: $1,000. **Number Awarded:** 3. **To Apply:** Applicants must submit completed application form; printed essay, completed as described on the application; transcript of college grades; and two letters of recommendation from teachers or employers. **Deadline:** May 17. **Contact:** Sonia E. Russell MT (ASCP); DCPA; 417 State Street, Webber W. Suite 541, Bangor, Maine 04401; 207-561-2413.

2909 ■ Club Managers Association of America (CMAA)

1733 King St.
Alexandria, VA 22314
Ph: (703) 739-9500
Fax: (703) 739-0124
E-mail: cmaa@cmaa.org
URL: www.cmaa.org

2910 ■ Club Managers Association of America Research Grants (CMAA) *(All/Grant)*

Purpose: To support research that is significant to the club management industry. **Focus:** Management. **Qualif.:** Applicants must submit a completed application; a detailed project description; a project budget; and appendixes. **Criteria:** Candidates are evaluated by The Club Foundation Allocation Committee (CFAC) using the following criteria: a) problem conceptualization; b) research technique; c) contribution to the field; d) clarity and thoroughness; e) project budget.

Funds Avail.: $2,500. **Number Awarded:** 2-4. **To Apply:** Applicants must download application form from the CMAA website. The application, narrative and other required attachments must be typed using 12-point font and one-inch margins. **Deadline:** November 5. **Contact:** Mr. Seth Gregg; Phone: 703-739-9500; Email at clubfoundation@clubfoundation.org.

2911 ■ CMAA Student Conference Travel Grants *(All/Grant)*

Purpose: To help student chapters offset the costs associated with attending the CMAA World Conference on Club Management. **Focus:** Management. **Qualif.:** Applicants must be student chapters of CMAA. **Criteria:** Recipients will be selected based on the quality of application material submitted.

Funds Avail.: $500. Funds must be used for expenditures related to the CMAA Annual Conference. **To Apply:** Applicant student chapters must hold a fundraising event; submit a president's annual report; submit the current chapter budget; submit an application for the grant; and submit a grantee form stipulating that funds will be used for its intended purpose. **Remarks:** Started in 1988. The grant is supported by contributions from E-Z-GO Textron, Inc. **Contact:** clubfoundation@clubfoundation.org.

Awards are arranged alphabetically below their administering organizations

---

2912 ■ Willmoore H. Kendall Scholarships
(Postgraduate/Scholarship)

Purpose: To provide tuition support to assist club managers interested in pursuing the Certified Club Manager (CCM) designation. **Focus:** Management. **Qualif.:** Candidate must be a CMAA member; an assistant manager; currently pursuing the CMMA designation; have at least one remaining BMI course to complete; must be nominated by their chapter. **Criteria:** Applicants who are recommended by The Club Foundation Allocation Committee and approved by The Club Foundation Board of Governors will be given preference.

Funds Avail.: No specific amount. **To Apply:** Applicants must submit an official application form; a letter provided by the applicant's chapter supporting his/her application and must be signed by a chapter officer; a letter of recommendation from a member and the general manager of the applicant's club; a resume; a 500-1000 words addressing the following components: a) a detailed description of the applicant's career objectives and goals; b) Detail the reason(s) he/she wished to pursue the CCM designation; c) What his/her specific interests within the private club management field?; d) A characteristic of Mr. Kendall's with which the applicant identifies and the reason why. **Deadline:** November 1. **Remarks:** Established in 2001 in memory of CMAA Past President Mr. Bill Kendall. **Contact:** clubfoundation@clubfoundation.org.

2913 ■ Joe Perdue Scholarships
(Undergraduate/Scholarship)

Purpose: To financially support the professional development of club managers through education, training and research initiatives. **Focus:** Management. **Qualif.:** Candidates must be pursuing managerial careers in the private club industry; must have completed their freshman year of college and be enrolled for the full academic year in an accredited four-year institution; and must have achieved and maintained a grade point average of at least 2.5 on a 4.0 scale, or 4.5 on a 6.0 scale. **Criteria:** Applicants who are CMAA student chapter members are given additional points.

Funds Avail.: No specific amount. **To Apply:** Candidates must submit an official application available online; a sealed copy of official college transcripts; a recommendation form and recommendation letter from a faculty advisor/professor and a private club industry professional; a resume; and a 500-1000 words addressing the following components: 1) the applicant's career objectives and goals; 2) the characteristics he/she possesses that will enable him/her to succeed as a club manager; 3) his/her perception of CMAA and the private club industry; 4) specific interests within the private club management field; 5) why the applicant feel that he/she should be a Club Foundation Scholarship recipient. **Contact:** joeperduescholarship@clubfoundation.org.

2914 ■ COACH: Canada's Health Informatics Association
250 Consumers Rd., Ste. 301
Toronto, ON, Canada M2J 4V6
Ph: (416) 494-9324
Fax: (416) 495-8723
Free: 888-253-8554
E-mail: info@coachorg.com
URL: www.coachorg.com

2915 ■ Steven Huesing Scholarships *(Graduate, Undergraduate/Scholarship)*

Purpose: To encourage health education by providing financial assistance for post-secondary education. **Focus:** Health education. **Qualif.:** Applicants must be enrolled in a health informatics or related program at an accredited post-secondary institution; and must demonstrate active involvement and achievement in health informatics. **Criteria:** Recipients will be selected based on academic standing and potential contribution to advance Health Informatics.

Funds Avail.: $1,000. **To Apply:** Applicants must submit a transcript of records and an assessment from academic advisor; must have proof of enrollment in a recognized Canadian post-secondary institution and current attendance in a health informatics and related program; must prepare a (500-word) description of their involvement and achievements in health informatics. **Deadline:** September 13. **Remarks:** Established in 1999 in recognition of Founding President Steven Huesing's contribution to COACH.

2916 ■ Coaching Association of Canada (CAC)
141 Laurier Ave. W, Ste. 300
Ottawa, ON, Canada K1P 5J3
Ph: (613) 235-5000
Fax: (613) 235-9500
E-mail: coach@coach.ca
URL: www.coach.ca

2917 ■ Women in Coaching National Coaching Institute Scholarships *(Undergraduate/Scholarship)*

Purpose: To financially assist women attending one of the seven National Coaching Institutes in Canada. **Focus:** General studies. **Qualif.:** Applicants must be Canadian citizens or landed immigrants currently coaching Canadian athletes; must be certified NCCP level 3; and must be accepted in a full-time or part-time diploma program at one of the seven National Coaching Institutes across Canada. **Criteria:** Recipients will be selected based on submitted application form and supporting documents.

Funds Avail.: No stated amount. **To Apply:** Applicants must contact Ms. Sheilagh Croxon for application form and needed materials. **Contact:** For further information, applicants may send an e-mail at scroxon@rogers.com.

2918 ■ Coalition of Higher Education Assistance Organizations (COHEAO)
1101 Vermont Ave. NW, Ste. 400
Washington, DC 20005-3586
Ph: (202) 289-3910
Fax: (202) 371-0197
E-mail: whuffman@wpllc.net
URL: www.coheao.com

2919 ■ COHEAO Scholarships *(Undergraduate/Scholarship)*

Purpose: To provide financial assistance to those students who are in need. **Focus:** General Studies. **Qualif.:** Applicants must be U.S citizens; must attend a COHEAO member school; must have a minimum GPA of 3.75 on a 4.0 scale. Only undergraduate students who are entering their sophomore, junior or senior year are eligible to apply; freshmen and graduate students are not eligible. **Criteria:**

Awards are arranged alphabetically below their administering organizations

Preference will be given to those students who meet the criteria.

Funds Avail.: $1,000. **Number Awarded:** 4. **To Apply:** Applicants must check the available website for the application process online. **Deadline:** March 31. **Contact:** Coalition of Higher Education Assistance Organizations at the above address.

2920 ■ Coast Guard Foundation

394 Taugwonk Rd.
Stonington, CT 06378
Ph: (860) 535-0786
Fax: (860) 535-0944
E-mail: info@cgfdn.org
URL: www.coastguardfoundation.org

2921 ■ Commander Ronald J. Cantin Scholarships *(Undergraduate/Scholarship)*

Purpose: To support Coast Guard enlisted personnel and their dependents. **Focus:** General studies. **Qualif.:** Applicants must be dependent children of enlisted men and women of the US Coast Guard on active duty, retired or deceased and dependent children of enlisted personnel in the Coast Guard Reserve currently on extended active duty 180 days or more. **Criteria:** Selection will be based on scholastic promise, motivation, moral character, leadership qualities and good citizenship.

Funds Avail.: $2,500. **Number Awarded:** 1. **To Apply:** Student must submit an application package which includes: completed foundation scholarship application form; student's college entrance scores; letter of recommendation from a school official where the student is currently attending high school, or college transcript signed by school official; letter to the president of the selection committee; letter of acceptance from the college or vocational school the student plans to attend; and completed Foundation financial statement. Application packages should include originals plus five copies of all original materials, with the exception of official transcripts which are to remain sealed. Submit completed application to Commandant (G-1112), Attention: Scholarship Program Manager, 2100 Second St., SW, Jemal 9-0733, Washington, DC 20593-0001. **Deadline:** April 1. **Remarks:** This fund is a gift from Mr. and Mrs. Stephen Wilcox to honor their brother-in-law, Commander Ronald J. Cantin. **Contact:** Mrs. Yvette Wright, 202-475-5159 or wright@uscg.mil.

2922 ■ Commander Daniel J. Christovich Scholarship Fund *(Undergraduate/Scholarship)*

Purpose: To support Coast Guard enlisted personnel and their dependents. **Focus:** General studies. **Qualif.:** Applicants must be dependent children of enlisted men and women of the US Coast Guard on active duty, retired or deceased and dependent children of enlisted personnel in the Coast Guard Reserve currently on extended active duty 180 days or more. **Criteria:** Selection will be based on scholastic promise, motivation, moral character, leadership qualities and good citizenship.

Funds Avail.: $2,500. **Number Awarded:** 1. **To Apply:** Student must submit an application package which includes: completed foundation scholarship application form; student's college entrance scores; letter of recommendation from a school official where the student is currently attending high school, or college transcript signed by school official; letter to the president of the selection committee;

letter of acceptance from the college or vocational school the student plans to attend; and completed Foundation financial statement. Application packages should include originals plus five copies of all original materials, with the exception of official transcripts which are to remain sealed. Submit completed application to Commandant (G-1112), Attention: Scholarship Program Manager, 2100 Second St., SW, Jemal 9-0733, Washington, DC 20593-0001. **Deadline:** April 1. **Remarks:** Established in honor of Commander Daniel J. Christovich. **Contact:** Mrs. Yvette Wright, 202-475-5159 or yvette.d.wright@uscg.mil.

2923 ■ Coast Guard Foundation Enlisted Education Grants *(All/Grant)*

Purpose: To support Coast Guard enlisted personnel and their dependents. **Focus:** General studies. **Qualif.:** Applicants must be active enlisted personnel in pay grades E-3 to E-9 with two or more years of Coast Guard service. **Criteria:** Selection will be based on scholastic promise, motivation, moral character, leadership qualities and good citizenship.

Funds Avail.: $350. **To Apply:** Applicants should complete the application form 1560/10a, available through the Coast Guard Institute. Mail completed form to: Commanding Officer, USCG Institute, 5900 SW 64th Street, Oklahoma City, OK 73169-6990. **Deadline:** December 1. **Remarks:** Established in 1999. **Contact:** 405-954-7240.

2924 ■ Coast Guard Foundation Scholarships *(Undergraduate/Scholarship)*

Purpose: To support Coast Guard enlisted personnel and their dependents. **Focus:** General studies. **Qualif.:** Applicants must be dependent children of enlisted men and women of the US Coast Guard on active duty, retired or deceased and dependent children of enlisted personnel in the Coast Guard Reserve currently on extended active duty 180 days or more. **Criteria:** Selection will be based on scholastic promise, motivation, moral character, leadership qualities and good citizenship.

Funds Avail.: $5,000. **Number Awarded:** Varies. **To Apply:** Student must submit an application package which includes: completed foundation scholarship application form; student's college entrance scores; letter of recommendation from a school official where the student is currently attending high school, or college transcript signed by school official; letter to the president of the selection committee; letter of acceptance from the college or vocational school the student plans to attend; and completed Foundation financial statement. Application packages should include originals plus five copies of all original materials, with the exception of official transcripts which are to remain sealed. Submit completed application to Commandant (G-1112), Attention: Scholarship Program Manager, 2100 Second St., SW, Jemal 9-0733, Washington, DC 20593-0001. **Deadline:** April 1. **Contact:** Mrs. Yvette Wright, 202-475-5159 or wright@uscg.mil.

2925 ■ The Fallen Heroes Scholarships *(Undergraduate/Scholarship)*

Purpose: To support Coast Guard enlisted personnel and their dependents. **Focus:** General Studies. **Qualif.:** Applicants must be families of Coast Guard personnel who die in the line of duty. **Criteria:** Selection will be based on scholastic promise, motivation, moral character, leadership qualities and good citizenship.

Funds Avail.: $2,500. **To Apply:** Applicants must submit a completed foundation application form; college entrance

Awards are arranged alphabetically below their administering organizations

scores; letter of recommendation from high school official or college transcript signed by college official; applicant letter to the president of the selection committee; letter of acceptance from the college the student plans to attend; and Foundation financial statement. **Contact:** Mrs. Yvette Wright, 202-475-5159 or yvette.d.wright@uscg.mil.

2926 ■ Captain Ernest Fox Perpetual Scholarships (Undergraduate/Scholarship)

Purpose: To assist the education and training endeavors of ARSC personnel. **Focus:** General studies. **Qualif.:** Applicants must be employees of Aircraft Repair and Supply Center (active duty, federal civil service and their dependents). **Criteria:** Selection will be based on scholastic promise, motivation, moral character, leadership qualities and good citizenship.

Funds Avail.: $1,000. **Number Awarded:** 1. **To Apply:** Applicants must submit an original and five copies of the application package to Aircraft Repair and Supply Center. **Deadline:** March 15. **Remarks:** Sponsored by Clay, Elizabeth and Dean Fox to honor the memory of their late son and brother, Captain Ernest W. Fox. **Contact:** MCPO Don Staubin, 252-335-6034.

2927 ■ Keiser College Coast Guard Scholarships (Undergraduate/Scholarship)

Purpose: To support Coast Guard enlisted personnel and their dependents. **Focus:** General Studies. **Qualif.:** Applicants must have a verification of high school graduation or GED completion and an entrance exam; must have a minimum of four years in the Coast Guard, second tour of duty, demonstrated leadership skill, an essay and a recommendation from his or her Commanding Officer. On-going requirements must also be met to remain in good standing. **Criteria:** Selection will be based on scholastic promise, motivation, moral character, leadership qualities and good citizenship.

Funds Avail.: $50,000. **Number Awarded:** 2. **To Apply:** Applications can be completed online through the internet at www.keiseruniversity.edu. A minimum 300-word essay on leadership will accompany the application. **Deadline:** December 15. **Contact:** Mrs. Belinda Keiser at belindak@keiseruniversity.edu or 866-534-7371.

2928 ■ Paul Resnick and Bruce Donnelly Scholarships (Undergraduate/Scholarship)

Purpose: To support Coast Guard enlisted personnel and their dependents. **Focus:** General Studies. **Qualif.:** Candidates must be enrolled at Cornell University and have a demonstrated financial need. **Criteria:** Preference will be given to students who have served in the US Coast Guard or who are dependents of a former or current member of the US Coast Guard.

Funds Avail.: No specific amount. **To Apply:** Applicants may contact and Cornell University, Financial Aid Office for application process. **Remarks:** Established by Mr. Resnick in honor of his father Paul Resnick, who served in the Coast Guard, and in memory of his father-in-law Bruce Donnelly. **Contact:** Jennifer L. Talcott, Financial Aid Office, Cornell University, 203 Day Hall, Ithaca, NY 14850; Phone: 607-255-5145; E-mail: jlt37@cornell.edu.

2929 ■ Arnold Sobel Scholarships (Undergraduate/Scholarship)

Purpose: To support Coast Guard enlisted personnel and their dependents. **Focus:** General studies. **Qualif.:** Applicants must be dependent children of enlisted men and women of the US Coast Guard on active duty, retired or deceased and dependent children of enlisted personnel in the Coast Guard Reserve currently on extended active duty 180 days or more. **Criteria:** Selection will be based on scholastic promise, motivation, moral character, leadership qualities and good citizenship.

Funds Avail.: $5,000. **Number Awarded:** 4. **To Apply:** Student must submit an application package which includes: completed foundation scholarship application form; student's college entrance scores; letter of recommendation from a school official where the student is currently attending high school, or college transcript signed by school official; letter to the president of the selection committee; letter of acceptance from the college or vocational school the student plans to attend; and completed Foundation financial statement. Application packages should include originals plus five copies of all original materials, with the exception of official transcripts which are to remain sealed. Submit completed application to Commandant (G-1112), Attention: Scholarship Program Manager, 2100 Second St., SW, Jemal 9-0733, Washington, DC 20593-0001. **Deadline:** April 1. **Contact:** Mrs. Yvette Wright, 202-475-5159 or wright@uscg.mil.

2930 ■ The Vander Putten Family Scholarships (All/Scholarship)

Purpose: To support Coast Guard enlisted personnel and their dependents. **Focus:** General studies. **Qualif.:** Applicants must be active enlisted personnel in pay grades E-3 to E-9 with two or more years of Coast Guard service. **Criteria:** Selection will be based on scholastic promise, motivation, moral character, leadership qualities and good citizenship.

Funds Avail.: $500. **To Apply:** Applicants should complete the application form 1560/10a, available through the Coast Guard Institute. Mail completed form to: Commanding Officer, USCG Institute, 5900 SW 64th Street, Oklahoma City, OK 73169-6990. **Deadline:** December 1. **Remarks:** Established in 1999. **Contact:** 405-954-7240.

2931 ■ Coastal Bend Community Foundation (CBCF)
600 Leopard St., Ste. 1716
Corpus Christi, TX 78473
Ph: (361) 882-9745
Fax: (361) 882-2865
URL: www.cbcfoundation.org

2932 ■ Alejandro "Alex" Abecia Reaching High Scholarships (Undergraduate, Vocational/Occupational/Scholarship)

Purpose: To provide resources for educational opportunities including vocational schools and two and four-year universities. **Focus:** General studies. **Qualif.:** Applicants must be senior members of the Mary Caroll High School Band or graduating senior members of the Mary Caroll High School soccer team; must be members of the A/B Honor Roll; must have taken honor classes in high school and maintained a course load of at least 12 hours per semester. **Criteria:** Applicants are evaluated based on merit.

Funds Avail.: $100. **Number Awarded:** 4. **To Apply:** Applicants must download the applications from the website of the Foundation. **Deadline:** March 1.

Awards are arranged alphabetically below their administering organizations

2933 ■ Chris Nance Adler Scholarship Fund
(High School/Scholarship)

Purpose: To provide financial assistance to graduating seniors at W.B. Ray High School to attend college. **Focus:** General studies. **Qualif.:** Applicants must be graduating seniors at W.B. Ray High School and chosen by the Hall of Honor Selection Committee from the students named to the permanent honor roll. **Criteria:** Applicants are evaluated based on financial need.

Funds Avail.: No specific amount. **To Apply:** Applicants must obtain applications from the Ray High School counselor's Office.

2934 ■ Allen - Marty Allen Scholarships *(High School, Undergraduate, Vocational/Occupational/ Scholarship)*

Purpose: To provide resources for educational opportunities including vocational schools and two and four-year universities. **Focus:** Music. **Qualif.:** Applicants must be graduating seniors of a Coastal Bend high school or college students who attended a Coastal Bend high school; must be majoring in music; must maintain GPA of 2.5 and course load of at least 12 college credits per semester. **Criteria:** Applicants who are jazz musicians will be given preference.

Funds Avail.: $200. **Number Awarded:** 1. **To Apply:** Applicants must submit all the required application information. **Deadline:** March 1.

2935 ■ Zachary Barriger Memorial Scholarships
(Undergraduate/Scholarship)

Purpose: To provide financial assistance to high school seniors who are planning to pursue a career in computer/ electrical engineering. **Focus:** Engineering, Computer; Engineering, Electrical. **Qualif.:** Applicants must be seniors at Tuloso-Midway High School; must be attending an accredited two or four-year college in Texas; must demonstrate interest in pursuing studies in the field of engineering or medicine; and must excel academically with A/B Honor Roll status and honor classes. **Criteria:** Applicants are evaluated based on merit.

Funds Avail.: $500. **Number Awarded:** 2. **To Apply:** Applicants must submit all the required application information. **Deadline:** March 1.

2936 ■ O.J. Beck, Jr. Memorial Scholarships
(Undergraduate/Scholarship)

Purpose: To provide educational assistance to students seeking a bachelor's degree in building construction. **Focus:** Construction. **Qualif.:** Applicants must be students at Texas A&M University - College Station who are seeking a bachelor's degree in building construction; must have maintained residency in the area served by the South Texas Chapter of Associated General Contractors. **Criteria:** Recipients are selected based on financial need.

Funds Avail.: $2,000. **Number Awarded:** 1. **To Apply:** Applicants must obtain application form from the Associated General Contractors office located at 518 S Enterprise Pkwy., Corpus Christi, TX 78405; Phone number: 361-289-0996.

2937 ■ Reverend E.F. Bennett Scholarships
(Undergraduate/Scholarship)

Purpose: To provide financial support to graduating seniors from a Coastal Bend high school. **Focus:** General studies.

Qualif.: Applicants must be: graduating seniors from a Coastal Bend high school; in the top 10% of their graduating class; attending Del Mar College, Texas A&M University-Corpus Christi or Texas A&M University-Kingsville. **Criteria:** Applicants are evaluated based on financial need.

Funds Avail.: $500. **Number Awarded:** 1. **To Apply:** Applicants must download the application form from the website of the Foundation or obtain it by calling the Foundation office at 361-882-9745. **Deadline:** March 1.

2938 ■ Marion Luna Brem/Pat McNeil Health and Education Scholarships *(Undergraduate/ Scholarship)*

Purpose: To provide financial assistance to teenage parents in Coastal Bend to pursue a college education while raising and supporting their children. **Focus:** General studies. **Qualif.:** Applicants must: attended high school in Coastal Bend; have a high school diploma or GED certification and a minimum GPA of 2.5; must attend Coastal Bend College, Del Mar College, Texas A&M University-Corpus Christi or Texas A&M University-Kingsville; must maintain a 2.0 GPA on a 4.0 scale and a minimum of 9 credit hours per semester. **Criteria:** Applicants are evaluated based on academic achievement and financial need.

Funds Avail.: $1,000. **Number Awarded:** 2. **To Apply:** Applicants must submit all the required application information. **Deadline:** March 1.

2939 ■ D.C. and Virginia Brown Scholarships
(High School, Undergraduate/Scholarship)

Purpose: To provide financial assistance to graduates of Mathis High School and current Mathis High School students to further their education in college. **Focus:** General studies. **Qualif.:** Applicants must be graduates or current students of Mathis High School who have earned their GED certificate and who have good potential and character; must maintain a course load of 12 semester hours and a 2.5 GPA on a 4.0 scale. **Criteria:** Applicants are evaluated based on academic merit and personal attributes.

Funds Avail.: $4,000 for four-year college student; $2,200 for two-year and trade school student; $1,000 for handicapped student. **Number Awarded:** 4. **To Apply:** Applicants must download application form from the website of the Foundation or obtain it from Mathis High School counseling office. **Deadline:** March 15.

2940 ■ Cecil E. Burney Scholarships
(Undergraduate/Scholarship)

Purpose: To provide financial assistance to high school seniors or graduates of a Coastal Bend high school in furthering their college education. **Focus:** Liberal arts; History; Political science; Music; Education. **Qualif.:** Applicants must be high school seniors or graduates of a Coastal Bend high school pursuing a liberal arts degree majoring in history, political science, music or education; have a high school GPA of 90 percent or higher; maintain a college 3.0 GPA or higher; at least 12 hours per semester; and must attend Coastal Bend College, Del Mar College, Texas A&M University-Corpus Christi or Kingsville Campus. **Criteria:** Applicants are evaluated based on academic performance.

Funds Avail.: $2,000. **Number Awarded:** 1. **To Apply:** Applicants must submit all the required application information. Application forms may be downloaded online or by calling the Foundation office. **Deadline:** March 1.

2941 ■ C.C.H.R.M.A. Scholarships *(High School, Undergraduate/Scholarship)*

Purpose: To assist students majoring in business with an interest in human resources. **Focus:** Business; Personnel

---

Awards are arranged alphabetically below their administering organizations

administration/human resources. **Qualif.:** Applicants must: be high school seniors or undergraduate college students majoring in business; be enrolled as full-time students in the Coastal Bend seven-county service area; maintain a 3.0 GPA on a 4.0 scale (85% on 100% scale if high school students). **Criteria:** Applicants are evaluated based on academic achievement and financial need.

Funds Avail.: $500. **Number Awarded:** 1. **To Apply:** Applicants must download application form from the website of the Foundation or obtain it by calling the Foundation at 361-882-9745. **Deadline:** March 15.

2942 ■ Justin Forrest Cox "Beat the Odds" Memorial Scholarships (Undergraduate/ Scholarship)

Purpose: To provide educational support for students who graduated from a Victoria ISD high school. **Focus:** General studies. **Qualif.:** Applicants must be students who graduated from a Victoria ISD high School; have a "C" average or better; be pursuing a four-year baccalaureate degree; complete at least 12 credit hours per semester; have overcome a significant difficulty in graduating from high school and have maintained a 2.5 GPA. **Criteria:** Applicants are evaluated based on academic achievement and financial need.

Funds Avail.: $2,500. **Number Awarded:** 1. **To Apply:** Applicants must obtain application form from Making the Grade-Victoria, 1908 Laurent Tower, Ste. 290 (PO Box 105), Victoria, TX 77902; Phone or Fax: 361-578-0270. **Deadline:** April 1. **Remarks:** Scholarship is to be used for books and tuition only.

2943 ■ Derek Lee Dean Soccer Scholarships (High School/Scholarship)

Purpose: To assist outstanding high school students of W.B. Ray High School who have a passion for soccer. **Focus:** General studies. **Qualif.:** Applicants must be outstanding W.B. Ray High School students and members of the soccer team who exhibit love for soccer, teamwork and sportsmanship. **Criteria:** Applicants are evaluated based on academic achievement and personal involvement in the sport.

Funds Avail.: $1,000. **Number Awarded:** 2. **To Apply:** Applicants must download the application form from the website of the Foundation or obtain it from the W.B. Ray High School counselor's office. **Deadline:** April 1.

2944 ■ Doraine Pursuit of Educational Excellence Scholarships (Undergraduate/Scholarship)

Purpose: To promote educational excellence in Coastal Bend. **Focus:** General studies. **Qualif.:** Applicants must be graduating high school seniors in the Coastal Bend; must be in the top 5% of the graduating class; and have maintained a GPA of 3.0 and enrolled in at least 12 hours per semester. **Criteria:** Applicants are evaluated based on academic performance and merit.

Funds Avail.: $2,000. **Number Awarded:** 1. **To Apply:** Applicants must download applications found at the website of the Foundation. **Deadline:** March 1.

2945 ■ Jay Downes Memorial Scholarships (Undergraduate/Scholarship)

Purpose: To provide financial assistance to graduating Alice High School senior students in pursuing college. **Focus:** General studies. **Qualif.:** Applicants must be graduating Alice High School seniors who lettered in UIL-sanctioned golf for at least two years; have an overall high school GPA of "B" or better; participated in extracurricular activities other than athletics; have high ideals, and spirit of good conduct and sportsmanship benefiting the "Fighting Alice Coyote"; must attend a four-year college or university, register for at least 12 hours of classes and maintain a minimum college GPA of 2.5 on 4.0 scale. **Criteria:** Applicants are evaluated based on academic achievement and financial need.

Funds Avail.: $1,000. **Number Awarded:** 1. **To Apply:** Applicants must be nominated by the athletic director and head golf coach at Alice High School.

2946 ■ John R. Eidson Jr., Scholarships (Undergraduate/Scholarship)

Purpose: To provide financial assistance to Coastal Bend students who intend to study engineering in college. **Focus:** Engineering. **Qualif.:** Applicants must be students who are in good standing with the Engineering Department; must be sophomores or higher; must exhibit academic potential; must have participated in professional and social societies; and maintained full-time status and a GPA of 3.0 higher. **Criteria:** Recipients are selected based on financial need.

Funds Avail.: $1,000. **Number Awarded:** 1. **To Apply:** Applicants must obtain application form from the financial aid office at Texas A&M University in College Station.

2947 ■ Barney Flynn Memorial Scholarships (High School/Scholarship)

Purpose: To provide financial assistance to graduating seniors of Corpus Christi, Flour Bluff or Tuloso-Midway ISD high schools in furthering their education. **Focus:** General studies. **Qualif.:** Applicants must be graduating seniors of Corpus Christi, Flour Bluff or Tuloso-Midway ISD high schools; must be members of the high school band with a high performance level in band. **Criteria:** Applicants are evaluated based on merit.

Funds Avail.: $1,000. **Number Awarded:** 1. **To Apply:** Applicants must submit all the required application information. Application forms may be downloaded online or by calling the Foundation office. **Deadline:** March 1.

2948 ■ Melissa Guerra Scholarships (Undergraduate/Scholarship)

Purpose: To provide educational assistance to senior students of Mary Caroll High School. **Focus:** General studies. **Qualif.:** Applicants must be Mary Carroll High School seniors; must attend a publicly funded college or university in Texas; and maintain a minimum of a 3.0 GPA and 12 credit hours per semester. **Criteria:** Applicants are evaluated based on academic performance.

Funds Avail.: $900. **Number Awarded:** 1. **To Apply:** Applicants must submit all the required application information. Applications are available online or by calling the foundation office. Applications are also available in the Mary Carroll High School counselor's office. **Deadline:** March 1.

2949 ■ Manuel Hernandez, Jr. Foundation Scholarships (Undergraduate, Vocational/ Occupational/Scholarship)

Purpose: To provide the high school graduating senior students of Roy Miller High School financial assistance for their college education. **Focus:** General studies. **Qualif.:** Applicants must be graduating seniors of Roy Miller High School; must have been accepted at a college, university, trade or vocational institution. **Criteria:** Applicants are evaluated based on financial need.

Awards are arranged alphabetically below their administering organizations

Funds Avail.: $500. **Number Awarded:** 4. **To Apply:** Applicants must submit all the required application information. Applications may be downloaded from the Foundation website or obtained from the Roy Miller High School Counselor's office. **Deadline:** March 1.

2950 ■ Puedo Scholarships - Joseph Huerta
(Undergraduate/Scholarship)

Purpose: To provide financial assistance to students in continuing their education in college. **Focus:** General studies. **Qualif.:** Applicants must have graduated from a CCISD high school and have a high school GPA of at least 90 percent on a 100-point scale; must be enrolled as full-time college students (at least 12 semester credits) at a four-year accredited college or university; and must maintain a course load of at least 12 college credits per semester and a GPA of 3.0 or higher. **Criteria:** Applicants are evaluated based on academic achievement and financial need.

Funds Avail.: $1,000 to $5,000. **Number Awarded:** 10. **To Apply:** Applicants must submit all the required application information. Application form can be downloaded at the website of the Foundation, www.cbcfoundation.org. **Deadline:** March 1.

2951 ■ Casey Laine Armed Forces Scholarships *(Undergraduate/Scholarship)*

Purpose: To assist high school students who are seeking financial resources to further their college education. **Focus:** General studies. **Qualif.:** Applicants must graduate in top 50% of high school class; maintain a GPA of 2.5 and enrolled in at least 12 hours per semester; must be graduating seniors or current graduates from a Coastal Bend high school, or members or honorably discharged veterans of the armed services, or R.O.T.C. members (high school seniors must agree to join an R.O.T.C. program upon entering college). **Criteria:** Applicants are evaluated based on academic performance.

Funds Avail.: $200. **Number Awarded:** 1. **To Apply:** Applicants must submit all the required application information. **Deadline:** March 1.

2952 ■ Sue Kay Lay Memorial Scholarships
(Undergraduate/Scholarship)

Purpose: To assist high school seniors seeking financial resources to further their education. **Focus:** General studies. **Qualif.:** Applicants must be high school seniors graduating at the end of the spring semester; must be enrolled in college full-time (12 hours or more); must have high school GPA of 95%; have graduated from a high school in Coastal Bend; and maintain a permanent residence in the Coastal Bend. **Criteria:** Applicants are evaluated based on financial need.

Funds Avail.: $1,500. **Number Awarded:** 5. **To Apply:** Applicants must submit all the required application information. Applications may be downloaded from the Foundation website or be calling the Foundation office at 361-882-9745. **Deadline:** March 1.

2953 ■ Brian and Colleen Miller Scholarships
(Undergraduate/Scholarship)

Purpose: To assist high school juniors or seniors attending a Coastal Bend high school. **Focus:** General studies. **Qualif.:** Applicants must be high school juniors or seniors attending a Coastal Bend high school; must attend any accredited four-year college or university. **Criteria:** Applicants are evaluated based on financial need.

Funds Avail.: $500. **Number Awarded:** 1. **To Apply:** Applicants must submit completed application form along with the documentation of participation and/or awards in the areas of mathematics and/or science. **Deadline:** March 1.

2954 ■ J.J. Rains Memorial Scholarships *(High School/Scholarship)*

Purpose: To provide graduating CCISD high school seniors financial assistance for their college education. **Focus:** General studies. **Qualif.:** Applicants must be graduating CCISD high school seniors with preference for students who have participated in speech or debate; have a cumulative high school GPA of 2.5; must maintain a cumulative college GPA of 2.5 on a 4.0 scale and enroll in a minimum of 12 semester hours. **Criteria:** Applicants are evaluated based on academic achievement and financial need.

Funds Avail.: $1,000. **Number Awarded:** 1. **To Apply:** Applicants must submit all the required application information. **Deadline:** March 1.

2955 ■ W.B. Ray HS Class of '56 Averill Johnson Scholarships *(Undergraduate/ Scholarship)*

Purpose: To provide financial assistance for graduating seniors of W.B. Ray High School. **Focus:** General studies. **Qualif.:** Applicants must be W.B. Ray high school seniors in the top 10% of their graduating class; enrolled as full-time (12 semester hours) students in an accredited college or university in the United States in the fall semester following graduation. **Criteria:** Recipients are selected based on academic achievement and financial need.

Funds Avail.: $1,000. **Number Awarded:** 2. **To Apply:** Applicants must submit all the required application information. **Deadline:** March 1.

2956 ■ Rotary Club of Corpus Christi Scholarships *(Undergraduate/Scholarship)*

Purpose: To advance higher education in the immediate Corpus Christi area. **Focus:** General studies. **Qualif.:** Applicants must be graduating seniors from the following: all CCISD high schools, Tuloso-Midway, Calallen, West Oso or Flour Bluff high schools, Incarnate Word Academy, Corpus Christi Academy or Annapolis Christian Academy; must attend Texas A&M Corpus Christi or Del Mar College; must maintain a minimum GPA of 2.0 on a 4.0 scale and courseload of at least 12 hours per semester. **Criteria:** Applicants are evaluated based on financial need.

Funds Avail.: $3,000 to $3,300. **Number Awarded:** 2. **To Apply:** Applicants must submit all the required application information and application form can be downloaded from the website of the Foundation. **Deadline:** March 1.

2957 ■ Seaman Family Scholarships
(Undergraduate/Scholarship)

Purpose: To provide financial assistance for Coastal Bend students who are home-schooled and need financial aid. **Focus:** General studies. **Qualif.:** Applicant must be a Coastal Bend or Calhoun County home-schooled student who demonstrates financial need; must be accepted at an accredited college or university; and must maintain a courseload of 12 semester hours. **Criteria:** Applicants are judged on the basis of academic performance and financial need.

Funds Avail.: $500. **To Apply:** Applicants must submit a completed application form; essay of 500 words about the topic "Freedom." **Deadline:** March 1.

Awards are arranged alphabetically below their administering organizations

2958 ■ Judge Terry Shamsie Scholarships
(High School/Scholarship)

Purpose: To assist graduating high school senior students in Coastal Bend, financially, to continue their education. **Focus:** General studies. **Qualif.:** Applicants must be graduating high school seniors in the Coastal Bend (Arkansas, Bee Jim Wells, Kleberg, Nueces, Refugio, San Patricio), Rostown, Banquete, and Nueces County or Kleberg County. Applicants must have a minimum of 3.5-3.0 high school GPA. **Criteria:** Applicants are evaluated based on academic achievement and financial need.

Funds Avail.: $1,000. **Number Awarded:** 4. **To Apply:** Applicants must submit completed applications which can be downloaded from the website of the Foundation. **Deadline:** March 1.

2959 ■ Jim Springer Memorial Scholarships
(Undergraduate/Scholarship)

Purpose: To provide financial assistance to further the education of deserving students in Coastal Bend. **Focus:** Public relations; Marketing and distribution; Advertising; Communications. **Qualif.:** Applicants must be Coastal Bend residents; full-time college sophomore, junior or senior students with grade point average of 2.5; majoring in public relations, marketing, advertising or communications. **Criteria:** Applicants are evaluated based on academic performance and financial need.

Funds Avail.: $500. **Number Awarded:** 1. **To Apply:** Applicants must submit all the required application information. **Deadline:** March 1.

2960 ■ Stewart Title Firefighters Scholarships
(High School, Undergraduate/Scholarship)

Purpose: To provide financial assistance to high school seniors and college students who are descendants of volunteer firefighters in Coastal Bend. **Focus:** General studies. **Qualif.:** Applicants must be high school seniors or college students in Coastal Bend; must be children of uniformed and volunteer firefighters for a fire department located in Coastal Bend; and must have maintained a 3.0 GPA and complete at least 12 credit hours per semester. **Criteria:** Applicants are evaluated based on academic performance and financial need.

Funds Avail.: $250. **Number Awarded:** 2. **To Apply:** Applicants must submit all the required application information. **Deadline:** March 11.

2961 ■ Talbert Family Memorial Accounting and Financial Management Scholarships
(Undergraduate/Scholarship)

Purpose: To provide financial assistance to deserving accounting students of Texas for furthering their education in the field. **Focus:** Accounting. **Qualif.:** Applicants must be full-time college juniors majoring in accounting at a Texas college with 3.25 grade point average; must have graduated from a Coastal Bend high school and permanently reside in Coastal Bend. **Criteria:** Applicants must submit all the required application information.

Funds Avail.: $2,000. **To Apply:** Applicants must submit all the required application information. **Deadline:** March 1.

2962 ■ Faye and Rendell Webb Scholarships
(Undergraduate/Scholarship)

Purpose: To help needy students in financing their college education. **Focus:** Education. **Qualif.:** Applicants must be students graduated from Miller or Moody high schools, with preference for students who attended Los Encinos, Lamar or Lozano elementary schools for at least one year; must be education majors who are attending college in the state of Texas; must be students who have an average of 85 percent or better or maintain 3.0 GPA on 4.0 scale and complete at least 12 credits per semester. **Criteria:** Applicants are evaluated based on academic achievement and financial need.

Funds Avail.: $1,000. **Number Awarded:** 2. **To Apply:** Applicants must download application form from the website of CBC Foundation or obtain it from Miller and Moody high school counselor's offices. **Deadline:** March 1.

2963 ■ Wheelchair Success Foundation Scholarships
(Undergraduate/Scholarship)

Purpose: To provide an opportunity for people permanently confined to a wheelchair to attend college or technical school. **Focus:** General school. **Qualif.:** Applicants must be graduates or GED certificate holders who attended a Coastal Bend high school; permanently confined to a wheelchair; must maintain nine credit hours per semester with GPA of 2.5 while attending an accredited university, college or technical school. **Criteria:** Applicants are evaluated based on scholastic performance and financial need.

Funds Avail.: $500. **Number Awarded:** 1. **To Apply:** Applicants must download application form from the website of CBC Foundation or inquire through telephone call to the Foundation. **Deadline:** March 1.

2964 ■ Dr. Dana Williams Scholarships
(Undergraduate/Scholarship)

Purpose: To provide educational assistance to students planning to become teachers or public school administrators. **Focus:** Education. **Qualif.:** Applicants must be: high school seniors graduating at the end of the spring semester; planning to become teachers or public school administrators; enrolled as full-time students in college (12 hours or more). Applicants must have a cumulative high school GPA of 90 percent or more; must be graduates from a high school in the Corpus Christi Independent School District and must be permanent residents of Corpus Christi. **Criteria:** Applicants are judged based on financial need.

Funds Avail.: $4,000. **Number Awarded:** 1. **To Apply:** Applicants must download an application form from the website of the CBC Foundation or obtain it by calling 361-882-9745. **Deadline:** March 1.

2965 ■ Coca-Cola Scholars Foundation
PO Box 442
Atlanta, GA 30301
Fax: (404) 733-5439
Free: 800-306-2653
E-mail: scholars@na.ko.com
URL: www.coca-colascholars.org

2966 ■ Coca-Cola Scholars Foundation Four-Year Awards for Seniors *(Undergraduate/Scholarship)*

Purpose: To provide scholarships to high school seniors. **Focus:** General studies. **Qualif.:** Applicants must be high school seniors attending school in the US; must be U.S. citizens, U.S. Nationals, or permanent residents; must be seniors anticipating completion of a high school diploma during the academic year in which application is made;

Awards are arranged alphabetically below their administering organizations

must be seniors planning to pursue a degree at an accredited U.S. postsecondary institution; and must be carrying a minimum 3.0 GPA at the end of their junior year of high school. **Criteria:** Selection will be based on the committee's criteria.

Funds Avail.: $10,000 and $20,000. **Number Awarded:** 250. **To Apply:** Applicants may apply online and must complete all parts of the application process. **Deadline:** October 31. **Contact:** Coca-Cola at the above address.

2967 ■ College Art Association (CAA)
275 7th Ave.
New York, NY 10001
Ph: (212) 691-1051
Fax: (212) 627-2381
E-mail: nyoffice@collegeart.org

2968 ■ College Art Association Professional Development Fellowships *(Graduate/Fellowship)*

Purpose: To help student artists and art historians bridge the gap between graduate studies and professional careers. **Focus:** Visual arts. **Qualif.:** Applicants must be graduate students in visual arts; must be CAA members; must be citizens and permanent residents of the United States; must have an MFA degree; and should demonstrate distinction in approach, technique or perspective in contribution to the visual arts. **Criteria:** Applicants will be evaluated based on submitted application materials.

Funds Avail.: $5,000. **To Apply:** Applicants must complete the application form and submit the following: a personal essay and resume in a CD format; visual documentation of work completed within the past two years; slide list with the number or title of each work. A (one-page) outline and description must be included in a CD or DVD; three letters of recommendation; an official copy of the birth certificate or driver's license as proof of citizenship; and a current graduate transcript that must be submitted in hard copy. **Deadline:** October 1. **Contact:** Questions may be addressed to Michael Fahlund at the above address or e-mail mfahlund@collegeart.org.

2969 ■ College Art Association Wyeth Publication Grants *(Professional development/Grant)*

Purpose: To support a book-length, scholarly manuscript in the history of American art, visual studies and related subjects that have been accepted by the publisher but cannot be published in the most desirable form without a subsidy. **Focus:** Visual arts. **Qualif.:** Applicants must be institutional CAA members. **Criteria:** Applicants will be selected based on published work. Committees will evaluate books based on the following criteria: 1) topics on art before 1970; 2) topics with a naturally small market or unusually high expenses; 3) works by disadvantaged scholars, including those at the earlier stages of a career, younger scholars, curators, issued by smaller museums, or undeserved constituencies.

Funds Avail.: Amount not specified. **Number Awarded:** 3. **To Apply:** Applicants must submit a curriculum vitae, narrative description, author's response to peer reviews, publisher's cover letter, partial manuscript and two or more peer reviews of the manuscript that have been submitted to the publisher. **Deadline:** October 1. **Contact:** For further information, applicants must contact Alex Gershuny at the above address.

2970 ■ College of Healthcare Information Management Executives (CHIME)
3300 Washtenaw Ave., Ste. 225
Ann Arbor, MI 48104-5184
Ph: (734) 665-0000
Fax: (734) 665-4922
E-mail: staff@cio-chime.org
URL: www.cio-chime.org

2971 ■ John Glaser Scholarships
(Undergraduate/Scholarship)

Purpose: To acknowledge IT staff members who show potential for advancement to a CIO and who are dedicated to professional development. **Focus:** Health care services. **Qualif.:** Candidates must be employed and nominated by a current CHIME member. **Criteria:** Recipients are selected based on Committee's review of the CIO potential and dedication to professional development.

Funds Avail.: $3,000. **Number Awarded:** 2. **To Apply:** Applicants must provide resume; and (500 to 1,000-word) essay describing: visions and goals; handling their responsibilities; financial challenges that prohibit them to participate in leadership development activities; and benefits they can get to the program they choose to attend. Applicant's direct supervisor is required to complete the questions on the application. **Deadline:** June 22. **Contact:** Application form and materials should be mailed to CHIME Scholarship Committee at the above address.

2972 ■ College Student Educators International
One Dupont Cir. NW, Ste. 300
Washington, DC 20036
Ph: (202) 835-2272
Fax: (202) 296-3286
E-mail: info@acpa.nche.edu
URL: www.myacpa.org

2973 ■ Educational Leadership Foundation Grants *(Undergraduate/Grant)*

Purpose: To enhance the student affairs profession; to generate and disseminate knowledge about college students. **Focus:** General studies. **Qualif.:** Applicants must be currently enrolled in a college, university and institution. **Criteria:** Recipients are selected based on the submitted project proposal.

Funds Avail.: $10,000. **To Apply:** Applicants must complete the online application form including the name and contact information. **Deadline:** February 1. **Contact:** Lynn Willet, lwillett@coastal.edu.

2974 ■ College Success Foundation (CSF)
1605 NW Sammamish Rd., Ste. 200
Issaquah, WA 98027-5388
Ph: (425) 416-2000
Fax: (425) 416-2001
Free: 877-655-4097
URL: www.collegesuccessfoundation.org

2975 ■ Chateau Ste. Michelle Scholarship Fund
(Undergraduate/Scholarship)

Purpose: To provide financial support for students to attend a four-year college degree. **Focus:** General studies. **Qualif.:** Applicants must have plan to attend, or currently

Awards are arranged alphabetically below their administering organizations

attending an eligible four-year college or university in Washington State; must be residents of Washington; must have plan to file or have already filed a FAFSA, if eligible; must have 2.75 cumulative GPA; and be enrolled full-time (12 credits per quarter or equivalent for semester) as college students. **Criteria:** Recipients will be selected based on submitted materials.

Funds Avail.: Amount not specified. **To Apply:** Applicants must complete the application form and contact CSF for further information. **Contact:** Barry Goren at 425-679-5546 or bgoren@collegesuccessfoundation.org.

2976 ■ Leadership 1000 Scholarships
(Undergraduate/Scholarship)

Purpose: To provide college scholarships to deserving students who need assistance attending an eligible four-year college or university in Washington State. **Focus:** General studies. **Qualif.:** Applicants must have plan to attend, or currently attending an eligible four-year college or university in Washington State; must be enrolled in a full-time basis; must be Washington State residents; must have plan to file or have already filed a FAFSA, if eligible; must have 2.75 cumulative GPA. **Criteria:** Recipients will be selected based on submitted materials.

Funds Avail.: $2,500-$5,000. **To Apply:** Applicants must complete the application form and must contact CSF office for other required materials. **Deadline:** March 23. **Contact:** For further information, applicants must contact 877-355-4617 or e-mail at helpdesk@collegesuccessfoundation.org.

2977 ■ Realize the Dream Scholarships
(Undergraduate/Scholarship)

Purpose: To support high school undergraduates who do not qualify for federal and state financial aid programs, but who do qualify for resident student status for state tuition and fees. **Focus:** General studies. **Qualif.:** Applicants must be undocumented residents of the United States and therefore do not qualify to apply for federal or state financial aid programs; must receive their high school diploma from a Washington State High School; must have 2.0 or higher high school GPA; must have plan to enroll in a college in full-time and complete an associate's and/or bachelor's degree at an eligible Washington educational institution; must be eligible to file the HB 1079 affidavit with public colleges and universities in order to permit them to quality for tuition rates that Washington State residents pay; and must have family size and income level that meets the program requirements. **Criteria:** Recipients will be evaluated based on GPA, cost of attendance, financial aid and scholarships awarded at the college or university to be attended.

Funds Avail.: $5,000. **To Apply:** Applicants must submit a completed application form. **Deadline:** June 18. **Remarks:** Applicants are eligible for HB 1079 if they have lived in Washington State for three years prior to receiving high school diploma or GED, lived continuously within the state since earning the diploma.

2978 ■ Washington State Governors' Scholarship for Foster Youth *(Undergraduate/Scholarship)*

Purpose: To help young men and women who are currently in an open dependency court order in Washington State, or an open dependency tribal court order, continue their education and earn a college degree. **Focus:** General studies. **Qualif.:** Applicants must be Washington State High School seniors and on track to graduate from high school; must have cumulative GPA of 2.0 or higher; must have

plan to enroll in a college on a full-time basis; must have resided in Washington State for at least three academic years prior to high school graduation; must be currently in an open dependency court order that resulted from intervention by Washington State on their behalf and have been placed in any of the following living situations: a) foster care; b) dependency guardianship; and c) guardianship. **Criteria:** Applicants will be selected based on eligibility and submitted materials.

Funds Avail.: $2,000-$4,000. **Number Awarded:** 40. **To Apply:** Applicants must contact CSF office for further information.

2979 ■ Collegiate Soaring Association (CSA)
PO Box 337081
Greeley, CO 80633
Ph: (970) 330-2050
E-mail: governor@coloradosoaring.org
URL: www.coloradosoaring.org/ssa/coll/home.htm

2980 ■ Gogos Scholarships *(Undergraduate/Scholarship)*

Purpose: To support young people in school, primarily college students, from first flight through advanced soaring. **Focus:** Aviation. **Qualif.:** Applicant must be a U.S. citizen or permanent resident student, aged 14-25 nominated by an FAI soaring badge holder within a sponsoring Soaring Club or Operator. **Criteria:** Candidates are judged based on criteria like the applicants' desire to soar, plans to help promote the amateur sport of soaring among young people in school, and financial need.

Funds Avail.: No specific amount. **Number Awarded:** 1. **To Apply:** Applicants must submit complete application form. **Deadline:** March 31.

2981 ■ Colorado Association of Stormwater and Floodplain Managers (CASFM)
c/o David Mallory, P.E.
2480 W 26th Ave., Ste. 156B
Denver, CO 80211
Ph: (303) 455-6277
E-mail: dmallory@udfcd.org
URL: www.casfm.org

2982 ■ CASFM-Ben Urbonas Scholarships
(Graduate/Scholarship)

Purpose: To provide financial assistance to students and to promote interest among themselves and the engineering community in CASFM. **Focus:** Hydrology; Meteorology; Atmospheric science. **Qualif.:** Applicants must be U.S. citizens enrolled in a graduate program closely related to CASFM's goals at a College or University in the State of Colorado and be registered to take at least three credit-hours of coursework per semester. Eligible programs of study include, but are not limited to hydrology, hydraulics, watershed management, floodplain management, stormwater management, stormwater quality, emergency response, meteorology and climatology. **Criteria:** Selection will be based on the evaluation of applications and specific criteria.

Funds Avail.: $2,500. **Number Awarded:** 3. **To Apply:** Applicants must submit a completed application form; a short essay (up to 500 words) describing personal and career goals. **Deadline:** March. **Contact:** Applicants must contact Shea Thomas at the above address or e-mail at sthomas@udfcd.org.

Awards are arranged alphabetically below their administering organizations

2983 ■ Colorado Broadcasters Association (CBA)

445 Union Blvd., Ste. 306
Lakewood, CO 80228
Ph: (720) 536-5427
Fax: (720) 536-5259
E-mail: cba@coloradobroadcasters.org.
URL: www.coloradobroadcasters.org

2984 ■ Colorado Broadcasters Association Continuing Education Scholarships *(Professional development/Scholarship)*

Purpose: To encourage enhanced educational opportunities for Colorado broadcasters and to foster an ever-improving work force in Colorado radio and television. **Focus:** Broadcasting. **Qualif.:** Applicants must be full-time employees of a Colorado broadcast station; must have been employed by that station for a minimum of one year; and the station must be a member in good standing of the CBA. Applicants must be residents of Colorado, as defined by the Colorado Commission of Higher Education. **Criteria:** Award will be on a first-come, first-served basis until funds are depleted.

Funds Avail.: $10,000. **Number Awarded:** 3. **To Apply:** Applicants must visit the CBA website to download the application form. Applications must be submitted using the official CBA Continuing Education Scholarship form and must be accompanied by the indicated attachments.

2985 ■ Colorado Christian University Alumni Association

c/o Alumni Relations
8787 W Alameda Ave.
Lakewood, CO 80226
Ph: (303) 963-3330
Fax: (303) 963-3331
Free: 800-44F-AITH
E-mail: alumni@ccu.edu
URL: www.ccu.edu/alumni

2986 ■ CCU Alumni Endowed Scholarships *(Undergraduate/Scholarship)*

Purpose: To assist students with the cost of post-secondary education. **Focus:** General studies. **Qualif.:** Applicant must be pursuing a baccalaureate degree; completed at least 85 credits, with a minimum of 24 credits earned at CCU; have a GPA of 3.3 or above; demonstrated the need of financial assistance; shows local church or community involvement; and have an alumni sponsor. **Criteria:** Selection is based on merit.

Funds Avail.: $20,000. **To Apply:** Applicants may contact the Alumni Relations for more details on the scholarship. **Remarks:** Funds established by the CCU Alumni Association.

2987 ■ Colorado Hotel and Lodging Association (CH&LA)

730 17th St., Ste. 920
Denver, CO 80202
Ph: (303) 297-8335
Fax: (303) 297-8104
E-mail: info@chla.com
URL: www.coloradolodging.com

2988 ■ Karl Mehlmann Scholarships *(Undergraduate/Scholarship)*

Purpose: To offer college students an opportunity to apply for this scholarship to overcome financial need. **Focus:** Culinary Arts. **Qualif.:** Applicants must be enrolled in an accredited four-year university or college and be majoring in hotel and/or restaurant management; must also be enrolled in the final year at the Culinary Institute of America; must be freshmen, sophomores, juniors or seniors who are going to graduate school; must carry a minimum workload of 12 hours per quarter or semester; must have maintain a minimum overall GPA of 3.0 on a 4.0 scale; must be U.S. citizens. **Criteria:** Recipients are selected based on the grammar and spelling of the essay.

Funds Avail.: No specific amount. **To Apply:** Applicants must submit one official transcript from current school or most recent if not currently attending school; must submit a brief autobiography; a one-page, typewritten essay answering why you've selected the hospitality industry for your career and what definition of hospitality is; must submit a type, signed and on letterhead recommendation letter from College or University; signature from Director/Dean. **Contact:** Questions can be addressed to Stephanie Van Cleve at the above address; E-mail: stephanie@chla.com.

2989 ■ Colorado Nurses Foundation (CNF)

7400 E Arapahoe Rd., No. 211
Centennial, CO 80112
Ph: (303) 694-4728
Fax: (303) 694-4869
E-mail: mail@cnfound.org
URL: www.cnfound.org

2990 ■ Roy Anderson Memorial Scholarships *(Graduate, Undergraduate/Scholarship)*

Purpose: To provide scholarships for qualified nursing students from both rural and urban settings. **Focus:** Nursing. **Qualif.:** Applicant must be a Colorado resident committed to practicing nursing in Colorado; must be a student in an approved Colorado Nursing Program; must have a minimum of 3.25 GPA (for undergraduate applicants) or 3.5 GPA (for graduate applicants); and must have one of the following student statuses: (1) Junior or senior level BSN undergraduate student; (2) RN enrolled in a baccalaureate or higher degree nursing program in a school of nursing; (3) Student in second year of nursing studies in an associate degree in nursing program; (4) RN with master's degree in nursing, currently practicing in Colorado and enrolled in a doctoral program; (5) Student in second or third year of a Doctorate Nursing Practice (DNP) program. **Criteria:** Scholarship application will be rated based on the following: (1) Professional philosophy and goals; (2) Dedication to the improvement of patient care in Colorado; (3) Demonstrated commitment to nursing, critical thinking skills and potential for leadership; (4) Involvement in community and professional organizations; (5) GPA-minimum of 3.25 undergraduate, 3.5 graduate; (6) Financial need; (7) Recommendation of one faculty member; and (8) Employer/Supervisor recommendation.

Funds Avail.: $5,000. **Number Awarded:** 2. **To Apply:** Applicants must submit a cover sheet, financial need statement, resume, recommendation form from Faculty and Employer in a separated sealed envelope, copy of transcript including the last semester grades. Student essay must be no more than three pages, double-spaced in a 12pt. font with 1″ each margin. **Deadline:** October 29. **Contact:** Ques-

Awards are arranged alphabetically below their administering organizations

tions and submission can be addressed to Vicki Carroll at the above address; Phone: 970-416-6811; Fax: 970-416-6820; E-mail: cnfscholarships@aol.com.

2991 ■ Banner Health System - McKee Medical Center, Loveland: Nightingale Scholarships
(Graduate, Undergraduate/Scholarship)

Purpose: To provide scholarships for qualified nursing students from both rural and urban settings. **Focus:** Nursing. **Qualif.:** Applicants must be Colorado residents committed to practicing nursing in Colorado; must be students in an approved Colorado Nursing Program; must have a minimum of 3.25 GPA (undergraduate) and 3.5 GPA (graduate); and must have one of the following student statuses: (1) Junior or senior level BSN undergraduate student; (2) RN enrolled in a baccalaureate or higher degree nursing program in a school of nursing; (3) Student in second year of nursing studies in an associate degree in nursing program; (4) RN with master's degree in nursing, currently practicing in Colorado and enrolled in a doctoral program; (5) Student in second or third year of a Doctorate Nursing Practice (DNP) program. **Criteria:** Scholarship application will be rated based on the following: (1) Professional philosophy and goals; (2) Dedication to the improvement of patient care in Colorado; (3) Demonstrated commitment to nursing, critical thinking skills, and potential for leadership; (4) Involvement in community and professional organizations; (5) GPA-minimum of 3.25 undergraduate, 3.5 graduate; (6) Financial need; (7) Recommendation of one faculty member, and (8) Employer/Supervisor recommendation.

Funds Avail.: $1,000. **Contact:** Vicki Carroll, RN, 728 Cherokee Dr., Ft. Collins, CO 80525 at 970-416-6811/970-416-6820 (fax) or cnfscholarships@aol.com.

2992 ■ Banner Health System - North Colorado Medical Center, Greeley: Nightingale Scholarships *(Graduate, Undergraduate/Scholarship)*

Purpose: To provide scholarships for qualified nursing students from both rural and urban settings. **Focus:** Nursing. **Qualif.:** Applicant must be a Colorado resident committed to practicing nursing in Colorado; must be a student in an approved Colorado Nursing Program; must have a minimum of 3.25 GPA for undergraduate and 3.5 GPA for a graduate applicant; and must have one of the following student statuses: (1) Junior or senior level BSN undergraduate student; (2) RN enrolled in a baccalaureate or higher degree nursing program in a school of nursing; (3) Student in second year of nursing studies in an associate degree in nursing program; (4) RN with master's degree in nursing, currently practicing in Colorado and enrolled in a doctoral program; (5) Student in second or third year of a Doctorate Nursing Practice (DNP) program. **Criteria:** Scholarship application will be rated based on the following: (1) Professional philosophy and goals; (2) Dedication to the improvement of patient care in Colorado; (3) Demonstrated commitment to nursing, critical thinking skills and potential for leadership; (4) Involvement in community and professional organizations; (5) GPA-minimum of 3.25 undergraduate, 3.5 graduate; (6) Financial need; (7) Recommendation of one faculty member, and (8) Employer/Supervisor recommendation.

Funds Avail.: $1,000. **To Apply:** Applicants are advised to contact the foundation at Colorado Nurses Foundation for further information. **Deadline:** October 31. **Contact:** Application form and supporting documents should be sent to: Vicki Carroll at the above address.

2993 ■ Colorado Nurses Association: Nightingale Scholarships *(Graduate, Undergraduate/Scholarship)*

Purpose: To provide scholarships for qualified nursing students from both rural and urban settings. **Focus:** Nursing. **Qualif.:** Applicant must be a Colorado resident committed to practicing nursing in Colorado; must be a student in an approved Colorado Nursing Program; must have a minimum of 3.25 GPA for undergraduate and 3.5 GPA for a graduate applicant; and must have one of the following student statuses: (1) Junior or senior level BSN undergraduate student; (2) RN enrolled in a baccalaureate or higher degree nursing program in a school of nursing; (3) Student in second year of nursing studies in an associate degree in nursing program; (4) RN with master's degree in nursing, currently practicing in Colorado and enrolled in a doctoral program; (5) Student in second or third year of a Doctorate Nursing Practice (DNP) program. **Criteria:** Scholarship application will be rated based on the following: (1) Professional philosophy and goals; (2) Dedication to the improvement of patient care in Colorado; (3) Demonstrated commitment to nursing, critical thinking skills and potential for leadership; (4) Involvement in community and professional organizations; (5) GPA-minimum of 3.25 undergraduate, 3.5 graduate; (6) Financial need; (7) Recommendation of one faculty member, and (8) Employer/Supervisor recommendation.

Funds Avail.: $1,000. **To Apply:** Applicants are advised to contact the foundation at Colorado Nurses Foundation for further information. **Deadline:** October 31. **Contact:** Application form and supporting documents should be sent to: Vicki Carroll at the above address.

2994 ■ Colorado Nurses Foundation Nightingale Scholarships *(Graduate, Undergraduate/Scholarship)*

Purpose: To provide scholarships for qualified nursing students from both rural and urban settings. **Focus:** Nursing. **Qualif.:** Applicant must be a Colorado resident committed to practicing nursing in Colorado; must be a student in an approved Colorado Nursing Program; must have a minimum of 3.25 GPA (for undergraduate applicants) or 3.5 GPA (for graduate applicants); and must have one of the following student statuses: (1) Junior or senior level BSN undergraduate student; (2) RN enrolled in a baccalaureate or higher degree nursing program in a school of nursing; (3) Student in second year of nursing studies in an associate degree in nursing program; (4) RN with master's degree in nursing, currently practicing in Colorado and enrolled in a doctoral program; (5) Student in second or third year of a Doctorate Nursing Practice (DNP) program. **Criteria:** Scholarship application will be rated based on the following: (1) Professional philosophy and goals; (2) Dedication to the improvement of patient care in Colorado; (3) Demonstrated commitment to nursing, critical thinking skills and potential for leadership; (4) Involvement in community and professional organizations; (5) GPA-minimum of 3.25 undergraduate, 3.5 graduate; (6) Financial need; (7) Recommendation of one faculty member; and (8) Employer/Supervisor recommendation.

Funds Avail.: $1,000. **Number Awarded:** 10. **To Apply:** Applicants must submit a cover sheet, financial need statement, resume, recommendation form from Faculty and Employer in a separated sealed envelope, copy of transcript including the last semester grades. Student essay must be no more than three pages, double-spaced in a 12pt. font with 1″ each margin. **Deadline:** October 29. **Contact:** Ques-

Awards are arranged alphabetically below their administering organizations

tions and submission can be addressed to Vicki Carroll at the above address; Phone: 970-416-6811; Fax: 970-416-6820; E-mail: cnfscholarships@aol.com.

2995 ■ Colorado Organization of Nursing Leaders Scholarships *(Graduate, Undergraduate/ Scholarship)*

Purpose: To provide scholarships for qualified nursing students from both rural and urban settings. **Focus:** Nursing. **Qualif.:** Applicant must be a Colorado resident committed to practicing nursing in Colorado; must be a student in an approved Colorado Nursing Program; must have a minimum of 3.25 GPA (for undergraduate applicants) or 3.5 GPA (for graduate applicants); and must have one of the following student statuses: (1) Junior or senior level BSN undergraduate student; (2) RN enrolled in a baccalaureate or higher degree nursing program in a school of nursing; (3) Student in second year of nursing studies in an associate degree in nursing program; (4) RN with master's degree in nursing, currently practicing in Colorado and enrolled in a doctoral program; (5) Student in second or third year of a Doctorate Nursing Practice (DNP) program. **Criteria:** Scholarship application will be rated based on the following: (1) Professional philosophy and goals; (2) Dedication to the improvement of patient care in Colorado; (3) Demonstrated commitment to nursing, critical thinking skills and potential for leadership; (4) Involvement in community and professional organizations; (5) GPA-minimum of 3.25 undergraduate, 3.5 graduate; (6) Financial need; (7) Recommendation of one faculty member; and (8) Employer/Supervisor recommendation.

Funds Avail.: $1,250. **To Apply:** Applicants must submit a cover sheet, financial need statement, resume, recommendation form from Faculty and Employer in a separated sealed envelope, copy of transcript including the last semester grades. Student essay must be no more than three pages, double-spaced in a 12pt. font with 1″ each margin. **Deadline:** October 29. **Contact:** Questions and submission can be addressed to Vicki Carroll at the above address; Phone: 970-416-6811; Fax: 970-416-6820; E-mail: cnfscholarships@aol.com.

2996 ■ Red and Lola Fehr: Nightingale Scholarships *(Graduate, Undergraduate/Scholarship)*

Purpose: To provide scholarships for qualified nursing students from both rural and urban settings. **Focus:** Nursing. **Qualif.:** Applicant must be a Colorado resident committed to practicing nursing in Colorado; must be a student in an approved Colorado Nursing Program; must have a minimum of 3.25 GPA (for undergraduate applicants) or 3.5 GPA (for graduate applicants); and must have one of the following student statuses: (1) Junior or senior level BSN undergraduate student; (2) RN enrolled in a baccalaureate or higher degree nursing program in a school of nursing; (3) Student in second year of nursing studies in an associate degree in nursing program; (4) RN with master's degree in nursing, currently practicing in Colorado and enrolled in a doctoral program; (5) Student in second or third year of a Doctorate Nursing Practice (DNP) program. **Criteria:** Scholarship application will be rated based on the following: (1) Professional philosophy and goals; (2) Dedication to the improvement of patient care in Colorado; (3) Demonstrated commitment to nursing, critical thinking skills and potential for leadership; (4) Involvement in community and professional organizations; (5) GPA-minimum of 3.25 undergraduate, 3.5 graduate; (6) Financial need; (7) Recommendation of one faculty member; and (8) Employer/Supervisor recommendation.

Funds Avail.: $1,000. **To Apply:** Applicants must submit a cover sheet, financial need statement, resume, recommendation form from Faculty and Employer in a separated sealed envelope, copy of transcript including the last semester grades. Student essay must be no more than three pages, double-spaced in a 12pt. font with 1″ each margin. **Deadline:** October 29. **Contact:** Questions and submission can be addressed to Vicki Carroll at the above address; Phone: 970-416-6811; Fax: 970-416-6820; E-mail: cnfscholarships@aol.com.

2997 ■ Johnson and Johnson: Nightingale Scholarships *(Graduate, Undergraduate/ Scholarship)*

Purpose: To provide scholarships for qualified nursing students from both rural and urban settings. **Focus:** Nursing. **Qualif.:** Applicant must be a Colorado resident committed to practicing nursing in Colorado; must be a student in an approved Colorado Nursing Program; must have a minimum of 3.25 GPA (for undergraduate applicants) or 3.5 GPA (for graduate applicants); and must have one of the following student statuses: (1) Junior or senior level BSN undergraduate student; (2) RN enrolled in a baccalaureate or higher degree nursing program in a school of nursing; (3) Student in second year of nursing studies in an associate degree in nursing program; (4) RN with master's degree in nursing, currently practicing in Colorado and enrolled in a doctoral program; (5) Student in second or third year of a Doctorate Nursing Practice (DNP) program. **Criteria:** Scholarship application will be rated based on the following: (1) Professional philosophy and goals; (2) Dedication to the improvement of patient care in Colorado; (3) Demonstrated commitment to nursing, critical thinking skills and potential for leadership; (4) Involvement in community and professional organizations; (5) GPA-minimum of 3.25 undergraduate, 3.5 graduate; (6) Financial need; (7) Recommendation of one faculty member, and (8) Employer/Supervisor recommendation.

Funds Avail.: $1,000. **To Apply:** Applicants are advised to contact the foundation at Colorado Nurses Foundation for further information. **Deadline:** October 31. **Contact:** Application form and supporting documents should be sent to: Vicki Carroll at the above address.

2998 ■ Kaiser Permanente: Nightingale Scholarships *(Graduate, Undergraduate/ Scholarship)*

Purpose: To provide scholarships for qualified nursing students from both rural and urban settings. **Focus:** Nursing. **Qualif.:** Applicant must be a Colorado resident committed to practicing nursing in Colorado; must be a student in an approved Colorado Nursing Program; must have a minimum of 3.25 GPA (for undergraduate applicants) or 3.5 GPA (for graduate applicants); and must have one of the following student statuses: (1) Junior or senior level BSN undergraduate student; (2) RN enrolled in a baccalaureate or higher degree nursing program in a school of nursing; (3) Student in second year of nursing studies in an associate degree in nursing program; (4) RN with master's degree in nursing, currently practicing in Colorado and enrolled in a doctoral program; (5) Student in second or third year of a Doctorate Nursing Practice (DNP) program. **Criteria:** Scholarship application will be rated based on the following: (1) Professional philosophy and goals; (2) Dedication to the improvement of patient care in Colorado; (3) Demonstrated commitment to nursing, critical thinking skills and potential for leadership; (4) Involvement in community and professional organizations; (5) GPA-minimum of 3.25 undergradu-

Awards are arranged alphabetically below their administering organizations

ate, 3.5 graduate; (6) Financial need; (7) Recommendation of one faculty member; and (8) Employer/Supervisor recommendation.

Funds Avail.: $1,000. **To Apply:** Applicants must submit a cover sheet, financial need statement, resume, recommendation form from Faculty and Employer in a separated sealed envelope, copy of transcript including the last semester grades. Student essay must be no more than three pages, double-spaced in a 12pt. font with 1" each margin. **Deadline:** October 29. **Contact:** Questions and submission can be addressed to Vicki Carroll at the above address; Phone: 970-416-6811; Fax: 970-416-6820; E-mail: cnfscholarships@aol.com.

2999 ■ H.M. Muffly Memorial Scholarships
(Graduate, Undergraduate/Scholarship)

Purpose: To provide scholarships for qualified nursing students from both rural and urban settings. **Focus:** Nursing. **Qualif.:** Applicant must be a Colorado resident committed to practicing nursing in Colorado; must be a student in an approved Colorado Nursing Program; must have a minimum of 3.25 GPA (for undergraduate applicants) or 3.5 GPA (for graduate applicants); and must have one of the following student statuses: (1) Junior or senior level BSN undergraduate student; (2) RN enrolled in a baccalaureate or higher degree nursing program in a school of nursing; (3) Student in second year of nursing studies in an associate degree in nursing program; (4) RN with master's degree in nursing, currently practicing in Colorado and enrolled in a doctoral program; (5) Student in second or third year of a Doctorate Nursing Practice (DNP) program. **Criteria:** Scholarship application will be rated based on the following: (1) Professional philosophy and goals; (2) Dedication to the improvement of patient care in Colorado; (3) Demonstrated commitment to nursing, critical thinking skills and potential for leadership; (4) Involvement in community and professional organizations; (5) GPA-minimum of 3.25 undergraduate, 3.5 graduate; (6) Financial need; (7) Recommendation of one faculty member; and (8) Employer/Supervisor recommendation.

Funds Avail.: $2,500. **Number Awarded:** 2. **To Apply:** Applicants must submit a cover sheet, financial need statement, resume, recommendation form from Faculty and Employer in a separated sealed envelope, copy of transcript including the last semester grades. Student essay must be no more than three pages, double-spaced in a 12pt. font with 1" each margin. **Deadline:** October 29. **Contact:** Questions and submission can be addressed to Vicki Carroll at the above address; Phone: 970-416-6811; Fax: 970-416-6820; E-mail: cnfscholarships@aol.com.

3000 ■ Colorado Nurses Association: Virginia Paulson Memorial Scholarships *(Graduate, Undergraduate/Scholarship)*

Purpose: To provide scholarships for qualified nursing students from both rural and urban settings. **Focus:** Nursing. **Qualif.:** Applicant must be a Colorado resident committed to practicing nursing in Colorado; must be a student in an approved Colorado Nursing Program; must have a minimum of 3.25 GPA (for undergraduate applicants) or 3.5 GPA (for graduate applicants); and must have one of the following student statuses: (1) Junior or senior level BSN undergraduate student; (2) RN enrolled in a baccalaureate or higher degree nursing program in a school of nursing; (3) Student in second year of nursing studies in an associate degree in nursing program; (4) RN with master's degree in nursing, currently practicing in Colorado and enrolled in a doctoral program; (5) Student in second or third year of a

Doctorate Nursing Practice (DNP) program. **Criteria:** Scholarship application will be rated based on the following: (1) Professional philosophy and goals; (2) Dedication to the improvement of patient care in Colorado; (3) Demonstrated commitment to nursing, critical thinking skills and potential for leadership; (4) Involvement in community and professional organizations; (5) GPA-minimum of 3.25 undergraduate, 3.5 graduate; (6) Financial need; (7) Recommendation of one faculty member, and (8) Employer/Supervisor recommendation.

Funds Avail.: $1,000. **To Apply:** Applicants must submit a cover sheet, financial need statement, resume, recommendation form from Faculty and Employer in a separated sealed envelope, copy of transcript including the last semester grades. Student essay must be no more than three pages, double-spaced in a 12pt. font with 1" each margin. **Deadline:** October 29. **Contact:** Questions and submission can be addressed to Vicki Carroll at the above address; Phone: 970-416-6811; Fax: 970-416-6820; E-mail: cnfscholarships@aol.com.

3001 ■ Poudre Valley Health System, Fort Collins: Nightingale Scholarships *(Graduate, Undergraduate/Scholarship)*

Purpose: To provide scholarships for qualified nursing students from both rural and urban settings. **Focus:** Nursing. **Qualif.:** Applicant must be a Colorado resident committed to practicing nursing in Colorado; must be a student in an approved Colorado Nursing Program; must have a minimum of 3.25 GPA (for undergraduate applicants) or 3.5 GPA (for graduate applicants); and must have one of the following student statuses: (1) Junior or senior level BSN undergraduate student; (2) RN enrolled in a baccalaureate or higher degree nursing program in a school of nursing; (3) Student in second year of nursing studies in an associate degree in nursing program; (4) RN with master's degree in nursing, currently practicing in Colorado and enrolled in a doctoral program; (5) Student in second or third year of a Doctorate Nursing Practice (DNP) program. **Criteria:** Scholarship application will be rated based on the following: (1) Professional philosophy and goals; (2) Dedication to the improvement of patient care in Colorado; (3) Demonstrated commitment to nursing, critical thinking skills, and potential for leadership; (4) Involvement in community and professional organizations; (5) GPA-minimum of 3.25 undergraduate, 3.5 graduate; (6) Financial need; (7) Recommendation of one faculty member; and (8) Employer/Supervisor recommendation.

Funds Avail.: $1,000. **Number Awarded:** 2. **To Apply:** Applicants must submit a cover sheet, financial need statement, resume, recommendation form from Faculty and Employer in a separated sealed envelope, copy of trancript including the last semester grades. Student essay must be no more than three pages, double-spaced in a 12pt. font with 1" each margin. **Deadline:** October 29. **Contact:** Questions and submission can be addressed to Vicki Carroll at the above address; Phone: 970-416-6811; Fax: 970-416-6820; E-mail: cnfscholarships@aol.com.

3002 ■ St. Anthony's Hospitals, Denver: Nightingale Scholarships *(Graduate, Undergraduate/Scholarship)*

Purpose: To provide scholarships for qualified nursing students from both rural and urban settings. **Focus:** Nursing. **Qualif.:** Applicant must be a Colorado resident committed to practicing nursing in Colorado; must be a student in an approved Colorado Nursing Program; must have a

Awards are arranged alphabetically below their administering organizations

minimum of 3.25 GPA (for undergraduate applicants) or 3.5 GPA (for graduate applicants); and must have one of the following student statuses: (1) Junior or senior level BSN undergraduate student; (2) RN enrolled in a baccalaureate or higher degree nursing program in a school of nursing; (3) Student in second year of nursing studies in an associate degree in nursing program; (4) RN with master's degree in nursing, currently practicing in Colorado and enrolled in a doctoral program; (5) Student in second or third year of a Doctorate Nursing Practice (DNP) program. **Criteria:** Scholarship application will be rated based on the following: (1) Professional philosophy and goals; (2) Dedication to the improvement of patient care in Colorado; (3) Demonstrated commitment to nursing, critical thinking skills and potential for leadership; (4) Involvement in community and professional organizations; (5) GPA-minimum of 3.25 undergraduate, 3.5 graduate; (6) Financial need; (7) Recommendation of one faculty member, and (8) Employer/Supervisor recommendation.

Funds Avail.: $1,000. **Number Awarded:** 2. **To Apply:** Applicants are advised to contact the foundation at Colorado Nurses Foundation for further information. **Deadline:** October 31. **Contact:** Application form and supporting documents should be sent to: Vicki Carroll at the above address.

3003 ■ Patty Walter Memorial Scholarships
(Graduate, Undergraduate/Scholarship)

Purpose: To provide scholarships for qualified nursing students from both rural and urban settings. **Focus:** Nursing. **Qualif.:** Applicant must be a Colorado resident committed to practicing nursing in Colorado; must be a student in an approved Colorado Nursing Program; must have a minimum of 3.25 GPA (for undergraduate applicants) or 3.5 GPA (for graduate applicants); and must have one of the following student statuses: (1) Junior or senior level BSN undergraduate student; (2) RN enrolled in a baccalaureate or higher degree nursing program in a school of nursing; (3) Student in second year of nursing studies in an associate degree in nursing program; (4) RN with master's degree in nursing, currently practicing in Colorado and enrolled in a doctoral program; (5) Student in second or third year of a Doctorate Nursing Practice (DNP) program. **Criteria:** Scholarship application will be rated based on the following: (1) Professional philosophy and goals; (2) Dedication to the improvement of patient care in Colorado; (3) Demonstrated commitment to nursing, critical thinking skills and potential for leadership; (4) Involvement in community and professional organizations; (5) GPA-minimum of 3.25 undergraduate, 3.5 graduate; (6) Financial need; (7) Recommendation of one faculty member, and (8) Employer/Supervisor recommendation.

Funds Avail.: $1,000. **To Apply:** Applicants are advised to contact the foundation at Colorado Nurses Foundation for further information. **Deadline:** October 31. **Contact:** Application form and supporting documents should be sent to: Vicki Carroll at the above address.

3004 ■ Colorado Society of Certified Public Accountants (COCPA)

7979 E Tufts Ave., Ste. 1000
Denver, CO 80237-2847
Ph: (303) 773-2877
Fax: (303) 773-6344
Free: 800-523-9082
E-mail: mmedley@cocpa.org
URL: www.cocpa.org

Awards are arranged alphabetically below their administering organizations

3005 ■ CSCPA College Scholarships *(Graduate, Undergraduate/Scholarship)*

Purpose: To support undergraduate and graduate accounting students. **Focus:** Accounting. **Qualif.:** Applicant must be an accounting major who has completed at least eight semester hours of accounting courses including one upper division accounting course; attend a Colorado college/university with an accredited accounting program; enrolled in courses equal to six semester/quarter hours or more for the semester/quarter for which the student is applying; have a college/university cumulative GPA of 3.0 or better on a 4.0 scale; and a U.S. citizen, or non-U.S. citizen legally living and studying in Colorado with a valid visa. **Criteria:** Selection is based on the application materials submitted.

Funds Avail.: $2,500. **Number Awarded:** Varies. **To Apply:** Applicants must submit a completed application form together with an official or unofficial transcript from the current school that includes cumulative overall GPA. **Deadline:** November 15.

3006 ■ CSCPA High School Scholarships *(Undergraduate/Scholarship)*

Purpose: To support high school seniors who plan to major in accounting at Colorado community colleges and Colorado colleges/universities. **Focus:** Accounting. **Qualif.:** Applicant must be a Colorado high school senior who will major in accounting at a Colorado community college or Colorado college or university with an accredited accounting program; enrolled in courses equal to six semester/quarter hours or more for the semester/quarter for which the student is applying; have a 3.0 or better cumulative GPA on a 4.0 scale; and a U.S. citizen, or non-U.S. citizen legally living and studying in Colorado with a valid visa. **Criteria:** Selection is based on the application materials submitted.

Funds Avail.: $1,000. **To Apply:** Applicants must submit a completed application form together with an official high school transcript that includes the applicant's cumulative GPA, class ranking and SAT/ACT test scores. **Deadline:** February 15.

3007 ■ CSCPA Sophomore Scholarships *(Undergraduate/Scholarship)*

Purpose: To financially support outstanding sophomore accounting students. **Focus:** Accounting. **Qualif.:** Applicant must be a sophomore who has maintained a 3.0 or better GPA on a 4.0 scale during the prior year and plans to major in accounting; enrolled in a Principles of Accounting class with a 3.0 GPA, and enroll in courses equal to six semester/quarter hours or more for the term for which the student is applying; and be a U.S. citizen, or non-U.S. citizen legally living and studying in Colorado with a valid visa. **Criteria:** Selection is based on the application materials submitted.

Funds Avail.: $1,000. **To Apply:** Applicants must submit a completed application form along with an official or unofficial transcript that includes the previous year's cumulative overall GPA. **Deadline:** November 15.

3008 ■ Columbian Lawyers Association of Westchester County

800 Westchester Ave., Ste. S608
Rye Brook, NY 10573
Ph: (914) 696-0006
E-mail: rgrlegal@optonline.net
URL: www.columbianlawyers.org/wcincludes/wchester.php

3009 ■ Columbian Lawyers Association of Westchester County Scholarships
(Undergraduate/Scholarship)

Purpose: To develop a program for Italian-American law students to give them an opportunity to serve as legal interns with judges who are associations members and to assist Italian-American educators and community members with their efforts to continue the teaching of the Italian language at several involving law, government, social, historical and contemporary issues. **Focus:** Law. **Qualif.:** Applicants must be residents of Westchester County who are enrolled in any law school; must not be children of CLAW member; and should be ranked in the upper half of their class. **Criteria:** Recipients are selected based on financial need.

Funds Avail.: $5,000. **To Apply:** Applicants must submit a complete application form and a resume; a letter to scholarship committee demonstrating the Italian descent, academic achievement, financial need, aspirations and goals; and a firm adherence to the ideals championed by the association.

3010 ■ PACE/Columbian Lawyers Association of Westchester County Endowed Scholarships
(Undergraduate/Scholarship)

Purpose: To develop a program for Italian-American law students to give them an opportunity to serve as legal interns with judges who are associations members and to assist Italian-American educators and community members with their efforts to continue the teaching of the Italian language at several involving law, government, social, historical and contemporary issues. **Focus:** Law. **Qualif.:** Applicants must be Pace Law School students; should be of an Italian-American heritage; and must maintain an overall minimum academic 3.0 GPA. **Criteria:** Recipients are selected based on financial need.

Funds Avail.: $5,000. **To Apply:** Applicants must submit completed application form.

3011 ■ Columbus Citizens Foundation
8 E 69th St.
New York, NY 10021
Ph: (212) 249-9923
Fax: (212) 737-4413
E-mail: ccf@columbuscitizens.org
URL: www.columbuscitizensfd.org

3012 ■ Columbus Citizens Foundation College Scholarships *(Undergraduate/Scholarship)*

Purpose: To provide financial assistance to underwrite the cost of Italian descent students' college tuition. **Focus:** General studies. **Qualif.:** Applicants must be students who are of Italian descent and who are from households where the total gross income does not exceed $25,000 per capita; must have a minimum grade average of 85% or a 3.25 GPA; and must be residents of one of the following states: NY, NJ, DE, DC, MD, PA, VT, RI, ME, MA, NH, or CT. **Criteria:** Applicants are evaluated based on existence of Italian-American ancestry; financial need; academic excellence; and service to school and community.

Funds Avail.: No specific amount. **To Apply:** Applicants must complete the application form; must submit a copy of their parent's or guardian's State and Federal Income Tax Returns; two letters of recommendation; an essay; academic performance verification; and must pay the $25 ap-

plication fee. **Deadline:** February 14.

3013 ■ Columbus Citizens Foundation High School Scholarships *(High School/Scholarship)*

Purpose: To provide educational assistance for students of Italian descent. **Focus:** General studies. **Qualif.:** Applicants must be students of Italian descent and must come from households where the total gross income does not exceed $20,000 per capita; must maintain 3.25 GPA and demonstrate that they have performed community service activities. **Criteria:** Applicants are evaluated based on existence of Italian-American ancestry; academic achievement and school/community service; and financial need.

Funds Avail.: No specific amount. **To Apply:** Applicants must complete the application form; must submit a copy of their parent's or guardian's State and Federal Income Tax Returns; three letters of recommendation; an essay; academic performance verification; and must pay the $25 application fee. **Deadline:** February 14.

3014 ■ Committee of 200 (C200)
980 N Michigan Ave., Ste. 1575
Chicago, IL 60611-7540
Ph: (312) 255-0296
Fax: (312) 255-0789
E-mail: info@c200.org
URL: www.c200.org

3015 ■ C200 Scholar Awards *(All/Scholarship)*

Purpose: To provide scholarship to outstanding MBA women students. **Focus:** Business. **Qualif.:** Applicants must be enrolled in business school hosting a C200 Outreach Seminar. **Criteria:** Selections are based on work experience, GPA, recommendations and essays.

Funds Avail.: $10,000. **Number Awarded:** 3. **To Apply:** Applicant must submit a recommendation and essay. **Contact:** Meghan McRae at mmcrae@c200.org.

3016 ■ Commonwealth Fund
1 E 75th St.
New York, NY 10021
Ph: (212) 606-3800
Fax: (212) 606-3500
E-mail: info@cmwf.org
URL: www.commonwealthfund.org

3017 ■ Association of Health Care Journalists Media Fellowships on Health Performance
(Professional development/Fellowship)

Purpose: To pursue a significant reporting project examining health care systems and support fellows for field reporting, health data and other research needs. **Focus:** Health care services. **Qualif.:** Applicants must be health care journalists. **Criteria:** Selection will be based on the committee's criteria.

Funds Avail.: No specific amount. **To Apply:** Applicants must visit the AHCJ website at www.healthjournalism.org to obtain an application form and other required attachments. **Remarks:** In collaboration with Association of Health Care Journalists.

3018 ■ Australian-American Health Policy Fellowships *(Doctorate, Graduate/Fellowship)*

Purpose: To offer a unique opportunity for outstanding, mid-career U.S. health policy researchers and practitioners

Awards are arranged alphabetically below their administering organizations

to spend up to 10 months in Australia. **Focus:** Health care services. **Qualif.:** Applicants must be citizens of the United States; must be mid-career health services researchers or practitioners; have demonstrated expertise in health policy issues and track record of informing health policy through research, policy analysis, health services or clinical leadership; have completed a master's degree, doctorate or equivalent in health services research, health administration, health policy or a related discipline, such as economics or political science; and if academically based, be at a mid-career level. **Criteria:** Candidates will be selected based on their qualifications and leadership potential; their commitment to improving health care through research and practice; quality of their research proposal; relevance of their proposed research to the Fund's areas of interest and to policy development in their home country and strength of their supporting letters.

Funds Avail.: $58,000 AUD. **To Apply:** Applicants must complete a formal application including an applicant summary sheet, statement of professional objectives, preliminary research proposal for a policy-oriented research project that fits within the program's priority areas, curriculum vitae, institutional letter of reference from the director of the applicant's institution or organization; two other professional references from senior health policymakers, managers or researchers who can comment on the applicant's past work and potential contributions of their proposed project and samples of up to three published articles or reports. **Deadline:** August 15. **Contact:** Robin Osborn, VP, Phone: 212-606-3809; Fax: 212-606-3875; Email:ro@cmwf.org.

3019 ■ Commonwealth Fund/Harvard University Fellowships in Minority Health Policy (Professional development/Fellowship)

Purpose: To promote health policies and practices that improve the access to high quality care at the national, state and/or local levels for minorities, the disadvantaged and most vulnerable populations. **Focus:** General studies. **Qualif.:** Applicants must be physicians who have completed residency, either BE/BC in the United States; must have additional experience beyond residency, such as chief residency is preferred; have experience or interest in addressing and improving the health needs of minorities, disadvantaged and vulnerable populations; have strong evidence of leadership experience or potential, especially as related to community efforts, quality improvements and/or health policy; have an intention to pursue a career in policy, public health practice or academia; and must be U.S. citizens. **Criteria:** Applications will be reviewed for academic and training qualifications; commitment to a multicultural perspective in program planning, program implementation and policy analysis; experience in projects devoted to increasing quality care and access and improving the capacity of the health care system to address health needs of minority, disadvantaged and vulnerable populations; and evidence of leadership potential.

Funds Avail.: No specific amount. **To Apply:** Applicants must complete the application form, both the Commonwealth Fund/Harvard University Fellowship in Minority Health Policy and the Master of Public Health Program of the Harvard School of Public Health, including application for financial aid at HSPH. For those applicants who already have an MPH degree, applications to both the Commonwealth Fund/Harvard University Fellowship (CFHUF) in Minority Health Policy and the Master of Public Administration Program of the Harvard Kennedy School will be required, including application for financial aid at HKS.

Once applicants have filled out and submitted all of the required information in the Request for Application Form, they should download the appropriate CFHUF application documents online. **Deadline:** January. **Contact:** 164 Longwood Ave., 2nd Fl., Boston, MA 02115-5815; Phone: 617-432-2922; Fax: 617-432-3834; Email: mfdp_cfhuf@hms.harvard.edu.

3020 ■ Harkness Fellowships in Health Care Policy and Practice (Doctorate, Graduate/Fellowship)

Purpose: To provide opportunities for mid-career health services researchers and practitioners from Australia, Germany, The Netherlands, New Zealand, Norway, Sweden, Switzerland and the United Kingdom. **Focus:** Health care services; Economics; Political science. **Qualif.:** Applicants must be citizens of Australia, Germany, New Zealand, The Netherlands, Norway, Sweden, Switzerland and the United Kingdom; must show significant promise as policy-oriented health services researchers or practitioners; have demonstrated expertise in health policy issues and a track record of informing health policy through research, policy analysis, health services or clinical leadership; have a master's degree or doctorate in health care services, health policy research or a related discipline, such as economics or political science. Consideration will be given to candidates with a bachelor's degree only, depending on work experience; and if academically based, be at a mid-career level. **Criteria:** Recipients will be selected based on their qualifications and leadership potential; their commitment to improving health care through research and practice; quality of their research proposal; relevance of their proposed research to the fund's areas of interest and to policy development in their home country and strength of their supporting letters.

Funds Avail.: No specific amount. **To Apply:** Candidates must complete a formal application, including: statement of professional objectives, curriculum vitae, five page preliminary proposal for a policy-oriented research project that fits within the fund's national program areas; letter of reference from the applicant's department chair or from the director of their institution; three professional references from senior health policy researchers, policymakers or senior level managers who can comment on the applicants' past work and the potential contribution of their proposed project. **Deadline:** September 12. **Contact:** Robin Osborn, VP, Phone: 212-606-3809; Fax: 212-606-3875; Email:ro@cmwf.org.

3021 ■ Communal Studies Association (CSA)
PO Box 122
Amana, IA 52203
Ph: (319) 622-6446
Fax: (319) 622-6446
E-mail: info@communalstudies.org
URL: www.communalstudies.info

3022 ■ Communal Studies Association Research Fellowships (Graduate/Grant)

Purpose: To provide financial support for qualified CSA members. **Focus:** General studies. **Qualif.:** Applicant must be a CSA member in good standing at the time of application and at presentation of the research. **Criteria:** Awards will be given to those who meet the qualifications.

Funds Avail.: $1200. **To Apply:** Applicant should provide: a curriculum vita or resume and letters from two relevant

Awards are arranged alphabetically below their administering organizations

references; a two-page description of the overall project, how he/she plans to accomplish such research, its goals, a timeline and how it will be presented at the CSA conference (paper, panel, A/V presentation, performance, exhibition, etc.); a bibliography of intended resources to be consulted during the grant project and a statement that these resources are open to the applicant; and a detailed budget (specify if funds other than this grant are to be used and their sources). **Deadline:** March 1. **Contact:** Christian Goodwillie, Chm. at president@communalstudies.org.

3023 ■ Communications Workers of America

7B-1050 Baxter Rd.
Ottawa, ON, Canada K2C 3P1
Ph: (613) 820-9777
Fax: (613) 820-8188
Free: 877-486-4292
E-mail: info@cwa-scacanada.ca
URL: www.cwa-scacanada.ca

3024 ■ Communications Workers of America Scholarships *(Undergraduate/Scholarship)*

Purpose: To raise professional standards and promote ethical business and journalistic practices. **Focus:** General studies. **Qualif.:** Applicants must be full-time students at an accredited college, university, community college, technical or trade school. **Criteria:** Recipients are selected based on academic performance.

Funds Avail.: $1,000. **To Apply:** Applicants must complete the application form. **Deadline:** October 31.

3025 ■ Communities Adolescents Nutrition Fitness (CANFIT)

2140 Shattuck Ave., Ste. 610
Berkeley, CA 94704
Ph: (510) 644-1533
Fax: (510) 644-1535
E-mail: info@canfit.org
URL: canfit.org

3026 ■ CANFIT Nutrition, Physical Education and Culinary Arts Scholarships *(Graduate, Undergraduate/Scholarship)*

Purpose: To encourage students to consider careers that will improve adolescent nutrition and fitness. **Focus:** Nutrition; Physical education; Culinary arts. **Qualif.:** Applicants must be California students of African-American, American Indian, Alaska Native, Asian-American, Pacific Islander or Latino/Hispanic descent; graduate applicants must be enrolled in an approved master level or doctoral graduate program in Nutrition, Public Health, Physical Education, or American Dietetic Association; must have approved preprofessional practice program at an accredited university in California; must have 12-15 units of graduate course work; must have 3.0 GPA or higher; applicants must be enrolled in an approved bachelor level program in Nutrition or Physical Education at an accredited university in California; must have 50 semester units of college credits completed; must have a 2.5 GPA or higher. **Criteria:** Selection will be based on the evaluation of submitted documents and specific criteria.

Funds Avail.: No specific amount. **To Apply:** Applicants must submit a completed application form; completed Statement of Financial Status; two recommendation letters

from two individuals; letter describing academic goals and involvement in community nutrition; a 500-1,000-word essay; photograph of own self (billfold size or larger); one copy of an official transcript of graduate course work to 12-15 units (for graduate applicants) or official transcripts of all college work to accrue 50 units (for undergraduate applicants). **Deadline:** March 31. Applicants must mail original and three additional copies of each document except transcript and photo.

3027 ■ Community and Economic Development Association (CEDA)

208 S Lasalle, Ste. 1900
Chicago, IL 60604
Ph: (312) 795-8844
Fax: (312) 795-1034
Free: 800-571-2332
URL: www.cedaorg.net

3028 ■ Charles David Hughes Scholarships *(Graduate/Scholarship)*

Purpose: To provide financial assistance to graduate students who have interest in careers that will give a significant contribution to society and not-for-profit organizations. **Focus:** Public service. **Qualif.:** Applicants must be U.S. citizens or permanent residents; must be residents of Cook County, Illinois; must be accepted in an accredited graduate program; must demonstrate academic achievement; must exhibit leadership ability through civic involvement and participation in community service activities. **Criteria:** Selection will be based on evaluation of the submitted documents and specific criteria.

Funds Avail.: $1,000. **To Apply:** Applicants must submit a completed application form; current transcript; one 500-word essay on "Why community service is important"; two letters of recommendation. **Deadline:** June.

3029 ■ Community Forestry and Environmental Research Partnerships (CEFRP)

101 Gianinni Hall 3100
Berkeley, CA 94720
Ph: (510) 642-3431
Fax: (510) 642-4612
E-mail: cffellow@nature.berkeley.edu
URL: www.cnr.berkeley.edu/community_forestry

3030 ■ CFERP Masters Fellowships *(Graduate/Fellowship)*

Purpose: To provide financial support to deserving students. **Focus:** Environmental science; Forestry. **Qualif.:** Applicants must be graduate students. **Criteria:** Preference will be given to those who meet the criteria.

Funds Avail.: $7,000 for Masters research - Eligible expenditures include living expenses in the field and transportation, communication and other research-related expenses. **To Apply:** Applicants must check the available website for more information regarding this fellowship. **Deadline:** February 2. **Contact:** Community Forestry and Environmental Research Partnerships at the above address.

3031 ■ Community-based Natural Resource Management Assistantships *(All/Internship)*

Purpose: To provide financial assistance to those students who are in need. **Focus:** Environmental science; General

Awards are arranged alphabetically below their administering organizations

studies. **Qualif.:** Applicants must be faculty or students at any U.S. college or university, in any department. **Criteria:** Priority will be given to those who meet the criteria.

Funds Avail.: $6,200. **To Apply:** Applicants must check the available website for more information. **Deadline:** April 14. **Contact:** Community Forestry and Environmental Research Partnerships at the above address.

3032 ■ Community Foundation of Calhoun County (CFCC)

PO Box 1826
Anniston, AL 36202-1826
Ph: (256) 231-5160
Fax: (256) 231-5161
E-mail: info@yourcommunityfirst.org
URL: www.yourcommunityfirst.org

3033 ■ Joe Bynum/Raymond James Investment Services Technical Excellence Scholarship Fund *(Undergraduate/Scholarship)*

Purpose: To help young men and women secure a college education. **Focus:** General studies. **Qualif.:** Applicants must be graduates of Oxford High School in Calhoun County; must have a 2.5 average on a 4.0 scale; must be enrolled as part- or full-time students. **Criteria:** Recipients are selected based on financial need, academic ability and good character.

Funds Avail.: $2,500. **To Apply:** Applicants must submit a completed application form and an essay describing their personal aspirations, educational or career goals and how this scholarship will help in achieving their career goals. **Deadline:** February 1.

3034 ■ Calhoun County Auduburn University Scholarships *(Undergraduate/Scholarship)*

Purpose: To provide financial resources enabling local students to pursue higher education at Auduburn University. **Focus:** General studies. **Qualif.:** Applicants must be graduates of any accredited public or private high school within Calhoun County; must have maintained 2.5 GPA on a 4.0 scale; must be ranked within the top 25% of high school graduating class. **Criteria:** Recipients are selected based on financial need.

Funds Avail.: No specific amount. **To Apply:** Applicants must submit a completed application form and an essay describing their personal aspirations, educational and career goals. **Deadline:** February 1. **Contact:** info@yourcommunityfirst.org.

3035 ■ Melanie and Todd Edmonson Memorial Scholarships *(Undergraduate/Scholarship)*

Purpose: To encourage young people to follow their dreams and to help lessen some of life's challenges. **Focus:** General studies. **Qualif.:** Applicants must be graduates of Oxford High School or its successor; must have 3.0 or "B" average; must be actively involved in their community, school and religious activities; must be full or part-time enrolled students at an accredited institution of higher learning in the United States; may be pursuing any field of academic study or technical training. **Criteria:** Recipients are selected based on financial need and academic performance.

Funds Avail.: No specific amount. **To Apply:** Applicants must submit a completed application form, transcript of records, an essay describing their personal aspirations, educational or career goals and how this scholarship will help in achieving their career goals. **Deadline:** February 1. **Contact:** info@yourcommunityfirst.org.

3036 ■ Gadsden State/McClellan Campus Nursing Scholarship Awards *(Undergraduate/ Scholarship)*

Purpose: To promote and celebrate the nursing profession. **Focus:** Nursing. **Qualif.:** Applicants must be graduates of an accredited public or private high school within Calhoun County currently attending Gadsden State/McClellan Campus; must be enrolled in LPN Nursing Program. **Criteria:** Recipients are selected based on character, academic ability, school/community service and financial need.

Funds Avail.: $2,500. **To Apply:** Applicants must submit a completed application form and an essay describing their personal aspirations and contributions to nursing profession. **Deadline:** February 1. **Contact:** info@yourcommunityfirst.org.

3037 ■ Farley Moody Galbraith Scholarship Fund *(Undergraduate/Scholarship)*

Purpose: To encourage high school seniors to attain a four-year college degree. **Focus:** General studies. **Qualif.:** Applicants must be graduating seniors from any public or private high school including home school; must have 3.0 average on a 4.0 scale; must be enrolled as part- or full-time students. **Criteria:** Recipients are selected based on financial need, academic ability and good character.

Funds Avail.: $2,500. **To Apply:** Applicants must submit a completed application form and an essay describing their personal aspirations, educational or career goals and how this scholarship will help in achieving their career goals. Guideline and applications are available from the Community Foundation or online at www.yourcommunityfirst.org. **Deadline:** February 1.

3038 ■ Whitney Laine Gallahar Memorial Scholarship Fund *(Undergraduate/Scholarship)*

Purpose: To provide supplement funding for full- or part-time enrolled students at an accredited state college or university within Alabama. **Focus:** General studies. **Qualif.:** Applicants must be graduating seniors of Ohatchee High school or its successor institution; must have 2.5 GPA; must be enrolled as part- or full-time. **Criteria:** Recipients are selected based on financial need, academic ability and good character.

Funds Avail.: $1,000. **To Apply:** Applicants must submit a completed application form and an essay describing their personal aspirations, educational or career goals and how this scholarship will help in achieving their career goals. **Deadline:** February 1.

3039 ■ Guin-Stanford Scholarships *(Professional development/Scholarship)*

Purpose: To enhance the quality of life in Calhoun County, Alabama. **Focus:** General studies. **Qualif.:** Applicants must have earned a bachelor's degree from an accredited college or university; must hold a current Teaching Certificate from the State of Alabama. **Criteria:** Recipients are selected based on financial need and character.

Funds Avail.: No specific amount. **To Apply:** Applicants must submit a completed application form, letter of enrollment and two letters of recommendation. **Contact:** info@yourcommunityfirst.org.

Awards are arranged alphabetically below their administering organizations

3040 ■ Cleve Holloway Memorial Scholarship Fund (Undergraduate/Scholarship)

Purpose: To provide full or supplemental funding for full-time enrolled students at an accredited state college or university within Alabama. **Focus:** General studies. **Qualif.:** Applicants must be graduating seniors of Anniston High School or its successor institution; must maintain high personal standards and moral character; must have a minimum of 2.5 or "C" average on a 4.0 scale; must be enrolled full-time. **Criteria:** Recipients are selected based on financial need, academic ability and good character.

Funds Avail.: No specific amount. **To Apply:** Applicants must submit a completed application form, transcript of records and an essay describing their personal aspirations, educational or career goals and how this scholarship will help in achieving their career goals. **Deadline:** February 1. **Contact:** info@yourcommunityfirst.org.

3041 ■ Edyie G. Kirby Nursing Scholarship Awards (Undergraduate/Scholarship)

Purpose: To promote and celebrate the nursing profession. **Focus:** Nursing. **Qualif.:** Applicants must be graduates of an accredited public or private high school within Calhoun County. **Criteria:** Recipients are selected based on character, academic ability, school/community service and financial need.

Funds Avail.: $2,500. **To Apply:** Applicants must submit a completed application form and an essay describing their personal aspirations and contributions to nursing profession. Applications are available from the Community Foundation of Calhoun County office or can be downloaded from www.yourcommunityfirst.org. Applications are also available from the CNHS at Jacksonville State University. **Deadline:** February 1. **Contact:** info@yourcommunityfirst.org.

3042 ■ E.C. Lloyd and J.C.U. Johnson Scholarship Fund (Undergraduate/Scholarship)

Purpose: To provide supplement funding for full or part-time enrolled students at any accredited two-or-four-year college or university within the United States. **Focus:** General studies. **Qualif.:** Applicants must be graduating seniors from any public or private high school including home schools; must have 2.5 or "C" average on a 4.0 scale; must be enrolled as part- or full-time students. **Criteria:** Preference will be given to applicants who are the first in their family to attend college.

Funds Avail.: $2,500. **To Apply:** Applicants must submit a completed application form and an essay describing their personal aspirations, educational or career goals and how this scholarship will help in achieving the career goal. **Deadline:** February 1.

3043 ■ Gertie S. Lowe Nursing Scholarship Awards (Undergraduate/Scholarship)

Purpose: To promote and celebrate the nursing profession. **Focus:** Nursing. **Qualif.:** Applicants must be full- or part-time students in the LPN or RN program at Gadsten State Community College; must be graduates of any accredited public or private high school within Calhoun County currently attending Gadsden State Community College. **Criteria:** Recipients are selected based on character, academic ability, school/community service and financial need.

Funds Avail.: $2,500. **To Apply:** Applicants must submit a completed application form and an essay describing their

personal aspirations and contributions to nursing profession. **Contact:** info@yourcommunityfirst.org.

3044 ■ Jerry Medforth Nursing Scholarship Awards (Undergraduate/Scholarship)

Purpose: To promote and celebrate the nursing profession. **Focus:** Nursing. **Qualif.:** Applicants must be graduates of any accredited public or private high school within Calhoun County possessing an unencumbered Registered Nurse License; must be full-time students enrolled at the Jacksonville State University Lurleen B. Wallace College of Nursing and Health Sciences RN to BSN Strategic Teaching for Enhanced Professional Preparation program. **Criteria:** Recipients are selected based on character, academic ability, school/community service and financial need.

Funds Avail.: $2,500. **To Apply:** Applicants must submit a completed application form and an essay describing their personal aspirations and contributions to nursing profession. An application is available from the CNHS and the Community Foundation of Calhoun office or from www.yourcommunityfirst.org. **Contact:** info@yourcommunityfirst.org.

3045 ■ Reverend John S. Nettled Scholarships (Undergraduate/Scholarship)

Purpose: To foster hope, self-confidence and ambition in the graduates of Anniston High School. **Focus:** General studies. **Qualif.:** Applicants must be graduating seniors from Anniston high School; must have 2.5 GPA or above on a 4.0 scale. **Criteria:** Recipients are selected based on character, academic ability, school, church and community service and financial need.

Funds Avail.: No specific amount. **To Apply:** Applicants must submit a completed application form and an essay describing the personal aspirations, educational and career goals. **Deadline:** February 1. **Contact:** info@yourcommunityfirst.org.

3046 ■ Gerald Powell Scholarships (Undergraduate/Scholarship)

Purpose: To support tuition assistance for students attending Sacred Heart of Jesus Catholic School in Anniston, Alabama. **Focus:** General studies. **Qualif.:** Applicants must be enrolled on a full-time basis at Sacred Heart of Jesus Catholic School either in elementary or high school levels; must maintain a GPA of 2.5 or "C" on a 4.0 scale. **Criteria:** Recipients are selected based on background, financial need and clarity and completeness of application.

Funds Avail.: No specific amount. **To Apply:** Applicants must submit a completed application form. **Deadline:** May 1.

3047 ■ Joseph and Amelia Saks Scholarship Fund (Undergraduate/Scholarship)

Purpose: To foster educational opportunities for graduates of Saks High School; to provide full or supplemental funding for full-time enrolled students over a four-year period at an accredited college or university within the United States. **Focus:** General studies. **Qualif.:** Applicants must be graduating senior students of Saks High School or its successor institution; must have maintained high personal standards and moral character; must have a minimum of 2.5 or "C" average on a 4.0 scale; must be full-time students completing academics aligned with their specific major or degree. **Criteria:** Recipients are selected based on financial need and academic performance.

Awards are arranged alphabetically below their administering organizations

Funds Avail.: No specific amount. **To Apply:** Applicants must submit: a completed application form; an essay describing their personal aspirations, educational or career goals and how this scholarship will help in achieving their career goals; a signed letter of acceptance; certified proof of enrollment from an institution and confirmation that the recipient is enrolled; and an official college or university transcript at the end of academic term. **Deadline:** February 1. **Contact:** info@yourcommunityfirst.org.

3048 ■ Leslie and Mary Ella Scales Memorial Scholarships *(Undergraduate/Scholarship)*

Purpose: To recognize the value of higher education and provide support for graduates of Anniston High School. **Focus:** General studies. **Qualif.:** Applicants must be full-time or part-time students attending any accredited institution of higher learning in United States; may pursue any field of academic study or technical training. **Criteria:** Recipients are selected based on financial need.

Funds Avail.: No specific amount. **To Apply:** Applicants must submit a completed application form. **Contact:** info@yourcommunityfirst.org.

3049 ■ Nathan Sparks Memorial Scholarships *(Undergraduate/Scholarship)*

Purpose: To provide supplemental funding for full or part-time enrolled students at an accredited college, university or technical institution within United States. **Focus:** General studies. **Qualif.:** Applicants must be graduating seniors of Saks High School or its successor institution. **Criteria:** Recipients are selected based on financial need.

Funds Avail.: $1,000. **To Apply:** Applicants must submit a completed application form, an essay describing their personal character and two letters of recommendation. **Deadline:** February 1. **Contact:** info@yourcommunityfirst.org.

3050 ■ Mary Katherine "Kathy" Williamson Scholarship Fund *(Undergraduate/Scholarship)*

Purpose: To enhance the quality of life in Calhoun County, Alabama. **Focus:** General studies. **Qualif.:** Applicants must be individuals who have a diploma from any accredited public or private high school or who have earned the General Education Development (GED) certificate; must be residents of Calhoun County; must have a 2.5 overall GPA or better on a 4.0 scale. **Criteria:** Recipients are selected based on financial need, passion to serve the needs of others and community service.

Funds Avail.: No specific amount. **To Apply:** Applicants must submit a completed application form, transcript of records, and an essay describing their personal aspirations, educational or career goals and how this scholarship will help in achieving their career goals. Applications are available to the guidance counselors at schools in Calhoun County or directly from the Community Foundation office or website (www.yourcommunityfirst.org). **Deadline:** February 1. **Contact:** info@yourcommunityfirst.org.

3051 ■ Community Foundation of the Eastern Shore (CFES)

1324 Belmont Ave., Ste. 401
Salisbury, MD 21804
Ph: (410) 742-9911
Fax: (410) 742-6638
E-mail: cfes@cfes.org
URL: www.cfes.org

3052 ■ William R. Bowen Scholarships *(Undergraduate/Scholarship)*

Purpose: To empower donors to make a profound difference in the quality of life in Maryland's Lower Eastern Shore; to provide community leadership through grants, non-profit support programs, charitable partnerships and local initiatives in Somerset, Wicomico and Worcester counties. **Focus:** General studies. **Qualif.:** Applicants must be graduating seniors of Snow Hill High School. **Criteria:** Recipients are selected based on academic performance and financial need.

Funds Avail.: $1,000. **To Apply:** Applicants must submit a completed application form. Application forms are available from Snow Hill High School Guidance Office.

3053 ■ William T. Burbage Family Memorial Scholarships *(Undergraduate/Scholarship)*

Purpose: To empower donors to make a profound difference in the quality of life in Maryland's Lower Eastern Shore; to provide community leadership through grants, non-profit support programs, charitable partnerships and local initiatives in Somerset, Wicomico and Worcester counties. **Focus:** General studies. **Qualif.:** Applicants must be graduating seniors of Stephen Decatur High School who have selected their college and have been accepted for admission as full-time students; must have 3.0 GPA. **Criteria:** Recipients are selected based on leadership potential.

Funds Avail.: $1,000. **To Apply:** Applicants must submit a completed application form; an official high school transcript of grades; letter of acceptance from college or university; two letters of recommendation from non-family members; a detailed listing by high school year of activities and an essay explaining how growing up on the Eastern Shore has contributed the individual leadership style. **Deadline:** April 15.

3054 ■ Irene Culver Collins and Louis Franklin Collins Scholarships *(Undergraduate/Scholarship)*

Purpose: To empower donors to make a profound difference in the quality of life in Maryland's Lower Eastern Shore; to provide community leadership through grants, non-profit support programs, charitable partnerships and local initiatives in Somerset, Wicomico and Worcester counties. **Focus:** General studies. **Qualif.:** Applicants must be past graduates or current 12th grade students of Parkside High School, Wicomico County, Maryland who have been accepted for admission as full-time college students; must have successfully completed a minimum of three advanced placement social studies during the enrollment at Parkside High School. **Criteria:** Recipients are selected based on academic performance and financial need.

Funds Avail.: $5,000. **To Apply:** Applicants must submit a completed application form; an official high school transcript of grades; letter of acceptance from college or university; an essay describing the personal character and two letters of recommendation from non-family members. **Deadline:** April 15.

3055 ■ Eastern Shore Building Industry Association Scholarships *(Undergraduate/Scholarship)*

Purpose: To empower donors to make a profound difference in the quality of life in Maryland's Lower Eastern Shore; to provide community leadership through grants, non-profit support programs, charitable partnerships and lo-

Awards are arranged alphabetically below their administering organizations

cal initiatives in Somerset, Wicomico and Worcester counties. **Focus:** General studies. **Qualif.:** Applicants must be current 12th grade students of high schools in Eastern Shore of Maryland counties of Kent, Queen Anne's, Caroline, Talbot, Dorchester, Somerset and Worcester who have been accepted for admission as full-time students; must have a minimum of 2.5 GPA on a 4.0 scale; must be participated in some extracurricular activities. **Criteria:** Recipients are selected based on academic performance, financial need and extracurricular activities.

Funds Avail.: $500. **To Apply:** Applicants must submit a completed application form; an official high school transcript of grades; letter of acceptance from college or university; must submit an essay describing the reasons of choosing the career path and two letters of recommendation from non-family members. **Deadline:** April 1.

3056 ■ Federalsburg Rotary Club Scholarships
(Undergraduate/Scholarship)

Purpose: To empower donors to make a profound difference in the quality of life in Maryland's Lower Eastern Shore; to provide community leadership through grants, non-profit support programs, charitable partnerships and local initiatives in Somerset, Wicomico and Worcester counties. **Focus:** General studies. **Qualif.:** Applicants must be graduating seniors of Colonel Richardson High School who have selected their college and have been accepted for admission as full-time students; must have 2.5 GPA. **Criteria:** Recipients are selected based on financial need.

Funds Avail.: $500. **To Apply:** Applicants must submit a completed application form; an official high school transcript of grades and letter of acceptance from college or university. **Deadline:** April 1.

3057 ■ Herb and Anne Fincher Memorial Scholarships *(Undergraduate/Scholarship)*

Purpose: To empower donors to make a profound difference in the quality of life in Maryland's Lower Eastern Shore; to provide community leadership through grants, non-profit support programs, charitable partnerships and local initiatives in Somerset, Wicomico and Worcester counties. **Focus:** Mathematics and mathematical sciences; Engineering. **Qualif.:** Applicants must be graduates of the four public high schools in Wicomico County, Maryland who have been accepted into a course of study for either math or engineering; must have a reputation of good character and be well-rounded young citizens who participated in extra-curricular school or community activities. **Criteria:** Recipients are selected based on demonstrated maturity and commitment to succeed in college level courses of study.

Funds Avail.: $6,000. **To Apply:** Applicants must submit a completed application form, an official high school transcript of grades, letter of acceptance from college or university and two letters of recommendation from non-family members. **Deadline:** April 1.

3058 ■ Green Hill Yacht and Country Club Scholarships *(Undergraduate, Vocational/Occupational/Scholarship)*

Purpose: To empower donors to make a profound difference in the quality of life in Maryland's Lower Eastern Shore; to provide community leadership through grants, non-profit support programs, charitable partnerships and local initiatives in Somerset, Wicomico and Worcester counties. **Focus:** General studies. **Qualif.:** Applicants must be graduating seniors of any Wicomico, Somerset or Worcester

County School; must be past graduates or current 12th grade students who have been accepted for admission as full-time students in an accredited four-year college or university or accredited two-year educational/vocational institution. **Criteria:** Recipients are selected based on academic achievement and financial need.

Funds Avail.: $1,000. **To Apply:** Applicants must submit a completed application form, an official high school transcript of grades and two letters of recommendation from non-family member. Completed application must be submitted to: Green Hill Yacht and Country Club, 5471 Whitehaven Rd., Quantico, MD 21856-2134. **Deadline:** April 15.

3059 ■ Gruwell Scholarships *(Undergraduate/Scholarship)*

Purpose: To empower donors to make a profound difference in the quality of life in Maryland's Lower Eastern Shore; to provide community leadership through grants, non-profit support programs, charitable partnerships and local initiatives in Somerset, Wicomico and Worcester counties. **Focus:** General studies. **Qualif.:** Applicants must be residents of Lake Forest School District, Kent County, Delaware who have selected their college and have been accepted for admission as full-time students. **Criteria:** Recipients are selected based on financial need, community involvement, academic achievement and extracurricular activities.

Funds Avail.: $1,000. **To Apply:** Applicants must submit a completed application form, an official high school transcript of grades and letter of acceptance from college or university; must submit a copy of parent/guardian and student's most recent income tax return and two letters of recommendation from non-family members.

3060 ■ Hancock Family Snow Hill High School Scholarships *(Undergraduate/Scholarship)*

Purpose: To empower donors to make a profound difference in the quality of life in Maryland's Lower Eastern Shore; to provide community leadership through grants, non-profit support programs, charitable partnerships and local initiatives in Somerset, Wicomico and Worcester counties. **Focus:** General studies. **Qualif.:** Applicants must be graduating seniors at Snow Hill High School who have been accepted by an Accredited academic college program; must have 2.5 GPA in appropriate course work indicating the students are able to be successful at the college level; must have three or more year residents of Snow Hill area; must be active in school activity, church, community and youth clubs; must have good moral character. **Criteria:** Recipients are selected based on academic performance, financial need and participation in extracurricular activities.

Funds Avail.: $2,000. **To Apply:** Applicants must submit a completed application form; an official high school transcript of grades; letter of acceptance from college or university; a copy of parent/guardian and student's most recent income tax return and two letters of recommendation from non-family members. **Deadline:** April 21.

3061 ■ Dick and Pat Hazel Minority Scholarships *(Professional development/Scholarship)*

Purpose: To empower donors to make a profound difference in the quality of life in Maryland's Lower Eastern Shore; to provide community leadership through grants, non-profit support programs, charitable partnerships and local initiatives in Somerset, Wicomico and Worcester counties. **Focus:** Education. **Qualif.:** Applicants must be members of a minority group and must commit teaching for

Awards are arranged alphabetically below their administering organizations

two years within the public education systems of Somerset, Wicomico or Worcester counties; must be minority residents of Wicomico, Somerset or Worcester County, Maryland who have selected their college and have been accepted for admission as full-time students whose pursuit must be education/teaching. **Criteria:** Recipients are selected based on financial need, community involvement, academic achievement and extracurricular activities.

Funds Avail.: $2,000. **To Apply:** Applicants must submit a completed application form; "one-page" describing the reasons of wanting to teach; an official high school transcript of grades; letter of acceptance from college or university and summary of financial assistance from college/university financial aid and office; must also submit a copy of parent/guardian and student's most recent income tax return and two letters of recommendation from non-family members. **Deadline:** May 1.

3062 ■ Martin S. Kane Memorial Community Service Award Scholarships *(Undergraduate/ Scholarship)*

Purpose: To empower donors to make a profound difference in the quality of life in Maryland's Lower Eastern Shore; to provide community leadership through grants, non-profit support programs, charitable partnerships and local initiatives in Somerset, Wicomico and Worcester counties. **Focus:** General studies. **Qualif.:** Applicants must be from Wicomico High School. **Criteria:** Recipients are selected based on financial need.

Funds Avail.: $600. **To Apply:** Application can be obtain from Wicomico High School Guidance Office.

3063 ■ TFC Edward A. Plank, Jr. Memorial Scholarships *(Undergraduate/Scholarship)*

Purpose: To empower donors to make a profound difference in the quality of life in Maryland's Lower Eastern Shore; to provide community leadership through grants, non-profit support programs, charitable partnerships and local initiatives in Somerset, Wicomico and Worcester counties. **Focus:** General studies. **Qualif.:** Applicants must be graduating seniors of any Wicomico, Somerset or Worcester County School; must have 3.0 overall GPA; must be accepted in a full-time basis at an accredited two-to-four-year college. **Criteria:** Recipients are selected based on academic achievement and financial need.

Funds Avail.: $2,000. **To Apply:** Applicants must submit a completed application form, a "500-word" essay on how crimes and/or drug abuse have been affected today's society and personal letters of recommendation from two responsible adults other than relatives. Submit completed application to Kristy Hickman. **Deadline:** March 31. **Contact:** Kristy Hickman, 33077 Peach Orchard Rd., Pocomoke City, MD 21851.

3064 ■ Progress Lane Scholarships *(Undergraduate/Scholarship)*

Purpose: To empower donors to make a profound difference in the quality of life in Maryland's Lower Eastern Shore; to provide community leadership through grants, non-profit support programs, charitable partnerships and local initiatives in Somerset, Wicomico and Worcester counties. **Focus:** General studies. **Qualif.:** Applicants must be current graduating 12th grade students of Washington High School, Princess Anne, Maryland who are financially advantaged and have been accepted for admission as students with a minimum of six credit hours in a course of study that will serve the educational requirements for their

chosen career. **Criteria:** Recipients are selected based on academic performance and financial need.

Funds Avail.: $500. **To Apply:** Applicants must submit a completed application form; an official high school transcript of grades; a letter of acceptance from college; university or training institute and "250-word" essay describing the reasons of wanting to attend college. **Deadline:** April 1.

3065 ■ Duane V. Puerde Memorial Scholarships *(Undergraduate, Vocational/Occupational/ Scholarship)*

Purpose: To empower donors to make a profound difference in the quality of life in Maryland's Lower Eastern Shore; to provide community leadership through grants, non-profit support programs, charitable partnerships and local initiatives in Somerset, Wicomico and Worcester counties. **Focus:** General studies. **Qualif.:** Applicants must be past graduates or current 12th grade students of Parkside High school who are residents of rural Eastern Wicomico County, Maryland including but not exclusive to the communities of Parsonburg, Pittsville, Powellville, Williards or Melson who have been accepted for admission as full-time college students or vocational school. **Criteria:** Recipients are selected based on academic performance and participation in extracurricular activities.

Funds Avail.: $500. **To Apply:** Applicants must submit a completed application form, an official high school transcript of grades and two letters of recommendation from non-family members. **Deadline:** April 1. **Contact:** Elaine W. Purdue, Chair, PO Box 5, Willards, MD 26874.

3066 ■ Elizabeth Pusey Scholarships *(Undergraduate/Scholarship)*

Purpose: To empower donors to make a profound difference in the quality of life in Maryland's Lower Eastern Shore; to provide community leadership through grants, non-profit support programs, charitable partnerships and local initiatives in Somerset, Wicomico and Worcester counties. **Focus:** General studies. **Qualif.:** Applicants must be graduating seniors at any Wicomico County high school who have selected their college and have been accepted from admission as full-time students; must be in the top 10% of their class. **Criteria:** Recipients are selected based on financial need.

Funds Avail.: $1,500. **To Apply:** Applicants must submit a completed application form, an official transcript of grades ad letter of acceptance from college or university. **Deadline:** April 1.

3067 ■ Lana K. Rinehart Scholarships *(Undergraduate/Scholarship)*

Purpose: To empower donors to make a profound difference in the quality of life in Maryland's Lower Eastern Shore; to provide community leadership through grants, non-profit support programs, charitable partnerships and local initiatives in Somerset, Wicomico and Worcester counties. **Focus:** General studies. **Qualif.:** Applicants must be graduating senior students at Parkside High School. **Criteria:** Recipients are selected based on academic performance and financial need.

Funds Avail.: $1,000. **Number Awarded:** 2. **To Apply:** Applicants must submit a completed application form. Applications are available from Parkside High School Guidance Office.

3068 ■ Drew Smith Memorial Scholarships *(Undergraduate/Scholarship)*

Purpose: To empower donors to make a profound difference in the quality of life in Maryland's Lower Eastern

Awards are arranged alphabetically below their administering organizations

Shore; to provide community leadership through grants, non-profit support programs, charitable partnerships and local initiatives in Somerset, Wicomico and Worcester counties. **Focus:** General studies. **Qualif.:** Applicants must be adults or graduating public or private high school seniors who are pursuing a degree in golf turf management from an accredited college or university and must be domiciled residents of the Eastern Shore Counties of Maryland and Virginia or the State of Delaware; must be enrolled in college for a minimum of six credit hours per scholastic year. **Criteria:** Recipients are selected based on academic record, financial need, extracurricular activities or community service.

Funds Avail.: $1,000. **To Apply:** Applicants must submit a completed application form, Career Goal Information, and two letters of recommendation to: PO Box 1607 Ocean Pines, MD 21811. **Deadline:** July 14.

3069 ■ Esther M. Smith Scholarships
(Undergraduate/Scholarship)

Purpose: To empower donors to make a profound difference in the quality of life in Maryland's Lower Eastern Shore; to provide community leadership through grants, non-profit support programs, charitable partnerships and local initiatives in Somerset, Wicomico and Worcester counties. **Focus:** General studies. **Qualif.:** Applicants must be graduating seniors with a disability as accepted defined by the Americans with Disabilities Act (ADA) who attended in Wicomico County; must be nominated by their school principal, guidance counselor or teacher; must have a minimum GPA of 2.0 and have been accepted for admission as full-time students at an accredited four-year college or university or a two-year education or career training institution. **Criteria:** Recipients are selected based on academic performance and financial need.

Funds Avail.: $2,000. **To Apply:** Applicants must submit completed application form; an official high school transcript of grades and letter of recommendation from non-family members. **Deadline:** April 15. **Contact:** Mr. Paul Rendine, Scholarship Chm., 935 Mt. Hermon Rd., Salisbury, MD 21804.

3070 ■ Wicomico High School Class of '55 Scholarships *(Undergraduate/Scholarship)*

Purpose: To empower donors to make a profound difference in the quality of life in Maryland's Lower Eastern Shore; to provide community leadership through grants, non-profit support programs, charitable partnerships and local initiatives in Somerset, Wicomico and Worcester counties. **Focus:** General studies. **Qualif.:** Applicants must be graduating senior students of Wicomico High School who have spent at least their junior and senior years in that school's program; must have selected their college and have been accepted for admission as full-time students; must have 3.0 cumulative GPA. **Criteria:** Recipients are selected based on community involvement, academic achievement and extracurricular activities.

Funds Avail.: $1,000. **To Apply:** Applicants must submit a completed application form; an official high school transcript of grades; letter of acceptance from college or university; three letters of recommendation from non-family members and "250-word" essay on "How they can make a difference". **Deadline:** April 15.

3071 ■ M. William and Frances J. Tilghman Scholarships *(Undergraduate/Scholarship)*

Purpose: To empower donors to make a profound difference in the quality of life in Maryland's Lower Eastern

Shore; to provide community leadership through grants, non-profit support programs, charitable partnerships and local initiatives in Somerset, Wicomico and Worcester counties. **Focus:** General studies. **Qualif.:** Applicants must be graduating high school senior students of Somerset County. **Criteria:** Recipients are selected based on academic achievement, extracurricular activities and financial need.

Funds Avail.: $1,000-$3,000. **To Apply:** Applicants must submit a completed application form; an official high school transcript of grades; letter of acceptance from a college or university and two letters of recommendation from non-family members. **Deadline:** April 15.

3072 ■ Community Foundation of the Fox River Valley
111 W Downer Pl., Ste. 312
Aurora, IL 60506-6106
Ph: (630) 896-7800
E-mail: info@communityfoundationfrv.org
URL: www.communityfoundationfrv.org

3073 ■ Community Foundation of the Fox River Valley Scholarships *(Undergraduate/Scholarship)*

Purpose: To enhance and support the quality of life in the Fox River Valley of Illinois. **Focus:** General studies. **Qualif.:** Applicants must be students who will attend an accredited institution of higher learning on a full-time basis and whose permanent residence is within the Foundation's service area. **Criteria:** Recipients are selected based on academic ability and financial need.

Funds Avail.: No specific amount. **To Apply:** Applicants must submit a completed application form. **Deadline:** January 15.

3074 ■ Community Foundation for Greater Atlanta
50 Hurt Plz., Ste. 449
Atlanta, GA 30303
Ph: (404) 688-5525
Fax: (404) 688-3060
E-mail: info@cfgreateratlanta.org
URL: www.cfgreateratlanta.org

3075 ■ Steve Dearduff Scholarships *(Graduate, Undergraduate/Scholarship)*

Purpose: To provide financial assistance to undergraduate and graduate students pursuing degrees in medicine and social work. **Focus:** Medicine; Social Work. **Qualif.:** Applicants must be legal residents of Georgia; must be enrolled or accepted in an accredited higher learning institution pursuing undergraduate or graduate degrees in medicine or social work; must have demonstrated history of commitment to community service; must have potential for success in chosen field; and have a minimum GPA of 2.0; must demonstrate financial need. **Criteria:** Recipients will be selected based on submitted documents and financial need.

Funds Avail.: $2,500. **Number Awarded:** 3. **To Apply:** Applicants must visit the Foundation's website to obtain the link for online application. **Deadline:** March 15.

3076 ■ George and Pearl Strickland Scholarships *(Graduate, Undergraduate/Scholarship)*

Purpose: To provide financial assistance to undergraduate and graduate students pursuing a degree at Atlanta

Awards are arranged alphabetically below their administering organizations

University Center colleges. **Focus:** General studies. **Qualif.:** Applicants must be legal residents of Georgia; must be enrolled or accepted at Clark Atlanta University, Morehouse College, Morehouse School of Medicine, Morris Brown College or Spelman College; and have a minimum GPA of 2.0. **Criteria:** Recipients will be selected based on demonstrated commitment to community service, potential for success in chosen field and financial need.

Funds Avail.: $1,000-$2,000. **Number Awarded:** 20-30. **To Apply:** Applicants must visit the Foundation's website to obtain the link for online application. **Deadline:** March 15.

3077 ■ Community Foundation for Greater New Haven

70 Audubon St.
New Haven, CT 06510-9755
Ph: (203) 777-2386
Fax: (203) 787-6584
E-mail: contactus@cfgnh.org
URL: www.cfgnh.org

3078 ■ Bambi Bailey Scholarships
(Undergraduate/Scholarship)

Purpose: To create positive and sustainable change in Greater New Haven by increasing the amount of and enhancing the impact of community philanthropy and to provide college scholarships based on financial need. **Focus:** General studies. **Qualif.:** Applicants must be students from New Haven who may not consider college as an option; must demonstrate an interest and ability in writing; must attend or plan to attend Wellesley College. **Criteria:** Recipients are selected based on financial need. Preference will be given to students demonstrating an interest and ability in writing and/or who plan to or do attend Wellesley College.

Funds Avail.: No specific amount. **To Apply:** Applicants must complete the application form and attach a personal essay; academic verification; letter of recommendation; and Parent/Guardian IRS Form. **Deadline:** March 31. **Contact:** 203-777-2386; 203-787-6584.

3079 ■ George J. Bysiewicz Scholarship Fund
(Undergraduate/Scholarship)

Purpose: To create positive and sustainable change in Greater New Haven by increasing the amount of and enhancing the impact of community philanthropy. **Focus:** General studies. **Qualif.:** Applicants must be students from New Haven, Catholic School planning to attend Sacred Heart Academy and Notre Dame High School. **Criteria:** Recipients are selected based on financial need.

Funds Avail.: No specific amount. **Number Awarded:** 2. **To Apply:** Applicants must complete the application form and attach a personal essay; academic verification; two letter of recommendation; letter of acceptance from either Sacred Heart Academy or Notre Dame; and Parent/Guardian IRS Form. **Deadline:** March 31. **Contact:** 203-777-7079; 203-787-6584.

3080 ■ Murtha Cullina Scholarships
(Undergraduate/Scholarship)

Purpose: To create positive and sustainable change in Greater New Haven by increasing the amount of and enhancing the impact of community philanthropy. **Focus:** General Studies. **Qualif.:** Applicants must be students from the greater New Haven area planning to attend a college or university. **Criteria:** Recipients are selected based on financial need.

Funds Avail.: No specific amount. **To Apply:** Applicants must complete the application form and attach a personal essay; academic verification; letter of recommendation; and Parent/Guardian IRS Form. **Deadline:** March 31. **Contact:** Bethany Watkins at 203-777-7079 or bwatkins@cfgnh.org.

3081 ■ John S. Martinez and Family Scholarship Fund *(Undergraduate/Scholarship)*

Purpose: To create positive and sustainable change in Greater New Haven by increasing the amount of and enhancing the impact of community philanthropy. **Focus:** General studies. **Qualif.:** Applicants must be students in an institution or university. **Criteria:** Recipients are selected based on financial need.

Funds Avail.: No specific amount. **To Apply:** Applicants must complete the application form and must attach a personal essay; academic verification; letter of recommendation; and Parent/Guardian IRS Form. **Deadline:** March 31. **Contact:** 203-777-7079; 203-787-6584.

3082 ■ Curtis M. Saulsbury Scholarship Fund
(Undergraduate/Scholarship)

Purpose: To create positive and sustainable change in Greater New Haven by increasing the amount of and enhancing the impact of community philanthropy. **Focus:** Music. **Qualif.:** Applicants must be graduating from secondary school in the region serviced by the community foundation. **Criteria:** Recipients are selected based on financial need.

Funds Avail.: No specific amount. **To Apply:** Applicants must complete the application form and attach a personal essay; academic verification; letter of recommendation; and Parent/Guardian IRS Form. **Deadline:** March 31. **Contact:** 203-777-7079; 203-787-6584.

3083 ■ Charles L. Terrell/New Haven Savings Bank Scholarship Fund *(Undergraduate/Scholarship)*

Purpose: To create positive and sustainable change in Greater New Haven by increasing the amount of and enhancing the impact of community philanthropy. **Focus:** General studies. **Qualif.:** Applicants must be high school students with financial need who have demonstrated a commitment to community service. **Criteria:** Recipients are selected based on financial need and demonstrated commitment to community service.

Funds Avail.: No specific amount. **To Apply:** Applicants must complete the application form and attach a personal essay; academic verification; letter of recommendation; and parent/Guardian IRS Form. **Deadline:** March 31. **Contact:** 203-777-7079; 203-787-6584.

3084 ■ Ruth and Sherman Zudekoff Scholarships *(Undergraduate/Scholarship)*

Purpose: To create positive and sustainable change in Greater New Haven by increasing the amount of and enhancing the impact of community philanthropy. **Focus:** General studies. **Qualif.:** Applicants must be students graduating from secondary school in regions served by the foundation. **Criteria:** Recipients are selected based on financial need.

Funds Avail.: No specific amount. **To Apply:** Applicants must complete the application form and attach a personal essay; academic verification; letter of recommendation; and

Awards are arranged alphabetically below their administering organizations

Parent/Guardian IRS Form. **Deadline:** March 31. **Contact:** 203-777-7097; 203-787-6584.

3085 ■ Community Foundation of Greene County (CFGC)

PO Box 768
Waynesburg, PA 15370
Ph: (724) 627-2010
Fax: (724) 627-2011
E-mail: cfgcpa@gmail.com
URL: www.cfgcpa.org

3086 ■ The William H. Davis, Jr. Scholarship Fund *(Undergraduate/Scholarship)*

Purpose: To maintain and enhance the educational, social, cultural, health and civic resources of the community through support of qualified non-profit organizations. **Focus:** General studies. **Qualif.:** Applicants must be graduating seniors of Southeastern Greene School District or its equivalent; must be accepted students at Westmoreland County Community College as full-time students or registered for a minimum of 12 credit hours; must be qualified for no more than three-quarters financial aid. **Criteria:** Recipients are selected based on financial need.

Funds Avail.: $500. **Number Awarded:** 3. **To Apply:** Applicants must submit five copies of their FAFSA, Special Condition Form, verification of GPA from the guidance counselor, copy of acceptance letter from WCCC and attendance record. **Deadline:** April 30.

3087 ■ The Thelma S. Hoge Memorial Scholarship Fund *(Undergraduate/Scholarship)*

Purpose: To maintain and enhance the educational, social, cultural, health and civic resources of the community through support of qualified non-profit organizations. **Focus:** General studies. **Qualif.:** Applicants must be graduating seniors from West Greene; must be accepted at a post-secondary or four-year college degree program; must have a minimum GPA of 3.0. **Criteria:** Recipients are selected based on essay, results of an interview and completed application.

Funds Avail.: $1,000. **Number Awarded:** 2. **To Apply:** Applicants must provide a brief essay about themselves; copy of high school transcript and two character references. **Deadline:** April 16. **Contact:** For additional information, applicants must call 724-499-5183 ext. 2220.

3088 ■ The Renardo A. Matteucci Scholarship Fund *(Undergraduate/Scholarship)*

Purpose: To provide an annual need-based scholarship to the Jefferson-Morgan High School. **Focus:** General studies. **Qualif.:** Applicants must be graduating students from Jefferson-Morgan High School; must be planning to pursue a Bachelor Degree, an Associate Degree or a Diploma from a trade school; must have a minimum GPA of 2.75. **Criteria:** Recipients are selected based on financial need.

Funds Avail.: $1,000. **Number Awarded:** 2. **To Apply:** Applicants must submit five copies of their FAFSA, Special Condition Form, verification of their GPA from guidance counselor, an official attendance record and post-secondary acceptance letter. **Deadline:** April 1.

3089 ■ The Walter Samek III Memorial Scholarship Fund *(Undergraduate/Scholarship)*

Purpose: To assist graduating senior class members of Carmichaels High School to continue post-secondary education. **Focus:** General studies. **Qualif.:** Applicants must be Carmichaels senior boys or girls who are enrolled in an approved post-secondary college/university; must have a 3.5 GPA. **Criteria:** Recipients are selected based on financial need and community service.

Funds Avail.: No specific amount. **To Apply:** Applicants must submit a completed application form. **Deadline:** April 15.

3090 ■ The Community Foundation of Middle Tennessee (CFMT)

3833 Cleghorn Ave., Ste. 400
Nashville, TN 37215-2519
Ph: (615) 321-4939
Fax: (615) 327-2746
Free: 888-540-5200
E-mail: mail@cfmt.org
URL: www.cfmt.org

3091 ■ Lt. Holly Adams Memorial Scholarships *(Undergraduate/Scholarship)*

Purpose: To help students in planning their post-secondary education. **Focus:** General studies. **Qualif.:** Applicants must be students from the Page High School area in Williamson County who not only achieve, but also possess the integrity, courage and caring spirit to help others achieve. **Criteria:** Recipients are selected based on financial need.

Funds Avail.: No specific amount. **To Apply:** Applicants must complete the application form; must submit two applicant appraisals; transcript of grades; student's essay describing educational plans and how these will help in career goals; and one recent photograph. **Deadline:** March 15. **Contact:** Contact Ms. Pat Cole at 615-321-4939 or e-mail pcole@cfmt.org.

3092 ■ Kathy D. and Stephen J. Anderson Scholarships *(Graduate/Scholarship)*

Purpose: To help students in planning their post-secondary education. **Focus:** General studies. **Qualif.:** Applicants must be graduate students from the Public High School area in Williamson County who have attended for a minimum of three years; must be in good standing as citizens in the school and community; have 3.2 or better GPA and minimum ACT score of 22 or SAT of 1100; and must be involved in at least one extracurricular activity. **Criteria:** Recipients are selected based on financial need.

Funds Avail.: Maximum amount of $10,000. **To Apply:** Applicants must complete the application form; must submit two applicant appraisals; transcript of grades; student's essay describing educational plans and how these will help in career goals; and one recent photograph. **Deadline:** March 15. **Contact:** Contact Ms. Pat Cole at 615-321-4939 or e-mail pcole@cfmt.org.

3093 ■ Cynthia and Alan Baran Fine Arts and Music Scholarships *(Undergraduate/Scholarship)*

Purpose: To help students in planning their post-secondary education. **Focus:** Fine arts; Music. **Qualif.:** Applicants must be rising sophomores, juniors, seniors in college and graduate students at an accredited college, university, or institute full-time or part-time (six or more credits); and must maintain at least 3.0 GPA or better. **Criteria:** Recipients are selected based on financial need, extracurricular and civic participation. Preference will be given to those

---

Awards are arranged alphabetically below their administering organizations

applicants pursuing a course of study in acoustic mandolin or acoustic guitar.

Funds Avail.: No specific amount. **To Apply:** Applicants must complete the application form; must submit two applicant appraisals; transcript of grades; student's essay describing educational plans and how these will help in career goals; and one recent photograph. **Deadline:** March 15. **Contact:** Contact Ms. Pat at 615-321-4939 or e-mail pcole@cfmt.org.

3094 ■ Belmont University Commercial Music Scholarships *(Undergraduate/Scholarship)*

Purpose: To help students in planning their post-secondary education. **Focus:** Music. **Qualif.:** Applicants must be high school seniors, college freshmen, sophomores, or juniors accepted to or attending Belmont University in Nashville, Tennessee as commercial music majors. **Criteria:** Recipients are selected based on financial need.

Funds Avail.: No specific amount. **To Apply:** Applicants must complete the application form; must submit two applicant appraisals; transcript of grades; student essay describing their educational plans and how these will help in career goals; and one recent photograph. **Deadline:** March 15. **Contact:** Contact Ms. Pat Cole at 615-321-4939 or e-mail pcole@cfmt.org.

3095 ■ George Oliver Benton Memorial Scholarships *(Undergraduate/Scholarship)*

Purpose: To help students in planning their post-secondary education. **Focus:** General studies. **Qualif.:** Applicants must be students who attend an accredited four-year college/university in the state of Tennessee; and must be residents of Tennessee. **Criteria:** Recipients will be selected based on extracurricular activities especially those indicative of an interest in government.

Funds Avail.: No specific amount. **To Apply:** Applicants must complete the application form; must submit two applicant appraisals; transcript of grades; student essay describing educational plans and how these will help in career goals; and one recent photograph. **Deadline:** March 15. **Contact:** Contact Ms. Pat Cole at 615-321-4939 or e-mail pcole@cfmt.org.

3096 ■ Dody Boyd Scholarships *(Undergraduate/Scholarship)*

Purpose: To help students in planning their post-secondary education. **Focus:** General studies. **Qualif.:** Applicants must be seniors graduating from Cheatham County Central High School and wishing to attend a two-year community college/technical school or four-year university; must have GPA of at least 2.5 or better and an ACT score of 20 or better. **Criteria:** Recipients are selected based on financial need.

Funds Avail.: No specific amount. **To Apply:** Applicants must complete the application form; must submit two applicant appraisals; transcript of grades; student's essay describing educational plans and how these will help in career goals; and one recent photograph. **Deadline:** March 15. **Contact:** Contact Ms. Pat Cole at 615-321-4939 or e-mail pcole@cfmt.org.

3097 ■ JoAhn Brown-Nash Memorial Scholarships *(Undergraduate/Scholarship)*

Purpose: To help students in planning their postsecondary education. **Focus:** General studies. **Qualif.:** Applicants must be female students at Fisk University, entering their junior year, who exemplify outstanding leadership skills, with a GPA of 3.2 or above. **Criteria:** Recipients are selected based on the financial need.

Funds Avail.: No specific amount. **To Apply:** Applicants must submit a completed application form along with a High School and/or College Transcripts (sealed in a separate envelope), and two appraisal letters (sealed in a separate envelope). **Deadline:** March 15.

3098 ■ William and Clara Bryan Scholarships *(Undergraduate/Scholarship)*

Purpose: To help students in planning their post-secondary education. **Focus:** General studies. **Qualif.:** Applicants must be high school seniors, or college freshmen, sophomores or juniors who are from Giles County, Tennessee and have lived there for the majority of their pre-college schooling. **Criteria:** Recipients are selected based on merit and financial need.

Funds Avail.: No specific amount. **To Apply:** Applicants must complete the application form; must submit two applicant appraisals; transcript of grades; student's essay describing educational plans and how these will help in career goals; and one recent photograph. **Deadline:** March 15. **Contact:** Contact Ms. Pat Cole at 615-321-4939 or e-mail pcole@cfmt.org.

3099 ■ Leigh Carter Scholarships *(Undergraduate/Scholarship)*

Purpose: To help students in planning their post-secondary education. **Focus:** Health care services. **Qualif.:** Applicants must be full-time students attending one of the nation's accredited chiropractic colleges or universities. **Criteria:** Recipients are selected based on financial need, interest in health care delivery, extracurricular and civic participation. Preference will be given to students from Tennessee.

Funds Avail.: No specific amount. **To Apply:** Applicants must complete the application form; must submit two applicant appraisals; transcript of grades; student's essay describing educational plans and how these will help in career goals; and one recent photograph. **Deadline:** March 15. **Contact:** Contact Ms. Pat Cole at 615-321-4939 or e-mail pcole@cfmt.org.

3100 ■ Cheatham County Scholarships *(Undergraduate/Scholarship)*

Purpose: To help students in planning their postsecondary education. **Focus:** General Studies. **Qualif.:** Applicants must be Cheatham County, Tennessee residents for a minimum period of one year. Applicants must have a high school diploma or GED with a GPA of 2.0 or better. Applicants must attend an accredited college, university, or technical school and maintain a grade point average of 2.0 or better. **Criteria:** Recipients are selected based on financial need, extracurricular and civic participation.

Funds Avail.: No specific amount. **To Apply:** Applicants must complete the application form. Applicants must submit two applicant appraisals; transcript of grades; student's essay describing educational plans and how these will help in career goals. Applicants must submit one recent photograph. **Deadline:** March 15. **Contact:** pcole@cfmt.org.

3101 ■ Choose Your Future Scholarships *(Undergraduate/Scholarship)*

Purpose: To help students in planning their post-secondary education. **Focus:** General studies. **Qualif.:** Applicants must be graduates of the Metropolitan Nashville Public

Awards are arranged alphabetically below their administering organizations

School of Davidson County with a minimum GPA of 2.5 and a score of 21 on the ACT; and must be attending a college or university in the United States. **Criteria:** Recipients are selected based on financial need, extracurricular and civic participation. Preference will be given to students who are the first in their families to attend college.

Funds Avail.: No specific amount. **To Apply:** Applicants must complete the application form; must submit two applicant appraisals; transcript of grades; student's essay describing educational plans and how these will help in career goals; one recent photograph. **Deadline:** March 15. **Contact:** Contact Ms. Pat Cole at 615-321-4939 or e-mail pcole@cfmt.org.

3102 ■ Howard A. Clark Horticulture Scholarships (Undergraduate/Scholarship)

Purpose: To help students in planning their post-secondary education. **Focus:** Horticulture. **Qualif.:** Applicants must be graduating seniors from Avery County High School, North Carolina attending a two or four-year college to study horticulture or agriculture; and must have at least a 2.5 GPA in high school. **Criteria:** Recipients are selected based on financial need, extracurricular and civic participation.

Funds Avail.: No specific amount. **To Apply:** Applicants must complete the application form; must submit two applicant appraisals; transcript of grades; student's essay describing educational plans and how these will help in career goals; and one recent photograph. **Deadline:** March 15. **Contact:** Contact Ms. Pat Cole at 615-321-4939 or e-mail pcole@cfmt.org.

3103 ■ The Community Foundation DBI Scholarships (Undergraduate, Vocational/Occupational/Scholarship)

Purpose: To help students in planning their post-secondary education. **Focus:** General studies. **Qualif.:** Applicants must be graduating high school seniors, undergraduates and graduates enrolling or enrolled at an accredited college/university, junior college or technical/vocational school on a full-time basis maintaining "B" average or better; must be the children of current employees of Ingram Entertainment Inc. or DBI Distributing Inc. with at least two years of service. **Criteria:** Recipients are selected based on financial need, extracurricular and civic participation.

Funds Avail.: No specific amount. **To Apply:** Applicants must complete the application form; must submit two applicant appraisals; transcript of grades; student's essay describing educational plans and how these will help in career goals; and one recent photograph. **Deadline:** March 15. **Contact:** Contact Ms. Pat Cole at 615-321-4939 or e-mail pcole@cfmt.org.

3104 ■ The Community Foundation Student Education Loans (Undergraduate/Loan)

Purpose: To help students in planning their postsecondary education. **Focus:** General studies. **Qualif.:** Applicants must be young men or women whose parents have discontinued financial support for their education because they are gay or lesbian. **Criteria:** Recipients are selected based on financial need, extracurricular and civic participation.

Funds Avail.: No specific amount. **To Apply:** Applicants must complete the application form; must submit two applicant appraisals; transcript of grades; student's essay describing the educational plans and how these will help in career goals; and one recent photograph. **Deadline:** March

15. **Contact:** Contact Ms. Pat Cole at 615-321-4939 or e-mail pcole@cfmt.org.

3105 ■ Colonel Richard M. Dawson Scholarships (Undergraduate/Scholarship)

Purpose: To help students in planning their post-secondary education. **Focus:** Criminal justice. **Qualif.:** Applicants must be children of employees of the Tennessee Highway Patrol who serve in uniform, undercover, or plainclothes; must be rising sophomores, juniors, or seniors in college who demonstrate a commitment to a career in criminal justice through their course of study. **Criteria:** Recipients are selected based on financial need, extracurricular and civic participation.

Funds Avail.: No specific amount. **To Apply:** Applicants must complete the application form; must submit two applicant appraisals; transcript of grades; student's essay describing educational plans and how these will help in career goals; and one recent photograph. **Deadline:** March 15. **Contact:** Contact Ms. Pat Cole at 615-321-4939 or e-mail pcole@cfmt.org.

3106 ■ B.J. Dean Scholarships (Undergraduate/Scholarship)

Purpose: To help students in planning their postsecondary education. **Focus:** General studies. **Qualif.:** Applicants must be a female preparing for full-time ministry, but scholarship is not limited to those seeking ordination or serving in any particular denomination. Applicant must be a resident of Tennessee or Texas or be enrolled in Yale Dignity School. **Criteria:** Recipients are selected based on financial need, extracurricular and civic participation.

Funds Avail.: No specific amount. **To Apply:** Applicants must complete the application form. Applicants must submit two applicant appraisals; transcript of grades; student essay describing educational plans and how these will help in career goals. Applicants must submit one recent photograph. **Deadline:** March 15. **Remarks:** Established in 1995.

3107 ■ Jimmy Edwards Scholarships (Undergraduate/Scholarship)

Purpose: To help students in planning their post-secondary education. **Focus:** General studies. **Qualif.:** Applicants must be past students or graduates of Donelson High School and descendents of alumni of Donelson High School. **Criteria:** Recipients are selected based on financial need, extracurricular and civic participation.

Funds Avail.: No specific amount. **To Apply:** Applicants must complete the application form; must submit two applicant appraisals; transcript of grades; student's essay describing educational plans and how these will help in career goals; and one recent photograph. **Deadline:** March 15. **Contact:** Contact Ms. Pat Cole at 615-321-4939 or e-mail pcole@cfmt.org.

3108 ■ Pauline LaFon Gore Scholarships (Undergraduate/Scholarship)

Purpose: To help students in planning their post-secondary education. **Focus:** General studies. **Qualif.:** Applicants must be high school seniors and current college underclassmen who are from Smith County, Tennessee and have lived there for the majority of their pre-college schooling. **Criteria:** Recipients are selected based on financial need, extracurricular and civic participation.

Funds Avail.: No specific amount. **To Apply:** Applicants must complete the application form; must submit two ap-

Awards are arranged alphabetically below their administering organizations

plicant appraisals; transcript of grades; student's essay describing educational plans and how these will help in career goals; and one recent photograph. **Deadline:** March 15. **Contact:** Contact Ms. Pat Cole at 615-321-4939 or e-mail pcole@cfmt.org.

3109 ■ Frank and Charlene Harris Scholarships
(Undergraduate/Scholarship)

Purpose: To help students in planning their post-secondary education. **Focus:** General studies. **Qualif.:** Applicants must be seniors of Cumberland Gap High School in Clairborne County, TN; and must have GPA of 3.0 or higher at the time of the application. **Criteria:** Recipients are selected based on financial need, extracurricular and civic participation.

Funds Avail.: No specific amount. **To Apply:** Applicants must complete the application form; must submit two applicant appraisals; transcript of grades; student's essay describing educational plans and how these will help in career goals; and one recent photograph. **Deadline:** March 15. **Contact:** Contact Ms. Pat Cole at 615-321-4939 or e-mail pcole@cfmt.org.

3110 ■ Regina Higdon Scholarships
(Undergraduate/Scholarship)

Purpose: To help students in planning their post-secondary education. To help graduates of Christ the King School of Nashville, Tennessee who have a desire to attend either Father Ryan High School or St. Cecilia Academy, both in Nashville, Tennessee. **Focus:** Art. **Qualif.:** Applicants must be graduating eighth graders of Christ the King School and/or former graduates of Christ the King School attending Father Ryan High School or St. Cecilia Academy; must have at least a 2.5 GPA or equivalent; and must exhibit a love for the arts. **Criteria:** Recipients are selected on financial need, extracurricular and civic participation.

Funds Avail.: No specific amount. **To Apply:** Applicants must complete the application form; must submit two applicant appraisals; transcript of grades; student's essay describing educational plans and how these will help in career goals; and one recent photograph. **Deadline:** March 16. **Contact:** Contact Ms. Pat Cole at 615-321-4939 or e-mail pcole@cfmt.org.

3111 ■ Jennifer Ingrum Scholarships
(Undergraduate/Scholarship)

Purpose: To help students in planning their post-secondary education. **Focus:** General studies. **Qualif.:** Applicants must be students who qualify academically for college but need financial assistance. **Criteria:** Recipients are selected based on financial need, extracurricular and civic participation.

Funds Avail.: $2,000. **Number Awarded:** 2. **To Apply:** Applicants must complete the application form; must submit two applicant appraisals; transcript of grades; student's essay describing educational plans and how these will help in career goals; and one recent photograph. **Deadline:** March 15. **Contact:** Contact Ms. Pat Cole at 615-321-4939 or e-mail pcole@cfmt.org.

3112 ■ Maude Keisling/Cumberland County Extension Homemakers Scholarships
(Undergraduate/Scholarship)

Purpose: To help students in planning their post-secondary education. **Focus:** Ecology; Education; Social work. **Qualif.:** Applicants must be residents of Cumberland County,

Tennessee for a period of four years or more; must be graduating high school seniors, GED graduates, or current college undergraduates with GPA of 2.5 or better; must pursue a field of study such as, but not limited to, human ecology, family and consumer science, education, and social services; and must be enrolled as full or part-time students with six or more semester hours at an accredited college, university, or community college. **Criteria:** Recipients are selected based on financial need, extracurricular and civic participation.

Funds Avail.: No specific amount. **To Apply:** Applicants must complete the application form; must submit two applicant appraisals; transcript of grades; student's essay describing educational plans and how these will help in career goals; and one recent photograph. **Deadline:** March 15. **Contact:** Contact Ms. Pat Cole at 615-321-4939 or e-mail pcole@cfmt.org.

3113 ■ Knox-Hume Scholarships
(Undergraduate/Scholarship)

Purpose: To help students in planning their post-secondary education. **Focus:** General studies. **Qualif.:** Applicants must be graduates of Hume-Fogg High School who exhibit academic merit and financial need. **Criteria:** Recipients are selected based on financial need, extracurricular and civic participation.

Funds Avail.: No specific amount. **To Apply:** Applicants must complete the application form; must submit two applicant appraisals; transcript of grades; student's essay describing educational plans and how these will help in career goals; and one recent photograph. **Deadline:** March 15. **Contact:** Contact Ms. Pat Cole at 615-321-4939 or e-mail pcole@cfmt.org.

3114 ■ Senator Carl O. Koella, Jr. Memorial Scholarships *(Undergraduate/Scholarship)*

Purpose: To help students in planning their post-secondary education. **Focus:** Law. **Qualif.:** Applicants must be legislative interns, either public or private, currently enrolled or planning to enroll in a four-year college the year of the application; and must be residents of Blount and Sevier Counties of Tennessee. **Criteria:** Recipients are selected based on financial need, extracurricular and civic participation. Extra consideration will be given to extracurricular activities in the areas of government and politics.

Funds Avail.: No specific amount. **To Apply:** Applicants must complete the application form; must submit two applicant appraisals; transcript of grades; student's essay describing educational plans and how these will help in career goals and one recent photograph. **Deadline:** March 15. **Contact:** Contact Ms. Pat Cole at 615-321-4939 or e-mail pcole@cfmt.org.

3115 ■ Michael B. Kruse Scholarships *(Graduate, Undergraduate/Scholarship)*

Purpose: To help students in planning their post-secondary education. **Focus:** Accounting. **Qualif.:** Applicants must be rising juniors, seniors and graduate students majoring in accounting; must be residents of Tennessee and attend an accredited college/university in the State of Tennessee; and must maintain a minimum GPA of 3.2 or better. **Criteria:** Recipients are selected based on financial need, extracurricular and civic participation. Special consideration will be given to married applicants.

Funds Avail.: No specific amount. **To Apply:** Applicants must complete the application form; must submit two ap-

Awards are arranged alphabetically below their administering organizations

plicant appraisals; transcript of grades; student's essay describing educational plans and how these will help in career goals; and one recent photograph. **Deadline:** March 15. **Contact:** Contact Ms. Pat Cole at 615-321-4939 or e-mail pcole@cfmt.org.

3116 ■ Heloise Werthan Kuhn Scholarships
(Undergraduate/Scholarship)

Purpose: To help students in planning their post-secondary education. **Focus:** General studies. **Qualif.:** Applicants must be pregnant or parenting teens living in the State of Tennessee; must be enrolled or planning to enroll in post-secondary education at an accredited college, university, junior college, technical school, or job training program as a way to increase their job skills and become more employable. **Criteria:** Recipients are selected based on financial need, extracurricular and civic participation.

Funds Avail.: No specific amount. **To Apply:** Applicants must complete the application form; must submit two applicant appraisals; transcript of grades; student's essay describing the educational plans and how these will help in career goals; and one recent photograph. **Deadline:** March 15. **Contact:** Contact Ms. Pat Cole at 615-321-4939 or e-mail pcole@cfmt.org.

3117 ■ Diane G. Lowe and John Gomez, IV Scholarships *(Undergraduate/Scholarship)*

Purpose: To help students in planning their post-secondary education. To provide financial assistance to students who would be otherwise unable to take qualifying entrance exams to institutions of higher learning and to provide gifted students financial assistance to attend academic programs that offer intellectually-accelerated content. **Focus:** General studies. **Qualif.:** Applicants must be students with financial need in Grades 6-12 who reside in Rutherford, Cannon, Dekalb, or Wilson Counties. **Criteria:** Recipients are selected based on financial need, extracurricular and civic participation.

Funds Avail.: No specific amount. **To Apply:** Applicants must complete the application form; must submit two applicant appraisals; transcript of grades; student's essay describing educational plans and how these will help in career goals; one recent photograph. **Deadline:** March 15. **Contact:** Contact Ms. Pat Cole at 615-321-4939 or e-mail pcole@cfmt.org.

3118 ■ Dr. Mac Scholarships *(Undergraduate/Scholarship)*

Purpose: To help students in planning their post-secondary education. **Focus:** Dentistry. **Qualif.:** Applicants must be enrolled at the University of Tennessee at Memphis School of Dentistry and entering their third year of school with a minimum of 2.7 GPA. **Criteria:** Recipients are selected based on financial need, extracurricular and civic participation.

Funds Avail.: No specific amount. **To Apply:** Applicants must complete the application form; must submit two applicant appraisals; transcript of grades; student's essay describing educational plans and how these will help in career goals; and one recent photograph. **Deadline:** March 15. **Contact:** Contact Ms. Pat Cole at 615-321-4939 or e-mail pcole@cfmt.org.

3119 ■ Edna Martin Scholarships
(Undergraduate/Scholarship)

Purpose: To help students in planning their post-secondary education. **Focus:** Education. **Qualif.:** Applicants must be

high school seniors, or individuals who previously graduated from the Davidson County-Metropolitan Nashville Public School System; must have desire to pursue a career in teaching in elementary, middle or high school. **Criteria:** Recipients are selected based on financial need, extracurricular and civic participation.

Funds Avail.: No specific amount. **To Apply:** Applicants must complete the application form; must submit two applicant appraisals; transcript of grades; student essay describing educational plans and how these will help in career goals; and one recent photograph. **Deadline:** March 15. **Contact:** Contact Ms. Pat Cole at 615-321-4939 or e-mail pcole@cfmt.org.

3120 ■ Juliann and Joseph Maxwell Scholarships *(Undergraduate/Scholarship)*

Purpose: To help students in planning their post-secondary education. **Focus:** General studies. **Qualif.:** Applicants must be high school seniors, college freshmen, sophomores and juniors who are dependent children, including adopted and stepchildren of full or part-time employees of the Tractor Supply Company. Employees must have minimum of one year of service with Tractor Supply Company by January 1 of the year in which the application is received. **Criteria:** Recipients are selected based on financial need, extracurricular and civic participation.

Funds Avail.: No specific amount. **To Apply:** Applicants must complete the application form; must submit two applicant appraisals; transcript of grades; student essay describing their educational plans and how these will help in career goals; and one recent photograph. **Deadline:** March 15. **Contact:** Contact Ms. Pat Cole at 615-321-4939 or e-mail pcole@cfmt.org.

3121 ■ Juliann King Maxwell Scholarships for Riverview High School Students *(Undergraduate, Vocational/Occupational/Scholarship)*

Purpose: To help students in planning their postsecondary education. **Focus:** General studies. **Qualif.:** Applicants must be graduating seniors from Riverview High School or prior recipients of the scholarship. **Criteria:** Recipients are selected based on financial need, extracurricular and civic participation.

Funds Avail.: No specific amount. **To Apply:** Applicants must complete the application form. Applicants must submit two applicant appraisals; transcript of grades; student essay describing educational plans and how these will help in career goals. Applicants must submit one recent photograph. **Deadline:** March 15. **Contact:** pcole@cfmt.org.

3122 ■ John E. Mayfield ABLE Scholarships
(Undergraduate/Scholarship)

Purpose: To help students in planning their post-secondary education. **Focus:** General studies. **Qualif.:** Applicants must be graduating seniors and be participants of the ABLE program; must attend an accredited college, university, junior college, technical school or job training program. Individuals who have previously received scholarship assistance are welcome to re-apply. **Criteria:** Recipients are selected based on financial need, extracurricular and civic participation.

Funds Avail.: No specific amount. **To Apply:** Applicants must complete the application form; must submit two applicant appraisals; transcript of grades; student essay describing educational plans and how these will help in career goals; and one recent photograph. **Deadline:** March

Awards are arranged alphabetically below their administering organizations

15. **Contact:** Contact Ms. Pat Cole at 615-321-4939 or e-mail pcole@cfmt.org.

3123 ■ John E. Mayfield Scholarships for Cheatham County Central High School
(Undergraduate/Scholarship)

Purpose: To help students in planning their post-secondary education. **Focus:** General studies. **Qualif.:** Applicants must be alumni and/or graduating seniors of Cheatham County Central High School in Cheatham County, Tennessee; must be residents of Cheatham County and have grade point average of 2.0 or better. **Criteria:** Recipients are selected based on financial need, extracurricular and civic participation.

Funds Avail.: No specific amount. **To Apply:** Applicants must complete the application form; must submit two applicant appraisals; transcript of grades; student essay describing educational plans and how these will help in career goals; one recent photograph. **Deadline:** March 15. **Contact:** Contact Ms. Pat Cole or e-mail pcole@cfmt.org.

3124 ■ John E. Mayfield Scholarships for Harpeth High School *(Undergraduate/Scholarship)*

Purpose: To help students in planning their post-secondary education. **Focus:** General studies. **Qualif.:** Applicants must be alumni and/or graduating seniors of Harpeth High School in Cheatham County, Tennessee; must be residents of Cheatham County and have GPA of 2.0 or better. **Criteria:** Recipients are selected based on financial need, extracurricular and civic participation.

Funds Avail.: No specific amount. **To Apply:** Applicants must complete the application form; must submit two applicant appraisals; transcript of grades; student essay describing educational plans and how these will help in career goals; one recent photograph. **Deadline:** March 15. **Contact:** Contact Ms. Pat Cole at 615-321-4939 or e-mail pcole@cfmt.org.

3125 ■ John E. Mayfield Scholarships Pleasant View Christian School *(Undergraduate/Scholarship)*

Purpose: To help students in planning their post-secondary education. **Focus:** General studies. **Qualif.:** Applicants must be alumni and/or graduating seniors of Pleasant View Christian School in Cheatham County, Tennessee; must be residents of Cheatham County and have GPA of 2.0 or better. **Criteria:** Recipients are selected based on financial need, extracurricular and civic participation.

Funds Avail.: No specific amount. **To Apply:** Applicants must complete the application form; must submit two applicant appraisals; transcript of grades; student essay describing educational plans and how these will help in career goals; and one recent photograph. **Deadline:** March 15. **Contact:** Contact Ms. Pat Cole at 615-321-4939 or e-mail pcole@cfmt.org.

3126 ■ John E. Mayfield Scholarships for Sycamore High School *(Undergraduate/Scholarship)*

Purpose: To help students in planning their post-secondary education. **Focus:** General studies. **Qualif.:** Applicants must be alumni and/or graduating seniors of Sycamore High School in Cheatham County, Tennessee; must be residents of Cheatham County and have GPA of 2.0 or better. **Criteria:** Recipients are selected based on financial need, extracurricular and civic participation.

Funds Avail.: No specific amount. **To Apply:** Applicants must complete the application form; must submit two applicant appraisals; transcript of grades; student essay describing educational plans and how these will help in career goals; and one recent photograph. **Deadline:** March 15. **Contact:** Contact Ms. Pat Cole 615-321-4939 or e-mail pcole@cfmt.org.

3127 ■ Archie Hartwell Nash Memorial Scholarships *(Graduate, Undergraduate/Scholarship)*

Purpose: To help students in planning their post-secondary education. **Focus:** General studies. **Qualif.:** Applicants must be Middle Tennessee State University sophomores or above including graduate students who are working at a minimum of 20 hours and have a GPA of 2.0 or better. **Criteria:** Recipients are selected based on financial need, extracurricular and civic participation.

Funds Avail.: No specific amount. **To Apply:** Applicants must complete the application form; must submit two applicant appraisals; transcript of grades; student essay describing educational plans and how these will help in career goals. Applicants must submit; and one recent photograph. **Deadline:** March 15. **Contact:** Contact Ms. Pat Cole at 615-321-4939 or e-mail pcole@cfmt.org.

3128 ■ Jerry Newson Scholarships
(Undergraduate/Scholarship)

Purpose: To help students in planning their post-secondary education. **Focus:** General studies. **Qualif.:** Applicants must currently reside in Davidson County, Tennessee; must have high school diploma or GED; must attend a four-year accredited institution of higher education which may be out-of-state; must be pursuing degree in the social sciences or areas where they will be helping and giving back to their community. High school graduates and adults are encouraged to apply. **Criteria:** Recipients are selected based on financial need, extracurricular and civic participation.

Funds Avail.: No specific amount. **To Apply:** Applicants must complete the application form; must submit two applicant appraisals; transcript of grades; student essay describing educational plans and how these will help in career goals; and one recent photograph. **Deadline:** March 15. **Contact:** Contact Ms. Pat Cole at 615-321-4939 or e-mail pcole@cfmt.org.

3129 ■ Eloise Pitts O'More Scholarships
(Undergraduate/Scholarship)

Purpose: To help students in planning their post-secondary education. **Focus:** Interior Design. **Qualif.:** Applicants must be interior design students who are currently pursuing a degree in interior design at O'More College of Design; must be classified as juniors or higher and have GPA of 3.0 or higher at the time of application; be actively participating members of either the American Society of Interior Design and/or International Design Association's student chapters. **Criteria:** Recipients are selected based on financial need, extracurricular and civic participation.

Funds Avail.: No specific amount. **To Apply:** Applicants must complete the application form; must submit two applicant appraisals; transcript of grades; student essay describing educational plans and how these will help in career goals; and one recent photograph. **Deadline:** March 15. **Contact:** Contact Ms. Pat Cole at 615-321-4939 or e-mail pcole@cfmt.org.

3130 ■ Buster Pool Memorial Scholarships
(Undergraduate/Scholarship)

Purpose: To help students in planning their post-secondary education. **Focus:** General studies. **Qualif.:** Applicants

Awards are arranged alphabetically below their administering organizations

must be graduating seniors of Meridian High School in Meridian, Mississippi and/or previous recipients of this scholarship; must have GPA of 2.5 or higher at the time of application. **Criteria:** Recipients are selected based on financial need, extracurricular and civic participation. Preference will be given to those applicants who are members of Meridian High School Golf Team and/or golfers in difference to Buster pool's passion for the game of golf.

Funds Avail.: No specific amount. **To Apply:** Applicants must complete the application form; must submit two applicant appraisals; transcript of grades; student essay describing educational plans and how these will help in career goals; and one recent photograph. **Deadline:** March 15. **Contact:** Contact Ms. Pat Cole at 615-321-4939 or e-mail pcole@cfmt.org.

3131 ■ Barbara Hagan Richards Scholarships
(Undergraduate/Scholarship)

Purpose: To help students in planning their post-secondary education. **Focus:** General studies. **Qualif.:** Applicants must be graduating seniors, undergraduates, and/or graduate students currently enrolled in a college/university and/or alumni of any high school located and serving Giles County, Tennessee; must have GPA of 3.0. **Criteria:** Recipients are selected based on financial need, extracurricular and civic participation.

Funds Avail.: No specific amount. **To Apply:** Applicants must complete the application form; must submit two applicant appraisals; transcript of grades; student essay describing educational plans and how these will help in career goals; and one recent photograph. **Deadline:** March 15. **Contact:** Contact Ms. Pat Cole at 615-321-4939 or e-mail pcole@cfmt.org.

3132 ■ James Edward "Bill" Richards Scholarships *(Undergraduate/Scholarship)*

Purpose: To help students in planning their post-secondary education. **Focus:** General studies. **Qualif.:** Applicants must be high school seniors, undergraduates or graduate students who have graduated from East High School in Nashville, Tennessee; and must have GPA of at least 3.0. **Criteria:** Recipients are selected based on financial need, extracurricular and civic participation.

Funds Avail.: No specific amount. **To Apply:** Applicants must complete the application form; must submit two applicant appraisals; transcript of grades; student's essay describing educational plans and how these will help in career goals; and one recent photograph. **Deadline:** March 15. **Contact:** Contact Ms. Pat Cole at 615-321-4939 or e-mail pcole@cfmt.org.

3133 ■ Meyer and Dorothy Silverman Scholarships *(Undergraduate/Scholarship)*

Purpose: To help students in planning their post-secondary education. **Focus:** General studies. **Qualif.:** Applicants must be students in Grade 7 to 12 in Oak Ridge Public Schools who are committed in developing their talents as string instrument players but who, otherwise, would be financially unable to take private string instruction; and must be recommended by an instructor. **Criteria:** Recipients will be selected based on financial need and demonstrated commitment to music.

Funds Avail.: No specific amount. **To Apply:** Applicants must complete the application form; must submit two applicant appraisals; transcript of grades; student essay describing educational plans and how these will help in

career goals; and one recent photograph. **Deadline:** March 15. **Contact:** Contact Ms. Pat Cole at 615-321-4939 or e-mail pcole@cfmt.org.

3134 ■ Drue Smith/Society of Professional Journalists Scholarships *(Undergraduate/Scholarship)*

Purpose: To help students in planning their post-secondary education. **Focus:** Journalism. **Qualif.:** Applicants must be college juniors, seniors or graduate students who have graduated from high school in Middle Tennessee and have chosen journalism or broadcast news for a career, or mid-career working journalists who seek training to develop professionally or further their careers. **Criteria:** Recipients are selected based on financial need, extracurricular and civic participation.

Funds Avail.: No specific amount. **To Apply:** Applicants must complete the application form; must submit two applicant appraisals; transcript of grades; student's essay describing educational plans and how these will help in career goals and one recent photograph. **Deadline:** March 15. **Contact:** Contact Ms. Pat Cole at 615-321-4939 or e-mail pcole@cfmt.org.

3135 ■ Richie Stevenson Scholarships
(Undergraduate, Vocational/Occupational/Scholarship)

Purpose: To help students in planning their post-secondary education. **Focus:** General studies. **Qualif.:** Applicants must be graduates of Benton Hall School who wish to attend a technical school, vocational school, community college, junior or four-year college or university. **Criteria:** Recipients are selected based on financial need, extracurricular and civic participation.

Funds Avail.: No specific amount. **To Apply:** Applicants must complete the application form; must submit two applicant appraisals; transcript of grades; student essay describing educational plans and how these will help in career goals; and one recent photograph. **Deadline:** March 15. **Contact:** Contact Ms. Pat Cole at 615-321-4939 or e-mail pcole@cfmt.org.

3136 ■ Tennessee Trucking Association Scholarships *(Undergraduate/Scholarship)*

Purpose: To help students in planning their post-secondary education. **Focus:** General studies. **Qualif.:** Applicants must be Tennessee residents who are dependent children, spouses or employees who are members in good standing of the Tennessee Trucking Association; must be entering their junior or senior years at accredited colleges or universities located in the State of Tennessee. **Criteria:** Recipients are selected based on financial need, extracurricular and civic participation.

Funds Avail.: No specific amount. **To Apply:** Applicants must complete the application form; must submit two applicant appraisals; transcript of grades; student's essay describing the educational plans and how these will help in career goals; and one recent photograph. **Deadline:** March 15. **Contact:** Contact Ms. Pat Cole at 615-321-4939 or e-mail pcole@cfmt.org.

3137 ■ Emmett H. Turner Scholarships
(Undergraduate/Scholarship)

Purpose: To help students in planning their postsecondary education. **Focus:** Criminal justice. **Qualif.:** Applicants must be students enrolling or currently enrolled at Tennes-

Awards are arranged alphabetically below their administering organizations

see University in the Criminal Justice program. **Criteria:** Recipients are selected based on financial need, extracurricular and civic participation.

Funds Avail.: No specific amount. **To Apply:** Applicants must complete the application form. Applicants must submit two applicant appraisals; transcript of grades; student essay describing educational plans and how these will help in career goals. Applicants must submit one recent photograph. **Deadline:** March 15. **Contact:** pcole@cfmt.org.

3138 ■ Teddy Wilburn Scholarships
(Undergraduate/Scholarship)

Purpose: To help students in planning their post-secondary education. **Focus:** General studies. **Qualif.:** Applicants must be students enrolling or currently enrolled at Tennessee State University or Vanderbilt University; must have at least "B" overall GPA during the last two years of high school; must have attended high school within the 40 counties of Middle Tennessee for the majority of high school. **Criteria:** Recipients are selected based on financial need, extracurricular and civic participation.

Funds Avail.: No specific amount. **To Apply:** Applicants must complete the application form; must submit two applicant appraisals; transcript of grades; student's essay describing educational plans and how these will help in career goals; and one recent photograph. **Deadline:** March 15. **Contact:** Contact Ms. Pat Cole at 615-321-4939 or e-mail pcole@cfmt.org.

3139 ■ The Woman's Club of Nashville Scholarships
(Undergraduate/Scholarship)

Purpose: To help students in planning their postsecondary education. **Focus:** General studies. **Qualif.:** Applicants must be women residing in Davidson County, Tennessee. Applicants must be graduating high school seniors or high school graduates with a GPA of 3.0 or higher. **Criteria:** Recipients are selected based on financial need, extracurricular and civic participation.

Funds Avail.: No specific amount. **To Apply:** Applicants must complete the application form. Applicants must submit two applicant appraisals; transcript of grades; student essay describing educational plans and how these will help in career goals. Applicants must submit one recent photograph. **Deadline:** March 15. **Remarks:** Established in 2001.

3140 ■ John W. Work III Memorial Foundation Scholarships
(Undergraduate/Scholarship)

Purpose: To help students in planning their post-secondary education. **Focus:** Music. **Qualif.:** Applicants must be undergraduate juniors, seniors or graduate students pursuing a degree in music at an accredited university, college or institute; must have "B" average and demonstrate potential for excellence in music. **Criteria:** Recipients are selected based on financial need, extracurricular and civic participation. Special preference will be given to African Americans.

Funds Avail.: No specific amount. **To Apply:** Applicants must complete the application form; must submit two applicant appraisals; transcript of grades; student's essay describing educational plans and how these will help in career goals; and one recent photograph. **Deadline:** March 15. **Contact:** Contact Ms. Pat Cole at 615-321-4939 or e-mail pcole@cfmt.org.

3141 ■ Community Foundation of Northern Illinois
946 N 2nd St.
Rockford, IL 61107

Ph: (815) 962-2110
Fax: (815) 962-2116
URL: www.cfnil.org

3142 ■ Charles Lee Anderson Memorial Scholarships
(Undergraduate/Scholarship)

Purpose: To serve the four county area (Boone, Ogle, Stephenson and Winnebago) through philanthropy; to provide leadership in meeting charitable needs. **Focus:** Education. **Qualif.:** Applicants must be Rock Valley or Sycamore High School graduating seniors who will enter a college or university to pursue a degree in education. **Criteria:** Recipients are selected based on demonstrated optimism, determination and love of neighbor.

Funds Avail.: No specific amount. **To Apply:** Applicants must submit a completed application form, verification form, an official college transcript in a sealed envelope and two completed recommendation forms. **Deadline:** March 1. **Contact:** jpatterson@cfnil.org.

3143 ■ Richard L. Bernardi Memorial Scholarships
(Undergraduate/Scholarship)

Purpose: To serve the four county area (Boone, Ogle, Stephenson and Winnebago) through philanthropy; to provide leadership in meeting charitable needs and to be a responsible steward to the Foundation's donors and of the Foundation's endowment. **Focus:** General studies. **Qualif.:** Applicants must be attending or planning to attend Rock Valley College; must be committed to completing a bachelor's degree; must have an at least 2.0 GPA. **Criteria:** Recipients are selected based on demonstrated enthusiasm and leadership.

Funds Avail.: No specific amount. **To Apply:** Applicants must submit a completed application form, verification form, an official college transcript in a sealed envelope and two completed recommendation forms. **Deadline:** March 1. **Contact:** jpatterson@cfnil.org.

3144 ■ Lindsay Buster Memorial Scholarships
(Undergraduate/Scholarship)

Purpose: To serve the four county area (Boone, Ogle, Stephenson and Winnebago) through philanthropy; to provide leadership in meeting charitable needs and to be a responsible steward to the Foundation's donors and of the Foundation's endowment. **Focus:** General studies. **Qualif.:** Applicants must be graduating senior athletes from Jefferson High school who have participated in high school sports for a minimum of three years including their senior year; must have 2.5 or higher cumulative GPA; must have plans to attend a two-or-four year college or university. **Criteria:** Recipients are selected based on financial need.

Funds Avail.: No specific amount. **To Apply:** Applicants must submit a completed application form, verification form, an official transcript in a sealed envelope and two letters of recommendation. **Deadline:** March 1. **Contact:** jpatterson@cfnil.org.

3145 ■ Harry H. and Floy B. Chapin Scholarships
(Undergraduate/Scholarship)

Purpose: To serve the four county area (Boone, Ogle, Stephenson and Winnebago) through philanthropy; to provide leadership in meeting charitable needs and to be a responsible steward to the Foundation's donors and of the Foundation's endowment. **Focus:** General studies. **Qualif.:** Applicants must be graduating senior students from Durand, Dakota or Pecatonica High school; must rank in top

Awards are arranged alphabetically below their administering organizations

15% of graduating class; must plan to attend a recognized college or university. **Criteria:** Recipients are selected based on financial need and involvement in school, community and/or church activities.

Funds Avail.: No specific amount. **To Apply:** Applicants must submit a completed application form, verification form, an official transcript in a sealed envelope and two letters of recommendation. **Deadline:** March 1. **Contact:** jpatterson@cfnil.org.

3146 ■ Community Foundation Scholarships
(Undergraduate/Scholarship)

Purpose: To serve the four county area (Boone, Ogle, Stephenson and Winnebago) through philanthropy; to provide leadership in meeting charitable needs and to be a responsible steward to the Foundation's donors and of the Foundation's endowment. **Focus:** General studies. **Qualif.:** Applicants must be graduating senior students and residents of Winnebago county; must have an at least 2.75 or higher GPA and have plans to attend a college, university or trade school. **Criteria:** Recipients are selected based on financial need.

Funds Avail.: No specific amount. **To Apply:** Applicants must submit a completed application form, verification form, an official transcript in a sealed envelope, two letters of recommendation and a copy of their FAFSA. **Deadline:** March 1. **Contact:** James Patterson, jpatterson@cfnil.org.

3147 ■ Margaret T. Craig Community Service Scholarships *(Undergraduate/Scholarship)*

Purpose: To serve the four county area (Boone, Ogle, Stephenson and Winnebago) through philanthropy; to provide leadership in meeting charitable needs and to be a responsible steward to the Foundation's donors and of the Foundation's endowment. **Focus:** General studies. **Qualif.:** Applicants must be high school graduates under the age of 23 or graduating seniors with a permanent address in Winnebago County; must have a plan to pursue a two or four-year degree at an accredited college, university or trade school; must have a minimum of 2.75 GPA. **Criteria:** Recipients are selected based on financial need, community involvement and strong commitment to improving the quality of life for people in their school, community and country.

Funds Avail.: No specific amount. **To Apply:** Applicants must submit a completed application form, verification form, an official transcript in a sealed envelope and two letters of recommendation. **Deadline:** March 1. **Contact:** jpatterson@cfnil.org.

3148 ■ William R. Durham/Theater Scholarships
(Undergraduate/Scholarship)

Purpose: To serve the four county area (Boone, Ogle, Stephenson and Winnebago) through philanthropy; to provide leadership in meeting charitable needs and to be a responsible steward to the Foundation's donors and of the Foundation's endowment. **Focus:** Theater Arts. **Qualif.:** Applicants must be high school graduates or graduating seniors with a permanent address within Winnebago or Boone county with a GPA of at least 3.0 on a 4.0 scale; must plan to attend an accredited four-year college or university to obtain an M.A. or B.A.; must intend to teach theater or work professionally as a performer or technician in theater. **Criteria:** Recipients are selected based on financial need.

Funds Avail.: No specific amount. **To Apply:** Applicants must submit a completed application form, verification form,

an official transcript in a sealed envelope and two letters of recommendation. **Deadline:** March 1. **Contact:** jpatterson@cfnil.org.

3149 ■ Helen R. Finley-Loescher and Stephen Loescher Scholarships *(Undergraduate/ Scholarship)*

Purpose: To serve the four county area (Boone, Ogle, Stephenson and Winnebago) through philanthropy; to provide leadership in meeting charitable needs and to be a responsible steward to the Foundation's donors and of the Foundation's endowment. **Focus:** Arts. **Qualif.:** Applicants must be Freeport High School students demonstrating academic achievement, self-motivation and an interest in the arts; must have exhibited artistic talent through participation in the high school arts curriculum; must have plans to pursue education in fine arts. **Criteria:** Recipients are selected based on financial need and demonstrated active involvement in social studies organizations, clubs and classes such as student government, political campaigns, social service and community service.

Funds Avail.: No specific amount. **To Apply:** Applicants must contact a Freeport High school Art Department Instructor for an application form. **Deadline:** March 1. **Contact:** jpatterson@cfnil.org.

3150 ■ John Flynn Memorial Scholarships
(Undergraduate/Scholarship)

Purpose: To serve the four county area (Boone, Ogle, Stephenson and Winnebago) through philanthropy; to provide leadership in meeting charitable needs and to be a responsible steward to the Foundation's donors and of the Foundation's endowment; to provide educational resources to Pecatonica High School senior students who are pursuing higher education. **Focus:** General studies. **Qualif.:** Applicants must be graduating Pecatonica High School senior students who are pursuing higher education; must have at least a 2.0 GPA on a 4.0 scale and have been involved in community service. **Criteria:** Recipients are selected based on financial need.

Funds Avail.: No specific amount. **To Apply:** Applicants must submit a completed application form, verification form, an official transcript in a sealed envelope and two letters of recommendation. **Deadline:** March 1. **Contact:** James Patterson, jpatterson@cfnil.org.

3151 ■ Susan Kay Munson Gilmore Memorial Scholarships *(Undergraduate, Vocational/ Occupational/Scholarship)*

Purpose: To serve the four county area (Boone, Ogle, Stephenson and Winnebago) through philanthropy; to provide leadership in meeting charitable needs and to be a responsible steward to the Foundation's donors and of the Foundation's endowment. **Focus:** General studies. **Qualif.:** Applicants must be graduating senior students or former graduates of a Guilford or Mendota Township high school; must have "C" or better average; and must be pursuing a vocational career. **Criteria:** Recipients are selected based on financial need.

Funds Avail.: No specific amount. **To Apply:** Applicants must submit a completed application form, verification form, an official transcript in a sealed envelope, two letters of recommendation and a copy of their FAFSA. **Deadline:** March 1. **Contact:** jpatterson@cfnil.org.

3152 ■ Nettie and Jesse Gorov Scholarships
(Undergraduate/Scholarship)

Purpose: To serve the four county area (Boone, Ogle, Stephenson and Winnebago) through philanthropy; to

Awards are arranged alphabetically below their administering organizations

provide leadership in meeting charitable needs and to be a responsible steward to the Foundation's donors and of the Foundation's endowment; to provide educational resources to graduating seniors, current college students or non-traditional students. **Focus:** General Studies. **Qualif.:** Applicants must plan to attend an accredited two or four-year school. **Criteria:** Recipients are selected based on financial need, character and academic achievement.

Funds Avail.: No specific amount. **To Apply:** Applicants must submit a completed application form, verification form, an official transcript in a sealed envelope, two letters of recommendation and a copy of their FAFSA. **Deadline:** March 1. **Contact:** jpatterson@cfnil.org.

3153 ■ Karen Harter Recruitment Scholarship Grants (Undergraduate/Scholarship)

Purpose: To serve the four county area (Boone, Ogle, Stephenson and Winnebago) through philanthropy; to provide leadership in meeting charitable needs and to be a responsible steward to the Foundation's donors and of the Foundation's endowment; to provide educational resources to students pursuing a career in education. **Focus:** Education. **Qualif.:** Applicants must be female Rockford College or Northern Illinois University sophomore or junior students who are pursuing a career in secondary math or science education. **Criteria:** Recipients are selected based on financial need.

Funds Avail.: No specific amount. **To Apply:** Applicants must submit a completed application form, verification form, an official transcript in a sealed envelope and two letters of recommendation. **Deadline:** March 1. **Contact:** jpatterson@cfnil.org.

3154 ■ Amber Huber Memorial Scholarships (Undergraduate/Scholarship)

Purpose: To serve the four county area (Boone, Ogle, Stephenson and Winnebago) through philanthropy; to provide leadership in meeting charitable needs and to be a responsible steward to the Foundation's donors and of the Foundation's endowment. **Focus:** General studies. **Qualif.:** Applicants must be graduating senior females from Byron High School who have participated in the Byron High School girls track program and/or Byron High School Cheerleading program for at least three seasons including their senior year; must have a minimum GPA of 5 on an 11 point scale or "C" average. **Criteria:** Recipients are selected based on financial need.

Funds Avail.: No specific amount. **To Apply:** Applicants must submit a completed application form, verification form, an official transcript in a sealed envelope and two letters of recommendation. **Deadline:** May 1. **Contact:** jpatterson@cfnil.org.

3155 ■ International Management Council Scholarships (IMC) (Undergraduate/Scholarship)

Purpose: To serve the four county area (Boone, Ogle, Stephenson and Winnebago) through philanthropy; to provide leadership in meeting charitable needs and to be a responsible steward to the Foundation's donors and of the Foundation's endowment; to provide educational resources to Winnebago County high school graduating seniors to pursue a degree in business. **Focus:** Business. **Qualif.:** Applicants must be graduating seniors residing in Winnebago County who are pursuing a degree in business; must have a GPA of at least 3.0 on a 4.0 scale and have been active in community service. **Criteria:** Recipients are selected based on financial need.

Funds Avail.: No specific amount. **To Apply:** Applicants must submit a completed application form, verification form, an official transcript in a sealed envelope and two letters of recommendation. **Deadline:** March 1. **Contact:** jpatterson@cfnil.org.

3156 ■ Ashley E. Ketcher Memorial Scholarships (Undergraduate/Scholarship)

Purpose: To serve the four county area (Boone, Ogle, Stephenson and Winnebago) through philanthropy; to provide leadership in meeting charitable needs and to be a responsible steward to the Foundation's donors and of the Foundation's endowment; to provide educational funds to support Auburn High school CAPA students planning to attend an accredited college or university. **Focus:** General studies. **Qualif.:** Applicants must be graduating Auburn High School seniors in the CAPA program who have an interest in and prior experience in the performing arts; must have a cumulative GPA of at least 2.5. **Criteria:** Recipients are selected based on financial need.

Funds Avail.: No specific amount. **To Apply:** Applicants must submit a completed application form, verification form, an official transcript in a sealed envelope, two letters of recommendation and a copy of FAFSA. **Deadline:** March 1. **Contact:** jpatterson@cfnil.org.

3157 ■ La Voz Latina Scholarships (Undergraduate/Scholarship)

Purpose: To serve the four county area (Boone, Ogle, Stephenson and Winnebago) through philanthropy; to provide leadership in meeting charitable needs and to be a responsible steward to the Foundation's donors and of the Foundation's endowment. **Focus:** Education. **Qualif.:** Applicants must be high school graduates of Hispanic origin who reside in Winnebago County; must be enrolled in a post-secondary education program; must be students completing high school who are pusuing the challenge and benefits of higher education, current college students, and non-traditional students seeking to return to school. **Criteria:** Recipients are selected based on financial need.

Funds Avail.: No specific amount. **To Apply:** Applicants must submit a completed application form. **Deadline:** March 14. **Contact:** 815-965-5784.

3158 ■ Leopold Education Project Scholarships (Undergraduate/Scholarship)

Purpose: To serve the four county area (Boone, Ogle, Stephenson and Winnebago) through philanthropy; to provide leadership in meeting charitable needs and to be a responsible steward to the Foundation's donors and of the Foundation's endowment. **Focus:** General studies. **Qualif.:** Applicants must be graduating high school seniors or high school graduates who are enrolled or planning to enroll in a full-time course of study at an accredited four-year college or university in a natural resources filed; must have a GPA of at least 3.0 on a 4.0 scale and have their permanent address in Boone, Cook, Dekalb, DuPage, Kane, Lake, Mchenry, Will or Winnebago counties; must be students completing high school who are pursuing the challenge and benefits of higher education, current college students, and non-traditional students seeking to return to school. **Criteria:** Recipients are selected based on financial need.

Funds Avail.: No specific amount. **To Apply:** Applicants must contact Jackie Falkenstein for more information. **Contact:** 815-544-2677.

Awards are arranged alphabetically below their administering organizations

3159 ■ May-Cassioppi Scholarships
(Undergraduate/Scholarship)

Purpose: To serve the four county area (Boone, Ogle, Stephenson and Winnebago) through philanthropy; to provide leadership in meeting charitable needs and to be a responsible steward to the Foundation's donors and of the Foundation's endowment. **Focus:** General studies. **Qualif.:** Applicants must be former Guilford High school swimmers and/or divers; must exhibit character traits of strength, discipline, leadership, teamwork and loyalty. **Criteria:** Recipients are selected based on financial need.

Funds Avail.: No specific amount. **To Apply:** Applicants must submit a completed application form, verification form, an official transcript in a sealed envelope, two letters of recommendation and a copy of their FAFSA. **Deadline:** March 1. **Contact:** jpatterson@cfnil.org.

3160 ■ Keith Miffioli Scholarships
(Undergraduate/Scholarship)

Purpose: To serve the four county area (Boone, Ogle, Stephenson and Winnebago) through philanthropy; to provide leadership in meeting charitable needs and to be a responsible steward to the Foundation's donors and of the Foundation's endowment; to provide awards to worthy scholars who otherwise might not receive a college or university education. **Focus:** General studies. **Qualif.:** Applicants must be graduating senior students from a Boone, Stephenson, Ogle or Winnebago County School who have a cumulative GPA of 3.0 or higher. **Criteria:** Recipients are selected based on financial need.

Funds Avail.: No specific amount. **To Apply:** Applicants must submit a completed application form, verification form, an official transcript in a sealed envelope, two letters of recommendation and a copy of their FAFSA. **Deadline:** March 1. **Contact:** jpatterson@cfnil.org.

3161 ■ Paul and Ruth Neidhold Business Scholarships *(Undergraduate/Scholarship)*

Purpose: To serve the four county area (Boone, Ogle, Stephenson and Winnebago) through philanthropy; to provide leadership in meeting charitable needs and to be a responsible steward to the Foundation's donors and of the Foundation's endowment. **Focus:** Business. **Qualif.:** Applicants must be Harvard High School seniors with a minimum GPA of 2.0; must have plans to pursue an education or training in a business field. **Criteria:** Recipients are selected based on financial need.

Funds Avail.: No specific amount. **To Apply:** Applicants must submit a completed application form, verification form, an official transcript in a sealed envelope, two letters of recommendation and a copy of their FAFSA. **Deadline:** March 1. **Contact:** jpatterson@cfnil.org.

3162 ■ Northwest Community Center Scholarships *(Undergraduate/Scholarship)*

Purpose: To serve the four county area (Boone, Ogle, Stephenson and Winnebago) through philanthropy; to provide leadership in meeting charitable needs and to be a responsible steward to the Foundation's donors and of the Foundation's endowment. **Focus:** General studies. **Qualif.:** Applicants must be graduating senior students or graduates from a Rockford high school who have a GPA of at least 2.0; must have plans to attend a college, university or trade school; must be residents of northwest Rockford or have a history of involvement at the Northwest Community Center as either a volunteer or participant. **Criteria:** Recipi-

ents are selected based on financial need.

Funds Avail.: No specific amount. **To Apply:** Applicants must submit a completed application form, verification form, an official transcript in a sealed envelope, two letters of recommendation and a copy of their FAFSA. **Deadline:** March 1. **Contact:** jpatterson@cfnil.org.

3163 ■ Katharine H. Obye Scholarship Awards
(Undergraduate/Scholarship)

Purpose: To serve the four county area (Boone, Ogle, Stephenson and Winnebago) through philanthropy; to provide leadership in meeting charitable needs and to be a responsible steward to the Foundation's donors and of the Foundation's endowment. **Focus:** General studies. **Qualif.:** Applicants must be female students who are graduating from a public high school within Boone or Winnebago county who have plans to teach at any level or in any field; must have done outstanding work on a high school publication staff such as newspaper or yearbook. **Criteria:** Recipients are selected based on financial need.

Funds Avail.: No specific amount. **To Apply:** Applicants must submit a completed application form, verification form, an official transcript in a sealed envelope, two letters of recommendation and a copy of their FAFSA. **Deadline:** March 1. **Contact:** jpatterson@cfnil.org.

3164 ■ William Pigott Memorial Scholarships
(Undergraduate/Scholarship)

Purpose: To serve the four county area (Boone, Ogle, Stephenson and Winnebago) through philanthropy; to provide leadership in meeting charitable needs and to be a responsible steward to the Foundation's donors and of the Foundation's endowment. **Focus:** Engineering. **Qualif.:** Applicants must be graduating senior students from McHenry, Boone or Winnebago county majoring in engineering. **Criteria:** Recipients are selected based on financial need.

Funds Avail.: No specific amount. **To Apply:** Applicants must submit a completed application form, verification form, an official transcript in a sealed envelope and two letters of recommendation. **Deadline:** March 1. **Contact:** jpatterson@cfnil.org.

3165 ■ Mark A. Reid Memorial Scholarship Grants *(Undergraduate/Scholarship)*

Purpose: To serve the four county area (Boone, Ogle, Stephenson and Winnebago) through philanthropy; to provide leadership in meeting charitable needs and to be a responsible steward to the Foundation's donors and of the Foundation's endowment; to encourage and support other students who are actively involved in extracurricular activities. **Focus:** Drama. **Qualif.:** Applicants must be graduating seniors at Oregon High School who actively participate in music or drama; must be students completing high school who are pursuing the challenge and benefits of higher education, current college students, and non-traditional students seeking to return to school. **Criteria:** Recipients are selected based on demonstrated leadership.

Funds Avail.: No specific amount. **To Apply:** Applicants must contact Mitch Lauer for more information. **Contact:** 815-732-6241.

3166 ■ Rockford Area Habitat for Humanity College Scholarships *(Undergraduate/Scholarship)*

Purpose: To serve the four county area (Boone, Ogle, Stephenson and Winnebago) through philanthropy; to

Awards are arranged alphabetically below their administering organizations

provide leadership in meeting charitable needs and to be a responsible steward to the Foundation's donors and of the Foundation's endowment. **Focus:** General studies. **Qualif.:** Applicants must have plans to attend an accredited junior college or university; must be current homeowner residents or dependents of homeowner residents of a home built by Rockford Area Habitat for Humanity; must be residing in that home at time of scholarship application. **Criteria:** Recipients are selected based on financial need.

Funds Avail.: No specific amount. **To Apply:** Applicants must submit a completed application form, verification form, an official transcript in a sealed envelope, two letters of recommendation and a copy of FAFSA. **Deadline:** March 1. **Contact:** jpatterson@cfnil.org.

3167 ■ Rockford Chapter Daughters of the American Revolution Memorial Scholarships
(Undergraduate/Scholarship)

Purpose: To serve the four county area (Boone, Ogle, Stephenson and Winnebago) through philanthropy; to provide leadership in meeting charitable needs and to be a responsible steward to the Foundation's donors and of the Foundation's endowment. **Focus:** General studies. **Qualif.:** Applicants must be graduating seniors from Winnebago or Boone County pursuing a two or four year degree; must be students completing high school who are pursuing the challenge and benefits of higher education, current college students, and non-traditional students seeking to return to school. **Criteria:** Recipients are selected based on academic achievement and financial need.

Funds Avail.: No specific amount. **To Apply:** Applicants must contact Audrey Johnson at 815-282-4395 for more information.

3168 ■ Deborah Jean Rydberg Memorial Scholarships *(Undergraduate/Scholarship)*

Purpose: To serve the four county area (Boone, Ogle, Stephenson and Winnebago) through philanthropy; to provide leadership in meeting charitable needs and to be a responsible steward to the Foundation's donors and of the Foundation's endowment. **Focus:** General studies. **Qualif.:** Applicants must be graduating female senior athletes at Guilford High school who have at least a "C" or better average and have plans to attend college. **Criteria:** Recipients are selected based on financial need.

Funds Avail.: No specific amount. **To Apply:** Applicants must submit a completed application form, verification form, an official transcript in a sealed envelope and two letters of recommendation. **Deadline:** March 1. **Contact:** jpatterson@cfnil.org.

3169 ■ Richard J. Schnell Memorial Scholarships *(Postdoctorate/Scholarship)*

Purpose: To serve the four county area (Boone, Ogle, Stephenson and Winnebago) through philanthropy; to provide leadership in meeting charitable needs and to be a responsible steward to the Foundation's donors and of the Foundation's endowment. **Focus:** General studies. **Qualif.:** Applicants must have been accepted into or enrolled in an American Dental Association accredited dental or dental hygiene program or a graduate post-doctoral program in United States. **Criteria:** Recipients are selected based on financial need.

Funds Avail.: No specific amount. **To Apply:** Applicants must submit a completed application form, verification form, an official transcript in a sealed envelope, two letters of

recommendation and a copy of their FAFSA. **Deadline:** July 1. **Contact:** jpatterson@cfnil.org.

3170 ■ Bonnie Sorenson Scudder Scholarships
(Undergraduate/Scholarship)

Purpose: To serve the four county area (Boone, Ogle, Stephenson and Winnebago) through philanthropy; to provide leadership in meeting charitable needs and to be a responsible steward to the Foundation's donors and of the Foundation's endowment. **Focus:** Physical education. **Qualif.:** Applicants must be female senior students at Harvard High School who have exhibited an interest in women's physical education and who wish to pursue a degree in women's physical education; must be students completing high school who are pusuing the challenge and benefits of higher education, current college students, and non-traditional students seeking to return to school. **Criteria:** Recipients are selected based on financial need.

Funds Avail.: No specific amount. **To Apply:** Applicants must submit a completed application form and must contact Melissa Laffey for more information. **Contact:** 1103 N Jefferson, Harvard, IL 60033.

3171 ■ Elisabeth Seegmiller Recruitment Scholarship Grants *(Undergraduate/Scholarship)*

Purpose: To serve the four county area (Boone, Ogle, Stephenson and Winnebago) through philanthropy; to provide leadership in meeting charitable needs and to be a responsible steward to the Foundation's donors and of the Foundation's endowment. **Focus:** General studies. **Qualif.:** Applicants must be female Rockford College sophomore or junior students who are pursuing a degree in education. **Criteria:** Recipients are selected based on financial need.

Funds Avail.: No specific amount. **To Apply:** Applicants must submit a completed application form, verification form, an official transcript in a sealed envelope and two letters of recommendation. **Deadline:** March 1. **Contact:** jpatterson@cfnil.org.

3172 ■ Senior Memorial Scholarships
(Undergraduate/Scholarship)

Purpose: To serve the four county area (Boone, Ogle, Stephenson and Winnebago) through philanthropy; to provide leadership in meeting charitable needs and to be a responsible steward to the Foundation's donors and of the Foundation's endowment. **Focus:** General studies. **Qualif.:** Applicants must be graduating senior students from a Rockford School District No. 205 high school; must plan to attend a college, university or higher institution of learning; must be students completing high school who are pursuing the challenge and benefits of higher education, current college students, and non-traditional students seeking to return to school. **Criteria:** Recipients are selected based on academic potential and financial need.

Funds Avail.: No specific Amount. **To Apply:** Applicants must be nominated by their high school principal. **Deadline:** March 1.

3173 ■ Ernest and Charlene Stachowiak Memorial Scholarships *(Undergraduate/Scholarship)*

Purpose: To serve the four county area (Boone, Ogle, Stephenson and Winnebago) through philanthropy; to provide leadership in meeting charitable needs and to be a responsible steward to the Foundation's donors and of the Foundation's endowment; to provide educational resources for residents in the four counties of Boone, Ogle, Stephen-

Awards are arranged alphabetically below their administering organizations

son and Winnebago. **Focus:** General studies. **Qualif.:** Applicants must be graduating seniors or college students with a permanent address within Boone, Ogle, Stephenson or Winnebago county; must have a GPA of at least 2.5 on 4.0 scale. **Criteria:** Recipients are selected based on financial need.

Funds Avail.: No specific amount. **To Apply:** Applicants must submit a completed application form, verification form, an official transcript in a sealed envelope, two letters of recommendation and a copy of their FAFSA. **Deadline:** March 1. **Contact:** jpatterson@cfnil.org.

3174 ■ Gary S. Wilmer RAMI Music Scholarships (Undergraduate/Scholarship)

Purpose: To serve the four county area (Boone, Ogle, Stephenson and Winnebago) through philanthropy; to provide leadership in meeting charitable needs and to be a responsible steward to the Foundation's donors and of the Foundation's endowment. **Focus:** Music. **Qualif.:** Applicants must be graduating senior students from Boone or Winnebago County who have a GPA of at least 2.5; must have plans to pursue a degree in music performance, education or composition and be actively involved in school or community musical groups; must be nominated by a music teacher. **Criteria:** Recipients are selected based on financial need.

Funds Avail.: No specific amount. **To Apply:** Applicants must submit a completed application form, verification form, an official transcript in a sealed envelope, two letters of recommendation and a five minute or less performance tape or C.D. **Deadline:** February 1. **Contact:** jpatterson@cfnil.org.

3175 ■ Women of Today's Manufacturing Scholarships (Undergraduate/Scholarship)

Purpose: To serve the four county area (Boone, Ogle, Stephenson and Winnebago) through philanthropy; to provide leadership in meeting charitable needs and to be a responsible steward to the Foundation's donors and of the Foundation's endowment. **Focus:** Manufacturing. **Qualif.:** Applicants must be male or female residents of Ogle, Winnebago, Boone, Stephenson or Rock County who are attending or plan to attend a college, university or trade/technical school; must demonstrate how their course work will impact manufacturing technology in the region. **Criteria:** Recipients are selected based on financial need.

Funds Avail.: No specific amount. **To Apply:** Applicants must submit a completed application form, verification form, an official transcript in a sealed envelope and two letters of recommendation. **Deadline:** March 1. **Contact:** jpatterson@cfnil.org.

3176 ■ Carolyn Wones Recruitment Scholarship Grants (Undergraduate/Scholarship)

Purpose: To serve the four county area (Boone, Ogle, Stephenson and Winnebago) through philanthropy; to provide leadership in meeting charitable needs and to be a responsible steward to the Foundation's donors and of the Foundation's endowment. **Focus:** General studies. **Qualif.:** Applicants must be females who graduated from a public high school within Boone or Winnebago county; must have plans to pursue a degree in secondary teaching; must exhibit academic potential and have participated in a number of high school activities. **Criteria:** Recipients are selected based on financial need.

Funds Avail.: No specific amount. **To Apply:** Applicants

must submit a completed application form, verification form, an official transcript in a sealed envelope and two letters of recommendation. **Deadline:** March 1. **Contact:** jpatterson@cfnil.org.

3177 ■ Margaret Wyeth Scholarships (Undergraduate/Scholarship)

Purpose: To serve the four county area (Boone, Ogle, Stephenson and Winnebago) through philanthropy; to provide leadership in meeting charitable needs and to be a responsible steward to the Foundation's donors and of the Foundation's endowment. **Focus:** General studies. **Qualif.:** Applicants must be graduating public high school senior students and residing in Boone, Ogle or Winnebago County; must plan to attend a college or university. **Criteria:** Recipients are selected based on financial need and demonstrated active involvement in social studies organizations, clubs and classes such as student government, political campaigns, social service and community service.

Funds Avail.: No specific amount. **To Apply:** Applicants must submit a completed application form, verification form, an official transcript in a sealed envelope, two letters of recommendation and a copy of their FAFSA. **Deadline:** March 1. **Contact:** jpatterson@cfnil.org.

3178 ■ Zeta Chapter Memorial Scholarship Awards (Undergraduate/Scholarship)

Purpose: To serve the four county area (Boone, Ogle, Stephenson and Winnebago) through philanthropy; to provide leadership in meeting charitable needs and to be a responsible steward to the Foundation's donors and of the Foundation's endowment. **Focus:** General studies. **Qualif.:** Applicants must be females who are graduating from a public high school within Boone or Winnebago county; must have plans to teach at any level; must exhibit academic potential and have participated in a number of high school activities. **Criteria:** Recipients are selected based on financial need and demonstrated active involvement in social studies organizations, clubs and classes such as student government, political campaigns, social service and community service.

Funds Avail.: No specific amount. **To Apply:** Applicants must submit a completed application form, verification form, an official transcript in a sealed envelope and two letters of recommendation. **Deadline:** March 1. **Contact:** jpatterson@cfnil.org.

3179 ■ Community Foundation of Prince Edward Island (CFPEI)
119-121 Quenn St., Ste. 105
Charlottetown, PE, Canada C1A 1Z4
Ph: (902) 892-3440
Fax: (902) 892-0880
Free: 800-566-7307
E-mail: cfpei@pei.aibn.com
URL: www.cfpei.ca

3180 ■ Architects Association of PEI Scholarships (Undergraduate/Scholarship)

Purpose: To provide financial assistance to qualified individuals who want to pursue their education. **Focus:** Architecture. **Qualif.:** Applicant must be a Prince Edward Island student who graduated from a PEI High School and has been accepted into a recognized architectural program. **Criteria:** Recipient will be selected based on the scholar-

Awards are arranged alphabetically below their administering organizations

ship application requirements.

Funds Avail.: $1,500. **To Apply:** Applicant must complete the application form available online; must submit an official transcript of marks, copy of letter of acceptance from the university, an essay, two reference letters and portfolio of work. Application form and other supporting documents must be sent to Community Foundation of Prince Edward Island, 119-121 Queen St. Ste. 105, Charlottetown, PE C1A 4B3. **Deadline:** June 1.

3181 ■ Joan Auld Scholarships *(Undergraduate/ Scholarship)*

Purpose: To provide financial assistance to qualified individuals who want to pursue their education. **Focus:** Art; Crafts; Design. **Qualif.:** Applicant must be a Canadian citizen; must have been a resident of P.E.I for at least the 6 months prior to application; must be undertaking full-time studies in a craft-related field at a recognized institution of applied art, craft and design; must demonstrate high school graduation or equivalence. **Criteria:** Recipient will be selected based on the scholarship application criteria.

Funds Avail.: No specific amount. **To Apply:** Applicants must complete the application form available online; must provide an outline of the proposed course of study and the name of the institution where they will attend the class; must submit an essay about their background, interest, aims and ambitions; must submit a letter of reference and portfolio demonstrating previous work, samples of craft-related work, sketches, video or pictures; must include written verification of acceptance. Application form and other supporting documents must be sent to Joan Auld Scholarship Fund c/o The Community Foundation of Prince Edward Island, 119-121 Queen St. Charlottetown, PE C1A 4B3. **Deadline:** June 1.

3182 ■ Lorne and Ruby Bonnell Scholarships *(Undergraduate/Scholarship)*

Purpose: To provide scholarship assistance to qualified individuals who want to pursue their studies. **Focus:** General studies. **Qualif.:** Applicant must be a graduate of a Prince Edward Island high school; must be a graduate of the University of Prince Edward Island with high academic standing; must be accepted into graduate studies in the sciences at a Canadian university. **Criteria:** Recipient will be selected by the selection committee following the guidelines of conditions of eligibility.

Funds Avail.: $1,000. **To Apply:** Applicant must complete the application form available online; must submit an official letter of acceptance from a Canadian graduate school. Application form and other supporting documents must be sent to Lorne and Ruby Bonnell Scholarship Fund c/o The Community Foundation of Prince Edward Island, 119-121 Queen St. Ste. 105, Charlottetown, PE C1A 4B3. **Deadline:** June 1. **Remarks:** Scholarship Fund was established on December 14, 2000 by the Honorable M. Lorne Bonnell, a prominent Prince Edward Island medical doctor, past Cabinet Minister of the Provincial Legislature and Senator.

3183 ■ Orin Carver Scholarships *(Undergraduate/Scholarship)*

Purpose: To provide financial assistance to qualified individuals who want to pursue their education. **Focus:** General studies. **Qualif.:** Applicants must be high school graduates in the top 25% of their class; must exhibit excellence and leadership in either athletics, arts and/or community service; must be accepted into a post-secondary program at UPEI or Holland College. **Criteria:** Recipient

will be selected based on the scholarship application requirements.

Funds Avail.: No specific amount. **To Apply:** Applicants must complete the application form available online; must have a formal statement of academic standing and official academic transcript for most recent academic year, as verified by educational institute attended; must have two letters of reference (one from the educational institution and one from a community member); must provide a 500-word essay or portfolio of their excellent works. Application form and other supporting documents must be sent to Orin Carver Scholarship Selection Committee, c/o Community Foundation of PEI, 119-121 Queen St. Ste. 105, Charlottetown, PE C1A 4b3. **Deadline:** June 1.

3184 ■ Phillips Scholarships *(Undergraduate/ Scholarship)*

Purpose: To provide financial assistance to qualified individuals who want to pursue their education. **Focus:** General studies. **Qualif.:** Applicant must be a high school graduate from the Western School District with a physical disability; must be a resident of Prince County; must have financial need; must have been accepted at a recognized post-secondary institution. **Criteria:** Recipient will be selected based on the scholarship application criteria.

Funds Avail.: No specific amount. **To Apply:** Applicant must complete the application form available online; must submit a copy of their final grades; must have a brief description of their physical disability and what they hope to gain from their studies; must have a letter of acceptance for the next year's study. Application form and other supporting documents must be sent to Lowell Phillips Scholarship Award c/o Community Foundation of Prince Edward Island, 119-121 Queen St. Ste. 105, Charlottetown, PEI C1A 4B3. **Deadline:** June 1.

3185 ■ Summerside-Natick Hockey Scholarships *(Undergraduate/Scholarship)*

Purpose: To provide financial assistance to qualified individuals who want to pursue their education. **Focus:** General studies. **Qualif.:** Applicant must be a high school graduate of Prince Edward Island; must be accepted at a post-secondary institution; must be entering the first year of study; must have played in the Summerside Area Minor Hockey Association. **Criteria:** Recipient will be selected based on the scholarship application criteria.

Funds Avail.: $500. **To Apply:** Applicant must complete the application form available online; must include a letter detailing how he/she meets the selection criteria; must have an official letter of acceptance from a recognized post-secondary institution; must submit two letters of reference; and most recent transcript. Application form and other supporting documents must be sent to The Summerside-Natick International Friendship Fund c/o The Community Foundation of Prince Edward Island, 119-121 Queen St. Ste. 105, Queen Square Place, Charlottetown, PE C1A 4B3. **Deadline:** June 1. **Remarks:** Founding members of the International Friendship Hockey Series Committee established the Summerside-Natick International Friendship Hockey Fund.

3186 ■ Community Foundation of Sarasota County
2635 Fruitville Rd.
Sarasota, FL 34237
Ph: (941) 955-3000
Fax: (941) 952-1951

Awards are arranged alphabetically below their administering organizations

E-mail: stewart@cfsarasota.org
URL: www.cfsarasota.org

3187 ■ American Business Women's Association Sarasota Sunrise Chapter Scholarships
(Undergraduate, Vocational/Occupational/ Scholarship)

Purpose: To encourage and enable caring individuals to easily and effectively support the charitable causes that they care about. **Focus:** Business. **Qualif.:** Applicants must be female students with 3.0 unweighted high school GPA and must be of good character and have a career goal related to their college or university studies. **Criteria:** Recipients are selected based on financial need.

Funds Avail.: No specific amount. **To Apply:** Applicants must complete the application form; must submit a parent or guardian's most recent 1040 federal tax form; must provide two letters of reference from people who know the applicant well; official acceptance letter from college or vocational school; and a copy of SAT and ACT scores.

3188 ■ byourself Scholarship Fund
(Undergraduate, Vocational/Occupational/ Scholarship)

Purpose: To encourage and enable caring individuals to easily and effectively support the charitable causes that they care about. **Focus:** Nursing. **Qualif.:** Applicants must be non-traditional students, males or females in Sarasota County pursuing RN, LPN, or CNA; must be accepted into the nursing programs at Manatee Community College or Sarasota County Technical Institute; and must maintain a 2.8 GPA to retain scholarship. **Criteria:** Recipients are selected based on financial need.

Funds Avail.: No specific amount. **To Apply:** Applicants must complete the application form; must submit a parent or guardian's most recent 1040 federal tax form; and must provide two letters of reference from people who know the applicant well; official acceptance letter from college or vocational school; and a copy of SAT and ACT scores.

3189 ■ Community Foundation of Sarasota County Adult Learner Scholarships
(Undergraduate, Vocational/Occupational/ Scholarship)

Purpose: To encourage and enable caring individuals to easily and effectively support the charitable causes that they care about. **Focus:** General studies. **Qualif.:** Applicants must be adult learners who are returning to vocational school or college after having been out of high school for a number of years. **Criteria:** Recipients are selected based on the objective and competitive academic and non-academic factors plus demonstrated financial need.

Funds Avail.: No specific amount. **To Apply:** Applicants must complete the application form; must submit a parent or guardian's most recent 1040 federal tax form; and must provide two letters of reference from people who know the applicant well. **Deadline:** September 19.

3190 ■ Davis Educational Scholarship Fund
(Undergraduate, Vocational/Occupational/ Scholarship)

Purpose: To encourage and enable caring individuals to easily and effectively support the charitable causes that they care about; to help students obtain a college degree or vocational training to pursue a career in nursing or the medical field. **Focus:** Medical education. **Qualif.:** Applicants must be accepted into a health related program. **Criteria:** Recipients are selected based on financial need and on their educational objectives that will lead to a career in the health care field.

Funds Avail.: No specific amount. **To Apply:** Applicants must complete the application form; must submit a parent or guardian's most recent 1040 federal tax form; must provide two letters of reference from people who know the applicant well; official acceptance letter from college or vocational school; and a copy of SAT and ACT scores.

3191 ■ Father Connie Dougherty Scholarships
(Undergraduate, Vocational/Occupational/ Scholarship)

Purpose: To further education at a college, university, or institution of higher learning including education in advanced vocational training. **Focus:** General studies. **Qualif.:** Applicants must be graduates of Sarasota County public and private school. **Criteria:** Recipients are selected based on academic performance and financial need.

Funds Avail.: $5,000. **To Apply:** Applicants must submit a completed application form; an official transcript; SAT or ACT scores; copy of Student Aid Report; and three letters of recommendation (one must come from a teacher and one from a community member who is not a teacher or relative). **Deadline:** April 2. **Contact:** Mimi Goodwill, Scholarship Manager, at mimi@cfssarasota.org.

3192 ■ James Franklin and Dorothy J. Warnell Scholarship Fund *(Undergraduate, Vocational/Occupational/Scholarship)*

Purpose: To encourage and enable caring individuals to easily and effectively support the charitable causes that they care about and to provide scholarships for adult learners in Sarasota County to pursue a professional certificate in hairdressing. **Focus:** General studies. **Qualif.:** Applicants must be residents of Sarasota County and post high school students. **Criteria:** Recipients are selected based on financial need and on their educational objectives.

Funds Avail.: No specific amount. **To Apply:** Applicants must submit completed application form; a parent or guardian's most recent 1040 federal tax form; two letters of reference from people who know the applicant well; official transcript of record; official acceptance letter from college or vocational school; and a copy of SAT and ACT scores.

3193 ■ Helen F. "Jerri" Rand Memorial Scholarships *(Undergraduate, Vocational/Occupational/ Scholarship)*

Purpose: To encourage and enable caring individuals to easily and effectively support the charitable causes that they care about and to provide scholarships for adult learners in Sarasota County to pursue a professional certificate in hairdressing. **Focus:** Cosmetology. **Qualif.:** Applicants must be adult learners who are accepted to any accredited beauty school in Sarasota County. **Criteria:** Recipients are selected based on financial need and on their educational objectives that will lead to a career.

Funds Avail.: No specific amount. **To Apply:** Applicants must complete the application form; must submit a parent or guardian's most recent 1040 federal tax form; must provide two letters of reference from people who know the applicant well; must provide official transcript of record, official acceptance letter from college or vocational school; and must submit a copy of SAT and ACT scores.

Awards are arranged alphabetically below their administering organizations

3194 ■ Traditional Student Scholarships
(Undergraduate/Scholarship)

Purpose: To encourage and enable caring individuals to easily and effectively support the charitable causes that they care about. **Focus:** General studies. **Qualif.:** Applicants must be high school seniors, or those who are 24 years old or younger who are currently attending college. **Criteria:** Recipients are selected based on financial need, leadership potential, academic performance, work experience, and commitment to school and community through volunteerism.

Funds Avail.: No specific amount. **To Apply:** Applicants must complete the application form; must submit a parent or guardian's most recent 1040 federal tax form; and must provide two letters of reference from people who know the applicant well. **Deadline:** March 1. **Contact:** Rebekah Fleming, Program Assistant at rebekah@cfsarasota.org.

3195 ■ Community Foundation for Southeast Michigan (CFSEM)
333 W Fort St., Ste. 2010
Detroit, MI 48226-3134
Ph: (313) 961-6675
Fax: (313) 961-2886
E-mail: cfsem@cfsem.org
URL: www.cfsem.org

3196 ■ Dick Depaolis Memorial Scholarships
(Undergraduate/Scholarship)

Purpose: To provide financial assistance to graduating senior male varsity athletes from North Farmington High School who demonstrate leadership, good grades and male varsity athlete who will enter college majoring in liberal studies, especially History and English. **Focus:** History; English language and literature. **Qualif.:** Applicants must be members of the graduating class at North Farmington High School; must demonstrate exemplary desire, ability and have a GPA of 3.0 or higher; must be male athletes demonstrating leadership, academic discipline and good sportsmanship on and off the field; must be playing varsity sports (football preferred); have applied or been accepted as full-time students in an accredited educational institution in the United States with a major in liberal studies, especially History and English. **Criteria:** Recipients are evaluated based on academic records, recommendations, statement of goals and financial need.

Funds Avail.: $500. **To Apply:** Application form contains the following: (a) scholarship guidelines and deadlines; (b) statement of academic and career goals; (c) recommendation form; and (d) transcript release form. Applicants must use a computer, typewriter or print neatly in blue or black ink in completing the application form. **Deadline:** March 23.

3197 ■ Detroit Economic Club Scholarships
(Undergraduate/Scholarship)

Purpose: To provide financial assistance to students of Southeast Michigan region for their education. **Focus:** General studies. **Qualif.:** Applicants must be high school seniors in public or private high schools in Wayne, Oakland or Macomb counties. **Criteria:** Recipients are selected based on scholastic, demonstrated character and leadership, personal statement and financial need.

Funds Avail.: $2,000. **Number Awarded:** 2. **To Apply:** Applicants must first be nominated by their counselor and then invited to apply, for scholarship consideration. Applicants must fill-out the Scholarship Application form. High school principal, advisor, counselor, or a teacher should be asked to complete the High School Certification Form and Applicant Recommendation Form. These forms should be filled-out by two different individuals. **Deadline:** April 2.

3198 ■ Robert Holmes Scholarships
(Undergraduate/Scholarship)

Purpose: To provide financial assistance to students of Southeast Michigan region for their education. **Focus:** General studies. **Qualif.:** Applicants must be dependents of eligible Michigan Teamsters and high school seniors who will attend a Michigan College or University as full-time students; and must be active or have been placed on a seniority list. **Criteria:** Recipients will be selected based on strong scholastic performance while in high school; class rank; and demonstrated qualities of leadership in school, extracurricular activities and community involvement.

Funds Avail.: $1,000. **Number Awarded:** 6. **To Apply:** Applicants must submit the completed application form; must ask a high school principal or advisor/counselor to complete the enclosed high School Certification Form and to a high school teacher or other adult to complete the enclosed the Applicant Recommendation Form. **Deadline:** April 2.

3199 ■ Detroit Tigers Willie Horton Scholarships
(Undergraduate/Scholarship)

Purpose: To provide financial assistance to students of Southeast Michigan region for education. **Focus:** General studies. **Qualif.:** Applicants must be graduating seniors at Northwestern High School in Detroit; must show leadership and character through extracurricular activities, volunteer involvement and work experience in school and in the community; have applied or have been accepted as full-time students in an accredited educational institution in the United States; and must demonstrate desire, ability and good grades. **Criteria:** Applicants are evaluated based on scholastic, personal attributes and experience in school or community.

Funds Avail.: $5,000. **Number Awarded:** 1. **To Apply:** Applicants must use a computer, typewriter or print neatly in blue or black ink all appropriate forms; must submit a complete application form including the following: (1) scholarship guidelines and deadlines; (2) student application; (3) statement of academic and career goals; (4) recommendation forms; and (5) transcript release form. **Deadline:** April 2.

3200 ■ Chris Kurzweil Scholarships
(Undergraduate/Scholarship)

Purpose: To provide financial assistance to students in the Southeast Michigan region for their education; to assist the legal dependents of employees of Intertape Polymer Group in pursuing a program of undergraduate education. **Focus:** General studies. **Qualif.:** Applicants must be dependents of members of the Intertape Polymer Group, formerly American Tape; and must be high school seniors. **Criteria:** Recipients will be selected based on strong scholastic performance; leadership qualities in school, extracurricular activities and community involvement; and class rank.

Funds Avail.: $2,000. **Number Awarded:** 2. **To Apply:** Applicants must use a computer, typewriter or print neatly in blue or black ink all appropriate forms; must complete the application form; must ask a high school principal or advisor/counselor to complete the High School Certification Form and a high school teacher or another adult to

Awards are arranged alphabetically below their administering organizations

complete the Applicant Recommendation Form. **Deadline:** April 2.

3201 ■ Imelda and Ralph LeMar Scholarship Program *(Undergraduate/Scholarship)*

Purpose: To provide educational assistance to students who are graduates from public high schools in Fowlerville. **Focus:** Chemistry; Physics; Engineering, Electrical; Engineering, Mechanical. **Qualif.:** Applicants must be members of a graduating class in a public high school in Fowlerville, Michigan; must demonstrate exemplary desire, ability and good grades; must show leadership and character through extracurricular activities, volunteer involvement and work experience in school and in the community; have applied or been accepted as full-time students in an accredited educational institution in the United States; must be planning to study chemistry, physics or electrical or mechanical engineering in college. **Criteria:** Applicants are evaluated based on academic records, recommendations and the student's statement of goals.

Funds Avail.: $800. **To Apply:** Forms may be computerized or typewritten or printed neatly in blue or black ink as appropriate; must submit a complete application form including the following: (1) scholarship guidelines and deadlines; (2) student application; (3) statement of academic and career goals; (4) recommendation form; (5) transcript release form. **Deadline:** March 30.

3202 ■ Virgil K. Lobring Scholarships *(Undergraduate/Scholarship)*

Purpose: To provide financial assistance to students of Southeast Michigan region for their education. **Focus:** General studies. **Qualif.:** Applicants must be members of the graduating class at Southwestern High School in Detroit, Michigan; must demonstrate exemplary desire, ability and good grades; demonstrate leadership and character through extracurricular activities, volunteer involvement and work experience in school and in the community; have applied or been accepted as full-time students in an accredited educational institution in the United States; must be students who have demonstrated the greatest improvement from the time during freshman year in high school as determined by the Lobring Scholarship committee; must demonstrate financial need. **Criteria:** Applicants are evaluated based on academic records, recommendations and statement of goals.

Funds Avail.: $1,500. **Number Awarded:** 1. **To Apply:** Applicants must submit the application containing scholarship guidelines and deadlines, student application, essay question, recommendation forms from counselor, teacher and community service forms; and transcripts release form. **Deadline:** April 2.

3203 ■ Cary Moore Memorial Scholarship Fund *(Undergraduate/Scholarship)*

Purpose: To provide financial assistance to the male varsity athlete from North Farmington High School who best personifies school spirit and good sportsmanship. **Focus:** General studies. **Qualif.:** Applicants must be members of the graduating class at North Farmington High School who demonstrate exemplary desire, ability and good grades; must be male athletes who show leadership, character and sportsmanship by participating in varsity athletics at North Farmington High School and Raiders Pride; have applied or been accepted as full-time students in an accredited educational institution in the United States. **Criteria:** Applicants are evaluated based on academic records, recom-

mendations and statement of goals.

Funds Avail.: $1,500. **Number Awarded:** 1. **To Apply:** Applicants must submit a completed application form including the following: (1) scholarship guidelines and deadlines; (2) student application (may substitute NFHS application); (3) statement of academic and career goals; (4) recommendation form; and (4) transcript release form. Applicants must use a computer, typewriter or print neatly in blue or black ink all appropriate forms. **Deadline:** March 25.

3204 ■ Jean and Tom Rosenthal Scholarship Program *(Undergraduate/Scholarship)*

Purpose: To provide financial assistance to students of Southeast Michigan region for their education. **Focus:** General studies. **Qualif.:** Applicants must be members of the graduating class at Pontiac Northern High School or Pontiac Central High School demonstrating exemplary desire, ability and good grades of at least 2.5 or higher; must show leadership and character through extracurricular activities, volunteer involvement and work experience in school and in the community; have applied or been accepted as full-time students in an accredited educational institution in the United States. **Criteria:** Applicant will be evaluated based on academic records, recommendations and the student's essay on personal commitment of service to others.

Funds Avail.: $1,000. **Number Awarded:** 2. **To Apply:** Applicants must submit the application containing scholarship guidelines and deadlines, student application, essay question, recommendation forms from counselor, teacher and community service forms; and transcripts release form. **Deadline:** April 2.

3205 ■ Jeptha Wade Schureman Scholarship Program *(Undergraduate/Scholarship)*

Purpose: To provide financial assistance to students of Southeast Michigan region for their education. **Focus:** Law; Nursing; Medicine; Dentistry. **Qualif.:** Applicants must be residents of Wayne, Oakland, Macomb, Lenawee, Monroe, Livingston, Washtenaw, or St. Clair counties at the time of high school graduation; must be fatherless either through death or through termination of parental rights; must be pursuing, or planning to pursue a degree in the fields of law, nursing, medicine or dentistry; must demonstrate a strong scholastic performance while in high school or college with an equivalent of 3.0 GPA on a 4.0 scale; must demonstrate leadership and character through extracurricular activities, school and community service, volunteer involvement and paid work experience; and must be admitted to one of the 15 non-profit public universities in Michigan. **Criteria:** Applicants are evaluated based on academic records; recommendations and statement of goals; and demonstrated financial need. Preference will be given to candidates between the ages of 17-27 at the time of application and pursuing a full-time education.

Funds Avail.: $7,500. **Number Awarded:** 8. **To Apply:** Applicants must submit the completed application form; and must provide a written personal statement which describes the following: (1) educational plans and career goals; (2) motivating factors and important experiences which may help them shape their personal philosophy and future goals. **Deadline:** June 1.

3206 ■ Community Foundation of Western Massachusetts
PO Box 15769
Springfield, MA 01115

Awards are arranged alphabetically below their administering organizations

Ph: (413) 732-2858
Fax: (413) 733-8565
E-mail: wmass@communityfoundation.org
URL: www.communityfoundation.org

3207 ■ Community Foundation of Western Massachusetts Community Scholarship Program
(Undergraduate/Scholarship)

Purpose: To help bring higher education within reach of residents in Massachusetts who might not otherwise be able to afford it. **Focus:** General studies. **Qualif.:** Applicants must be residents from Franklin, Hampden, Hampshire or combination or city/town; must be freshmen, sophomores, juniors, graduating seniors or graduates of specific high school. **Criteria:** Applicants are evaluated based on scholastic ability, financial need, extracurricular activities, volunteer and community services or athletic activities.

Funds Avail.: $25,000. **To Apply:** Applicants must submit all the required application information. **Deadline:** March 30.

3208 ■ Composite Panel Association (CPA)
19465 Deerfield Ave., Ste. 306
Leesburg, VA 20176
Ph: (703) 724-1128
Fax: (703) 724-1588
E-mail: tjulia@cpamail.org
URL: compositepanel.org

3209 ■ Robert E. Dougherty Scholarships
(Undergraduate/Scholarship)

Purpose: To provide financial assistance to students pursuing a career in the composite panel and affiliated industries. **Focus:** Forestry; Chemistry; Engineering. **Qualif.:** Applicant must be a North American citizen; and be nominated by a member of the Robert E. Dougherty Education Foundation. **Criteria:** Member companies are permitted to nominate one or more individuals for scholarship consideration.

Funds Avail.: 5,000. **Number Awarded:** 5. **To Apply:** Scholarship Application forms can be downloaded at the website and must be filled out and returned to the Foundation. **Deadline:** March 1.

3210 ■ Conference on Asian Pacific American Leadership (CAPAL)
PO Box 65073
Washington, DC 20035
Fax: (877) 892-5427
E-mail: info@capal.org
URL: www.capal.org

3211 ■ Conference on Asian Pacific American Leadership Scholarships *(Graduate, Undergraduate/Scholarship)*

Purpose: To provide financial assistance to students with leadership potential to pursue public service internships in Washington, DC. **Focus:** Public service. **Qualif.:** Applicants must be undergraduate and graduate students working in a full-time summer internship in the public sector within the Washington, DC metropolitan area or students graduating in spring 2011. **Criteria:** Selection will be based on demonstrated commitment to public service, including service to the APA community, demonstrated leadership and potential for continued growth in leadership skills, relevance and consistency with overall public sector goals, academic achievement and financial need.

Funds Avail.: $2,000. **Number Awarded:** 3. **To Apply:** Applicants must submit a completed online application form; resume and academic transcripts; one to three letters of recommendation; a statement of purpose that answers two out of three questions found on the online application. **Deadline:** February 1. **Contact:** Applicants may e-mail their questions to scholarships@capal.org.

3212 ■ Conference of State Bank Supervisors (CSBS)
1129 20th St. NW, 9th Fl.
Washington, DC 20036
Ph: (202) 296-2840
Fax: (202) 296-1928
E-mail: jryan@csbs.org
URL: www.csbs.org

3213 ■ Conference of State Bank Supervisors Graduate School Scholarships *(Graduate/Award)*

Purpose: To encourage and assist qualified bank and trust examiners to prepare themselves for expanded duties and responsibilities in their banking departments; broaden the examiner's understanding of banking or trust operations; encourage excellence in bank and trust examination; provide the opportunity for State Bank Supervisors to recognize their outstanding examiners; and raise the level of proficiency of state banking departments. **Focus:** Banking. **Qualif.:** Program is open to outstanding and deserving examiners who demonstrate excellence in their work by supporting their attendance at the graduate banking or graduate trust school of their choice. Nominees must have 3 years of experience in bank or trust supervision as examiners-in-charge or 3 years of experience as bank or trust examiners plus 2 years of experience in a bank or trust company; must have a degree from an accredited college and must have successfully completed the CSBS Senior School; must have demonstrated fully to the State Bank that they have the potential to assume senior-level responsibilities; must continue to be employed by a state banking department. **Criteria:** Recipients are selected based on experience, education, promotion potential and other requirements set by the schools and the banking departments.

Funds Avail.: $3,000. **Number Awarded:** 3. **To Apply:** State Bank Supervisors must nominate candidates using nomination forms provided by the Foundation. **Deadline:** December 1. **Contact:** Roger Stromberg, Senior VP - Education, Conference of State Bank Supervisors; 1155 Connecticut Ave., Ste. 500, Washington, DC 20036-4306; 800-886-2727 ext. 714 (Toll Free); 202-728-5714 (Direct); 202-296-1928 (Fax); rstromberg@csbs.org.

3214 ■ Congressional Black Caucus Foundation (CBCF)
1720 Massachusetts Ave. NW
Washington, DC 20036
Ph: (202) 263-2800
Fax: (202) 775-0773
E-mail: info@cbcfinc.org

Awards are arranged alphabetically below their administering organizations

URL: www.cbcfinc.org

3215 ■ CBC Spouses Cheerios Brand Health Initiative Scholarships *(Undergraduate/ Scholarship)*

Purpose: To increase the number of minority students pursuing degrees in the fields of medicine, engineering, technology, nutrition and other health-related professions. **Focus:** Medicine; Engineering; Technology; Nutrition; Health care services. **Qualif.:** Applicant must be preparing to pursue an undergraduate degree full-time or be a current full-time student in good academic standing at an accredited college/university; planning to pursue a degree in the fields of medicine, engineering, technology, nutrition, or other health related studies; have a minimum 2.5 GPA; have exhibit leadership ability and participate in community service activities; and reside or attend school in a congressional district represented by a CBC member. **Criteria:** Selection is based on submitted application and materials.

Funds Avail.: No specific amount. **To Apply:** Applicants must submit a completed CBC Spouses scholarship application; a sealed official high school or college transcript; a personal statement essay from the student (500 words or more) that addresses all four (4) of the topics listed on the application in one essay; two letters of recommendation (one should come from a community or public service leader-church leader, community leader, etc.); if a first year student, an acceptance letter from the college/university where the student will enroll; and a recent photograph suitable for publication. **Deadline:** June 1. **Remarks:** This award was established in 1998. **Contact:** jcarter@cbcfinc.org.

3216 ■ CBC Spouses Education Scholarship Fund *(Doctorate, Graduate, Undergraduate/ Scholarship)*

Purpose: To support highly motivated students in pursuing their educational goals. **Focus:** General studies. **Qualif.:** Applicant must intend to pursue full-time undergraduate, graduate or doctoral degrees at an accredited college/ university; have a minimum 2.5 GPA; exhibit leadership ability and participate in community service activities; and reside or attend school in a congressional district represented by a CBC member. **Criteria:** Selection is based on submitted application and materials.

Funds Avail.: No specific amount. **To Apply:** Applicants must submit a completed CBC Spouses scholarship application; a sealed official high school or college transcript; a personal statement essay from the student (500 words or more) that addresses all four (4) of the topics listed on the application in one essay; two letters of recommendation (one should come from a community or public service leader-church leader, community leader, etc.); if a first year student, an acceptance letter from the college/university where the student will enroll; and a recent photograph suitable for publication. **Contact:** jcarter@cbcfinc.org.

3217 ■ CBC Spouses Flexible Education Scholarships *(Graduate, Master's, Undergraduate/Scholarship)*

Purpose: to advance educational opportunities for underrepresented and nontraditional groups in higher education. **Focus:** General studies. **Qualif.:** Applicant must be a U.S. citizen or permanent resident and not an employee or a family member of the Apollo Group, Inc. or its subsidiaries. **Criteria:** Preference will be given to applicants who are economically disadvantaged and who have experienced hardships, such as homelessness or inability to complete a previously started degree program.

Funds Avail.: Full tuition. **Number Awarded:** 25. **To Apply:** Applicants must submit a completed application along with all supplemental materials. **Contact:** jcarter@cbcfinc.org.

3218 ■ CBC Spouses Heineken USA Performing Arts Scholarships *(Undergraduate/ Scholarship)*

Purpose: To support students pursuing a career in the performing arts to achieve their goals. **Focus:** Performing arts. **Qualif.:** Applicant must be preparing to pursue a degree full-time, or be a current full-time student in good academic standing at an accredited college/university; have a minimum 2.5 GPA; and exhibit leadership ability and participate in community service activities. **Criteria:** Selection is based on submitted application and materials.

Funds Avail.: $3,000. **Number Awarded:** 10. **To Apply:** Applicants must submit a completed CBC Spouses scholarship application together with a personal statement; an official sealed transcript(s) from all institutions attended; letter of acceptance from intended institution; two letters of recommendation (one from community involvement experience); one page resume listing extracurricular activities, honors, employment, community service and special skills; recent photograph (no group or social photos); and a two minute CD-R or DVD of a recent performance. **Deadline:** May 3. **Remarks:** Established in the year 2000 in honor of the late Curtis Mayfield. **Contact:** jcarter@cbcfinc.org.

3219 ■ CBC Spouses Visual Arts Scholarships *(Undergraduate/Scholarship)*

Purpose: To support students pursuing a career in the visual arts to achieve their goals. **Focus:** Visual arts. **Qualif.:** Applicant must be preparing to pursue an undergraduate degree full-time, or be a current full-time student in good academic standing at an accredited college/university; have a minimum 2.5 GPA; and exhibit leadership ability and participate in community service activities. **Criteria:** Selection is based on submitted application and materials.

Funds Avail.: $3,000. **Number Awarded:** 10. **To Apply:** Applicants must submit a completed CBC Spouses scholarship application together with a personal statement; official sealed transcript(s) from all institutions attended; letter of acceptance from intended institution; two letters of recommendation (one from community involvement experience); one page resume listing extracurricular activities, honors, employment, community service and special skills; recent photograph (no group or social photos); and a CD-R of five original pieces of artwork (an art sample must be provided). Each piece should be titled with the dimension and media. **Deadline:** May 3. **Contact:** jcarter@cbcfinc.org.

3220 ■ CBCF Congressional Fellows Program *(Professional development/Fellowship)*

Purpose: To increase the number of African Americans working as professional staff in the U.S. Congress. **Focus:** General studies. **Qualif.:** Applicant must be a U.S. citizen or permitted to work in the U.S.; a graduate or have professional degree completed prior to the start date fellowship program; familiar with the federal legislative process, Congress and the Congressional Black Caucus (CBC) and its members; and have demonstrated interest in public policy and commitment to creating and implementing policy to improve the living conditions for underserved and underrepresented individuals. **Criteria:** Selection is based on a

Awards are arranged alphabetically below their administering organizations

combination of the following criteria: a record of academic and professional achievement; evidence of leadership skills and the potential for further growth; demonstrated interest in public policy; and quality of paper application and interview performance.

Funds Avail.: $40,000 with benefits. **To Apply:** Applicants must submit a completed application form along with a resume; three letters of recommendation; three Transcript (at least one must be an official transcript); and three essays (each essay no more than two pages in length). Submit three copies of the complete application under one cover. Bind application with paperclips (do not use staples). **Deadline:** May 23.

3221 ■ Louis Stokes Health Scholars Program
(Undergraduate, Vocational/Occupational/Scholarship)

Purpose: To increase the number of qualified, yet under-represented, college students entering the health workforce. **Focus:** Health sciences; Health care services; Health education; Health services administration; Occupational safety and health; Public health; Allied health. **Qualif.:** Applicant must be a U.S. citizen or legal U.S. resident who have a minimum 3.0 GPA on a 4.0 scale; currently enrolled or planning to enroll in a full-time undergraduate course of study at an accredited two- or four-year college, university, vocational or technical school (degree must be in a subject that will lead to a career in a health field); planning seek work in an underserved community; and have demonstrated financial need. Employees or immediate family members of UnitedHealth Group and its affiliates, CBC Members, the CBC Foundation staff, the CBC Foundation Board of Directors or the CBC Foundation Corporate Advisory Council are not eligible. **Criteria:** Preference will be given to students who demonstrate an interest to work in underserved communities.

Funds Avail.: Up to $8,000. **Number Awarded:** 10. **To Apply:** Applicants must complete the online application form. In addition, the following items should all arrive in one package: official transcript from current institution; two letters of recommendation (in sealed envelopes with signature across seal); one-page resume listing extracurricular activities, honors, employment, community service and special skills; recent photograph (no group or social photos); and a copy of Federal Student Aid Report (SAR). **Deadline:** March 29. **Contact:** jcarter@cbcfinc.org.

3222 ■ Louis Stokes Urban Health Policy Fellows Program
(Graduate, Professional development/Fellowship)

Purpose: To increase the pool of qualified, minority health policy professionals who are committed to eliminating health disparities in the United States and abroad. **Focus:** Behavioral sciences; Social sciences; Biological and clinical sciences; Health sciences. **Qualif.:** Applicant must be a U.S. citizen or permitted to work in the United States; a graduate or have a professional degree in a health-related field (behavioral science, social sciences, biological sciences and health professions) from an accredited institution completed prior to the fellowship start date; familiar with the federal legislative process, Congress and the Congressional Black Caucus (CBC); and have demonstrated interest in public policy, and commitment to creating and implementing policy to improve the living conditions for underserved and underrepresented individuals. **Criteria:** Selection is based on a combination of the following criteria: a record of academic and professional achievement;

evidence of leadership skills and the potential for further growth; study of how health policies affect African Americans and minorities; demonstrated interest in public health policy; and quality of paper application and interview performance.

Funds Avail.: $40,000 with benefits. **To Apply:** Applicants must submit a completed application form along with a resume; three letters of recommendation; three transcripts (at least one must be an official transcript); and three essays (each essay no more than two pages in length). Submit three copies of the complete application under one cover. Bind application with paperclips (do not use staples). **Deadline:** May 23.

3223 ■ Congressional Hispanic Caucus Institute (CHCI)
911 2nd St. NE
Washington, DC 20002
Ph: (202) 543-1771
Fax: (202) 546-2143
Free: 800-EXCEL-DC
E-mail: sgrosa@chci.org
URL: www.chci.org

3224 ■ Congressional Hispanic Caucus Institute Graduate and Young Professional Fellowships
(Doctorate, Graduate/Fellowship)

Purpose: To enhance participants' leadership abilities, strengthen professional skills and produce more competent and competitive Latino professionals in underserved public policy issue areas. **Focus:** Public affairs. **Qualif.:** Applicant must poses a graduate degree or higher in an area of study related to his/her chosen policy issue area from an accredited educational institution and must be within three years of program start date; have high academic achievement; have evidence of leadership skills and potential for leadership growth; demonstrate commitment to public service-oriented activities; have superior analytical skills, outstanding oral and written communication skills; and be a U.S. citizen or have legal permanent resident status. **Criteria:** Selection is based on the quality of the application and the interview scores.

Funds Avail.: $2,700 monthly. **To Apply:** Applicants must complete the application online. **Deadline:** September 17.

3225 ■ Congressional Hispanic Caucus Institute Public Policy Fellowships
(Graduate/Fellowship)

Purpose: To enhance participants' leadership abilities, strengthen professional skills and produce more competent and competitive Latino professionals in public policy areas. **Focus:** Public affairs. **Qualif.:** Applicant must have earned a Bachelor's Degree within two years of the program start date and not have received credits towards an advanced degree; have high academic achievement (preference of 3.0 GPA or higher); evidence of leadership skills and potential for leadership growth; demonstrated commitment to public service-oriented activities; have superior analytical skills, outstanding oral and written communication skills; and be a U.S. citizen or have legal permanent resident status. **Criteria:** Selection is based on the quality of the application and the interview scores.

Funds Avail.: $2,200 monthly. **To Apply:** Applicants must complete the application online. **Deadline:** February 18.

Awards are arranged alphabetically below their administering organizations

3226 ■ Congressional Hispanic Caucus Institute Scholarships (Community College, Graduate, Undergraduate/Scholarship)

Purpose: To provide assistance to Latino college students. **Focus:** General studies. **Qualif.:** Applicant must be a full-time student enrolled in a United States Department of Education accredited community college, four-year university, or graduate/professional program during the period for which scholarship is requested; have demonstrated financial need; have consistent, active participation in public and/or community service activities; have strong writing skills; and be a U.S. citizen or have legal permanent residency status. **Criteria:** Selection is based on the application materials submitted.

Funds Avail.: $1,000-$5,000. **To Apply:** Applications must be completed online.

3227 ■ Connecticut Association of Land Surveyors (CALS)

78 Beaver Rd.
Wethersfield, CT 06109
Ph: (860) 563-1990
Fax: (860) 529-9700
E-mail: kathy@ctsurveyor.com
URL: www.ctsurveyor.com

3228 ■ Connecticut Association of Land Surveyors Memorial Scholarships (Undergraduate/Scholarship)

Purpose: To provide information about land surveying in Connecticut to the growing global surveying/internet community. **Focus:** Surveying. **Qualif.:** Applicants must be residents of Connecticut; must be enrolled in a program leading to a degree in surveying or related fields; must be accepted to attend the program and could be a freshman; must show an interest or work history in being a part of the surveying profession. **Criteria:** Recipients are selected based on academic performance and interest in surveying profession.

Funds Avail.: No stated amount. **To Apply:** Applicants must submit a statement outlining qualifications, transcript, resume and other pertinent information. **Deadline:** June 1. **Contact:** 49 Arlington St., West Haven, CT 06516.

3229 ■ Connecticut Association of Latinos in Higher Education (CALAHE)

950 Main St., Ste. 1104
Hartford, CT 06103-1207
Ph: (860) 906-5234
E-mail: ca-calahe@ccc.commnet.edu
URL: www.calahe.org

3230 ■ Thomas M. Blake Memorial Scholarships (Undergraduate/Scholarship)

Purpose: To promote the participation of Latinos in different areas of postsecondary education in Connecticut. **Focus:** Education. **Qualif.:** Applicant must be accepted for admission to an accredited institution of higher education; have a "B" average (3.0 GPA) for all completed enrollment periods at the time of application; a U.S. citizen or permanent resident; have been a Connecticut resident during the preceding 12 months; a Latino student from Connecticut; and must demonstrate financial need. **Criteria:**

Selection is based on the application materials.

Funds Avail.: $1,000. **To Apply:** Applicants must submit a completed scholarship application together with an official copy of educational transcripts; copy of Student Aid Report (SAR) sent by the U.S. Department of Education; and an essay on "How do you feel education is going to impact your ability to continue assisting others to pursue an education?" (maximum 2 page typewritten, double spaced statement). Send application to: Dr. Wilson Luna, Gateway Community College, 60 Sargent Dr., New Haven, CT 06511. **Deadline:** April 15.

3231 ■ Rosa Quezada Memorial Education Scholarships (Undergraduate/Scholarship)

Purpose: To promote the participation of Latinos in different areas of postsecondary education in Connecticut. **Focus:** Education. **Qualif.:** Applicant must be accepted for admission to an accredited institution of higher education; have a "B" average (3.0 GPA) for all completed enrollment periods at the time of application; a U.S. citizen or permanent resident; have been a Connecticut resident during the preceding 12 months; a Latino student from Connecticut; and must demonstrate financial need. **Criteria:** Selection is based on the application materials.

Funds Avail.: $1,000. **To Apply:** Applicants must submit a completed scholarship application together with an official copy of educational transcripts; copy of Student Aid Report (SAR) sent by the U.S. Department of Education; and an essay on "How do you feel education is going to impact your ability to continue assisting others to pursue an education?" (maximum 2 page typewritten, double spaced statement). Send application to: Dr. Wilson Luna, Gateway Community College, 60 Sargent Dr., New Haven, CT 06511. **Deadline:** April 15.

3232 ■ John Soto Scholarships (Undergraduate/Scholarship)

Purpose: To promote the participation of Latinos in different areas of postsecondary education in Connecticut. **Focus:** Education. **Qualif.:** Applicant must be accepted for admission to an accredited institution of higher education; have a "B" average (3.0 GPA) for all completed enrollment periods at the time of application; a U.S. citizen or permanent resident; have been a Connecticut resident during the preceding 12 months; a Latino student from Connecticut; and must demonstrate financial need. **Criteria:** Selection is based on the application materials.

Funds Avail.: $1,000. **To Apply:** Applicants must submit a completed scholarship application together with an official copy of educational transcripts; copy of Student Aid Report (SAR) sent by the U.S. Department of Education; and an essay on "How do you feel education is going to impact your ability to continue assisting others to pursue an education?" (maximum 2 page typewritten, double spaced statement). Send application to: Dr. Wilson Luna, Gateway Community College, 60 Sargent Dr., New Haven, CT 06511. **Deadline:** April 15.

3233 ■ Marta Vallin Memorial Scholarships (Undergraduate/Scholarship)

Purpose: To promote the participation of Latinos in different areas of postsecondary education in Connecticut. **Focus:** Education. **Qualif.:** Applicant must be attending Gatewau Community College; have a "B" average (3.0 GPA) for all completed enrollment periods at the time of application; a U.S. citizen or permanent resident; have been a Connecticut resident during the preceding 12 months; a

Awards are arranged alphabetically below their administering organizations

Latino student from Connecticut; and must demonstrate financial need. **Criteria:** Selection is based on the application materials.

Funds Avail.: $1,000. **To Apply:** Applicants must submit a completed scholarship application together with an official copy of educational transcripts; copy of Student Aid Report (SAR) sent by the U.S. Department of Education; and an essay on "How do you feel education is going to impact your ability to continue assisting others to pursue an education?" (maximum 2 page typewritten, double spaced statement). Send application to: Dr. Wilson Luna, Gateway Community College, 60 Sargent Dr., New Haven, CT 06511. **Deadline:** April 15.

3234 ■ Connecticut Construction Industries Association (CCIA)
912 Silas Deane Hwy.
Wethersfield, CT 06109-3433
Ph: (860) 529-6855
Fax: (860) 563-0616
E-mail: ccia-info@ctconstruction.org
URL: www.ctconstruction.org

3235 ■ Associated General Contractors of Connecticut Scholarships *(Undergraduate/Scholarship)*

Purpose: To provide constant resource of information services and educational seminars; to maintain strong working relationships with federal and state agencies; to utilize lobbying efforts focused on removing unnecessary regulatory inefficiencies and costly restrictions that hinder progress and stifle the economy. **Focus:** Construction; Civil Engineering. **Qualif.:** Applicants must be graduating high school seniors entering college as freshmen or entering a two-year technical school with a construction course of study with the intent of entering a four-year college upon completion of the technical school; must desire a career in construction; must pursue a B.S. degree in construction technology or construction civil engineering; must be U.S. citizens or documented residents of the United States. **Criteria:** Recipients are selected based on academic performance and interest in the field of construction.

Funds Avail.: $5,000. **To Apply:** Applicants must complete the "four-page" signed application; must submit one faculty evaluation form completed by high school faculty member with scholastic achievement and school history, two personal evaluation forms and official transcript of records. **Deadline:** March 31.

3236 ■ Connecticut League for Nursing (CLN)
377 Research Pkwy., Ste. 2D
Meriden, CT 06450-7160
Ph: (203) 235-6873
Fax: (860) 276-8798
E-mail: lisa@ctleaguefornursing.org
URL: www.ctleaguefornursing.org

3237 ■ CLN Scholarships *(Graduate, Undergraduate/Scholarship)*

Purpose: To support the education of Connecticut nursing students. **Focus:** Nursing. **Qualif.:** Applicant must be a Connecticut resident enrolled in a Connecticut accredited nursing program (NLN or AACN, program must be a CLN Supporting Member); must demonstrate scholastic ability,

professional potential, and financial need. Baccalaureate degree applicants must have completed the third year of a four-year program. Associate degree applicants must have completed the first year of a two-year program. Diploma applicants must have completed the first year of a two-year program. Registered Nurse applicants in an upper division nursing program must be entering the senior year of the nursing curriculum as verified by the dean/director of the program. Graduate degree applicants must have completed 18 credits in the nursing program as verified by the dean/director of the program. **Criteria:** Selection is based on the submitted applications.

Funds Avail.: Amount is based on the applicant's qualifications and the available fund. **Number Awarded:** Varies. **To Apply:** Applicants must submit a completed Nursing Scholarship Award Application along with an official academic transcript from current school inclusive of all data up to the present fall semester; a completed reference form from the dean/director or nursing faculty from current school; and the verification of student status form if enrolled in a BSN completion program or graduate program. **Deadline:** October 12. **Contact:** Renee Ryan at the above address.

3238 ■ Constangy, Brooks and Smith, LLP
230 Peachtree St. NW, Ste. 2400
Atlanta, GA 30303-1557
Ph: (404) 525-8622
Fax: (404) 525-6955
E-mail: humanresources@constangy.com
URL: www.constangy.com

3239 ■ Diversity Scholars Awards *(Graduate/Award)*

Purpose: To recognize the achievements of law students who have demonstrated academic achievement, a commitment to diversity in their community, school or work environment, and personal achievements in overcoming challenges to reach goals. **Focus:** Law. **Qualif.:** Applicants must be second-year students enrolled in an accredited law school that is located in one of the following three regions: Southern; Mid-West/West Coast; Eastern. **Criteria:** Scholarship will be awarded based on accomplishments in academics, a commitment to diversity in the community, school or work environment, and personal achievement in overcoming challenges to reach goals.

Funds Avail.: $3,000. **To Apply:** Interested applicants must visit the website for the application process.

3240 ■ Construction Financial Management Association (CFMA)
100 Village Blvd., Ste. 200
Princeton, NJ 08540
Ph: (609) 452-8000
Fax: (609) 452-0474
E-mail: sbinstock@cfma.org
URL: www.cfma.org

3241 ■ Cindy P. Dennis Scholarship Fund *(Undergraduate/Scholarship)*

Purpose: To provide resources to meet challenges of construction financial professionals. To support the qualified individual who want to pursue a degree in business or construction management. **Focus:** Business, Construction.

Awards are arranged alphabetically below their administering organizations

Qualif.: Applicant must be a resident of Atascosa, Bandera, Bexar, Comal, Guadalupe, Kendall, Medina, or Wilson County; must be a candidate for a degree in business or construction management at any accredited college or university taking a minimum of 12 hours; must have a high school scholastic B average at the end of fall semester of senior year or have a minimum 3.0 cumulative GPA, if already in college. **Criteria:** Applicants will be selected based on scholarship criteria and by the scholarship application materials.

Funds Avail.: $500. **To Apply:** Applicant must submit the following: name, address and telephone numbers; must have the high school transcript through fall semester of senior year or cumulative college transcripts for classes taken to date; must prepare an essay (not to exceed 500 words); must have a letter of recommendation from a non-family member; must have a summary of extracurricular and outside activities. Application and other supporting documents must be sent to: CFMA - San Antonio Chapter Scholarship Committee, 100 NE Loop 410, Ste. 1100, San Antonio, TX 78216. **Deadline:** March 31.

3242 ■ Contra Costa County Bar Association (CCCBA)
2300 Clayton Rd., Ste. 520
Concord, CA 94520
Ph: (925) 686-6900
Fax: (925) 686-9867
E-mail: agee@bcglegal.com
URL: www.cccba.org

3243 ■ Court Scholarships *(Undergraduate/ Scholarship)*

Purpose: To help adults or juveniles gain the education they need to get ahead. **Focus:** Criminal justice. **Qualif.:** Applicants must be adults or juveniles currently residing in Contra Costa County who have been through the criminal justice system resulting in a conviction; must be out of custody as of March 31st of the current year and not in a residential treatment program or on electronic home detention. **Criteria:** Award is based on education expenses.

Funds Avail.: $2,500. **To Apply:** Applicants must submit a completed application form. If selected for consideration, applicants must provide references and documentation to support their request, including school transcripts. **Deadline:** April 30. **Contact:** Theresa Hurley at 925-370-2548; thurley@cccba.org.

3244 ■ John Kent Cooke Foundation (JKCF)
44325 Woodridge Pkwy.
Lansdowne, VA 20176
Ph: (703) 723-8000
Fax: (703) 723-8030
Free: 800-498-6478
URL: www.jkcf.org

3245 ■ John Kent Cooke Foundation Graduate Scholarships *(Graduate/Scholarship)*

Purpose: To support students pursuing graduate or professional study. **Focus:** General studies. **Qualif.:** Applicant must be a college senior or a recent graduate (within the last five years) from an accredited college/university in the U.S.; have a cumulative GPA of 3.50 or better on a 4.0 scale (or equivalent); plan to begin his/her first graduate

degree program; and be nominated by his/her undergraduate institution. **Criteria:** Selection is based on academic achievement and critical thinking ability, financial need, will to succeed and a breadth of interest and activities.

Funds Avail.: $50,000. **Number Awarded:** Approximately 35. **To Apply:** Applicants must be nominated by their undergraduate institutions (students cannot apply directly). Applicants must contact the Foundation's Faculty Representative at his/her institution.

3246 ■ John Kent Cooke Foundation Undergraduate Transfer Scholarships *(Undergraduate/Scholarship)*

Purpose: To support community college students to transfer and complete their bachelor's degrees at the top four-year colleges/universities. **Focus:** General studies. **Qualif.:** Applicant must be a current student at an accredited U.S. community college or two-year institution with sophomore status, or a recent graduate; plan to enroll full-time in a baccalaureate program at an accredited college/university; have a cumulative undergraduate GPA of 3.50 or better on a scale of 4.0 (or the equivalent); nominated by his/her two-year institution; have unmet financial need; and have not previously been nominated for the Jack Kent Cooke Foundation Undergraduate Transfer Scholarship. **Criteria:** Selection is based on academic excellence and critical thinking ability, financial need, will to succeed and breadth of interest and activities.

Funds Avail.: No specific amount. **Number Awarded:** Approximately 50. **To Apply:** Applicants must contact the Faculty Representative at their two-year college.

3247 ■ John Kent Cooke Foundation Young Scholars *(High School/Scholarship)*

Purpose: To support students in their educational pursuits. **Focus:** General studies. **Qualif.:** Applicant must be in the 7th grade entering 8th grade; have mostly 'A' grades and no 'Cs' or below in the past two years; have a family with unmet financial need; and planning to attend high school in the U.S. **Criteria:** Selection is based on academic ability and high achievement and intelligence, unmet financial need, will to succeed, leadership and public service, critical-thinking ability and appreciation for, or participation in, the arts and humanities, music, art, literature or similar fields.

Funds Avail.: No specific amount. **Number Awarded:** Approximately 75. **To Apply:** Applicants must submit a completed application (application checklist: student application, parent/guardian form, custodial parent(s)/guardian(s) financial form and tax forms; noncustodial parent(s)/guardian(s) financial form and tax forms (if applicable); school report; teacher recommendation; personal recommendation; survey form). **Deadline:** April 16.

3248 ■ Cooley Godward Kronish LLP
Five Palo Alto Sq.
3000 El Camino Real
Palo Alto, CA 94306-2155
Ph: (650) 843-5000
Fax: (650) 857-0663
URL: www.cooley.com

3249 ■ Cooley Godward Kronish Diversity Fellowships *(Graduate, Undergraduate/Fellowship)*

Purpose: To financially assist law students. **Focus:** Law. **Qualif.:** Applicant must be a law student enrolled full-time

Awards are arranged alphabetically below their administering organizations

in an ABA accredited law school and in the 1L year at the time of application; committed to join the Firm's Summer Associate Program following the 2L year; and must not be a recipient of a similar diversity award from other law firm for the same time period. **Criteria:** Selection is based on the student's commitment to promoting goals of diversity; academic performance; personal achievements; leadership abilities; community service; and commitment to joining the Cooley Godward Kronish Summer Associate Program.

Funds Avail.: Up to $15,000. **Number Awarded:** 8. **To Apply:** Applicants must submit a completed application form along with a brief personal statement; a current resume; law school transcript; and undergraduate transcript. In addition, applicants may also submit up to two letters of recommendation; up to three references; and a legal writing sample. **Contact:** diversityfellowship@cooley.com.

3250 ■ Cooley's Anemia Foundation (CAF)

330 7th Ave., No. 200
New York, NY 10001
Fax: (212) 279-5999
Free: 800-522-7222
E-mail: info@cooleysanemia.org
URL: www.cooleysanemia.org

3251 ■ Cooley's Anemia Foundation Research Fellowships *(Postdoctorate/Fellowship)*

Purpose: To serve people afflicted with various forms of thalassemia. **Focus:** Cooley's anemia. **Qualif.:** Applicants must be a postdoctoral or junior faculty member interested in clinical or basic research related to thalassemia. **Criteria:** Selection will be based on the submitted applications.

Funds Avail.: $40,000. **To Apply:** Applicants must complete and return an original and twelve (12) copies of applications together with letters of reference to Gina Cioffi, National Dir., 330 Seventh Ave., No. 200, New York, NY 10001. **Deadline:** February 2.

3252 ■ Copper and Brass Servicenter Association (CBSA)

6734 W 121st St.
Overland Park, KS 66209
Ph: (913) 396-0697
Fax: (913) 345-1006
E-mail: cbsahq@copper-brass.org
URL: www.copper-brass.org

3253 ■ Copper and Brass Servicenter Association Inc. Scholarship Program *(Undergraduate/ Scholarship)*

Purpose: To provide financial educational assistance to a child of CBSA employees or any associate member companies. **Focus:** General studies. **Qualif.:** Applicants must be dependents of an individual employed in CBSA's service center or any associate member company; must be college students entering Sophomore, Junior or Senior year in the fall; must be taking at least six credit hours in the upcoming year; and must have a GPA of at least 3.0 on a 4.0 scale. **Criteria:** Scholarships will be granted only to children of CBSA's service center or associate member companies. Applicants will be selected based on academic performance and financial need.

Funds Avail.: No specific amount. **To Apply:** Candidates

must fill out the online application form. Must submit two letters of recommendation (one from an educator and one from a past or present employer); 500-word essay explaining the reason of pursuing the chosen field; and transcript of records. Freshmen candidates must submit a high school transcript. **Deadline:** March 1. **Contact:** For more information, applicants must contact Jean McClure at the above address or may send an e-mail at jmcclure@copper-brass.org.

3254 ■ Coro

c/o Manatt Phelps
700 12th St. NW, Ste. 1100
Washington, DC 20005-4075
Ph: (202) 585-6548
Fax: (202) 585-6548
E-mail: info@coro.org
URL: www.coro.org

3255 ■ Coro Fellows Program in Public Affairs *(Graduate/Fellowship)*

Purpose: To train and prepare committed individuals for effective and ethical leadership in the public affairs arena. **Focus:** Public affairs. **Qualif.:** Applicant must be a graduate student committed to effective and ethical leadership in the public affairs arena. **Criteria:** Selection is based on the application materials submitted.

Funds Avail.: No specific amount. **Number Awarded:** 68. **To Apply:** Applicants must first complete the online pre-application form. Applicants may then submit electronically the three written essays; resume (maximum of 2 pages); three letters of recommendation; official academic transcripts for all higher education institutions attended; and a $75 non-refundable application fee. **Deadline:** January 20. **Remarks:** The Fellows Program is offered in Los Angeles, New York, Pittsburgh, San Francisco and St. Louis. **Contact:** Coro Southern California: 1000 N Alameda St., Ste. 240 Los Angeles, CA 90012-4295, corosocal@coro.org, P: 213-346-3219; Coro New York: 42 Broadway, Ste. 1827-35 New York, NY 10004, recruitny@coro.org, p: 212-248-2935, x-242; Coro Center for Civic Leadership: 33 Terminal Way, Ste. 429-A Pittsburgh, PA 15219, recruitpgh@coro.org, p: 412-258-2671; Coro San Francisco: 601 Montgomery St., Ste. 800 San Francisco, CA 94111, corosfapply@coro.org, p: 415-986-0521, x-102; Coro St. Louis: 1325 N Highway Dr. Fenton, MO 63099, kari@coro.org, p: 636-827-9806.

3256 ■ The Corp Students of Georgetown Inc.

1324 Leavey Ctr.
3700 O St. NW
Washington, DC 20057
Ph: (202) 687-6079
Fax: (202) 687-8904
URL: www.thecorp.org

3257 ■ The Corp - Students of Georgetown Inc. Coke Scholarships *(Undergraduate/Scholarship)*

Purpose: To help students pursue their education. **Focus:** General studies. **Qualif.:** Applicants must be undergraduate students at Georgetown University. **Criteria:** Awarded to the three students that best reflect the Corp's mission of student serving students. Applicants will be judged based on thoughtfulness, creativity and passion.

Funds Avail.: $1,000. **Number Awarded:** 3. **To Apply:**

Awards are arranged alphabetically below their administering organizations

Applicants must submit a completed application form. **Deadline:** April 24.

3258 ■ The Corp - Students of Georgetown Inc. Textbook Scholarships (Undergraduate/ Scholarship)

Purpose: To help students pay for their textbooks. **Focus:** General studies. **Qualif.:** Applicants must be high school senior students who have been accepted to Georgetown University. **Criteria:** Applicants will be judged based on dedication to their high school student services.

Funds Avail.: $500. **Number Awarded:** 6. **To Apply:** Applicants must submit a resume via attachment. **Contact:** Application form must be submitted to philanthropy@thecorp.org.

3259 ■ The Corp - Students of Georgetown Inc.-Word Scholarships (Undergraduate/ Scholarship)

Purpose: To encourage students to submit their written piece. **Focus:** General studies. **Qualif.:** Students are eligible for the award. **Criteria:** Applicants will be judged on their submitted piece based on thoughtfulness, relevancy to chosen word, and degree of the expressed ideas.

Funds Avail.: $500. **Number Awarded:** 6. **To Apply:** Applicants must submit a written piece relevant to the chosen word. Piece includes a one-page cover sheet. **Contact:** Written piece must be sent through attachment to philanthropy@thecorp.org.

3260 ■ More Uncommon Grounds Scholarships (MUG) (Undergraduate/Scholarship)

Purpose: To help students pursue their education. **Focus:** General studies. **Qualif.:** Applicants must be undergraduate Georgetown students. **Criteria:** Recipients will be selected based on submitted applications.

Funds Avail.: $8,000. **Number Awarded:** 10. **To Apply:** Applicants must submit a completed application form and resume. **Deadline:** April 13. **Contact:** Application materials must be sent to mug@thecorp.org.

3261 ■ Corporate Counsel Women of Color (CCWC)

PO Box 2095
New York, NY 10101-2095
Ph: (646) 483-8041
E-mail: info@ccwomenofcolor.org
URL: www.ccwomenofcolor.org

3262 ■ My Life As A Lawyer Scholarships (Graduate, Undergraduate/Scholarship)

Purpose: To support law students with their educational pursuit. **Focus:** Law. **Qualif.:** Applicant must be a first or second year student enrolled in an accredited law school in any state of the United States of America. **Criteria:** Selection is based on the submitted application materials.

Funds Avail.: No specific amount. **To Apply:** Applicants must submit a completed application form together with a list any publications, academic awards, honors, scholarships, memberships, and/or extracurricular activities; an essay of no more 350 words; and a copy of law school transcript. **Deadline:** June 30.

3263 ■ Corporation for Public Broadcasting (CPB)

401 9th St. NW
Washington, DC 20004-2129

Ph: (202) 879-9600
Free: 800-272-2190
E-mail: nstaples@cpb.org
URL: www.cpb.org

3264 ■ Producers Academy Scholarships (All/ Scholarship)

Purpose: To facilitate the development of and ensure universal access to non-commercial high quality programming and telecommunications services. **Focus:** Broadcasting. **Qualif.:** Applicants must have an interest in broadcasting. **Criteria:** Recipients are selected based on the research proposal.

Funds Avail.: No specific amount. **Number Awarded:** 25. **To Apply:** Applicants must complete the application form.

3265 ■ Correctional Education Association (CEA)

8182 Lake Brown Rd., Ste. 202
Elkridge, MD 21075
Ph: (443) 459-3080
Fax: (443) 459-3088
Free: 800-783-1232
E-mail: office@ceanational.org
URL: www.ceanational.org/index2.htm

3266 ■ Correctional Education Association Scholarships (Graduate, Undergraduate/ Scholarship)

Purpose: To encourage students to continue a course of study in correctional education. **Focus:** Criminal justice. **Qualif.:** Applicant must be a graduate or undergraduate student in correctional education; must be a voting member of the Correctional Education Association and have been a member for a minimum of two years prior to application. **Criteria:** Application materials (quality of the application will be taken into consideration) will be evaluated by the Scholarship Committee. Priority will be given to first time applicants.

Funds Avail.: $500. **Number Awarded:** Scholarship Committee will determine the number of scholarships to be awarded. **To Apply:** Application forms are available in the website (application format must be completed in full in order to be considered by the Committee). Application materials must be sent to: Correctional Educational Association, Scholarship Committee, 8182 Lark Brown Rd., Ste. 202, Elkridge, MD 21075.

3267 ■ Council for the Advancement of Science Writing (CASW)

PO Box 910
Hedgesville, WV 25427
Ph: (304) 754-6786
E-mail: diane@nasw.org
URL: www.casw.org

3268 ■ Taylor/Blakeslee University Fellowships (Professional development, Undergraduate/ Fellowship)

Purpose: To provide financial support to students who want to pursue a career in science writing. **Focus:** Journalism. **Qualif.:** Applicants must be professional journalists and students enrolled in a U.S graduate-level science writing program; must be U.S citizens. **Criteria:** Scholarship ap-

Awards are arranged alphabetically below their administering organizations

plication will be evaluated by CASW Selection Committee based on criteria. Journalists with at least two years of mass media experience will receive preferential treatment in the selection process.

Funds Avail.: $5,000. **To Apply:** Applicants must complete the application form; must submit resume; samples of writing; description of science-writing program and list of courses to be pursued; and statement (not to exceed 500 words). **Deadline:** July 1. **Contact:** Rennie Taylor at the above address.

3269 ■ Council of American Overseas Research Centers (CAORC)

PO Box 37012
Washington, DC 20013-7012
Ph: (202) 633-1599
Fax: (202) 786-2430
E-mail: lane.maryellen@caorc.org
URL: www.caorc.org

3270 ■ Multi-Country Research Fellowships
(Doctorate/Fellowship)

Purpose: To support advanced regional or trans-regional research in the humanities, social sciences or allied natural sciences for US doctoral candidates and scholars who have already earned their PhD. **Focus:** Humanities; Social sciences; natural sciences. **Qualif.:** Applicants must be US citizens; must have a PhD or be doctoral candidates who have completed all PhD requirements with the exception of the dissertation; must be engaged in the study of and research in the humanities, social sciences and allied natural sciences; must wish to conduct research of regional or trans-regional significance in two or more countries outside the US, one of which must host a participating American overseas research center (ORC). **Criteria:** Selection will be based on the following criteria: merits of the proposal for significance, relevance and potential contribution to regional and/or trans-regional scholarly research; qualifications; research design and methodology; significance to the applicants' field; significance to needs and interests of host country and CAORC; feasibility in terms of resources and amount of time allocated to the project; need for residence in host country to accomplish the project; proficiency in language required to complete research project, if applicable.

Funds Avail.: $12,000. **Number Awarded:** Nine. **To Apply:** A complete application must consists the following: application form; project description; project bibliography/ literature review; two separate letters of recommendation; a maximum three pages curriculum vitae; graduate transcripts. The project description must be 1,500 words or less, describing the nature of the applicants' proposed project and their competence to carry out the required research. State their research question and the methods and procedures they will use to conduct their research. Give the reasons why their project requires their presence in the countries they indicated and indicate the facilities that they plan to use while conducting their research. Applicants must also indicate the relationship they will have with the host-country ORC(s) and the extent to which they have investigated other funding sources. Submit the application form, project description, project bibliography/ literature review and curriculum vitae, in MS Word format, via email. Letters of recommendation must be sent directly from the applicants' referee. Transcript must be mailed directly to CAORC. **Deadline:** January 17. **Contact:** fellowships@caorc.org.

Awards are arranged alphabetically below their administering organizations

3271 ■ Council of Energy Resource Tribes (CERT)

c/o Greenberg Traurig
1200 17th St., No. 2400
Denver, CO 80202
Ph: (303) 282-7576
Fax: (303) 282-7584
E-mail: info@certredearth.com
URL: 74.63.154.129

3272 ■ CERT College Scholarships *(Graduate, Undergraduate/Scholarship)*

Purpose: To meet the unforeseen need of today's Indian college students. **Focus:** Business; Engineering; Science; Mathematics and mathematical sciences; Computer and information sciences. **Qualif.:** Applicants must have been selected and/or successfully participated in one of the CERT education programs: TRIBES Program (1981-2005), CERT Intern Program (1986-2009), CERT Scholars Program (2006-2008); must be a full-time undergraduate (12 hrs/semester) or graduate (9 hrs/semester) student enrolled at an accredited two or four year tribal, private, or public university/college; majoring in business, engineering, science, math, computer technology, or related fields; and maintain an acceptable GPA (2.5 cumulative GPA or higher) according to CERT Scholarship guidelines. **Criteria:** Selection is based on the application.

Funds Avail.: No specific amount. **To Apply:** Applicants must submit a completed application form together with university/college enrollment verification for forthcoming semester/quarter (if not shown on transcript); and most recent official transcripts from university/college registrar's office after completion of each semester or quarter. **Deadline:** September 15 (Fall); February 15 (Spring). **Contact:** Clint LeBeau by email at clebeau@certredearth.com or 3545 S Tamarac Drive, Suite 320, Denver, CO 80237.

3273 ■ Council for European Studies (CES)

Columbia University
420 W 118th St.
MC 3307
New York, NY 10027
Ph: (212) 854-4172
Fax: (212) 854-8808
E-mail: ces@columbia.edu
URL: www.councilforeuropeanstudies.org

3274 ■ CES Conference Travel Grants *(Graduate, Professional development/Grant)*

Purpose: To provide trans-Atlantic travel for junior faculty and graduate students already scheduled to present at the Council's International Conference of Europeanists. **Focus:** European studies. **Qualif.:** Presenters must be accepted to present a paper at the International Conference of Europeanists; must be currently working at and affiliated with an academic, research or policy institution in North America; must be graduate students or hold the rank of Assistant Professor (or its equivalent) and below; must be committed to presenting at the CES conference regardless of eventual grant status. **Criteria:** Selection will be based on the committee's criteria.

Funds Avail.: $500. **To Apply:** Selection will be based on the committee's criteria. **Deadline:** January 7.

3275 ■ CES Dissertation Completion Fellowships *(Graduate/Fellowship)*

Purpose: To facilitate the timely completion of the doctoral degree by late-stage graduate students on topics that focus on European Studies. **Focus:** European studies. **Qualif.:** Applicants must be ABD; must be enrolled at a higher education institution in the US that is a member of the CES Academic Consortium; must have no more than one full year of dissertation work remaining at the start of the fellowship year as certified by their dissertation advisor. Applicants must also have exhausted the dissertation completion funding normally provided by their academic department or university, and must be working on a topic within or substantially overlapping European Studies. **Criteria:** Selection will be based on the committee's criteria.

Funds Avail.: A stipend of $25,000. **To Apply:** Interested applicants must contact the Council for the application process. **Deadline:** February 4.

3276 ■ CES Pre-Dissertation Research Fellowships *(Graduate/Fellowship)*

Purpose: To conduct the exploratory phase of a projected dissertation project in the social sciences or humanities which will require a subsequent stay in Europe. **Focus:** European studies. **Qualif.:** Applicants must be enrolled in a doctoral program at a university that is a member of the council for European Studies Academic Consortium; must possess any language skills required to carry out the proposed research; must have completed the majority of doctoral coursework; must have not yet begun substantial dissertation research in Europe. **Criteria:** Selection will be based on the committee's criteria.

Funds Avail.: $4,000. **To Apply:** Applicants must submit the CES Pre-Dissertation Fellowship Application Form and return three completed Faculty Recommendation Forms. Also, applicants must submit a Language Competency Form for every language in which they will require functional knowledge to complete their proposed research. **Deadline:** February 1.

3277 ■ First Article Prize *(Professional development/Prize)*

Purpose: To honor the writers of the best first articles in European studies published within a two-year period. **Focus:** Social sciences; Humanities; European studies. **Qualif.:** Nominated article must be the first article published by the nominee in the field of European Studies in a peer-reviewed journal; must be published between January 1, 2010 and December 31, 2011; must be the work of one author only or be an article on which the nominee is the first author; must be authored by a member of the Council for European Studies or a faculty/student of an institution that is a member. **Criteria:** Strong preference will be given to submissions in English, French, German and Spanish.

Funds Avail.: $500. **Number Awarded:** Two. **To Apply:** Nominations must be submitted by the publisher, editor, author or admiring colleagues, and must be accompanied by a nomination form and digital copy of the nominated article.

3278 ■ Council on Library and Information Resources (Council on Library Resources)
1752 N St., Ste. 800
Washington, DC 20036-2124
Ph: (202) 939-4750
Fax: (202) 939-4765

E-mail: info@clir.org
URL: www.clir.org

3279 ■ Mellon Fellowships *(Doctorate, Graduate/Fellowship)*

Purpose: To help junior scholars in the humanities and related social science fields gain skill and creativity in developing knowledge from original sources. **Focus:** Humanities; Social sciences. **Qualif.:** Applicants must be enrolled in a doctoral program in a graduate school in the United States; have completed all doctoral requirements except the dissertation; planning to do dissertation research primarily in original source material in the holdings of archives, libraries, historical societies, museums, related repositories or a combination. Candidates for the Ed.D, J.D., or D.D. degrees are not eligible. **Criteria:** Selection of applicants will be based on quality of the research proposal with reference to the following category: (1) originality and creativity; (2) importance of the proposed dissertation to the applicant's field; (3) appropriateness of the primary source collection(s) and institutions in which the applicant proposes to do research; (4) competence of the research; and (5) prospects for completing specified research within the time projected and funds awarded.

Funds Avail.: $2,000 per month plus $1,000 upon participating in symposium on research. **Number Awarded:** 15. **To Apply:** Applicants must complete and submit the online application form; official transcripts; a letter from the appropriate dean, department head or dissertation advisor certifying that the candidate has completed or will complete all doctoral work except the dissertation; and three letters of reference. All documents must be submitted in triplicate by mail. **Deadline:** November 13. **Contact:** mellon@clir.org.

3280 ■ A.R. Zipf Fellowships *(Graduate/Fellowship)*

Purpose: To support students in graduate school in early stages of study. **Focus:** General studies. **Qualif.:** Applicants must be citizens or permanent residents of the United States; must be enrolled in a graduate school that and shows exceptional promise for leadership and technical achievement in information management. **Criteria:** Selection is based on the application.

Funds Avail.: $10,000. **To Apply:** Applicants must complete and submit the online application form; four letters of reference; undergraduate and graduate school transcripts; and scores of Graduate Record Examinations (if taken). **Deadline:** March 30. **Contact:** Questions for the application should be directed to: Alice Bishop, Special Projects Associate at abishop@clir.org.

3281 ■ Council on Social Work Education
1701 Duke St., Ste. 200
Alexandria, VA 22314
Ph: (703) 683-8080
Fax: (703) 683-8099
E-mail: info@cswe.org
URL: www.cswe.org

3282 ■ Council on Social Work Education Minority Fellowship Programs *(Postdoctorate/Fellowship)*

Purpose: To educate ethnic minority social work professionals to prepare them for leadership roles in mental health

Awards are arranged alphabetically below their administering organizations

research and in the delivery of mental health services. **Focus:** Mental health; Social work. **Qualif.:** Applicants must be currently enrolled in a doctoral program in a school of social work. **Criteria:** Recipients are selected based on the academic standing and letters of recommendation.

Funds Avail.: No specific amount. **To Apply:** Applicants must submit an application instruction sheet. All permanent residents must provide the following: photocopy of Permanent Resident Card signed by the notary public; official transcript of records; GRE and MAT scores; letter of admission; resume; financial list of information including the resources applied for, personal financial costs and anticipated income. **Deadline:** March 15.

3283 ■ Council on Social Work Education Scholars Program *(Postdoctorate/Scholarship)*

Purpose: To provide opportunities for senior and junior scholars to work on research projects or programmatic initiatives of their choosing that is in line with the priorities of CSWE. **Focus:** Social work. **Qualif.:** Program is open to senior scholars, faculty members and junior scholars such as doctoral students or individuals recently completing their doctoral dissertation. **Criteria:** Selection is based on proposed research.

Funds Avail.: No specific amount. **To Apply:** Applicants must submit completed application together with project proposal; budget; task list; and curriculum vitae. **Contact:** Jessica Holmes, jholmes@cswe.org.

3284 ■ Carl A. Scott Book Scholarships *(Undergraduate/Scholarship)*

Purpose: To promote equity and social justice in social work. **Focus:** Social work. **Qualif.:** Applicants must be in the last year of study for a social work degree in a baccalaureate or master's degree program accredited by the Council on Social Work Education; must be African American, American Indian, Asian American, Mexican American or Puerto Rican; must have a cumulative GPA of at least 3.0 on a 4.0 scale; and must be enrolled in 12 credit hours. **Criteria:** Recipients are selected based on the demonstrated commitment in promoting equity and social justice.

Funds Avail.: $500. **Number Awarded:** 2. **To Apply:** Applicants must submit a two-three page, double-spaced, typewritten statement that include professional interests, and experiences; two letters of recommendation preferably from a professor, a field instructor, or a community-based leader; an official letter from the school's registrar verifying that the applicant is enrolled and in good standing with the university or college; and an official academic transcript from university/college. **Deadline:** May 9.

3285 ■ Courage to Grow

PO Box 2507
Chelan, WA 98816
Ph: (509) 731-3056
E-mail: kimberlyjohnson@couragetogrowscholarship.com
URL: couragetogrowscholarship.com

3286 ■ Courage to Grow Scholarships *(Undergraduate/Scholarship)*

Purpose: To help fund college educations. **Focus:** General studies. **Qualif.:** Applicants must be high school seniors or college students with a minimum GPA of 2.5; must be U.S. citizens. **Criteria:** Recipients will be selected based on

submitted application materials.

Funds Avail.: $500. **Number Awarded:** 1 award per month. **To Apply:** Applicants must provide proof of enrollment obtained from the college administration department, proof of GPA and maximum of 250 words description on why the applicant deserves to get the award. **Deadline:** August 31.

3287 ■ Creative Glass Center of America (CGCA)

1501 Glasstown Rd.
Millville, NJ 08332
Ph: (856) 825-6800
Fax: (856) 825-2410
Free: 800-998-4552
E-mail: cgca@wheatons.org
URL: www.wheatonarts.org/creativeglasscenteramerica

3288 ■ Creative Glass Center of America Fellowships *(All/Fellowship)*

Purpose: To provide focused, self-directed artists with three-month and six-week fellowships. **Focus:** General studies. **Qualif.:** Applicants must be artists with young families, artists whose professional commitments do not afford them the option of a three-month residency and for teams of artists wishing to collaborate on a particular project. **Criteria:** Applicants will be evaluated by the Fellowship Selection Committee based on their designed criteria.

Funds Avail.: No specific amount. **Number Awarded:** 10. **To Apply:** Applicants must submit completed application form; two letters of recommendation; a CD containing ten images of the applicant's work, image information sheet, one paragraph biography, statement of intent and current resume/CV. **Deadline:** October 26.

3289 ■ Crisis Intervention and Suicide Prevention Centre of British Columbia

763 E Broadway
Vancouver, BC, Canada V5T 1X8
Ph: (604) 872-1811
Fax: (604) 879-6216
Free: 800-784-2433
E-mail: info@crisiscentre.bc.ca
URL: www.crisiscentre.bc.ca

3290 ■ Steve Cowan Memorial Scholarships *(Undergraduate/Scholarship)*

Purpose: To recognize and support individuals who have made a positive contribution to their school and/or local or global community. **Focus:** General studies. **Qualif.:** Applicants must be involved in voluntary humanitarian work; demonstrated outstanding leadership and community service during the course of their studies; must be currently in graduating year at a Lower Mainland or Sea-to-sky Corridor high school, or graduated from a Lower Mainland or Sea-to-sky Corridor high school in the last year; must be entering first year of full-time studies leading to a post-secondary diploma or degree at an accredited college, university or technical school; must possess the academic skills to successfully enter and complete a post-secondary education; must be Canadian citizens or landed immigrants; must not be employees or immediate family members of a Crisis Intervention and Suicide Prevention Centre of BC employee. **Criteria:** Selection will be based on applicant's

Awards are arranged alphabetically below their administering organizations

dedication to the humanitarian ideals and community service ideals of the Crisis Centre, their volunteer experience, community leadership and their participation in community service. **Funds Avail.:** $250-$500. **To Apply:** Applicants must submit an application form, two reference letters and an official transcript of the past two years of schooling. **Deadline:** March 6.

3291 ■ Crohn's and Colitis Foundation of America (CCFA)

386 Park Ave. S, 17th Fl.
New York, NY 10016-8804
Free: 800-932-2423
E-mail: info@ccfa.org
URL: www.ccfa.org

3292 ■ CCFA Career Development Awards
(Doctorate, Graduate/Grant)

Purpose: To support a research that will help prepare for a career of independent basic or clinical investigation in the area of inflammatory bowel disease. **Focus:** Medicine. **Qualif.:** Applicants must be employed in an institution; engaged in health care or health-related research within the United States; have MD, PhD or equivalent; must not be in excess of ten years beyond the attainment of the doctoral degree; and have at least two years of documented post-doctoral research relevant to IBD. Proposals must be relevant to inflammatory bowel disease (Crohn's Disease or ulcerative colitis). **Criteria:** Applicants will be selected on the basis of intellectual background; mentor's record; number of important techniques to be learned; importance of the research area; relevance to IBD; and applicant's career objectives.

Funds Avail.: $35,000-$100,000. **To Apply:** Applicants must download, complete and submit the application form, CDA Letter of Intent and CDA forms available at the website. Only compiled application on a CD or disk will be considered. **Deadline:** January 14 or July 1.

3293 ■ CCFA Research Fellowship Awards
(Doctorate, Graduate/Fellowship)

Purpose: To support a research that will help prepare for a career of independent basic or clinical investigation in the area of Crohn's disease and ulcerative colitis. **Focus:** Medicine. **Qualif.:** Applicants must be employed in an institution; engaged in health care or health related research within the United States; have MD, PhD or equivalent. Applicants with MD degrees must have at least two years of post doctoral experience. Candidates with PhD degrees must have at least one year of post-doctoral research experience related to IBD. Proposals must be relevant to inflammatory bowel disease (Crohn's Disease or ulcerative colitis). **Criteria:** Applicants will be selected on the basis of intellectual background; research experience; mentor's track record; number of important techniques to be learned; importance of the research area; relevance to IBD; and career objectives.

Funds Avail.: $25,000-$65,000. **To Apply:** Applicants must download, complete and submit the application form, RFA Letter of Intent and RFA forms available at the website. **Deadline:** January 14 and July 1.

3294 ■ CCFA Student Research Fellowship Awards *(Graduate, Undergraduate/Grant)*

Purpose: To fund a research on topics relevant to inflammatory bowel disease. **Focus:** Medicine. **Qualif.:** Ap-

plicants must be undergraduate, medical, or graduate students at an accredited institution in United States. **Criteria:** Applicants will be judged based on novelty, feasibility and significance of the proposal; attributes of the candidate; mentor's record; evidence of the institutional commitment and laboratory environment.

Funds Avail.: $3,000. **Number Awarded:** 16. **To Apply:** Applicants must download, complete and submit the application form and SRFA forms available at the website. **Deadline:** March 15.

3295 ■ Crohn's and Colitis Foundation of America Senior Research Awards *(Doctorate, Graduate/Grant)*

Purpose: To provide funds for research to generate sufficient preliminary data from other sources such as National Institute of Health (NIH). **Focus:** Medicine. **Qualif.:** Applicants must have MD, PhD or equivalent degree; must be employed in an institution or engaged in health care or health related research; must have attained independence from their mentors. Proposals must be relevant to inflammatory bowel disease (Crohn's Disease or ulcerative colitis). **Criteria:** Awards will be given on the basis of scientific merit; relevance to IBD; excellence of investigator and research environment.

Funds Avail.: $50,000-$150,000. **To Apply:** Applicants must download, complete and submit the application form, SRA Letter of Intent and SRA forms available at the website; must submit a research plan with evidence; curriculum vitae; appendix and application index (optional). Formats for all attachments must be .doc, .xls or .pdf only. **Deadline:** January 14 or July 1. **Contact:** E-mail: grants@ccfa.org.

3296 ■ CrossLites

c/o Samuel Certo
1000 Holt Ave.
Winter Park, FL 32789
E-mail: crosslites@gmail.com
URL: crosslites.com

3297 ■ CrossLites Scholarships *(Graduate, High School, Undergraduate/Scholarship)*

Purpose: To provide financial aid to students who wish to pursue their education. **Focus:** General studies. **Qualif.:** Applicant must be a high school, college or graduate school student. **Criteria:** Selection is based on the submitted essay's originality, reflection, punctuation/grammar, and content.

Funds Avail.: 1st Place: $2,000; 2nd Place: $1,500; 3rd Place: $1,000; 4th Place: $750; 5th Place: $500; 6th Place: $250. **To Apply:** Applicants must submit their name; email address; name of the institution that the applicant is attending or planning to attend; a 400-600 word reflective essay (based on Dr. Parker's quotes or messages). Official transcripts must be sent via snail mail. **Deadline:** December 15. **Remarks:** Students will be competing against other students in their level, thus 9th-12th graders will be competing for a chance to win 1st, 2nd or 3rd place just as undergraduate students (freshmen-senior) will be competing to win their own 1st, 2nd, or 3rd place.

3298 ■ CSA Fraternal Life

122 W 22nd St.
Oak Brook, IL 60523
Ph: (630) 472-0500

Awards are arranged alphabetically below their administering organizations

Fax: (630) 472-1100
Free: 800-543-3272
URL: www.csafraternallife.org

3299 ■ CSA Fraternal Life Scholarships
(Undergraduate/Scholarship)

Purpose: To help students on their financial needs for studying in college. **Focus:** General studies. **Qualif.:** Applicants must be student-members with satisfactory class standing no less than a "B" or Better or 3.0 in average (minimum of two years); have at least $5,000 face value in permanent life insurance or $1,000 in a CSA annuity at the time of application. **Criteria:** Selection will be made based on class rank, grade point average, college placement test scores, extracurricular activities including CSA activities, and essay made.

Funds Avail.: $1,250. **Number Awarded:** Varies. **To Apply:** Applicants must submit a completed application form to the Fraternal Department; a complete official transcript to be sent to CSA; submit a photo for publication in the Journal to be attached to the first page of the application over the cap and diploma and a 400-600 words essay about the applicant's interests. **Deadline:** March 8. **Remarks:** Scholarship grants are only available for undergraduate studies on a full-time basis at an accredited junior college, college, university, or technical institute.

3300 ■ Cuban American Bar Association (CABA)
2 S Biscayne Blvd., 21st Fl.
Miami, FL 33131
Ph: (305) 646-0046
Fax: (305) 646-0633
E-mail: info@cabaonline.com
URL: www.cabaonline.com

3301 ■ Cuban American Bar Association Scholarships *(All/Scholarship)*

Purpose: To provide financial assistance for students enrolled in accredited law schools. **Focus:** Law. **Qualif.:** Applicant must be a Cuban-American law student who has distinguished himself/herself academically and/or in service-oriented activities; any law student who has distinguished himself/herself in research, writing, community services, and/or other activities of importance to the Cuban-American community; must not be currently enrolled at the University of Miami, Florida International University, University of Florida, St. Thomas University, Nova Southern University and Florida State University. **Criteria:** Selection will be based on the committee's criteria.

Funds Avail.: $2,500. **Number Awarded:** 2. **To Apply:** Applicants must submit a completed formal application together with a competitive essay (no more than 1,000 words) focusing on and describing in detail the activities and achievements that the applicant qualify for the award; an updated resume; and a copy of applicant's transcript. **Deadline:** October 14. **Contact:** Victoria Mendez, victoriamendez@aol.com; Sandra Ferrera, sferrera@melandrussin.com.

3302 ■ Culinary and Hospitality Foundation of San Benito County
PO Box 1153
Tres Pinos, CA 95075
Ph: (831) 628-3320

E-mail: info@chfsbc.com
URL: chfsbc.com

3303 ■ Culinary and Hospitality Foundation of San Benito County Scholarships
(Undergraduate/Scholarship)

Purpose: To encourage professional development within the culinary, hospitality, tourism or related industry. **Focus:** Culinary Arts. **Qualif.:** Applicants must be high school senior students who are permanent residents of San Benito County and are graduating from an accredited high school; must plan to seek a career in the culinary, hospitality or tourism related industry; and must have a high school GPA of 2.0 or above. **Criteria:** Recipients are selected based on financial need.

Funds Avail.: $1,000. **Number Awarded:** 2. **To Apply:** Applicants must submit a completed application form; two letters of recommendation; official high school transcript; and a personal essay.

3304 ■ The Culinary Trust (TCT)
PO Box 273
New York, NY 10013
Ph: (646) 224-6989
Free: 888-345-4666
E-mail: info@theculinarytrust.org
URL: www.theculinarytrust.org

3305 ■ L'Academie de Cuisine Culinary Arts Scholarships *(All, Professional development/ Scholarship)*

Purpose: To assist individuals who wish to advance their knowledge in the culinary arts. **Focus:** Culinary arts. **Qualif.:** Applicant must be a new student toward the 12-month Culinary Arts Certificate Program; have a GPA of 3.0 or higher (for applicants who have been students during the five years prior to the application). **Criteria:** Recipients are selected based on merit, work experience, culinary goals and skills and references.

Funds Avail.: $5,000. **Number Awarded:** 1. **To Apply:** Applicants must submit a completed Culinary Trust Scholarship application form; a project proposal (two pages, double-spaced) illustrating their culinary goals; two letters of reference on business or personal letterhead; a current academic transcript; a non-refundable application fee of $35. **Deadline:** March 1. **Remarks:** For information about L'Academie de Cuisine visit www.lacademie.com. **Contact:** scholarships@theculinarytrust.com.

3306 ■ The French Culinary Institute Classic Pastry Arts Scholarships *(Professional development, Undergraduate/Scholarship)*

Purpose: To assist individuals who wish to advance their knowledge in the culinary arts. **Focus:** Culinary arts. **Qualif.:** Applicant must be a new student or career professional toward the nine months Classic Pastry Arts Diploma Program; have a GPA of 3.0 or higher (for applicants who have been students during the five years prior to the application). **Criteria:** Recipients are selected based on merit, work experience, culinary goals and skills, and references.

Funds Avail.: $5,000. **Number Awarded:** 1. **To Apply:** Applicants must submit a completed Culinary Trust Scholarship application form; a project proposal (two pages, double-spaced) illustrating their culinary goals; two letters

Awards are arranged alphabetically below their administering organizations

of reference on business or personal letterhead; a current academic transcript; a non-refundable application fee of $35. **Deadline:** March 1.

3307 ■ The French Culinary Institute Culinary Arts Scholarships (All, Professional development/ Scholarship)

Purpose: To assist individuals who wish to advance their knowledge in the culinary arts. **Focus:** Culinary arts. **Qualif.:** Applicant must be a new student or career professional toward the nine months Classic Culinary Arts Diploma Program; have a GPA of 3.0 or higher (for applicants who have been students during the five years prior to the application). **Criteria:** Recipients are selected based on merit, work experience, culinary goals and skills, and references.

Funds Avail.: $5,000. **Number Awarded:** 1. **To Apply:** Applicants must submit a completed Culinary Trust Scholarship application form; a project proposal (two pages, double-spaced) illustrating their culinary goals; two letters of reference on business or personal letterhead; a current academic transcript; a non-refundable application fee of $35. **Deadline:** March 1. **Contact:** scholarships@ theculinarytrust.com.

3308 ■ Cultural Vistas
10400 Little Patuxent Pkwy., Ste. 250
Columbia, MD 21044-3519
Ph: (410) 997-2200
Fax: (410) 992-3924
E-mail: info@culturalvistas.org
URL: culturalvistas.org

3309 ■ IAESTE United States Scholarships (Undergraduate/Scholarship)

Purpose: To help defray some of the costs associated with relocating overseas. **Focus:** General studies. **Qualif.:** Applicant must be of IAESTE United States at the time of internship. **Criteria:** Recipient will be based on the choice of destination which enables a student to leave the familiar and thereby grow professionally, culturally, and personally ; a drive to use the international experience as a springboard to further develop the skills and competencies needed to fulfill a successful career of lifelong learning; choice of a region that directly relates to a student's academic, personal, and cultural interests.

Funds Avail.: No specific amount. **Number Awarded:** 3. **To Apply:** Applicant must submit a scholarship application form; a photo of the internship experience; a 500-word essay explaining the meaning and value of IAESTE internship.

3310 ■ Jessica King Scholarships (Professional development/Scholarship)

Purpose: To help defray some of the costs associated with relocating overseas. **Focus:** Hospitals-Administration. **Qualif.:** All applicants must be 18 years old and not older than 35; must have an offer of training/work contract from an employer in the hospitality industry for a position outside the US; must be participants in an AIPT program; must have an educational degree (Associate or Bachelor degree or ACF certification) from a hospitality/culinary school or program; must have had at least 2 years of employment in the hospitality industry; must be US citizens. **Criteria:** Committee will evaluate the application based upon the merit, and not on the financial need.

Funds Avail.: $2,000. **To Apply:** An applicant must complete and submit a filled-out application form and must include two letters of reference, two copies of resume and a copy of school transcripts. Applicants must also submit an essay of at least 500 words but not exceeding 1000 words, describing the applicant's motivation for participating in a practical work experience abroad; describing the skills that he/she expect to learn from his/her international work experience. Applicants must also include how they will apply the experience to their future endeavors upon return to the US. **Contact:** aipt@aipt.org.

3311 ■ Cystic Fibrosis Foundation (CFF)
6931 Arlington Rd.
Bethesda, MD 20814
Ph: (301) 951-4422
Fax: (301) 951-6378
Free: 800-344-4823
E-mail: info@cff.org
URL: www.cff.org

3312 ■ Cystic Fibrosis Scholarship Foundation (Undergraduate, Vocational/Occupational/ Scholarship)

Purpose: To provide financial assistance for individuals with Cystic Fibrosis intending to pursue studies in undergraduate or vocational schools. **Focus:** General studies. **Qualif.:** Applicants may either be individuals entering college or vocational school or those who have already completed two semesters of college or vocational school. **Criteria:** Scholarships are awarded based on a combination of financial need, academic achievement and leadership.

Funds Avail.: $1,000. **To Apply:** Application forms and instructions are available at the website. **Deadline:** March 21. **Contact:** Cystic Fibrosis Scholarship Foundation, 1555 Sherman Avenue, 116 Evanston, IL 60201.

3313 ■ Dade Community Foundation, Inc. (DCF)
200 S Biscayne Blvd., Ste. 505
Miami, FL 33131-5330
Ph: (305) 371-2711
Fax: (305) 371-5342
E-mail: ruth.shack@dadecommunityfoundation.org
URL: www.dadecommunityfoundation.org

3314 ■ Judge Sidney M. Aronovitz Memorial Scholarships (High School, Undergraduate/ Scholarship)

Purpose: To provide financial assistance to Miami-Dade County minority students planning to continue their education at the university level and pursue a career in South Florida. **Focus:** General studies. **Qualif.:** Applicants must be minority high school seniors or GED recipients no older than 19 years of age attending a Miami Dade County public school with a minimum high school grade point average of 3.0. **Criteria:** Recipients are selected based on personal statement/goals; recommendations; academic achievement; financial need; and, volunteer/work experience.

Funds Avail.: $500. **Number Awarded:** 1. **To Apply:** Applicants must submit the completed application form and enclose all proper attachments. **Deadline:** March 20. **Contact:** Ted Seijo at the above address.

Awards are arranged alphabetically below their administering organizations

3315 ■ Jennet Colliflower Nursing Scholarships
(Undergraduate/Scholarship)

Purpose: To provide financial assistance to students in their junior or senior year of undergraduate nursing degree, who are Florida residents and enrolled full-time in a Florida public or private university. **Focus:** Nursing. **Qualif.:** Applicants must be entering junior or senior year undergraduate studies; must be full-time students (minimum of 12 credits hours per semester) in a public or private four-year Florida university or college; and must be seeking an undergraduate degree in Nursing. **Criteria:** Recipients are selected based on the volunteer experience, work experience and school activities; academic achievement; financial need; and, personal aspirations/career goals and relationship with nursing.

Funds Avail.: $1,000. **Number Awarded:** 2. **To Apply:** Applicants must submit the completed application form along with the required materials. **Deadline:** May 8. **Remarks:** Established in 1997 by Jennet Colliflower Key's family to memorialize the life of Jennet Colliflower Keys.

3316 ■ The Continental Group Scholarship
Fund *(High School, Undergraduate/Scholarship)*

Purpose: To provide educational opportunities for the children of current, full-time employees of The Continental Group, Inc and its subsidiaries. **Focus:** General studies. **Qualif.:** Applicants must be graduating high school seniors with a minimum 3.0 GPA and have a parent who is a full-time employee of The Continental Group, Inc. or one of its Subsidiaries for at least one year. **Criteria:** Applicants are evaluated based on financial need.

Funds Avail.: $1,000. **Number Awarded:** 4. **To Apply:** Applicants must submit all the required application information. **Deadline:** March 27.

3317 ■ Alan R. Epstein "Reach for the Stars"
Scholarships *(Undergraduate/Scholarship)*

Purpose: To provide financial assistance to deserving students in Dade County who have successfully dealt with life's obstacles. **Focus:** General studies. **Qualif.:** Applicants must be high school seniors graduating in June; must be accepted to a college or university. **Criteria:** Applicants are evaluated based on financial need.

Funds Avail.: $10,000. **To Apply:** Applicants must submit completed application form; high school official transcript; college acceptance letter(s); two letters of recommendation; volunteer/work experience and school activities; personal statement; one or two paragraphs describing the importance of scholarship. **Deadline:** April 10.

3318 ■ Randy Green Memorial Scholarship
Fund *(High School/Scholarship)*

Purpose: To provide financial assistance to students at Miami Springs Senior High School who are enrolled in a college program related to public education, political science, history or social work. **Focus:** Political science; History; Social work; Public relations. **Qualif.:** Applicants must be permanent residents or citizens of the U.S. and domiciled in South Florida; must have minimum high school grade point average of 3.0; must be Miami Springs high-school seniors demonstrating merit and financial need; must be accepted into accredited university and plan to be enrolled in two year or four year university programs concentrating in public education, political science, history, social work, or other major related to community service. **Criteria:** Recipients are selected based on academic

achievement; personal statement/career goals; volunteer/ work experience and school activities; recommendations; and financial need.

Funds Avail.: $1,000. **Number Awarded:** 2. **To Apply:** Applicants must submit the completed application form and all other required application information. **Deadline:** June 3.

3319 ■ Dr. Felix H. Reyler Memorial Scholarships
(Undergraduate/Scholarship)

Purpose: To provide financial assistance to business students entering their junior/senior year of undergraduate studies. **Focus:** Business; Finance. **Qualif.:** Applicants must be permanent residents or citizens of the U.S. and domiciled in Florida; must be business students entering their junior/senior year of undergraduate studies; must be students graduating from the Academy for International Business and Finance at Miami Jackson Senior High and the children of FIBA members; must be currently or enrolling as full-time students in four-year Florida college/ university and seeking for a degree in Business. **Criteria:** Recipients are selected based on financial need; academic achievement; personal aspirations/career goals and interests within Business and Finance; volunteer/work experience; and, school activities.

Funds Avail.: $2,500. **Number Awarded:** 2. **To Apply:** Applicants must submit completed application form; personal statement; official transcript; original recommendation letter on school letterhead; and, one photocopy of the entire completed application. **Deadline:** April 24.

3320 ■ Samalot - Sebastian Scholarship Fund
(High School/Scholarship)

Purpose: To support minority high school students in need of financial assistance. **Focus:** General studies. **Qualif.:** Applicants must be permanent residents or citizens of the U.S. and domiciled in South Florida; must have minimum high school grade point average of 3.5; must be minority high school senior; must be enrolling as full-time students (minimum of 12 credit hours per semester) in a four-year college/university. **Criteria:** Recipients are selected based on merit and financial need.

Funds Avail.: $2,000. **Number Awarded:** 3. **To Apply:** Applicants must submit all the required application information. **Deadline:** April 3.

3321 ■ Leo Suarez Journalism Scholarships
(Undergraduate/Scholarship)

Purpose: To help talented South Florida students for aspiring a career in journalism, broadcast or mass communications. **Focus:** Journalism; Broadcasting; Communications. **Qualif.:** Applicants must be high school seniors in Miami-Dade or Broward public school; must have minimum of 3.0 grade point average; must intend to major in journalism, broadcast or mass communications in undergraduate studies at four year university and/or two year college. **Criteria:** Applicants are evaluated based on career goals; writing samples; teacher recommendation; and academic achievement.

Funds Avail.: $1,000. **To Apply:** Applicants must submit the completed application form together with the three writing samples that have been published and letter of recommendation from the journalism sponsor or English professor at their high school. **Deadline:** March 23.

3322 ■ The Rodney Thaxton Justice Fund
(Undergraduate/Scholarship)

Purpose: To assist students pursuing career in the insurance industry and business. **Focus:** Social sciences; Law.

Awards are arranged alphabetically below their administering organizations

Qualif.: Applicants must be committed to the goal of social justice, and must be able to demonstrate that commitment to the scholarship committee; must be African descent and resident of Miami-Dade County who plans to take a four-year degree in college or university. **Criteria:** Applicants are evaluated based on personal statement/goals, essay on ethics; academic achievement; volunteer/work experience.

Funds Avail.: $1,000. **Number Awarded:** 5. **To Apply:** Applicants must submit completed application form and all required application materials and information. **Deadline:** April 17.

3323 ■ Jacki Tuckfield Memorial Graduate Business Scholarship Fund (Doctorate, Graduate, Master's/Scholarship)

Purpose: To provide financial assistance to African-American students to pursue their professional careers. **Focus:** Business. **Qualif.:** Applicants must be African American United States citizen, resident of South Florida, enrolled in a graduate business degree program (master's or doctoral), at Florida University; must be planning to pursue professional career in South Florida. **Criteria:** Recipients are selected based on merit.

Funds Avail.: $1,000. **Number Awarded:** 40. **To Apply:** Applicants must submit the completed application form; essay; transcripts; color passport photo; letter of recommendation; and resume. **Deadline:** May 31.

3324 ■ Seitlin Franklin E. Wheeler Scholarship Fund (Undergraduate/Scholarship)

Purpose: To assist students pursuing careers in the insurance industry and business. **Focus:** Insurance and insurance-related fields; Business. **Qualif.:** Applicants must be high school seniors with minimum high school grade point average of 3.0 and demonstrate interest in pursuing career in business or the insurance industry. **Criteria:** Recipients are selected on the basis of personal statement/goals, essay on ethics; academic achievement; and, volunteer/work experience.

Funds Avail.: $1,500. **Number Awarded:** 2. **To Apply:** Applicants must submit a completed application; one-page essay on "Ethics"; high school official transcript; and one photocopy of the entire completed application. **Deadline:** May 8.

3325 ■ Daedalian Foundation
PO Box 249
Universal City, TX 78148-0249
Ph: (210) 945-2113
Fax: (210) 945-2112
E-mail: daedalus@daedalians.org
URL: www.daedalians.org

3326 ■ Descendant Scholarships
(Undergraduate/Scholarship)

Purpose: To encourage the youth to become military pilots. **Focus:** Aerospace sciences. **Qualif.:** Applicant must be a direct descendant (natural or adopted) of a Founder, Named, or Hereditary member in good standing (living or deceased) of the Order of Daedalians; a citizen of the United States of America; accepted by or attending an accredited college/university and enrolled in an academic program which leads to a baccalaureate or higher degree; physically and mentally qualified with demonstrated

aptitude for commissioned US military service; in good scholastic standing; and not a recipient of another Daedalian scholarship in the same year. **Criteria:** Selection is based on the application.

Funds Avail.: Amount not specified. **To Apply:** Applicants must submit a completed application form together with a 3" x 5" photograph and a letter stating the rank, name and number of the sponsoring Daeldalian.

3327 ■ John and Alice Egan Multi-Year Mentioning Scholarships (Undergraduate/Scholarship)

Purpose: To encourage the youth to become military pilots. **Focus:** Aerospace sciences. **Qualif.:** Applicant must be a college/university student pursuing a career as a military aviator. Freshmen are not qualified. **Criteria:** Selection is based on the application.

Funds Avail.: $500-$2000. **To Apply:** Applicants must submit a completed application form together with a 3" x 5" photograph; complete transcripts (sent directly by the educational institution); a copy of FAA medical certificate and annotated copy of the Flight Physical Standards Questionnaire. **Deadline:** August 1. **Remarks:** The scholarship is not tied to the Matching Program, students may apply for both programs.

3328 ■ Matching Scholarships Program (Undergraduate/Scholarship)

Purpose: To encourage the youth to become military pilots. **Focus:** Aerospace sciences. **Qualif.:** Applicant must be a college/university student pursuing a career as a military aviator. **Criteria:** Selection is based on the application.

Funds Avail.: No specific amount. **To Apply:** Applicants must submit a completed application form together with a 3" x 5" photograph to the Chairman, Daedalian Foundation, PO Box 249 Randolph AFB, TX 78148-0249.

3329 ■ Navy, Army or Air Force ROTC Scholarship Program (Undergraduate/Scholarship)

Purpose: To encourage the youth to become military pilots. **Focus:** Aerospace sciences. **Qualif.:** Applicant must be a college/university student pursuing a career in military and must be nominated by local commander. **Criteria:** Selection is made by various ROTC headquarters.

Funds Avail.: No specific amount. **To Apply:** Applicants may contact the foundation for application information.

3330 ■ Dairy Farmers of America Inc.
10220 N Ambassador Dr.
Kansas City, MO 64153-2312
Ph: (816) 801-6455
Free: 888-332-6455
E-mail: webmail@dfamilk.com
URL: www.dfamilk.com

3331 ■ Dairy Farmers of America Scholarships
(Undergraduate/Scholarship)

Purpose: To recognize outstanding students pursuing careers in the dairy industry. **Focus:** Dairy science. **Qualif.:** Applicant must be pursuing a career in the dairy industry and enrolled in a two- or four-year accredited college, university or trade school. **Criteria:** Selection is based on applicant's commitment and passion to have a career in the dairy industry, and responses to essay questions;

Awards are arranged alphabetically below their administering organizations

extracurricular activities, awards, recognition and work experience; academic achievement; and financial need.

Funds Avail.: $1,500. **Number Awarded:** 5. **To Apply:** Applicants must submit a completed application form along with a recent transcript and two letters of recommendation. Application is also available online. **Deadline:** January 13. **Contact:** For further information, applicants must call 816-801-6432 and application materials must be submitted at scholarships@dfamilk.com.

3332 ■ Dalai Lama Trust

241 E 32nd St.
New York, NY 10016
Ph: (212) 213-5010
Fax: (212) 779-9245
E-mail: info@dalailamatrust.org
URL: www.dalailamatrust.org

3333 ■ Dalai Lama Trust Graduate Scholarships *(Graduate/Scholarship)*

Purpose: To further human capital development of the Tibetan people by supporting the pursuit of excellence among Tibetan students in the graduate field of their choice. **Focus:** General studies. **Qualif.:** Applicants must be enrolled in or already accepted to a graduate degree program in a university in Europe or North America and must demonstrate proof of Tibetan heritage. **Criteria:** Selection will be based on submitted documents and selected applicants will be contacted for a phone interview.

Funds Avail.: $15,000. **To Apply:** Applicants must submit a completed application form; photograph of themselves in digital format attached to the application form; official undergraduate transcript of records; curriculum vitae; copy of acceptance letter or enrollment form for intended graduate institution; two written letters of recommendation; two essay responses; copy of valid Green Book; financial statement: copy of most recent income tax return, or SAR/FAFSA forms if applicable. **Deadline:** May 31. **Contact:** E-mail at scholarship@dalailamatrust.org.

3334 ■ Dalcroze Society of America

c/o William R. Bauer, Pres.
The College of Staten Island/CUNY
2800 Victory Blvd.
Staten Island, NY 10314
Ph: (718) 982-2534
E-mail: president@dalcrozeusa.org
URL: www.dalcrozeusa.org

3335 ■ Dalcroze Society of America Memorial Scholarships *(Graduate/Scholarship)*

Purpose: To provide financial aid to students attending institutions offering Dalcroze certification or graduate credits devoted to the Dalcroze approach. **Focus:** Music education. **Qualif.:** Applicants must be attending an institution offering Dalcroze graduate credits and must not have been previously awarded a DSA scholarship. **Criteria:** Committees will award scholarships based on merit, financial need, intention to work towards Dalcroze certification within United States, residency and previous experience.

Funds Avail.: No specific amount. **To Apply:** Applicants must submit a resume, proof of acceptance at a Dalcroze Training Center, three letters of recommendation, statement of financial need such as recent tax return or other

documents, and a personal statement describing teaching and Dalcroze experiences or reasons for pursuing the training. **Deadline:** March 1.

3336 ■ Dallas Hispanic Bar Association (DHBA)

2101 Ross Ave.
Dallas, TX 75201
Ph: (214) 989-4306
E-mail: christievillarreal@sbcglobal.net
URL: www.dallashispanicbar.com

3337 ■ Dallas Hispanic Bar Association Scholarships *(Undergraduate/Scholarship)*

Purpose: To provide financial assistance for Texas law school students. **Focus:** Law. **Qualif.:** Applicants must have high academic performance and demonstrated leadership and must be enrolled in a Texas law school. **Criteria:** Selection of recipients will be based on financial need and academic standing.

Funds Avail.: $1,000-$2,000. **Number Awarded:** 5. **To Apply:** Applicants must complete the application form available online and must send it to Martinez Ramirez Siewcynski LLC. **Deadline:** June 17. **Contact:** Maricela Siewczynski at maricela@texemploymentlaw.com; Martinez Ramirez Siewcynski LLC, 6318 Gaston Ave., Ste. 201, Dallas, TX 75214.

3338 ■ Danish America Heritage Society (DAHS)

925 NE 5th St.
Salem, OR 97301
Ph: (503) 588-1331
E-mail: egonb@teleport.com
URL: www.danishamericanheritagesociety.org

3339 ■ Edith and Arnold N. Bodtker Grants *(All/Grant)*

Purpose: To provide stipends for students interested in studying and performing research in the area of Danish immigration to North America. **Focus:** General studies. **Qualif.:** Applicants must be currently enrolled in or graduated from a university-level institution. **Criteria:** Candidates must have a well-defined research or internship project that make them to stay in United States of America (for Danish or North American students) or in Denmark (for North American students).

Funds Avail.: $5,000. **Number Awarded:** Varies. **To Apply:** Applicants planned projects must be for a three to four-month period of residence in the United States or in Denmark, during the next calendar year. Proposals for residence in June-August will also be considered. **Deadline:** April 15 or September 15. **Remarks:** Established in 1998. **Contact:** Egon Bodtker, Pres. at the above address.

3340 ■ Dante Society of America (DSA)

PO Box 1558
Arlington, MA 02474-0023
E-mail: dsa@dantesociety.org
URL: www.dantesociety.org

3341 ■ Dante Prizes *(Undergraduate/Prize)*

Purpose: To support best student essay in competition on a subject related to the life or works of Dante. **Focus:**

Awards are arranged alphabetically below their administering organizations

General studies. **Qualif.:** Applicants must be undergraduates in any American or Canadian college or university, or by anyone not enrolled as graduate students who have received the degree of A.B., or its equivalent, within the past year. **Criteria:** Selection will be based on the committee's criteria.

Funds Avail.: $500. **To Apply:** All submissions must be made by e-mail attachment of a file in either Word or Word-Perfect and sent to the Dante Society. Files should have the extension .doc or .rtf if saved in Word, .wpd if saved in WordPerfect. Undergraduate essays should be no longer than 5,000 words in length, including bibliographies and any other material. The writer's name should not appear on the essay title page or on any other page of the essay since the essays are submitted anonymously to the readers. Quotations from Dante's works should be cited in the original language and the format of an essay should conform to either the Chicago or MLA Style Sheet guidelines. **Deadline:** June 30.

3342 ■ Charles Hall Grandgent Awards
(Graduate/Award)

Purpose: To support best student essay in competition on a subject related to the life or works of Dante. **Focus:** General studies. **Qualif.:** Applicants must be American or Canadian students enrolled in any graduate program. **Criteria:** Selection will be based on the committee's criteria.

Funds Avail.: $750. **To Apply:** All submissions must be made by e-mail attachment of a file in either Word or Word-Perfect and sent to the Dante Society. Files should have the extension .doc or .rtf if saved in Word, .wpd if saved in WordPerfect. Graduate essays should be no longer than 7,500 words in length, including bibliographies and any other material. Each writer should provide a cover page giving the writer's name, local, permanent and email addresses, the title of the essay, the essay category and the writer's institutional affiliation. The writer's name should not appear on the essay title page or on any other page of the essay since the essays are submitted anonymously to the readers. Quotations from Dante's works should be cited in the original language and the format of an essay should conform to either the Chicago or MLA Style Sheet guidelines. **Deadline:** June 30.

3343 ■ David Library of the American Revolution
1201 River Rd.
Washington Crossing, PA 18977
Ph: (215) 493-6776
Fax: (215) 493-9276
E-mail: librarian@dlar.org
URL: www.dlar.org

3344 ■ David Library Fellowships *(Doctorate, Postdoctorate/Fellowship)*

Purpose: To promote advanced scholarship. **Focus:** General studies. **Qualif.:** Open to both doctoral and post-doctoral applicants. Doctoral candidates must have passed their general examinations before beginning their fellowships. **Criteria:** Selection will be based on the committee's criteria.

Funds Avail.: $1,600. **To Apply:** Applicants should submit seven sets of the following: cover sheet with applicants name, mailing address, email address, phone number, academic affiliation and title of project; a brief project statement (3 to 5 pages) describing the project and stating what

David Library resources will be used; a detailed C.V.; writing sample (10 to 20 pages of recent work, preferably from the proposed fellowship project). Each application must be supported by two letters of reference sent directly by the referee, not sent by the applicant). All application materials must be submitted in a single package. **Deadline:** March 1. **Contact:** Meg McSweeney, Chief Operating Officer, 215-493-2233, ext.106 or mcsweeney@dlar.org.

3345 ■ Davis Memorial Foundation
465 Fairchild Dr., Ste. 210
Mountain View, CA 94043
Ph: (650) 938-5405
Fax: (650) 938-5407
E-mail: dmf@wsrca.com
URL: www.davisfoundation.org

3346 ■ Davis Memorial Foundation Scholarship Awards Program *(Graduate, Undergraduate/Scholarship)*

Purpose: To develop qualified professionals through education and to award those who have the desire to continue to improve their quality of life. **Focus:** General studies. **Qualif.:** Applicants must be high school students, undergraduate or graduate students or technical trade school students who are provisionally accepted as students into undergraduate or graduate degree programs for the coming academic year by accredited colleges or universities; must be WSRCA members in good standing, their employees or their respective immediate family (spouse or child). The child may be natural, legally adopted or a step child. **Criteria:** Applicants are evaluated based on academic performance.

Funds Avail.: $4,000. **To Apply:** Applicants must submit 6 copies of each: official application form; official transcript of all high school and college records; letter from college, university or technical trade school where the undergraduate or graduate work will be undertaken, indicating provisional acceptance of the proposed course of study; and current picture. **Deadline:** April 15.

3347 ■ Davis Wright Tremaine LLP (DWT)
701 W Eighth Ave.
Anchorage, AK 99501-3468
Ph: (907) 257-5300
Fax: (907) 257-5399
Free: 877-398-8416
E-mail: info@dwt.com
URL: www.dwt.com

3348 ■ Davis Wright Tremaine 1L Diversity Scholarships *(Undergraduate/Scholarship)*

Purpose: To provide financial assistance for qualified students intending to pursue their law degree. **Focus:** Law. **Qualif.:** Applicants must be first-year law students; must have a record of academic achievement in both undergraduate school and the first year of law school; must demonstrate promise for a successful career in law; must be committed to civic involvement that promotes diversity; be willing to continue that commitment upon entering the legal profession; and must commit to become a Summer Associate in DWT's Seattle Office between the student's first and second years of law school. **Criteria:** Applicants will be selected based on their academic performance and

Awards are arranged alphabetically below their administering organizations

commitment to a successful career in law. **Funds Avail.:** $7,500 for the student's second year tuition and expenses. **Number Awarded:** 2. **To Apply:** Applicants must submit a current resume; a complete undergraduate transcript; a grade from the first semester of law school; a short, personal essay indicating the applicant's eligibility for and interest in the scholarship, and a legal writing sample; and two or three references (one of whom should be a person qualified to comment on the applicant's law school work). **Deadline:** January 19. **Contact:** Carol Yuly at carolyuly@dwt.com; Davis Wright Tremaine LLP, IL Diversity Scholarship Program, 1201 Third Ave., Suite 2200, Seattle, WA 98101-3045.

3349 ■ Deafness Research Foundation (DRF)

363 7th Ave., 10th Fl.
New York, NY 10001-3904
Ph: (212) 257-6140
Fax: (212) 257-6139
Free: 866-454-3924
E-mail: info@hearinghealthfoundation.org
URL: www.drf.org

3350 ■ Deafness Research Foundation Research Grants *(Doctorate/Grant)*

Purpose: To promote hearing health possible for all people through research and education. **Focus:** Medical Research. **Qualif.:** Applicant should hold the M.D., Ph.D., or equivalent degrees as well as a faculty or post-doctoral appointment; and should demonstrate experience and strong research training as well as sufficient institutional support to carry out the proposed work. **Criteria:** Priority is given to new investigators in the field of hearing and balance and to projects that are likely to open new lines of inquiry.

Funds Avail.: $25,000 per year. **Number Awarded:** Varies. **To Apply:** For first year application, application must be clear and legible with a minimum font size of 11 points. Figures, charts, tables, legends and footnotes may be smaller in size but must be legible. For second year applications, applicant must submit a letter of intent to apply for second year funding to DRF. **Deadline:** December 1 for first year application. **Contact:** Trisha Donaldson at 212-328-9483, or grants@drf.org or tdonaldson@drf.org.

3351 ■ Death Valley '49ers

PO Box 101
Amargosa Valley, NV 89020
Ph: (310) 544-1207
Fax: (310) 544-2178
E-mail: information@deathvalley49ers.org
URL: www.deathvalley49ers.org

3352 ■ Death Valley '49ers Scholarships *(Undergraduate/Scholarship)*

Purpose: To assist high school graduates living in the Death Valley Unified School District. **Focus:** Historic preservation. **Qualif.:** Applicants must be residents of the Death Valley Unified School District and/or Death Valley National Park for a minimum of two years and/or parent(s) are employed within the boundaries of Death Valley National Park and/or attended Death Valley Elementary School for a minimum of two years; must have completed all the required subjects for high school graduation in their junior and senior academic years at Beatty, Pahrump, or Shoshone High Schools; must maintain 24 to 30 required units per academic year. Freshmen must have 2.5 GPA, Sophomores must have 2.75, Juniors and Seniors must have 3.0 GPA. **Criteria:** Scholarships are awarded based on a four-year program and will be renewed each year based on the academic progress of the student. The scholarship committee will review academic progress at the end of each semester.

Funds Avail.: $4,000. **Number Awarded:** 1. **To Apply:** Applicants must submit a Death Valley '49ers Scholarship Application to the Scholarship Committee by the application deadline in the senior year of high school. **Deadline:** December 20. **Contact:** Lawrence C. Baker Jr. at the above address.

3353 ■ Michael E. DeBakey International Surgical Society (MEDISS)

c/o Kenneth L. Mattox, MD, Sec.-Treas.
1 Baylor Plz.
Houston, TX 77030
Ph: (713) 798-4557
Fax: (713) 796-9605
Free: 800-914-3709
E-mail: redstart@aol.com
URL: www.mediss.org

3354 ■ DeBakey International Society Fellowship Awards *(Professional development/Award)*

Purpose: To support individuals for training in Houston at Baylor College of Medicine-affiliated hospitals for medicine's surgical program. **Focus:** Cardiology. **Qualif.:** Applicants must have completed a general surgical residency and must have passed the ECFMG or any other certifying examinations necessary to obtain a temporary license to practice medicine in Texas. **Criteria:** Candidates will be evaluated based on criteria by the committee of the society.

Funds Avail.: $25,000. **To Apply:** Applicants must submit a letter of support from their program director, documents confirming applicant's eligibility for an institutional or temporary Texas license to practice medicine and their current photograph should be submitted to the Office of the Secretary. Following receipt of these documents, the secretary will send a formal application to applicants. **Contact:** Kenneth L. Mattox, M.D. at the above address.

3355 ■ Decorative Arts Trust

106 Bainbridge St.
Philadelphia, PA 19147
Ph: (215) 627-2859
Fax: (215) 925-1144
URL: www.decorativeartstrust.org

3356 ■ Dewey Lee Curtis Scholarships *(All/Scholarship)*

Purpose: To support individuals actively working in the field of American decorative arts with their education. **Focus:** Art. **Qualif.:** Applicants must be individuals who are actively working in the field of American decorative arts. **Criteria:** Candidates will be selected based on the application.

Funds Avail.: No specific amount. **Number Awarded:** 1. **To Apply:** Applicants may contact the organization or their Institute's office for the application information.

Awards are arranged alphabetically below their administering organizations

3357 ■ Delaware Community Foundation (DCF)

PO Box 1636
Wilmington, DE 19899
Ph: (302) 571-8004
Fax: (302) 571-1553
E-mail: info@delcf.org
URL: www.delcf.org

3358 ■ Chrysler Technical Scholarship Fund
(Undergraduate/Scholarship)

Purpose: To provide college scholarship assistance to those worthy students based on demonstrated academic ability, leadership traits and financial need. **Focus:** General Studies. **Qualif.:** Applicants must be residents of Delaware and not older than 23 years of age at the time of application; must have an at least 2.75 GPA and provide evidence of a commitment to leadership in the community; must plan to obtain a degree or certificate from a community college, trade school or university in a technical field related to the design, engineering, manufacturing or repair of automotive products, including but not limited to, automotive repair, skilled trades and engineering. **Criteria:** Recipients will be selected based on demonstrated academic ability, leadership traits and financial need.

Funds Avail.: $1,000 per academic year. **Number Awarded:** 20. **To Apply:** Applicants must download and fill out the application form at the Delaware Community Foundation website. **Deadline:** April 1. **Contact:** For further information, applicants must contact Richard Gentsch at the above address.

3359 ■ Delta Delta Delta

2331 Brookhollow Plaza Dr.
Arlington, TX 76006
Ph: (817) 633-8001
Fax: (817) 652-0212
E-mail: info@trideltaeo.org
URL: www.tridelta.org

3360 ■ Nancy Ashley Adams/Ashley Adams Koetje Scholarships *(Undergraduate/Scholarship)*

Purpose: To provide financial assistance to qualified undergraduate students. **Focus:** General studies. **Qualif.:** Applicant must be an Alpha Eta chapter member in Florida State University; must be an initiated sophomore or junior member. **Criteria:** Preference is given to officer or members from out-of-state. Applicants will be evaluated based on their academic achievement, chapter and campus activities, and financial need.

Funds Avail.: No stated amount. **To Apply:** Application forms are available on the website. Applicant must provide a personal statement about their educational and vocational goals; must have a recommendation letter from a faculty member; must have an official transcript from each undergraduate institution. Application materials must be sent to: Delta Delta Delta, PO Box 5987, Arlington, TX 76005. **Deadline:** March 1. **Contact:** tbraeutigam@trideltaeo.org or 817-633-8001.

3361 ■ Adams Family Scholarships
(Undergraduate/Scholarship)

Purpose: To provide financial assistance to qualified undergraduate students. **Focus:** General studies. **Qualif.:** Applicant must be a Chi member at the University of Mis-sissippi chapter; must be an initiated sophomore or junior member. **Criteria:** Applicants will be judge based on academic achievement, campus and community involvement, and financial need.

Funds Avail.: No stated amount. **To Apply:** Application forms are available in the website. Applicant must provide a personal statement about educational and vocational goals; must have a recommendation letter from a faculty member; must have an official transcript from each undergraduate institution. Application materials must be sent to: Delta Delta Delta, PO Box 5987, Arlington, TX 76005. **Deadline:** March 1. **Contact:** For further information, applicants must e-mail Tawnya Braeutigam at tbraeutigam@rideltaeo.org.

3362 ■ Margaret M. Alkek Scholarships
(Undergraduate/Scholarship)

Purpose: To provide financial assistance to qualified undergraduate students. **Focus:** Education, Music, Theater arts. **Qualif.:** Applicant must be a Theta Xi chapter member at the University of Southern California; must have academic achievement at the collegiate level of 3.0 or better; must be an initiated sophomore or junior members. **Criteria:** Preference will be given to those majoring in education, music or theater.

Funds Avail.: No stated amount. **To Apply:** Application forms are available on the website. Applicant must provide a personal statement about their educational and vocational goals; must have a recommendation letter from a faculty member; must have an official transcript from each undergraduate institution. Application materials must be sent to: Delta Delta Delta, PO Box 5987, Arlington, TX 76005. **Deadline:** March 1.

3363 ■ Alpha Eta Scholarships *(Undergraduate/ Scholarship)*

Purpose: To provide financial assistance to qualified undergraduate students. **Focus:** General studies. **Qualif.:** Applicant must be a member of Alpha Eta chapter member at Florida State University; must be an initiated sophomore or junior member. **Criteria:** Applicants are judged based on academic standing, chapter and campus activities, and financial need.

Funds Avail.: No stated amount. **To Apply:** Application forms are available on the website. Applicant must provide a personal statement about their educational and vocational goals; must have a recommendation letter from a faculty member; must have an official transcript from each undergraduate institution. Application materials must be sent to: Delta Delta Delta, PO Box 5987, Arlington, TX 76005. **Deadline:** March 1. **Contact:** Applicants must contact Tawnya Braeutigam at the Foundation office, tbraeutigam@trideltaeo.org.

3364 ■ Alpha Rho Leadership Scholarships
(Undergraduate/Scholarship)

Purpose: To provide financial assistance to qualified undergraduate students. **Focus:** General studies. **Qualif.:** Applicant must be an Alpha Rho chapter member at the University of Georgia; must be an initiated sophomore or junior member. **Criteria:** Applicants are judge based on academic standing, chapter and campus activities, and financial need.

Funds Avail.: No stated amount. **To Apply:** Application forms are available on the website. Applicant must provide a personal statement about their educational and vocational

Awards are arranged alphabetically below their administering organizations

goals; must have a recommendation letter from a faculty member; must have an official transcript from each undergraduate institution. **Deadline:** March 1. **Contact:** Applicants must contact Tawnya Braeutigam at the Foundation office, tbraeutigam@trideltaeo.org.

3365 ■ Jane E. Anderson Scholarships
(Undergraduate/Scholarship)

Purpose: To provide financial assistance to qualified undergraduate students. **Focus:** General studies. **Qualif.:** Applicant must be a Kappa chapter member at the University of Nebraska; must have academic achievement at the collegiate level; must be "without favor or prejudice"; must be an initiated sophomore or junior member. **Criteria:** Applicants will be judged based on their academic achievement, campus and community involvement, and financial need.

Funds Avail.: No stated amount. **To Apply:** Application forms are available on the website. Applicant must provide a personal statement about educational and vocational goals; must have a recommendation letter from a faculty member; must have an official transcript from each undergraduate institution. Application materials must be sent to: Delta Delta Delta, PO Box 5987, Arlington, TX 76005. **Deadline:** March 1.

3366 ■ Atlanta Alumnae Achievement Scholarships *(Undergraduate/Scholarship)*

Purpose: To provide financial assistance to qualified undergraduate students. **Focus:** General studies. **Qualif.:** Applicant must be currently enrolled in an undergraduate Tri Delta member in good standing at any public or private college or university; must be a collegiate member who graduated from a Georgia high school in one of the following four counties: Fulton, Dekalb, Cobb or Gwinnett; must be a junior during the application year. **Criteria:** Selection of applicant will be based on the following criteria: (1) Must have a minimum GPA of 3.3 on a 4.0 scale - 50%; (2) Collegiate Chapter Service (must have served or be serving at an elected or appointed position(s)) - 30%; (3) Leadership or community service on campus - 20%.

Funds Avail.: No stated amount. **To Apply:** Application forms are available on the website. Applicant must provide a personal statement about educational and vocational goals; must have a recommendation letter from a faculty member; must have an official transcript from each undergraduate institution. Application materials must be sent to: Delta Delta Delta, PO Box 5987, Arlington, TX 76005. **Deadline:** March 1.

3367 ■ Avery Bayle Barth Scholarships
(Undergraduate/Scholarship)

Purpose: To provide financial assistance to qualified undergraduate students. **Focus:** Education. **Qualif.:** Applicant must be a Theta Xi chapter member at the University of Southern California; must have an academic achievement at the collegiate level; must be an initiated sophomore and junior members. **Criteria:** Preference will be given to those majoring in education.

Funds Avail.: No stated amount. **To Apply:** Application forms are available on the website. Applicant must provide a personal statement about educational and vocational goals; must have a recommendation letter from a faculty member; must have an official transcript from each undergraduate institution. Application materials must be sent to: Delta Delta Delta, PO Box 5987, Arlington, TX 76005. **Deadline:** March 1.

3368 ■ Beta Gamma Memorial Scholarships
(Undergraduate/Scholarship)

Purpose: To provide financial assistance to qualified undergraduate students. **Focus:** General studies. **Qualif.:** Applicant must be a Beta Gamma chapter member at Jacksonville University; must be a full time undergraduate at Jacksonville University; must have a minimum GPA of 2.5; must be a member who has overcome personal hardship or life struggle. **Criteria:** Applicants are judged based on academic standing, chapter and campus activities, and financial need.

Funds Avail.: No stated amount. **To Apply:** Application forms are available on the website. Applicant must provide a personal statement about their educational and vocational goals; must have a recommendation letter from a faculty member; must have an official transcript from each undergraduate institution. **Deadline:** March 1. **Contact:** Applicants must contact Tawnya Braeutigam at the Foundation office, tbraeutigam@trideltaeo.org or 817-633-8001.

3369 ■ Chi Chapter Undergraduate Scholarships *(Undergraduate/Scholarship)*

Purpose: To provide financial assistance to a qualified undergraduate student. **Focus:** General studies. **Qualif.:** Applicant must be Chi member at the University of Mississippi chapter; must be an initiated sophomore or junior member. **Criteria:** Applicants will be judged based on academic achievement, campus and community involvement, and financial need.

Funds Avail.: No stated amount. **To Apply:** Application forms are available on the website. Applicant must provide a personal statement about their educational and vocational goals; must have a recommendation letter from a faculty member; must have an official transcript from each undergraduate institution. Application materials must be sent to: Delta Delta Delta, PO Box 5987, Arlington, TX 76005. **Deadline:** March 1.

3370 ■ Durning Sisters Scholarships *(Graduate/Scholarship)*

Purpose: To provide financial assistance to graduate students. **Focus:** General studies. **Qualif.:** Applicant must be a Tri Delta member who has completed 12 hours of graduate study and is unmarried. **Criteria:** Applicants will be evaluated based on academic merit, chapter and campus or community activities.

Funds Avail.: $3,000. **To Apply:** Applicant must complete the application form available on the website; must have a personal statement about educational and vocational goals; must have two letters of academic recommendation and one Tri Delta recommendation letter; must provide a transcript and financial information. Application documents must be sent to: Delta Delta Delta at PO Box 5987, Arlington, TX 76005. **Deadline:** March 1.

3371 ■ Harriet Erich Graduate Fellowships
(Graduate/Fellowship)

Purpose: To provide financial assistance to graduate students. **Focus:** General studies. **Qualif.:** Applicant must be a Tri Delta member enrolled in an accredited graduate program at the University of Alabama. **Criteria:** Applicants are judged based on academic merit as well as chapter and campus or community activities.

Funds Avail.: No stated amount. **To Apply:** Applicant must complete the application form available on the website; must have a personal statement about educational and

Awards are arranged alphabetically below their administering organizations

vocational goals; must have two letters of academic recommendation and one Tri Delta recommendation letter; must provide a transcript and financial information. Application documents must be sent to: Delta Delta Delta at PO Box 5987, Arlington, TX 76005. **Deadline:** March 1. **Contact:** Applicants must contact Tawnya Braeutigam at the Foundation office, tbraeutigam@trideltaeo.org.

3372 ■ Louise Bales Gallagher Scholarships
(Undergraduate/Scholarship)

Purpose: To provide financial assistance to qualified undergraduate students. **Focus:** General studies. **Qualif.:** Applicant must be a Delta Epsilon chapter member at Millikin University; must be an initiated sophomore or junior members. **Criteria:** Scholarship application will be based on the following criteria: (1) Financial need - 50%; (2) Academic achievement - 25%; (3) Chapter and campus involvement - 25%.

Funds Avail.: No stated amount. **To Apply:** Application forms are available on the website. Applicant must provide a personal statement about educational and vocational goals; must have a recommendation letter from a faculty member; must have an official transcript from each undergraduate institution. Application materials must be sent to: Delta Delta Delta, PO Box 5987, Arlington, TX 76005. **Deadline:** March 1. **Contact:** For further information, applicants must e-mail Tawnya Braeutigam at tbraeutigam@rideltaeo.org.

3373 ■ Peg Hart Harrison Memorial Scholarships
(Undergraduate/Scholarship)

Purpose: To provide financial assistance to qualified undergraduate students. **Focus:** General studies. **Qualif.:** Applicant must be a Beta Lambda chapter member at the University of Central Florida; must be a member who has overcome insurmountable odds; must be an initiated sophomore or junior member. **Criteria:** Applicants are judge based on academic standing, chapter and campus activities, and financial need.

Funds Avail.: No stated amount. **To Apply:** Application forms are available in the website. Applicant must provide a personal statement about their educational and vocational goals; must have a recommendation letter from a faculty member; must have an official transcript from each undergraduate institution. **Deadline:** March 1. **Contact:** tbraeutigam@trideltaeo.org or 817-633-8001.

3374 ■ Erin Kumelos Heard Memorial Scholarships
(Undergraduate/Scholarship)

Purpose: To provide financial assistance to qualified undergraduate students. **Focus:** General studies. **Qualif.:** Applicant must be a member of the Beta Pi chapter at California/Davis; must be an initiated sophomore or junior member in good standing with the foundation; must be a full-time student and active member. **Criteria:** Application will be evaluated by Rae Ann and her committee.

Funds Avail.: No specific amount. **To Apply:** Application forms are available in the website. Applicant must provide a personal statement about educational and vocational goals; must have a recommendation letter from a faculty member; must have an official transcript from each undergraduate institutions. Application materials must be sent to: Delta Delta Delta, PO Box 5987, Arlington, TX 76005. **Deadline:** March 1.

3375 ■ Houston Alumnae Chapter Graduate Fellowships
(Graduate/Fellowship)

Purpose: To provide financial assistance to graduate students. **Focus:** General studies. **Qualif.:** Applicant must be a Tri Delta member enrolled in an accredited graduate program full-time whose permanent residence is in Houston, Texas. **Criteria:** Candidates will be selected based on academic merit as well as chapter and campus or community activities.

Funds Avail.: $3,000. **To Apply:** Applicant must complete the application form available on the website; must have a personal statement about educational and vocational goals; must have two letters of academic recommendation and one Tri Delta recommendation letter; must provide a transcript and financial information. Application documents must be sent to: Delta Delta Delta at PO Box 5987, Arlington, TX 76005. **Deadline:** March 1.

3376 ■ Hazel D. Isbell Fellowships *(Graduate/Fellowship)*

Purpose: To provide financial assistance to graduate students. **Focus:** General studies. **Qualif.:** Applicant must be a Tri Delta member pursuing a graduate study. **Criteria:** Preference will be given to Theta Delta alumnae attending the University of Oregon, Theta Mu chapter members.

Funds Avail.: No stated amount. **To Apply:** Applicant must complete the application form available on the website; must have a personal statement about educational and vocational goals; must have two letters of academic recommendation and one Tri Delta recommendation letter; must provide a transcript and financial information. Application documents must be sent to: Delta Delta Delta at PO Box 5987, Arlington, TX 76005. **Deadline:** March 1. **Contact:** Applicants must contact Tawnya Braeutigam at the Foundation office, tbraeutigam@trideltaeo.org.

3377 ■ Kappa Chapter Centennial Scholarships
(Undergraduate/Scholarship)

Purpose: To provide financial assistance to qualified undergraduate students. **Focus:** General studies. **Qualif.:** Applicant must be a Kappa chapter member at the University of Nebraska; must be an initiated sophomore or junior member. **Criteria:** Applicants will be judged based on academic achievement, campus and community involvement, and financial need.

Funds Avail.: No stated amount. **To Apply:** Application forms are available on the website. Applicant must provide a personal statement about educational and vocational goals; must have a recommendation letter from a faculty member; must have an official transcript from each undergraduate institution. Application materials must be sent to: Delta Delta Delta, PO Box 5987, Arlington, TX 76005. **Deadline:** March 1.

3378 ■ Luella Akins Key Scholarships
(Undergraduate/Scholarship)

Purpose: To provide financial assistance to qualified undergraduate students. **Focus:** General studies. **Qualif.:** Applicant must be an initiated sophomore or junior member in good standing of Delta Delta; must be a full-time student and active member. **Criteria:** Applicants are judged based on academic standing, chapter and campus activities, and financial need.

Funds Avail.: No stated amount. **To Apply:** Application forms are available on the website. Applicant must provide a personal statement about educational and vocational goals; must have a recommendation letter from a faculty member; must have an official transcript from each undergraduate institution. Application materials must be sent to: Delta Delta Delta, PO Box 5987, Arlington, TX 76005. **Deadline:** March 1.

Awards are arranged alphabetically below their administering organizations

3379 ■ Sarah Shinn Marshall Scholarships
(Undergraduate/Scholarship)

Purpose: To provide financial assistance to qualified undergraduate students. **Focus:** General studies. **Qualif.:** Applicant must be an initiated sophomore or junior member in good standing of Delta Delta; must be a full-time student and active member. **Criteria:** Applicants are judge based on academic standing, chapter and campus activities, and financial need.

Funds Avail.: $1,000-$3,000. **To Apply:** Application forms are available on the website. Applicant must provide a personal statement about educational and vocational goals; must have a recommendation letter from a faculty member; must have an official transcript from each undergraduate institution. Application materials must be sent to: Delta Delta Delta, PO Box 5987, Arlington, TX 76005. **Deadline:** March 1.

3380 ■ Martin Sisters Scholarships
(Undergraduate/Scholarship)

Purpose: To provide financial assistance to qualified undergraduate students. **Focus:** General studies. **Qualif.:** Applicant must be an initiated sophomore or junior members in good standing of Delta Delta; must be a full-time student and active member. **Criteria:** Applicants are judged based on academic standing, chapter and campus activities, and financial need.

Funds Avail.: No stated amount. **To Apply:** Application forms are available in the website. Applicant must provide a personal statement about educational and vocational goals; must have a recommendation letter from a faculty member; must have an official transcript from each undergraduate institutions. Application materials must be sent to: Delta Delta Delta, PO Box 5987, Arlington, TX 76005. **Deadline:** March 1. **Contact:** Applicants must contact Tawnya Braeutigam at the Foundation office, tbraeutigam@trideltaeo.org.

3381 ■ McKinney Sisters Undergraduate Scholarships *(Undergraduate/Scholarship)*

Purpose: To provide financial assistance to qualified undergraduate students. **Focus:** General studies. **Qualif.:** Applicant must be a graduate from high school in San Antonio, TX or has permanent residence in San Antonio; must be an initiated sophomore or junior member. **Criteria:** Applicants will be judged based on academic achievement, campus and community involvement, and financial need.

Funds Avail.: No stated amount. **To Apply:** Application forms are available on the website. Applicant must provide a personal statement about educational and vocational goals; must have a recommendation letter from a faculty member; must have an official transcript from each undergraduate institution. Application materials must be sent to: Delta Delta Delta, PO Box 5987, Arlington, TX 76005. **Deadline:** March 1. **Contact:** Applicants must contact Tawnya Braeutigam at the Foundation office, tbraeutigam@trideltaeo.org.

3382 ■ Virginia Nicklas Scholarships
(Undergraduate/Scholarship)

Purpose: To provide financial assistance to qualified undergraduate students. **Focus:** Literature, Science, Arts. **Qualif.:** Applicant must be an Iota chapter member at the University of Michigan; must be a permanent resident outside of Michigan; must live in Iota chapter house; must be currently enrolled in Literature, Science, and Arts. **Crite-**ria: Applicants will be judged based on academic achievement, campus and community involvement, and financial need.

Funds Avail.: No stated amount. **To Apply:** Application forms are available on the website. Applicant must provide a personal statement about educational and vocational goals; must have a recommendation letter from a faculty member; must have an official transcript from each undergraduate institution. Application materials must be sent to: Delta Delta Delta, PO Box 5987, Arlington, TX 76005. **Deadline:** March 1.

3383 ■ Northern Virginia Alumnae Chapter Scholarships *(Undergraduate/Scholarship)*

Purpose: To provide financial assistance to qualified undergraduate students. **Focus:** General studies. **Qualif.:** Applicant must have academic achievement of 3.0 or better GPA; must have a financial need; must be an initiated sophomore or junior member. **Criteria:** Priority is given to a member from a Virginia Tri Delta chapter, then a member of any Tri Delta chapter with a permanent residence in Northern Virginia.

Funds Avail.: No stated amount. **To Apply:** Application forms are available on the website. Applicant must provide a personal statement about educational and vocational goals; must have a recommendation letter from a faculty member; must have an official transcript from each undergraduate institution. Application materials must be sent to: Delta Delta Delta, PO Box 5987, Arlington, TX 76005. **Deadline:** March 1. **Contact:** Applicants must contact Tawnya Braeutigam at the Foundation office, tbraeutigam@trideltaeo.org.

3384 ■ Cissy McDaniel Parker Scholarships
(Undergraduate/Scholarship)

Purpose: To provide financial assistance to qualified undergraduate students. **Focus:** General studies. **Qualif.:** Applicant must be a Theta Zeta chapter member at the University of Texas; must have an academic achievement of 3.0 or better GPA; must be an initiated sophomore or junior members. **Criteria:** Applicants will be judged based on academic achievement, campus and community involvement, and financial need.

Funds Avail.: No stated amount. **To Apply:** Application forms are available on the website. Applicant must provide a personal statement about educational and vocational goals; must have a recommendation letter from a faculty member; must have an official transcript from each undergraduate institution. Application materials must be sent to: Delta Delta Delta, PO Box 5987, Arlington, TX 76005. **Deadline:** March 1.

3385 ■ Zoe Gore Perrin Scholarships
(Undergraduate/Scholarship)

Purpose: To provide financial assistance to qualified undergraduate students. **Focus:** General studies. **Qualif.:** Applicant must be an initiated sophomore and junior member in good standing of Delta Delta; must be a full-time student and active member. **Criteria:** Applicants are judged based on academic achievement, past and present Tri Delta involvement, campus and community involvement, and financial need.

Funds Avail.: No specific amount. **To Apply:** Application forms are available on the website. Applicant must provide a personal statement about their educational and vocational goals; must have a recommendation letter from a faculty

Awards are arranged alphabetically below their administering organizations

member; must have an official transcript from each undergraduate institution. Application materials must be sent to: Delta Delta Delta, PO Box 5987, Arlington, TX 76005. **Deadline:** March 1.

3386 ■ Cheryl White Pryor Memorial Scholarships (Undergraduate/Scholarship)

Purpose: To provide financial assistance to qualified undergraduate students. **Focus:** General studies. **Qualif.:** Applicant must be a member of Delta Sigma chapter member at Tennessee; must be an initiated sophomore or junior members. **Criteria:** Scholarship selection committee shall determine the number of recipients and amounts of each scholarship. Applicants will be evaluated based on the following criteria: (1) Past and present service to the Delta Sigma chapter at the University of Tennessee - 60%; (2) Academic achievement - 30%; (3) Financial need - 10%.

Funds Avail.: $500. **To Apply:** Application forms are available on the website. Applicant must provide a personal statement about educational and vocational goals; must have a recommendation letter from a faculty member; must have an official transcript from each undergraduate institution. Application materials must be sent to: Delta Delta Delta, PO Box 5987, Arlington, TX 76005. **Deadline:** March 1.

3387 ■ Susan E. Riley Scholarships (Undergraduate/Scholarship)

Purpose: To provide financial assistance to a qualified undergraduate student. **Focus:** General studies. **Qualif.:** Applicant must be a Theta Mu chapter member at Oregon State University; must be currently a Tri Delta member in good standing; must show academic achievements at the collegiate level; must participate in community service; must be an initiated sophomore or junior member. **Criteria:** Applicants will be judged based on academic achievement, campus and community involvement, and financial need.

Funds Avail.: No stated amount. **To Apply:** Application forms are available on the website. Applicant must provide a personal statement about their educational and vocational goals; must have a recommendation letter from a faculty member; must have an official transcript from each undergraduate institution. Application materials must be sent to: Delta Delta Delta, PO Box 5987, Arlington, TX 76005. **Deadline:** March 1.

3388 ■ Jean Wiggin Roach Scholarships (Undergraduate/Scholarship)

Purpose: To provide financial assistance to qualified undergraduate students. **Focus:** General studies. **Qualif.:** Applicant must be a Phi Lambda chapter member at Texas Christian University; must have academic achievement at the collegiate level; must be an initiated sophomore and junior members. **Criteria:** Applicants will be judged based on academic achievement, campus and community involvement, and financial need.

Funds Avail.: No stated amount. **To Apply:** Application forms are available on the website. Applicant must provide a personal statement about educational and vocational goals; must have a recommendation letter from a faculty member; must have an official transcript from each undergraduate institution. Application materials must be sent to: Delta Delta Delta, PO Box 5987, Arlington, TX 76005. **Deadline:** March 1.

3389 ■ Jeanne Graves Ryland Scholarships (Undergraduate/Scholarship)

Purpose: To provide financial assistance to qualified undergraduate students. **Focus:** General studies. **Qualif.:**

Applicant must be a Phi Theta chapter member at Auburn University; must be an initiated sophomore or junior member. **Criteria:** Applicants will be judged based on academic achievement, campus and community involvement, and financial need.

Funds Avail.: No stated amount. **To Apply:** Application forms are available on the website. Applicant must provide a personal statement about educational and vocational goals; must have a recommendation letter from a faculty member; must have an official transcript from each undergraduate institution. Application materials must be sent to: Delta Delta Delta, PO Box 5987, Arlington, TX 76005. **Deadline:** March 1.

3390 ■ Julie Anne Sadlier Memorial Scholarships (Undergraduate/Scholarship)

Purpose: To provide financial assistance to qualified undergraduate students. **Focus:** General studies. **Qualif.:** Applicant must be a Theta Pi chapter member at UCLA; must have overcome a personal hardship or life struggle; must be an initiated sophomore or junior members. **Criteria:** Applicants will be judged based on academic achievement, campus and community involvement, and financial need.

Funds Avail.: No stated amount. **To Apply:** Application forms are available on the website. Applicant must provide a personal statement about educational and vocational goals; must have a recommendation letter from a faculty member; must have an official transcript from each undergraduate institution. Application materials must be sent to: Delta Delta Delta, PO Box 5987, Arlington, TX 76005. **Deadline:** March 1.

3391 ■ Virginia Hartford Saharov Memorial Scholarships (Undergraduate/Scholarship)

Purpose: To provide financial assistance to qualified undergraduate students. **Focus:** General studies. **Qualif.:** Applicant must be a Delta Pi chapter member at Illinois; must be an initiated sophomore or junior member. **Criteria:** Applicants will be judged based on academic achievement, campus and community involvement, and financial need.

Funds Avail.: No stated amount. **To Apply:** Application forms are available on the website. Applicant must provide a personal statement about educational and vocational goals; must have a recommendation letter from a faculty member; must have an official transcript from each undergraduate institution. Application materials must be sent to: Delta Delta Delta, PO Box 5987, Arlington, TX 76005. **Deadline:** March 1.

3392 ■ Edith Scandlyn/Sammie Lynn Scandlyn Puett Memorial Scholarships (Undergraduate/Scholarship)

Purpose: To provide financial assistance to a qualified undergraduate student. **Focus:** General studies. **Qualif.:** Applicant must be a Delta Sigma chapter member at the University of Tennessee; must be an initiated sophomore or junior members. **Criteria:** Preference will be given to: (a) Applicants with strong academic records (3.5+); (b) Applicants who rely on the financial support of a single parent (mother) to go to college.

Funds Avail.: No stated amount. **To Apply:** Application forms are available on the website. Applicant must provide a personal statement about educational and vocational goals; must have a recommendation letter from a faculty member; must have an official transcript from each undergraduate institution. Application materials must be sent to:

Awards are arranged alphabetically below their administering organizations

Delta Delta Delta, PO Box 5987, Arlington, TX 76005. **Deadline:** March 1.

3393 ■ Donna Axum Whitworth Scholarships
(Undergraduate/Scholarship)

Purpose: To provide financial assistance to qualified undergraduate students. **Focus:** General studies. **Qualif.:** Applicant must be a Delta Iota member at Arkansas; must be an initiated sophomore or junior member. **Criteria:** Applicants will be judge based on academic achievement, campus and community involvement, and financial need.

Funds Avail.: No stated amount. **To Apply:** Application forms are available on the website. Applicant must provide a personal statement about educational and vocational goals; must have a recommendation letter from a faculty member; must have an official transcript from each undergraduate institution. Application materials must be sent to: Delta Delta Delta, PO Box 5987, Arlington, TX 76005. **Deadline:** March 1. **Contact:** For further information, applicants must e-mail Tawnya Braeutigam at tbraeutigam@rideltaeo.org.

3394 ■ Delta Epsilon Sigma (DES)
University of St. Thomas
2115 Summit Ave.
St. Paul, MN 55105-1048
E-mail: desnational@stthomas.edu
URL: www.deltaepsilonsigma.org

3395 ■ Delta Epsilon Sigma Graduate Fellowships *(Graduate/Fellowship)*

Purpose: To provide financial support for the education of member students. **Focus:** General studies. **Qualif.:** Applicants must be junior year members. **Criteria:** Candidates will be judged by the Scholarship Committee based on scholastic achievement, leadership and service activities.

Funds Avail.: $1,000. **To Apply:** Applicants must submit typed application accompanied by three letters of recommendation including one from the Chapter Advisor and official transcripts of all college work through the current fall semester. **Deadline:** March 1. **Contact:** Dr. Thomas Connery at the above address.

3396 ■ Delta Epsilon Sigma Undergraduate Scholarships *(Undergraduate/Scholarship)*

Purpose: To provide financial support for the education of member students. **Focus:** General studies. **Qualif.:** Applicants must be junior year members. **Criteria:** Candidates will be judged by the Scholarship Committee based on scholastic achievement, leadership and service activities.

Funds Avail.: $1,000. **To Apply:** Applicants must submit typed application accompanied by three letters of recommendation including one from the Chapter Advisor and official transcripts of all college work through the current fall semester. **Deadline:** March 1. **Contact:** Dr. Thomas Connery at the above address.

3397 ■ Delta Gamma
3250 Riverside Dr.
Upper Arlington, OH 43221-1725
Ph: (614) 481-8169
Fax: (614) 481-0133
E-mail: dginfo@deltagamma.org
URL: www.deltagamma.org

3398 ■ Delta Gamma Scholarships
(Undergraduate/Scholarship)

Purpose: To encourage the Delta Gammas to pursue a career in science. **Focus:** Science. **Qualif.:** Candidates must have a 3.0 or higher GPA; must be participants in chapter, campus and community leadership activities; must have completed at least three semesters or four quarters of college work. **Criteria:** Grants awarded on a competitive basis.

Funds Avail.: No specific amount. **To Apply:** Applicants must submit a complete Delta Gamma Foundation scholarship application. **Deadline:** January 15. **Contact:** Christine Boring, Dir. of Scholarships and Fellowships at fnscholarfellow@deltagamma.org.

3399 ■ Delta Nu Alpha Transportation Fraternity (DNA)
1720 Manistique Ave.
South Milwaukee, WI 53172-2932
Ph: (414) 764-3063
Fax: (630) 499-8505
E-mail: admin@deltanualpha.org
URL: deltanualpha.org

3400 ■ Delta Nu Alpha Foundation Scholarships *(Undergraduate/Scholarship)*

Purpose: To emphasize financial assistance and mentoring for students, excellent continuing education opportunities for the work force, and vigilance in communicating changes in regulations. **Focus:** Transportation; Logistics. **Qualif.:** Program is open to all students studying in the field of Transportation, Logistics and Supply Chain Management. Students pursuing associate and bachelor degrees are encouraged to apply. **Criteria:** Recipients are selected based on academic success, potential, motivation, career plans, recommendation, evaluation of Faculty members and internship experience related to transportation and logistics.

Funds Avail.: No amount specified. **To Apply:** Applicants must submit a completed application form along with transcripts of all college/university level work completed and two letters of recommendation (one should be from the transportation, logistics or supply chain management instructor). **Deadline:** May 31. **Contact:** Tom Bock DNA Foundation Scholarship Chair, 4123 Apple blossom Rd. Lutz, FL 33558; Phone: 813-288-2640; E-mail:tbock@oilpursys.com.

3401 ■ Delta Phi Epsilon (DPHIE)
251 S Camac St.
Philadelphia, PA 19107
Ph: (215) 732-5901
Fax: (215) 732-5906
E-mail: info@dphie.org
URL: www.dphie.org

3402 ■ Delta Phi Epsilon Educational Foundation Scholarships *(Undergraduate/Scholarship)*

Purpose: To develop social conscience and a willingness to think in terms of the common good in order to assure for its members continuous development and achievement in the collegiate and fraternity world. **Focus:** General studies. **Qualif.:** Applicants must be members of Delta Phi Epsilon

Awards are arranged alphabetically below their administering organizations

or the sons or daughters of members; must be enrolled in undergraduate studies during the academic year. **Criteria:** Scholarships are based on three criteria: service and involvement, academics, and need.

Funds Avail.: $1,000. **Number Awarded:** 4-6. **To Apply:** Application forms are available on the website. Applicant must submit an official transcript of grades, letter of introduction and need for scholarship, typed autobiographical sketch (1,000 words max), two recent photos suitable for publication, letter of recommendation from (must provide at least 2): Chapter President; Chapter Advisor; College Professor or Administrator; High School Teacher/Principal; Alumna; Employer. Applicant must provide a name and address of financial aid director for the school. **Deadline:** March 17. **Contact:** Nicole DeFeo, at ndefeo@dphie.org.

3403 ■ Delta Tau Lambda Sorority (DTL)

PO Box 7714
Ann Arbor, MI 48107
E-mail: dtl-info@deltataulambda.org
URL: www.deltataulambda.org

3404 ■ Lydia Cruz and Sandra Maria Ramos Scholarships *(Undergraduate/Scholarship)*

Purpose: To assist young Latinas in reaching their goals through education. **Focus:** General studies. **Qualif.:** Applicants must be current Latina high school seniors who are entering their first year of college at a two or four year higher learning institution. **Criteria:** Selection of applicant will be based on academic excellence and community service.

Funds Avail.: No specific amount. **Number Awarded:** 1. **To Apply:** Applicant must complete the application form available on the website; must provide the official high school transcript and a copy of University/College Acceptance Letter. Scholarship application materials must be sent to Delta Tau Lambda Sorority, Inc.

3405 ■ Delta Zeta Sorority

202 E Church St.
Oxford, OH 45056
Ph: (513) 523-7597
Fax: (513) 523-1921
E-mail: dzs@dzshq.com
URL: www.deltazeta.org

3406 ■ Sandra Sebrell Bailey Scholarships *(Undergraduate/Scholarship)*

Purpose: To provide financial assistance to all qualified undergraduate students. **Focus:** General studies. **Qualif.:** Applicant must be a junior or senior woman who has been an initiated member at least one year and is in good standing. **Criteria:** Applicants will be evaluated based on academic achievements, financial need, campus leadership and activities, and services to Delta Zeta. Preference will be given to those members entering the field of education.

Funds Avail.: $1,000-$2,500. **To Apply:** Scholarship applications are available on the website and must be completed properly. Applicant must have the FAFSA reply form. **Deadline:** February 15.

3407 ■ Charline Chilson Scholarships *(Undergraduate/Scholarship)*

Purpose: To provide financial assistance for qualified graduate students. **Focus:** Science. **Qualif.:** Applicant must

be a Delta Zeta member in good standing; must be in their junior or senior year or as graduate students; must have a high grade point in their major; must show financial need; must have a history of active leadership and participation in Delta Zeta activities; and must have a commitment to a degree in science. **Criteria:** Applicants will be selected based on academic achievements and financial need.

Funds Avail.: $1,000-$2,500. **To Apply:** Scholarship applications are available on the website and must be completed properly. Applicant must have the FAFSA reply form. **Deadline:** February 15.

3408 ■ Arlene Davis Scholarships *(Undergraduate/Scholarship)*

Purpose: To provide financial assistance to all qualified undergraduate students. **Focus:** Aviation. **Qualif.:** Applicant must be an initiated, active, continuing member entering her sophomore or junior year, who is enrolled in courses showing an interest in aviation; must have a 3.0 grade average. **Criteria:** Candidates will be selected based on academic standing and financial need.

Funds Avail.: $1,000-$2,500. **To Apply:** Scholarship applications are available on the website and must be completed properly. Applicant must have the FAFSA reply form. **Deadline:** February 15.

3409 ■ Delta Zeta Undergraduate Scholarships *(Undergraduate/Scholarship)*

Purpose: To provide financial assistance to all qualified undergraduate students. **Focus:** General studies. **Qualif.:** Applicant must be an initiated, active, continuing member of Delta Zeta entering junior or senior year; must be outstanding in campus and chapter activities, and have maintained at least a B average (3.0). **Criteria:** Scholarship applications will be reviewed and evaluated by the committee. Recommendation for scholarship recipients will be made by the scholarship committees to the Foundation Board of Trustees for final selection.

Funds Avail.: $1,000-$2,500. **To Apply:** Scholarship applications are available on the website and must be completed properly. Applicant must have the FAFSA reply form. **Deadline:** February 15. **Contact:** dzfoundation@dzshq.com.

3410 ■ Elizabeth M. Gruber Scholarships *(Graduate/Scholarship)*

Purpose: To provide financial assistance to all qualified undergraduate student. **Focus:** Liberal arts. **Qualif.:** Applicant must be a Delta Zeta graduate student working toward a degree in a liberal arts area. **Criteria:** Preference will be given to an Alpha Beta Chapter member or to a Delta Zeta attending a university in the Midwest.

Funds Avail.: $1,000-$15,000. **To Apply:** Applicant must provide a transcript of record; must submit a statement indicating their special service to Delta Zeta, activities and/or community involvement, academic honors and/or honor societies, and personal statement about their need and desire to get the award; must have a list of employment records and at least two recommendation letter from a Delta Zeta (Alumnae Chapter President, College Chapter Director, and/or Regional Collegiate Coordinator), and one from Academic Graduate Advisor and/or Employer. **Deadline:** February 15.

3411 ■ Edith Head Scholarships *(Undergraduate/Scholarship)*

Purpose: To provide financial assistance to all qualified undergraduate students. **Focus:** Fashion design. **Qualif.:**

Awards are arranged alphabetically below their administering organizations

Applicant must be an initiated, active, continuing member of Delta Zeta pursuing a course study leading to a career in design, production, and merchandising of textile and apparel products, and/or costume design; must be a junior or senior student, graduate level, or a professional school which offers fashion merchandising, textiles, and clothing or costume design; must have at least a 3.0 average. **Criteria:** Candidates will be selected based on their academic standing and financial need.

Funds Avail.: $1,000-$2,500. **To Apply:** Scholarship applications are available on the website and must be completed properly. Applicant must have the FAFSA reply form. **Deadline:** February 15.

3412 ■ Lavonne Heghinian Scholarships
(Undergraduate/Scholarship)

Purpose: To provide financial assistance to all qualified undergraduate students. **Focus:** General studies. **Qualif.:** Applicant must be an initiated, active, continuing member of Delta Zeta in need of financial assistance; must have a 3.0 average. **Criteria:** Application will be evaluated based on the sorority service, campus involvement and employment. Preference will be given to Southern California applicants in accordance with Mrs. Heghinian's will.

Funds Avail.: $1,000-$2,500. **To Apply:** Scholarship applications are available on the website and must be completed properly. Applicant must have the FAFSA reply form. **Deadline:** February 15.

3413 ■ Houston/Nancy Holliman Scholarships
(Undergraduate/Scholarship)

Purpose: To provide financial assistance to all qualified undergraduate students. **Focus:** Speech and language pathology/audiology; Hearing and deafness; Allied health. **Qualif.:** Applicant must be a junior or senior active, continuing member majoring in hearing and speech, audiology or an allied field; must have an academic achievements (maintaining a 3.0 average), campus honors and activities, and service to Delta Zeta. **Criteria:** Candidates will be selected based on academic standing, honors, and financial need.

Funds Avail.: $1,000-$2,500. **To Apply:** Scholarship applications are available on the website and must be completed properly. Applicant must have the FAFSA reply form. **Deadline:** February 15.

3414 ■ Sarah Jane Houston Scholarships
(Undergraduate/Scholarship)

Purpose: To provide financial assistance to all qualified undergraduate students. **Focus:** Education, English as a second language. **Qualif.:** Applicant must be an undergraduate Delta Zeta member in good standing with 3.0 or higher grade point average; must have a major field in English or in related fields such as speech, debate, drama, theater, or education. **Criteria:** Applicants from Delta Zeta chapters in Illinois will be given preferences if all other qualifications are equal. Applicants will be evaluated based on academic achievements and campus activities.

Funds Avail.: $1,000-$2,500. **To Apply:** Scholarship applications are available in the website and must be completed properly. Applicant must have the FAFSA reply form. **Deadline:** February 15.

3415 ■ Huenefeld/Denton Scholarships
(Undergraduate/Scholarship)

Purpose: To provide financial assistance to all qualified undergraduate students. **Focus:** Child development,

Education, Library and archival sciences. **Qualif.:** Applicant must be a junior or senior initiated, active continuing members in need of financial help, seeking an undergraduate degree in child development/primary education or library science. **Criteria:** Applicants will be evaluated based on their academic achievements, campus activities, and service to Delta Zeta.

Funds Avail.: $1,000-$2,500. **To Apply:** Scholarship applications are available on the website and must be completed properly. Applicant must have the FAFSA reply form. **Deadline:** February 15.

3416 ■ Betsy B. and Garold A. Leach Scholarships for Museum Studies *(Undergraduate/Scholarship)*

Purpose: To provide financial assistance to all qualified undergraduate students. **Focus:** Museum science. **Qualif.:** Applicant must be an initiated, continuing member of Delta Zeta pursuing a course of study that could lead to a career in museum work; must be entering his/her junior or senior year or graduate level; must have a financial need and have at least 3.0 average. **Criteria:** Selection of candidates will be based on academic achievements, and campus activities.

Funds Avail.: $1,000-$2,500. **To Apply:** Scholarship applications are available on the website and must be completed properly. Applicant must have the FAFSA reply form. **Deadline:** February 15.

3417 ■ Elsa Ludeke Graduate Scholarships
(Graduate/Scholarship)

Purpose: To provide financial assistance to all qualified graduate students. **Focus:** General studies. **Qualif.:** Applicant must be an initiated member in need of financial assistance; must have at least a B average (3.0); must be outstanding in undergraduate campus activities and in special service and leadership to Delta Zeta chapter. **Criteria:** Selection of applicant will be based on financial need and academic achievements.

Funds Avail.: $1,000-$15,000. **To Apply:** Applicant must provide a transcript of record; must submit a statement indicating special service to Delta Zeta, activities and/or community involvement, academic honors and/or honor societies, and personal statement about their need and desire to get the award; must have a list of employment records and at least two recommendation letters from a Delta Zeta (Alumnae Chapter President, College Chapter Director, and/or Regional Collegiate Coordinator), and one from Academic Graduate Advisor and/or Employer. **Deadline:** February 15.

3418 ■ John L. and Eleanore I. Mckinley Scholarships *(Undergraduate/Scholarship)*

Purpose: To provide financial assistance to all qualified undergraduate students. **Focus:** General studies. **Qualif.:** Applicant must be a junior or senior Delta Zeta member in good standing; must have earned a B or better average at the conclusion of their sophomore year; must have achieved a high level of service to the Delta Zeta Sorority and her college community. **Criteria:** Financial need is considered.

Funds Avail.: $1,000-$2,500. **To Apply:** Scholarship applications are available on the website and must be completed properly. Applicant must have the FAFSA reply form. **Deadline:** February 15.

Awards are arranged alphabetically below their administering organizations

3419 ■ Helen Woodruff Nolop Scholarships in Audiology and Allied Fields *(Graduate/Scholarship)*

Purpose: To assist qualified female students in pursuing an education. **Focus:** Speech and language pathology/audiology; Allied health. **Qualif.:** Applicant must be a graduate student in audiology or in allied field; must be an initiated continuing member in good standing in a collegiate chapter with 3.0 cumulative grade average. **Criteria:** Selection of applicant will be based on academic achievement and financial need.

Funds Avail.: $1,000-$15,000. **To Apply:** Applicant must provide a transcript of record; must submit a statement indicating special service to Delta Zeta, activities and/or community involvement, academic honors and/or honor societies, and personal statement about need and desire to get the award; must have a list of employment records and at least two recommendation letters from a Delta Zeta (Alumnae Chapter President, College Chapter Director, and/or Regional Collegiate Coordinator), and one from Academic Graduate Advisor and/or Employer. **Deadline:** February 15.

3420 ■ Gail Patrick Charitable Trust Scholarships *(Undergraduate/Scholarship)*

Purpose: To provide financial assistance to all qualified undergraduate student. **Focus:** General studies. **Qualif.:** Applicant must be an initiated, active, continuing Delta Zeta member in need of financial assistance; must be entering her junior or senior year. **Criteria:** Applicant will be evaluated based on academic achievements and campus activities.

Funds Avail.: $15,000-$20,000. **Number Awarded:** Two. **To Apply:** Scholarship applications are available on the website and must be completed properly. Applicant must have the FAFSA reply form. **Deadline:** February 15.

3421 ■ Dorothy Worden Ronken Scholarships *(Graduate/Scholarship)*

Purpose: To provide financial assistance to all qualified graduate students. **Focus:** Education, Business. **Qualif.:** Applicant must be a Delta Zeta graduate student working on a degree in education or business; must be a initiated continuing member in good standing in a collegiate chapter with 3.0 cumulative grade average. **Criteria:** Preference will be given to applicants from the Alpha Alpha chapter of Northwestern University.

Funds Avail.: Amount of the awards may vary depending upon the fund earnings. **To Apply:** Applicant must provide a transcript of record; must submit a statement indicating their special service to Delta Zeta, activities and/or community involvement, academic honors and/or honor societies, and personal statement about need and desire to get the award; must have a list of employment records and at least two recommendation letters from a Delta Zeta (Alumnae Chapter President, College Chapter Director, and/or Regional Collegiate Coordinator), and one from Academic Graduate Advisor and/or employer. **Deadline:** February 15.

3422 ■ Elizabeth Coulter Stephenson Scholarships *(Undergraduate/Scholarship)*

Purpose: To provide financial assistance to all qualified undergraduate students. **Focus:** General studies. **Qualif.:** Applicant must be outstanding in campus and chapter activities; must have held, or must currently hold, an executive board position; must have at least 3.0 average; must have been adversely affected, or parents have been adversely affected by a disaster. **Criteria:** Preference will be given to initiated, active, continuing members of Delta Zeta in their junior or senior year who need a financial assistant.

Funds Avail.: $750. **To Apply:** Application forms are available in the website. Applicant must provide the official transcript; must have statement about special service to Delta Zeta, campus activities and/or community involvement, and academic honors; must have the list of employment record; must submit a recommendation letter from the college chapter director (CCD) and if chapter has no CCD, a letter from RCC will suffice. Application materials must be sent to: Delta Zeta Foundation, 202 E Church St., Oxford, OH 45056. **Deadline:** February 15.

3423 ■ Thornberg/Havens Scholarships *(Undergraduate/Scholarship)*

Purpose: To provide financial assistance to all qualified undergraduate students. **Focus:** General studies. **Qualif.:** Applicant must be an undergraduate and/or graduate Delta Zeta in good standing; must be an initiated member in need of financial assistance who has shown outstanding campus and chapter activities; must have at least 3.0 undergraduate average. **Criteria:** Candidates will be selected based on their academic standing and financial need.

Funds Avail.: $1,000-$2,500. **To Apply:** Scholarship applications are available on the website and must be completed properly. Applicant must have the FAFSA reply form. **Deadline:** February 15.

3424 ■ DeMolay International

10200 NW Ambassador Dr.
Kansas City, MO 64153
Ph: (816) 891-8333
Fax: (816) 891-9062
Free: 800-336-6529
E-mail: demolay@demolay.org
URL: www.demolay.org

3425 ■ Frank S. Land Scholarships *(Undergraduate/Scholarship)*

Purpose: To provide financial assistance for eligible members of DeMolay. **Focus:** General studies. **Qualif.:** Applicants must be active members of DeMolay who have not yet reached their majority or 21st birthday. **Criteria:** Applicants are evaluated based on personal attributes.

Funds Avail.: $1,000. **Number Awarded:** 1. **To Apply:** Applicants may download the scholarship application form from the Foundation's website. **Deadline:** April 1.

3426 ■ York Rite Grand Chapter Royal Arch Masons Scholarships *(Undergraduate/Scholarship)*

Purpose: To support the post-baccalaureate education of the members of DeMolay. **Focus:** General studies. **Qualif.:** Applicants must be active senior DeMolay members. **Criteria:** Applicants are evaluated based on merit.

Funds Avail.: $1,000. **To Apply:** Applicants may download scholarship application form from the foundation's website. **Deadline:** April 1.

3427 ■ Denver Scholarship Foundation (DSF)

303 E 17th Ave., Ste. 200
Denver, CO 80203

Awards are arranged alphabetically below their administering organizations

Ph: (303) 951-4140
Fax: (720) 746-5139
E-mail: info@denverscholarship.org
URL: www.denverscholarship.org

3428 ■ Denver Scholarship Foundation Scholarships *(Undergraduate/Scholarship)*

Purpose: To inspire and empower Denver Public School (DPS) students to achieve their post-secondary goals. **Focus:** General studies. **Qualif.:** Applicant must be a DPS graduate, enrolled and included in the State Census (October 1st Count) at a participating DPS school for at least one year immediately preceding graduation; and eligible to receive federal student financial aid; must be a U.S. citizen, permanent resident or other eligible non-citizen. **Criteria:** Awards are given based on merit and need.

Funds Avail.: $5,000. **To Apply:** Applicants must complete and submit the DSF Scholarship Application online. **Deadline:** April 1. **Remarks:** All mailings, fax coversheets or e-mail messages must include the student's full name, student ID number, phone number and e-mail address.

3429 ■ Department of Business and Professional Regulation (DBPR)

1940 N Monroe St.
Tallahassee, FL 32399-1027
Ph: (850) 487-1395
Fax: (352) 333-2508
Free: 866-532-1440
E-mail: call.center@dbpr.state.fl.us
URL: www.myflorida.com/dbpr

3430 ■ DBPR Division of CPA - BOA Minority Scholarships *(Undergraduate/Scholarship)*

Purpose: To encourage students to remain in school for the fifth year required to sit for the CPA exam. **Focus:** Accounting. **Qualif.:** Applicant must have financial need; a minority; enrolled full-time and must be in the fifth year of an accounting program at an accredited Florida institution and must have a declared major in accounting; must have a minimum GPA of 2.5 on a 4.0 scale; be academically in good standing; and must be a Florida resident. **Criteria:** Selection is based on merit and need.

Funds Avail.: $3,000 per semester. **To Apply:** Applicants must submit a completed application form along with a copy current transcripts; a copy of most recent FAFSA; and a financial release form completed by the financial aid office. **Deadline:** June 1. **Contact:** Veloria A. Kelly at the above address.

3431 ■ Development Fund for Black Students in Science and Technology (DFBSST)

2705 Bladensburg Rd. NE
Washington, DC 20018
Ph: (202) 635-3604
URL: www.dfbsstscholarship.org/

3432 ■ Development Fund for Black Students in Science and Technology Scholarships *(Undergraduate/Scholarship)*

Purpose: To provide scholarships to African American undergraduate students. **Focus:** Science; Technology. **Qua-**

lif.: Applicants must meet the following criteria: African-American heritage; undergraduate students majoring (or intending to major) in a technical field of study (i.e., engineering, math, science, etc.); enrollment at one of the predominantly Black colleges or universities; U.S. citizenship or permanent residency. **Criteria:** Awards will be based on academic achievement, personal essay describing career goals, current and past relevant extracurricular activities, recommendations from teachers and guidance counselors and financial need.

Funds Avail.: $2,000. **To Apply:** Applicants must submit a completed application form. **Deadline:** June 15. **Contact:** Development Fund for Black Students in Science and Technology at the above address.

3433 ■ Diabetes Hope Foundation

6150 Dixie Rd., No. 1
Mississauga, ON, Canada L5T 2E2
Ph: (905) 670-0557
Fax: (905) 565-7296
E-mail: info@diabeteshopefoundation.com
URL: www.diabeteshopefoundation.com

3434 ■ Diabetes Hope Foundation Scholarships *(Undergraduate/Scholarship)*

Purpose: To provide financial assistance to deserving post secondary individuals who are engaged in healthy self management of their diabetes. **Focus:** General studies. **Qualif.:** Applicant must be a resident of Ontario, Canada; must be in the transition year of Diabetes Care by a Pediatric Health Care team; must have received care for type 1 or 2 Diabetes by a Pediatric Health Care team for a minimum of 1 year; must demonstrate competence in self management. **Criteria:** Preference will be given for those who are in need.

Funds Avail.: $2,500. **Number Awarded:** 20. **To Apply:** Applicant must provide an endorsement letter from a member of their Pediatric Health Care team confirming their attendance and documenting successful self-management. **Deadline:** March 5. **Contact:** trisha @ diabeteshopefoundation.com.

3435 ■ Dialog

2250 Perimeter Park Dr., Ste. 300
Morrisville, NC 27560
Ph: (919) 804-6400
Fax: (919) 804-6410
Free: 800-334-2564
E-mail: customer@dialog.com
URL: www.dialog.com

3436 ■ Roger K. Summit Scholarships for North America *(Graduate/Scholarship)*

Purpose: To financially assist students from North America studying library science and related disciplines. **Focus:** Library and archival sciences. **Qualif.:** Applicant must be a student from North America in a graduate degree program in library science and related disciplines. **Criteria:** Award is given based on the application materials submitted.

Funds Avail.: $5,000. **Number Awarded:** 1. **To Apply:** Applicants may contact Betty Jo Hibberd for more information about the scholarships. **Deadline:** April 30. **Remarks:** Established in 1993 in honor of Dialog founder Roger K.

Awards are arranged alphabetically below their administering organizations

Summit. **Contact:** Gabrielle Derriks at gabrielle.derriks@ dialog.com.

3437 ■ Dickey Rural Networks (DRN)

9628 Hwy. 281
Ellendale, ND 58436
Ph: (701) 344-5000
Fax: (701) 344-4300
Free: 877-559-4692
URL: www.drtel.net

3438 ■ Dickey Rural Networks College Scholarship Program (Undergraduate, Vocational/ Occupational/Scholarship)

Purpose: To provide financial assistance for rural high school seniors to further their college education. **Focus:** Telecommunications systems. **Qualif.:** Applicants must be graduating high school seniors; must receive local telecommunications service from a current NTCA member (except for students sponsored by an associate member company); must be accepted by an accredited two or four-year college, university or vocational-technical school; must have at least a C grade point average (GPA); must have academic credentials within an average to above-average range; must express an interest to return to a rural community following graduation; and must be sponsored by a contributor to, or supporter of, the Foundation for Rural Service. **Criteria:** Applicants are evaluated based on academic credentials and financial need.

Funds Avail.: $3,000. **Number Awarded:** 30. **To Apply:** Applicants must complete and print the DRN/FRS Scholarship Application online, which is also available from the school counselor, with the complete instructions and checklist of items to be considered. **Deadline:** February 15.

3439 ■ Bill Dickey Scholarship Association

1140 E Washington St. Ste. 103
Phoenix, AZ 85034
Ph: (602) 258-7851
Fax: (602) 258-3412
E-mail: andrea@bdscholar.org
URL: www.nmjgsa.org

3440 ■ Bill Dickey Scholarship Association Scholarships (Undergraduate/Scholarship)

Purpose: To provide financial support to deserving undergraduate students. **Focus:** General studies. **Qualif.:** Applicants must be high school seniors who are already in BDSA database as well as undergraduate students that previously received a scholarship as freshmen. **Criteria:** Selection will be based on academic achievement, entrance exam scores, financial need, references, evidence of community service and golfing ability.

Funds Avail.: $1,000-$3,500. **To Apply:** Applicants must check the available website to enter their database profile and to gain information regarding this award. **Deadline:** April 30. **Contact:** at the above address.

3441 ■ Dietetics in Health Care Communities (DHCC)

c/o Marla Carlson, Exec. Dir.
2219 Cardinal Dr.
Waterloo, IA 50701
Ph: (319) 235-0991
Fax: (319) 235-7224
E-mail: dhccdpg@mchsi.com
URL: www.dhccdpg.org

3442 ■ DHCC Board Scholarships (Graduate, Professional development, Undergraduate/ Scholarship)

Purpose: To award scholarships to junior or senior level college students, dietetic interns, or graduate students in dietetics who are pursuing an advanced degree. **Focus:** Health care services. **Qualif.:** Applicants must be juniors or senior level college students, dietetic interns, or graduate students who have an interest in practicing as consultant dietitians in health care facilities. **Criteria:** The fund and candidate selection is administered by the ADA Foundation.

Funds Avail.: No specific amount. **To Apply:** Applicants must send an application form (available at the website). **Deadline:** February.

3443 ■ Gaynold Jensen Education Stipends (Postdoctorate, Professional development/ Scholarship)

Purpose: To provide learning programs to improve the contributions of consultant dietitians to health care. **Focus:** Health care services. **Qualif.:** Applicants must be American Dietetic Association members; must be at least a two-year member in Consultant Dietitians in Health Care Facilities; a registered dietitian; currently practicing as a consultant dietitian; planning to expand knowledge in the consultant role. **Criteria:** Recipients are selected based on the committee's review of how and why the program will improve the applicant's contributions as a consultant dietitian in health care.

Funds Avail.: No specific amount. **To Apply:** Applicants must send the application forms (available at the website).

3444 ■ Direct Marketing Educational Foundation (DMEF)

1120 Ave. of the Americas
New York, NY 10036-6700
Ph: (212) 768-7277
Fax: (212) 790-1561
E-mail: dmef@directworks.org
URL: www.the-dma.org/dmef

3445 ■ Mike Buoncristiano Memorial Scholarship Fund (Undergraduate/Scholarship)

Purpose: To help students further their education in the area of direct and interactive marketing. **Focus:** Marketing and distribution. **Qualif.:** Applicants must be U.S. citizens or permanent residents; must be enrolled in an accredited four-year undergraduate institution; must have a minimum GPA of 3.0 on a 4.0 scale in major and have 3.0 overall; must show a commitment to pursue a career in direct/ interactive marketing. **Criteria:** Selection is based on evaluation of submitted documents and specific criteria.

Funds Avail.: $1,000 to $5,000. **To Apply:** Applicants must submit a completed application form; official transcripts and resume. **Contact:** Jim Wu at jwu@directworks.org.

3446 ■ Mark Duda Scholarship Fund (Graduate, Undergraduate/Scholarship)

Purpose: To provide financial assistance to students studying data and targeting strategies in direct and interactive

Awards are arranged alphabetically below their administering organizations

marketing. **Focus:** Marketing and distribution. **Qualif.:** Applicants must be U.S. citizens or permanent residents; must be enrolled in an accredited four-year undergraduate institution or be graduate students; must have a minimum GPA of 3.0 on a 4.0 scale in major and have 3.0 overall; must show a commitment to pursue a career in direct/interactive marketing. **Criteria:** Selection is based on evaluation of submitted documents and specific criteria.

Funds Avail.: $1,000 to $5,000. **To Apply:** Applicants should submit a completed application form, official transcripts and resume. **Contact:** Jim Wu at jwu@directworks.org.

3447 ■ Lee Epstein Scholarship Fund *(Graduate, Undergraduate/Scholarship)*

Purpose: To help students further their education in the area of direct and interactive marketing. **Focus:** Marketing and distribution. **Qualif.:** Applicants must be U.S. citizens or permanent residents; must be enrolled in an accredited four-year undergraduate institution or should be graduate students; must have a minimum GPA of 3.0 on a 4.0 scale in major and have 3.0 overall; must show a commitment to pursue a career in direct/interactive marketing. **Criteria:** Selection is based on evaluation of submitted documents and specific criteria.

Funds Avail.: $1,000 to $5,000. **To Apply:** Applicants must submit a completed application form, an official transcript of records and resume. **Contact:** Jim Wu at jwu@directworks.org.

3448 ■ Dave Florence Scholarship Fund *(Undergraduate/Scholarship)*

Purpose: To help students further their education in the area of direct and interactive marketing. **Focus:** Marketing and distribution. **Qualif.:** Applicants must be U.S. citizens or permanent residents; must be enrolled in an accredited four-year undergraduate institution; must have a minimum GPA of 3.0 on a 4.0 scale in major and have 3.0 overall; must show a commitment to pursue a career in direct/interactive marketing. **Criteria:** Selection is based on evaluation of submitted documents and specific criteria.

Funds Avail.: $1,000 to $5,000. **To Apply:** Applicants must submit a completed application form, official transcripts and resume. **Contact:** Jim Wu at jwu@directworks.org.

3449 ■ Don Kuhn Memorial Scholarship Fund *(Graduate/Scholarship)*

Purpose: To provide financial assistance to deserving graduate students with a demonstrated commitment to pursue a career in non-profit direct/interactive marketing. **Focus:** Marketing and distribution. **Qualif.:** Applicants must be U.S. citizens or permanent residents; must be graduate students enrolled in an accredited four-year institution; must have a minimum GPA of 3.0 on a 4.0 scale in major and have 3.0 overall; must show commitment to pursue a career in direct/interactive marketing. **Criteria:** Selection is based on evaluation of submitted documents and specific criteria.

Funds Avail.: $1,000 to $5,000. **To Apply:** Applicants must submit a completed application form, official transcripts and resume. **Contact:** Jim Wu at jwu@directworks.org.

3450 ■ Willa Yeck Memorial Scholarship Fund *(Undergraduate/Scholarship)*

Purpose: To help students further their education in the area of direct and interactive marketing. **Focus:** Marketing and distribution. **Qualif.:** Applicants must be U.S. citizens

or permanent residents; must be enrolled in an accredited four-year undergraduate institution; must have a minimum GPA of 3.0 on a 4.0 scale in major and have 3.0 overall; must show a commitment to pursue a career in direct/interactive marketing. **Criteria:** Selection is based on evaluation of submitted documents and specific criteria.

Funds Avail.: $1,000 to $5,000. **To Apply:** Applicants must submit a completed application form, official transcripts and resume. **Contact:** Jim Wu at jwu@directworks.org.

3451 ■ Lorraine Zitone Memorial Scholarship Fund *(Undergraduate/Scholarship)*

Purpose: To help students further their education in the area of direct and interactive marketing. **Focus:** Marketing and distribution. **Qualif.:** Applicants must be U.S. citizens or permanent residents; must be enrolled in an accredited four-year undergraduate institution; must have a minimum GPA of 3.0 on a 4.0 scale in major and have 3.0 overall; must show a commitment to pursue a career in direct/interactive marketing. **Criteria:** Selection is based on evaluation of submitted documents and specific criteria.

Funds Avail.: $1,000 to $5,000. **To Apply:** Applicants must submit a completed application form, official transcripts and resume. **Contact:** Jim Wu at jwu@directworks.org.

3452 ■ Direct Marketing Fundraisers Association (DMFA)
PO Box 1038
New York, NY 10028
Ph: (646) 675-7314
Fax: (201) 266-4006
E-mail: info@dmfa.org
URL: www.dmfa.org

3453 ■ Sanky Perlowin Memorial Scholarships *(Undergraduate/Scholarship)*

Purpose: To enhance the skills of a new member in direct marketing fundraising. **Focus:** Marketing and distribution. **Qualif.:** Students must be involved or interested in fundraising by direct mail and related techniques. **Criteria:** Recipients are selected based on the on information submitted in writing by current DMFA members.

Funds Avail.: $500 plus membership to DMFA for one year. **To Apply:** Applicants must be nominated by a current DMFA member. Nomination forms are available online. **Remarks:** Mrs. Sanky Perlowin was the head of Sanky Perlowin Associates, a direct mail fundraising consulting firm.

3454 ■ Directed Energy Professional Society (DEPS)
7770 Jefferson St. NE, Ste. 440
Albuquerque, NM 87109
Ph: (505) 998-4910
Fax: (505) 998-4917
E-mail: office@deps.org
URL: www.deps.org

3455 ■ DEPS Graduate Scholarship Program *(Graduate/Scholarship)*

Purpose: To foster research and development of DE technology for national defense and civil applications through professional communication and education. **Focus:**

Awards are arranged alphabetically below their administering organizations

Physics; Engineering, Electrical; Engineering, Chemical; Chemistry; Materials research/science; Optical engineering; Engineering, Aerospace/Aeronautical/Astronautical; Engineering, Optical. **Qualif.:** Applicants must be U.S. citizens or individuals who have demonstrated interest in American citizenship; must be full-time graduate students at a U.S. school; must be pursuing or currently studying DE technology areas of HEL or HPM with scopes similar to those researches published in the Journal of Directed Energy. **Criteria:** Applicants are selected based on the reviews conducted by the DEPS Board of Scientific and Engineering Advisors' (BSEA).

Funds Avail.: $10,000. **To Apply:** Applicants must submit completed application form available at the website; official transcripts of undergraduate and graduate studies sent directly from the school; letter of interest in DE technology and statement of proposed research; and a reference letter from a potential or current research advisor including an assessment of the applicant's potential and description of facilities to be employed for the research; and letter of intent to become U.S. citizen. **Deadline:** April 2. **Contact:** Questions should be directed to Dr. Sam Blankenship at the above address or e-mail him at sam@deps.org.

3456 ■ Directors of Health Promotion and Education

1015 18th St. NW, 3rd Fl.
Washington, DC 20036
Ph: (202) 659-2230
Fax: (202) 659-2339
URL: www.dhpe.org

3457 ■ Scholarships for Leadership Training and Coaching (Professional development/ Scholarship)

Purpose: To provide financial assistance for individuals intending to enroll in leadership-related courses. **Focus:** Leadership, Institutional and community; Public health. **Qualif.:** Program is open to DHPE dues-paid members seeking professional development through leadership-related courses or leadership coaching. **Criteria:** Applicant will be assessed based on the application form submitted describing the leadership training opportunity in sufficient detail to evaluate its credentials and content (for training awards), goals and outcomes of coaching (for coaching awards), commitment by the supervisor to allow participation in the training and amount requested.

Funds Avail.: $500 up to $2,000. **To Apply:** Applicants must submit the completed application form provided by the scholarship committee. **Contact:** Jo Schram, jo.schram@bluopal.com; Pam Edison, pam.edison@dhpe.org.

3458 ■ Disabled American Veterans (DAV)

PO Box 14301
Cincinnati, OH 45250-0301
Ph: (859) 441-7300
Free: 877-426-2838
URL: www.dav.org

3459 ■ Jesse Brown Memorial Youth Scholarship Program (All/Scholarship)

Purpose: To provide financial assistance to young volunteers who play active roles in the Department of Veterans Affairs Voluntary Service programs to continue their education. **Focus:** General studies. **Qualif.:** Applicants must be any volunteers who are at the age of 21 or younger and have volunteered for a minimum of 100 hours at a VA medical center during the previous year; immediate family members of the DAV national organization are also eligible. **Criteria:** Applicants will be evaluated based on criteria designed by the Scholarship Selection Committee.

Funds Avail.: No specific amount. **To Apply:** Nominations must be submitted by the Voluntary Service Program Manager at the VA medical center, DAV Department Commander. Students must submit a self-nomination form which is available online, including an essay and any supporting documentation. **Deadline:** February 26.

3460 ■ Distinguished Flying Cross Society (DFCS)

PO Box 530250
San Diego, CA 92153
Free: 866-332-6332
E-mail: dfcs@dfcsociety.org
URL: www.dfcsociety.org

3461 ■ Distinguished Flying Cross Society Scholarships (Undergraduate/Scholarship)

Purpose: To support dependents of DFC Society members in the pursuit of continuing higher education. **Focus:** Aviation. **Qualif.:** Applicants must be descendants (or legally adopted children) of a DFC Society member; must be attending the Spring Semester at an accredited institution of higher education in the pursuit of an undergraduate degree. **Criteria:** Recipients will be selected based on academic achievement.

Funds Avail.: $1,000. **Number Awarded:** Four. **To Apply:** Applicants must provide (500-word) essay on why they deserve a DFCS Scholarship; SAT/SCAT scores; official high school transcript; and a letter from DFCS member attesting that he/she is a descendant of a DFCS member. **Deadline:** November 15.

3462 ■ Distinguished Young Women

751 Government St.
Mobile, AL 36602
Ph: (251) 438-3621
Fax: (251) 431-0063
Free: 800-256-5435
E-mail: beckyjo@distinguishedyw.org
URL: www.ajm.org

3463 ■ Distinguished Young Women Scholarships (Undergraduate/Scholarship)

Purpose: To give every young woman the opportunity to further their education and prepare for a successful future. **Focus:** General studies. **Qualif.:** Applicant must be enrolled in her chosen field of study at an approved school or institution. **Criteria:** Selection will be based on the submitted application.

Funds Avail.: No specific amount. **To Apply:** Applicant must submit a completed application and must complete a Scholarship Funds Request and Transcript Release Statement from and return it to the Foundation.

3464 ■ Dixon Hughes Goodman, LLP

440 Monticello Ave., Ste. 1400
Norfolk, VA 23510

Awards are arranged alphabetically below their administering organizations

Ph: (757) 624-5100
Fax: (757) 624-5233
Free: 866-455-3261
URL: www.dhgllp.com

3465 ■ Dixon Hughes Goodman LLP Annual Scholarship *(Undergraduate/Scholarship)*

Purpose: To help promising students pursue public accounting as a profession. **Focus:** Accounting. **Qualif.:** Applicant must be a U.S. citizen; a junior or senior accounting major; currently enrolled in an accredited Virginia college or university with the intent to take the CPA Exam; and have a minimum overall and accounting GPA of 3.0 or higher. **Criteria:** Award is given based on the merit of the application.

Funds Avail.: $2,500. **Number Awarded:** 1. **To Apply:** Applicants must submit a completed scholarship application together with the essay; letter of recommendation from a faculty member; a current resume; and recent official transcript reflecting GPA; application must be typed or printed.

3466 ■ Dollar-A-Day Scholarship Fund

PO Box 811882
Boca Raton, FL 33481-1882
Free: 888-728-2521
E-mail: info@muslimscholarship.org
URL: www.muslimscholarship.org

3467 ■ Dollar-A-Day Academic Scholarships *(Graduate, Undergraduate/Scholarship)*

Purpose: To provide educational assistance to Muslim university students in their chosen field of study. **Focus:** General studies. **Qualif.:** Applicants must be college or graduate students; must be Muslims; be U.S. citizens or permanent residents in the United States; must demonstrate financial need; and have filed the FAFSA for the applicable year. **Criteria:** Selection will be based on evaluation of submitted documents and specific criteria.

Funds Avail.: $1,000. **To Apply:** Applicants must submit a completed application form; university enrollment form; most recent transcripts; two recommendation letters; student aid report; and updated resume. **Deadline:** August 26.

3468 ■ Dolphin Scholarship Foundation

4966 Euclid Rd., Ste. 109
Virginia Beach, VA 23462
Ph: (757) 671-3200
Fax: (757) 671-3330
E-mail: info@dolphinscholarship.org
URL: www.dolphinscholarship.org

3469 ■ Dolphin Scholarships *(Undergraduate/ Scholarship)*

Purpose: To support the education of children/stepchildren of members or former members of the Submarine Force or who have served in the Submarine Force. **Focus:** General studies. **Qualif.:** Applicant must be a high school senior or college student; child or stepchild of a member or former member of the U.S. Navy Submarine Force; unmarried; under age 24; must attend a four-year accredited college or university and intend to work toward a BS or BA degree.

Criteria: Scholarships are awarded based on academic proficiency, financial need and commitment to and excellence in school and community activities.

Funds Avail.: Varies. **Number Awarded:** Varies. **To Apply:** Applicants must submit a completed scholarship application form. **Contact:** scholars@dolphinscholarship.org.

3470 ■ Dominican Bar Association (DBA)

PO Box 203
New York, NY 10013
E-mail: president@dominicanbarassociation.com
URL: www.dominicanbarassociation.org

3471 ■ DBA Law School Scholarship Program *(Undergraduate/Scholarship)*

Purpose: To help undergraduate students pursue their education in a law school. **Focus:** Law. **Qualif.:** Applicants must be first, second or third year undergraduate students in the field of law; must be enrolled full-time or part-time. **Criteria:** Applicants will be evaluated based on demonstrated involvement in and commitment to serve the Latino community through the legal profession, academic, personal achievement and financial need.

Funds Avail.: $3,000. **To Apply:** Applicants must submit a completed and signed DBA scholarship application form, current resume, cover letter, an official undergraduate transcript or a photocopy and letter from the law school's financial aid office indicating the amount of aid awarded. **Deadline:** May 15.

3472 ■ Douglas-Coldwell Foundation (DCF)

300-279 Laurier Ave. W
Ottawa, ON, Canada K1P 5J9
Ph: (613) 232-1918
Fax: (613) 230-9950
E-mail: info@dcf.ca
URL: www.dcf.ca

3473 ■ Beverlee Bell Scholarships in Human Rights and Democracy *(Graduate/Scholarship)*

Purpose: To provide support to qualified students who want to pursue their education. **Focus:** Human rights. **Qualif.:** Applicants must be graduate students making a significant contribution to human rights and democracy in developing countries. **Criteria:** Applicants are selected based on the committee's review of the application materials.

Funds Avail.: $1,000. **To Apply:** Applicants are advised to contact the Carleton University, Academic Department, 1125 Colonel By Dr., Ottawa, ON for further information about the scholarship application form and requirements. **Deadline:** January. **Remarks:** Established in 2002 to honor the memory of NDP activist Beverlee Bell, by her family and the Douglas-Coldwell Foundation.

3474 ■ Douglas-Coldwell Foundation Scholarships in Social Affairs *(Graduate/Scholarship)*

Purpose: To support deserving student who wants to pursue their study. **Focus:** Education, English as a second language; History; Political science; Social work; Sociology. **Qualif.:** Applicants must be fully-qualified graduate students preparing a thesis on a topic involving some aspect of Canadian social theory or history. **Criteria:** Applicants are selected based on the Scholarship Commit-

Awards are arranged alphabetically below their administering organizations

tee's review of the application materials.

Funds Avail.: $3,000. **To Apply:** Scholarship application form and requirements are available at University of Regina, Graduate Studies and Research. **Deadline:** October 31.

3475 ■ Kalmen Kaplansky Scholarships in Economic and Social Rights (Graduate/Scholarship)

Purpose: To provide support to qualified students who want to pursue their education. **Focus:** Economics; Civil rights. **Qualif.:** Applicants must be graduate students researching economic and social rights in a School or Department in the Faculty of Public Affairs and Management at Carleton University. **Criteria:** Recipients will be selected based on their research work.

Funds Avail.: $1,000. **To Apply:** Applicants are advised to contact the Carleton University, Academic Unit, 1125 Colonel By Dr., Ottawa, ON for further information about the scholarship application form and other requirements. **Deadline:** February 1. **Remarks:** Scholarship was established in 1998 by the Douglas-Coldwell Foundation in honor of the lifetime achievement of Dr. Kalmen Kaplansky, labor and human rights advocate, in the field of economic and social rights.

3476 ■ Downeast Energy and Building Supply

18 Spring St.
Brunswick, ME 04011
Free: 800-339-9921
URL: www.downeastenergy.com

3477 ■ Downeast Energy Scholarships
(Undergraduate/Scholarship)

Purpose: To provide financial assistance to children of full-time or seasonal Downeast Energy's Maine and New Hampshire employees who are seeking higher education. **Focus:** General studies. **Qualif.:** Applicants must be students who are high school seniors or graduates planning to enroll, or students already enrolled in a full-time course of study leading to a bachelor's degree at an accredited post-secondary college or university, an associate's degree at a junior or community post secondary school, or a certificate at an approved vocational technical institute. **Criteria:** Award will be based on a combination of selection factors including, but not limited to, scholastic merit and participation in extracurricular activities.

Funds Avail.: $1,000. **To Apply:** Applicant must submit completed word process application; transcripts of high school; two or more non-family character references; and a word processed cover letter describing your intended course of study and anything else that might help us in our decision. **Deadline:** April 1. **Contact:** Betsy Morrell at 207-319-1321 or betsy@downeastenergy.com.

3478 ■ Drake University Law School

2621 Carpenter Ave.
Des Moines, IA 50311
Ph: (515) 271-2824
Free: 800-443-7253
URL: www.law.drake.edu/

3479 ■ William Stone Ayres Scholarships
(Undergraduate/Scholarship)

Purpose: To support the education of law students. **Focus:** Law. **Qualif.:** Applicants must be students of Drake University law school. **Criteria:** Recipients are selected based on academic record and financial need.

Funds Avail.: No specific amount. **To Apply:** Applicants must file FAFSA and application form. **Remarks:** Established by a bequest from Gladys L. Ayres in memory of her husband, a 1894 Law School graduate. **Contact:** Office of Admission and Financial Aid at 515-271-2782.

3480 ■ Beverly Estate Scholarships
(Undergraduate/Scholarship)

Purpose: To support the education of law students. **Focus:** Law. **Qualif.:** Applicants must be students of Drake University law school. **Criteria:** Recipients are selected based on academic record and financial need.

Funds Avail.: No specific amount. **To Apply:** Applicants must file FAFSA and application form. **Remarks:** Awards are made possible by bequests from Francis Cecile Beverly, LW'15, and Adda Brown Beverly, ED'14. **Contact:** Office of Admission and Financial Aid at 515-271-2782.

3481 ■ George and Mary Brammer Scholarships (Undergraduate/Scholarship)

Purpose: To support the education of law students. **Focus:** Law. **Qualif.:** Applicants must be students of Drake University law school. **Criteria:** Recipients are selected based on academic record and financial need.

Funds Avail.: No specific amount. **To Apply:** Applicants must file FAFSA and application form. **Remarks:** Established by Mary and John Harper as a memorial to Mary's parents, 1908 and 1907 graduates of the Law School. **Contact:** Office of Admission and Financial Aid at 515-271-2782.

3482 ■ Gregory Brunk Scholarships
(Undergraduate/Scholarship)

Purpose: To support the education of law students. **Focus:** Law. **Qualif.:** Applicants must be students of Drake University law school. **Criteria:** Recipients are selected based on academic record and financial need.

Funds Avail.: No specific amount. **To Apply:** Applicants must file the FAFSA and application form. **Remarks:** The scholarship was made available by the late Gregory Brunk, LW'19. **Contact:** Office of Admission and Financial Aid at 515-271-2782.

3483 ■ Donald C. and Doris K. Byers Scholarships (Undergraduate/Scholarship)

Purpose: To support the education of law students. **Focus:** Law. **Qualif.:** Applicants must be entering first year students. **Criteria:** Recipients are selected based on merit and financial need. Preferences are given to residents of Newton, Iowa and the surrounding area of Jasper County, Iowa.

Funds Avail.: No specific amount. **To Apply:** Applicants must submit a completed application form. **Deadline:** April 1. **Remarks:** Sponsored by Donald C. and Doris K. Byers. **Contact:** Office of Admission and Financial Aid at 515-271-2782.

3484 ■ Raymond DiPaglia Endowment Scholarships (Undergraduate/Scholarship)

Purpose: To support the education of law students. **Focus:** Law. **Qualif.:** Applicants must be returning law students who are in good standing at the Drake University law school. **Criteria:** Recipients are selected based on aca-

Awards are arranged alphabetically below their administering organizations

demic record and financial need.

Funds Avail.: No specific amount. **To Apply:** Applicants must file FAFSA and application form. **Contact:** Office of Admission and Financial Aid at 515-271-2782.

3485 ■ Grace O. Doane Scholarships
(Undergraduate/Scholarship)

Purpose: To support the education of law students. **Focus:** Law. **Qualif.:** Applicants must be second year Iowa residents who rank in the top one-half of their class. **Criteria:** Recipients are selected based on academic record and financial need.

Funds Avail.: No specific amount. **To Apply:** Applicants must file FAFSA and an application form. **Contact:** Office of Admission and Financial Aid at 515-271-2782.

3486 ■ Joseph M. Dorgan Scholarships
(Undergraduate/Scholarship)

Purpose: To support the education of law students. **Focus:** Law. **Qualif.:** Applicants must be African American law students. **Criteria:** Recipients are selected based on academic record and financial need.

Funds Avail.: No specific amount. **To Apply:** Applicants must file FAFSA and application form. **Contact:** Office of Admission and Financial Aid at 515-271-2782.

3487 ■ Drake University Law School Law Opportunity Scholarships - Disadvantage
(Undergraduate/Scholarship)

Purpose: To support the education of disadvantaged law students. **Focus:** Law. **Qualif.:** Applicants must have been admitted to the Law School and must demonstrate financial need as determined by the Free Application for Federal Student Aid. **Criteria:** Recipients will be selected based on the following factors: (1) applicant's showing of diversity, disadvantage or both; (2) academic record; (3) personal achievements and leadership; and (4) financial need. Preferences are given to students whose enrollment will significantly contribute to the diversity of the Drake Law School student body, or to those who have overcome economic, educational or other significant disadvantages.

Funds Avail.: One-quarter tuition to full-tuition awards. **To Apply:** Applicants must have the FAFSA form completed between January 1 and March 1, and must submit the completed scholarship application form. **Remarks:** Disadvantaged student is defined as: "one who, despite facing significant obstacles, has prepared himself or herself for a college education.". **Contact:** Office of Admission and Financial Aid at 515-271-2782.

3488 ■ Drake University Law School Law Opportunity Scholarships - Diversity
(Undergraduate/Scholarship)

Purpose: To promote the diversity of students in Drake University. **Focus:** Law. **Qualif.:** Applicants must have been admitted to the law school and must demonstrate financial need as determined by the Free Application for Federal Student Aid. **Criteria:** Recipients will be selected based on the following factors: (1) applicant's showing of diversity, disadvantage or both; (2) academic record; (3) personal achievements and leadership; and (4) financial need. Preferences are given to students whose enrollment will significantly contribute to the diversity of the Drake University law school student body, or to those who have overcome economic, educational or other significant disadvantages.

Funds Avail.: One-quarter tuition to full-tuition awards. **To Apply:** Applicants must have the FAFSA form completed between January 1 and March 1, and must submit the completed scholarship application form. **Contact:** Office of Admission and Financial Aid at 515-271-2782.

3489 ■ Drake University Law School Public Service Scholarships *(Undergraduate/ Scholarship)*

Purpose: To support the education of law students. **Focus:** Law. **Qualif.:** Applicants must exhibit an extraordinary history of public service work and plan to continue that commitment during and after law school. **Criteria:** Recipients are selected based on merit and need.

Funds Avail.: Full-tuition. **Number Awarded:** 2. **To Apply:** Applicants must submit completed application form along with essay, a short description of past work experiences/ activities, letters of recommendation, relevant academic curriculum and statement of reasons for award. **Deadline:** March 1. **Contact:** Office of Admission and Financial Aid at 515-271-2782.

3490 ■ Robert E. Early Memorial Scholarships
(Undergraduate/Scholarship)

Purpose: To support the education of law students. **Focus:** Law. **Qualif.:** Applicants must be second or third year full time students who are in need of financial assistance. **Criteria:** Recipients are selected based on academic records and financial need.

Funds Avail.: No specific amount. **To Apply:** Applicants must file FAFSA and application form. **Remarks:** Sponsored by Margaret M. Early in memory of her husband, LW'41. **Contact:** Office of Admission and Financial Aid at 515-271-2782.

3491 ■ Electric Cooperative Pioneer Trust Fund Scholarships *(Undergraduate/Scholarship)*

Purpose: To support the education of law students. **Focus:** Law. **Qualif.:** Applicants must be second or third year law students interested in agricultural law. **Criteria:** Recipients are selected based on merit. Preference is given to students planning to practice in Iowa.

Funds Avail.: No specific amount. **To Apply:** Applicants may contact Office of Admission and Financial Aid for more information. **Contact:** Office of Admission and Financial Aid at 515-271-2782.

3492 ■ Herman E. Elgar Memorial Scholarships
(Undergraduate/Scholarship)

Purpose: To support the education of law students. **Focus:** Law. **Qualif.:** Applicants must be third year law students. **Criteria:** Recipients are selected based on academic record and financial need.

Funds Avail.: No specific amount. **To Apply:** Applicants must file FAFSA and application form. **Remarks:** Established in memory of Mr. Elgar, LW'11, by his wife and children, John, LW'50, and Alanson, LW'51 and Elizabeth Elgar Anderson, ED'41. **Contact:** Office of Admission and Financial Aid at 515-271-2782.

3493 ■ D.J. Fairgrave Education Trust
(Undergraduate/Scholarship)

Purpose: To support the education of law students. **Focus:** Law. **Qualif.:** Applicants must be students of Drake University law school. **Criteria:** Recipients are selected based on financial need; character; academic record;

Awards are arranged alphabetically below their administering organizations

personal achievements; future goals and anticipated contributions to the profession.

Funds Avail.: No specific amount. **Number Awarded:** 1. **To Apply:** Applicants must file FAFSA and application form. **Remarks:** Established by Denio John Fairgrave. **Contact:** Office of Admission and Financial Aid at 515-271-2782.

3494 ■ Leland Stanford Forrest Scholarships
(Undergraduate/Scholarship)

Purpose: To support the education of law students. **Focus:** Law. **Qualif.:** Applicants must be students who are graduates of Iowa high schools or colleges; must be students whose high school and college experiences took place outside the state. **Criteria:** Recipients are selected from among entering students who are graduates of Iowa high schools or colleges.

Funds Avail.: No specific amount. **To Apply:** Applicants must fill up the General Information Form of Scholarship. **Remarks:** Scholarship was established through the bequest of Leland Stanford Forrest, former dean of the law school.

3495 ■ Lex and Scott Hawkins Endowed Scholarships *(Undergraduate/Scholarship)*

Purpose: To support the education of law students. **Focus:** Law. **Qualif.:** Applicants must be the president of the Law School's Moot Court Board. **Criteria:** Recipients are selected based on merit.

Funds Avail.: No specific amount. **To Apply:** Applicants may contact Office of Admission and Financial Aid for more information. **Remarks:** Established by Lex Hawkins, LW'51 and Scott Hawkins, LW'81. **Contact:** Office of Admission and Financial Aid at 515-271-2782.

3496 ■ Edward and Cora Hayes Scholarships
(Undergraduate/Scholarship)

Purpose: To support the education of law students. **Focus:** Law. **Qualif.:** Applicants must be accepted as first year students at Drake University law school and not a graduate of Iowa high schools or colleges; and must be students whose high school and college experiences took place outside the state. **Criteria:** Recipients are selected based on merit.

Funds Avail.: No specific amount. **To Apply:** Applicants must fill up the General Information Form of Scholarship. **Remarks:** Established by the former associate dean Edward Hayes and his wife.

3497 ■ Annamae Heaps Law Scholarships
(Undergraduate/Scholarship)

Purpose: To support the education of law students. **Focus:** Law. **Qualif.:** Applicants must be second year students demonstrating financial need. **Criteria:** Recipients are selected based on academic record and financial need.

Funds Avail.: No specific amount. **To Apply:** Applicants must file FAFSA and application form. **Contact:** Office of Admission and Financial Aid at 515-271-2782.

3498 ■ John M. Helmick Law Scholarships
(Undergraduate/Scholarship)

Purpose: To support the education of law students. **Focus:** Law. **Qualif.:** Applicants must be students of Iowa backgrounds planning to enter the legal or educational professions in Iowa. **Criteria:** Recipients are selected based on academic record and financial need.

Funds Avail.: No specific amount. **To Apply:** Applicants must file FAFSA and application form. **Remarks:** Sponsored by Robert H. Helmick, LW'60, in memory of his grandfather, John Miller Helmick. **Contact:** Office of Admission and Financial Aid at 515-271-2782.

3499 ■ James P. Irish Scholarships
(Undergraduate/Scholarship)

Purpose: To support the education of law students. **Focus:** Law. **Qualif.:** Applicants must be from Southeast Polk High School or members of the Law Review Board of Editor. **Criteria:** Recipients are selected based on merit.

Funds Avail.: No specific amount. **To Apply:** Applicants may contact Office of Admission and Financial Aid for more information. **Remarks:** Established by Edwin Skinner and Donald Beattie in honor of their associate and law partner, James P. Irish, LW'31. **Contact:** Office of Admission and Financial Aid at 515-271-2782.

3500 ■ Edward H. Jones Scholarships
(Undergraduate/Scholarship)

Purpose: To support the education of law students. **Focus:** Law. **Qualif.:** Applicants must be second year law students. **Criteria:** Recipients are selected based on merit.

Funds Avail.: $2,000. **To Apply:** Applicants must submit a completed scholarship application form. **Remarks:** Established in honor of the late Edward H. Jones, former executive director of the Iowa State Bar Association. **Contact:** Office of Admission and Financial Aid at 515-271-2782.

3501 ■ Martin Luther King Law Scholarships
(Undergraduate/Scholarship)

Purpose: To support the education of law students. **Focus:** Law. **Qualif.:** Applicants must be female African-American law students who embodies the spirit and values of Martin Luther King and who have demonstrated financial need. **Criteria:** Recipients are selected based on academic record and financial need.

Funds Avail.: No specific amount. **To Apply:** Applicants must file FAFSA and application form. **Remarks:** Established by Naomi Mercer, LW'68. **Contact:** Office of Admission and Financial Aid at 515-271-2782.

3502 ■ Forest A. King Scholarships
(Undergraduate/Scholarship)

Purpose: To support the education of law students. **Focus:** Law. **Qualif.:** Applicants must be students of Drake University law school. **Criteria:** Recipients are selected based on academic record and financial need.

Funds Avail.: No specific amount. **To Apply:** Applicants must file FAFSA and application form. **Remarks:** Established in memory of Mr. King, LW'25, by his wife, Nonnie. **Contact:** Office of Admission and Financial Aid at 515-271-2782.

3503 ■ Verne Lawyer Scholarships
(Undergraduate/Scholarship)

Purpose: To support the education of law students. **Focus:** Law. **Qualif.:** Applicants must be students of Drake University Law School. **Criteria:** Recipients are selected based on academic record and financial need.

Funds Avail.: No specific amount. **To Apply:** Applicants must file FAFSA and application form. **Remarks:** Established in 1992 in honor of D. Verne Lawyer, a 1949 graduate of the Law School. **Contact:** Office of Admission and

Awards are arranged alphabetically below their administering organizations

Financial Aid at 515-271-2782.

3504 ■ League of Attorneys' Wives Scholarships (Undergraduate/Scholarship)

Purpose: To support the education of law students. **Focus:** Law. **Qualif.:** Applicants must be second year or third year female law students planning a career in public interest law. **Criteria:** Recipients are selected based on academic record and financial need.

Funds Avail.: No specific amount. **To Apply:** Applicants must file FAFSA and application form. **Contact:** Office of Admission and Financial Aid at 515-271-2782.

3505 ■ Legal Research Service Scholarships (Undergraduate/Scholarship)

Purpose: To support the education of law students. **Focus:** Law. **Qualif.:** Applicants must be the presidents of the Student Legal Research Service. **Criteria:** Recipients are selected based on merit.

Funds Avail.: No specific amount. **To Apply:** Applicants may contact Office of Admission and Financial Aid for more information. **Contact:** Office of Admission and Financial Aid at 515-271-2782.

3506 ■ Frederick D. Lewis Jr. Scholarships (Undergraduate/Scholarship)

Purpose: To support the education of law students. **Focus:** Law. **Qualif.:** Applicants must be students of Drake University law school. **Criteria:** Recipients are selected based on academic record and financial need.

Funds Avail.: No specific amount. **To Apply:** Applicants must file FAFSA and application form. **Remarks:** Established by Patrick D. Kelly, LW'53, in memory of Frederick D. Lewis Jr., a professor at Drake Law School from 1949 to 1959. **Contact:** Office of Admission and Financial Aid at 515-271-2782.

3507 ■ Gordon and Delores Madson Scholarships (Undergraduate/Scholarship)

Purpose: To support the education of law students. **Focus:** Law. **Qualif.:** Applicants must be students of Drake University law school. **Criteria:** Recipients are selected based on academic record and financial need.

Funds Avail.: No specific amount. **To Apply:** Applicants must file FAFSA and application form. **Remarks:** Established by Gordon Madson, LW'57, and his wife, Delores. **Contact:** Office of Admission and Financial Aid at 515-271-2782.

3508 ■ Jake S. More Scholarships (Undergraduate/Scholarship)

Purpose: To support the education of law students. **Focus:** Law. **Qualif.:** Applicants must be students of Drake University law school. **Criteria:** Recipients are selected based on academic record and financial need.

Funds Avail.: No specific amount. **To Apply:** Applicants must file FAFSA and scholarship application form. **Remarks:** Established by Jake S. More, LW'28. **Contact:** Office of Admission and Financial Aid at 515-271-2782.

3509 ■ Dwight D. Opperman Scholarships (Undergraduate/Scholarship)

Purpose: To support the education of law students. **Focus:** Law. **Qualif.:** Applicants must be accepted as first year students at Drake Law School; must show evidence of superior academic record and potential; must have a high score in law entrance exam; and demonstrate significant community and extracurricular experiences. **Criteria:** Recipients are selected based on achievement and potential.

Funds Avail.: Full-tuition plus $10,000 to help pay for books and living expenses while attending Drake Law School. **Number Awarded:** 5. **To Apply:** Applicants must complete the application packet (application for admission and the general scholarship information sheet). **Contact:** Kara Blanchard at the above address.

3510 ■ Jerome S. Petz, S.J., Scholarships (Undergraduate/Scholarship)

Purpose: To support the education of law students. **Focus:** Law. **Qualif.:** Applicants must be students of Drake University law school. **Criteria:** Recipients are selected based on academic record and financial need.

Funds Avail.: No specific amount. **To Apply:** Applicants must file FAFSA and application form. **Remarks:** Established by the faculty as a memorial in honor of Father Jerome Petz, who taught at the Law School from 1971 to 1979. **Contact:** Office of Admission and Financial Aid at 515-271-2782.

3511 ■ Janet Reynoldson Memorial Scholarships (Undergraduate/Scholarship)

Purpose: To support the education of law students. **Focus:** Law. **Qualif.:** Applicants must be students of Drake University law school. **Criteria:** Recipients are selected based on student's contributions to community and family, academic achievement, need and significant change in career.

Funds Avail.: No specific amount. **To Apply:** Applicants must file FAFSA and application form. **Remarks:** Established by the family of Janet Reynoldson, LW'65. **Contact:** Office of Admission and Financial Aid at 515-271-2782.

3512 ■ Isador M. Robinson Endowment Scholarships (Undergraduate/Scholarship)

Purpose: To support the education of law students. **Focus:** Law. **Qualif.:** Applicants must be second or third year law students of Drake University law school. **Criteria:** Recipients are selected based on leadership and academic achievement.

Funds Avail.: No specific amount. **To Apply:** Applicants must file FAFSA and application form. **Contact:** Office of Admission and Financial Aid at 515-271-2782.

3513 ■ Walter and Rita Selvy Scholarships (Undergraduate/Scholarship)

Purpose: To support the education of law students. **Focus:** Law. **Qualif.:** Applicants must be students of Drake University law school. **Criteria:** Recipients are selected based on academic record and financial need.

Funds Avail.: No specific amount. **To Apply:** Applicants must file FAFSA and application form. **Remarks:** Established by Walter, LW'28, and his late wife, Rita Selvy. **Contact:** Office of Admission and Financial Aid at 515-271-2782.

3514 ■ Charles "Buck" and Dora Taylor Endowed Law Scholarships (Undergraduate/Scholarship)

Purpose: To support the education of law students. **Focus:** Law. **Qualif.:** Applicants must be students with financial

Awards are arranged alphabetically below their administering organizations

need and have demonstrated a history of academic success while participating in sports at the undergraduate school level. **Criteria:** Recipients are selected based on merit and need.

Funds Avail.: No specific amount. **To Apply:** Applicants must submit the General Information Form for Scholarships along with the application for admission. **Remarks:** Established in honor of 1933 Drake Law School graduate Charles Taylor. **Contact:** Mail application form and other supporting documents to Office of Admission and Financial Aid at 2507 University Ave., Des Moines, IA 50311-4505; Phone: 515-271-2782.

3515 ■ Haemer Wheatcraft Scholarships
(Undergraduate/Scholarship)

Purpose: To support the education of law students. **Focus:** Law. **Qualif.:** Applicants must be students of Drake University law school. **Criteria:** Recipients are selected based on academic record and financial need.

Funds Avail.: No specific amount. **To Apply:** Applicants must file the FAFSA and the scholarship application. **Remarks:** Established by friends and associates in honor of Haemer Wheatcraft, LW'33. **Contact:** Office of Admission and Financial Aid at 515-271-2782.

3516 ■ Zarley, McKee, Thomte, Voorhees, Sease Law Scholarships *(Undergraduate/Scholarship)*

Purpose: To support the education of law students. **Focus:** Law. **Qualif.:** Applicants must be students interested in intellectual property law. **Criteria:** Recipients are selected based on academic record and financial need.

Funds Avail.: No specific amount. **To Apply:** Applicants must file FAFSA and application form. **Remarks:** Established by Donald H. Zarley, LW'54; Bruce W. McKee; Dennis L. Thomte; Michael G. Voorhees, LW'68; Edmund J. Sease, LW'67; and John Beehner. **Contact:** Office of Admission and Financial Aid at 515-271-2782.

3517 ■ The Drama Therapy Fund
1626 Leavenworth St.
Manhattan, KS 66502
E-mail: info@dramatherapyfund.org
URL: www.dramatherapyfund.org

3518 ■ The Drama Therapy Fund Graduate Research Grants *(Graduate/Grant)*

Purpose: To support students pursuing research in the field of drama therapy. **Focus:** Theater Arts. **Qualif.:** Applicants must be conducting an approved empirical investigation about some aspect of drama therapy which will be undertaken as part of thesis or dissertation in fulfillment of a graduate degree in drama therapy or an academic discipline related to drama therapy; research may be qualitative, quantitative, or both and may utilize standard and/or drama therapy measurement methods; research must have been approved by the graduate committee and the University's Internal Review Board for Research Projects. **Criteria:** Selection will be based on evaluation of submitted documents and specific criteria.

Funds Avail.: Up to $300. **To Apply:** Applicants must submit a cover letter which includes contact information, name of school, contact and degree, addresses problem of the research, demographics, relationship and importance of research to the advancement of drama therapy, brief outline

of methodology to be used, plan for dissemination of findings; a letter of support from faculty supervisor; copy of IRB approval for the study. Send via online or send via mail (applicants must send four hard copies for mail applications). **Deadline:** May 15 and October 15. **Contact:** Sally Bailey, Treasurer, The Drama Therapy Fund at the above address or e-mail at dtfund@dramatherapy.org.

3519 ■ The Drama Therapy Fund Graduate Student Research Awards *(Graduate/Grant)*

Purpose: To encourage research in the field of drama therapy. **Focus:** Theater Arts. **Qualif.:** Applicants must have completed empirical investigation in the field, utilizing standard and/or drama therapy measurement methods as part of a thesis or dissertation in fulfillment of graduate degrees in drama therapy or an academic discipline related to drama therapy; research may be qualitative, quantitative, or both. **Criteria:** Selection will be based on evaluation of submitted documents and specific criteria.

Funds Avail.: $1,000. **To Apply:** Applicants must submit an abstract of thesis or dissertation addressing demographics, problem, relationship and importance of research to the advancement of drama therapy, brief outline of methodology used; cover letter addressing contact information, name of school, contact and degree, plan for dissemination of findings, date thesis or dissertation was successfully defended; letter of support from faculty supervisor; copy of IRB approval for the study. **Deadline:** September 1. **Contact:** Sally Bailey at the above address or e-mail at dtfund@dramatherapy.org.

3520 ■ Wilder Dimension Scholarships for Advanced Study in Theatre Arts *(Graduate/Scholarship)*

Purpose: To provide financial assistance to drama therapists. **Focus:** Theater Arts. **Qualif.:** Applicants must be registered drama therapists working on continuing education and graduate students preparing for careers as drama therapists either through an approved NADT university program or through NADT alternative learning program. **Criteria:** Selection will be based on evaluation of submitted documents and specific criteria. Applications will be reviewed by a team of three registered drama therapists.

Funds Avail.: Up to $400. **To Apply:** Applicants must submit a contact information page along with a letter of intent which includes contact information, name of proposed course, where the course will be offered, dates of the course, rational for wanting to study theater history or literature and contribution to practice as drama therapist. Send via online or send via mail (applicants must send four hard copies for mail applications). **Contact:** Sally Bailey at the above address or e-mail at dtfund@dramatherapy.org.

3521 ■ Doris Duke Charitable Foundation (DDCF)
650 5th Ave., 19th Fl.
New York, NY 10019
Ph: (212) 974-7000
Fax: (212) 974-7590
URL: www.ddcf.org

3522 ■ Clinical Research Fellowship for Medical Students *(Graduate/Fellowship)*

Purpose: To encourage medical students to pursue careers in clinical research. **Focus:** Clinical sciences. **Qualif.:** Applicants must be students matriculated at any US medical school who are in good academic standing and have

Awards are arranged alphabetically below their administering organizations

completed two or more years of medical school prior to the start of the fellowship. **Criteria:** Selection will be based on the committee's criteria.

Funds Avail.: $28,000 stipend. **To Apply:** Applicants must visit the website for the online application form. Complete all sections of the online application form, which requests the following information: contact information; education history; areas of clinical research you are interested in during the fellowship year; schools to which you are applying (this information will be released to all schools you apply to); names and emails of medical school dean and faculty submitting letters of support; descriptions of prior research experience, if applicable. Completed application should include the following: online application form; letter from the dean; letter of support; personal statement, curriculum vitae; medical school transcript; additional school requirements. **Deadline:** January 12.

3523 ■ Duluth-Superior Area Community Foundation

324 W Superior St., Ste. 212
618 Missabe Bldg.
Duluth, MN 55802
Ph: (218) 726-0232
Fax: (218) 726-0257
E-mail: info@dsacommunityfoundation.com

3524 ■ Darrell and Palchie Asselin Scholarships *(Undergraduate/Scholarship)*

Purpose: To provide financial assistance to the non-traditional, older students in financial resources for their education. **Focus:** General studies. **Qualif.:** Applicants must be students over the age of 22 who are the primary care givers to one or more children under the age of 18; must have a grade point average of 2.5 (based on a 4.0 system) or higher for a completed of at least 50% of the course of instruction at the time of the award. **Criteria:** Applicants are evaluated based on academic achievement; financial need; written recommendations; seriousness of purpose.

Funds Avail.: $2,000. **To Apply:** Applicants must complete the application form; academic transcript; letters of recommendation; and financial need documentation. **Deadline:** January 15.

3525 ■ William E. Barto Scholarships
(Undergraduate/Scholarship)

Purpose: To provide financial assistance for art students. **Focus:** Arts; Visual arts. **Qualif.:** Applicants must be graduating seniors of public and private high schools in Duluth and Superior; must be planning to major in arts or visual arts at the University of Minnesota Duluth or the University of Wisconsin-Superior; must rank in the upper 25% of their class. **Criteria:** Applicants are evaluated based on financial need; academic record; written recommendations; and, seriousness of purpose.

Funds Avail.: $1,500. **Number Awarded:** 1. **To Apply:** Applicants must submit a completed application form; academic transcript; letters of recommendation; and financial need documentation. **Remarks:** Scholarship may be accepted in addition to other awards, provided that the combined amount does not exceed the full amount of tuition, books, fees, room and board charges. Established in 1995.

3526 ■ Bernard B. and Mary L. Brusin Scholarships *(Undergraduate/Scholarship)*

Purpose: To provide assistance to Jewish and Roman Catholic students who are in need financial of aid for their college education. **Focus:** General studies. **Qualif.:** Applicants must be either Jewish or Roman Catholic graduating seniors from St. Louis County public or private high schools who are in the top 25% of their high school. **Criteria:** Applicants are evaluated based on financial need; academic record; written recommendations (one of which must be from a clergy) and seriousness of purpose.

Funds Avail.: $5,000. **To Apply:** Applicants should complete and submit an application form; academic transcript (including standardized test scores); recommendations from one educator and one to the clergy; and financial need documentation. **Remarks:** The award is co-payable to the institution and the recipient. Established in 1987.

3527 ■ Duluth Building and Construction Trades Council Scholarships *(Undergraduate, Vocational/Occupational/Scholarship)*

Purpose: To provide financial assistance to students entering/attending any post secondary vocational college, community college or other college or university. **Focus:** General studies. **Qualif.:** Applicants must be graduating high school seniors, whose parent/guardian is a member of one of the 17 unions affiliated with the Duluth Building Trades Council; must have grade point average of 2.75, based on 4.0 scale, or higher; must be students from the Foundation's geographic service areas. **Criteria:** Applicants are evaluated based on academic record (including GPA, class rank, and test scores when relevant); written recommendations; and, seriousness of purpose.

Funds Avail.: $2,500. **Number Awarded:** 2. **To Apply:** Applicants must submit all the required application information. **Remarks:** The award is co-payable to the institution and the recipient.

3528 ■ Duluth Central High School Alumni Scholarships *(Undergraduate/Scholarship)*

Purpose: To assist the worthy student who customarily would be eliminated from scholarship consideration on the basis of level achievement attained in class work. **Focus:** General studies. **Qualif.:** Applicants must be graduating seniors from Duluth Central High School who will attend the College of St. Scholastica, University of Minnesota-Duluth, University of Wisconsin-Superior, Lake Superior College, or Wisconsin Indianhead Technical College. **Criteria:** Applicants are evaluated based on academic record; financial need; written recommendations; and, seriousness of purpose.

Funds Avail.: $1,000. **Number Awarded:** 1. **To Apply:** Applicants must submit a completed application form; academic transcript (including standardized test scores); two letters of recommendation; and financial need documentation. **Deadline:** January 15. **Remarks:** The Award is co-payable to the institution and the recipient.

3529 ■ Peter M. Gargano Scholarship Fund
(Undergraduate/Scholarship)

Purpose: To provide financial assistance for post-secondary education to the children of employees of Ulland Brothers. **Focus:** General studies. **Qualif.:** Applicants must be children of Ulland Brothers employees who have been employed with the company for a minimum of two years

Awards are arranged alphabetically below their administering organizations

(for salaried employees) or for a minimum of two seasons (for seasonal employees); must be students who are unmarried child under age 25 who is not self-supporting and who are full-time high school seniors or post-secondary students; must have a grade point average of 3.0 (based on 4.0 system) or higher; must be graduating high school seniors from the Geographic Service Areas. **Criteria:** Applicants are evaluated based on academic record (including GPA, class rank, and test scores when relevant); financial need; written recommendations; and, seriousness of purpose.

Funds Avail.: $2,000. **Number Awarded:** 1. **To Apply:** Applicants must submit completed application form and recently completed Student Aid Report (SAR) from the Free Application for Federal Student Aid (FAFSA). A complete application will also include an academic transcript (inlcuding standardized test scores), one recommendation and financial need documentation. **Remarks:** The award is co-payable to the institution and the recipient.

3530 ■ Patricia S. Gustafson '56 Memorial Scholarships (Undergraduate/Scholarship)

Purpose: To provide financial assistance to graduating female seniors from Denfeld High School or the Marshall School who exemplifies the characteristics and life exhibited by Patricia Gustafson. **Focus:** General studies. **Qualif.:** Applicants must be young women who will graduate from Denfeld High School or Marshall High School; must plan to attend either the University of Minnesota Duluth, Lake Superior College or the College of St. Scholastica; must have a high school grade point average of 3.4 or higher; must be active participants or leaders in school activities; must have some measure of financial need. **Criteria:** Recipients are selected based on ability to live a full life following the example of Patricia Gustafson; contributions to their schools; high academic achievement; potential and intention to make contributions in the field of education; high level of moral character; and, level of financial need.

Funds Avail.: $800. **To Apply:** Applicants must submit a completed application form and a personal statement answering the question "Considering what you know of Patricia Gustafson, why do you think you would be a worthy recipient of a scholarship honoring her memory?" **Deadline:** January 15. **Remarks:** The award is co-payable to the institution and the recipient.

3531 ■ Jeanne H. Hemmingway Scholarships (Undergraduate/Scholarship)

Purpose: To assist students with financial need from the three counties of Minnesota's Arrowhead region. **Qualif.:** Applicants must be graduate seniors of public or private high schools in St. Louis, Lake and Cook counties who are planning to attend UMD; must be in the top 15% of their high school. **Criteria:** Applicants are evaluated based on financial need; academic record; written recommendations; and, seriousness of purpose.

Funds Avail.: $2,250. **Number Awarded:** 3. **To Apply:** Applicants must submit a completed application form and a recently completed Student Aid Report (SAR) from the Free Application for Federal Student Aid (FAFSA). **Remarks:** The award is co-payable to the institution and the recipient. Established in 1990.

3532 ■ Gus and Henrietta Hill Scholarships (Undergraduate/Scholarship)

Purpose: To provide financial assistance to graduates of Duluth East High School. **Focus:** Environmental Science.

Qualif.: Applicants must be graduating seniors from Duluth East High School who are active in the sport of pole vaulting and/or music activities; must be on top third of their high school class. **Criteria:** Applicants will be evaluated based on participation in pole vaulting and/or music activities; financial need; academic record; written recommendations; and seriousness of purpose.

Funds Avail.: $4,500. **Number Awarded:** 1. **To Apply:** Applicants must submit a completed application form; academic transcript (including standardized test scores); two letters of recommendation; and financial documentation. **Deadline:** January 15. **Remarks:** The Award is co-payable to the institution and the recipient.

3533 ■ Max and Julia Houghton Duluth Central Scholarships (Undergraduate/Scholarship)

Purpose: To provide financial assistance for students of all backgrounds to enable them to pursue higher education. **Focus:** General studies. **Qualif.:** Applicants must be graduating seniors from Duluth Central High School who are in the top 25% of their high school class. **Criteria:** Applicants are evaluated based on financial need; academic performance; and, involvement in community and/or school activities.

Funds Avail.: $3,000. **To Apply:** Applicants must submit all the required application information. **Deadline:** January 15. **Remarks:** The award is co-payable to the institution and the recipient.

3534 ■ Greg Irons Student Scholarships (Undergraduate/Scholarship)

Purpose: To provide opportunities to students who are seeking for financial resources for their education in college. **Focus:** General studies. **Qualif.:** Applicants must be 12th grade students who have been able to attain their personal goals through self motivation, perseverance and through guidance of a mentor who characterizes Greg Irons; must have positive influences through their enthusiastic participation in school activities; and must be students with academic, physical, or emotional needs. **Criteria:** Recipients will be selected based on academic record and other factors described on the application. Preference will be given to students who have desire to enter the teaching profession or other helping professions.

Funds Avail.: $1,000. **To Apply:** Applicants must submit a completed application form including transcript of records. **Deadline:** January 15. **Remarks:** The award is co-payable to the institution and the recipient.

3535 ■ The Jackson Club Scholarships (Undergraduate/Scholarship)

Purpose: To provide financial assistance to the residents of Hermantown and graduates of Hermantown High School. **Focus:** General studies. **Qualif.:** Applicants must be residents of Hermantown and graduates of Hermantown High School planning to attend any accredited post-secondary institution on a full-time basis; must have a 2.3 grade point average. **Criteria:** Applicants are evaluated based on academic record; written recommendation; and involvement in community activities.

Funds Avail.: $500. **To Apply:** Applicants must submit a completed application form; transcript of records (including standardized test scores); one letter of recommendation; and an essay stating the meaning of growing up in Hermantown. **Remarks:** The award is co-payable to the institution and the recipient. Established in 1910.

Awards are arranged alphabetically below their administering organizations

3536 ■ Cory Jam Awards (Undergraduate/Scholarship)

Purpose: To provide financial assistance to students who intend to pursue further education or training at any accredited university, college or technical school. **Focus:** General studies. **Qualif.:** Applicants must be graduating seniors from Duluth East High School who attended Congdon Park Elementary School, Homecroft Elementary School or Lowell Elementary School; must have participated in at least two extracurricular activities sponsored by Duluth East High School and at least one community based activity during their high school enrollment years; must intend to pursue education or training at any accredited university, college or technical school; must possess a 3.5 grade point average or higher based on 4.0 system. **Criteria:** Applicants are evaluated based on academic records; written recommendations; and involvement in community and church activities.

Funds Avail.: $750. **Number Awarded:** 1. **To Apply:** Applicants must submit a completed application form; academic transcript (including standardized test scores); and two letters of recommendation. **Deadline:** January 15. **Remarks:** The payment is co-payable to the institution and recipient.

3537 ■ Minnesota Power Community Involvement Scholarships (Undergraduate/Scholarship)

Purpose: To provide financial assistance to high school seniors residing within Minnesota Power's service territory. **Focus:** General studies. **Qualif.:** Applicants must be high school seniors residing within Minnesota Power's service territory; must be full-time high school students who have a 3.0 GPA or above. **Criteria:** Applicants are evaluated based on community involvement and financial need.

Funds Avail.: $2,500. **Number Awarded:** 20. **To Apply:** Applicants must submit an application form; supporting documentation from community leaders; a copy of the applicant's parents' 1040 form; and a high school transcript. **Deadline:** January 14. **Remarks:** The award is co-payable to the institution and the recipient.

3538 ■ Modern Woodmen of America Scholarships (Undergraduate/Scholarship)

Purpose: To provide financial assistance to students with their educational needs. **Focus:** General studies. **Qualif.:** Applicants must be single parents who are the primary care-givers to one or more children; must have completed at least 50 percent of their course of instruction at the time of the award. **Criteria:** Applicants are evaluated based on academic record; written recommendations; and, involvement in community and church activities.

Funds Avail.: $1,000. **Number Awarded:** 1. **To Apply:** Applicants must submit a completed application form together with academic transcript (including standardized test scores), two recommendations, and financial need documentation. **Deadline:** January 15. **Remarks:** The award is co-payable to the institution and the recipient.

3539 ■ Hubert A. Nelson Scholarships (Undergraduate/Scholarship)

Purpose: To provide financial assistance for students studying business and accounting. **Focus:** Business; Accounting. **Qualif.:** Applicants must be graduating seniors of public or private high schools in Duluth and Superior; must be planning to major in business/accounting at the University of Minnesota-Duluth or the University of Wisconsin-

Superior; must be in the top 25% of their high school. **Criteria:** Applicants are evaluated based on academic record; financial need; written recommendations; involvement in community; and extra-curricular activities.

Funds Avail.: $2,000. **To Apply:** Applicants must submit a completed application form; academic transcript (including standardized test scores); one letter of recommendation; and financial need documentation. **Remarks:** The award is co-payable to the institution and the recipient. Established in 1995.

3540 ■ Amelia and Emanuel Nessell Scholarships (Undergraduate/Scholarship)

Purpose: To provide educational opportunities for students who are in financial need. **Focus:** General studies. **Qualif.:** Applicants must be graduating seniors of Duluth public or private high schools; must be Jewish students who are planning to pursue a post-secondary education, including community colleges, four-year colleges and universities; must be in the top 25% of their high school class. **Criteria:** Applicants are evaluated based on academic record; financial need; written recommendations (one of which must come from a clergy); involvement in community and extra-curricular activities. Priority consideration will be given to Jewish applicants.

Funds Avail.: $1,000. **To Apply:** Applicants must submit a completed DSACF Common Scholarship Application form; academic transcript (including standardized test scores); two letters of recommendation (one from educator and the other one must come from the clergy); and financial documentation. **Remarks:** The award is co-payable to the institution and the recipient. Established in 1997.

3541 ■ Anderson Niskanen Scholarships (Undergraduate/Scholarship)

Purpose: To provide financial assistance for students to achieve higher education. **Focus:** General studies. **Qualif.:** Applicants must be graduating seniors from Duluth public high schools who will attend either the University of Minnesota-Duluth or the University of Minnesota-Twin Cities; and must be in the top 25% of their class. **Criteria:** Applicants are evaluated based on financial need; academic achievement; written recommendations and seriousness of purpose.

Funds Avail.: $2,000. **To Apply:** Applicants must submit a completed application form; academic transcript (including standardized test scores); two letters of recommendation; and financial documentation. **Remarks:** Established in 1998.

3542 ■ Dr. Mark Rathke Family Scholarships (Undergraduate/Scholarship)

Purpose: To help future generations of Marshall School students to pursue their educational goals. **Focus:** General studies. **Qualif.:** Applicants must be graduating seniors of the Marshall School who will be attending a college or university as full-time students; must have a grade point average of 2.75 (on a 4.0 scale) or higher; and must have demonstrated school and/or community involvement, leadership qualities and hardworking behavior. **Criteria:** Applicants are evaluated based on academic record; hardworking behavior; good citizenship; leadership qualities; serious commitment to college education; written recommendations; and involvement in community and extra-curricular activities. Preference will be given to those students who are not in the top ten percent of their graduating class.

Awards are arranged alphabetically below their administering organizations

Funds Avail.: $1,000. **Number Awarded:** 1. **To Apply:** Applicants must submit a completed application form; academic transcript (including standardized test scores); and two letter of recommendation. **Deadline:** January 15.

3543 ■ Lawrence E. & Mabel Jackson Rudberg Scholarships *(Undergraduate/Scholarship)*

Purpose: To provide financial assistance to students pursuing a college degree. **Focus:** General studies. **Qualif.:** Applicants must be graduating seniors from Duluth public and Two Harbors Senior High; must intend to pursue a post-secondary education at an accredited four-year public or private college or university. **Criteria:** Applicants are evaluated based on academic record; financial need; written recommendations; involvement in community and extra-curricular activities. Two Harbors graduates will be given preference.

Funds Avail.: $5,000. **To Apply:** Applicants must submit a completed DSACF Common Scholarship Application form; academic transcript (including standardized test scores); two letters of recommendation; and financial need documentation. **Remarks:** Established in 1999. The award is co-payable to the institution and the recipient. Award is renewable for four years, assuming proper academic progress (2.5 GPA or greater) is maintained.

3544 ■ Phil Shykes Memorial Scholarships *(Undergraduate, Vocational/Occupational/ Scholarship)*

Purpose: To provide financial assistance to those in need to pursue trade or career. **Focus:** General studies. **Qualif.:** Applicants must be graduating seniors from Hermantown High School who are intending to pursue post-secondary education at a vocational college, community college, or other college or university on a full-time basis; must have achieved a 2.5 or higher cumulative GPA (on a 4.0 scale) in high school. **Criteria:** Recipients will be selected based on the following criteria: (1) financial need; (2) family profile; (3) involvement in community service; (4) major field of interest; (5) determination to pursue a higher education or vocation; and (6) employment (optional).

Funds Avail.: $2,000. **To Apply:** Applicants must submit a completed DSACF Common Scholarship Application form; academic transcript (including standardized test scores); one letter of recommendation; and financial need documentation. **Deadline:** January 15. **Remarks:** The award is co-payable to the institution and the recipient.

3545 ■ Dale and Betty George Sola Scholarships *(Undergraduate/Scholarship)*

Purpose: To provide financial assistance for graduating high school seniors living in or attending school in the central areas of Duluth. **Focus:** General studies. **Qualif.:** Applicants must be students of Duluth Central High School, the Marshall School, Lakeview Christian Academy and alternative schools (including Unity School and the Harbor City International School) in the central areas of Duluth; or, graduates residing within the Central Hillside or Park Point areas who have a grade point average of 2.75 (on a 4.0 scale) or higher. **Criteria:** Recipients will be selected based on the following criteria: (1) demonstrated leadership; (2) hard-working behavior; (3) financial need; (4) good work ethic; (5) involvement in community and school activities; and (6) academic performance. Preference will be given to students who are not in the top ten percent of the graduating class.

Funds Avail.: $2,000. **To Apply:** Applicants must complete

the DSACF Common Scholarship Application available from the Guidance Offices; academic transcript (including standardized test scores); two letters of recommendation; and financial need documentation. **Deadline:** January 15.

3546 ■ John A. Sullivan Scholarships *(Undergraduate/Scholarship)*

Purpose: To provide financial assistance for students majoring in education who are in financial need. **Focus:** Education. **Qualif.:** Applicants must be graduates of Senior High in Superior, Wisconsin who will attend their junior and senior years at the University of Wisconsin-Superior majoring in education. **Criteria:** Recipients will be selected based on financial need; academic record; written recommendations; and seriousness of purpose.

Funds Avail.: $1,000. **Number Awarded:** 1. **To Apply:** Applicants must contact the University of Wisconsin Education Department for application form. **Deadline:** January 15.

3547 ■ Robert B. and Sophia Whiteside Scholarships *(Undergraduate/Scholarship)*

Purpose: To provide financial assistance to students who are going to attend college. **Focus:** General studies. **Qualif.:** Applicants must be high school seniors graduating from schools, including home schools, in Duluth and seek admission to any fully-accredited, degree granting college or university; and must be in top 10% of their class. **Criteria:** Applicants are evaluated based on academic achievement.

Funds Avail.: $6,000. **To Apply:** Applicants must submit a completed application form; academic transcript (including standardized test scores); and two letters of recommendation. **Remarks:** Established in 1976 in memory of Robert and Sophia Whiteside by the will of their daughter Marion Whiteside Meining.

3548 ■ Dumbarton Oaks Research Library and Collection
1703 32nd St. NW
Washington, DC 20007
Ph: (202) 339-6401
Fax: (202) 339-6419
E-mail: blazinac@doaks.org
URL: www.doaks.org

3549 ■ Dumbarton Oaks Fellowships *(Doctorate, Graduate/Fellowship)*

Purpose: To promote research in Byzantine studies, Pre-Columbian studies and Garden and Landscape Studies. **Focus:** Byzantine studies; Pre-Columbian studies. **Qualif.:** Applicant must be a graduate student who expects to have a PhD prior to taking up residence at Dumbarton Oaks. **Criteria:** Selection is based on the submitted application materials.

Funds Avail.: Maximum of $47,000. **To Apply:** Applicants are required to complete the application online. In addition, applicants must submit three letters of recommendation. **Deadline:** November 1. **Remarks:** Successful applicants will revert to the status and stipend of Junior Fellows if the degree has not been conferred by the beginning of the term of residence.

3550 ■ Dumbarton Oaks Junior Fellowships *(Graduate/Fellowship)*

Purpose: To promote research in Byzantine studies, Pre-Columbian studies and Garden and Landscape Studies.

Awards are arranged alphabetically below their administering organizations

Focus: Byzantine studies; Pre-Columbian studies. **Qualif.:** Applicant must be a degree candidate who, at the time of application, has fulfilled all preliminary requirements for a PhD (or appropriate final degree) and will be working on a dissertation or final project at Dumbarton Oaks. **Criteria:** Selection is based on the submitted application materials.

Funds Avail.: $27,000. **To Apply:** Applicants are required to complete the application online. In addition, applicants must submit three letters of recommendation and a transcript of graduate record (sent by university registrar). **Deadline:** November 1.

3551 ■ Post-Doctoral Teaching Fellowships
(Postdoctorate/Fellowship)

Purpose: To promote research in Byzantine studies, Pre-Columbian studies, and Garden and Landscape Studies. **Focus:** Byzantine studies; Pre-Columbian studies. **Qualif.:** Applicant must have completed all requirements for the doctoral degree; a citizen of the U.S. or Canada or a graduate of a North American university; and must have an excellent command of spoken and written English. **Criteria:** Selection is based on demonstrated scholarly accomplishment and overall academic excellence and promise; potential future impact on the field of Byzantine studies through teaching and writing; significance and quality of the research project(s) to be carried out at Dumbarton Oaks; knowledge of the relevant ancient and modern languages; and ability to contribute to the academic community at Dumbarton Oaks and local area universities.

Funds Avail.: $60,000/year and $1,000/year research expenses. **To Apply:** Applicants must submit six copies of an application consisting of a cover letter that includes a statement of teaching experience and proposed courses; a curriculum vitae; a writing sample of not more than forty pages; a 1000-word description of the research project(s) to be carried out during the term of the fellowship; and three letters of recommendation. **Deadline:** January 1. **Contact:** Margaret Mullett at the above address.

3552 ■ DuPage County Bar Association (DCBA)
126 S County Farm Rd.
Wheaton, IL 60187
Ph: (630) 653-7779
Fax: (630) 653-7870
URL: www.dcba.org

3553 ■ Hartman E. Stime Scholarships
(Undergraduate/Scholarship)

Purpose: To promote the study of law. **Focus:** Paralegal studies. **Qualif.:** Applicants must be DuPage County, IL residents who will begin their second, third or fourth year of law school. **Criteria:** Selection will be based on submitted application and personal interview.

Funds Avail.: No specific amount. **To Apply:** Applicant must submit an application form (available on the website) and their resume. **Deadline:** March 22. **Remarks:** Established in memory of Harman Stime, a long-time DCBA member distinguished for his many years of pro bono work and community service efforts on behalf of the poor and elderly. **Contact:** Glenda Berg Sharp, at the above address; Fax: 630-653-7870.

3554 ■ Dutchess County Bar Association (DCBA)
PO Box 4865
Poughkeepsie, NY 12602

Ph: (845) 473-2488
Fax: (845) 485-1484
E-mail: janna@dutchesscountybar.org
URL: www.dutchesscountybar.org

3555 ■ Joseph H. Gellert/Dutchess County Bar Association Scholarships *(Undergraduate/ Scholarship)*

Purpose: To provide financial assistance for the residents of Dutchess County intending to attend an accredited law school. **Focus:** Law. **Qualif.:** Applicants must be Dutchess County residents who completed at least one year of law school. **Criteria:** Applicants will be evaluated based on financial need.

Funds Avail.: $1,000. **To Apply:** Applicants must submit application; copy of law school transcript; essay of approximately 500 words describing interest in the law and career aspirations; letter of recommendation; and resume. **Deadline:** April 1.

3556 ■ Dystonia Medical Research Foundation (DMRF)
1 E Wacker Dr., Ste. 2810
Chicago, IL 60601-1905
Ph: (312) 755-0198
Fax: (312) 803-0138
Free: 800-377-DYST
E-mail: dystonia@dystonia-foundation.org
URL: www.dystonia-foundation.org

3557 ■ Dystonia Medical Research Foundation Fellowships *(Postdoctorate/Fellowship)*

Purpose: To assist post-doctoral fellows in establishing careers in research relevant to dystonia. **Focus:** Muscular dystrophy. **Qualif.:** Applicants must be in their post-doctoral degree. **Criteria:** Applicant will be selected based on their proposal.

Funds Avail.: $50,000 per year for two years. **To Apply:** Applicants must submit a proposal. In addition, applicants should include the following attachments: Application Cover Sheet (use form provided); Budget (use form provided); biographical sketch of principal investigator and all key personnel (Use standard NIH form); Research Funding Terms and Conditions, signed by applicant and applicant's institutional official; letters of support (one letter from a mentor); and relevant articles, video clips, or other items, if applicable. **Deadline:** December 15. **Contact:** Jody Roosevelt, Grants Manager, at 312-447-5150 or jroosevelt@dystonia-foundation.org.

3558 ■ Fernandez Earle Scholarship Foundation
1868 Marine Dr., Ste. 204
West Vancouver, BC, Canada V7V 1J6
Ph: (604) 638-1802
E-mail: info@fernandezearle.com
URL: www.fernandezearle.com

3559 ■ Fernandez Earle Undergraduate Entrance Scholarships *(Undergraduate/ Scholarship)*

Purpose: To support the education of undergraduate students from a high school in the Queens Charlotte Islands. **Focus:** General studies. **Qualif.:** Applicant must

Awards are arranged alphabetically below their administering organizations

be a graduating student with scholastic achievement as well as strong leadership qualities and concern for their community. **Criteria:** Preference will be based on merit and need.

Funds Avail.: $15,000. **Number Awarded:** 3. **To Apply:** Applicant must provide a transcript, letter of recommendation from school officials and community representatives, and a letter from the applicant describing their educational and career goals.

3560 ■ Early American Industries Association (EAIA)
PO Box 524
Hebron, MD 21830-0524
E-mail: execdirector@eaiainfo.org
URL: www.eaiainfo.org

3561 ■ EAIA Research Grants *(Professional development/Grant)*
Purpose: To preserve and present historic trades, crafts and tools that will reflect their impact in our lives. **Focus:** Industry and trade; Crafts. **Qualif.:** Applicants must be individuals with a research related to trades, crafts and tools. **Criteria:** Recipients will be evaluated based on submitted research.

Funds Avail.: $2,000. **To Apply:** Applicants must submit a research. The project must be related to the purpose of the EAIA. The total length including the form may not exceed ten pages. Successful applicants will be required to file a report on the project attached on a form. One copy of the final form of the completed project must be deposited to the Research Grants Committee, whether or not the final form is published. Applicants are asked to give the names and addresses of their local newspapers, so the Research Grants Committee can announce new grant recipients. **Deadline:** March 15.

3562 ■ Earthquake Engineering Research Institute (EERI)
499 14th St., Ste. 320
Oakland, CA 94612-1934
Ph: (510) 451-0905
Fax: (510) 451-5411
E-mail: eeri@eeri.org
URL: www.eeri.org

3563 ■ EERI/FEMA Graduate Fellowships *(Graduate/Scholarship)*
Purpose: To support study and research that may contribute to the science and practice of earthquake hazard mitigation. **Focus:** Earth sciences. **Qualif.:** Applicant must be enrolled in a graduate degree program at an accredited U.S. college/university and must hold U.S. citizenship or permanent resident status. **Criteria:** Selection is based on the submitted application and materials.

Funds Avail.: $12,000 with $8,000 for tuition, fees and research expenses. **Number Awarded:** 1. **To Apply:** Applicant must submit a completed application form along with the letter of nomination by faculty sponsor; academic transcript; a statement (maximum of 300 words) of educational and career goals; and a resume (maximum of two pages). In addition, two letters of recommendation must be sent by the author directly to EERI. **Deadline:** May 14.

3564 ■ East Tennessee Foundation (ETF)
625 Market St., Ste. 1400
Knoxville, TN 37902

Ph: (865) 524-1223
Fax: (865) 637-6039
Free: 877-524-1223
E-mail: etf@etf.org
URL: www.easttennesseefoundation.org

3565 ■ B&W Y-12 Scholarship Fund *(Undergraduate/Scholarship)*
Purpose: To benefit graduating high school seniors wishing to pursue careers in science, math or pre-engineering related fields. **Focus:** Science; Mathematics and mathematical sciences; Engineering. **Qualif.:** Applicants must be enrolled as full-time students at either Roane State Community College or Pellissippi State Technical College; must be U.S citizens; must have a minimum GPA of at least 3.0; be a graduating senior from a high school located in Anderson, Blount, Campbell, Claiborne, Cocke, Knox, Loudon, Morgan, Roane or Sevier counties. **Criteria:** A selection committee will be pre-selected and approved by ETF's board of Directors. The committee's primary function shall be the one to select the scholarship recipient, not only by considering the applicants' qualifications under criteria established above but also in consideration of the following factors: Scholastic and academic achievements; general aptitude for advanced educational work and seriousness of purpose; qualities of citizenship in school and in community such as volunteer work and employment history; participation in extracurricular activities at school or in the community; demonstrated financial need.

Funds Avail.: $1,300. **Number Awarded:** 1. **To Apply:** Applicants must check the application process online. **Deadline:** February 18. **Contact:** Application packet should be mailed to Beth Heller at the above address; E-mail: bheller@etf.org.

3566 ■ Ruby A. Brown Memorial Scholarships *(Undergraduate/Scholarship)*
Purpose: To benefit health nurses seeking to continue their nursing education. **Focus:** Nursing. **Qualif.:** Applicants must be currently employed as a public health nurse; must be residents in one of 15 counties (Anderson, Blount, Campbell, Claiborne, Cocke, Grainger, Hamblen, Jefferson, Loudon, Monroe, Morgan, Roane, Scott, Sevier or Union); may pursue their education at any accredited, not-for-pofit nursing program on a full-time or part-time basis. **Criteria:** Selection of recipient and alternate will be based upon current level of education, additional training being pursued, length of employment, current county of employment, financial need and GPA.

Funds Avail.: $3,000. **To Apply:** Applicant must check the application process online and must submit two reference letters. Applicants must send five copies of the application and attachments plus the originals. **Deadline:** April 29. **Contact:** Application packet should be mailed to Beth Heller at the above address; E-mail: bheller@etf.org.

3567 ■ Gordon W. and Agnes P. Cobb Scholarships *(Undergraduate/Scholarship)*
Purpose: To benefit graduates of high schools in Blount, Loudon, and Knox counties in Tennessee who wish to pursue or who are pursuing college education in a health care or medical-related field. **Focus:** Health Sciences. **Qualif.:** Applicants must show proof of maintaining full-time enrollment and a 3.0 or better academic standing in a health care or medical related curriculum each year through the submission of academic transcripts to the foundation at

Awards are arranged alphabetically below their administering organizations

the end of each semester. **Criteria:** Selection will be based on the following criteria: Academic promise and achievement; enrolled in a health care or medical-related curriculum; desire to pursue advanced education in a health care or medical-related field; evidence of a strong work or volunteer history; must demonstrate financial need.

Funds Avail.: $10,000 per year. **To Apply:** Applicants must check the application process online. **Deadline:** April 8. **Remarks:** Applicants from single-parent families will be given special consideration. **Contact:** Application packet should be mailed to Beth Heller at the above address; E-mail: bheller@etf.org.

3568 ■ Steven L. Coffey Memorial Scholarships
(Undergraduate/Scholarship)

Purpose: To assist students who possess the potential for excellence but may require some additional support in achieving their educational goals. **Focus:** General Studies. **Qualif.:** Applicants must either be Anderson County residents and graduates of Anderson County High School, Clinton Senior High School or Oak Ridge High School. **Criteria:** Grants are awarded based on academic excellence; must have financial need; must also present an evidence of a 2.5 GPA or better; and the desire to pursue a post secondary education.

Funds Avail.: $1,200 Annually. **To Apply:** Applicants must check the application online for the required materials. **Deadline:** April 15. **Contact:** Application packet should be mailed to Beth Heller at the above address; E-mail: bheller@etf.org.

3569 ■ R.G. and Ruth Crossno Memorial Scholarships *(Undergraduate/Scholarship)*

Purpose: To benefit graduating seniors of Anderson County High School who wish to pursue an advanced degree. **Focus:** General studies. **Qualif.:** Applicants must be enrolled as full-time students in an accredited public or private not-for-profit university or community college. **Criteria:** Selection of scholars will be based on applicants' demonstrated financial need, career motivation, academic promise and evidence of strong work experience.

Funds Avail.: $1,400. **To Apply:** Applicants must check the application process online as well as the required materials. **Deadline:** April 15. **Remarks:** Mr. R.G. Crossno, past mayor of Norris, Tennessee and 21-year member of the Anderson County School Board dedicated his life to promoting better education throughout the state of Tennessee. **Contact:** Application packet should be mailed to Beth Heller at the above address; E-mail: bheller@etf.org.

3570 ■ Michael D. Curtin Renaissance Student Memorial Scholarships *(Undergraduate/ Scholarship)*

Purpose: To recognize and benefit students who demonstrate leadership or achievement in a balanced array of activities, including the arts, athletics, citizenship, community/religious service and academics. **Focus:** General Studies. **Qualif.:** Applicants must be enrolled as full time students in an accredited public or private not-for-profit university. **Criteria:** Selection of scholars will be selected by the scholarship committee consisting of five faculty members from Anderson County High School; they will review all applications, conduct interviews and make funding recommendations to East Tennessee Foundation Board of Directors.

Funds Avail.: Up to $1,000. **To Apply:** Applicants must

check the application process online. **Deadline:** March 11.

3571 ■ Easter Seals Ontario
1 Concorde Gate, Ste. 700
Toronto, ON, Canada M3C 3N6
Ph: (416) 421-8377
Fax: (416) 696-1035
Free: 800-668-6252
E-mail: info@easterseals.org
URL: www.easterseals.org

3572 ■ The Leaders of Tomorrow Scholarships
(Undergraduate, Vocational/Occupational/ Scholarship)

Purpose: To assist young adults with physical disabilities with the cost of post-secondary education or vocational training. **Focus:** Education, Vocational-technical. **Qualif.:** Applicants must be seeking for post-secondary education; demonstrated consistent level of scholastic achievement throughout their secondary school curriculum; participated as a spokesperson for The Easter Seal Society; must served as models and inspirations to fellow students; and have applied for alternate financial assistance and still require assistance. **Criteria:** Applicants are evaluated based on financial need.

Funds Avail.: No specific amount. **To Apply:** Applicants must submit the completed application form along with typed, one-page letter outlining the qualifications for the award, including scholastic achievement, motivation, initiative and extra-curricular activities; copy of secondary and, if applicable, post-secondary transcripts; any interim marks that are available before the deadline; and, proof of application to applicable alternate sources of financial assistance. **Deadline:** May 11. **Contact:** Tina Shier at scholarships@easterseals.org.

3573 ■ Beatrice Drinnan Spence Scholarships
(Undergraduate, Vocational/Occupational/ Scholarship)

Purpose: To assist young adults with physical disabilities with the cost of post-secondary education or vocational training. **Focus:** Education, Vocational-technical. **Qualif.:** Applicants must be resident students of Ontario with disabilities who are currently applying to or enrolled in a post-secondary educational facility like university or community college. **Criteria:** Applicants are evaluated based on personal attributes and financial need.

Funds Avail.: $5,000. **Number Awarded:** 1. **To Apply:** Applicants must submit the completed application form along with a one-page letter outlining qualifications for the award including scholastic achievement, motivation, initiative and extra-curricular activities; copy of secondary and, if applicable, post-secondary transcripts; any interim marks that are available before the deadline; and, proof of application to applicable alternate sources of financial assistance. **Deadline:** May 11. **Contact:** Tina Shier at scholarships@easterseals.org.

3574 ■ Eastern Communication Association (ECA)
Duquesne University
Department of Communication & Rhetorical Studies
340 College Hall
600 Forbes Ave.
Pittsburgh, PA 15219

Awards are arranged alphabetically below their administering organizations

E-mail: info@ecasite.org
URL: associationdatabase.com

3575 ■ ECA Applied Urban Communication Research Grants (Professional development/ Grant)

Purpose: To fund the development of the original research related to urban communication. **Focus:** Communications. **Qualif.:** Applicants must be members of the Eastern Communication Association. **Criteria:** Applicants will be evaluated based on potential impact of their work as well as the quality and rigor of their contributions.

Funds Avail.: $1,000. **To Apply:** Applicants must include the following: 1) a cover letter explaining why the applicant deserves the award; 2) 500-word essay describing their career goals, outlining the anticipated outcomes, intended mode of dissemination of the research; 3) anticipated budget and timetable for completion of the project; 4) copy of the curriculum vitae; and at least one supporting letter from someone well-acquainted with the nominee. **Deadline:** March 5. **Contact:** Janie Harden Fritz at harden@duq.edu.

3576 ■ ECA Centennial Scholarships (Master's, Doctorate/Scholarship)

Purpose: To financially assist deserving PhD and M.A. students. **Focus:** General studies. **Qualif.:** Applicants must be PhD or M.A. students. **Criteria:** Recipients will be selected based on submitted materials and academic achievement.

Funds Avail.: Amount not specified. **To Apply:** Nominations must include a letter of nomination from the thesis/dissertation advisor attesting the nominee's student status. Must submit a four page, 1500-word project summary. **Deadline:** March 15. **Contact:** Janie Harden Fritz at harden@duq.edu.

3577 ■ Eastman Community Music School (ECMS)

University of Rochester
Eastman School of Music
26 Gibbs St.
Rochester, NY 14604
Ph: (585) 274-1400
Fax: (585) 274-1005
E-mail: community@esm.rochester.edu
URL: www.esm.rochester.edu/community

3578 ■ ECMS Scholarships (Undergraduate/ Scholarship)

Purpose: To financially assist ECMS students. **Focus:** Music. **Qualif.:** Applicant must be an ECMS student enrolled in a diploma program. **Criteria:** Selection is based on merit and financial need.

Funds Avail.: No specific amount. **To Apply:** Applicants must submit a completed application form along with Financial Assistance Application Form; teacher recommendation; and copy of the first page of the applicant's federal tax form. **Deadline:** May 1, August 1, December 1.

3579 ■ Ecological Society of America (ESA)

1990 M St. NW, Ste. 700
Washington, DC 20036
Ph: (202) 833-8773
Fax: (202) 833-8775

E-mail: esahq@esa.org
URL: www.esa.org

3580 ■ Jasper Ridge Restoration Fellowships Jasper Ridge Biological Preserve (Graduate, Postdoctorate/Fellowship)

Purpose: To provide financial support to deserving students. **Focus:** General studies. **Qualif.:** Applicants must be post-doctoral students up to senior faculty. **Criteria:** Applications will be assessed based on an individual's past accomplishments and on potential to take full advantage of the ecosystems and past research at Jasper Ridge, as well as the intellectual community at Stanford.

Funds Avail.: $80,000. **To Apply:** Applicants must submit a CV, a 3-page description of their proposed program, and contact information for 3 references. **Deadline:** May 1. **Contact:** For additional information or to submit an application, please contact: Dr. Philippe Cohen at philippe.cohen@stanford.edu. Administrative Director, Jasper Ridge Biological Preserve, 4001 Sand Hill Road, Woodside, CA 94062. Applications should be submitted as email attachments.

3581 ■ Economic History Association (EHA)

Department of Economics
University of Arizona
McClelland Hall, 401GG
1130 E Helen St
Tucson, AZ 85721-0108
Ph: (520) 621-4421
Fax: (520) 621-8450
E-mail: fishback@email.arizona.edu
URL: eh.net/eha

3582 ■ Arthur H. Cole Grants in Aid (Doctorate/ Grant)

Purpose: To support research in economic history, regardless of time period or geographic area. **Focus:** History, Economic. **Qualif.:** Applicant must be a member of the association and must hold a Ph.D. degree. **Criteria:** Applicants with recent PhD degrees are given preference.

Funds Avail.: $5,000. **To Apply:** Applicants must email required information: name, home address, institutional affiliation and contact information; submit a (five-page, single-spaced) proposal, inclusive of any footnotes, tables, and bibliography. Proposal should discuss how this grant will facilitate completion of the research; a curriculum vitae; and a project budget. **Deadline:** March 1. **Contact:** Questions should be forwarded to Prof. Robert McGuire at rmcquire@uakron.edu.

3583 ■ EHA Exploratory Travel and Data Grants (Doctorate/Grant)

Purpose: To provide funding for doctoral students intending to write a dissertation in economic history. **Focus:** History, Economic. **Qualif.:** Applicants must be doctoral students and current association members. **Criteria:** Recipients will be selected based on Committee's review of the application materials submitted.

Funds Avail.: $2,500. **To Apply:** Applicants must e-mail required information: name, home address, institutional affiliation, contact information and the name of the chair of the dissertation committee; submit a copy of current curriculum vitae; a (one-page) itemized budget; a (three-page, single-spaced) proposal (inclusive of any footnotes, tables,

Awards are arranged alphabetically below their administering organizations

and bibliography) that describes the topic, how the fellowship will help to complete the thesis, describes the work to date, time-table of completion and a brief bibliography. **Deadline:** January 13. **Contact:** Questions should be forwarded to Prof. Robert McGuire at rmcquire@uakron.edu.

3584 ■ EHA Graduate Dissertation Fellowships
(Doctorate/Fellowship)

Purpose: To support students whose thesis topics have been approved and who have made some progress towards writing their dissertation. **Focus:** History, Economic. **Qualif.:** Applicants must be current association members. **Criteria:** Recipients will be selected based on the committee's review of the application materials submitted.

Funds Avail.: $10,000. **To Apply:** Applicants must e-mail required information: name, home address, institutional affiliation, contact information and two reference letters (one from the chair of the thesis committee); submit a copy of current curriculum vitae; (five-page, single-spaced) proposal (inclusive of any footnotes, tables, and bibliography) that describes the topic, how the fellowship will help to complete the thesis, describes the work to date, time-table of completion and a brief bibliography; and a draft of a completed thesis chapter. **Deadline:** January 13. **Contact:** Questions should be forwarded to Prof. Robert McGuire at rmcquire@uakron.edu.

3585 ■ EDiS Company
One Riverwalk Ctr.
110 S Poplar St.
Wilmington, DE 19801
Ph: (302) 421-5700
Fax: (302) 421-5715
URL: www.ediscompany.com

3586 ■ Generation III Scholarships
(Undergraduate/Scholarship)

Purpose: To recognize members of the community who played a part in the growth of EDiS. **Focus:** Architecture; Engineering; Business. **Qualif.:** Applicant must be a resident within the community in which EDiS is currently working; must not be any employee of an EDiS Company or a relative of an employee of an EDiS Company; must be pursuing either an Associate's degree or Bachelor's degree; field of study is limited to business or construction-related degrees; and must have a cumulative GPA of 2.5 or greater for renewal. **Criteria:** Awards are given based on academic achievement, financial aid and field of study.

Funds Avail.: $1,000 renewable. **To Apply:** Applicants must submit a completed scholarship application together with official transcript (from current institution) and a copy of best SAT score. **Deadline:** April 13. **Contact:** Ms. Leslie Rensi at the above address.

3587 ■ Editors Association of Canada (EAC)
505-27 Carlton St.
Toronto, ON, Canada M5B 1L2
Ph: (416) 975-1379
Fax: (416) 975-1637
Free: 866-226-3348
E-mail: info@editors.ca
URL: www.editors.ca

3588 ■ Claudette Upton Scholarships
(Undergraduate/Scholarship)

Purpose: To support continuing professional development in editing. **Focus:** Editors and editing. **Qualif.:** Applicants must be student members of EAC. **Criteria:** Scholarship will be given to a student who demonstrates an aptitude for editing, commitment to pursuing a career as an editor, and other qualifications reminiscent of honorary life member Claudette Upton.

Funds Avail.: $1,000. **To Apply:** Applicants must submit the following documents: 1) a reference letter from an instructor; 2) maximum two-page resume; and 3) 300-word statement in response to the question "At the end of a long career as an editor, what would be the one thing you hope to be the most proud of?" **Deadline:** January 29. **Contact:** Application form and supporting documents may be sent via e-mail at claudetteuptonscholarship@editors.ca.

3589 ■ Edmonton Epilepsy Association (EEA)
11007 - 124 St. NW
Edmonton, AB, Canada T5M 0J5
Ph: (780) 488-9600
Fax: (780) 447-5486
Free: 866-374-5377
E-mail: info@edmontonepilepsy.org
URL: www.edmontonepilepsy.org

3590 ■ Edmonton Epilepsy Continuing Education Scholarships *(Undergraduate/Scholarship)*

Purpose: To open doors for incoming or continuing Canadian college students who are under epilepsy care. **Focus:** General studies. **Qualif.:** Applicants must be Greater-Edmonton area students aged 17-29 years of age who are Canadian Citizens or who have Landed Immigrant status and who are currently under a Canadian physician's care for epilepsy. Visa students are not eligible for this award. **Criteria:** Recipients will be selected based on Committee's review of all applications and supporting documents.

Funds Avail.: $1,000. **Number Awarded:** 2. **To Apply:** Applicants must submit a completed application form available from the website; a short essay (600-1,200 words) on "How Can I Personally Help Increase Epilepsy Education in my Community?"; three letters of recommendation of which one must come from someone from academia; copy of immigration papers (if landed immigrant); an unofficial copy of the current academic transcript; and a copy of university, college, or graduate school application(s)/acceptance letter, or confirmation of enrollment. Complete application package must be submitted to: Scholarship Awards, Edmonton Epilepsy Association, 11007-124 St., Edmonton, AB T5M 0J5. **Deadline:** March 1. **Contact:** info@edmontonepilepsy.org.

3591 ■ Edon Farmers Cooperative Association Inc.
205 S Michigan St.
Edon, OH 43518
Ph: (419) 272-2121
Fax: (419) 272-2304
Free: 800-878-4093
E-mail: rdunbar@edonfarmerscoop.com
URL: www.edonfarmerscoop.com

Awards are arranged alphabetically below their administering organizations

3592 ■ Edon Farmers Cooperative Scholarships (Undergraduate/Scholarship)

Purpose: To provide financial assistance for high school seniors to further their education as full-time students in any post high school institution. **Focus:** Agricultural sciences. **Qualif.:** Applicants must be dependents of a stockholder going into any field of study or any students going into an agricultural field; and must be high school seniors in any post high school institutions. **Criteria:** Recipients are selected based on demonstrated scholarship potential, spirit of hard work, leadership ability, interest in extracurricular activities and commitment to reach personal goals. Financial need will be one of the considerations but not necessarily the primary factor.

Funds Avail.: $1,000. **To Apply:** Applicants must submit all the required application information. **Deadline:** April 1.

3593 ■ Educational Audiology Association (EAA)
3030 W 81st Ave.
Westminster, CO 80031
Ph: (800) 460-7322
Fax: (303) 458-0002
Free: 800-460-7322
E-mail: admin@edaud.org
URL: www.edaud.org

3594 ■ Fred Berg Awards (All/Award)

Purpose: To promote educational audiology. **Focus:** Speech and language pathology/ audiology. **Qualif.:** Applicants may be members or nonmembers of EAA. **Criteria:** Awards will be given based on the committee's criteria. The Nominations and Awards Committee reviews the nominations and makes recommendations to the EAA Executive Committee for approval.

Funds Avail.: No specific amount. **Number Awarded:** Varies. **To Apply:** Nominator must submit a letter stating the applicant's specific qualifications for the award; two additional letters of support; and the applicant's vitae.

3595 ■ Educational Audiology Association Doctoral Scholarships (Doctorate/Scholarship)

Purpose: To promote the educational audiology. **Focus:** Speech and language pathology/audiology. **Qualif.:** Applicant must be a member of EAA; practicing as an educational audiologist; be matriculated in an official doctoral program. **Criteria:** Recipient is awarded based on committee's review of their application.

Funds Avail.: $500. **Number Awarded:** Three. **To Apply:** Applicants must submit all supporting documentation. **Deadline:** Rolling submissions will be accepted all year.

3596 ■ Noel D. Matkin Awards (Undergraduate/Award)

Purpose: To promote educational audiology. **Focus:** Speech and language pathology/audiology. **Qualif.:** Applicant must be a member of EAA. **Criteria:** Award will be given to practitioners and students who are EAA members.

Funds Avail.: No specific amount. **Number Awarded:** Varies. **To Apply:** Members are encouraged to submit proposals for these awards. The proposals should be typed, double-spaced, and should include the requested information on the pdf rule. The proposals should include section headings and number pages. Applicants must submit a letter of support from their academic advisor, research mentor

or program director. **Deadline:** February 1. **Contact:** EAA Headquarters, 3030 W 81st Ave., Westminster, Colorado 80031.

3597 ■ Educational Foundation for Women in Accounting (EFWA)
136 S Keowee St.
Dayton, OH 45402
Ph: (937) 424-3391
Fax: (937) 222-5794
E-mail: info@efwa.org
URL: www.efwa.org

3598 ■ EFWA Moss Adams Foundation Scholarships (Graduate, Undergraduate/Scholarship)

Purpose: To provide financial assistance to female reentry students who wish to pursue a degree in accounting. **Focus:** Accounting. **Qualif.:** Applicants must be women returning to school with undergraduate status; incoming, current, or reentry junior or seniors; must be minority women; or pursuing their fifth year requirement through either general studies or within a graduate program. **Criteria:** Scholarship recipients will be selected based on commitment of the career goals, aptitude for accounting and business and financial need. Preference will be given to those individuals who have demonstrated financial need.

Funds Avail.: $1,000. **To Apply:** Applicants must submit a completed application with all attachments (scholastic record; employment record; volunteer activities; professional activities; honors; career goals; personal goals; financial need; tax returns; references; and complete school contact information) to Educational Foundation for Women in Accounting. **Deadline:** April 30.

3599 ■ Michele L. McDonald Scholarships (Undergraduate/Scholarship)

Purpose: To provide financial assistance to female reentry students who wish to pursue a degree in accounting. **Focus:** Accounting. **Qualif.:** Applicants must be women returning to college from the work force or after raising children. **Criteria:** Scholarship recipients will be selected based on commitment of the career goals, aptitude for accounting and business, established plans for achieving goals, both personal and professional, financial need and demonstration of how this scholarship will impact their lives. Preference will be given to those female applicants returning to college from the work force or after raising children.

Funds Avail.: $1,000. **To Apply:** Applicants must submit a completed application with all attachments (scholastic record; employment record; volunteer activities; professional activities; honors; career goals; personal goals; financial need; tax returns; references; and complete school contact information) to Educational Foundation for Women in Accounting. **Deadline:** April 30. **Remarks:** Established by the Albuquerque chapter of the American Society of Women Accountants in memory of one of their members and was transferred to EFWA in 2006.

3600 ■ Seattle Chapter ASWA Scholarships (Undergraduate/Scholarship)

Purpose: To provide financial assistance for students pursuing a degree in accounting. **Focus:** Accounting. **Qualif.:** Applicants must be women who are enrolled in an accounting program at an accredited school in the State of

Awards are arranged alphabetically below their administering organizations

Washington. **Criteria:** Scholarship recipients will be selected based on commitment of the career goals, aptitude for accounting and business, financial need and demonstration of how the scholarship will impact her life.

Funds Avail.: $2,000. **To Apply:** Applicants must submit a completed application with all attachments (scholastic record; employment record; volunteer activities; professional activities; honors; career goals; personal goals; financial need; tax returns; references; and complete school contact information) to Educational Foundation for Women in Accounting.

3601 ■ Women In Need Scholarships
(Undergraduate/Scholarship)

Purpose: To provide financial assistance to female reentry students who wish to pursue a degree in accounting. **Focus:** Accounting. **Qualif.:** Applicants should be incoming, current, or reentry juniors or seniors. **Criteria:** Scholarship recipients will be selected based on commitment of the career goals, aptitude for accounting and business, established plans for achieving goals, both personal and professional, financial need and demonstration of how this scholarship will impact their lives.

Funds Avail.: $2,000. **Number Awarded:** 1. **To Apply:** Applicants must submit a completed application with all attachments (scholastic record; employment record; volunteer activities; professional activities; honors; career goals; personal goals; financial need; tax returns; references; and complete school contact information) to Educational Foundation for Women in Accounting. **Deadline:** April 30. **Remarks:** Created by the Board of Trustees in 2000.

3602 ■ Women In Transition Scholarships
(Undergraduate/Scholarship)

Purpose: To provide financial assistance to female reentry students who wish to pursue a degree in accounting. **Focus:** Accounting. **Qualif.:** Applicants should be incoming or current freshmen and women returning to school with a freshman status. **Criteria:** Applicants will be judged based on the following criteria: 1) Commitment to the goal of pursuing a degree in accounting, including evidence of continued commitment after receiving the award; 2) Aptitude for accounting and business; 3) Clear evidence that the candidate has established goals and a plan for achieving those goals, both personal and professional; 4) Financial need; and 5) Demonstration of how the scholarship will impact her life.

Funds Avail.: Up to $16,000. **Number Awarded:** 1. **To Apply:** Applicants must submit a completed application with all attachments (scholastic record; employment record; volunteer activities; professional activities; honors; career goals; personal goals; financial need; tax returns; references; and complete school contact information) to Educational Foundation for Women in Accounting. **Deadline:** April 30. **Remarks:** Established in 1990 to commemorate the 25th Anniversary of the Educational Foundation. **Contact:** Audrey Hutchinson.

3603 ■ Educational Portal of the Americas
1889 F St. NW
Washington, DC 20006
Ph: (202) 458-6166
E-mail: portal@oas.org
URL: www.educoas.org

3604 ■ Educational Portal of the Americas Graduate Scholarships *(Postgraduate/Scholarship)*

Purpose: To award a person to undertake undergraduate or graduate studies that lead to a degree and/or graduate research at a university or higher learning institution of member state. **Focus:** General Studies. **Qualif.:** Applicants must be enrolled in a Master's or Doctorate's degree. **Criteria:** Recipients are selected based on merit and financial need.

Funds Avail.: $30,000. **Number Awarded:** 2. **To Apply:** Applicants must present a complete application form. **Contact:** scholarships@oas.org.

3605 ■ Educational Portal of the Americas Undergraduate Scholarships *(Undergraduate/Scholarship)*

Purpose: To award a person to undertake undergraduate or graduate studies that lead to a degree and/or graduate research in a university or higher learning institution of a member state. **Focus:** General Studies. **Qualif.:** Applicants must be accepted into the university where they plan to study the last two years of undergraduate degree. **Criteria:** Recipients are selected based on the available financing.

Funds Avail.: $30,000. **To Apply:** Applicants must present complete application form. **Contact:** scholarships@oas.org.

3606 ■ Educational Research Center of America (ERCA)
PO Box 9012
Lynbrook, NY 11563
Ph: (561) 882-9800
E-mail: info@studentresearch.org
URL: www.studentresearch.org

3607 ■ ERCA Community Contribution Scholarships *(Undergraduate/Scholarship)*

Purpose: To help high school students further their education and professional development. **Focus:** General studies. **Qualif.:** Applicant must be a high school student and a legal resident of the United States. Applicant must also have recognized a need/problem in his/her community and has determined a way to address this need or solve the problem with a developed action plan. **Criteria:** Applications are sorted by graduation year. Judges will select 25 finalists from the 50 semi-finalists based on project quality, grades, honors and activities.

Funds Avail.: $1,000. **Number Awarded:** 25. **To Apply:** Applicants must submit a completed official ERCA Community Contribution Scholarship Competition Application. **Deadline:** July 13.

3608 ■ Educational Testing Service
225 Phillips Blvd.
Ewing, NJ 08628
Ph: (609) 921-9000
Fax: (609) 734-5410
URL: www.ets.org

3609 ■ ETS Postdoctoral Fellowships
(Postdoctorate/Fellowship)

Purpose: To increase the number of women and underrepresented minority professionals conducting research in

Awards are arranged alphabetically below their administering organizations

educational measurement and related fields. **Focus:** Psychology; Linguistics; Speech and language pathology/audiology; Teaching; Statistics. **Qualif.:** Applicant must be a doctorate in a relevant discipline within the past three years and has evidence of prior research. **Criteria:** Selection is based on the applicant's scholarship and the technical strength of the proposed research topic.

Funds Avail.: $55,000. **To Apply:** Applicant must send a one-page abstract about the research and a letter of intent. If the submitted abstract is approved, applicants must submit a detailed proposal (approximately 5 double-spaced pages) describing the research that will be carried out at ETS and how it relates to current ETS research; a current curriculum vita; official graduate academic transcripts; and names and e-mail addresses of three individuals familiar with the applicant's work and willing to complete a recommendation form. Submit all application materials via e-mail at internfellowships@ets.org as PDF attachments, except for the transcripts which must be sent via regular mail. **Contact:** 609-734-5543 or internfellowships@ets.org.

3610 ■ Harold Gulliksen Psychometric Research Fellowships *(Doctorate, Graduate/Fellowship)*

Purpose: To increase the number of well-trained scientists in educational measurement, psychometrics and statistics. **Focus:** Psychology; Linguistics; Speech and language pathology/audiology; Teaching; Statistics. **Qualif.:** Applicant must be enrolled in a doctoral program; have completed all the coursework toward the PhD; be at the dissertation stage of the program (dissertation topics in the areas of psychometrics, statistics, educational/psychological measurement, or quantitative methods will be given priority). **Criteria:** Selection is based on the strength of the applicant's academic credentials and the suitability and technical strength of the proposed research project.

Funds Avail.: $15,000 stipend, $7,500 for tuition, fees and work-study program commitments. **To Apply:** For Preliminary application, applicants must submit a letter of interest (approximately five double-spaced pages) describing the research that would be undertaken during the award year and how the research fits with ETS research efforts; a nomination letter (either as an e-mail or as an e-mail with a PDF attachment) from an academic advisor; and a current curriculum vitae. For final application, applicants must submit a detailed project description (approximately 15 double-spaced pages) of the research the applicant will carry out at the host university, including the purpose, goals and methods of the research; official graduate academic transcripts; and evidence of scholarship (presentations, manuscripts, etc.). Submit all application materials via e-mail at internfellowships@ets.org as PDF attachments. **Deadline:** December 1 (preliminary application), February 1 (final application). **Contact:** 609-734-5543 or internfellowships@ets.org.

3611 ■ Sylvia Taylor Johnson Minority Fellowships in Educational Measurement *(Doctorate/Fellowship)*

Purpose: To encourage original and significant research for early-career scholars. **Focus:** Psychology; Linguistics; Speech and language pathology/audiology; Teaching; Statistics. **Qualif.:** Applicant must have received doctorate within the past ten years and be a U.S. citizen or permanent resident. **Criteria:** Selection is based on applicant's record of accomplishments, proposed topic of research, commitment to education and independent body of scholarship

that signals the promise of continuing outstanding contributions to educational measurement.

Funds Avail.: No specific amount. **To Apply:** Applicants must submit a letter of interest; a detailed proposal (approximately five double-spaced pages in length) of the type of research the applicant will conduct at ETS; current curriculum vita; the names and e-mail addresses of three individuals familiar with the applicant's work and willing to complete a recommendation form; samples of published research; and official graduate academic transcripts. Submit all application materials via e-mail at internfellowships@ets.org as PDF attachments. **Contact:** 609-734-5543 or internfellowships@ets.org.

3612 ■ Eisenhower World Affairs Institute
818 Connecticut Ave. NW, 18th Fl.
Washington, DC 20006
Ph: (202) 628-4444
Fax: (202) 628-4445
E-mail: ei@eisenhowerinstitute.org
URL: www.eisenhowerinstitute.org

3613 ■ Conrad N. Hilton Scholarships *(Undergraduate/Scholarship)*

Purpose: To help American students study abroad. **Focus:** Social sciences. **Qualif.:** Applicant must be a Gettysburg College senior or junior undergraduate student planning to study abroad; have at least a 3.0 cumulative GPA (can be waived for applicants with strong needs or qualifications); and must be social science or interdisciplinary majors. **Criteria:** Selection is based on merit.

Funds Avail.: $4,000. **Number Awarded:** 3. **To Apply:** Applicant must submit an academic transcript; a resume; a statement of career aspirations (maximum of 1,000 words); a letter of recommendation from the candidate's faculty advisor or department chair; and a copy of a (10-15 page) paper (within the last four months) from a course in the applicant's major field of study. Submit it at Gettysburg College. **Deadline:** January 24.

3614 ■ Clifford Roberts Graduate Fellowships *(Doctorate/Fellowship)*

Purpose: To support study and education dealing with the role of government in a free society, the relationship between international and domestic issues and improved understanding of world affairs. **Focus:** Public affairs. **Qualif.:** Applicant must be at an advanced stage of their doctoral candidacies, preferably preparing a dissertation. **Criteria:** Selection is based on merit. The Institute will consider the applications of less advanced graduate students or persons who recently earned their PhD and pursuing the Institute's field of interest.

Funds Avail.: $10,000. **Number Awarded:** 2. **To Apply:** Applicants must submit a curriculum vitae; a statement describing the nature and scope of the dissertation; a 10- to 15-page writing sample on a topic related to the dissertation; a 1,000-word statement of career aspirations; two letters of recommendation; and other required materials by the university. Submit materials at the participating universities. **Deadline:** April 10. **Remarks:** The program is available only at the participating universities. **Contact:** Rick Farwell at 202-628-4444, or rfarwell@gettysburg.edu.

3615 ■ Ann Cook Whitman Scholarships for Perry High School *(Undergraduate/Scholarship)*

Purpose: To help students obtain undergraduate degrees in furtherance of education and leadership skills. **Focus:**

Awards are arranged alphabetically below their administering organizations

General studies. **Qualif.:** Applicant must be a high school senior student at Perry High School planning to receive an undergraduate education; and have an average of B and above (can be waived for applicants with strong needs or qualifications). **Criteria:** Selection is based on need and merit.

Funds Avail.: $4,000. **Number Awarded:** 2. **To Apply:** Applicant must submit an academic transcript; a resume; a statement of career aspirations (maximum of 1,000 words); a letter of recommendation from the candidate's faculty advisor or guidance counselor; another letter of recommendation from a member of the Perry, Ohio community other than a family member; and documentation from Perry High School on its needs-based assessment procedures for its nominees. Submit materials at the Perry High School. **Deadline:** April 10.

3616 ■ Ann Cook Whitman Washington, DC Scholarships *(Undergraduate/Scholarship)*

Purpose: To assist graduating African-American seniors from the District of Columbia public education system in obtaining an undergraduate degree in furtherance of their education and leadership skills. **Focus:** General studies. **Qualif.:** Applicant must be an African-American senior student from any of four eligible high schools (Spingarn, H.D. Woodson, Ballou, and Eastern) pursuing an undergraduate education; and have a 2.8 GPA or above (can be waived for applicants with strong needs or qualifications). **Criteria:** Selection is based on need and merit.

Funds Avail.: $4,000 each year for four years. **Number Awarded:** 2. **To Apply:** Applicants must submit a completed application form; academic transcript; a statement of career aspirations (maximum of 500 words); identification of colleges/universities applied to; a letter of recommendation from a faculty member or the guidance counselor; and another letter of recommendation from a member of the Washington, DC community, other than a family member. Submit materials at the applicant's respective high school. **Deadline:** April 10.

3617 ■ EJLB Foundation

1350 Sherbrooke St. W, Ste. 1050
Montreal, QC, Canada H3G 1J1
Fax: (514) 843-4080
URL: www.ejlb.qc.ca

3618 ■ EJLB Foundation's Scholar Research Programme *(Graduate, Postgraduate/Scholarship)*

Purpose: To support scientific research through financial assistance. **Focus:** Science technologies. **Qualif.:** Applicants must be scientists who have earned an M.D. and/or a Ph.D. degree; must have completed their post-graduate training and have been admitted in the preceding seven years as faculty members of a leading university and affiliated non profit research center. **Criteria:** Recipients will be selected by the Scientific Advisory Committee.

Funds Avail.: $350,000. **Number Awarded:** 3. **To Apply:** For further information applicants are advised to contact the foundation at The EJLB Foundation, 1350 Sherbrooke St. W, Ste. 1050, Montreal, QC H3G 1J1.

3619 ■ El Dorado County Mineral and Gem Society

PO Box 950
Placerville, CA 95667-0950

Ph: (530) 676-2472
URL: www.eldoradomineralandgem.org

3620 ■ El Dorado County Mineral and Gem Society Scholarships *(Graduate, Undergraduate/Scholarship)*

Purpose: To provide scholarships to residents of El Dorado County who are pursuing a degree and/or career in earth sciences, lapidary arts and other related fields at an accredited college or university. **Focus:** Earth sciences. **Qualif.:** Applicant must be a graduate of an El Dorado County high school, who may now be attending a college or graduate school outside of the County. **Criteria:** Selection is based on the application.

Funds Avail.: $500-$1,000. **Number Awarded:** 1. **To Apply:** Applicants must submit a completed application form along with a current transcript; a personal essay of 300-500 words; and two letters of reference, one of which is from a faculty member and the other from someone who is not a member of the applicant's family. **Deadline:** May 1.

3621 ■ El Pomar Foundation

10 Lake Cir.
Colorado Springs, CO 80906
Ph: (719) 633-7733
Fax: (719) 577-5702
Free: 800-554-7711
E-mail: communications@elpomar.org
URL: www.elpomar.org

3622 ■ El Pomar Fellowships *(Graduate/Fellowship)*

Purpose: To encourage and promote current well-being of the people of Colorado. **Focus:** General studies. **Qualif.:** Applicant must be a graduate of a four-year university/college; have a Colorado connection (a Colorado resident, have attended a Colorado college/university, or have immediate family who are residents or past residents); must demonstrate strong leadership capability and potential; must exhibit the highest standards of professionalism and behavior; possess strong verbal and writing skills; must demonstrate personal initiative and determination; and have the ability to travel throughout the state of Colorado on official Foundation business. **Criteria:** Selection is based on submitted application materials.

Funds Avail.: No specific amount. **To Apply:** Applicants must submit a 1-2 page letter on leadership experience, career objectives, and interest in the Fellowship program; a resume; college transcript(s); and two letters of recommendation. **Contact:** Gary Butterworth at 719-577-7037 or fellowship@elpomar.org.

3623 ■ Electrochemical Society (ECS)

65 S Main St., Bldg. D
Pennington, NJ 08534-2839
Ph: (609) 737-1902
Fax: (609) 737-2743
E-mail: ecs@electrochem.org
URL: www.electrochem.org

3624 ■ Oronzio de Nora Industrial Electrochemistry Fellowships *(Postdoctorate/Fellowship)*

Purpose: To provide financial support to a postdoctoral scientist or engineer for research in the field of industrial

Awards are arranged alphabetically below their administering organizations

electrochemistry. **Focus:** Electrochemistry. **Qualif.:** Applicant must be a postdoctoral scientist or engineer continuing research in industrial electrochemistry. **Criteria:** Selection is based on the proposed research topics in the areas of electrochemistry.

Funds Avail.: $25,000. **Number Awarded:** 1. **To Apply:** Applicants must submit an essay (1,000 words or less) addressing personal interests/career goals related to the fellowship position, and talents brought to the fellowship, along with a curriculum vitae; three letters of recommendation (should include letter of support from the group receiving the fellow); and transcripts. **Deadline:** January 1. **Remarks:** Established in 2003. **Contact:** awards@electrochem.org.

3625 ■ Summer Fellowships of The Electrochemical Society *(Graduate/Fellowship)*

Purpose: To assist a student in the pursuit of work in a field of interest to The Electrochemical Society. **Focus:** Electrochemistry. **Qualif.:** Applicant must be a graduate student pursuing work between the degrees of BS and PhD in a college/university, and who will continue his/her studies after the summer period. **Criteria:** Selection is based on the application materials submitted.

Funds Avail.: $5,000. **Number Awarded:** 1-5. **To Apply:** Applicants must submit a completed application form along with the required materials to: Dr. Vimal H. Desai, Office of the VP for Research, New Mexico State University, MSC 3RES-Box 30001, Las Cruces, NM 88033-8001, USA. **Deadline:** January 1. **Contact:** Dr. Vimal H. Desai, E-mail: vimalc@nmsu.edu; Tel: 505-646-3425; Fax: 505-646-2480.

3626 ■ Electronic Document Systems Foundation (EDSF)
1845 Precinct Line Rd., Ste. 212
Hurst, TX 76054
Ph: (817) 849-1145
Fax: (817) 849-1185
E-mail: info@edsf.org
URL: www.edsf.org

3627 ■ Document Management and Graphic Communications Industry Scholarships *(Undergraduate/Scholarship)*

Purpose: To recognize and support the next generation of professionals for the document management and communication companies worldwide. **Focus:** Computer and information sciences; Engineering; Communications technologies. **Qualif.:** Applicants must be full-time students who are committed to pursuing careers in document management and communications marketplace which include computer science and engineering, graphic and media communications and those students interested in Business in the document management and communications industry; must have a minimum GPA of 3.0 or a 'B' average; must be technical, trade school, community college, undergraduate and advanced-degree students in the U.S. and/or diploma or tertiary students outside of the U.S. may be considered for scholarships; must be students who are attending full-time, an accredited college or university. **Criteria:** Applicants are evaluated based on any one or a combination of the following: Scholastic achievement, application essay, participation in school activities, community service, honors and organizational affiliations and education objectives.

Funds Avail.: $1000-$5,000. **To Apply:** Applicants must

submit all the required application information. **Deadline:** May 1. **Contact:** May 2.

3628 ■ Elks National Foundation (ENF)
2750 N Lakeview Ave.
Chicago, IL 60614-2256
Ph: (773) 755-4728
Fax: (773) 755-4729
E-mail: enf@elks.org
URL: www.elks.org

3629 ■ Elks National Foundation Scholarships *(Undergraduate/Scholarship)*

Purpose: To build stronger communities. **Focus:** General studies. **Qualif.:** Applicants must be undergraduates in an institution, college, or university. **Criteria:** Recipients are selected based on financial need and scholastic standing.

Funds Avail.: No specific amount. **To Apply:** Applicants must complete the application form. **Contact:** scholarship@elks.org.

3630 ■ Clay Elliott Scholarship Foundation
975-A Elgin St. W, Ste. 263
Cobourg, ON, Canada K9A 5J3
Ph: (905) 372-7549
E-mail: info@attitudesforeducation.com
URL: www.attitudesforeducation.com

3631 ■ Clay Elliott Scholarship Foundation Scholarships *(Undergraduate/Scholarship)*

Purpose: To provide financial support to qualified high school students who want to pursue their education. **Focus:** General studies. **Qualif.:** Applicant must be a graduating student in the current school year; must be a Canadian citizen; must have notification of acceptance into a full-time post-secondary program; must be a current resident of Northumberland County; must be attending a high school within Northumberland County. **Criteria:** Selection is based on the application materials.

Funds Avail.: $1,500 for the first academic year; $1,000 for each additional year. **To Apply:** Applicant must submit a personal information and two reference letter (one must be an academic reference); must provide a written future academic plan. **Deadline:** May 4.

3632 ■ Emergency Nurses Association (ENA)
915 Lee St.
Des Plaines, IL 60016-6569
Ph: (847) 460-4120
Fax: (847) 460-4002
Free: 800-900-9659
E-mail: execoffice@ena.org
URL: www.ena.org

3633 ■ BCEN Undergraduate Scholarships *(Undergraduate/Scholarship)*

Purpose: To promote education or research on emergency care. **Focus:** Nursing. **Qualif.:** Applicants must be nurses with a current BCEN credential (CEN, CPEN, CFRN or CTRN) who are pursuing a baccalaureate degree in nursing; must be ENA members for at least one year; and with a minimum GPA of 3.0 **Criteria:** Applicants will be evalu-

Awards are arranged alphabetically below their administering organizations

ated by the ENA Foundation review panel.

Funds Avail.: $3,000. **Number Awarded:** 1. **To Apply:** Applicants must provide a letter verifying the school's current accreditation with the application (visit the website for the application). If not a member, applicant must provide a letter of reference from an ENA member. Applications submitted electronically must include scanned copies of the required documents: signed copy of the application; official transcripts; and reference letters. Applications must be mailed or e-mailed only. **Deadline:** June 1. **Remarks:** Do not staple materials, use paper clips or binder clips. Faxed materials will be disqualified. **Contact:** ENA Foundation Office, 800-900-9659 x-4100 or 847-460-4100, foundation@ena.org.

3634 ■ Emergency Nurses Association Undergraduate Scholarships (Undergraduate/Scholarship)

Purpose: To promote education or research on emergency care. **Focus:** Nursing. **Qualif.:** Applicants must be attending a NLN, CCNE, or AACN accredited school; must be ENA members for at least one year; and must have a minimum GPA of 3.0. **Criteria:** Applicants will be evaluated by the ENA Foundation review panel.

Funds Avail.: No specific amount. **To Apply:** Applicants must provide a letter verifying the school's current accreditation together with the application form. If not a member, applicant must provide a letter of reference from an ENA member. **Deadline:** June 1. **Remarks:** Do not staple materials, use paper clips or binder clips. Faxed materials will be disqualified. **Contact:** For further information, applicants may e-mail foundation@ena.org or contact a member of the Development Department at 847-460-4100.

3635 ■ Faculty Doctoral Scholarships (Doctorate/Scholarship)

Purpose: To promote education or research on emergency care. **Focus:** Nursing. **Qualif.:** Applicants must be attending a NLN or AACN accredited school; must be ENA members for at least one year; working on a dissertation related to emergency nursing. **Criteria:** Applicants will be evaluated by the ENA Foundation review panel.

Funds Avail.: $10,000 and $5,000. **Number Awarded:** 2. **To Apply:** Applicants must provide a letter verifying the school's current accreditation with the applications (visit the website for the application); proof of acceptance in an accredited doctoral program in nursing; and a statement about the applicant's career intent. **Deadline:** June 1. **Remarks:** Do not staple materials, use paper clips or binder clips. Faxed materials will be disqualified. **Contact:** ENA Foundation Office, 800-900-9658 x-4100, foundation@ena.org.

3636 ■ Endocrine Society
8401 Connecticut Ave., Ste. 900
Chevy Chase, MD 20815-5817
Ph: (301) 941-0200
Fax: (301) 941-0259
Free: 888-363-6274
E-mail: societyservices@endo-society.org
URL: www.endo-society.org

3637 ■ Amgen Scholars Fellowships (Doctorate, Professional development/Fellowship)

Purpose: To support fellows who perform clinical research related to osteoporosis and bone disorders. **Focus:** Medi-

cine, Osteopathic. **Qualif.:** Applicants must be MD, PhD or DO fellows either enrolled in their first through third year of training in a U.S. adult or pediatric clinical endocrinology program, or have completed an adult or pediatric clinical endocrinology-training program who are proposing to do a research fellowship in a U.S. training program. **Criteria:** Selection will be based on the committee's criteria.

Funds Avail.: No specific amount. **To Apply:** Applicants may contact the society for the application process. **Deadline:** February. **Contact:** awards@endo-society.org.

3638 ■ Lilly Endocrine Scholars Fellowship Awards (Doctorate, Professional development/Fellowship)

Purpose: To support fellows who perform clinical research related to pituitary disorders, bone disorders or diabetes mellitus. **Focus:** Endocrinology. **Qualif.:** Applicants must be DO, MD or MD/PhD fellows either enrolled in their first through third year of training in a U.S. adult or pediatric clinical endocrinology program, or have completed an adult or pediatric endocrinology training program who are now proposing to do a research fellowship in a U.S. training program. **Criteria:** Selection will be based on the committee's criteria.

Funds Avail.: No specific amount. **To Apply:** Applicants may contact the society for the application process. **Deadline:** February. **Contact:** awards@endo-society.org.

3639 ■ Summer Research Fellowships (Graduate, Undergraduate/Fellowship)

Purpose: To encourage promising undergraduate students, medical students and first year graduate school students to pursue careers in endocrinology. **Focus:** Endocrinology. **Qualif.:** Applicants must be currently enrolled full-time in school and may not be employed as research assistants. Students' academic levels must fall into one of the three categories at the time they apply: undergraduate students who are currently in their third year of schooling or beyond; first year graduate students; medical students who are beyond their first year of schooling. Mentors must be active members of the Endocrine Society and projects must be under the direction of the mentor. Only one application per mentor must be submitted. **Criteria:** Selection will be based on the committee's criteria.

Funds Avail.: No specific amount. **To Apply:** Applicants must contact the society for the application process. **Contact:** awards@endo-society.org.

3640 ■ Endourological Society
4100 Duff Pl., Lower Level
Seaford, NY 11783
Ph: (516) 520-1224
Fax: (516) 520-1225
URL: www.endourology.org

3641 ■ Endourological Society Fellowships (Professional development/Fellowship)

Purpose: To establish endourology at academic centers outside the United States of America. **Focus:** Urology. **Qualif.:** Applicants must be chief residents, junior academic faculty and members of the Endourological Society with an academic appointment; must have plan to continue their academic career after completing their fellowship training. **Criteria:** Recipients will be selected based on qualifications and submitted materials.

Awards are arranged alphabetically below their administering organizations

Funds Avail.: $2,000 monthly. **Number Awarded:** 3. **To Apply:** Applicants must submit a curriculum vitae, letters of recommendation from three urologists who have practiced with the individual and are familiar with their surgical abilities, letter from the Chairman of department or division of Urology; must provide a one to two-page narrative outlining the following: 1) reasons for seeking the fellowship position; 2) reasons for selecting one or two places they plan to visit; and 3) how fellowship will impact their career future plans once completed; must submit a one-page description of the research project and letter of support from the head of endourological program. **Contact:** Michele Paoli at the above address.

3642 ■ Energy and Mineral Law Foundation (EMLF)

340 S Broadway, Ste. 101
Lexington, KY 40508
Ph: (859) 231-0271
Fax: (859) 226-0485
E-mail: info@emlf.org
URL: www.emlf.org

3643 ■ EMLF Law Student Scholarships
(Undergraduate/Scholarship)

Purpose: To provide educational assistance to encourage the study of energy, environmental, natural resources, and mineral law. **Focus:** Environmental science, Natural resources, Mineralogy, Energy-related areas; Environmental law. **Qualif.:** Applicants must be law school students for the current academic year and must demonstrate an interest in the study of natural resources, energy or mineral law. **Criteria:** Recipient will be selected based on the following criteria: a) potential to make a significant contribution in the field of energy, mineral and natural resources law; b) academic ability; c) leadership ability; and d) financial need.

Funds Avail.: $1,000-$3,000. **To Apply:** Applicants must submit a complete application form; transcript of records; and two letters of recommendation from school dean, faculty member, or member of the legal profession. **Deadline:** April 18. **Contact:** Application form and other supporting documents may be sent electronically at carolyn@emlf.org.

3644 ■ Enlisted Association of National Guard of the United States (EANGUS)

3133 Mt. Vernon Ave.
Alexandria, VA 22305-2640
Ph: (703) 519-3846
Fax: (703) 519-3849
Free: 800-234-EANG
E-mail: eangus@eangus.org
URL: www.eangus.org

3645 ■ CSM Virgil R. Williams Scholarships
(Undergraduate/Scholarship)

Purpose: To support the education of EANGUS members, their spouses and their unmarried children. **Focus:** General studies. **Qualif.:** Applicant must be EANGUS Auxiliary members; must be unmarried, dependent sons and daughters of EANGUS Auxiliary members; must be spouses of EANGUS Auxiliary members. **Criteria:** Awards will be made based on the applicant's character, leadership and financial need.

Funds Avail.: $2,000. **Number Awarded:** 2. **To Apply:** Applicant must submit a transcript of high school credits and/or a transcript of college credits for applicants already in an institution of higher learning; must have a letter from the applicant with personal, specific facts as to his/her desire to continue his/her education and why financial assistance is required; must have three letters of academic recommendation verifying the application and giving moral, personal and leadership traits. Application form and other documents must be submitted electronically via the internet to the Chairman of the Scholarship Committee except the school transcript. **Deadline:** July 1.

3646 ■ Ennis Arts Association (EAA)

PO Box 201
Ennis, MT 59729
E-mail: info@ennisartsassociation.org
URL: www.ennisartsassociation.org

3647 ■ EAA Tuition Scholarships *(College, Vocational/Occupational/Scholarship)*

Purpose: To help students pursue their education in an arts curriculum. **Focus:** Arts. **Qualif.:** Applicants must be college or vocational technical school students who are currently or have plans to enroll in an arts curriculum; must be living or have lived within the boundaries of the Ennis/Harrison School Districts. **Criteria:** Recipients will be evaluated based on submitted materials.

Funds Avail.: $350. **To Apply:** Applicants must contact the Guidance Counselor at their prospective school. **Deadline:** April 15.

3648 ■ EAA Workshop Scholarships *(College, Vocational/Occupational/Scholarship)*

Purpose: To help students pursue their education in an arts curriculum. **Focus:** Arts. **Qualif.:** Applicants must be college or vocational technical school students who are currently or have plans to enroll in an arts curriculum; must be living or have lived within the boundaries of the Ennis/Harrison School Districts. **Criteria:** Recipients will be evaluated based on submitted materials.

Funds Avail.: $350. **To Apply:** Applicants must contact the Guidance Counselor at their prospective school. **Deadline:** April 15.

3649 ■ Entertainment Software Association (ESA)

575 7th St. NW, Ste. 300
Washington, DC 20004
Ph: (202) 223-2400
E-mail: esa@theesa.com
URL: www.theesa.com

3650 ■ ESA Foundation Computer and Video Game Scholarship Program *(Undergraduate/Scholarship)*

Purpose: To assist women and minority students who plan to continue their education in fields supporting Video Game Development. **Focus:** Graphic Arts and Design; Computer and Information Sciences. **Qualif.:** Applicants must be women or minority students; pursuing degrees leading to careers in computer and video game arts (high school seniors must already be accepted into a program); enrolling or enrolled in a full-time undergraduate course of study

Awards are arranged alphabetically below their administering organizations

at an accredited four-year college or university in the United States; maintaining a GPA of 2.75 or above on a 4.0 scale (or its equivalent); and must be US citizens. **Criteria:** Recipients are selected based on academic standing.

Funds Avail.: $3,000. **Number Awarded:** 30. **To Apply:** Applicants must complete an online application form. Applicants must provide a proof that they are currently enrolled in a college, university, or institution. **Deadline:** May 15. **Contact:** For further information, applicants must call 877-525-8491 or by email at info@applyists.com.

3651 ■ Entomological Society of America (ESA)

10001 Derekwood Ln., Ste. 100
Lanham, MD 20706-4876
Ph: (301) 731-4535
Fax: (301) 731-4538
E-mail: esa@entsoc.org
URL: www.entsoc.org

3652 ■ Stan Beck Fellowships *(Graduate, Undergraduate/Fellowship)*

Purpose: To provide educational assistance for needy students at the graduate or undergraduate level of their education in entomology and related disciplines at a college or university in the United States, Mexico, or Canada. **Focus:** Entomology. **Qualif.:** Applicants must be graduate or undergraduate students in entomology or related disciplines at colleges or universities in the United States, Mexico, or Canada. **Criteria:** Recipients are selected based on physical limitation, economic, minority, or environmental condition; recommendation of the professors and advisors; enthusiasm, interest and achievement in entomology or related disciplines; notable academic plans; and impact of need.

Funds Avail.: No specific amount. **To Apply:** Applicants must submit a letter of nomination; description of applicant's academic studies including academic plan; a statement of the applicant's need or challenge (not more than 2 pages); letter of recommendation from the applicant's academic advisor; and two letters of support demonstrating the applicant's need or challenge. **Deadline:** July 1. **Contact:** Entomological Foundation, 9331 Annapolis Rd. Ste. 210, Lanham, MD 20706.

3653 ■ BioQuip Undergraduate Scholarships *(Undergraduate/Scholarship)*

Purpose: To help students achieve their goal of obtaining a degree in entomology or pursuing a career as an entomologist. **Focus:** Biology. **Qualif.:** Applicants must be enrolled as undergraduate students in entomology in any college or university in the United States, Mexico, and Canada. **Criteria:** Selection will be based on academic credentials; personal statement; extracurricular activities including research, meeting presentations, awards and honors, and professional memberships and affiliations; letters of recommendation; and enthusiasm for entomology as culled from their personal statement and letters of recommendation.

Funds Avail.: $2,000. **To Apply:** Applicants must fill out an application form. Applicants must submit a letter of nomination; statement not exceeding two-pages in length stating interest in entomology, career goals, financial need, and other pertinent factors which illustrate qualifications for the scholarship; three statements from school officials or other knowledgeable individuals attesting to entomological

interests, character, aptitude and financial need; and current official transcript of college grades. **Deadline:** July 1. **Contact:** Entomological Foundation, 9332 Annapolis Rd. Ste. 210, Lanham MD 20706.

3654 ■ Pioneer Hi-Bred International Graduate Student Fellowships *(Graduate/Fellowship)*

Purpose: To recognize and encourage innovative research and graduate education in the area of entomology with a focus on key insects or complexes of insects that effect corn, soybeans, canola, alfalfa, or other significant commodity crops. **Focus:** Biology. **Qualif.:** Applicants must be graduate students; must have a GPA of 3.5 or higher; must attend college/university in the United States; must have demonstrated excellence in the study of entomology or a related discipline. **Criteria:** Recipients are selected based on the demonstrated excellence in the study of entomology or related discipline.

Funds Avail.: $12,500. **To Apply:** Applicants must complete the application form. Applicants must submit an official transcript of college grades; three letters of recommendation; description of the student's completed and proposed program of academic studies including brief statement of the goals, rationale and justification for the proposed project; short essay on why the student is interested in the study of insects impacting crops including significant commodity crops; statement of long range career goals and description of how the graduate program will help the student to attain the goals; up to three letters of endorsement from professional colleagues and clientele. **Remarks:** This award is given only once every 4 years. **Contact:** Entomological Foundation, 9332 Annapolis Rd. Ste. 210, Lanham, MD 20706.

3655 ■ Environmental Law Institute (ELI)

2000 L St. NW, Ste. 620
Washington, DC 20036
Ph: (202) 939-3800
E-mail: law@eli.org
URL: www.eli.org

3656 ■ Public Interest Environmental Law Fellowships *(Postgraduate/Fellowship)*

Purpose: To provide a recent law school graduate a year of legal experience and training. **Focus:** Law. **Qualif.:** Applicant must be a law school graduate or a candidate who has graduated recently, and have a top academic record and possess superior legal research and writing skills. **Criteria:** Selection is based on the application materials.

Funds Avail.: Approximately $35,000, with benefits. **To Apply:** Applicants must submit a complete application package which must include: cover letter; current resume; completed "ELI Application for Employment"; law school transcript; three references; and writing sample of approximately 10 (but no more than 15) pages. Application package must be sent via email (preferred method) to law@eli.org (subject line: Law Fellow No. 100707), or by U.S. mail. **Deadline:** December 9.

3657 ■ Environmental Research and Education Foundation (EREF)

3301 Benson Dr., Ste. 301
Raleigh, NC 27609
Ph: (919) 861-6876
Fax: (919) 861-6878

Awards are arranged alphabetically below their administering organizations

E-mail: foundation@erefdn.org
URL: www.erefdn.org

3658 ■ Environmental Research and Education Foundation Scholarships *(Doctorate, Postdoctorate/Scholarship)*

Purpose: To recognize excellence in master's, doctoral or post-doctoral waste management research and education. **Focus:** Waste Management. **Qualif.:** Applicant must be a full-time master's student, doctoral or post-doctoral researcher; must have demonstrated interest in waste management research. **Criteria:** Recipients are selected based on academics; professional performance; relevance of one's work to the advancement of solid waste management; potential for success.

Funds Avail.: $12,000 for doctoral and post-doctoral; $5,000 for master's degree. **To Apply:** Applicant must complete an application form; must submit an official college transcript; admission test scores; three recommendations; an essay of not more than 500 words that includes an autobiographical statement and discussion of research topic. Essay should be typewritten, double-spaced, unbound and unstapled. **Contact:** Bryan Staley, PhD, at scholarships@erefdn.org.

3659 ■ Epilepsy Foundation
8301 Professional Pl.
Landover, MD 20785-2223
Ph: (301) 459-3700
Fax: (301) 577-2684
Free: 800-332-1000
E-mail: contactus@efa.org
URL: www.epilepsyfoundation.org

3660 ■ Behavioral Sciences Post-Doctoral Fellowships *(Postdoctorate/Fellowship)*

Purpose: To provide financial assistance for post-doctoral training of behavioral scientists committed to epilepsy research. **Focus:** Social sciences; Behavioral Sciences; Epilepsy. **Qualif.:** Applicants must receive their doctoral degrees in the field of social sciences by the time the fellowship commences; have an acceptable research plan; and have an access to institutional resources in conducting the project. **Criteria:** Applications are evaluated based on the quality of the proposed project; applicant's and preceptor's qualifications; and adequacy of the facility.

Funds Avail.: $40,000. **To Apply:** Applicants must complete an application form with letters of recommendation included. **Deadline:** March 21.

3661 ■ Behavioral Sciences Student Fellowships *(Graduate, Undergraduate/Fellowship)*

Purpose: To encourage individuals to pursue careers in epilepsy in either the research or practice setting. **Focus:** Behavioral sciences; Epilepsy. **Qualif.:** Applicants must be undergraduates or graduate students who are studying a field related to epilepsy research or clinical care; have (three months) free period to conduct the research; have qualified mentor; and have an access to institutional resources including clinics and laboratories to conduct the project. **Criteria:** Applications are evaluated based on the quality of the proposed project; interest in the field; applicant's and mentor's qualifications; adequacy of facilities and quality of the training environment.

Funds Avail.: $3,000. **To Apply:** Applicants must complete

an application form with letters of recommendation included. **Deadline:** March 21.

3662 ■ Epilepsy Foundation Post-doctoral Research Fellowships *(Postdoctorate, Professional development/Fellowship)*

Purpose: To develop academic physicians and scientists committed to research related to epilepsy. **Focus:** Epilepsy; Neuroscience. **Qualif.:** Applicants must be physicians or PhD neuroscientists. **Criteria:** Applications are evaluated based on the quality of the proposed project. Applications are considered from individuals interested in acquiring experience either in basic laboratory research or in the conduct of human clinical studies.

Funds Avail.: $45,000. **To Apply:** Applicants may visit the website or contact Epilepsy Foundation for more details. **Deadline:** August 31.

3663 ■ Epilepsy Foundation Pre-doctoral Research Training Fellowships *(Graduate/Grant)*

Purpose: To financially support dissertation research related to epilepsy. **Focus:** Epilepsy; Neuroscience; Physiology; Pharmacology; Psychology; Biochemistry; Genetics; Nursing; Pharmacy. **Qualif.:** Applicants must be graduate students enrolled in a full-time doctoral (PhD) program with academic focus on Neuroscience, Physiology, Pharmacology, Psychology, Biochemistry, Genetics, Nursing, or Pharmacy. **Criteria:** Applications are evaluated based on the quality of the proposed project.

Funds Avail.: $20,000. **To Apply:** Applicants may visit the website or contact Epilepsy Foundation for more details. **Deadline:** August 31.

3664 ■ Epilepsy Foundation Research Grants *(All/Grant)*

Purpose: To stimulate epilepsy research by providing funds for biological or behavioral researches by young clinical investigators. **Focus:** Behavioral sciences; Epilepsy. **Qualif.:** Applicants must be conducting a biological or behavioral research that may advance the treatment, understanding and prevention of epilepsy. **Criteria:** Applications are evaluated based on the quality of the proposed project.

Funds Avail.: $50,000. **To Apply:** Applicants may visit the website or contact Epilepsy Foundation for more details. **Deadline:** August 31.

3665 ■ Epilepsy Foundation Research and Training Fellowships for Clinicians *(Doctorate, Professional development/Grant)*

Purpose: To provide support for study and research by clinically trained professionals. **Focus:** Epilepsy; Neurology; Internal medicine; Psychiatry. **Qualif.:** Applicants must be clinically trained professionals (PharmD, Doctor of Nursing); have an MD or DO who have completed residency training in neurology, neurosurgery, pediatrics, internal medicine, or psychiatry by the time the fellowship commences. **Criteria:** Applications are evaluated based on the quality of the proposed project.

Funds Avail.: $50,000. **To Apply:** Applicants may visit the website or contact Epilepsy Foundation for more details. **Deadline:** October 1.

3666 ■ Health Sciences Student Fellowships *(Doctorate, Graduate/Fellowship)*

Purpose: To stimulate individuals to pursue careers in epilepsy in either research or practice settings. **Focus:**

Awards are arranged alphabetically below their administering organizations

Health sciences; Epilepsy. **Qualif.:** Applicants must be pre-doctoral training students in Health Sciences; be enrolled or accepted for enrollment in medical school, in doctoral program or other graduate program; have an epilepsy-related study or research plan; have three months free period; have a qualified mentor; have an access to institutional resources including clinics or laboratories in conducting the project. **Criteria:** Applications are evaluated based on the quality of the proposed project; relevance of the proposed work to epilepsy; interest in the field of epilepsy; applicant's qualifications; adequacy of facility and quality of the training environment.

Funds Avail.: $3,000. **To Apply:** Applicants must complete an application form with letters of recommendation included. **Deadline:** March 21.

3667 ■ Partnership for Pediatric Epilepsy Research (Doctorate/Grant)

Purpose: To support innovative investigator-initiated studies on epilepsies that begin in infancy and childhood. **Focus:** Epilepsy. **Qualif.:** Applicants must hold a relevant advanced degree (MD or PhD); must have completed all research training; and must be based at corporations and academic/university settings. **Criteria:** Applications are evaluated based on the quality of the proposed project. Grants will be awarded to applicants based on need and timetable for the proposed work.

Funds Avail.: $75,000. **To Apply:** Applicants may visit the website or contact Epilepsy Foundation for more details. **Deadline:** August 31.

3668 ■ Targeted Research Initiative for Health Outcomes (Doctorate/Grant)

Purpose: To support research that generates initial data leading to more extensive projects that will generate knowledge and will ultimately improve the healthcare of persons with epilepsy. **Focus:** Behavioral sciences; Epilepsy. **Qualif.:** Applicants must hold a relevant advanced degree; have completed all research training; and must be based at corporations as well as academic/university settings. **Criteria:** Applications are evaluated based on proposal's scientific validity; relevance to the program's goals and feasibility; applicant's qualifications and adequacy of the research. Grants will be awarded to applicants who have provided a clear justification based on need and timetable of the work proposed.

Funds Avail.: $50,000. **To Apply:** Applicants may visit the website or contact Epilepsy Foundation for more details. **Deadline:** March 21.

3669 ■ Targeted Research Initiative for Mood Disorders (Doctorate/Grant)

Purpose: To provide financial support for behavioral researches leading to new insights in the treatment and understanding of epilepsy and mood disorders. **Focus:** Behavioral sciences; Epilepsy. **Qualif.:** Applicants must hold a relevant advanced degree (MD, PhD, MS or PharmD); must have completed all research training appropriate to the project proposed; and must be based at corporations as well as academic/university settings. **Criteria:** Applications are evaluated based on the quality of the proposed project such as research plan and its goal; applicant's qualifications; and adequacy of the facility where the research has been conducted. Grants will be awarded to applicants who have provided a clear justification based on need and timetable of the work proposed.

Funds Avail.: $50,000. **To Apply:** Applicants must com-plete an application form including letters of recommendation. **Deadline:** March 22. **Contact:** pcsupport@altum.com.

3670 ■ Targeted Research Initiative for Seniors (Doctorate/Grant)

Purpose: To encourage a breakthrough in behavioral science by funding a pilot research in the fundamental knowledge of aging and epilepsy. **Focus:** Behavioral sciences; Epilepsy. **Qualif.:** Applicants must hold a relevant advanced degree (MD or PhD); and must have completed all research trainings appropriate to the project proposed; have a research which is conducted in U.S. **Criteria:** Applications are evaluated based on the scientific quality of the research plan; applicant's qualifications; and adequacy of the facility where the research has been conducted.

Funds Avail.: $50,000. **To Apply:** Applicants must complete an application form with letters of recommendation included. **Deadline:** March 22.

3671 ■ Epilepsy Newfoundland and Labrador (ENL)

351 Kenmount Rd.
St. John's, NL, Canada A1B 3P9
Ph: (709) 722-0502
Fax: (709) 722-0999
Free: 866-EPI-LEPSY
E-mail: info@epilepsynl.com
URL: www.epilepsynl.com

3672 ■ Jim Hierlihy Memorial Scholarships (Undergraduate/Scholarship)

Purpose: To widen horizons of ENL student members by providing financial support as they pursue college or university studies. **Focus:** General studies. **Qualif.:** Applicants must be diagnosed with epilepsy and be members in good standing of Epilepsy Newfoundland and Labrador at the time of scholarship application. Scholarship is not open to current ENL board and staff members. Former board or staff members and/or their family members may apply for scholarships if they have been out of the service of Epilepsy Newfoundland and Labrador for two years. **Criteria:** Recipient is chosen based on grades, extracurricular activities and financial need.

Funds Avail.: $1,000. **Number Awarded:** 1. **To Apply:** Applicants must submit the completed application form available from the website along with a copy of the most recent academic transcript. **Deadline:** November 1.

3673 ■ Mature Student Scholarships (Undergraduate/Scholarship)

Purpose: To widen horizons of ENL student members by providing financial support as they pursue college or university studies. **Focus:** General studies. **Qualif.:** Applicants must be 21 years or older; must be diagnosed with epilepsy; and be members in good standing of Epilepsy Newfoundland and Labrador at the time of the scholarship application. Scholarship is not open to current ENL board and staff members. Former board or staff members and/or their family members can apply for scholarships if they have been out of the service of Epilepsy Newfoundland and Labrador for two years. **Criteria:** Selection is based on the review of application records.

Funds Avail.: $1,000. **Number Awarded:** 1. **To Apply:** Applicants must complete application form available at the website and submit it along with a copy of the most recent

Awards are arranged alphabetically below their administering organizations

academic transcript to: Epilepsy Newfoundland and Labrador, 261 Kenmount Rd., St. John's, NF A1B 3P9. **Deadline:** November 1.

3674 ■ Equal Justice Works

1730 M St., NW Ste. 1010
Washington, DC 20036-4511
Ph: (202) 466-3686
E-mail: info@equaljusticeworks.org
URL: www.equaljusticeworks.org

3675 ■ Equal Justice Works Fellowship Program *(Graduate, Undergraduate/Fellowship)*

Purpose: To address the shortage of attorneys working on behalf of traditionally under-served populations and causes in the United States and its territories while encouraging partnerships between law firms, corporations and public interest organizations to fund fellowships. **Focus:** Law. **Qualif.:** Applicants must be third year law students, graduates or experienced attorneys from an EJW law school who are committed to public interest. **Criteria:** Applications will be judged based on quality of the proposed project.

Funds Avail.: No specific amount. **To Apply:** Applicants must provide a completed application, including a project proposal, a fellowship candidate to carry out the project, and a nonprofit public interest organization identified to host the project; Applicants must also submit a certification form and two hard copies of letters of recommendation; and must attend a scheduled interview if evaluated successfully. **Deadline:** September 15.

3676 ■ Equity Foundation

PO Box 5696
Portland, OR 97228
Ph: (503) 231-5759
E-mail: info@equityfoundation.org
URL: www.equityfoundation.org

3677 ■ Gregori Jakovina Endowment Scholarships *(Undergraduate/Scholarship)*

Purpose: To encourage and facilitate post-secondary education in the arts for people who are gay, lesbian, bisexual or transgender (GLBT). **Focus:** Art. **Qualif.:** Applicants must be Oregon or Clark County Washington residents who demonstrate financial need. **Criteria:** Preference will be given to those who meet the criteria.

Funds Avail.: No specific amount. **To Apply:** Applicants must check the application process online. **Deadline:** May 28. **Contact:** Equity Foundation at the above address.

3678 ■ Just Out Scholarship Fund *(Undergraduate/Scholarship)*

Purpose: To provide financial assistance to those post secondary LGBT students. **Focus:** General Studies. **Qualif.:** Applicants must be members of the gay, lesbian, bisexual or transgendered communities; must be gay/lesbian/bi/transgender or the child of a gay/lesbian/bi/transgender parent(s); must be residents of either Oregon or southwest Washington (Clark, Cowlitz, or Skamania County) for at least one year prior to submitting an application, with additional consideration given to applicants who live in rural areas; must be pursuing education beyond the secondary level as an undergraduate at a college, university, trade or technical school; must be accepted for enroll-

ment in an accredited educational program beyond the secondary level. **Criteria:** Preference will be given to people outside the Portland area.

Funds Avail.: No specific amount. **To Apply:** Applicants must check the available website for the required materials. **Deadline:** June 30. **Contact:** Equity Foundation at the above address.

3679 ■ Kaiser Permanente Northwest Pride Scholarships *(Undergraduate/Scholarship)*

Purpose: To provide financial assistance and to encourage members of the gay, lesbian, bisexual and transgender communities and their children, in Northwest Oregon and Southwest Washington to pursue careers in healthcare. **Focus:** Health care services. **Qualif.:** Applicants must be members of the LGBT communities; must be residents of either northwest Oregon (Benton, Clackmas, Columbia, Hood River, Linn, Marion, Multnomah, Polk, Washington or Yamhill County) or southwest Washington (Clark, Cowlitz, Lewis, Skamania or Wahkiakum County) for at least one year prior to submitting an application; must be pursuing education beyond the secondary level as an undergraduate or graduate student at a college, university, trade or technical school. **Criteria:** Preference will be given to those who meet the criteria.

Funds Avail.: No specific amount. **To Apply:** Applicants must check the available website for the required materials. **Deadline:** June 30. **Contact:** Equity Foundation at the above address.

3680 ■ Larry McDonald Scholarships *(Undergraduate/Scholarship)*

Purpose: To provide financial assistance to those who are in need. **Focus:** Art; Humanities. **Qualif.:** Applicants must be adults in mid-life who are gay, lesbian, bisexual or transgender who seek to make a significant change in their lives or vocations by taking classes in the arts or humanities. **Criteria:** Preference will be given to those students who meet the criteria.

Funds Avail.: No specific amount. **To Apply:** Applicants must check the application process online. **Deadline:** December 31. **Contact:** Equity Foundation at the above address.

3681 ■ Portland Area Business Association Scholarships *(Undergraduate/Scholarship)*

Purpose: To provide financial assistance to post secondary GLBT students. **Focus:** General Studies. **Qualif.:** Applicants must be members of the gay, lesbian, bisexual or transgendered communities. **Criteria:** Preference will be given to those who meet the criteria.

Funds Avail.: No specific amount. **To Apply:** Applicants must check the available website for the required materials. **Deadline:** June 30. **Contact:** Equity Foundation at the above address.

3682 ■ Pride of the Rose Scholarship Fund *(Undergraduate/Scholarship)*

Purpose: To provide financial assistance to those students who are in need. **Focus:** General studies. **Qualif.:** Applicants must be post-secondary education to members of the gay, lesbian, bisexual and transgender communities and their children residing in the Quad-county area of Portland, OR and Clark County, WA. **Criteria:** Preference will be given to those who meet the criteria.

Funds Avail.: No specific amount. **To Apply:** Applicants

Awards are arranged alphabetically below their administering organizations

must check the application process online. **Deadline:** July 30. **Contact:** Equity Foundation at the above address.

3683 ■ Bill and Ann Sheperd Legal Scholarship Fund (Undergraduate/Scholarship)

Purpose: To provide financial support to those who are in need. **Focus:** Law. **Qualif.:** Applicants must be third year law students dedicated to keeping Oregon a hate-free state; be committed to equal rights and justice for gays, lesbians, bisexuals and transgendered persons; be citizens of the United States; must demonstrate the potential to complete their law program successfully; and demonstrate the intent to practice law and promote the rights of the gay, lesbian, bisexual and transgendered community. **Criteria:** Preference will be given to those who meet the criteria.

Funds Avail.: No specific amount. **To Apply:** Applicants must check the available website for the required materials. **Deadline:** June 30. **Contact:** Equity Foundation at the above address.

3684 ■ Boomer Esiason Foundation (BEF)

483 10th Ave., Ste. 300
New York, NY 10018
Ph: (646) 292-7930
Fax: (646) 292-7945
E-mail: info@esiason.org
URL: www.esiason.org

3685 ■ Boomer Esiason Foundation Scholarship Program (All/Scholarship)

Purpose: To provide educational assistance for students with cystic fibrosis. **Focus:** General studies. **Qualif.:** Applicants must be proven to have been diagnosed with cystic fibrosis. **Criteria:** Grantees will be selected based on scholastic ability, character, leadership potential, service to the community and financial need.

Funds Avail.: $500-$2500. **Number Awarded:** 10-15. **To Apply:** Applicants must submit a completed application form available at the website; recent photo; letter from physician confirming CF diagnosis and therapy routine; letter from social worker confirming need for financial assistance; recent W2 form; one-page essay stating goals; letter of acceptance from an academic institution; detailed breakdown of tuition costs; and transcript of records. **Deadline:** Scholarships are granted quarterly: March 15, June 15, September 15 and December 15. **Contact:** Materials should be submitted to Jerry Cahill at the above address or e-mail him at jcahillbef@aol.com.

3686 ■ Exercise For Life Athletic Scholarships Program (Undergraduate/Scholarship)

Purpose: To provide educational assistance for student athletes with cystic fibrosis. **Focus:** General studies. **Qualif.:** Applicants must be high school senior athletes pursuing undergraduate degrees. **Criteria:** Grantees will be selected according to financial need, academic accomplishment and athletic ability.

Funds Avail.: $10,000. **Number Awarded:** 2. **To Apply:** Applicants must submit an application form (available at the website); EFL training log (print from website); an essay (one-page, single-spaced) on the importance of exercise and compliance; recent photo; letter from physician (on letterhead) confirming CF diagnosis and therapy routine; recent W2 form verification for both parents; high school transcript; letter of acceptance from a college institu-

tion; and signed waiver. Requirements must be mailed to: Boomer Esiason Foundation, Jerry Cahill, 483 10th Ave., Ste. 300, New York, NY 10018. **Deadline:** June 25. **Contact:** Materials should be submitted to Jerry Cahill at the above address or e-mail him at jcahill@esiason.org.

3687 ■ Sacks For CF Scholarships (All/Scholarship)

Purpose: To provide educational assistance for students with cystic fibrosis. **Focus:** General studies. **Qualif.:** Applicants must be proven to have been diagnosed with cystic fibrosis. **Criteria:** Grantees will be selected based on scholastic merits and type of lifestyle.

Funds Avail.: $3,000 to $10,000. **To Apply:** Applicants must submit an application form (downloaded from the website); recent photo; letter from a doctor confirming diagnosis of cystic fibrosis and list of daily medication routine; essay; an official/unofficial high school/college transcript; tuition breakdown; and W2 form for verification for both parents. **Deadline:** January 13. **Remarks:** A joint program by Novartis and Boomer Esiason Foundation. **Contact:** Materials should be submitted to Jerry Cahill at the above address or e-mail him at jcahill@esiason.org.

3688 ■ Scholarships of the Arts (Graduate, Undergraduate/Scholarship)

Purpose: To provide educational assistance for students engaged in arts. **Focus:** Art. **Qualif.:** Applicants must be artists with cystic fibrosis (CF). **Criteria:** Grantees will be selected according to credits.

Funds Avail.: No specific amount. **To Apply:** Applicants must submit an application form (available at the website); a recent photo; letter from the doctor confirming diagnosis of cystic fibrosis and list of daily medication routine; 2-part essay; an official/unofficial high school/college transcript; tuition breakdown; W2 form for verification for both parents and picture of the art entry. **Deadline:** February 15.

3689 ■ Bonnie Strangio Education Scholarships (Graduate, Undergraduate/Scholarship)

Purpose: To provide educational assistance for students with cystic fibrosis. **Focus:** General studies. **Qualif.:** Applicants must be undergraduate or graduate students who have cystic fibrosis. **Criteria:** Grantees will be selected by a majority vote.

Funds Avail.: $500 to $1,000. **To Apply:** Applicants must submit an application form (available at the website); an essay on post-graduation goals; a recent photo; a letter from a physician confirming CF diagnosis; most recent W2 form verification for both parents; transcript (high school, college, or graduate); and letter of acceptance from an academic institution. **Deadline:** June 18. **Contact:** Materials should be submitted to Jerry Cahill at the above address or e-mail him at jcahillbef@aol.com.

3690 ■ Eurasia Foundation

1350 Connecticut Ave. NW, Ste. 1000
Washington, DC 20036
Ph: (202) 234-7370
Fax: (202) 234-7377
E-mail: eurasia@eurasia.org
URL: www.eurasia.org

3691 ■ Bill Maynes Fellowships (Professional development/Fellowship)

Purpose: To build personal and professional bridges between emerging leaders in the Eurasia region and their

Awards are arranged alphabetically below their administering organizations

counterparts in the United States. **Focus:** General studies. **Qualif.:** Applicants must be: citizens of Armenia, Azerbaijan, Belarus, Georgia, Kazakhstan, Kyrgyzstan, Moldova, Russia, Tajikistan, Turkmenistan, Ukraine or Uzbekistan; individuals working at local, national and international levels with a record of achievement or exceptional future promise in the fields of micro and small business, independent media, open and responsive governance, community development, youth or gender advocacy or other areas that support civil society; have a commitment to fully take advantage of a rigorous program of meetings, speaking engagements, presentations and practical involvement at various institutions during the course of the fellowship; be an experienced partners of the Eurasia Foundation Network; be candidates with a good command of the English language. **Criteria:** Selection will be based on the committee's criteria.

Funds Avail.: No specific amount. **To Apply:** Interested applicants must contact Zhenya Khilji for the application process and further inquiries. **Contact:** Zhenya Khilji at zkhilji@eurasia.org.

3692 ■ Executive Women International (EWI)

7414 S State St.
Midvale, UT 84047
Ph: (801) 355-2800
Fax: (801) 355-2852
Free: 877-4EWI-NOW
E-mail: ewi@ewiconnect.com
URL: www.ewiconnect.com

3693 ■ Adult Students in Scholastic Transition Scholarships (ASIST) *(All/Scholarship)*

Purpose: To provide financial support for adult students in a variety of transitional situations and to enable recipients to improve their self-esteem and to have a positive impact on the recipient's personal life, employment, family and community. **Focus:** General studies. **Qualif.:** Applicants must be single parents or non-traditional students including individuals past high school age who are entering a college, university or trade school and/or the workforce for the first time; or either be non-traditional students already enrolled who are in need of re-training due to changes in the workplace; must be 18 years of age or older; and must be residing within the boundaries of the EWI chapter to which application is submitted. **Criteria:** Recipients are selected based on: financial need; socially, physically and economically challenged adults; responsibility for small children.

Funds Avail.: $2,500. **Number Awarded:** 12. **To Apply:** Applicants must complete the application form; must include a copy of the most recent federal or state tax return and W-2 form; must enclosed personal recommendation form; and must obtain an official transcript of grades from the educational provider or ACT scores. Applicants must contact the nearest EWI Chapter for more information. **Deadline:** April.

3694 ■ Executive Women International Scholarship Program (EWISP) *(High School/Scholarship)*

Purpose: To financially help qualified applicants achieve their academic goals. **Focus:** General studies. **Qualif.:** Applicants must be full-time junior students currently enrolled in a school located within the geographical boundaries of a participating EWI Chapter; and must have plan to pursue a degree at an accredited post-secondary institution. **Criteria:**

Applicants will be selected based on character, personal merit and background.

Funds Avail.: No specific amount. **Number Awarded:** 6. **To Apply:** Applicants must submit a completed application form available on the website; two letters of recommendation (use the Personal Recommendation Form) and official transcript of grades. Applications should be submitted to the EWI Chapter near the applicant's residency.

3695 ■ ExeptionalNurse.com

13019 Coastal Cir.
Palm Beach Gardens, FL 33410
Ph: (561) 627-9872
E-mail: exceptionalnurse@aol.com
URL: www.exceptionalnurse.com

3696 ■ ExeptionalNurse.com College Scholarships *(Graduate, Undergraduate/Scholarship)*

Purpose: To support students with disabilities who wish to continue their education in a nursing education program. **Focus:** Nursing. **Qualif.:** Applicant must be a student with a documented disability who has applied to, or has already been admitted to, a college/university program on a full-time basis. **Criteria:** Selection is based on the submitted application materials.

Funds Avail.: $250. **To Apply:** Applicants must submit a completed and signed application form along with three letters of recommendation attesting to the applicant's academic abilities and personal character (may not be relatives); a 1-2 page essay; official transcripts of high school/ and or college courses completed; and Medical Verification of Disability Form. **Deadline:** June 1.

3697 ■ Explorers Club

46 E 70th St.
New York, NY 10021
Ph: (212) 628-8383
Fax: (212) 288-4449
E-mail: ect@studytours.org
URL: www.explorers.org

3698 ■ Scott Pearlman Field Awards for Science and Exploration *(Professional development/ Award)*

Purpose: To promote the scientific exploration of land, sea, air, and space by supporting research and education in the physical, natural, and biological sciences. **Focus:** Photography; Filmmaking; Journalism. **Qualif.:** Applicants must be professional artists, writers, photographers, filmmakers and journalists. **Criteria:** Selection will be based on the committee's criteria.

Funds Avail.: $1,500. **To Apply:** Applicants may visit the website to download the application form. Four copies of the completed application, samples of the candidate's work, letters from two peers familiar with the candidate's work and a written recommendation from the expedition leader must be received together for consideration.

3699 ■ Fadel Educational Foundation (FEF)

PO Box 212135
Augusta, GA 30917-2135
Ph: (484) 694-1783
E-mail: secretary@fadelfoundation.org

Awards are arranged alphabetically below their administering organizations

URL: fadelfoundation.wordpress.com

3700 ■ FEF Scholarships *(Graduate/Scholarship)*

Purpose: To encourage American Muslims to pursue higher education. **Focus:** General studies. **Qualif.:** Applicant must be a U.S. citizen or permanent resident; an American Muslim; and a graduating college senior pursuing higher education. **Criteria:** Selection is based on merit and financial need.

Funds Avail.: $3,500. **To Apply:** Applicants must submit a completed scholarship application along with the FAFSA. **Deadline:** May 31.

3701 ■ Faegre & Benson LLP
2200 Wells Fargo Ctr.
90 S 7th St.
Minneapolis, MN 55402-3901
Ph: (612) 766-7000
Fax: (612) 766-1600
Free: 800-328-4393
E-mail: info@faegre.com
URL: www.faegre.com

3702 ■ Faegre & Benson Diversity Scholarships *(Undergraduate/Scholarship)*

Purpose: To encourage and support individuals intending to pursue their legal profession. **Focus:** Law. **Qualif.:** Applicants must be enrolled full-time at an accredited law school in the United States. **Criteria:** Applicants will be selected based on a short essay that explores how diversity has influenced their lives and how it affects the legal profession.

Funds Avail.: $12,000. **Number Awarded:** 2. **To Apply:** Applicants must complete the application form, available online; must submit a resume and cover letter; must provide a personal statement explaining their interest in the scholarship program and how diversity has influenced their life and how it impacts the legal profession; must have an undergraduate transcript(s), legal writing sample and two professional recommendations, one of which must be from a law school professor. **Deadline:** January 9. **Contact:** Application form and other supporting documents must be sent to Faegre & Benson LLP, 2200 Wells Fargo Center, 90 S 7th St., Minneapolis, MN 55402; Dana Gray, Manager of Legal Personnel Services at dgray@faegre.com.

3703 ■ Families of Freedom Scholarship Fund
Scholarship America
One Scholarship Way
Saint Peter, MN 56082
Fax: (507) 931-1682
Free: 800-537-4180
E-mail: info@familiesoffreedom.org
URL: www.familiesoffreedom.org

3704 ■ Families of Freedom Scholarship Fund - America Scholarships *(Undergraduate, Vocational/Occupational/Scholarship)*

Purpose: To provide education assistance for post-secondary study to dependents - children and spouses - of those killed of permanently disabled as a result of terrorist attacks on September 11, 2001 and during the rescue activities to those attacks. **Focus:** General studies. **Qualif.:** Applicants must be dependents of those killed or permanently disabled as a result of the terrorist attacks on September 11, 2001 and during the rescue activities relating to those attacks. Specifically, families of Freedom benefits children and spouses of the victims, including airplane crew and passengers, World Trade Center and Pentagon workers and visitors, and relief workers, including firefighters and emergency medical personnel and law enforcement personnel. Participants must enroll in a course of study at an accredited two- or four-year college, university or vocational-technical school based in the United States. **Criteria:** Recipients are selected based on merit.

Funds Avail.: $1,000. **To Apply:** Applicants must submit all the required application information.

3705 ■ Families USA
1201 New York Ave. NW, Ste. 1100
Washington, DC 20005
Ph: (202) 628-3030
Fax: (202) 347-2417
E-mail: info@familiesusa.org
URL: www.familiesusa.org

3706 ■ Villers Fellowships for Health Care Justice *(Graduate/Fellowship)*

Purpose: To develop a network of young leaders who share a passion for social and health care justice. **Focus:** Health care services. **Qualif.:** Applicant must be authorized to work in the United States and have a college degree or plan to receive a degree. **Criteria:** Selection is based on applicant's demonstrable passion for justice in the health care system.

Funds Avail.: $38,000 and health care benefits. **Number Awarded:** 1. **To Apply:** Applicants must submit a completed application form along with a personal essay and a resume. In addition, Families USA must receive an official copy of most recent college or graduate school transcript sent directly from the school registrar's office, three letters of recommendation from academic and/or professional references who can attest the applicant's community involvement sent directly from the references themselves. Send application materials by mail or email to: villersfellowship@familiesusa.org. **Deadline:** January 10. **Contact:** Melissa Rosenblatt at villersfellowship@familiesusa.org.

3707 ■ Wellstone Fellowships for Social Justice *(Graduate/Fellowship)*

Purpose: To foster the advancement of social justice through participation in health care advocacy work that focuses on the unique challenges facing many communities of color. **Focus:** Social work. **Qualif.:** Applicant must be authorized to work in the United States and have a college degree or plan to receive a degree. **Criteria:** Selection is based on the applicant's demonstrable passion for social justice.

Funds Avail.: $38,000 and health care benefits. **Number Awarded:** 1. **To Apply:** Applicants must submit a completed application form along with a personal essay and a resume. In addition, Families USA must receive an official copy of most recent college or graduate school transcript sent directly from the school registrar's office, three letters of recommendation from academic and/or professional references who can attest the applicant's community involvement. Send application materials by mail or email to

Awards are arranged alphabetically below their administering organizations

wellstonefellowship@familiesusa.org. **Deadline:** January 27. **Contact:** Melissa Rosenblatt at wellstonefellowship@familiesusa.org.

3708 ■ Family, Career and Community Leaders of America (FCCLA)

1910 Association Dr.
Reston, VA 20191-1584
Ph: (703) 476-4900
Fax: (703) 860-2713
Free: 800-234-4425
E-mail: mbenjamin@fcclainc.org
URL: www.fcclainc.org

3709 ■ Beth Middleton Memorial Scholarships
(Undergraduate/Scholarship)

Purpose: To expand leadership potential and develop skills for lifeplanning, goal setting, problem solving, decision making and interpersonal communications. **Focus:** General studies. **Qualif.:** Applicant must be a member for a minimum of two years (not necessarily consecutive); a current or former FCCLA state or national officer; he/she must be a senior and have a 3.5 GPA; and has made a significant contribution to a state or national project exemplary of the goals and ideals of FCCLA. **Criteria:** Recipients will be selected based on academic records and contributions made as an officer.

Funds Avail.: $400 for tuition, room and/or board. **Number Awarded:** 1. **To Apply:** Applicant must fill out the on-line application form using a 10pt. Times New Roman font; must attach the most recent official high school transcript of record including the first semester of the senior year including standardized college entrance exam scores(ACT and/or SAT); must provide a copy of the chapter affiliation verifying national dues paid by March 1, 2011; applicants must include recommendations from their local adviser, state adviser, and one other person knowledgeable of student's non-FCCLA activities; **Deadline:** April 1.

3710 ■ National Technical Honor Society Scholarships *(Undergraduate/Scholarship)*

Purpose: To promote educational excellence; to enhance career opportunities for the NTHS membership. **Focus:** General studies. **Qualif.:** Applicant must be a member who has held the office of the President of the State FCCLA Association; must be a senior and must have taken the ACT or SAT examination; must have applied to a degree granting institution leading to an associate's or bachelor's degree in any field of study. **Criteria:** Recipients will be selected based on outstanding leadership, academic excellence and significant volunteer experience; also, judges will base the evaluation to the style and expression as well as content.

Funds Avail.: $1,000. **Number Awarded:** 2. **To Apply:** Applicant must fill out the online application form using the 10pt. Times New Roman font; most recent official high school transcript including the first semester grades of the senior year and standardized college entrance exam scores(ACT and/or SAT); a copy of the chapter affiliation verifying national dues paid by January 1, 2011; applicants must include a letter of recommendation from their local adviser, state adviser, and one other person knowledgeable of student's non-FCCLA activities; all signatures must be included. **Deadline:** April 1.

3711 ■ Wiley Publishing Inc. Scholarships
(Undergraduate/Scholarship)

Purpose: To help students set goals, make plans, become leaders at work, and prepare for career success. **Focus:**
General studies. **Qualif.:** Applicants must be students who have outstanding leadership qualities gain through FCCLA membership and other experiences in family, school, and community; applicants must be seniors who have affiliated with national FCCLA by March 1; must have taken the ACT or SAT examination; must have applied to a degree-granting institution leading to an associate's or bachelor's degree in any field of study. **Criteria:** Scholarship Committee will evaluate the application based on the style and expression as well as content.

Funds Avail.: $1,000. **Number Awarded:** 1. **To Apply:** Applicant must fill out the online application form; he/she must complete the requirements for Outstanding Leader Recognition found on the Career Connection and Leaders at Work CD; an applicant must submit the completed Outstanding Leader application form; he/she must attach recent official high school transcript; a letter of recommendation from the food production and services, or hospitality, tourism, and recreation instructor; and must submit a two-minute videotape(VHS or DVD format) which addresses the question, "How will the leadership skills you have developed through FCCLA help you reach the family and consumer sciences career goal?"; and a copy of the chapter affiliation form verifying national dues payment by May 1. **Deadline:** April 1.

3712 ■ Fanconi Anemia Research Fund

1801 Williamette St., Ste. 200
Eugene, OR 97401
Ph: (541) 687-4658
Fax: (541) 687-0548
Free: 888-326-2664
E-mail: info@fanconi.org
URL: www.fanconi.org

3713 ■ Fanconi Anemia Research Grants
(Postdoctorate/Grant)

Purpose: To help researchers advance the science relating to Fanconi anemia. **Focus:** Health sciences. **Qualif.:** Applicants must be principal investigators, postdoctoral fellows or grant coordinators. **Criteria:** Selection will be based on the committee's criteria.

Funds Avail.: No specific amount. **To Apply:** Applicants must contact the Fanconi Anemia Research Fund office to request an application packet. The packet contains application forms and guidelines, conditions of award and criteria for peer review. **Contact:** Beverly Mayhew at the above address.

3714 ■ Farella Braun Martel LLP

Russ Bldg.
235 Montgomery St., 17th Fl.
San Francisco, CA 94104
Ph: (415) 954-4400
Fax: (415) 954-4480
E-mail: cloof@fbm.com
URL: www.fbm.com

3715 ■ Farella Braun Martel LLP Diversity Scholarships *(Undergraduate/Scholarship)*

Purpose: To support outstanding, diverse Bay Area law students. **Focus:** Law. **Qualif.:** Applicants must be current first-year, full or part-time law students who are students of color or from underrepresented backgrounds, who currently

Awards are arranged alphabetically below their administering organizations

attend one of the following local law schools: University of California, Berkeley (Boalt Hall); University of California, Davis (King Hall); University of California, Hastings College of the Law; Golden Gate University; Stanford University; Santa Clara University; or the University of San Francisco. **Criteria:** Recipients will be selected based on a combination of merit and financial need. Preference will be given to applicants who demonstrate a commitment to working and living in the Bay Area.

Funds Avail.: A total of $25,000 is available. **Number Awarded:** 3-5. **To Apply:** Applicants must submit the completed application form. **Contact:** Jennifer Peneyra, Recruiting and Diversity Manager, jpeneyra@fbm.com.

3716 ■ Federal Circuit Bar Association (FCBA)

1620 I St. NW, Ste. 900
Washington, DC 20006
Ph: (202) 466-3923
Fax: (202) 833-1061
E-mail: brookshire1@fedcirbar.org
URL: www.fedcirbar.org

3717 ■ Howard T. Markey Memorial Scholarships (Undergraduate/Scholarship)

Purpose: To provide financial support for qualified individuals intending to pursue their studies. **Focus:** Law. **Qualif.:** Applicants must be law students showing financial need, demonstrated academic promise, and service, either in undergraduate or in law school. **Criteria:** Awards will be given based on a written submission of no more than one page setting out the applicant's financial need, any interests in particular areas of the law, and any qualifications for the awards considered relevant by the applicant. Application materials will be considered, and prior academic performance will not be the primary criteria for selection.

Funds Avail.: $10,000. **Number Awarded:** 1. **To Apply:** Applicants must submit a college and law school transcript and a one-page curriculum vitae. **Deadline:** April 15.

3718 ■ Helen W. Nies Memorial Scholarships (Undergraduate/Scholarship)

Purpose: To provide financial support for qualified individuals intending to pursue their studies. **Focus:** Law. **Qualif.:** Applicants must be women law students showing financial need, demonstrated academic promise and service, either in undergraduate or in law school. **Criteria:** Award is given based on a written submission of no more than one page setting out the applicant's financial need, any interests in particular areas of the law, and any qualifications for the awards considered relevant by the applicant. Application materials will be considered and prior academic performance will not be the primary criteria for selection.

Funds Avail.: $10,000. **Number Awarded:** 1. **To Apply:** Applicants must submit a college and law school transcript and a one-page curriculum vitae. **Deadline:** April 1.

3719 ■ Federal Communication Bar Association Foundation (FCBA)

1020 19th St. NW, Ste. 325
Washington, DC 20036-6101
Ph: (202) 293-4000
Fax: (202) 293-4317
E-mail: fcba@fcba.org
URL: www.fcba.org

3720 ■ Federal Communication Bar Association Foundation Scholarships (Undergraduate/Scholarship)

Purpose: To provide financial assistance for local high school students intending to pursue college studies. **Focus:** General studies. **Qualif.:** Applicants must be high school students attending in any of the 8 high schools located in the District of Columbia. **Criteria:** Scholarship is given based on academic achievement and honors, communication/presentation skills, financial need, motivation, attendance record, service to school, service to community and interest in communications or information technology (not required but will be considered if applicable).

Funds Avail.: Up to $32,000. **To Apply:** Applicants must complete the application and make sure that they have completed and attached all information required. If an applicant does not have certain information specified, that applicant should so note, and provide a brief explanation. Please note that applicants are required to certify that they are legal residents of the United States or must explain, in detail, their residency status in order to be considered for an FCBA Foundation scholarship. Applicants must attach copies of any essays, awards, letters of recommendation or appreciation (in addition to the recommendations specified in the application), or any other documentation or representation of excellence or achievement that demonstrates their future potential or would provide additional insight to the foundation as it reviews the written applications according to the criteria. **Deadline:** February 29. **Contact:** Kerry Loughney at the above address; E-mail: kerry@fcba.org.

3721 ■ Federal Court Clerks Association (FCCA)

US District Ct., Eastern District of Tennessee
800 Market St., Ste. 130
Knoxville, TN 37902
Ph: (865) 545-4244
E-mail: chuck_diard@alsd.uscourts.gov
URL: www.fcca.ws

3722 ■ Carol C. Fitzgerald Scholarship Program (Professional development/Scholarship)

Purpose: To assist deserving, qualified individuals to continue their education. **Focus:** General studies. **Qualif.:** Applicant must be a member in good standing of FCCA for a minimum of two consecutive years and must be a deputy clerk, employed by the U.S. Courts. **Criteria:** Committee will review all applications and award scholarships to deserving individuals who meet the qualifications, within the financial limitations of the program. Committee may consider the years of membership, economic need, FCCA contributions, and the applicant's interest in continuing education.

Funds Avail.: Amount awarded per individual scholarship may vary, as determined by the committee. **To Apply:** applicant must submit a complete application forms to: U.S District Court, Northern District of California, 450 Golden Gate Ave., San Francisco, CA 94102-3489. **Deadline:** April 30.

3723 ■ Federal Employee Education and Assistance Fund (FEEA)

3333 S Wadsworth Blvd., Ste. 300
Lakewood, CO 80227

Awards are arranged alphabetically below their administering organizations

Ph: (303) 933-7580
Fax: (303) 933-7587
Free: 800-323-4140
E-mail: fedshelpingfeds@feea.org
URL: www.feea.org

3724 ■ Federal Employee Education and Assistance Fund Scholarships *(Undergraduate/Scholarship)*

Purpose: To provide financial assistance to civilian employees of the US Federal Government. **Focus:** General studies. **Qualif.:** Applicants must be civilian federal and postal employees with at least three years of federal service and their dependent family members (children and spouses) are eligible to apply during their senior year in high school; must be full-time students enrolled or planning to enroll in an accredited post-secondary school in a course of study that will lead to a two-year, four-year or graduate degree; and must have a GPA of 3.0 on a 4.0 scale. **Criteria:** Recipients will be selected based on academic merit.

Funds Avail.: $250 to 2,500. **To Apply:** Applicants must submit complete academic record, including fall semester grades; recommendation (character reference); list of extracurricular and community service activities; and essay. **Contact:** Niki Logan at the above address.

3725 ■ FEEA-NTEU Scholarships *(Graduate, Postgraduate, Undergraduate/Scholarship)*

Purpose: To provide financial assistance to civilian employees of the US Federal Government. **Focus:** General studies. **Qualif.:** Applicants must be current civilian federal employees and their dependent family members (spouse/child); adult children and other relatives are eligible if claimed on the sponsoring employee's tax return; active duty military members and their dependents are eligible only through a sponsoring civilian employee spouse; military retirees and dependents are eligible if the retiree (or retiree's spouse) is a current civilian federal employee; must have at least three (3) years of civilian federal service; must have at least a 3.0 cumulative grade point average (CGPA) unweighted on a 4.0 scale; must be current high school seniors or college students working toward an accredited degree and enrolled in a two or four year undergraduate, graduate or postgraduate program; dependents must be full-time students; and federal employees may be part-time students. **Criteria:** Applicants will be judged by Scholarship Committee.

Funds Avail.: $5,000. **Number Awarded:** 7. **To Apply:** Applicants must submit FEEA Scholarship Application Form; essay; written recommendation/character reference; transcript; a list and brief description of awards, extracurricular and community service activities; copy of ACT, SAT or other examination scores; copy of most recent standard form 50 "notice of personnel action", and two self-addressed, stamped, No. 10 business-size envelopes with first class postage properly affixed. **Deadline:** March 26.

3726 ■ Federal Law Enforcement Officers Association (FLEOA)

PO Box 326
Lewisberry, PA 17339
Ph: (717) 938-2300
Fax: (717) 932-2262
E-mail: fleoa@fleoa.org
URL: www.fleoa.org

3727 ■ FLEOA Foundation Scholarship Program *(Undergraduate/Scholarship)*

Purpose: To provide educational assistance for the children of current, retired or deceased Federal Law Enforcement Officers. **Focus:** General studies. **Qualif.:** Applicants must be high school graduates; dependents of a current, retired or deceased Federal Law Enforcement Officer. **Criteria:** Scholarship will be awarded to the applicant with the highest cumulative ranking as independently reviewed by FLEAO Foundation Scholarship Committee; scholastic ability; and social character. Special consideration will be given to those applicants who are the children of federal law enforcement officers killed or disabled in the line of duty.

Funds Avail.: $1,000. **Number Awarded:** 40. **To Apply:** Applicants must submit completed application form available from the website; transcript of records (with class ranking, SAT scores); and an acceptance letter from a college or university. **Deadline:** July 16.

3728 ■ Federal Managers Association (FMA)

1641 Prince St.
Alexandria, VA 22314-2818
Ph: (703) 683-8700
Fax: (703) 683-8707
E-mail: info@fedmanagers.org
URL: www.fedmanagers.org

3729 ■ FMA-FEEA Scholarship Program *(Undergraduate/Scholarship)*

Purpose: To provide financial assistance for the educational pursuits of current civilian employees and retirees who are FMA members and their dependent family members. **Focus:** General studies. **Qualif.:** Applicants must be at least college freshmen; must have a 3.0 cumulative grade point average on 4.0 scale; must be current high school seniors or college students working toward an accredited degree and enrolled in two- or four-year post-secondary, graduate or postgraduate program; full-time students (if dependents); and part-time students (if federal employees). **Criteria:** Candidates will be evaluated based on academic performance.

Funds Avail.: $1,000. **To Apply:** Applicants must submit complete application package containing the FMA-FEEA Scholarship Application Form; essay; written recommendation/character reference; transcript of scholastic record; brief description of awards, extracurricular and community service activities; copy of ACT, SAT or other examination scores; copy of most recent standard Form 50 "Notice of Personnel Action"; and two self-addressed, stamped, No. 10 business-size envelopes with first class postage properly affixed. **Deadline:** March 30. **Contact:** Mail the application package to: FEEA Scholarship Program, 3333 S Wadsworth Blvd., Ste. 300, Lakewood, CO 80227.

3730 ■ The Federalist Society

1015 18th St. NW, Ste. 425
Washington, DC 20036
Ph: (202) 822-8138
Fax: (202) 296-8061
E-mail: info@fed-soc.org
URL: www.fed-soc.org

3731 ■ Olin/Searle Fellows in Law *(Professional development/Fellowship)*

Purpose: To support young legal thinkers in developing their skills. **Focus:** Law. **Qualif.:** Applicant must be a J.D.

Awards are arranged alphabetically below their administering organizations

and have extremely strong academic qualifications; committed to the rule of law and intellectual diversity and legal academia; and have the promise of a distinguished career as a legal scholar and teacher. **Criteria:** A distinguished group of academics will select the Fellows based on qualifications and the submitted application materials.

Funds Avail.: $50,000 plus benefits. **Number Awarded:** Up to three. **To Apply:** Applicants must submit a resume and law school transcript; academic writing sample(s) (50 page limit); a brief discussion of the applicant's areas of intellectual interest (approximately 2 pages); a statement of commitment to teaching law; and at least two, and generally no more than three, letters of support. **Deadline:** March 15. **Contact:** Barrett Young at barrett.young@fed-soc.org.

3732 ■ Searle Young Legal Scholars Research Fellowships *(Professional development/ Fellowship)*

Purpose: To support junior tenure-track faculty members in developing their skills. **Focus:** Law. **Qualif.:** Applicants must be tenure-track faculty members at a law school in the second to fifth years of their tenure-track teaching careers. **Criteria:** Selection is based on academic talent, commitment and current teaching load.

Funds Avail.: Awards will be set at a level reasonably comparable to the fellows salary for half a year. **Number Awarded:** Up to two. **To Apply:** Applicants must submit a description of the project for which the applicant seeks the fellowship (including its current status); a list and copies of completed or close-to-complete articles (published or not), with a notation indicating the single non-coauthored article that represents the applicant's best work; a curriculum vitae; preliminary information concerning the applicant's school's policies on granting academic leave for the pursuit of research funded by an outside entity, including any minimum financial commitment generally required in those circumstances. In addition, applicants may also submit two-to-three letters of recommendation from faculty members or other academic authorities familiar with the applicant's work; and any information relevant to the applicant's qualifications. **Deadline:** September 13. **Contact:** Erin Sheley at erin.sheley@fed-soc.org.

3733 ■ Federated Women's Institutes of Ontario

7382 Wellington Rd. 30, RR5
Guelph, ON, Canada N1H 6J2
Ph: (519) 836-3078
Fax: (519) 836-9456
URL: fwio.on.ca

3734 ■ Ontario Women's Institute Scholarships *(Undergraduate/Scholarship)*

Purpose: To assist students studying at the University of Guelph, College of Social and Applied Human Sciences. **Focus:** Hotel, institutional, and restaurant management; Management. **Qualif.:** Applicants must be female students from Ontario with a minimum of 70% cumulative average at the end of the second semester of the BASc Program or the Marketing Management, Housing and Real Estate Management, or Hotel and Food Administration majors who have been involved in extracurricular activities; must be currently studying at the University of Guelph. **Criteria:** Recipients will be selected based on submitted materials.

Funds Avail.: $1,000. **Number Awarded:** 3. **To Apply:** Applicants must visit the website for further information. **Deadline:** April 1.

3735 ■ Federation of American Consumers and Travelers (FACT)

318 Hillsboro Ave.
Edwardsville, IL 62025
Ph: (618) 656-5369
Fax: (618) 656-5369
Free: 800-USA-FACT
E-mail: cservice@usafact.org
URL: www.usafact.org

3736 ■ FACT Graduating Senior Scholarship Program *(Undergraduate/Scholarship)*

Purpose: To assure the continuation of FACT's selfless intents and purposes; to maintain high level of professionalism at the director level; to prevent any special-interest groups or self-serving individuals from assuming control of FACT for their own gain. **Focus:** General studies. **Qualif.:** Program is open to FACT members. Applicants must be graduating from an accredited public, private or parochial high school or equivalent during the 2011-2012 school year; must maintain a "C" grade point average to remain in the funds (if considered). Applicants may be students currently enrolled in two- or four-year education in accredited colleges or universities. **Criteria:** Applicants will be evaluated by the Scholarship Committee based on academic records and quality of the essay submitted.

Funds Avail.: $10,000 and $2,500. **Number Awarded:** 2. **To Apply:** Applicants must submit completed application form; Release Authorization and Membership Verification Form; Certification Form; Official Copy of High School Transcript signed by the applicant's high school principal or academic advisor; and a two-page, double-spaced essay. **Deadline:** January 15. **Contact:** FACT Membership Office at the above address.

3737 ■ Federation of Diocesan Liturgical Commissions (FDLC)

415 Michigan Ave. NE, Ste. 70
Washington, DC 20017
Ph: (202) 635-6990
Fax: (202) 529-2452
E-mail: nationaloffice@fdlc.org
URL: www.fdlc.org

3738 ■ The Tabat Scholarship Fund *(Graduate/ Scholarship)*

Purpose: To support graduate students in liturgical studies by providing assistance with the payment of tuition, the purchase of books, or the continuation of research. **Focus:** Religion; Theology. **Qualif.:** Applicants must be pursuing a graduate degree in a program of liturgical studies to prepare for service in the Church of the United States in an academic, diocesan, or parish setting. **Criteria:** Candidates will be evaluated by the Scholarship Committee.

Funds Avail.: $1,000. **To Apply:** Applicants must submit curriculum vitae; a short description of how the grant will be used; and two letters of recommendation, in a sealed envelope, from professors or from someone knowledgeable about the person's work. **Deadline:** June 30.

3739 ■ FEI Company

5350 NE Dawson Creek Dr.
Hillsboro, OR 97124
Ph: (503) 726-7500

Awards are arranged alphabetically below their administering organizations

Fax: (503) 726-2767
Free: 866-693-3426
E-mail: sales@feico.com
URL: www.fei.com

3740 ■ Casey Bennett Scholarships
(Undergraduate/Scholarship)

Purpose: To assist high school seniors who plan careers in the fields of Physical Sciences or Materials Sciences. **Focus:** Physical sciences. **Qualif.:** Applicant must be a high school senior (from either the Beaverton or Hillsboro School Districts); planning to pursue a career in Physical Sciences or Materials Sciences; has 3.5 GPA or above; financial need. **Criteria:** Awards are given based on the application.

Funds Avail.: $2,000. **Number Awarded:** 1. **To Apply:** Applicants must complete the online scholarship application; submit a brief essay (approximately 1/2-1 page) explaining why they should receive the award and an explanation of education/career "roadmap"; a letter of recommendation from a science-related faculty member; and high school transcript (copy or scan). Applications are to be submitted online to scholarships@fei.com (include your name in the subject line of the email). **Deadline:** April 20.

3741 ■ Field Museum
1400 S Lake Shore Dr.
Chicago, IL 60605-2496
Ph: (312) 922-9410
E-mail: collections@fieldmuseum.org
URL: fieldmuseum.org

3742 ■ Field Museum Graduate Student Fellowships *(Graduate/Fellowship)*

Purpose: To support graduate students engaged in dissertation research associated with the Field Museum. **Focus:** General Studies. **Qualif.:** Applicants must be graduate students residing in the Chicago area. **Criteria:** Selection will be based on evaluation of submitted research including relevance of the Field museum's collections to the project, collaboration(s) with Field Museum curators (if any), procedures and methods used in the project.

Funds Avail.: No specific amount. **To Apply:** Applicants must submit proposed research summary (one or two pages, double-spaced); full curriculum vitae with names and contact information of two references in addition to sponsor; copy of thesis proposal uploaded as supplemental material with the application; two reference letters sent 10 days after the application deadline. **Deadline:** February 1.

3743 ■ Fields Institute
222 College St.
Toronto, ON, Canada M5T 3J1
E-mail: geninfo@fields.utoronto.ca
URL: www.fields.utoronto.ca

3744 ■ Fields Research Immersion Fellowships
(Postdoctorate/Fellowship)

Purpose: To support individuals with high potential to re-enter an active research career after an interruption due to family responsibilities. **Focus:** Mathematics and mathematical sciences. **Qualif.:** Applicant must have been in a post-doctoral or faculty position at the time his/her active career was interrupted; may be in complete or partial hiatus from research activities at the time of application; and should not be engaged in full-time paid research activities. **Criteria:** Selection is based on the submitted application materials.

Funds Avail.: No specific amount. **To Apply:** Applicants must submit a cover sheet indicating applicant's interest; a CV; and a research proposal which includes the name(s) of faculty who may be appropriate as supervisors/research advisors. **Contact:** director@fields.utoronto.ca.

3745 ■ Postdoctoral Fellowships at the Fields Institute *(Postdoctorate/Fellowship)*

Purpose: To support postdoctoral fellows in the field of mathematical sciences. **Focus:** Mathematics and mathematical sciences. **Qualif.:** Applicant must be expecting to receive a PhD in a related area of the mathematical sciences. **Criteria:** Applicants must submit their applications before the deadline to be considered.

Funds Avail.: $20,000. **To Apply:** Applicants must submit online a cover letter; curriculum vitae; a research statement; publication list; and three reference letters (submitted by the reference writers). **Deadline:** December 15. **Contact:** programs@fields.utoronto.ca.

3746 ■ Film Studies Association of Canada
4401 University Dr.
Lethbridge, AB, Canada T1K 3M4
Ph: (403) 394-3922
E-mail: emathijs@interchange.ubc.ca
URL: www.filmstudies.ca

3747 ■ Gerald Pratley Awards *(Doctorate, Graduate/Award)*

Purpose: To inspire Quebec or Canadian cinema development by providing financial support for graduate students doing cinema researches. **Focus:** Cinema. **Qualif.:** Applicants must be students entering or completing a graduate program in Film Studies (or any related discipline) at any recognized post-secondary institution in or outside Canada. Applicants need not be Canadian citizens. **Criteria:** Selection is based on the student's previous academic performance and his or her intentions for a specific paper or body of research on Canadian/Quebec cinema.

Funds Avail.: $1,000. **To Apply:** Applicants must prepare a brief research proposal (500 words) including bibliography; two letters of recommendation; one sample of previous work (3000 to 5000 words); and official university transcripts. **Deadline:** July 30. **Remarks:** Established in 1991. **Contact:** Return applications to: Marc Furstenau, Assistant Professor, Film Studies School for Studies in Art and Culture Carleton University at 409 St. Patrick's Bldg. 1125 Colonel By Dr. Ottawa, ON K1S 5B6. Phone: 613-520-2600, Fax: 613-520-3575, or email marc_furstenau@carleton.ca.

3748 ■ Fine Arts Association (FAA)
38660 Mentor Ave.
Willoughby, OH 44094
Ph: (440) 951-7500
Fax: (440) 975-4592
E-mail: faa@fineartsassociation.org
URL: www.fineartsassociation.org

3749 ■ Fine Arts Association Minority Scholarships *(Undergraduate/Scholarship)*

Purpose: To ensure that the opportunity for art education is available to all who deserve it and to create customized

---

Awards are arranged alphabetically below their administering organizations

educational arts experiences in music, dance, drama, visual arts and music therapy. **Focus:** Fine arts. **Qualif.:** Students applying must be residents of Lake County who are members of a minority population as defined by the Ohio Arts Council. **Criteria:** Recipients are selected based on financial need.

Funds Avail.: No specific amount. **To Apply:** Applicants must complete the application form with parents/guardians if they are dependents. Forms are available at the FAA Customer Service Center and are also available for download at the website. First time applicants must include a copy of the first page of their most recent IRS 1040 form. **Contact:** Peter Grossetti, Director of Development at 440-951-7500.

3750 ■ Fine Arts Association United Way Scholarships *(Undergraduate/Scholarship)*

Purpose: To ensure that the opportunity for art education is available to all who deserve it and to create customized educational arts experiences in music, dance, drama, visual arts and music therapy. **Focus:** Fine Arts. **Qualif.:** Applicants must be students residing in Lake County and must have total family income not exceeding $22,400 annually, unless there are extenuating financial circumstances. **Criteria:** Recipients are selected based on financial need.

Funds Avail.: No specific amount. **To Apply:** Applicants must complete the application form with parents/guardians if they are dependents. Forms are available at the FAA Customer Service Center and are also available for download at the website. First time applicants must include a copy of the first page of their most recent IRS 1040 form. **Contact:** Peter Grossetti, Director of Development at 440-951-7500.

3751 ■ Gwen Yarnell Theatre Scholarships *(Undergraduate/Scholarship)*

Purpose: To ensure that the opportunity for art education is available to all who deserve it and to create customized educational arts experiences in music, dance, drama, visual arts and music therapy. **Focus:** Fine arts; Theater arts. **Qualif.:** Program is open to new and returning Fine Arts students intending to study theatre. **Criteria:** Recipients are selected based on merit.

Funds Avail.: No specific amount. **To Apply:** Forms can be requested by calling the association's Customer Service Center. **Contact:** For more information, please contact registration staff at 440-951-7500.

3752 ■ Finnegan, Henderson, Farabow, Garrett & Dunner LLP

901 New York Ave. NW
Washington, DC 20001-4413
Ph: (202) 408-4000
Fax: (202) 408-4400
E-mail: info@finnegan.com
URL: www.finnegan.com

3753 ■ Finnegan, Henderson, Farabow, Garrett & Dunner, LLP Diversity Scholarships *(Undergraduate/Scholarship)*

Purpose: To develop diversity in the workplace and in the field of intellectual property law. **Focus:** Law. **Qualif.:** Applicant must be enrolled in an American Bar Association accredited law school either as a first year full-time student or second-year part-time student. **Criteria:** Recipients must

have demonstrated a commitment to pursuing a career in intellectual property law; exceptional academic performance at the undergraduate, graduate (if applicable), and law school level; a degree in the life sciences, engineering, computer science, or substantial prior trademark experience; and relevant work experience, community service, leadership skills and special accomplishment.

Funds Avail.: $15,000. **To Apply:** Applicants must submit current resume; completed scholarship application; undergraduate and, if applicable, graduate transcripts; law school transcripts; a legal writing sample (10 pages); and one to three letters of recommendation. **Deadline:** March 1. **Contact:** diversityscholarship@finnegan.com.

3754 ■ First Community Foundation of Pennsylvania, Williamsport-Lycoming

330 Pine St., Ste. 401
Williamsport, PA 17701
Ph: (570) 321-1500
Fax: (570) 321-6434
Free: 866-901-2372
E-mail: fcfpa@fcfpa.org
URL: www.wlfoundation.org

3755 ■ Ken and Pat Ackerman Family Scholarship Fund *(Undergraduate/Scholarship)*

Purpose: To provide scholarship for Danville Area High School seniors who have been accepted or will attend an accredited 4-year college, full-time. **Focus:** General studies. **Qualif.:** Applicants must have been a varsity wrestler and/or varsity football player and have the highest cumulative 4-year average in English. **Criteria:** Selection will be based on the committee's criteria.

Funds Avail.: No specific amount. **To Apply:** Applicants may request an application from the guidance counselor of Danville Area School District. **Contact:** Gary Grozier, Guidance Counselor of Danville Area School District, 600 Walnut St., Danville, PA 17821; 570-271-3268 ext. 2006; ggrozier@danville.k12.pa.us.

3756 ■ Ruth D. Adams Fund *(Undergraduate/Scholarship)*

Purpose: To provide financial assistance for Montoursville Area High School seniors who are seeking higher education beyond graduation from high school (full-time) and who represent the top 10% GPA of graduating seniors. **Focus:** General studies. **Qualif.:** Applicants shall be approved for full-time admission to any accredited two or four-year college or university of their choice and be enrolled in a course of study of their choice which leads to a degree. **Criteria:** Selection will be based on the committee's criteria and financial need. Preference will be given to those who should not otherwise be able to pursue a higher education by any other means.

Funds Avail.: No specific amount. **To Apply:** Applicants may contact and request an application from the Montoursville Area High School. **Contact:** Ronda Albert, Montoursville Area High School, 100 N Arch St, Montoursville, PA 17754; 570-368-3509; ralbert@montoursville.k12.pa.us.

3757 ■ Anne L. Alexander and Blaise Robert Alexander Memorial Scholarships *(Undergraduate/Scholarship)*

Purpose: To provide scholarship for graduating seniors from Mount Carmel Area High School and Montoursville

Awards are arranged alphabetically below their administering organizations

Area High School respectively, who have been accepted into a full-time undergraduate, business or technical program at an accredited institution of higher education. **Focus:** General studies. **Qualif.:** Applicants must have exhibited good citizenship and community involvement; must be a leader with a sense of humor; must be grounded; must show tolerance to others; must be honest; must have integrity; and must make a difference in the school community. **Criteria:** Selection will be based on the committee's criteria.

Funds Avail.: No specific amount. **To Apply:** Applicants may contact and request an application from the Montoursville Area High School and the Mount Carmel School District. **Deadline:** April 1. **Contact:** Betty Gilmour, Program Officer, at 570-321-1500 or bettyg@fcfpa.org.

3758 ■ B-Brave McMahon/Stratton Scholarship Fund *(Undergraduate/Scholarship)*

Purpose: To provide financial assistance for graduates who have been in the foster care system or have legal adopted status and who have shown remarkable achievement despite the obstacles in their life. **Focus:** General studies. **Qualif.:** Applicant must be a graduating senior from a Lycoming County High School or Clinton County High School that has believed in herself/himself; must have been accepted into a full-time continuing education program, preferably in Pennsylvania; must have exhibited good citizenship and have no known drug or alcohol record or juvenile offenses; have an unmet financial need; and must show evidence that they have a current minimum GPA of 2.8. **Criteria:** Selection will be based on the committee's criteria.

Funds Avail.: No specific amount. **To Apply:** Candidates must complete the application and submit it along with any requested additional information to the Williamsport-Lycoming Community Foundation. **Deadline:** April 1. **Contact:** Candy Bower, Manager of Program and Scholarship Services candyb@fcfpa.org.

3759 ■ Gina L. Barnhart Memorial Scholarship Fund *(Undergraduate/Scholarship)*

Purpose: To provide financial assistance for Milton Area High school seniors planning to pursue a major in elementary education. **Focus:** Education, Elementary. **Qualif.:** Candidates must be seniors in good standing and members of the cheerleading squad; must have been accepted by a qualified institution of higher education and plan to major in elementary education. Applicants who are planning to major in secondary education may be considered if there are no candidates that are planning to major in elementary education. Preference will be given to applicants with educational and/or career objectives focused on working with children or community service. **Criteria:** Selection will be based on the committee's criteria.

Funds Avail.: No specific amount. **To Apply:** Candidates must submit of a 200-word short essay on the following topic: "How has my participating in cheerleading and sports helped to prepare me for a career in elementary education or other work on behalf of children?" **Contact:** Leslie Robinson, Milton Senior High School, 700 Mahoning St., Milton, PA 17847, 570-742-7611.

3760 ■ Bloch-Selinger Education Fund *(Undergraduate/Scholarship)*

Purpose: To provide financial assistance for honor students from the Danville Area High School. **Focus:** General studies. **Qualif.:** Applicants must be attending a full-time ac-

credited school or university and be in good standing. **Criteria:** Selection will be based on the committee's criteria.

Funds Avail.: No specific amount. **To Apply:** Applicants may request an application from the guidance counselor of Danville Area School District. **Contact:** Gary Grozier, Guidance Counselor of Danville Area School District, 600 Walnut St., Danville, PA 17821; 570-271-3268 ext. 2006; ggrozier@danville.k12.pa.us.

3761 ■ Diane Booth Memorial Scholarships *(Undergraduate/Scholarship)*

Purpose: To provide scholarship to the Danville Area High School seniors. **Focus:** General studies. **Qualif.:** Applicants must be accepted into a full-time undergraduate, associate or technical program in an institution of higher education; have exhibited good citizenship and community involvement; and a strong potential for success. **Criteria:** Selection will be based on the committee's criteria.

Funds Avail.: No specific amount. **To Apply:** Applicants may request an application from the Danville Area School District. **Contact:** Gary Grozier, Guidance Counselor, Danville Area School District, 570-271-3268, ggrozier@danville.k12.pa.us.

3762 ■ Eleanor McWilliams Burke Fund *(Undergraduate/Scholarship)*

Purpose: To provide academic support for Danville Area High School seniors who have been accepted into a full-time undergraduate program at an accredited institution of higher education and who are entering a health-related field. **Focus:** Medicine; Nursing; Nutrition; Pharmacy; or Physical therapy. **Qualif.:** Applicants must be entering a health related field. **Criteria:** Selection is based on character, academic performance, career goals and participation in school and/or community activities.

Funds Avail.: No specific amount. **To Apply:** Applicants may request an application from the Guidance Counselor of Danville Area School District. **Contact:** Gary Grozier, Guidance Counselor of Danville Area School District, 600 Walnut St., Danvilled, PA 17821; 570-271-3268 ext. 2006; ggrozier@danville.k12.pa.us.

3763 ■ Joseph R. Calder, Jr., MD Scholarship Fund *(Undergraduate/Scholarship)*

Purpose: To support the education of current and/or aspiring Lycoming County medical professionals who plan to dedicate their lives to helping others. **Focus:** Medicine; Nursing; Pharmacy; Allied health. **Qualif.:** Applicants must be accepted into a full-time or part-time medical or any other related specialty at an accredited institution of higher education. Applicants should be residents of Lycoming County. **Criteria:** Selection will be based on merit.

Funds Avail.: No specific amount. **To Apply:** Applicant must submit an essay not to exceed one page outlining why he/she is pursuing a career in the medical field and summarizing his/her ultimate career objectives. Applicants may download an application form the Foundation's web site. **Contact:** Betty Gilmour, Program Officer, at 570-321-1500 or bettyg@fcfpa.org.

3764 ■ Warren E. "Whitey" Cole American Society of Highway Engineers Scholarships *(Undergraduate/Scholarship)*

Purpose: To provide scholarship awards for students enrolled in a Civil Engineering curriculum. **Focus:** Civil engineering. **Qualif.:** Applicants must be enrolled in a civil

Awards are arranged alphabetically below their administering organizations

engineering, civil engineering technology or civil technology curriculum; have completed at least the sophomore year of a four-year curriculum or the freshman year of a two-year curriculum; be either enrolled at Pennsylvania State University, Bucknell University or Pennsylvania College of Technology or have residence in the counties of Bradford, Columbia, Lycoming, Montour, Northumberland, Snyder, Sullivan, Tioga or Union and attend another college. **Criteria:** Selection will be based on the committee's criteria.

Funds Avail.: $500-$1,000. **To Apply:** Candidates must complete the application and submit it along with any requested additional information to the Williamsport-Lycoming Community Foundation. **Contact:** Ken Klingerman, American Society of Highway Engineers, 570-368-4231.

3765 ■ Cotner Family Scholarships
(Undergraduate/Scholarship)

Purpose: To provide scholarship for Danville Area High School seniors who will attend an accredited 2 or 4-year college. **Focus:** Agricultural economics. **Qualif.:** Applicants must be high school seniors attending an accredited 2 or 4-year college and must be pursuing studies in agriculture or agricultural related fields on a full-time basis. **Criteria:** Selection will be based on the committee's criteria.

Funds Avail.: No specific amount. **To Apply:** Applicants may request an application from the Guidance Counselor of Danville Area School District. **Contact:** Betty Gilmour, Program Officer, at 570-321-1500 or bettyg@fcfpa.org.

3766 ■ Danville Education Association Scholarship Fund *(Undergraduate/Scholarship)*

Purpose: To provide financial assistance for Danville Area High School seniors who have been accepted into a full-time undergraduate program at an accredited institution of higher education, preferably in Pennsylvania. **Focus:** General studies. **Qualif.:** Applicants must have exhibited good citizenship and community involvement; must have unmet financial need; and must have not been the recipient of other major scholarship awards. **Criteria:** Selection will be based on the committee's criteria.

Funds Avail.: No specific amount. **To Apply:** Applicants may request an application from the Guidance Counselor of Danville Area School District. **Contact:** Gary Grozier, Guidance Counselor of Danville Area School District, 600 Walnut St., Danvilled, PA 17821; 570-271-3268 ext. 2006; ggrozier@danville.k12.pa.us.

3767 ■ Danville High School Class of 1963 Scholarship Fund *(Undergraduate/Scholarship)*

Purpose: To provide financial assistance for Danville Area High School seniors who have been accepted and will be pursuing a Bachelor of Arts or Sciences degree in an accredited institution of higher education. **Focus:** General studies. **Qualif.:** Applicants must have exhibited good citizenship and community involvement. The recipients must have experience with community service and volunteering. **Criteria:** Selection will be based on financial need.

Funds Avail.: No specific amount. **To Apply:** Applicants may request application form from the Guidance Counselor of Danville Area School District. **Contact:** Gary Grozier, Guidance Counselor of Danville Area School District, 600 Walnut St., Danvilled, PA 17821; 570-271-3268 ext. 2006; ggrozier@danville.k12.pa.us.

3768 ■ Danville Rotary Scholarships
(Undergraduate/Scholarship)

Purpose: To provide financial assistance for Danville Area High School seniors who have been accepted and will at-

tend an accredited 2 or 4-year college as full-time students. **Focus:** General studies. **Qualif.:** Applicants must have exhibited good citizenship, honesty, integrity, and volunteerism in the community and/or charity that demonstrate the Rotary's motto. **Criteria:** Selection will be based on the committee's criteria.

Funds Avail.: No specific amount. **To Apply:** Applicants must submit a completed application form along with the essay; activity sheet; reference letters; transcript; and parent's tax return (if required). **Contact:** Betty Gilmour at bettyg@fcfpa.org or 570-321-1500.

3769 ■ Marian Jones Donaldson Scholarship Fund *(Undergraduate/Scholarship)*

Purpose: To provide financial assistance for Canton Area High School seniors intending to pursue a course of study in elementary or secondary education. **Focus:** Education, Elementary; Education, Secondary. **Qualif.:** Applicants shall have a four-year overall minimum grade average of 85%. **Criteria:** Selection will be based on involvement in community service, extra-curricular activities, and financial need.

Funds Avail.: No specific amount. **Number Awarded:** 1. **To Apply:** Candidate must complete and submit an application, a 500-word or less essay describing why he or she wants to enter the field of education, and three letters of reference. **Deadline:** April 1. **Contact:** Jamie May, Guidance Counselor, Canton Area High School, 570-673-5134, jmay@canton.k12.pa.us.

3770 ■ Lindsay M. Entz Memorial Scholarships
(Undergraduate/Scholarship)

Purpose: To provide financial assistance for the Jersey Shore High School seniors intending to pursue a course of study in elementary education, preferably with an emphasis on education of special-needs children. **Focus:** Education, elementary. **Qualif.:** Candidates must plan to pursue a course of study in elementary education, preferably with an emphasis on education of special-needs children; must have exhibited good citizenship and community involvement; must be a leader with a sense of humor; must be grounded; must show tolerance to others; must be honest; must have integrity; and must make a difference in the school community. **Criteria:** Selection will be based on the committee's criteria.

Funds Avail.: $1,000. **Number Awarded:** 1. **To Apply:** Candidate must complete an application; attach a cover letter (not to exceed two pages) outlining why he or she is applying for the scholarship and summarizing his/her ultimate career objectives; must provide proof that he or she has been accepted to an accredited two-/four-year college/university; and must provide at least one letter of reference. **Deadline:** April 15. **Contact:** Jeannie Rombach, Guidance Counselor, Jersey Shore Area Senior High School, 570-398-7174 ext. 1009, jrombach@jsasd.k12.pa.us.

3771 ■ Nolan W. Feeser Scholarship Fund
(Undergraduate/Scholarship)

Purpose: To provide financial assistance for South Williamsport Area High School seniors who are pursuing a higher education degree at an accredited college or university. **Focus:** General studies. **Qualif.:** Applicants must have displayed academic achievements; must have unmet financial need; and must be planning to enroll at or pursuing a degree at Lycoming College, Gettysburg College or Pennsylvania College of Technology. **Criteria:** Se-

Awards are arranged alphabetically below their administering organizations

lection will be based on the committee's criteria.

Funds Avail.: No specific amount. **Number Awarded:** 2. **To Apply:** Applicants may contact and request an application from the South Williamsport Area High School. **Contact:** Verna Correll, Guidance Counselor, South Williamsport Jr./Sr. High School, 700 Percy St., S Williamsport, PA 17702; 570-326-2684; vcorrell@mounties.k12.pa.us.

3772 ■ Daniel G. and Helen I. Fultz Scholarship Fund *(Undergraduate/Scholarship)*

Purpose: To encourage educational pursuits by providing scholarship for Indian Valley High School seniors. **Focus:** General studies. **Qualif.:** Program is open to Indian Valley High School seniors who have been accepted into a full-time undergraduate program at Lycoming College, Williamsport, PA. If there are no applicants from Indian Valley High School, then applicants may be chosen from Lewistown High School in Mifflin County, again, who have been accepted into a full-time undergraduate degree program at Lycoming College, Williamsport, PA. Applicants must have good citizenship and community involvement; be a leader with a sense of humor; be grounded; must show tolerance of others; be honest; have integrity; and make a difference in the school community. Unmet financial need is also considered. **Criteria:** Selection will be based on the committee's criteria.

Funds Avail.: No specific amount. **To Apply:** Applicants may contact and request an application from the Indian Valley High School. **Deadline:** April 15. **Contact:** Jane A. Floor, Guidance Counselor, Indian Valley High School, 717-248-5444, jaf53@mcsdk12.org; Frank A. Zook, Guidance Counselor, Lewistown High School, 717-242-1401, faz42@mcsdk12.org.

3773 ■ Adam Hampton Memorial Scholarship Fund *(Undergraduate/Scholarship)*

Purpose: To provide scholarship for Danville Area High School seniors who have been accepted into a full-time undergraduate program. **Focus:** General studies. **Qualif.:** Applicants must have good citizenship and community involvement; must be a leader with a sense of humor; must be grounded; must show tolerance of others; must be honest; must have integrity; and must make a difference in the school community. Applicants must also have an unmet financial need and must hold a "B" average or above. **Criteria:** Selection will be based on the committee's criteria.

Funds Avail.: No specific amount. **To Apply:** Applicants may request an application from the Guidance Counselor of Danville Area School District. **Contact:** Gary Grozier, Guidance Counselor of Danville Area School District, 600 Walnut St., Danville, PA 17821; 570-271-3268 ext. 2006; ggrozier@danville.k12.pa.us.

3774 ■ Morton Harrison Scholarship Fund *(Undergraduate/Scholarship)*

Purpose: To provide financial assistance for Lycoming County young adults who demonstrate the potential to succeed in pursuing higher education goals. **Focus:** General studies. **Qualif.:** Candidates shall be young adults who, as a result of legal offenses as juveniles or young adults, have come to the attention of Lycoming County's Probation Department; must demonstrate a strong willingness to make positive changes in their lives and pursue educational and/or job training goals that will enable them to fulfill their human potential; and plan to attend a qualified institution of higher education, including but not limited to a 2- or 4-year college or university, a technical college, trade school, or other approved education or training program. **Criteria:** Selection will be based on the committee's criteria.

Funds Avail.: No specific amount. **To Apply:** Candidates must complete the application and submit it along with any requested additional information to the Williamsport-Lycoming Community Foundation. **Contact:** Candy Bower, Manager of Program and Scholarship Services candyb@fcfpa.org.

3775 ■ Mollie Harter Memorial Fund *(Undergraduate/Scholarship)*

Purpose: To provide financial assistance for Danville Area High School seniors intending to pursue higher education goals, preferably in the field of secondary education. **Focus:** Education, Secondary. **Qualif.:** Applicants must be planning to pursue a Bachelor of Arts or Sciences degree from a qualified institution of higher education. Applicants' experience with community service and volunteering, as well as their interest in working with children and the potential to succeed in pursuing their goals may be considered. Preference will be given to applicants interested in a career in education, ideally secondary education, and then to other careers working with children. **Criteria:** Selection will be based on the committee's criteria.

Funds Avail.: $500. **To Apply:** Applicants must submit a completed application form along with the essay; activity sheet; reference letters; transcript; and parent's tax return (if required). **Contact:** Betty Gilmour at bettyg@fcfpa.org or 570-321-1500.

3776 ■ Jane Hood Memorial Fund *(Undergraduate/Scholarship)*

Purpose: To provide financial assistance for Danville Area High School seniors who have been accepted into a full-time undergraduate program. **Focus:** Visual arts; Mathematics and mathematical science; Science; Engineering. **Qualif.:** Applicants must be accepted in a full-time undergraduate program at an institution of higher education to study graphic-visual arts, math and/or science (including engineering). Applicants must have exhibited good citizenship and community involvement. **Criteria:** Selection will be based on the committee's criteria.

Funds Avail.: No specific amount. **Number Awarded:** 2. **To Apply:** Applicants must submit a completed application form along with the essay; activity sheet; reference letters; transcript; and parent's tax return (if required). **Contact:** Betty Gilmour at bettyg@fcfpa.org or 570-321-1500.

3777 ■ ISCALC International Scholarship Fund *(Undergraduate/Scholarship)*

Purpose: To provide financial assistance for Lycoming County high school seniors who have demonstrated an interest in furthering their education in international studies. **Focus:** International affairs and relations; Foreign languages. **Qualif.:** Applicant must be a high school senior within Lycoming county who will be attending an accredited institution of higher education and who plans to pursue major coursework in the area of international studies, including but not limited to international affairs, foreign languages, overseas exchange programs, multicultural studies, and related areas. **Criteria:** Selection will be based on the committee's criteria.

Funds Avail.: $250-$400. **Number Awarded:** 2-4. **To Apply:** Applicants may request an application form from any Lycoming County High School Guidance Office or by contacting the Williamsport-Lycoming Community Founda-

Awards are arranged alphabetically below their administering organizations

tion. Applicants must submit a completed application from together with their high school transcript, a typed essay of 500 words or less describing why they want to enter the field of international studies, and at least one letter of reference. **Deadline:** March 31. **Contact:** Betty Gilmour, Program Officer, at 570-321-1500 or bettyg@fcfpa.org.

3778 ■ Carl and Lucille Jarrett Scholarship Fund *(Graduate, Undergraduate/Scholarship)*

Purpose: To provide scholarship for Montgomery Area High School seniors and/or graduated alumni who have been accepted and will attend an accredited 2 or 4-year college or university, full-time or part-time. **Focus:** General studies. **Qualif.:** The applicants must exhibit good citizenship; must be honest; must have integrity; must have shown through job or volunteer history his/her ability to succeed; must be self-motivated; and must have strong ethics. **Criteria:** Selection will be based on the committee's criteria.

Funds Avail.: $1,000. **To Apply:** Applicants must complete the application. Applicants may request an application by contacting the Guidance Counselors of Montgomery Area High School or download it through the Foundation's web site. **Deadline:** May 1. **Contact:** Tara Bozella or Stacey Roman, Guidance Counselors, Montgomery Area High School, 570-547-1608 ext. 116; tbozella@montasd.org; sroman@montasd.org or sroman@montast.org.

3779 ■ Gerald J. Levandoski Memorial Scholarship Fund *(Undergraduate/Scholarship)*

Purpose: To provide financial support for Danville Area High School seniors who are pursuing their studies in the field of engineering or science. **Focus:** Engineering. **Qualif.:** Applicants must have exhibited good citizenship and community involvement. **Criteria:** Selection will be based on the committee's criteria.

Funds Avail.: No specific amount. **To Apply:** Applicants must submit a completed application form along with the essay; activity sheet; reference letters; transcript; and parent's tax return (if required). **Contact:** Betty Gilmour at bettyg@fcfpa.org or 570-321-1500.

3780 ■ Carl J. Marrara Memorial Scholarship Fund *(Undergraduate/Scholarship)*

Purpose: To provide financial assistance for Danville Area High School seniors who have been accepted into a full-time undergraduate program at an accredited institution of higher education, preferably in Pennsylvania. **Focus:** General studies. **Qualif.:** Applicants must have exhibited good citizenship and community involvement; must be a leader with a sense of humor; must be grounded; must show tolerance of others; must be honest; must have integrity and make a difference in the school community; and must have an unmet financial need. **Criteria:** Selection will be based on the committee's criteria.

Funds Avail.: No specific amount. **To Apply:** Applicants may request an application from the guidance counselor of Danville Area School District. **Contact:** Gary Grozier, Guidance Counselor of Danville Area School District, 600 Walnut St., Danville, PA 17821; 570-271-3268 ext. 2006; ggrozier@danville.k12.pa.us.

3781 ■ Walter A. and Nan C. McCloskey Memorial Scholarships *(Undergraduate/Scholarship)*

Purpose: To provide financial assistance for Danville Area High School seniors who have been accepted into a full-time undergraduate program at an accredited institution of higher education, preferably in Pennsylvania. **Focus:** General studies. **Qualif.:** Applicants must have attained a Boys or Girls letter in basketball (or football or baseball in the event basketball is discontinued at Danville High School). The award recipient shall be a good school and community citizen in addition to his/her scholastic and athletic qualities. **Criteria:** Selection will be based on the committee's criteria.

Funds Avail.: No specific amount. **To Apply:** Applicants may request an application from the guidance counselor of Danville Area School District. **Contact:** Gary Grozier, Guidance Counselor of Danville Area School District, 600 Walnut St., Danville, PA 17821; 570-271-3268 ext. 2006; ggrozier@danville.k12.pa.us.

3782 ■ Joseph and Catherine Missigman Memorial Nursing Scholarships *(Undergraduate/Scholarship)*

Purpose: To provide financial assistance for Bloomsburg University students who are pursuing a career in nursing. **Focus:** Nursing. **Qualif.:** Candidates must be Bloomsburg University students who have identified nursing as their major; must be completing their second or third year's curricula in the University's nursing education program; have a GPA of 2.5 or greater for all nursing coursework; and have a demonstrated financial need as determined by Bloomsburg University's methods and practices for assessing its student's financial capacities. **Criteria:** Selection will be based on the committee's criteria.

Funds Avail.: No specific amount. **To Apply:** Candidates must have completed and filed an application for the scholarship and must include a one-page cover letter describing his/her rational for applying for the scholarship as well as his/her interest in the nursing field. **Contact:** Margie Eckroth-Bucher, Associate Professor Department of Nursing, Bloomsburg University, 570-389-4607, mekroth@bloomu.edu.

3783 ■ Missigman Scholarship Fund *(Undergraduate/Scholarship)*

Purpose: To provide financial assistance for Sullivan County High School seniors who have been accepted into a full-time undergraduate program at an accredited institution of higher education, preferably in Pennsylvania. **Focus:** General studies. **Qualif.:** Candidate must be a graduating senior at Sullivan County High School and must demonstrate a strong potential to succeed in pursuing their higher education objectives. **Criteria:** Selection will be based on the committee's criteria.

Funds Avail.: No specific amount. **To Apply:** Applicants may request an application from the Sullivan County High School or from the First Community Foundation of Pennsylvania. **Contact:** Jill Sysock, Guidance Office, Sullivan County High School, Beech and South St., Laporte, PA 18626, 570-947-7001, sysojill@sulcosd.k12.pa.us.

3784 ■ Robert E. and Judy More Scholarship Fund *(Undergraduate/Scholarship)*

Purpose: To provide financial assistance for Montgomery Area High School students intending to pursue higher education in finance, engineering, business or science. **Focus:** Finance; Engineering; Business; Science. **Qualif.:** Candidates must exhibit leadership qualities, academic excellence and a cooperative spirit. **Criteria:** Selection will be based on the committee's criteria.

Funds Avail.: No specific amount. **To Apply:** Candidates

Awards are arranged alphabetically below their administering organizations

must complete and submit the application. Scholarship application can be requested from Montgomery Area High School or may be downloaded from the Foundation's web site. **Deadline:** April 15. **Contact:** Betty Gilmour, Program Officer, at 570-321-1500 or bettyg@fcfpa.org.

3785 ■ Muncy Rotary Club Scholarship Fund
(Undergraduate/Scholarship)

Purpose: To provide financial assistance for Muncy High School seniors who have been accepted into a full-time continuing education program. **Focus:** General studies. **Qualif.:** Applicants must have exhibited community involvement. Other than a strong potential for success, such factors as class rank and GPA will not be criteria in making a selection unless, in the judgment of the Muncy Rotary Club Scholarship Committee, such factors are needed to distinguish between multiple potential candidates. **Criteria:** Financial need will be a considering factor.

Funds Avail.: No specific amount. **To Apply:** Applicants may request an application from Erik Berthold of Muncy High School. **Deadline:** April 1. **Contact:** Erik Berthold, Guidance Counselor, Muncy High School, 200 West Penn St., Muncy, PA 17756, 570-546-3127 ext. 3260, eberthold@muncysd.org.

3786 ■ Muncy Scholars Award Fund
(Undergraduate/Award)

Purpose: To provide financial assistance for graduating seniors in the Muncy Area School District who have completed grades 9, 10, and 11 at the Muncy High School and who have been accepted and will attend a 4-year college, full-time. **Focus:** General studies. **Qualif.:** Applicants must have exhibited continued growth in his/her citizenship; must be a leader; must be honest; must have integrity; and must be determined to succeed. **Criteria:** Selection will be based on the committee's criteria.

Funds Avail.: No specific amount. **To Apply:** Applicants will be selected from the top 10 academic performers and must have attained at least one varsity letter (either n sports or band). **Contact:** Erik Berthold, guidance counselor, Muncy High School, 200 W Penn St., Muncy, PA 17756; 570-546-3127 ext. 3260; eberthold@muncysd.org.

3787 ■ Albert and Alice Nacinovich Music Scholarships *(Undergraduate/Scholarship)*

Purpose: To provide financial assistance for Lycoming County high school seniors graduating from public or private schools with a demonstrated interest in music who plan to attend a qualified institution of higher education in a music-related field of study. **Focus:** Music. **Qualif.:** Applicants must be graduating high school seniors from any Lycoming County high school, public or private (secular or Christian), or as part of a qualified home-schooling arrangement within Lycoming County; must have been accepted to a qualified institution of higher education with the intention of pursuing further education or a career in music in a degree-granting program in music education or a music-related field of study; and must have a demonstrated interest in music, which may include participation in band, chorus, music theory and composition, and performance service at school, church, or community. **Criteria:** Selection will be based on the committee's criteria.

Funds Avail.: $1,000. **To Apply:** Applicants will be required to complete an application, provide copies of transcripts, and attach a 500-word of essay or less outlining his or her interest in music and how a scholarship award will help to advance his or her goals within a musical field or discipline.

A recording of the applicant's work must also be submitted with completed application and essay. **Deadline:** May 1. **Contact:** Betty Gilmour, Program Officer at 570-321-1500/866-901-2372 or bettyg@fcfpa.org.

3788 ■ Rechsteiner Family Scholarship Fund
(Undergraduate/Scholarship)

Purpose: To provide financial assistance for Danville Area High School graduating seniors who have been accepted into a full-time undergraduate program at an institution of higher education to study education or science. **Focus:** Education; Science. **Qualif.:** Applicants must be students studying education or science and who maintain a GPA of 2.7 on a 4.0 scale after the end of their freshman year and for the rest of their undergraduate education. **Criteria:** Selection will be based on the committee's criteria.

Funds Avail.: No specific amount. **To Apply:** Applicants may request an application from the Guidance Counselor of Danville Area School District. **Contact:** Gary Grozier, Guidance Counselor of Danville Area School District, 600 Walnut St., Danville, PA 17821; 570-271-3268 ext. 2006; ggrozier@danville.k12.pa.us.

3789 ■ Kimberly Marie Rogers Memorial Scholarship Fund *(Undergraduate, Vocational/Occupational/Scholarship)*

Purpose: To provide scholarship for Montoursville Area High School seniors who are planning to attend a vocational/technical college or a two or four-year accredited college. **Focus:** General studies. **Qualif.:** Applicants must be Montoursville Area High School seniors who are planning to attend a vocational/technical college or a two or four-year accredited college. Their major should fall under the vocational/technical field. **Criteria:** Selection will be based on financial need but with equal emphasis on academics. The recipient must have a GPA of 3.0 or higher.

Funds Avail.: No specific amount. **To Apply:** Applicants may contact and request an application from the Montoursville Area High School. **Contact:** Ronda Albert, Montoursville Area High School, 100 N Arch St, Montoursville, PA 17754; 570-368-3509; ralbert@montoursville.k12.pa.us.

3790 ■ Dr. Wayne F. Rose Scholarship Fund
(Undergraduate/Scholarship)

Purpose: To provide financial assistance for Loyalsock High School seniors intending to attend a qualified institution of higher education in pursuit of a career in education who have a demonstrated interest in working with children and who exhibit an appreciation of the arts. **Focus:** General studies. **Qualif.:** Applicants must demonstrate family financial need; must demonstrate active involvement working or volunteering with children outside of their own school and typical class responsibilities; must demonstrate participation in the arts while in school and/or through extracurricular activities; and must be in good academic standing with potential for success. **Criteria:** Selection will be based on the committee's criteria.

Funds Avail.: No specific amount. **To Apply:** Applicants may request an application to the Loyalsock Township High School. Applicants must have a recommendation of at least one teacher. **Contact:** Diane Stanzione, Loyalsock Township High School, 1801 Loyalsock Drive, Williamsport, PA 17701, 570-326-3581 ext. 1307, dstanzio@ltsd.k12.pa.us.

3791 ■ Jane Salanky-Onzik Scholarship Fund
(Undergraduate/Scholarship)

Purpose: To provide financial assistance for South Williamsport Area High School seniors. **Focus:** Spanish stud-

Awards are arranged alphabetically below their administering organizations

ies. **Qualif.:** Applicants must be high school seniors who have been accepted into a full-time undergraduate program at an institution of higher education (preferably in Pennsylvania) to study secondary education (preferably to teach Spanish) or to study Spanish in preparation for a career that would utilize the Spanish language. Applicants must have exhibited good citizenship and community involvement, must have unmet financial need and must not have been the recipient of other major scholarship awards. **Criteria:** Selection will be based on the committee's criteria.

Funds Avail.: No specific amount. **To Apply:** Applicant must submit an application to the Guidance Counselor's office. **Contact:** Verna Correll, Guidance Counselor, s Williamsport Jr./Sr. High School, 700 Percy St., S Williamsport, PA 17702; 570-326-2684; vcorrell@mounties.k12.pa.us.

3792 ■ John A. Savoy Scholarship Fund
(Undergraduate/Scholarship)

Purpose: To provide financial assistance for South Williamsport Area High School seniors who have been accepted into a full-time undergraduate program at an accredited institution of higher education, preferably in Pennsylvania. **Focus:** General studies. **Qualif.:** Applicants must have exhibited good citizenship and community involvement; have unmet financial need; and must not have been the recipient of other major scholarship awards. **Criteria:** Selection will be based on committee's criteria.

Funds Avail.: $500. **To Apply:** Scholarship is renewable as long as the recipient remains in good standing at an accredited college or university but shall not exceed a maximum of 4 years. Applicant must submit an application to the Guidance Counselor's Office; must include a cover letter (not to exceed two pages) outlining why he or she is applying for the scholarship and summarizing his/her ultimate career objectives; must provide at least one letter of reference; and must provide proof that he or she has been accepted to a qualified two or four-year college/university. **Deadline:** May 1. **Contact:** Verna Correll, Guidance Counselor, South Williamsport Jr./Sr. High School, 700 Percy St., S Williamsport, PA 17702; 570-326-2684; vcorrell@mounties.k12.pa.us.

3793 ■ Ralph and Josephine Smith Scholarship Fund *(Undergraduate/Scholarship)*

Purpose: To defray all or a portion of the costs of attending college or other undergraduate institutions of higher learning beyond the secondary level for Warrior Run High School seniors. **Focus:** General studies. **Qualif.:** Candidate must maintain a GPA of 2.5. Candidate's financial needs shall always be a primary consideration. Extra-curricular activities will not be considered in the selection process. **Criteria:** Selection will be based on the committee's criteria.

Funds Avail.: $625. **Number Awarded:** 4. **To Apply:** Applicants may request an application from the Guidance Office of Warrior Run High School. **Contact:** Jenna Brown or Jim Houser, Guidance Office, Warrior Run High School, 4800 Susquehanna Trail, Turbotville, PA 17772, 570-649-5166 ext. 105, jbrown@wrsd.org or jhouser@wrsd.org.

3794 ■ Margaret E. Waldron Scholarship Fund
(Undergraduate/Scholarship)

Purpose: To provide financial assistance for Muncy High School seniors who are pursuing higher education. **Focus:** General studies. **Qualif.:** Candidates must have completed grades 10, 11, 12 at Muncy High School and have graduated from academic courses at Muncy High School; must rank in upper 1/5 of the class during junior and senior years;

must present letter of acceptance from a postsecondary institution of higher learning. **Criteria:** Selection will be based on the committee's criteria.

Funds Avail.: $3,000 - freshman and sophomore years; $4,000 - junior and senior years. **To Apply:** Applicants may contact Guidance Office of Muncy High School to request an application or download the application from the Foundation's web site. Applicant must submit a copy of his/her parents' current U.S. Individual Income Tax Return and a copy of his or her school transcript through the third marking period of his or her senior year. **Deadline:** April 1. **Contact:** Betty Gilmour, Program Officer at 570-321-1500/866-901-2372 or at bettyg@fcfpa.org.

3795 ■ Monica M. Weaver Memorial Fund
(Undergraduate/Scholarship)

Purpose: To provide scholarship for Montoursville Area High School seniors of high scholastic standing who are enrolled at a college or other educational institution pursuing a major in physical therapy. **Focus:** Physical therapy. **Qualif.:** Students must have resided in the Montoursville Area School District for a minimum of three years prior to graduation. **Criteria:** Selection will be based on the committee's criteria. Preference will be given to a student who has not received other scholarships and demonstrates financial need.

Funds Avail.: No specific amount. **To Apply:** Applicants may contact and request an application from the Montoursville Area High School. **Contact:** Ronda Albert, Montoursville Area High School, 100 N Arch St, Montoursville, PA 17754; 570-368-3509; ralbert@montoursville.k12.pa.us.

3796 ■ Williamsport-Lycoming Community Foundation - Benjamin Franklin Scholarships
(Undergraduate, Vocational/Occupational/ Scholarship)

Purpose: To provide academic support for students who are attending Pennsylvania College and have graduated from Bradford County, Clinton County, Lycoming County, Potter County, Sullivan County or Tioga County. **Focus:** General studies. **Qualif.:** Applicants must be enrolled at the Pennsylvania College of Technology; must be enrolled in an approved Tech prep high school program and subsequently enroll in a Certificate, Associate or Bachelor's Degree program at the Pennsylvania College of Technology. In schools without approved Tech Prep programs, students must enroll in a high school vocational-technical program and subsequently enroll in a Certificate, Associate, or Bachelor's Degree program at the Pennsylvanian College of Technology. Applicants must have a GPA of "B" or higher and must be enrolled full-time. Preference will be given to continuing students in subsequent years if a cumulative GPA of 2.80 is maintained in the program. **Criteria:** Selection will be based on the committee's criteria.

Funds Avail.: No specific amount. **To Apply:** Applicants must submit a writing sample as defined by the Pennsylvania College of Technology Prep office. **Contact:** Betty Gilmour, Program Officer, bettyg@fcfpa.org.

3797 ■ Eleanor M. Wolfson Memorial Scholarship Fund *(Undergraduate/Scholarship)*

Purpose: To provide scholarship for Montoursville Area High School seniors who will be attending Yale College. **Focus:** Creative writing. **Qualif.:** Students must be graduating seniors at Montoursville Area High School. If there are no graduating students planning to attend Yale College, a

Awards are arranged alphabetically below their administering organizations

graduating student with an outstanding academic record and a demonstrated talent in creative writing will be considered. **Criteria:** Selection will be based on academic merit and potential.

Funds Avail.: No specific amount. **To Apply:** Applicants may contact and request an application from the Montoursville Area High School. **Contact:** Ronda Albert, Montoursville Area High School, 100 N Arch St, Montoursville, PA 17754; 570-368-3509; ralbert@montoursville.k12.pa.us.

3798 ■ Wendy Y. Wolfson Memorial Scholarship Fund (Undergraduate/Scholarship)

Purpose: To provide scholarship for Montoursville Area High School seniors who will be attending Yale College. **Focus:** Music; Drama criticism. **Qualif.:** Students must be graduating seniors of Montoursville Area High School. If there are no graduating students planning to attend Yale College, graduating students with an outstanding academic record and a demonstrated talent in music or drama will be considered. **Criteria:** Selection will be based on academic merit and potential.

Funds Avail.: No specific amount. **To Apply:** Applicants may contact and request an application from the Montoursville Area High School. **Contact:** Ronda Albert, Montoursville Area High School, 100 N Arch St, Montoursville, PA 17754; 570-368-3509; ralbert@montoursville.k12.pa.us.

3799 ■ Fish & Richardson P.C.
One Marina Park Dr.
Boston, MA 02210
Ph: (617) 542-5070
Fax: (617) 542-8906
E-mail: info@fr.com
URL: www.fr.com

3800 ■ Fish & Richardson 1L Diversity Fellowships (Undergraduate/Scholarship)

Purpose: To promote diversity in the legal profession. **Focus:** Law. **Qualif.:** Applicant must be a first year law student. **Criteria:** Selection is based on the submitted application and materials.

Funds Avail.: $5,000. **Number Awarded:** 5. **To Apply:** Applicants must submit a completed application which includes an essay question, a resume, undergraduate transcript, legal writing sample, and a letter of recommendation from a law school or college professor. **Deadline:** January 13.

3801 ■ Fisher Communications Inc.
100 4th Ave. N, Ste. 510
Seattle, WA 98109-4983
Ph: (206) 404-7000
Fax: (206) 404-6037
E-mail: Info@fsci.com
URL: www.fsci.com

3802 ■ Fisher Broadcasting Scholarships for Minorities (Undergraduate, Vocational/Occupational/Scholarship)

Purpose: To attract minority students into careers in broadcasting. **Focus:** Broadcasting. **Qualif.:** Applicant must be of non-white origin; a U.S. citizen; have a minimum cumulative GPA of 2.5; at least a sophomore; and enrolled in a broadcast oriented curriculum leading to a baccalaureate degree at an accredited four-year college/university, or to a broadcast curriculum at an accredited community college, transferable to such a four-year baccalaureate degree program or to a broadcast curriculum at an accredited vocational-technical school. **Criteria:** Selection is based on need, academic achievement and personal qualities.

Funds Avail.: No specific amount. **Number Awarded:** Varies. **To Apply:** Applicants must submit a completed scholarship application form along with a copy of college/technical school transcripts; two letters of recommendation from non-family members (at least one should be from a former instructor); written essay explaining the applicant's financial need (list scholarships, grants and loans received and applied for), educational and career goals, involvement in school activities, and experience or interest in broadcast communications; estimated expense/income spreadsheet; and proof of citizenship. **Deadline:** May 31.

3803 ■ Allison E. Fisher Memorial Fund
PO Box 43402
Baltimore, MD 21236
Ph: (410) 679-0595
E-mail: fishers@verizon.net
URL: www.allisonfisherfund.org

3804 ■ St. Stephen A.M.E. Allison E. Fisher Book Awards (Undergraduate/Scholarship)

Purpose: To provide financial assistance to graduating senior students who have been accepted to a two-year community college or four-year college or university. **Focus:** General studies. **Qualif.:** Applicants must be graduating senior students who attended St. Stephen A.M.E. and who have been accepted to a two-year community college or four-year college or university. **Criteria:** Recipients are selected based on the criteria designed by the Scholarship Selection Committee.

Funds Avail.: $300. **To Apply:** Applicants must submit all the required application information.

3805 ■ Allison E. Fisher Scholarships (Graduate, Undergraduate/Scholarship)

Purpose: To provide financial assistance to students who are attending an accredited four-year university. **Focus:** Journalism; Photography; Radio and television. **Qualif.:** Applicants must be any foreign or U.S. students who are majoring in journalism-print, photography or radio and television or planning a career in one of those fields; must be currently attending accredited four-year university; must have cumulative grade point average of 3.0 and be enrolled in undergraduate or graduate school during the award year. **Criteria:** Applicants are evaluated based on academic and financial need.

Funds Avail.: $2,500. **To Apply:** Applicants must submit all the required application information.

3806 ■ Spirit of Allison Graduation Awards (Undergraduate/Award)

Purpose: To provide financial assistance and recognize graduating seniors at Perry Hall High School. **Focus:** General studies. **Qualif.:** Applicants must be graduating seniors at Perry Hall High School. **Criteria:** Applicants are judged based on their essay which exemplified leadership; artistic expression; courage; congeniality and volunteerism.

Funds Avail.: $500. **To Apply:** Applicants must submit

Awards are arranged alphabetically below their administering organizations

completed application form along with the essay. **Deadline:** March 31.

3807 ■ Flamenco de la Isla Society
2560 Vancouver St.
Victoria, BC, Canada V8T 4A7
Ph: (250) 380-3927
E-mail: info@flamencodelaisla.org
URL: www.flamencodelaisla.org

3808 ■ Flamenco Student Scholarships
(Undergraduate/Scholarship)

Purpose: To help students defray the cost of obtaining an education. **Focus:** Dance. **Qualif.:** Applicants must be members of the Flamenco de la Isla Society; must have a minimum of two years flamenco dance training; must be taking a minimum of two classes per week; must be willing to, or have in the past, volunteered for the society's events. **Criteria:** Preference will be given to those students who meet the criteria.

Funds Avail.: $500. **To Apply:** Applicants must submit a completed application form and must provide a statement (no more than half a page) stating the importance of the scholarship. **Deadline:** May 1.

3809 ■ Flexible Packaging Association (FPA)
971 Corporate Blvd., Ste. 403
Linthicum, MD 21090
Ph: (410) 694-0800
Fax: (410) 694-0900
E-mail: fpa@flexpack.org
URL: www.flexpack.org

3810 ■ Flexible Packaging Academic Scholarships & Summer Internships Program
(Undergraduate/Internship, Scholarship)

Purpose: To provide a learning experience on the flexible packaging industry. **Focus:** Industrial design; Industrial education. **Qualif.:** Applicants must be enrolled in an AA, BA, BS or MS degree program; have a 2.7 GPA; have 24 credit hours, nine credits of which are in packaging, printing or other areas in the converting industry. **Criteria:** Recipient is selected based on submitted application and supporting materials.

Funds Avail.: $3,000. **To Apply:** Applicants are advised to visit the website for the online application system. Prepare a recommendation letter (academic or professional); and an essay (maximum of 500 words). **Remarks:** Introduced in 2005.

3811 ■ Flexographic Technical Association (FTA)
3920 Veterans Memorial Hwy., Ste. 9
Bohemia, NY 11716
Ph: (631) 737-6020
Fax: (631) 737-6813
E-mail: memberinfo@flexography.org
URL: www.flexography.org

3812 ■ FIRST Operator Certification Scholarships *(Undergraduate/Scholarship)*

Purpose: To assist individuals who desire to improve their skills in the pursuit of certification training. **Focus:** Printing trades and industries. **Qualif.:** Applicants must pursue FIRST Operator Certification (Levels I, II & III) in one of the two areas of concentration: Press or Prepress; must have at least two years of full-time direct work experience in any area related to flexographic printing/converting. **Criteria:** Selection will be based on submitted applications.

Funds Avail.: $1,050. **To Apply:** Applicants must submit an electronic format of a completed application form together with supporting documents such as work history, letters of recommendation and must attach a school transcript. **Contact:** Shelley Rubin at 631-737-6020 or srubin@flexography.org.

3813 ■ Florida Association Directors of Nursing Administration (FADONA)
200 Butler St., Ste. 305
West Palm Beach, FL 33407
Ph: (561) 659-2167
Fax: (561) 659-1291
E-mail: fadona@fadona.org
URL: www.fadona.org

3814 ■ Imogene Ward Nursing Scholarships
(Undergraduate/Scholarship)

Purpose: To provide financial assistance to individuals in nursing looking to continue their education in the LTC setting. **Focus:** Nursing. **Qualif.:** Applicants must be pursuing education to become registered nurses; must be enrolled in an accredited Florida Nursing program; must be willing to pledge a minimum of two years, working full-time in long-term care in the state of Florida. **Criteria:** Recipients are selected based on demonstrated determination to overcome personal and/or professional obstacles to pursue nursing education, track record of excellence and the potential for future leadership in long-term care.

Funds Avail.: No specific amount. **To Apply:** Applicants must submit a completed application form including name and full contact information; must submit a 300-word or less narrative essay which outlines what it takes to be an exceptional nurse and also expresses reasons they should be considered for the Imogene Ward Nursing Scholarship Award.

3815 ■ Florida Association for Media in Education (FAME)
1876-B Eider Ct.
Tallahassee, FL 32308
Ph: (850) 531-8351
Fax: (850) 531-8344
E-mail: info@floridamedia.org
URL: www.floridamedia.org

3816 ■ Sandy Ulm Scholarships *(Undergraduate/ Scholarship)*

Purpose: To help every student in Florida be involved in and have open access to a quality school library media program, administered by a highly competent, certified library media specialist. **Focus:** Media Arts. **Qualif.:** Applicants must be students studying to be school library media specialists. **Criteria:** Recipients are selected based on academic performance.

Funds Avail.: $No specific amount. **To Apply:** Applicants must submit a completed application form and submit a

Awards are arranged alphabetically below their administering organizations

copy of the transcript of all college credits for the graduate program in which they are currently enrolled, two letters of recommendation (one must come from a professor) and a notarized statement (found in application). **Deadline:** September 15 and February 15.

3817 ■ Florida Atlantic Planning Society (FAPS)
777 Glades Rd.
Boca Raton, FL 33431
Ph: (561) 297-3000
E-mail: fauweb@fau.edu
URL: www.fau.edu/durp/faps

3818 ■ Delores A. Auzenne Fellowships
(Postgraduate/Fellowship)

Purpose: To encourage minority students to pursue graduate degree in areas where they are historically underrepresented at Florida Atlantic University. **Focus:** Engineering; Mathematics and mathematical sciences; Computer and information science; Psychology. **Qualif.:** Applicants must be pursuing graduate degrees in a discipline in which minority students are underrepresented; must be citizens or permanent residents of the United States. **Criteria:** Recipients are selected based on academic performance and financial need.

Funds Avail.: $5,000. **To Apply:** Applicants must submit a transcript from all institutions attended; one-two page statement on how fellowship will assist in the achievement of their career goals and three current letters of recommendation from which one must come from a professor who is familiar with their academic work. **Deadline:** May 11.

3819 ■ Florida Atlantic Planning Society Graduate Fellowships for Academic Excellence
(Postgraduate/Fellowship)

Purpose: To provide financial assistance in the form of a fellowship to outstanding graduate students. **Focus:** General studies. **Qualif.:** Applicants must be degree-seeking students with a minimum GPA of 3.5; must have completed a minimum of one semester in a FAU graduate program. **Criteria:** Recipients are selected based on academic performance and financial need.

Funds Avail.: $5,000. **To Apply:** Applicants must submit two letters of recommendation from FAU Faculty, unofficial transcript of all graduate works attempted by the nominee and application form. **Deadline:** May 11. **Contact:** Nancy Diamond, diamond@fau.edu.

3820 ■ Royal Palm Audubon Society Environmental Fellowships *(Postgraduate/Fellowship)*

Purpose: To provide funds to graduate students preparing for a career in the promotion of environmentalism, environmental preservation or environmental protection. **Focus:** Environmental science. **Qualif.:** Applicants must be graduate students conducting research towards increasing public understanding of environmental problems and solutions. **Criteria:** Recipients are selected based on academic performance and financial need.

Funds Avail.: $1,500. **To Apply:** Applicant must submit a one-two page description of academic background, interest and research project and one letter of recommendation from a faculty member who is familiar with the student and his or her research. **Deadline:** April 27.

3821 ■ Florida Education Fund (FEF)
201 E Kennedy Blvd., Ste. 1525
Tampa, FL 33602

Ph: (813) 272-2772
Fax: (813) 272-2784
E-mail: office@fefonline.org
URL: www.fefonline.org

3822 ■ Florida Education Fund McKnight Doctoral Fellowships *(Graduate/Fellowship)*

Purpose: To address the under-representation of African American and Hispanic faculty at colleges and universities in the state of Florida by increasing the pool of citizens qualified with PhD degrees to teach at the college and university levels. **Focus:** Arts; Science; Business; Engineering; Health Sciences; Nursing; Visual arts; Performing arts. **Qualif.:** Applicants must be African American or Hispanic, US citizens, and hold a minimum of a bachelor's degree from a regionally accredited college or university. Currently enrolled doctoral students are not eligible to apply. The Fellowships must be used at one of the participating Florida universities and will be awarded only to those eligible individuals who have been accepted for graduate study at one of the participating universities. **Criteria:** Selection will be based on the committee's criteria.

Funds Avail.: $5,000 plus annual stipend of $12,000. **Number Awarded:** 50. **To Apply:** Interested applicants may visit the website for the application process. Paper application forms are also available upon request. **Deadline:** January 15.

3823 ■ Florida Engineering Society (FES)
PO Box 750
Tallahassee, FL 32302-0750
Ph: (850) 224-7121
Fax: (850) 222-4349
E-mail: fes@fleng.org
URL: www.fleng.org

3824 ■ Cesar A. Calas/FES Miami Chapter Scholarships *(Undergraduate/Scholarship)*

Purpose: To encourage and assist students in pursuing engineering careers; to educate the public about engineering; and to promote and enhance engineering education in Florida in order to position the state as a technological leader in global economy. **Focus:** Engineering. **Qualif.:** Applicants must be attending an accredited college of higher learning and enrolled in an engineering program approved by the Florida Engineering Society Scholarship Committee; must have at least 3.0 GPA; must maintain 12 credit hours per semester; and must be permanent residents of Miami-Dade or Monroe County. **Criteria:** Recipients are selected based on academic performance and financial need.

Funds Avail.: $1,000. **To Apply:** Applicants must submit completed application form; an official transcript; and letter of recommendation from any appropriate source. **Deadline:** February 15. **Contact:** dbroer@fleng.org.

3825 ■ Fecon Scholarships *(Undergraduate/Scholarship)*

Purpose: To encourage and assist students in pursuing engineering careers; to educate the public about engineering; and to promote and enhance engineering education in Florida in order to position the state as a technological leader in global economy. **Focus:** Engineering. **Qualif.:** Applicant must be currently enrolled or accepted into a Florida university engineering program; must be in or entering his/her junior or senior year; must have at least 3.0 average on

Awards are arranged alphabetically below their administering organizations

a 4.0 scale; must be recommended by an engineering faculty member; and must be interested in pursuing a career in the field of construction. **Criteria:** Recipients are selected based on academic performance and financial need.

Funds Avail.: $1,000. **To Apply:** Applicants must submit a complete application form and an official transcript. **Deadline:** February 15. **Contact:** 850-224-7121.

3826 ■ FICE Scholarships (Undergraduate/Scholarship)

Purpose: To encourage and assist students in pursuing engineering careers; to educate the public about engineering; and to promote and enhance engineering education in Florida in order to position the state as a technological leader in global economy. **Focus:** Engineering. **Qualif.:** Applicants must be U.S. citizens pursuing a bachelor's degree in an Accreditation Board Engineering and Technology (ABET) program and must be entering their junior, senior or fifth year of college. **Criteria:** Recipients are selected based on academic performance and financial need.

Funds Avail.: $5,000. **To Apply:** Applicants must submit completed application form and an official transcript. **Deadline:** February 15.

3827 ■ Florida Engineering Society Junior College Scholarships (Undergraduate/Scholarship)

Purpose: To encourage and assist students in pursuing engineering careers; to educate the public about engineering; and to promote and enhance engineering education in Florida in order to position the state as a technological leader in global economy. **Focus:** Engineering. **Qualif.:** Applicants must be enrolled in the final year of a pre-engineering program in a Florida Junior Community College; must have at least 3.0 grade point average on a 4.0 scale; must be recommended by an engineering faculty member; and must be United States citizens or residents of Florida. **Criteria:** Recipients are selected based on academic performance and financial need, work experience, activities, honors, letters of recommendation along with the evidence of leadership, motivation, character and self-reliance.

Funds Avail.: $1,000. **To Apply:** Applicants must submit a completed application form; an official transcript; and letter of recommendation from any appropriate source. **Deadline:** February 15.

3828 ■ Florida Engineering Society University Scholarships (Undergraduate/Scholarship)

Purpose: To encourage and assist students in pursuing engineering careers; to educate the public about engineering; and to promote and enhance engineering education in Florida in order to position the state as a technological leader in global economy. **Focus:** Engineering. **Qualif.:** Applicant must be entering his or her junior or senior year in the Florida University Engineering Program; must have at least 3.0 grade point average on a 4.0 scale; must be recommended by an engineering faculty member; and must be a U.S. citizen or resident of Florida. **Criteria:** Recipients are selected based on academic performance and financial need.

Funds Avail.: Up to $30,000. **To Apply:** Applicants must submit a completed application form; an official transcript; and letter of recommendation from an engineering faculty member. **Deadline:** February 15.

3829 ■ David F. Ludovici Scholarships (Undergraduate/Scholarship)

Purpose: To encourage and assist students in pursuing engineering careers; to educate the public about engineering; and to promote and enhance engineering education in Florida in order to position the state as a technological leader in global economy. **Focus:** Engineering. **Qualif.:** Applicants must be enrolled in an ABET-accredited Florida engineering school and must be interested in civil, structural or consulting engineering. **Criteria:** Recipients are selected based on academic performance and financial need.

Funds Avail.: $1,000. **To Apply:** Applicants must submit completed application form; an official transcript; and letter of recommendation from any appropriate source. **Deadline:** February 15. **Contact:** dbroer@fleng.org.

3830 ■ Raymond W. Miller, PE and Alice E. Miller Scholarships (Undergraduate/Scholarship)

Purpose: To encourage and assist students in pursuing engineering careers; to educate the public about engineering; and to promote and enhance engineering education in Florida in order to position the state as a technological leader in global economy. **Focus:** Engineering. **Qualif.:** Applicants must be enrolled in an ABET-accredited Florida engineering school and must plan to attend the University of Florida. **Criteria:** Recipients are selected based on academic performance and financial need.

Funds Avail.: $1,000. **To Apply:** Applicants must submit completed application form; an official transcript; and letter of recommendation from any appropriate source. **Deadline:** February 15. **Contact:** dbroer@fleng.org.

3831 ■ Raymond W. Miller, PE Scholarships (Undergraduate/Scholarship)

Purpose: To encourage and assist students in pursuing engineering careers; to educate the public about engineering; and to promote and enhance engineering education in Florida in order to position the state as a technological leader in global economy. **Focus:** Engineering. **Qualif.:** Applicants must be enrolled in an ABET-accredited Florida engineering school and must plan to attend the University of Florida. **Criteria:** Recipients are selected based on academic performance and financial need.

Funds Avail.: $2,500. **To Apply:** Applicants must submit a complete application form; an official transcript; and letter of recommendation from any appropriate source. **Deadline:** February 15. **Contact:** dbroer@fleng.org.

3832 ■ Eric Primavera Memorial Scholarships (Undergraduate/Scholarship)

Purpose: To encourage and assist students in pursuing engineering careers; to educate the public about engineering; and to promote and enhance engineering education in Florida in order to position the state as a technological leader in global economy. **Focus:** Engineering. **Qualif.:** Applicants must be enrolled in an ABET-accredited Florida engineering school and plan to attend the Florida Institute of Technology. **Criteria:** Recipients are selected based on academic performance and financial need. Preference will be given to students desiring to attend Florida Institute of Technology.

Funds Avail.: $1,000. **To Apply:** Applicants must submit completed application form; an official transcript; and letter of recommendation from any appropriate source. **Deadline:** February 15. **Contact:** dbroer@fleng.org.

Awards are arranged alphabetically below their administering organizations

3833 ■ Florida Fertilizer and Agrichemical Association (FFAA)

302 S Massachusetts Ave., Ste. 199
Lakeland, FL 33801
Ph: (863) 293-4827
Fax: (863) 294-8626
E-mail: mhartney@ffaa.org
URL: www.ffaa.org

3834 ■ Florida Fertilizer and Agrichemical Association Scholarships *(Graduate, Undergraduate/Scholarship)*

Purpose: To promote the study of agriculture in higher education and to encourage students pursuing agriculture studies. **Focus:** Agricultural sciences. **Qualif.:** Applicants must be agriculture junior, senior, or graduate students at the University of Florida, Florida A&M or Florida Southern; must plan to enroll for the semester immediately following the fall semester; must have a minimum GPA of 3.0 on a 4.0 scale. **Criteria:** Recipients are selected based on academic performance and financial need.

Funds Avail.: No specific amount. **To Apply:** Applicants must submit a completed application form. **Deadline:** October 15. **Contact:** 863-293-4827.

3835 ■ Florida Institute of Certified Public Accountants (FICPA)

PO Box 5437
Tallahassee, FL 32314
Ph: (850) 488-6602
Fax: (850) 222-8190
Free: 800-342-3197
E-mail: msc@ficpa.org
URL: www.ficpa.org/ficpa/Home

3836 ■ FICPA Educational Foundation 1040K Race Scholarships *(Undergraduate/Scholarship)*

Purpose: To help offset the educational costs for accounting students at Florida's colleges and universities. **Focus:** Accounting. **Qualif.:** Applicant must be an African American; a permanent resident of Miami-Dade, Broward, Palm Beach, or Monroe Counties; and must be a full-time, 4th or 5th year accounting major at: Barry University, Florida Atlantic University, Florida International University, Florida Memorial College, Nova Southeastern University, St. Thomas University, and University of Miami. **Criteria:** Awards will be given based on the application materials submitted.

Funds Avail.: $2,000. **Number Awarded:** Varies. **To Apply:** Applicants must submit a completed application along with a complete official transcript to the Accounting Scholarship Chairman at their school. **Deadline:** February 15. **Contact:** Betsy Wilson at wilsonb@ficpa.org.

3837 ■ Florida Nursery, Growers and Landscape Association (FNGLA)

1533 Park Center Dr.
Orlando, FL 32835-5705
Ph: (407) 295-7994
Fax: (407) 295-1619
Free: 800-375-3642
E-mail: info@fngla.org
URL: www.fngla.org

3838 ■ James H. Davis Scholarships
(Undergraduate/Scholarship)

Purpose: To encourage students to pursue careers in Florida's horticulture industry and related pursuits by providing financial assistance for undergraduate, post-graduate, or other advanced education programs in Florida. **Focus:** Horticulture. **Qualif.:** Applicants must be incoming college freshmen, sophomores, juniors, seniors and/or graduate students planning to attend a community college, college or university in the state of Florida; must be full-time students in horticulture program or related field with the intent to graduate in the field; must have a 2.0 or above GPA. **Criteria:** Recipients are selected based on financial need and students' ability to maintain a 2.0 grade point average.

Funds Avail.: No specific amount. **To Apply:** Applicants must complete the application form; must submit a high school or college transcript; an essay and two letters of recommendation. **Deadline:** January 15.

3839 ■ Florida Nurses Association (FNA)

1235 E Concord St.
Orlando, FL 32803
Ph: (407) 896-3261
Fax: (407) 896-9042
E-mail: info@floridanurse.org
URL: www.floridanurse.org

3840 ■ Florida Nurses Foundation Scholarships
(All/Scholarship)

Purpose: To serve and support all registered nurses through professional development, advocacy and the promotion of excellence at every level of professional nursing practice. **Focus:** Nursing. **Qualif.:** Applicants must be enrolled in a nationally accredited nursing program; must be students including those in associate, baccalaureate, and master's degree nursing programs or doctoral programs; and must have a minimum GPA of 2.5 for undergraduate and 3.0 GPA for graduate students. **Criteria:** Recipients are selected based on academic performance and potential contribution to the Nursing Professionals Society.

Funds Avail.: No specific amount. **To Apply:** Applicants must submit all necessary documents with the application form online. **Deadline:** June 1. **Contact:** foundation@floridanurse.org.

3841 ■ Florida Outdoor Writers Association (FOWA)

24 NW, 33rd Ct., Ste. A
Gainesville, FL 32607
Ph: (352) 284-1763
E-mail: info@fowa.org
URL: www.fowa.org

3842 ■ Florida Outdoor Writers Association Scholarships *(Undergraduate/Scholarship)*

Purpose: To motivate and encourage young people to enter outdoor communications career fields. **Focus:** Communications; Journalism. **Qualif.:** Applicants must be students at Florida Colleges and universities, or must be students whose applications are endorsed by a FOWA member or a faculty advisor. **Criteria:** Recipients are selected based on the essay, endorsement of the faculty advisor or FOWA member, scholastic merit and extracur-

Awards are arranged alphabetically below their administering organizations

ricular activities as indicated in the applicant's resume or supporting materials submitted.

Funds Avail.: $500-$1,000. **To Apply:** Applicants must submit a completed application form; must submit an essay, 500-1,000-words, that expresses their appreciation for the outdoor experience; an up-to-date resume; a letter of endorsement from a FOWA member or faculty advisor. **Deadline:** May 14.

3843 ■ Florida Police Chiefs Association (FPCA)

924 N Gadsden St.
Tallahassee, FL 32303
Ph: (850) 219-3631
Fax: (850) 219-3640
Free: 800-332-8117
E-mail: amercer@fpca.com
URL: www.fpca.com

3844 ■ Police Explorer Scholarships Program
(Undergraduate/Scholarship)

Purpose: To promote public safety legislation. **Focus:** Government. **Qualif.:** Applicants must have been involved in a police explorer post, and have been a member of the post for a minimum of one year by the time of award presentation; must maintain a minimum of a 2.0 overall grade point average and should be completing their senior year in high school, already enrolled in college or planning to attend college. **Criteria:** Recipients are selected based on the information they submit to the foundation.

Funds Avail.: $1,000. **To Apply:** Applicants must submit a completed application form; must submit a 4x5 glossy, black and white or colored headshot photo, in uniform, if possible. **Deadline:** April 15.

3845 ■ Florida Public Health Association (FPHA)

1605 Pebble Beach Blvd.
Green Cove Springs, FL 32043-8077
Ph: (904) 529-1401
Fax: (904) 529-7761
E-mail: floridapha@bellsouth.net
URL: fpha.org

3846 ■ Florida Public Health Association Public Health Graduate Scholarships *(Graduate/Scholarship)*

Purpose: To support graduate or undergraduate students studying public health. **Focus:** Public health. **Qualif.:** Applicant must be a FPHA member; must be in a Master's Degree or Doctoral Degree program in the field of public health; must intend to remain in Florida and contribute to Florida's Public Health System following graduation. **Criteria:** Selection is based on the application.

Funds Avail.: $500. **To Apply:** Applicants must submit the complete application form together with a narrative (1-2 pages) that explains professional goals and reasons for seeking Master's or Doctoral degree, curriculum vitae, two original letters of recommendation from two non-family references, and copy of current transcript showing GPA. Send application to: Max Salfinger M.D. Florida Department of Health, Bureau of Laboratories, 4052 Bald Cypress Way, HQ, Bin No. A-15, Tallahassee, FL 32399. **Deadline:** May 31.

3847 ■ Florida Public Health Association Public Health Undergraduate Scholarships
(Undergraduate/Scholarship)

Purpose: To support graduate or undergraduate students studying public health **Focus:** Public health. **Qualif.:** Applicants must be working on degrees in health-related or public health programs. **Criteria:** Selection is based on the application.

Funds Avail.: $300. **To Apply:** Applicants must submit the completed application form together with a narrative (1-2 pages) that explains professional goals and reasons for interest in health or public health, curriculum vitae, two original letters of recommendation from two non-family references, and a copy of current transcript showing GPA. Send application to: Max Salfinger M.D. Florida Department of Health, Bureau of Laboratories, 4052 Bald Cypress Way, HQ, Bin No. A-15, Tallahassee, FL 32399. **Deadline:** May 31.

3848 ■ Fluid Power Distributor Association (FPDA)

PO Box 1420
Cherry Hill, NJ 08034-0054
Ph: (856) 424-8998
Fax: (856) 424-9248
E-mail: info@fpda.org
URL: www.fpda.org

3849 ■ Tom D. Ralls Memorial Scholarships
(Professional development/Scholarship)

Purpose: To promote the ongoing professional development of industry executives. **Focus:** Engineering, Industrial. **Qualif.:** Applicants must be employees in good standing of an FPDA Regular (Distributor) Member organization and members of FPDA Young Executives. **Criteria:** Applications will be reviewed and evaluated by FPDA Executive Committee.

Funds Avail.: Full tuition. **Number Awarded:** 1. **To Apply:** Applicants must submit a completed application form along with a letter of recommendation and an essay about the applicant's interest to attend the University Industrial Distribution program. **Deadline:** November 14. **Remarks:** Established in memory of Tom D. Ralls, former FPDA President and Chairman. **Contact:** Patricia A. Lilly, Exec. Dir. at plilly@fpda.org.

3850 ■ Flying Physicians Association (FPA)

11626 Twain Dr.
Montgomery, TX 77356
Ph: (936) 588-6505
Fax: (832) 415-0287
E-mail: info@fpadrs.org
URL: www.fpadrs.org

3851 ■ FPA Aviation Scholarships *(Graduate, Undergraduate/Scholarship)*

Purpose: To provide academic and flight scholarships to deserving students who need financial assistance. **Focus:** Aviation. **Qualif.:** Applicants must possess a student pilot certificate, or higher, with a current third-class medical certificate. **Criteria:** Selection of applicants will be based on financial need.

Funds Avail.: $250. **To Apply:** Applicants must submit a

Awards are arranged alphabetically below their administering organizations

brief letter expressing aviation situation and ambitions; must submit the application along with copy of student pilot/pilot certificate, medical certificate and copy of logbook. **Deadline:** June 1.

3852 ■ Food and Drug Law Institute (FDLI)

1155 15th St. NW, Ste. 800
Washington, DC 20005
Ph: (202) 371-1420
Fax: (202) 371-0649
Free: 800-956-6293
E-mail: service@fdli.org
URL: www.fdli.org

3853 ■ H. Thomas Austern Memorial Writing Competition *(Undergraduate/Prize)*

Purpose: To encourage students interested in the areas of law. **Focus:** Law. **Qualif.:** Applicants must be currently enrolled in a J.D. program at any of the nations' "ABA accredited" law schools. **Criteria:** Committees of practicing attorneys and law professors with relevant food and drug expertise will judge the papers according to the following category: 1) thoroughness and depth of legal analysis; 2) originality and difficulty of topic; 3) evaluation of judicial precedents, status and regulations; 4) discussion of conclusions and future impact; 5) quality of legal research; 6) writing style; 7) conciseness; 8) form and quality of citations; and 9) conformity with rules and competition.

Funds Avail.: $4,000 (1st Place); $1,000 (2nd Place). **Number Awarded:** 2. **To Apply:** Submissions shall be typewritten, double-spaced on 81/2 x 11 inch paper. Electronic submissions in word documents are acceptable. Students joining the short paper competition shall not exceed 40 pages in length including appendices and footnotes, which may be single-spaced. Candidates submitting in a long paper category shall reach the 100 pages including footnotes. Text and footnote shall be type-written, 12 pt. Times New Roman format. Papers shall have one-inch margin in all sides. Applicants must also include a cover sheet with entrant's full name and contact information, law school, year of study and date of submission. **Deadline:** June 8. **Contact:** Materials should be submitted to Sarah Sansolo at the above address; Phone: 202-222-0894; Toll free: 800-956-6293; E-mail: sks@fdli.org.

3854 ■ Food Processing Suppliers Association (FPSA)

1451 Dolley Madison Blvd., Ste. 101
McLean, VA 22101-3847
Ph: (703) 761-2600
Fax: (703) 761-4334
E-mail: info@fpsa.org
URL: www.fpsa.org

3855 ■ Career Development Scholarships *(Postdoctorate, Postgraduate/Scholarship)*

Purpose: To attract and retain qualified personnel for the food processing industry. **Focus:** Food science and technology; service food careers. **Qualif.:** Applicants can be FPSA member employees who work full-time or their immediate family members (spouse and children). Applicants must be high school seniors, college students, or graduate students. **Criteria:** Selection is based on academic achievement; character & integrity; essay content;

community involvement and leadership.

Funds Avail.: $3,000. **Number Awarded:** 10. **To Apply:** Candidates must complete the online application. In addition, candidates must mail or fax a 500-word essay, the cover page, and all required documents. **Deadline:** April 1. **Remarks:** Established in 1983. **Contact:** Robyn Roche at rroche@fpsa.org.

3856 ■ For the Love of Chocolate Scholarship Foundation

226 W Jackson Blvd., Ste. 106
Chicago, IL 60606
Ph: (312) 726-2419
Fax: (312) 726-2446
E-mail: info@fortheloveofchocolatefoundation.org
URL: www.fortheloveofchocolatefoundation.org

3857 ■ For the Love of Chocolate Foundation Scholarships *(Graduate, Professional development, Undergraduate/Scholarship)*

Purpose: To encourage and assist aspiring students, career changers and culinary career professionals to advance their knowledge of the pastry arts. **Focus:** Culinary arts. **Qualif.:** Applicant must demonstrate a desire to develop pastry art skills; accepted into L'Art de la Patisserie program; must work a minimum of 40 hours in a food-service establishment prior to the beginning of the semester (work must be documented by a direct supervisor); must demonstrate financial need; must be accepted by The French Pastry School for the upcoming semester; and must be U.S. citizens. **Criteria:** Selection is based on application materials and demonstrated financial need.

Funds Avail.: No stated amount. **To Apply:** Applicants must submit a completed scholarship application form along with a personal essay, two letters of recommendation and a copy of previous year's tax return. **Deadline:** May 1 and October 1.

3858 ■ Forest History Society (FHS)

701 William Vickers Ave.
Durham, NC 27701-3162
Ph: (919) 682-9319
Fax: (919) 682-2349
E-mail: stevena@duke.edu
URL: www.foresthistory.org

3859 ■ Alfred D. Bell Travel Grants *(All/Grant)*

Purpose: To provide financial assistance for researchers conducting in-depth studies using resources in the society's archive and library. **Focus:** General studies. **Qualif.:** Candidates must be researchers conducting in-depth studies and who use FHS research resources to support their work. **Criteria:** Preference is given to applicants whose research topics are well-covered in the FHS library and archives. Preference is also given to young scholars per the wishes of the Bell family.

Funds Avail.: Travel and lodging expenses of up to $950. **To Apply:** Applicants must submit a completed hard copy of the application form at the FHS office. **Remarks:** The grant is given in honor of Alfred D. Bell, Jr., former VP of Forest History Society (FHS). **Contact:** Cheryl Oakes at coakes@duke.edu.

3860 ■ Frederick K. Weyerhaeuser Forest History Fellowships *(Graduate/Fellowship)*

Purpose: To support the research of a Duke University graduate student whose research examines in some way

Awards are arranged alphabetically below their administering organizations

forest and conservation history. **Focus:** Forestry; Environmental conservation; History. **Qualif.:** Applicants must be Duke University graduate students pursuing research in the fields of forest, conservation or environmental history. **Criteria:** Fellowship recipient is selected on the basis of merit. Proposals are judged in terms of overall significance and quality of presentation.

Funds Avail.: The fellowship consists of an $11,000 stipend, distributed quarterly. **To Apply:** Applicants must submit a narrative description of research (up to eight pages), including significance of topic, research approach, author's background, research and writing schedule and budget. Attachments are not necessary but may include previous publications, written chapters and basic bibliography; curriculum vitae and 2-3 letters of recommendation from persons knowledgeable of the applicant's research. Letters of recommendation should address the author's qualifications and may describe the significance of the topic to forest and conservation history; five hard copies of the proposal and an electronic copy of the proposal without supporting documents. Applicants must provide a cover letter that states the title of the proposed research, a one-paragraph summary of the significance of the project and a description of the historical nature of the project. **Deadline:** January 31. **Remarks:** The fellowship was established in 1986 to honor the memory of Frederick K. Weyerhaeuser. **Contact:** Andrea Anderson at the above address.

3861 ■ Fort Atkinson Community Foundation
244 N Main St.
Fort Atkinson, WI 53538
Ph: (920) 563-3210
E-mail: facf@idcnet.com
URL: www.fortfoundation.org

3862 ■ Walter and Louise Buell Graduate Scholarships *(Graduate/Scholarship)*

Purpose: To provide financial assistance to students residing within the Fort Atkinson area. **Focus:** General studies. **Qualif.:** Applicants must be residents of the Fort Atkinson area or graduates of Fort Atkinson High School; must be accepted into a graduate school at an accredited college or university in a program leading to an advanced degree within the United States; must be full or part-time graduate students with ongoing registration; must make steady progress towards a degree; and must demonstrate financial need. **Criteria:** Applicants will be evaluated based on academic achievement, interest and potential for community involvement, citizenship and need for financial assistance.

Funds Avail.: No specific amount. **To Apply:** Applicants must submit a completed application form; an essay consisting of career goals and how obtaining their education will be an advantage for the community; appended college transcripts including undergraduate study and any graduate work completed; two recommendation letters. **Deadline:** May 15. **Contact:** Helen M. Rose at the above address or e-mail at admin@fortfoundation.org.

3863 ■ Jason Dahnert Memorial Scholarships *(Graduate, Undergraduate/Scholarship)*

Purpose: To provide financial assistance to students residing within Fort Atkinson area. **Focus:** Engineering. **Qualif.:** Applicants must be residents of Fort Atkinson area; must be in current high school senior years, college undergraduate or graduate students concentrating in any disciplines

involving engineering; must be pursuing degrees at a recognized U.S. college or university. **Criteria:** Selection will be based on academic records, financial need, participation in extra-curricular activities and community involvement.

Funds Avail.: No specific amount. **Number Awarded:** 1. **To Apply:** Applicants must submit a completed application form; an essay consisting of interest in technology and career goals; high school or college transcripts including undergraduate study and any graduate work completed to date; test scores; two recommendation letters. **Deadline:** January 20 for high school students and February 15 for undergraduate and graduate students. **Contact:** Helen M. Rose at the above address or e-mail at admin@fortfoundation.org.

3864 ■ Jerome Hake Engineering Scholarships *(Graduate, Undergraduate/Scholarship)*

Purpose: To provide financial assistance to students who are currently pursuing a degree in engineering at a college or university. **Focus:** Engineering. **Qualif.:** Applicants must be current high school seniors graduating in the top one-third of their class, college undergraduate or graduate students pursuing engineering degrees (candidates studying electrical engineering should be given special consideration assuming that all other selection criteria are met); must be residents of the Fort Atkinson area; must attend a four-year degree granting college or university. **Criteria:** Selection will be based on financial need, academic records especially in math and science courses, good character and strong work ethic.

Funds Avail.: No specific amount. **To Apply:** Applicants must submit a completed application form; an essay describing interest in technology; high school or college transcripts including undergraduate study and any graduate work completed to date; test scores; two recommendation letters. **Deadline:** January 20 for high school seniors; February 15 for undergraduate and graduate students. **Contact:** Helen M. Rose at the above address or e-mail at admin@fortfoundation.org.

3865 ■ Gene Halker Memorial Scholarships *(Graduate, Undergraduate/Scholarship)*

Purpose: To provide financial assistance to students residing at Fort Atkinson area. **Focus:** Economics; Business; Literature. **Qualif.:** Applicants must be residents of the Fort Atkinson area or graduates of Fort Atkinson High School pursuing degrees in economics, business, literature or any related fields; undergraduate applicants must be full-time students at a four-year degree granting college or university with junior standing in the next academic year; graduate applicants may be either full-time or part-time students at an accredited U.S college or university which grants post-graduate degrees; must have a minimum GPA of 3.0 in post-secondary study. **Criteria:** Selection is based on academic records, indication of potential success from letters of reference and financial need.

Funds Avail.: No specific amount. **To Apply:** Applicants must submit a completed application form; an essay consisting of career goals and explanation for choosing area of study; high school and college transcripts including undergraduate study and any graduate work completed to date; test scores; two letters of recommendation. **Deadline:** May 15. **Contact:** Helen M. Rose at the above address or e-mail at admin@fortfoundation.org.

Awards are arranged alphabetically below their administering organizations

3866 ■ Eileen Harrison Education Scholarships
(Graduate, Undergraduate/Scholarship)

Purpose: To provide financial assistance to graduates of Fort Atkinson High School, Fort Atkinson residents or employees of Fort Atkinson School District. **Focus:** Education. **Qualif.:** Applicants must be residents of Fort Atkinson area, graduates of Fort Atkinson High School or employees of Fort Atkinson School District; must be currently pursuing an undergraduate or graduate degree in Education (graduate students may be full or part-time students); must attend a four-year degree granting college or university; must obtain a GPA of 3.0 on a 4.0 scale; must be in good standing in undergraduate/graduate program. **Criteria:** Selection will be based on evaluation of submitted documents and specific criteria.

Funds Avail.: No specific amount. **To Apply:** Applicants must submit a completed application form; an essay describing commitment to education; high school or college transcripts including undergraduate study and any graduate work completed to date; test scores; two recommendation letters. **Deadline:** April 1. **Contact:** Helen M. Rose at the above address or e-mail at admin@fortfoundation.org.

3867 ■ Robert C. and Judith L. Knapp Scholarships *(Graduate, Undergraduate/Scholarship)*

Purpose: To financially assist students who have the potential for achieving their professional goals. **Focus:** Mathematics and mathematical sciences; Physics; Engineering; Music education. **Qualif.:** Applicants must be residents of the Fort Atkinson area pursuing undergraduate or graduate degrees in mathematics, mathematics education, physics, physics education, engineering, engineering education, music performance or music education at a college or university; must have completed at least one year full-time college study and earned at least 3.0 GPA in post secondary study; must attend a four-year degree granting college or university. **Criteria:** Evaluations will be based on academic records plus indication of potential success from letters of reference.

Funds Avail.: No specific amount. **To Apply:** Applicants must submit a completed application form; an essay consisting of career goals and choosing of area of study; high school and college transcripts including undergraduate study and any graduate work completed to date; two letters of recommendation. **Deadline:** May 15. **Contact:** Helen M. Rose at the above address or e-mail at admin@fortfoundation.org.

3868 ■ Jane Shaw Knox Graduate Scholarships
(Graduate/Scholarship)

Purpose: To provide tuition aid to women pursuing postgraduate degrees. **Focus:** General studies. **Qualif.:** Applicants must be residents of Fort Atkinson area (graduates of Fort Atkinson High School, employed in Fort Atkinson, have a Fort Atkinson mailing address or phone number). **Criteria:** Selection will be based on evaluation of submitted documents and specific criteria.

Funds Avail.: $1,500. **Number Awarded:** 1. **To Apply:** Applicants must submit a completed application form; official copy of university transcript(s); personal resume; three recommendation letters; financial data. **Deadline:** April 15. **Contact:** Rhona Quinn, Chair, AAUW Scholarship Committee, 1133 Grant St., Fort Atkinson, WI 53538; Call at 920-563-4451.

3869 ■ Ralph and Clara Rutledge Memorial Scholarships *(Graduate/Scholarship)*

Purpose: To provide financial assistance to students residing within Fort Atkinson area. **Focus:** General studies. **Qua-**

lif.: Applicants must be residents of Fort Atkinson area or graduates of Fort Atkinson High School; must be accepted into a graduate school at an accredited college or university in a program leading to an advanced degree within the United States; must be full or part-time graduate students with an ongoing registration; must be making steady progress towards a degree. **Criteria:** Applicants will be evaluated based on academic achievement, interest and potential for community involvement and citizenship.

Funds Avail.: No specific amount. **To Apply:** Applicants must submit a completed application form; an essay consisting of career goals and how obtaining their education will be an advantage for the community; appended college transcripts including undergraduate study and any graduate work completed; two recommendation letters. **Deadline:** May 15. **Contact:** Helen M. Rose at the above address or e-mail at admin@fortfoundation.org.

3870 ■ Foster Care to Success (FC2S)
21351 Gentry Dr., Ste. 130
Sterling, VA 20166
Ph: (571) 203-0270
Fax: (571) 203-0273
E-mail: info@fc2success.org
URL: www.fc2success.org

3871 ■ Casey Family Scholars Scholarships
(Undergraduate, Vocational/Occupational/Scholarship)

Purpose: To provide opportunities and resources for America's foster youth to pursue their education and succeed in life. **Focus:** Health care services. **Qualif.:** Applicants must be accepted or enrolled in an accredited postsecondary program at the undergraduate level in a college, university, vocational or technical institute. Applicants must be children under the age of 25, who have spent at least 12 months in foster care and who were not subsequently adopted. **Criteria:** Recipients are selected based on financial needs and scholastic standing.

Funds Avail.: $10,000. **To Apply:** Applicants must complete the application form. **Deadline:** January 1. **Contact:** scholar@orphan.org.

3872 ■ Dr. Nancy Foster Scholarship Program
c/o Dr. Priti Brahma
NOAA Office of Education
1315 E W Hwy. SSMC-3 Rm. 10600
Silver Spring, MD 20910
E-mail: fosterscholars@noaa.gov
URL: fosterscholars.noaa.gov

3873 ■ Dr. Nancy Foster Scholarships *(Doctorate, Graduate/Scholarship)*

Purpose: To provide support for outstanding students and to encourage independent graduate-level research in oceanography, marine biology or maritime archaeology, particularly by women and members of minority groups. **Focus:** Oceanography; Marine biology; Maritime studies. **Qualif.:** Applicant must be a U.S. citizen; enrolled or accepted at an accredited U.S. graduate institution; and pursuing or intending to pursue a master's or doctoral level degree in oceanography, maritime archaeology or marine biology. **Criteria:** Selection is based on: academic record and statement of intent (25%); quality of project and ap-

Awards are arranged alphabetically below their administering organizations

plicability to program priorities (35%); recommendations and/or endorsement letters (15%); relevant experience related to diversity of education, extra-curricular activities, honors and awards, interpersonal, written and oral communication skills (15%) and financial need (10%).

Funds Avail.: $30,000. **Number Awarded:** Varies. **To Apply:** Applicants must apply online through grants.gov.

3874 ■ Foundation for Appalachian Ohio

PO Box 456
Nelsonville, OH 45764
Ph: (740) 753-1111
Fax: (740) 753-3333
E-mail: cbrook@ffao.org
URL: www.appalachianohio.org

3875 ■ Ora E. Anderson Scholarships
(Undergraduate/Scholarship)

Purpose: To provide financial support to the most outstanding eligible scholars who are committed to environmental protection and conservation. **Focus:** Natural sciences. **Qualif.:** Applicants must be graduating high school seniors who possess a GED; must be residents of and attending school within any of the 32 counties of Appalachian Ohio; must have a plan to pursue post-secondary studies associated with the natural sciences, including but not limited to, forest and wildlife management, environmental restoration, natural and historical interpretation, ecotourism and related disciplines associated with broadly protecting plants, animals and the environment; must have a proof of acceptance at an accredited vocational school, college or university. **Criteria:** Applicants will be selected based on academic performance and demonstrated commitment to environmental protection and conservation.

Funds Avail.: $2,500. **Number Awarded:** 2. **To Apply:** Applicants must complete the application form available online; must attach a transcript of records and personal statement. **Deadline:** March 31.

3876 ■ Zelma Gray Medical School Scholarships *(Doctorate/Fellowship)*

Purpose: To provide scholarship assistance to promising medical provider from Guernsey County High School in order to improve the medical access and healthcare in Ohio. **Focus:** Medical education. **Qualif.:** Applicants must be residents and high school graduates of Guernsey County who are pursuing a Doctor of Medicine or Doctor of Osteopathic Medicine degree; must be enrolled full-time in an accredited medical school and must remain in good standing as defined by the policy in effect at the individual's school enrollment. **Criteria:** Applicants will be selected based on MCAT scores and college transcripts on a non-discriminatory basis without regard to race, creed, national origin, religion, or sex and the amount is at the discretion of the Fund Trustee.

Funds Avail.: No specific amount. **To Apply:** Applicants must complete the application form; must submit a certified copy of academic transcripts from all colleges or undergraduate institutions attended, indicating grades per class or course, and cumulative undergraduate grade point average; must provide proof of scores on the Medical College Admission Test (MCAT) or other test designed to measure their ability and aptitude for medical school; must have a copy of Free Application for Federal Student Aid (FAFSA) or the most recent federal income tax return. **Deadline:** March 31.

3877 ■ Susan K. Ipacs Nursing Legacy Scholarships *(Undergraduate/Scholarship)*

Purpose: To provide financial assistance to nursing students. **Focus:** Nursing. **Qualif.:** Applicants must be second year Hocking College students pursuing a degree in a nursing program; must have at least 3.0 GPA on a 4.00 scale. **Criteria:** Selection of applicants will be based on financial need and character as evidenced by personal conduct, values, attitude and behavior applicable to the nursing field, and submitted statement and nomination forms. Application requirements will be evaluated by the Scholarship Committee and the final approval is made by the Foundation's Board of Trustees.

Funds Avail.: $500. **To Apply:** Applicants must submit a complete application which includes the following: original application form available on the website, including all required signatures; current Hocking College transcript of records signed by the school official; two applicant nominations in a sealed envelope; student aid report listing their EFC from the FAFSA. **Deadline:** March 31.

3878 ■ Wayne F. White and Bob Evans Legacy Scholarships *(Undergraduate/Scholarship)*

Purpose: To financially assist senior high school students in Appalachian Ohio. **Focus:** General studies. **Qualif.:** Applicants must be graduating high school seniors who possess a GED; must be residents of and attending school within any of the 32 counties of Appalachian Ohio; must demonstrate outstanding character, academic excellence and involvement with extra-curricular activities; must have an Expected Family Contribution (EFC) of $8,000 or less. **Criteria:** Preference will be given to those with financial need, who demonstrate the desire to succeed and overcome obstacles.

Funds Avail.: No specific amount. **To Apply:** Applicants must complete the application form available online; must attach a transcript of records and personal statement. **Deadline:** March 31.

3879 ■ Foundation for the Carolinas (FFTC)

220 N Tryon St.
Charlotte, NC 28202
Ph: (704) 973-4500
Free: 800-973-7244
E-mail: infor@fftc.org
URL: www.fftc.org

3880 ■ Henry S. and Carolyn Adams Scholarship Fund *(Undergraduate/Scholarship)*

Purpose: To provide educational assistance for deserving students with financial need who are residents of Union County, NC. **Focus:** General studies. **Qualif.:** Applicants must have a minimum cumulative grade point average of 3.0 (on a 4.0 scale); must be legal residents of Union County, NC; must be nominated by the principal of their high school; and must demonstrate a substantial need for financial assistance. **Criteria:** Recipients are selected based on academic achievement; school and community involvement and personal achievements.

Funds Avail.: $4,000. **To Apply:** Applicants must submit completed application form; official copy of high school transcript(s), including SAT/ACT scores; one to two-paged typed statement expressing qualifications for the scholarship, educational goals and financial need for scholarship assistance; two completed recommendation forms includ-

Awards are arranged alphabetically below their administering organizations

ing at least one from a current teacher; and a copy of SAR from FAFSA. **Deadline:** April.

3881 ■ Herb Adrian Memorial Scholarship Fund
(Undergraduate/Scholarship)

Purpose: To provide financial assistance for students at the University of North Carolina at Charlotte who have expressed an interest in the multi-family housing field. **Focus:** Finance; Construction; Management. **Qualif.:** Applicants must be rising UNC Charlotte juniors or seniors; must have interest in the multi-housing industry, including but not limited to finance, construction and management; and must demonstrate financial need. **Criteria:** Recipients are selected based on financial need.

Funds Avail.: No specific amount. **To Apply:** Applicants must contact the UNC Charlotte Student Financial Aid Office at 704-687-2461 for application.

3882 ■ African American Network - Carolinas Scholarship Fund *(Undergraduate/Scholarship)*

Purpose: To provide scholarships for college-bound students from North and South Carolina who are pursuing a major in engineering, math, science, computer science, accounting, finance or business administration. **Focus:** Engineering; Mathematics and mathematical sciences; Science; Computer and information sciences; Accounting; Finance; Business administration. **Qualif.:** Applicants must be graduating seniors at a North or South Carolina high school; must attend a four-year college or university located in North or South Carolina; must plan to major in engineering, computer science, the sciences, accounting, finance or business administration. **Criteria:** Applicants are judged based on grade point average; residence; leadership skills and financial need.

Funds Avail.: No specific amount. **Number Awarded:** 3. **To Apply:** Applicants must submit all the required application information.

3883 ■ William Tasse Alexander Scholarship Fund *(Undergraduate/Scholarship)*

Purpose: To provide financial assistance for undergraduate students from Mecklenburg County, NC, primarily in the field of education. **Focus:** Education. **Qualif.:** Applicants must be legal residents of Mecklenburg County, NC who are matriculating full-time juniors or seniors in college; must have a minimum cumulative grade point average of 3.0 on a 4.0 scale; and must be majoring in the field of education or taking courses leading to a career in teaching. **Criteria:** Applicants are evaluated based on academic performance; school and community involvement and personal achievements; and demonstrated potential for a career as an educator.

Funds Avail.: $1,000 to $3,500. **To Apply:** Applicants must submit completed application form; official transcript(s) of academic coursework and grades for at least the last two years; copy of applicants' NTE/Praxis Series scores, if available; three recommendation forms (two from instructors or other campus administrators and one from an employer or other non-related individual); one to two pages typewritten statement expressing reasons for applying for scholarship, qualifications, and educational/career goals; and a copy of the estimated expense budget for tuition, room and board, books, etc. at the school they attended. **Deadline:** March 30. **Contact:** Online submission of the application package should be directed to scholars@fftc.org.

3884 ■ Andersen Nontraditional Scholarships for Women's Education and Retraining
(Undergraduate/Scholarship)

Purpose: To provide financial support and encouragement for adult women age 25 and older who are raising school-age children (grades K-12) and hope to earn a two-year nursing degree or a four-year undergraduate degree in the field of their choice. **Focus:** General studies. **Qualif.:** Applicants must be nontraditional female students age 25 or older at the time of the application deadline; legal residents of Mecklenburg County, NC or contiguous county in North Carolina or South Carolina; enrolled or planning to enroll as full-time, degree-seeking students at an accredited institution in North Carolina or South Carolina; and must be primary caregivers to at least one school-age child (enrolled in K-12). This includes natural born or legally adopted children for whom legal guardianship has been granted. **Criteria:** Applicants who are single parents are given preference, with the following basis criteria: financial need as determined by the costs of college attendance compared with an applicants' household income and other financial factors; demonstrated potential for academic success.

Funds Avail.: No specific amount. **To Apply:** Applicants must submit a completed application form; copy of the Student Aid Report from FAFSA; official transcripts of grades for the applicant's most recently completed coursework; three recommendation forms from non-related adults such as instructors or other campus administrators, employers, mentors, etc.; updated, typed resume; one to two-page typed personal statement expressing why the applicant is applying for the scholarship and the applicant's educational and career goals; and copy of the applicant's federal tax return for the preceding year showing dependents and adjusted gross income. **Deadline:** March. **Contact:** Electronic submission must be directed to scholars@fftc.org.

3885 ■ Bank of America Junior Achievement Scholarship Fund *(Undergraduate/Scholarship)*

Purpose: To provide financial support for undergraduate students who have expressed an interest in business through their service to Junior Achievement in Atlanta, GA. **Focus:** Business; Technology. **Qualif.:** Applicants must be graduating high school seniors with a minimum cumulative GPA of 3.0 on a 4.0 scale and who have actively participated in Junior Achievement of Georgia; and must be planning to major in business or computer technology. **Criteria:** Applicants are evaluated based on academic merit and financial need.

Funds Avail.: No specific amount. **To Apply:** Applicants must submit all the required application information. **Contact:** Applicants must contact Junior Achievement by calling 404-257-1932.

3886 ■ Pete and Ellen Bensley Memorial Scholarship Fund *(Undergraduate/Scholarship)*

Purpose: To assist graduating seniors at East Mecklenburg High School in Charlotte, NC, who demonstrate interest in foreign languages and/or journalism. **Focus:** Foreign languages; Journalism. **Qualif.:** Applicants must be legal residents of Mecklenburg County and graduating seniors at East Mecklenburg High School who are planning to major in foreign languages and/or journalism. **Criteria:** Applicants are selected based on the criteria designed by the Scholarship Selection Committee.

Funds Avail.: Amount not specified. **To Apply:** Applicants must submit all the required materials and complete application information. **Contact:** The Scholarship Coordina-

Awards are arranged alphabetically below their administering organizations

tor at East Mecklenburg High School, 980-343-6430.

3887 ■ Donald H. Bernstein/John B. Talbert, Jr. Scholarships *(Undergraduate/Scholarship)*

Purpose: To provide financial support for children of Hanes Companies, Inc., USA employees. **Focus:** General studies. **Qualif.:** Applicants must be graduating high school seniors who have a minimum cumulative grade point average of 3.0 (on a 4.0 scale). Parents or legal guardians of applicants must be employees who have completed at least two years (24 months) of full-time service with Hanes Companies, Inc. USA prior to the application deadline. Applicants shall be defined to include natural-born or legally-adopted dependent children, stepchildren, and wards of employees. **Criteria:** Applicants are evaluated based on academic/personal achievement; financial need; school and community involvement.

Funds Avail.: $1,200. **To Apply:** Applicants must submit a completed application form; copy of high school transcript(s), including SAT/ACT scores; three recommendation forms (two from teachers or other school personnel and one from an employer or other non-related adult); one to two-paged typed statement expressing the reason for applying for the scholarship, qualifications, and educational/ career goals; and letter from an official of Hanes Companies, Inc. USA where parent or legally-appointed guardians are employed. **Deadline:** March.

3888 ■ T. Frank Booth Memorial Scholarship Fund *(Undergraduate/Scholarship)*

Purpose: To provide financial assistance for accounting students at East Carolina University. **Focus:** Accounting. **Qualif.:** Applicants must be legal residents of North Carolina who are juniors or seniors with a 3.0 minimum cumulative grade point average (on 4.0 scale) who have declared major in accounting. **Criteria:** Applicants are evaluated based on merit and financial need.

Funds Avail.: No specific amount. **To Apply:** Applicants must submit all the required application information. **Contact:** For further information, contact East Carolina University Accounting Department at 252-328-6623.

3889 ■ Cadmus Communications Corporation Graphics Scholarship Endowment Fund *(Undergraduate/Scholarship)*

Purpose: To assist students who are enrolled in the associate degree in Graphic Arts Management Program at Central Piedmont Community College. **Focus:** Graphic art and design. **Qualif.:** Applicants must have completed at least two semesters of the CPCC Graphic Arts and Imaging Technology Program with 3.0 minimum cumulative grade point average on 4.0 scale. **Criteria:** Applicants are evaluated based on criteria designed by the Scholarship Selection Committee.

Funds Avail.: No specific amount. **To Apply:** Applicants must submit all the required application information and materials. **Contact:** CPCC Graphic Arts and Imaging Technology Program; 704-330-4437.

3890 ■ Kasie Ford Capling Memorial Scholarship Endowment Fund *(Undergraduate/ Scholarship)*

Purpose: To provide financial assistance for high school seniors graduating from Charlotte-Mecklenburg high schools (public or private) who have experienced the death of one or both parents. **Focus:** General studies. **Qualif.:**

Applicants must be graduating high school seniors from a high school located in Mecklenburg County, NC (public or private) planning to enter a four-year degree program at an accredited institution; must be legal residents of Mecklenburg County, NC; must have experienced the death of one or both parents; and must be in good standing at the time of application. **Criteria:** Recipients will be selected based on academic achievements; record of leadership as evidenced by the school, athletic and community involvement; and financial need. Preference will be given to students planning to attend a college in North Carolina.

Funds Avail.: $1,000. **Number Awarded:** 1. **To Apply:** Applicants must complete the application form; must submit a copy of Student Aid Report (SAR); official transcript of high school and/or college coursework and grades for at least the last two years, including SAT/ACT scores if taken; and two recommendation forms: one from a teacher or other school personnel and one from a non-related adult such as employer, mentor, coach, etc. **Deadline:** March 28. **Contact:** Application form and supporting documents should be sent via e-mail at zscholars@fftc.org.

3891 ■ Julian E. Carnes Scholarship Fund *(Undergraduate/Scholarship)*

Purpose: To provide financial assistance to students of Clemson University and the University of North Carolina at Charlotte who are preparing for a career in a technological field appropriate to meet the requirements of the U.S. Patent Office as a patent agent or attorney. **Focus:** Engineering; Chemistry; Physics; Biology; Computer and information sciences. **Qualif.:** Applicants must be legal residents of North or South Carolina; must be rising juniors or seniors at Clemson University or UNC Charlotte whose academic major is appropriate to meet the requirements of the U.S. Patent Office for admission as a patent agent or attorney (including but not limited to engineering, chemistry, physics, biology and computer science); and must have at least a 3.0 cumulative grade point average (on a 4.0 scale). **Criteria:** Applicants are evaluated based on merit.

Funds Avail.: No specific amount. **To Apply:** Applicants must submit all the required application information. **Contact:** Clemson University Office of Student Financial Aid, 864-656-2280 or the UNC Charlotte Student Financial Aid Office, 704-687-2461.

3892 ■ Carolina Panthers Scholarship Fund *(Graduate/Scholarship)*

Purpose: To provide graduate level scholarships for athletes in North and South Carolina. **Focus:** General studies. **Qualif.:** Applicants must have earned an intercollegiate varsity letter in college; must be graduating senior athletes at an accredited North or South Carolina college or university; have minimum cumulative grade point average of 3.0 on a 4.0 scale; must receive a nomination for scholarship consideration from their current Athletic Director. Female athletes may letter in any sport and male athletes must letter in football. **Criteria:** Applicants are evaluated based on academic performance; record of leadership and citizenship; school and community involvement and personal achievements.

Funds Avail.: $10,000. **To Apply:** Applicants must submit a completed application form; official transcript; copy of score report from the Graduate Record Exam (GRE), Law School Admissions Test (LSAT), Medical College Admissions Test (MCAT) or other appropriate graduate admission test scores, if available; three recommendation forms which include one from a faculty member in major course of study,

Awards are arranged alphabetically below their administering organizations

one from a member of the Athletic Department and one from another school official or other non-related individual familiar with the applicants' extracurricular and leadership involvement; and a typed double-spaced personal statement not to exceed 1,000 words expressing the reason for applying for the scholarship, involvement in athletics, and educational/career goals. **Deadline:** April. **Contact:** Online submission of the application package should be directed to scholars@fftc.org.

3893 ■ Carolinas-Virginias Retail Hardware Scholarships *(Undergraduate/Scholarship)*

Purpose: To support the children of employees of member firms of the Carolinas-Virginias Region of the National Retail Hardware Association. **Focus:** General studies. **Qualif.:** Applicants must have a minimum cumulative grade point average of 2.5 on a 4.0 scale; whose parents or legally-appointed guardians are employees who have completed at least two years of full-time service with a member firm of the Carolinas-Virginias Region of the National Retail Hardware Association; children of employees shall be defined to include natural-born or legally-adopted dependent children, stepchildren, and wards of employees. **Criteria:** Applicants are evaluated based on academic achievement including grade point average and performance on tests designed to measure preparation and ability for postsecondary study; school and community involvement and personal achievements; work experience particularly in retail hardware.

Funds Avail.: $500 up to $2,000. **To Apply:** Applicants must submit a completed application form; copy of the Student Aid Report (SAR) from FAFSA; official transcript(s) of high school and/or college coursework and grades for at least the last two years, including SAT/ACT scores if taken; three recommendation forms, two from teachers or other school personnel and one from an employer or other non-related adult; one to two-page typed statement expressing the reason on why applicant is applying for the scholarship, qualifications and educational and career goals; a letter from an official of the member firm of the Carolinas-Virginias Region of the National Retail Hardware Association where parent or legally-appointed guardian is employed. **Deadline:** March.

3894 ■ Charlotte Housing Authority Scholarship Fund (CHASF) *(Undergraduate, Vocational/Occupational/Scholarship)*

Purpose: To provide educational assistance for young residents of housing owned or managed by the Charlotte Housing Authority. **Focus:** General studies. **Qualif.:** Applicants must be residents of public housing owned or managed by the Charlotte Housing Authority. Applicants attending a college, vocational or technical school for the first time must not be over 21 years of age as of September 1 of the school year for which the scholarship award is to be made; those who have previously attended a college, vocational or technical school must not be over 24 years of age as of September 1 of the school year for which the scholarship award is to be made. **Criteria:** Applicants are evaluated based on financial need; academic performance; personal achievements; school and community involvement; and commitment to and demonstrated potential for success in college, technical or vocational school.

Funds Avail.: Ranging from $500 to $3,400. **To Apply:** Applicants must submit a completed application form; official transcript(s) of coursework and grades for at least the first two years, including SAT/ACT scores if taken; three recommendation forms (one from an adult in the housing

community where the applicant lives, one from a teacher, counselor or other school administrator, and one from an employer, minister, community leader or other non-related adult); one to two pages typed personal statement expressing the applicant's educational and career goals and financial need for scholarship assistance; and a copy of the applicant's FAFSA or student aid report. **Deadline:** March. **Contact:** Application form and supporting documents must be submitted by mail: Southside Aurora Ctr., 306 Benjamin St., Charlotte, NC 28203; Phone: 704-336-5782; E-mail: mmcclune@cha-nc.org.

3895 ■ Charlotte-Mecklenburg Schools Scholarship Incentive Program *(Undergraduate/Scholarship)*

Purpose: To provide motivation and encouragement for Charlotte-Mecklenburg public high school students with financial need to stay in school, graduate and pursue post-secondary education. **Focus:** General studies. **Qualif.:** Applicants must be graduating seniors at a Charlotte-Mecklenburg public high school; must be participants in the Communities In Schools ThinkCOLLEGE Program or the Charlotte-Mecklenburg Schools AVID Program; must be legal residents of Mecklenburg County, NC; and must have 2.5 minimum cumulative grade point average on a 4.0 scale. **Criteria:** Applicants will be evaluated based on financial need; academic/personal achievement; and school/community involvement.

Funds Avail.: Ranging from $800 to $1,500. **To Apply:** Applicants must submit completed application form; official copy of high school transcript(s), including SAT/ACT scores; two recommendation forms from a teacher, counselor or other school administrator, and the other one from an employer, community leader or non-related adult; one to two pages typed personal statement; and copy of SAR from FAFSA. **Deadline:** March 1. **Contact:** Application materials must be submitted through e-mail at scholars@fftc.org.

3896 ■ Children's Scholarship Fund of Charlotte *(Undergraduate/Scholarship)*

Purpose: To assist children in grades K-8 intending to attend tuition-based schools which their families could not otherwise afford. **Focus:** General studies. **Qualif.:** Applicants must be legal resident children of Mecklenburg County, NC in grades K-8 attending or planning to attend a tuition-based school in the Charlotte-Mecklenburg region. **Criteria:** Recipients are selected based on financial need.

Funds Avail.: No specific amount. **To Apply:** Applicants must submit all the required application information. **Contact:** Carla McCrorey at the above address.

3897 ■ Lula Faye Clegg Memorial Scholarship Fund *(Undergraduate/Scholarship)*

Purpose: To provide financial assistance for students majoring in education at the University of North Carolina at Charlotte. **Focus:** Education. **Qualif.:** Applicants must be graduates of a high school in the Charlotte-Mecklenburg public school system; must rank in the top 10% of graduating high school class; and must have strong interest and commitment to a career in teaching. **Criteria:** Applicants are evaluated based on the criteria designed by the Scholarship Selection Committee.

Funds Avail.: No specific amount. **To Apply:** Applicants must submit all the required application information. **Contact:** UNC Charlotte Student Financial Aid Office, 704-687-2461.

Awards are arranged alphabetically below their administering organizations

3898 ■ Cole Foundation Undergraduate Scholarship Program *(Undergraduate/ Scholarship)*

Purpose: To increase the number of high school graduates from Richmond County, NC pursuing a post-secondary education. **Focus:** General studies. **Qualif.:** Applicants must be legal residents of Richmond County, NC; must be high school seniors scheduled to graduate in the spring of the current school year. Students applying for four-year scholarships must have a minimum cumulative grade point average of 3.0 (on 4.0 scale). Students applying for two-year scholarships must have a minimum cumulative grade point average of 2.5 (on a 4.0 scale). **Criteria:** Preference is given to applicants whose parents do not have a college degree and will be evaluated based on financial need; academic achievement; school and community involvement; and personal achievements.

Funds Avail.: $5,000. **To Apply:** Applicants must submit a completed application form; copy of SAR from FAFSA; official copy of the applicant's high school transcript(s), including SAT/ACT scores if taken; type-written statement expressing educational and career goals, reasons for applying for the scholarship and why they deserve the scholarship; and copy of both parents' federal tax return(s) for the preceding year showing dependents and adjusted gross income. **Deadline:** March.

3899 ■ Sally Cole Visual Arts Scholarship Fund *(Undergraduate/Scholarship)*

Purpose: To provide financial assistance to Richmond County, NC students with demonstrated talent and career interests in the visual arts. **Focus:** Visual arts. **Qualif.:** Applicants must be planning to attend an accredited two-year or four-year post-secondary institution with a degree program in visual arts; must be high school seniors in good academic standing scheduled to graduate in the spring of the current school year; must have an expressed and demonstrated interest in the visual and/or studio arts which primarily includes, but are not limited to, painting, drawing, sculpture, illustration and ceramics; must be legal residents of Richmond County, NC. **Criteria:** Applicants are evaluated based on academic achievement; school and community involvement and personal achievements; and demonstrated aptitude and career potential in the visual arts.

Funds Avail.: $7,500. **To Apply:** Applicants must submit a completed application form; official copy of high school transcript(s), including SAT/ACT scores if taken; three recommendation forms, two of which must come from individuals able to evaluate the applicants' aptitude and career potential in the visual arts; one to two pages type-written statement expressing a) applicants' reasons for applying for the scholarship, b) applicants' interest in the arts, c) applicants' educational and career goals in the field of visual arts; and samples (3-5 labeled color slides) of applicants' original artwork. **Deadline:** March.

3900 ■ Judy Crocker Memorial Scholarship Fund *(Undergraduate/Scholarship)*

Purpose: To provide financial assistance for Winthrop University students with an interest in Education, Human Services and related majors. **Focus:** Education. **Qualif.:** Applicants must be legal residents of York County, SC; must be rising juniors or seniors at Winthrop University, located in Rock Hill, SC, majoring in education, human services or a related field; must have 2.9 minimum cumulative grade point average (on a 4.0 scale) and who demon-

strate financial need. **Criteria:** Recipients are selected based on financial need.

Funds Avail.: No specific amount. **To Apply:** Applicants must submit all the required application information. **Contact:** Winthrop University Office of Financial Aid, 704-973-4541.

3901 ■ Crowder Scholarships *(Undergraduate/ Scholarship)*

Purpose: To provide financial assistance for children of employees of general contracting companies headquartered in Mecklenburg County, NC. **Focus:** General studies. **Qualif.:** Applicants must be defined as natural-born or legally-adopted dependent children, stepchildren, and wards of employees. Parents or legally-appointed guardians of applicants must have worked for their respective general contracting company for at least three years prior to the application deadline. A minimum cumulative grade point average of 2.0 (on a 4.0 scale) is required. **Criteria:** Applicants are evaluated based on academic achievement; financial need; school and community involvement; and personal achievements. Preference will be given to children of employees of Crowder Construction Company.

Funds Avail.: $1,000. **To Apply:** Applicants must submit a completed application form; copy of SAR from FAFSA; official transcript(s) of high school and/or college coursework and grades for at least the last two years, including SAT/ACT scores if taken; three recommendation forms; a one to two-paged typed statement expressing why the applicant is applying for the scholarship, applicant's qualifications and the applicant's educational and career goals; a letter from an official of the general contracting company where the applicant's parent is employed, certifying that the parent is an employee and stating the employee's position and length of service; and a copy of both parents' federal tax return for the preceding year showing dependents and adjusted gross income. **Deadline:** March.

3902 ■ The E.R. and Lilian B. Dimmette Scholarship Fund *(Undergraduate/Scholarship)*

Purpose: To provide financial assistance for undergraduate students who "fall between the cracks" of financial aid and/or scholarship programs. **Focus:** General studies. **Qualif.:** Applicants must be nominated by the Superintendent of Schools in their county; must have a minimum cumulative grade point average of 2.5 (on a 4.0 scale); and must be legal residents of Gaston, Iredell, Mecklenburg, Rowan or Wilkes County, North Carolina. **Criteria:** Applicants are evaluated based on demonstrated substantial need for financial assistance.

Funds Avail.: Ranging from $1,000 to $4,000. **To Apply:** Applicants must submit completed application form; copy of the SAR from FAFSA; official copy of high school transcript(s), including SAT/ACT scores; three recommendation forms (two from teachers or other school personnel and one from an employer or other non-related adult); one to two-paged typed statement expressing qualifications for the scholarship, educational goals and financial need for scholarship assistance; copy of both parents' federal tax return for the preceding year showing dependents and adjusted gross income; and copy of estimated expense budget for tuition, fees, room, board, books, etc. for the school planning to attend. **Deadline:** February 16.

3903 ■ Laura M. Fleming Scholarships *(Undergraduate, Vocational/Occupational/ Scholarship)*

Purpose: To provide financial assistance for children of Founders Federal Credit Union members intending to at-

Awards are arranged alphabetically below their administering organizations

tend an accredited college, vocational or technical school of their choice. **Focus:** General studies. **Qualif.:** Applicants must be children of Founders Federal Credit Union members defined as natural born or legally adopted children and stepchildren and wards of employees; must be high school seniors graduating in the spring of the current school year; must have a minimum 3.5 cumulative grade point average (on a 4.0 scale). Applicant's parents or legally appointed guardians must be Founders Credit Union members in good standing for a minimum of two years (24 months) prior to the application deadline. **Criteria:** Applicants are evaluated based on financial need; record of good citizenship evidenced by school and community involvement; and academic achievement.

Funds Avail.: $1,000 up to $2,500. **To Apply:** Applicants must submit completed application form; official copy of most recent high school transcript; three recommendation forms (two from current teachers or other school personnel and one from an employer or other non-relative); two typed essays of 400 words or less on topics provided in the application form; documentation of school and community involvement; and a copy of Student Air Report (SAR) from FAFSA. **Deadline:** March 2.

3904 ■ Foundation for the Carolinas Rotary Scholarship Fund (Undergraduate/Scholarship)

Purpose: To provide financial assistance for students intending to pursue college but who are not capable of paying the school expenses. **Focus:** General studies. **Qualif.:** Applicants must be at least college juniors or seniors at a four-year institution enrolling as full-time students; must have a minimum 3.0 cumulative grade point average (on a 4.0 scale); and must demonstrate financial need. **Criteria:** Recipients are selected based on academic merit, financial need and community service.

Funds Avail.: No specific amount. **To Apply:** Applicants must submit completed application form; copy of Student Aid Report (SAR) from Free Application for Federal Student Aid; official transcript(s) of academic coursework and grades for at least the last two years; three recommendation forms (two from instructors or other campus administrators and one from an employer or other non-related individual in Charlotte-Mecklenburg area); one to two-paged typed statement expressing reasons for applying for the scholarship; and a copy of the estimated expense budget for tuition, room and board, books, etc. **Deadline:** April 2.

3905 ■ Richard Goolsby Scholarship Fund (Graduate, Undergraduate/Scholarship)

Purpose: To provide financial assistance to graduate undergraduate students who have shown a career interest or demonstrate practical experiences in the plastics industry. **Focus:** General studies. **Qualif.:** Applicants must be full-time rising college sophomore, junior or senior students at a four-year college or two-year technical school, who are in good academic standing and majoring in or taking courses that would be suited to a career in the plastics industry; or must be graduate students seeking to obtain a post-secondary graduate degree. **Criteria:** Applicants are evaluated on the basis of academic performance; demonstrated interest in plastics industry; financial need; school and community involvement; and personal achievements. Preference will be given to applicants living in the Geographical area served by the Carolinas Section of the Society of Plastics Engineers (central and western North Carolina and all South Carolina).

Funds Avail.: $4,000. **To Apply:** Applicants must submit a

completed application form; copy of the Student Aid Report (SAR) from Free Application for Federal Student Aid; official transcript(s) of academic coursework and grades for at least the last two years; three recommendation forms (two from teachers or other school administrators and one from an employer or other non-related individual); and a personal statement expressing reasons for applying for the scholarship, qualifications, educational and career goals in plastics industry. **Deadline:** February. **Contact:** Online submission of the application package should be directed to scholars@fftc.org.

3906 ■ Howard B. Higgins South Carolina Dental Scholarships (Undergraduate/Scholarship)

Purpose: To provide financial assistance for students attending the College of Dental Medicine at the Medical University of South Carolina. **Focus:** Dentistry. **Qualif.:** Applicants must be students at the College of Dental Medicine at the Medical University of South Carolina; must have at least 3.0 cumulative grade point average (on a 4.0 scale); and must be legal residents of South Carolina. **Criteria:** Applicants are evaluated based on the criteria designed by the Scholarship Selection Committee.

Funds Avail.: No specific amount. **To Apply:** Applicants must submit all the required application information. **Contact:** College of Dental Medicine Office of Academic and Student Affairs; 843-792-2344.

3907 ■ Wilbert L. and Zora F. Holmes Scholarship Endowment Fund (Undergraduate, Vocational/Occupational/Scholarship)

Purpose: To provide financial assistance for graduating seniors from South Carolina's York School District One intending to attend an accredited college or technical school of their choice. **Focus:** Vocational-technical education. **Qualif.:** Applicants must be graduating seniors at York Comprehensive High School (currently the only high school in the York School District One) and must have been students at York Comprehensive High School for a minimum of two years as of the application deadline; must be legal residents of York County, South Carolina; and must have a minimum of 3.0 cumulative grade point average (on 4.0 scale) at the end of the first semester of senior year. **Criteria:** Recipients are selected based on academic achievement and financial need.

Funds Avail.: No specific amount. **To Apply:** Applicants must submit all the required application information. **Contact:** Guidance Office at York Comprehensive High School at 803-684-2336.

3908 ■ James V. Johnson Scholarship Fund (Undergraduate/Scholarship)

Purpose: To provide financial assistance for students at Pfeiffer University in Misenheimer, NC and Mitchell Community College in Statesville, NC. **Focus:** General studies. **Qualif.:** Applicants must be legal residents of Iredell or Alexander County in North Carolina; must be incoming freshmen at Pfeiffer University in Misenheimer, NC or first-year students at Mitchell Community College in Statesville, NC. **Criteria:** Applicants are evaluated based on criteria designed by the Scholarship Selection Committee.

Funds Avail.: No specific amount. **To Apply:** Applicants must submit all the required application information. **Contact:** Pfeiffer University Office Admissions and Financial Aid, 704-463-1360 or the Mitchell Community College Office of Financial Aid, 704-878-3200.

Awards are arranged alphabetically below their administering organizations

3909 ■ Annabel Lambeth Jones Scholarships
(Undergraduate/Scholarship)

Purpose: To provide undergraduate scholarships for students of Queens University of Charlotte in Charlotte, NC and Brevard College in Brevard, NC. **Focus:** General studies. **Qualif.:** Applicants must be incoming freshmen; must have high academic merit; and must have demonstrated leadership potential. **Criteria:** Applicants are evaluated based on personal attributes.

Funds Avail.: No specific amount. **To Apply:** Applicants must submit all the required application information.

3910 ■ Mary and Millard Kiker Scholarships
(Undergraduate/Scholarship)

Purpose: To support deserving students with financial need who are residents of Anson or Union Countries in North Carolina. **Focus:** General studies. **Qualif.:** Applicants must be legal residents of Anson or Union County, NC who are nominated by the Superintendent of Schools in their county with a minimum cumulative grade point average of 2.5 (on a 4.0 scale) and must demonstrate substantial need for financial assistance. **Criteria:** Applicants are evaluated based on financial need.

Funds Avail.: $1,000 to $4,000. **To Apply:** Applicants must submit a completed application form; copy of the Student Aid Report from FAFSA; official copy of high school transcript(s), including SAT/ACT scores; three recommendation forms (two from teachers or other school personnel and one from an employer or other non-related adult); one to two-paged typed statement expressing qualifications for the scholarship, educational goals and financial need for scholarship assistance; and a copy of both parents' federal tax return for the preceding year showing dependents and adjusted gross income. **Deadline:** April.

3911 ■ Law Enforcement Memorial Scholarship Fund *(Undergraduate/Scholarship)*

Purpose: To provide financial support for students studying law enforcement at Central Piedmont Community College and the University of North Carolina at Charlotte. **Focus:** Law enforcement. **Qualif.:** Applicants must be students at Central Piedmont Community College or the University of North Carolina at Charlotte who have a 2.5 minimum cumulative grade point average (on a 4.0 scale); and majoring in a law enforcement field. **Criteria:** Applicants are judged based on academic merit.

Funds Avail.: No specific amount. **To Apply:** Applicants must submit all the required application information. **Contact:** CPCC Financial Aid Office, 704-330-6942 or the UNC Charlotte Student Financial Aid Office, 704-687-2461.

3912 ■ George T. Lewis, Jr. Academic Scholarship Fund *(Undergraduate/Scholarship)*

Purpose: To provide motivation and encouragement to George T. Lewis, Jr. Academic Center graduates intending to pursue post-secondary education or training. **Focus:** General studies. **Qualif.:** Applicants must meet or exceed the benchmark goals for attendance set for the George T. Lewis, Jr. Academic Center during their senior year; must have earned a minimum 2.0 cumulative grade point average (on a 4.0 scale) at the end of the first semester of senior year; and must be graduating seniors at the George T. Lewis, Jr. Academic Center and must have at least one full academic year of enrollment and participation in the ThinkCOLLEGE Program (upon graduation). **Criteria:** Applicants are evaluated based on academic achievement; school involvement and personal achievements and financial need.

Funds Avail.: No specific amount. **To Apply:** Applicants must submit completed application form; copy of the SAR from FAFSA; official copy of high school transcript(s), including SAT/ACT scores; two recommendation forms (one from a teacher, counselor or other school administrator and one from employer, community leader or other non-related adult); a one to two-paged typed personal statement on one of the following topics: (1) Discuss who or what has been the biggest influence on your decisions to attend college and why or (2) Present and explain the 'personal mission' or 'personal vision' you have adopted for yourself and discuss why you think these goals are important; and a copy of the applicant's completed FAFSA. **Deadline:** March.

3913 ■ Albert and Eloise Midyette Memorial Scholarship Fund *(Undergraduate/Scholarship)*

Purpose: To provide undergraduate scholarships for students attending Limestone College in Gaffney, South Carolina. **Focus:** Nursing; Education, Medical. **Qualif.:** Applicants must be full-time U.S. citizen students at Limestone College; must be majoring in the fields of religious and ministry studies, nursing or other medical academic fields; and must have a cumulative unweighted grade point average of at least 2.5 (on a 4.0 scale). **Criteria:** Applicants are evaluated on the basis of academic achievement and financial need.

Funds Avail.: No specific amount. **To Apply:** Applicants must submit all the required application information and materials. **Contact:** For further information, applicants must contact Limestone College's Office of Financial Aid at 864-488-8231.

3914 ■ Carolina Panthers Players Sam Mills Memorial Scholarship Fund *(Undergraduate/Scholarship)*

Purpose: To assist high school athletes from Mecklenburg County, NC and Spartanburg County, SC who wish to pursue a four-year undergraduate degree. **Focus:** General studies. **Qualif.:** Applicants must be graduating senior athletes at high schools (public or private) located in Mecklenburg County, NC or Spartanburg County, SC; have earned a varsity letter in high school; with 3.0 minimum cumulative unweighted grade point average on a 4.0 scale; demonstrated outstanding leadership and citizenship; and must attend an accredited four-year college or university as full-time students. **Criteria:** Applicants are evaluated based on academic achievement; school and community involvement; evidence of leadership and citizenship.

Funds Avail.: $2,500. **Number Awarded:** 2. **To Apply:** Applicants must submit a completed application form; copy of the Student Aid Report (SAR) from Free Application for FAFSA; official copy of high school transcript, including SAT/ACT scores; three recommendation forms, one from a faculty member/school official and one from a member of the coaching staff of the sport in which the athletes participate; and must attend a personal interview with the Selection Committee, if requested. **Deadline:** April. **Contact:** Application form and supporting documents may send by e-mail at scholars@fftc.org.

3915 ■ North Carolina League for Nursing Academic Scholarships *(Graduate/Scholarship)*

Purpose: To provide financial assistance for graduate students pursuing either a master's degree in nursing or a doctoral degree in nursing or a related discipline. **Focus:**

Awards are arranged alphabetically below their administering organizations

Nursing. **Qualif.:** Applicants must be legal residents of North Carolina; must have completed a minimum of six semester hours of course work in their graduate program of study by the application deadline; and must be granted unconditional admission to a master's degree program in nursing or doctoral degree program in nursing or a related discipline and be classified as a graduate degree student by the college or university. **Criteria:** Applicants are evaluated based on academic performance and financial need.

Funds Avail.: $1,000 to $2,000. **To Apply:** Applicants must submit a completed application form; copy of the Student Aid Report from Free Application for Federal Student Aid; official transcripts; two recommendation forms (one from a faculty member familiar with the applicant's progress in the program and one from any other non-related individual); a one to two-paged typed statement expressing qualifications for the scholarship; and commitment to full-time employment in North Carolina either in nursing practice or in teaching in a nursing education program. **Deadline:** March.

3916 ■ North Mecklenburg Teachers' Memorial Scholarships *(Undergraduate/Scholarship)*

Purpose: To provide financial assistance for North Mecklenburg High School students intending to pursue a degree in education. **Focus:** Education. **Qualif.:** Applicants must be graduating seniors with a grade point average of 3.0 on a 4.0 scale at North Mecklenburg High School; must be planning to attend a four-year college or university; and must be majoring in education. **Criteria:** Applicants are evaluated based on academic achievement; extracurricular and community involvement; statement of personal aspirations and educational goals; and financial need.

Funds Avail.: No stated amount. **To Apply:** Applicants must submit a completed application form; copy of the Student Aid Report (SAR) from Free Application for Federal Student Aid; official transcript of academic coursework and grades; and a typewritten statement expressing the applicants' educational and career goals and reasons for applying for the scholarship. **Contact:** North Mecklenburg High School Guidance Office at 980-343-3840.

3917 ■ Ted H. Ousley Scholarship Fund *(Undergraduate/Scholarship)*

Purpose: To provide undergraduate scholarships for graduating seniors at North Mecklenburg High School in Huntersville, NC. **Focus:** General studies. **Qualif.:** Applicants must be graduating seniors at North Mecklenburg High School; must have a minimum cumulative grade point average of 2.5 (on a 4.0 scale); and must be planning to attend a post-secondary institution in North Carolina. **Criteria:** Applicants are evaluated based on criteria designed by the Scholarship Selection Committee.

Funds Avail.: No specific amount. **To Apply:** Applicants must submit all the required application information. **Contact:** For further information, contact Scholarship Coordinator at North Mecklenburg High School by calling 980-343-3840.

3918 ■ Henry DeWitt Plyler Scholarship Fund *(Undergraduate/Scholarship)*

Purpose: To provide financial support for students from Lancaster County, SC intending to attend Winthrop University. **Focus:** General studies. **Qualif.:** Applicants must be graduating seniors or graduates of Lancaster County public high schools; must have 3.0 minimum cumulative grade point average (on a 4.0 scale); and must be legal residents of Lancaster County, SC. **Criteria:** Ap-

plicants are evaluated based on financial need as determined by the costs of college attendance compared with an applicants' household income and other financial factors; academic performance and achievement; and school and community involvement. Preference will be given to students with a career interest in the field of teaching.

Funds Avail.: $500 to $1,000. **To Apply:** Applicants must submit completed application form; copy of the SAR from FAFSA; official transcript(s) of high school and/or college coursework and grades for at least the last two years, including SAT/ACT scores if taken; three recommendation forms (two from teachers or other school personnel and one from employer or other non-related adult); one to two-paged typed statement expressing reason for applying for the scholarship, qualifications and the educational and career goals. **Deadline:** February 9.

3919 ■ Ben Robinette Scholarship Endowment Fund *(Undergraduate/Scholarship)*

Purpose: To assist graduates of high schools in Charlotte-Mecklenburg (public or private schools) to attend the University of North Carolina at Chapel Hill. **Focus:** General studies. **Qualif.:** Applicants must be graduating seniors at public or private high school in Charlotte-Mecklenburg with minimum of 3.0 grade point average on 4.0 scale. **Criteria:** Preference will be given to competitive runners who have been members of their high school track or cross country teams.

Funds Avail.: No specific amount. **To Apply:** Applicants must submit all the required application information. **Contact:** UNC Chapel Hill Office of Scholarships and Student Aid, 919-962-4168.

3920 ■ Rotary Public Safety Scholarships *(Undergraduate/Scholarship)*

Purpose: To provide financial assistance for the children of Charlotte area public safety personnel. **Focus:** Public service. **Qualif.:** Applicants must be high school seniors intending to enter a two-year or four-year degree program with a minimum of 2.5 cumulative grade point average (on a 4.0 scale), whose mother or father are full time employees of the Charlotte Fire Department, Charlotte-Mecklenburg Police Department, Mecklenburg County Sheriff's Office or MEDIC with minimum of one year of service. **Criteria:** Recipients are selected based on academic performance; financial need; and record of good citizenship as evidenced by school and community involvement beyond required activities.

Funds Avail.: $1,500. **To Apply:** Applicants must submit a completed application form; copy of SAR from FAFSA; official transcripts of academic coursework and grades for at least the last two years; four recommendation forms (two from instructors or other school administrators and two from employers or other non-related individuals in the Charlotte-Mecklenburg area); one to two-paged typed statement expressing reasons for applying for the scholarship, qualifications, and educational and career goals; and a copy of estimated expense budget for tuition, room and board, books, etc. at the school the applicant wants to attend. **Deadline:** March.

3921 ■ Tacy Ana Smith Memorial Scholarships *(Undergraduate/Scholarship)*

Purpose: To provide financial support for graduating seniors at Providence High School in Charlotte, NC. **Focus:** General studies. **Qualif.:** Applicants must be graduating seniors at Providence High School with a 2.5 minimum

Awards are arranged alphabetically below their administering organizations

cumulative grade point average (on a 4.0 scale), planning to attend a four-year college or university. **Criteria:** Applicants are evaluated based on criteria designed by the Scholarship Committee.

Funds Avail.: No specific amount. **To Apply:** Applicants must submit all the required application information. **Contact:** Scholarship Coordinator at Providence High School, 980-343-5390.

3922 ■ The Spirit Square Center for Arts and Education Scholarship Fund *(Undergraduate/ Scholarship)*

Purpose: To provide financial assistance for undergraduate students who can demonstrate aptitude and career potential in arts. **Focus:** General studies. **Qualif.:** Applicants must be rising college juniors or senior students in good academic standing who have demonstrated talent and with a declared major that indicates potential for a significant career contribution to arts. **Criteria:** Recipients are selected based on academic performance; school and community involvement and personal achievements; and commitment to and demonstrated potential for a career in arts. Preference will be given to students who are legal residents of Mecklenburg or contiguous counties in North or South Carolina and those who attend colleges and universities in North Carolina.

Funds Avail.: $4,000. **To Apply:** Applicants must submit a completed application form; official transcript(s) of academic coursework and grades for at least the last two years; three recommendation forms, two of which must come from individuals who are able to evaluate the applicants' aptitude and career potential in arts; one to two pages typed statement expressing 1) reasons for applying for the scholarship, 2) interest in arts, 3) educational and career goals in arts; and 4) a copy of the estimated expense budget for tuition, room and board, books, etc. **Deadline:** March. **Contact:** Online submission of the application package should be directed to scholars@fftc.org.

3923 ■ Mary Stewart and William T. Covington, Jr. Scholarship Fund *(Undergraduate/ Scholarship)*

Purpose: To provide financial support to students who are about to graduate from a public high school located in Hoke County, NC. **Focus:** General studies. **Qualif.:** Applicants must be legal residents of Hoke county, NC who are graduating seniors at Hoke County High School; must have 2.75 minimum cumulative grade point average (on a 4.0 scale); and must attend a four-year college or university. **Criteria:** Applicants are evaluated based on the criteria designed by the Scholarship Selection Committee.

Funds Avail.: No specific amount. **To Apply:** Applicants must submit all the required application information and materials. **Contact:** Scholarship Coordinator at Hoke County High School, 910-875-2156.

3924 ■ Jack Tate/ThinkCOLLEGE Scholarship Fund *(Undergraduate/Scholarship)*

Purpose: To provide scholarship assistance for ThinkCOLLEGE Program participants planning to attend Central Piedmont Community College. **Focus:** General studies. **Qualif.:** Applicants must achieve 90% of the benchmark goal for attendance set for their high school during their senior year (Charlotte-Mecklenburg School System sets individual school goals each year for attendance, academics and behavior, copies are available in the school offices);

must have earned a minimum 2.5 cumulative grade point average (on a 4.0 scale) at the end of the first semester of senior year; must be graduating seniors at Communities In Schools site; and must have at least one full academic year of enrollment and participation in the ThinkCOLLEGE Program (upon graduation). **Criteria:** Recipients are selected based on financial need; academic achievement; school and community involvement; and personal achievements.

Funds Avail.: $800. **To Apply:** Applicants must submit a completed application form; official copy of high school transcript(s), including SAT/ACT scores; two recommendation forms (one from a teacher, counselor or other school administrator and one from an employer, community leader or other non-related adult); one to two-paged typed personal statement; and a copy of Student Aid Report from Free Application for Federal Student Aid (FAFSA). **Deadline:** March. **Contact:** Application form and supporting documents should be sent to Communities in Schools of Charlotte-Mecklenburg, Inc. located at 601 E Fifth St., Ste. 300, Charlotte, NC 28202.

3925 ■ Turner Family Scholarships *(Undergraduate, Vocational/Occupational/ Scholarship)*

Purpose: To provide financial assistance for graduating high school seniors in Mecklenburg County intending to attend an accredited college or vocational school in Mecklenburg County. **Focus:** Vocational-technical education. **Qualif.:** Applicants must be graduating high school seniors who have a minimum cumulative grade point average of 2.5 (on a 4.0 scale) and whose parents or legally appointed guardians are full-time employees who worked for National Welders Supply Company, Inc. for at least two years. Children of employees shall be defined to include natural born or legally adopted dependent children and stepchildren and wards of employees (in the case of stepchildren and wards, the applicant must live in the home with the eligible employee). **Criteria:** Applicants are evaluated based on academic achievement including grade point average and performance on tests designed to measure preparation and ability for postsecondary study; involvement in extracurricular activities and leadership roles held; and record of community service and other personal achievements. Preference will be given to applicants who are children of National Welders Suppliers employees.

Funds Avail.: $1,000 to 4,000. **To Apply:** Applicants must submit completed application form; copy of the Student Aid Report (SAR) from Free Application for Federal Student Aid (FAFSA); three recommendation forms (two from teachers or other school personnel and one from an employer or other non-related adult); one to two pages typed statement expressing reasons for applying for the scholarship, qualifications and educational/career goals; and a letter from an official of National Welders Supply Company, Inc. where the applicants' parents or legally appointed guardians are employed. **Deadline:** March.

3926 ■ The Sibyl Jennings Vorheis Memorial Undergraduate Scholarships *(Undergraduate/ Scholarship)*

Purpose: To assist North Iredell High School graduates in obtaining a degree in physical therapy, medicine or nursing from a post-secondary accredited institution. **Focus:** Physical therapy; Medicine; Nursing. **Qualif.:** Applicants must have graduated from North Iredell High School with a minimum cumulative grade point average of 3.0 (on 4.0

Awards are arranged alphabetically below their administering organizations

scale). **Criteria:** Recipients are selected on the basis of academic achievement; school and community involvement; and personal achievements.

Funds Avail.: $1,500-$3,000. **To Apply:** Applicants must submit completed application form; verification of acceptance into the accredited graduate program; official copy of college transcript; two recommendation forms and letters of recommendation; and a typewritten application statement of eligibility expressing applicant's educational and career goals, reasons for applying for the scholarship, and why the applicant feels they are a good candidate for the scholarship. **Deadline:** April. **Contact:** Tiffany Capers at 704-973-4537 or tcapers@fftc.org.

3927 ■ Laramie Walden Memorial Fund
(Undergraduate/Scholarship)

Purpose: To provide financial assistance to children of Charlotte, NC firefighters. **Focus:** General studies. **Qualif.:** Applicants must be seniors scheduled to graduate in the spring of the academic year; must have 3.5 minimum cumulative weighted grade point average (on a 4.0 scale) whose parent(s) are full-time employees of the Charlotte Fire Department with at least one year of service; and must participate in state-sanctioned school sport. **Criteria:** Applicants are evaluated based on academic merit and extracurricular involvement.

Funds Avail.: $500. **To Apply:** Applicants must submit completed application form; official transcript(s) of academic coursework and grades for at least the last two years; three recommendation forms (two from instructor or other school administrator and one from a non-related adult in the Charlotte-Mecklenburg area such as an employer, coach, scout leader, etc.); and a one-paged typed statement expressing the reason for applying for the scholarship, qualifications, educational and career goals. **Deadline:** March 1.

3928 ■ Fred C. Wikoff, Jr. Scholarships
(Undergraduate, Vocational/Occupational/ Scholarship)

Purpose: To provide undergraduate college and/or vocational scholarships for children of employees of Wikoff Color Corporation and its subsidiaries. **Focus:** General studies. **Qualif.:** Applicants must be children of employees (defined to include natural-born or legally-adopted dependent children and stepchildren and wards of employees). Parents or legally-appointed guardians of applicants must be full-time employees who have worked for Wikoff Color Corporation for at least two years prior to the application deadline. Applicants enrolled in high school at the time of application must have a minimum cumulative grade point average 2.5 (on a 4.0 scale). Applicants enrolled in college at the time of application must have a minimum cumulative grade point average of 2.0 (on a 4.0 scale). Applicant's age must not be over 25 as of the application deadline but a student over the age of 25 will be considered on a case to case basis if the student is permanently disabled or has some other special circumstance that requires him or her to be financially dependent upon their parents. **Criteria:** Applicants are evaluated based on academic achievement; school and community involvement and personal achievements; and financial need.

Funds Avail.: $500 to $2,000. **To Apply:** Applicants must submit a completed application form; copy of SAR from FAFSA; official transcript(s) of high school and/or college coursework and grades for at least the last two years, including SAT/ACT scores if taken; three recommendation

forms (two from teachers or other school personnel and one from an employer or other non-related adult); one to two-page typed statement expressing the reason for applying for the scholarship, qualifications and educational and career goals; and a letter from an official of Wikoff Color Corporation where parents or legally appointed guardians are employed. **Deadline:** March.

3929 ■ The Wilmore Scholarship Fund
(Undergraduate, Vocational/Occupational/ Scholarship)

Purpose: To provide financial assistance for residents of the Wilmore neighborhood in Charlotte, NC intending to attend a college or vocational school. **Focus:** Vocational-technical education. **Qualif.:** Applicants must be residents of the Wilmore Neighborhood which is defined by Summit Avenue on the north, Interstate 77 on the west, South Tryon Street on the east and Wilmore Drive on the south; must have lived in Wilmore Neighborhood for at least one year (12 months) prior to the application deadline; and must have a minimum cumulative grade point average of 2.0 (on a 4.0 scale) for the last completed years of education. **Criteria:** Applicants are judged based on academic achievement; financial need; and leadership potential evidenced by school and/or community involvement. Preference will be given to applicants who are current high school seniors.

Funds Avail.: $500 to $2,000. **To Apply:** Applicants must submit a completed application form; official transcript(s) of high school and/or college coursework and grades for at least the last two years attended, including SAT/ACT score reports if taken; one recommendation form from a teacher, other school personnel or employer; one to two page personal statement expressing the applicants' educational and career goals and financial need for scholarship assistance; and a copy of the Student Aid Report (SAR) from Free Application for Federal Student Aid (FAFSA). **Deadline:** April. **Contact:** Application form and supporting documents may send by e-mail at scholars@fftc.org.

3930 ■ Mary and Elliot Wood Foundation Graduate Scholarship Fund *(Graduate/ Scholarship)*

Purpose: To provide merit-based graduate scholarships for North Carolina students, primarily in Guilford, Moore and Randolph Counties. **Focus:** Humanities; Environmental science; Ecology; Nutrition; Economics; Peace Studies; Government; Education. **Qualif.:** Candidates must have chosen as recipients or finalists for MEWF undergraduate scholarships; must commit a course of graduate study and an eventual career that will contribute to the goals of the foundation; must maintain a full-time enrollment (nine semester hours) for which the scholarship is paid. **Criteria:** Applicants are evaluated on the basis of academic achievement, extracurricular activities and statement of personal goals and references.

Funds Avail.: No specific amount. **To Apply:** Applicants must submit a completed application form, curriculum vitae, personal statement, letters of recommendation and official transcripts in a sealed envelope. **Deadline:** April 1. **Contact:** For more information, applicants are advised to contact the Foundation for the Carolinas Scholarship Team at 704-973-4537.

3931 ■ Mary and Elliot Wood Foundation Undergraduate Scholarship Fund
(Undergraduate/Scholarship)

Purpose: To provide financial support for the most gifted future leaders who have the capability, desire, energy,

Awards are arranged alphabetically below their administering organizations

enthusiasm and determination to improve our civilization and to enhance the quality of all life cultural, civic, and ecological. **Focus:** General studies. **Qualif.:** Applicants must be students graduating from high schools in the districts in Guilford County, Davidson County, Randolph County, Moore County; must have a GPA of atleast 4.0 and 1800 on SAT total scores. **Criteria:** Applicants are evaluated based on personal character; leadership potential; and scholastic achievement.

Funds Avail.: No specific amount. **To Apply:** Applicants must submit completed application form and all other required materials for the scholarship. **Contact:** For more information, applicants are advised to contact the Foundation for the Carolinas Scholarship Team at 704-973-4537.

3932 ■ Foundation for Community Association Research

6402 Arlington Blvd., Ste. 500
Falls Church, VA 22042
Ph: (703) 970-9220
Fax: (703) 970-9558
Free: 888-224-4321
E-mail: foundation@caionline.org
URL: www.cairf.org

3933 ■ Byron Hanke Fellowships *(Doctorate, Graduate, Undergraduate/Fellowship)*

Purpose: To promote positive charge for all stakeholders who live in homeowner associations by discovering future trends and opportunities; to support and conduct research; to facilitate and promote cooperation among industry partners and provide resources that help educate the public. **Focus:** General studies. **Qualif.:** Applicants must be enrolled in an accredited master's, doctoral or law program in United States of America or Canada. Students in all discipline are welcome to apply provided their research projects or studies are related to community associations. **Criteria:** Recipients are selected based on academic achievements; faculty recommendations; research and writing ability; and the nature of the proposed topic and its benefit to the study and understanding of community associations.

Funds Avail.: Maximum amount of $4,000. **To Apply:** Applicants must submit a completed application form and research proposal. **Deadline:** May 1. **Contact:** foundation@caionline.org.

3934 ■ Foundation for Enhancing Communities

200 N Third St.
Harrisburg, PA 17108-0678
Ph: (717) 236-5040
Fax: (717) 231-4463
E-mail: dawn@tfec.org
URL: www.tfec.org

3935 ■ G. Thomas Balsbaugh Memorial Scholarship Fund *(Undergraduate/Scholarship)*

Purpose: To provide financial assistance for a Dauphin County high school senior planning to attend a four-year college or university. **Focus:** General studies. **Qualif.:** Applicants must be high school seniors from Dauphin County planning to attend a four-year college or university; must be legal residents of Dauphin County; have high academic standing and achievement; must exemplify good character;

must exhibit a variety of interests and activities in both academic and personal life; and must demonstrate financial need. **Criteria:** Recipients will be selected based in demonstrated good character; interest and activities in both academic and personal life; and financial need.

Funds Avail.: $1,000. **Number Awarded:** 1. **To Apply:** Application for the scholarship should include: official academic transcript issued by school; completed personal information; completed financial statement; and personal statement describing current interests and activities as well as future goals and ambitions; FAFSA Student Aid Report Form; and two personal reference letters. One letter should come from a high school teacher. **Deadline:** April 1. **Contact:** Jennifer Kuntch, Program Officer at the above address.

3936 ■ Robbie Baron Memorial Scholarships *(Undergraduate/Scholarship)*

Purpose: To provide financial support for a graduating senior of Cedar Cliff High School who attended Hillside Elementary School. **Focus:** General studies. **Qualif.:** Applicant must be a graduating senior at Cedar Cliff High School and have attended Hillside Elementary. **Criteria:** Scholarship will be given based on the following: academic achievement; extracurricular activities; services to the community; an essay which identifies the applicant's opinion on values and youth leadership; and financial need.

Funds Avail.: No specific amount. **Number Awarded:** 1. **To Apply:** Applicant may download the application at the TFEC web site. Applicant must submit the following required attachments: completed student application; high school transcript; completed student essay (question attached); and one personal reference letter. Applicants may return their completed application to the High School Guidance Office. **Contact:** Dawn Morris at the above address.

3937 ■ Chambersburg/Fannett-Metal School District Scholarship Fund *(Undergraduate/Scholarship)*

Purpose: To provide educational assistance to students of Chambersburg High School and Fannett-Metal High School. **Focus:** Engineering, computer; Computer and information sciences. **Qualif.:** Applicants must be graduating students from Chambersburg Area High School and Fanett-Metal High School; have a desire to pursue a career in computer engineering or computer science; and must have an academic achievement of a cumulative GPA of 2.0 or higher on a 4.0 scale. **Criteria:** Selection will be based on financial need; submitted essay; academic achievement; extracurricular activities; volunteer services to the community; and demonstrated financial need.

Funds Avail.: No specific amount. **To Apply:** Applicants must submit a completed scholarship application form; a high school transcript with GPA; completed personal essay identifying their interest in computer science and/or computer engineering including professional goals; FAFSA Student Aid Report; and two letters of recommendation from a teacher and the other one must be from an employer or a supervisor of a community service volunteer agency. Letters from family members will not be accepted. **Remarks:** Established in 1999. **Contact:** Applications and supporting documents should be submitted to Dawn Morris at the above address.

3938 ■ CODY Foundation Fund *(Undergraduate/Scholarship)*

Purpose: To promote Christian initiatives through education and athletics. **Focus:** General studies. **Qualif.:** Ap-

Awards are arranged alphabetically below their administering organizations

plicants must be graduating high school senior students from Greenwood High School, Susquenita High School, West Perry High School or Newport High School. **Criteria:** Selection will be based on the following: GPA (academic achievements); community involvement; recommendation letters (one from a teacher, the other from an employer, supervisor, or community advisor); completed essay; high moral character (must attend and/or be involved in church activities); and financial need.

Funds Avail.: $500. **Number Awarded:** 2. **To Apply:** Applicants must complete the required attachments: completed application; official high school transcript; FAFSA student aid report; completed student essay; and two personal reference letters. To the persons writing the reference letters should list the applicant's leadership attributes and examples where they demonstrate their faith or belief system. **Deadline:** April 1. **Contact:** Applications and supporting documents should be sent to Jennifer Kuntch at the above address or e-mail her at jkuntch@tfec.org.

3939 ■ Jan DiMartino Delany Memorial Scholarships *(Undergraduate/Scholarship)*

Purpose: To assist students with their college tuition expenses. **Focus:** General studies. **Qualif.:** Applicant must be a graduating senior of Cumberland Valley High School who will attend a two or four-year institution of higher learning. **Criteria:** Selection criteria will be based on financial need; scholastic ability; leadership abilities within the school or community; community service; essay; and personal challenges that have been overcome. Preference will be given to those applicants who are graduating seniors of Cumberland Valley High School.

Funds Avail.: $2,000. **To Apply:** Applicant must complete and submit the application to the Cumberland Valley High School Guidance Office. Include an official transcript of complete high school records with GPA, through the first half of final year on which the raised school seal is imprinted. On a separate sheet of paper, applicant must list his/ her most significant extracurricular or non-academic activities, noting work experience and community service with the dates of these activities. Attach an essay answering the question: "What are some of the obstacles that you have overcome or challenges that you have met in your life and how do they impact your future goals?" The essay should be titled, typewritten, double-spaced and must not exceed 300 words. Return the completed application and attachments to the CVHS Guidance Department. **Deadline:** April 1. **Contact:** Dawn Morris at the above address.

3940 ■ Lou Drane Music Scholarships *(Undergraduate/Scholarship)*

Purpose: To provide educational assistance to deserving music students in the areas of classical music composition, teaching, and/or performance. **Focus:** Classical music. **Qualif.:** Applicant must have a serious interest in classical music and display unusual ability and/or creativity; must apply for financial aid from the school he/she plans to attend; must attend an accredited post-secondary institution of higher learning or have been accepted and plan to attend same; be a citizen of the United States and must maintain a permanent residence on one of the following counties in central Pennsylvania: Adams, Cumberland; Dauphin, Franklin, Fulton, Juniata, Lancaster, Lebanon, Montour, Northumberland, Perry, Snyder or York. **Criteria:** Recipients will be selected based on technical quality of their recording.

Funds Avail.: Up to $5,000. **To Apply:** Applicant must at-

tach FAFSA Student Aid Report and a letter detailing applicant's financial need; and must submit, along with the application, an example of their ability, in one of the following fields: Composition or composition-teaching - a CD not to exceed 20 minutes in length - and a written music score - of two separate works of you own composition. Identify yourself, your instrument and title at the beginning of the tape. Label the recording with this information also. Audition recordings of original compositions must be of live performances. MIDI and other electronic performances are not accepted. For applications in Performance or performance-teaching submit a CD, not to exceed 20 minutes in length, of two separate works reflecting a variety of style. Identify yourself, your instrument and title at the beginning of the recording. Label the tape with this information also. All instruments with the exception of piano and classical guitar must be accompanied, but avoid lengthy introductions by accompaniment. **Deadline:** March 30. **Contact:** Allison Moesta at the above address.

3941 ■ Sue and Ken Dyer Foundation Travel Scholarships *(Undergraduate/Scholarship)*

Purpose: To assist students with travel expenses for educational or service trips. **Focus:** Travel and tourism. **Qualif.:** Applicants must be junior or senior students enrolled at one of the following schools: Cedar Cliff, Camp Hill, Mechanicsburg, Trinity or the Harrisburg Academy. **Criteria:** Selection criteria include purpose of the travel; financial need; character of the applicants and information provided by the written references.

Funds Avail.: $2,000. **To Apply:** Applicants must complete and return the application and required attachments to the Foundation. Required attachments include: scholastic record and extracurricular activities; an essay on the topic: "The purpose of my proposed trip and what I expect to gain from this experience". Essay should be titled, type-written, double-spaced and maximum of 300 words; two reference letters from individuals who can speak to the quality of your character, your academic prowess and/or your likelihood of utilizing the proposed travel experience as a tool for personal growth; also include financial information. **Deadline:** April 1. **Contact:** Jennifer Doyle at the above address.

3942 ■ Family and Children's Services of Lebanon County Fund *(Undergraduate/Scholarship)*

Purpose: To provide financial assistance for Lebanon County residents pursuing higher education degrees. **Focus:** Medicine; Nursing, Social work, Mental health. **Qualif.:** Applicants must be enrolled full-time in schools of advanced education in the fields of medicine, nursing, social work, mental health and other specialized therapies in the treatment of physical and mental disabilities; must demonstrate financial need, academic aptitude and achievement, and commitment to a career in human services; and must be residents of Lebanon County. **Criteria:** Applicants will be judged based on financial need, academic aptitude and achievement, and commitment to a career in human services.

Funds Avail.: $1,200. **To Apply:** Applicants may obtain the application online. Applicants must provide the most recent, either a certified high school transcript or a certified college transcript; (300-word) essay. It should be typewritten, 12 pt. font and double-spaced; and one personal reference letter who can attest their commitment in human services career. **Deadline:** March 30. **Contact:** Allison Moesta at the above address.

Awards are arranged alphabetically below their administering organizations

3943 ■ Adrienne Zoe Fedok Art and Music Scholarships (Undergraduate/Scholarship)

Purpose: To award scholarship to a student from either Central Dauphin High School or Central Dauphin East High School. **Focus:** Art; Music. **Qualif.:** Applicant must be from either Central Dauphin High School or Central Dauphin East High School entering his or her freshman year in post-secondary education in the field of Art and Music. **Criteria:** Selection will be based on the following criteria: interest in art and/or music education; financial need; SAT scores; GPA; demonstrated leadership and community service; and personal essay on the applicant's educational and career goals.

Funds Avail.: $1,000. **Number Awarded:** 1. **To Apply:** The application and the required attachments must be completed and postmarked on or before the deadline. Required attachments include: completed application; high school transcript including GPA; SAT scores; FAFSA Student Aid Report Form (Financial Aid Form); two letters of recommendation (one from a faculty member in the art or music department); a list of extra-curricular activities demonstrating leadership and community service; and personal essay on the applicant's educational and career goals. **Deadline:** April 1. **Contact:** Application form and supporting documents should be submitted to Jennifer Kuntch at the above address or e-mail her at jkuntch@tfec.org.

3944 ■ Friends of Megan Bolton Memorial Fund (Undergraduate/Scholarship)

Purpose: To assist students with their college expenses. **Focus:** General studies. **Qualif.:** Applicants must be graduating high school seniors of Camp Hill High School; must have high academic standing and achievement; and must exemplify good character. **Criteria:** Selection will be based on: financial need; high academic standing and achievement; leadership; and character.

Funds Avail.: $1,000. **Number Awarded:** Varies. **To Apply:** Application form can be obtained online. Applicants must submit an official school transcript of their complete high school records including GPA, through the first half of final year, on which the raised school seal is imprinted. Students should indicate evidence of meaningful leadership and positive character traits, volunteer work or involvement in community or church activities/charities that contribute to the betterment of that community or organization. Submit a resume if available, though not required, and a reference letter written by one of the contacts from the resume. Students are also asked to submit an essay (300 words or less) describing their idea of friendship and the significance of having close friends in their lives. **Deadline:** April 1. **Contact:** Dawn Morris at the above address.

3945 ■ Norma Gotwalt Scholarship Fund (Undergraduate/Scholarship)

Purpose: To assist students with their college tuition expenses. **Focus:** Education, Elementary. **Qualif.:** Applicants must be female junior or senior students studying Elementary Education at the Penn State Capital College and who have maintained a minimum of 3.0 cumulative GPA while at Capital College. **Criteria:** Recipients will be selected based on financial need; community service; submitted essay; and career goals.

Funds Avail.: $3,000. **Number Awarded:** 1. **To Apply:** Applicants must complete the application form; must submit an official transcript of post-secondary academic records; FAFSA Student Aid Report Form; (300-word) personal es-

say; and a written recommendation from a professor who can assess the potential ability as an elementary school teacher. **Deadline:** March 15. **Contact:** Allison Moesta at the above address.

3946 ■ Roberta L. Houpt Scholarship Fund (Undergraduate/Scholarship)

Purpose: To assist students from Cumberland, Dauphin and Perry Counties studying nursing at a college or university of their choice. **Focus:** Nursing. **Qualif.:** Applicants must be nursing undergraduate students and residents of Dauphin, Cumberland or Perry Counties. **Criteria:** Selection will be based on the following criteria: desire to pursue a career in nursing; academic achievement; extracurricular activities; services to the community; an essay which identifies the applicant's interest in nursing; and financial need.

Funds Avail.: $2,000. **Number Awarded:** Varies. **To Apply:** Application and the required attachments must be completed and postmarked on or before the deadline. Required attachments include: completed student background sheet; high school transcript or college transcript; letter of acceptance in nursing program or college transcript showing enrollment in program; FAFSA student aid report form (financial aid form); completed essay (question attached); and two personal reference letters (one letter should be from a science teacher and the other letter should be from an individual who can speak to applicant's ability to successfully complete studies), such as a teacher, employer, or mentor. Application form can be obtained online. **Deadline:** April 1. **Remarks:** Established in 1998. **Contact:** Dawn Morris, Program Officer at the above address.

3947 ■ Carol Hoy Scholarship Fund (Undergraduate/Scholarship)

Purpose: To assist students from Mechanicsburg Area High School planning to pursue a career in elementary or early childhood education. **Focus:** Elementary Education; Early childhood education. **Qualif.:** Applicants must be graduating seniors from Mechanicsburg Area High School; must have desire to pursue a career in elementary education or early childhood education. **Criteria:** Selection will be based on the following criteria: academic achievements; leadership and community service; one or two paragraph essay; personal interview; and financial need.

Funds Avail.: No specific amount. **Number Awarded:** 1. **To Apply:** Application and the required attachments must be completed and postmarked on or before the deadline. The required attachments include: completed student background sheet; high school transcript; FAFSA student aid report form (financial aid form); completed student essay; resume including leadership and community service; and two personal reference letters. One letter should be from a teacher and the other letter should be from an individual who can speak to applicant's ability to successfully complete studies, such as a teacher, employer, or mentor. Application form can be obtained online. **Deadline:** April 1. **Remarks:** Established in 2006. **Contact:** Dawn Morris at the above address.

3948 ■ Erin L. Jenkins Memorial Scholarship Fund (Undergraduate/Scholarship)

Purpose: To award scholarships for deserving students attending Cumberland Valley High School. **Focus:** General studies. **Qualif.:** Students must reside in the area defined by the Cumberland Valley School District or its successor;

Awards are arranged alphabetically below their administering organizations

must have desire to a career in elementary education or early childhood education. **Criteria:** Recipients will be selected based on financial need; academic achievement; community service; and essay.

Funds Avail.: $1,500. **Number Awarded:** 1. **To Apply:** Students must complete and return the application and attachments to the Foundation. Students must also submit the following: official school transcript; two recommendations; FAFSA Student Aid Report Form; and (300-word) personal essay. **Deadline:** April 1. **Contact:** Dawn Morris, Program Officer at the above address.

3949 ■ Ken and Romaine Kauffman Scholarship Fund (Undergraduate/Scholarship)

Purpose: To assist students with college tuition expenses. **Focus:** Automotive technology. **Qualif.:** Students must be residents of Cumberland Perry Counties pursuing a degree in the mechanical or technical field; must be graduating seniors of Cumberland Valley High School or Cumberland-Perry Vo-Tech planning to attend a four-year college, university, technical school or community college. **Criteria:** Selection will be based on the committee's criteria. Preference will be given to students studying an automotive technology.

Funds Avail.: $1,500. **Number Awarded:** 1. **To Apply:** Applicants must complete the application form; must submit an official transcript including GPA; FAFSA Student Aid Report Form; and one personal reference letter from an individual such as teacher, employer or mentor. **Deadline:** April 1. **Contact:** Dawn Morris, Program Officer at the above address.

3950 ■ Leon I. Lock and Barbara R. Lock Scholarship Fund (Undergraduate/Scholarship)

Purpose: To assist students with their college tuition expenses. **Focus:** Automotive technology. **Qualif.:** Applicants must be graduating seniors in any high school in the Harrisburg School District (including Bishop McDevitt High School) who will attend Harrisburg Area Community College, or Penn State, or students who have graduated from one of the two high schools in no more than five years before the year of application; must have minimum GPA of 2.5 on a 4.0 scale; must be enrolled in an automotive technology either at HACC or Penn State. **Criteria:** Recipients will be selected based on financial need; academic achievements; demonstrated work and study ethic from an employer or volunteer group supervisors; and impact of essay. Preference will be given to those students enrolled at Harrisburg Area Community College in an automotive technology field.

Funds Avail.: $500. **To Apply:** Applicants must complete the application form; must submit an official transcript including GPA; FAFSA Student Aid Report; reference letter from an employer or a volunteer group about how students demonstrate a good work or study ethic; and maximum of 300 words essay explaining the choice of the course undertaken. Essay should be in 12-point font and double-spaced. **Deadline:** April 1. **Contact:** Allison Moesta at the above address.

3951 ■ Carie and George Lyter Scholarship Fund (Undergraduate/Scholarship)

Purpose: To provide educational assistance for students attending Greenwood High School, Newport High School, Susquenita High School and West Perry High School. **Focus:** Education, Elementary; Science; Mathematics and mathematical sciences. **Qualif.:** Applicants must have a

desire to pursue a career in elementary or middle school education with emphasis in science or mathematics; an academic achievement of a cumulative GPA of 2.5 to 3.0 on a 4.0 scale in their junior/senior year; demonstrated talent for leadership; a high moral character (must have attended and be involved in church activities); and must demonstrate financial need. **Criteria:** Selection will be based on the committee's criteria.

Funds Avail.: No specific amount. **Number Awarded:** 1. **To Apply:** Applicants must submit the following required attachments: completed student background sheet; official high school transcript with raised school seal; FAFSA student aid report; completed student 300-word essay identifying their interest in Elementary or Middle School Education with an emphasis in science and mathematics (include professional goals); and two personal reference letters. One letter should be from a teacher and the other letter should be from an employer or a supervisor of a community service volunteer agency. Letters of reference may not be from a family member. **Deadline:** April 1. **Contact:** Application form and supporting documents should be submitted to Jennifer Kuntch at the above address or e-mail her at jkuntch@tfec.org.

3952 ■ Sam Mizrahi Memorial Scholarships (Undergraduate/Scholarship)

Purpose: To assist students with their college tuition expenses. **Focus:** General studies. **Qualif.:** Applicants must be students from Northern York High School who plan to attend a two or four-year college, university or trade school; must demonstrate financial need; must have a minimum 2.5 GPA; and must have a high moral character. **Criteria:** Recipients will be selected based on financial need; leadership/community service; character; and personal essay.

Funds Avail.: No specific amount. **To Apply:** Applicants must complete the attached form and any other requested supporting documents and return on or before the deadline to the guidance counselor at Northern York High School. Applicants must include an official transcript of complete high school records including GPA, through first half of final year, on which the raised school seal is imprinted. On a separate sheet of paper, list the most significant extracurricular or nonacademic activities, noting work experience and community service with the dates of these activities. Applicants must also write a one to two-page essay on the subject "My biggest life challenge and what I learned from the experience". **Deadline:** April 1. **Contact:** Dawn Morris, Program Officer at the above address.

3953 ■ Leo F. Moro Baseball Memorial Scholarships (Undergraduate/Scholarship)

Purpose: To assist students with their college tuition expenses. **Focus:** General studies. **Qualif.:** Applicants must be graduating senior students of Malden High School or Malden Catholic High School in Malden, Massachusetts who will attend a two or four-year college or university; must have accomplishments in baseball at the high school level and have plan to continue a baseball career in college; and must have success in the sport of baseball. **Criteria:** Recipients will be selected based on financial need; leadership ability; academic achievement based on GPA and SAT scores; and sportsmanship.

Funds Avail.: No specific amount. **Number Awarded:** 1. **To Apply:** Applicants must complete and return the attached form and other requested supporting documents to the foundation. Applicants must include an official transcript

Awards are arranged alphabetically below their administering organizations

of complete high school records including GPA, through the first half of final year, on which the raised school seal is imprinted. On a separate sheet of paper, list the most significant extracurricular or no-academic activities, noting work experience and community service with the dates of these activities. Please include a photocopy of your FAFSA with your completed scholarship application; and must attach a baseball information sheet. Application form can be obtained online. **Deadline:** May 31. **Contact:** Jennifer Kuntch, Program Officer at the above address.

3954 ■ Pathways to Success Scholarships
(Undergraduate/Scholarship)

Purpose: To provide high school students a meaningful, educational and highly-involved look at law and law-related career opportunities. **Focus:** Law; Paralegal studies. **Qualif.:** Applicants must be minority students accepted by (in the case of high school students) or enrolled in an accredited institution of higher learning at its main campus or a branch campus located in Central Pennsylvania. **Criteria:** Recipients will be selected based on academic achievement, financial need, and contribution to society and legal profession.

Funds Avail.: $2,500. **To Apply:** Application form can be obtained online. Applicants must provide a copy of high school or college transcript, certified as true and accurate by your guidance counselor, Registrar's Office or equivalent. Applicants must respond to the essay question (maximum of 500 words and typed). If you are in high school, attach a copy of your letter of acceptance to your application. Applicants pursuing post-secondary education should attach a copy of a certification of good standing from the educational institution which they are attending. Submit two letters of recommendation endorsing your candidacy for the Pathways to Success scholarship with your application. Letters of recommendation from teachers, administrators, or community members may be submitted and must reference at least one example of personal interaction with the applicant to underscore the applicant's academic/leadership and/or contribution to community. Must attach a copy of FAFSA Student Aid Report and a signed statement of intention with student and parent/guardian signatures. **Deadline:** March 1. **Contact:** Central PA Chapter, Association of Corporate Counsel, c/o Frank Miles, Esq., 27 West Chocolate Ave., Hershey, PA 17033.

3955 ■ Dr. Harry V. Pfautz Memorial Scholarship Fund *(Undergraduate/Scholarship)*

Purpose: To assist Susquenita High School students with their college expenses in the field of Forestry and/or Agriculture with an emphasis in forestry. **Focus:** Forestry. **Qualif.:** Applicants must be graduating senior students of Susquenita High School who have a GPA of 2.5 on a 4.0 point scale. **Criteria:** Selection will be based on financial need, community involvement and work ethic, scholastic performance and student essay.

Funds Avail.: No specific amount. **Number Awarded:** 1. **To Apply:** Applicants must complete the attached form and requested supporting documents and send to the foundation. The supporting documents include: official transcript of the complete high school records including GPA, through the first half of final year, on which the raised school seal is imprinted; FAFSA Student Aid Report Form; completed personal essay explaining the reasons of choosing the Forestry as a career path and description of educational plans in achieving goals; and two personal reference letters from a teacher. Letters from family members will not be accepted. References should be sealed in an envelope. **Dead-**line: April 10. **Contact:** For further information, contact Jennifer Doyle, Program Officer at the above address or by e-mail at jdoyle@tfec.org.

3956 ■ Ruth Cook Pfautz Memorial Scholarship Fund *(Undergraduate/Scholarship)*

Purpose: To assist Susquenita High School students with their college expenses in the field of Elementary Education. **Focus:** Education, Elementary. **Qualif.:** Applicants must be graduating senior students of Susquenita High School who have a GPA of 2.5 on a 4.0 point scale. **Criteria:** Selection will be based on financial need, community service, leadership qualities and career plans.

Funds Avail.: No specific amount. **Number Awarded:** 1. **To Apply:** Application form can be obtained online. Applicants must complete the attached form and requested supporting documents and send to the Foundation. The supporting documents include: official transcript of the complete high school record, including GPA, through the first half of final year, on which the raised school seal is imprinted; list of extracurricular or non-academic activities; reference letter; and a 300-word student essay explaining why they have chosen Elementary Education as a career path and describing their educational plans to achieve their career goal. **Contact:** For further information, contact Jennifer Doyle, Program Officer at the above address or by e-mail at jdoyle@tfec.org.

3957 ■ Bertha and Byron L. Reppert Scholarship Fund *(Undergraduate/Scholarship)*

Purpose: To encourage and recognize two senior students from the Mechanicsburg Area School District who demonstrate good citizenship. **Focus:** Political science; Horticulture. **Qualif.:** Applicants must have an interest in political science or horticulture; must be in the top one-third of the graduating class; must be accepted to an accredited college or university; must demonstrate good citizenship within the school and local community; and must complete an essay explaining how they meet the criteria. **Criteria:** Selection will be based on the committee's criteria.

Funds Avail.: No specific amount. **Number Awarded:** 2. **To Apply:** Application form can be obtained online. Applicants must attach the following documents: official transcript of the complete high school/college records including GPA, through the first half of the present year, with the raised school seal imprinted; list of extracurricular or non-academic activities; FAFSA Student Aid Report; and an essay describing how they meet the eligibility criteria of this scholarship. **Deadline:** April 1. **Contact:** Dawn Morris, Program Officer at the above address.

3958 ■ Ollie Rosenberg Educational Trust *(Undergraduate/Scholarship)*

Purpose: To assist students with business, technical or trade school tuition expenses. **Focus:** General studies. **Qualif.:** Students must attend a state supported school in Pennsylvania; must have a job; must have a Pennsylvania student loan; and must demonstrate financial need. **Criteria:** Selection will be based on the committee's criteria; extracurricular and/or non-academic activities; completed personal essay; and financial need.

Funds Avail.: $2,000. **To Apply:** Applicants must complete and submit the application and required documents to the Foundation. Required documents include official transcript of the complete high school records including GPA, through first half of final year, on which the raised school seal is imprinted, and a 300-word essay explaining how applicant

Awards are arranged alphabetically below their administering organizations

has overcome the challenges in life and how he or she will apply these lessons to his or her vocation. Applicants must list their most significant extracurricular or non-academic activities, emphasizing work experience and community volunteer service. Scholarships require a copy of SAR to be included in application. Applications missing the SAR will not be considered. **Deadline:** April 16. **Contact:** Dawn Morris, Program Officer at the above address.

3959 ■ Ollie Rosenberg Scholarship Travel Fund *(Undergraduate/Scholarship)*

Purpose: To assist students with business, technical or trade school tuition expenses. **Focus:** Travel and tourism. **Qualif.:** Applicants must be graduating seniors who wish to travel to Israel to study traditional Jewish customs and culture. **Criteria:** Selection will be based on the committee's criteria.

Funds Avail.: No specific amount. **To Apply:** Applicants must complete the following required attachments: completed student background sheet, verification of family income, completed student essay and two personal reference letters. One letter should be from your Guidance Counselor and the other letter should be from an individual who can speak to your ability to successfully complete your studies, such as a teacher, employer, or mentor. Your letter of reference should not be from a family member. **Deadline:** April 11. **Contact:** Dawn Morris, Program Officer at the above address.

3960 ■ J. Ward Sleichter and Frances F. Sleichter Memorial Scholarship Fund *(Undergraduate/Scholarship)*

Purpose: To provide aid for needy and deserving students who otherwise would not have the financial means to obtain a four-year college education. **Focus:** General studies. **Qualif.:** Applicants must be full-time students who maintain a "B" average or equivalent; must reside in the area defined by the Shippensburg Area School District, or its successor; and must have plan to attend a four-year college or university. **Criteria:** Recipients will be selected based on financial need; and demonstrated motivation, character, ability and potential.

Funds Avail.: $5,000. **Number Awarded:** 1. **To Apply:** Applicants must complete the following required attachments: application; official school transcript; two recommendations (one from the student's guidance counselor and one from a teacher who can discuss the student's personal characteristics such as motivation, character, ability and potential); and FAFSA Student Aid Report (make sure to include the cover letter of the report, which will indicate the student's Estimated Family contribution). **Deadline:** April 3. **Contact:** Inquiries should be directed to: Erica Frontino, Guidance Councilor, Shippensburg Area High School, 317 N Morris St., Shippensburg, PA 17257.

3961 ■ Soroptimist International of Chambersburg Scholarship Fund *(Undergraduate/Scholarship)*

Purpose: To provide assistance for female seniors of Chambersburg Area Senior High School. **Focus:** General studies. **Qualif.:** Applicants must be female senior students of Chambersburg Area High School; and must be accepted at an accredited college or university at the time the awards are made. **Criteria:** Selection will be based on academic performance; citizenship; interest and aptitude; leadership qualities; responsibility; enthusiasm; motivation to learn and improve; attitude and cooperative spirit; dependability;

financial need; and recommendations from a teacher and also a counselor.

Funds Avail.: $500. **To Apply:** Applicants must complete the required attachments. Required attachments include: application; two letters of recommendation (one from your guidance counselor, containing your GPA, course of study and general character assessment and the other from one of your teacher containing a general character assessment of you as a person and a student); FAFSA Student Aid Report; a paragraph of approximately 150 words answering the question "Why I Have Chosen to Continue My Education". **Deadline:** April 18. **Contact:** Chris Butler, Guidance Counselor, Chambersburg Area Senior High School, 511 S Sixth High School, Chambersburg, PA 17201.

3962 ■ Joseph L. and Vivian E. Steele Music Scholarship Fund *(Undergraduate/Scholarship)*

Purpose: To assist needy students of classical music in the fields of composition, teaching and performance. **Focus:** Music. **Qualif.:** Applicants must have a serious interest in classical music and display unusual ability and/or creativity; must apply for financial aid from the school they plan to attend; must attend an accredited post-secondary institution of higher learning or have been accepted and plan to attend same; must be citizens of the United States and must maintain permanent residence in one of the following counties in central Pennsylvania: Adams, Cumberland, Dauphin, Franklin, Fulton, Juniata, Lancaster, Lebanon, Montour, Northurberland, Perry, Snyder or York. **Criteria:** Recipients will be selected based on financial need and technical quality of recording.

Funds Avail.: $5,000. **Number Awarded:** Varies. **To Apply:** Each applicant is required to submit the attached application on or before the deadline. Submit along with the application, an example of ability in one of the following fields: Composition or composition-teaching - a CD not to exceed 20 minutes in length and a written music score for two separate works of own composition. Identify self, instrument and title at the beginning of the tape. Label the tape with this information also; Performance or performance-teaching - a CD, not to exceed 20 minutes in length, of two separate works reflecting a variety of style. Identify self, instrument and title at the beginning of the recording. **Deadline:** March 30. **Contact:** Allison Moesta at the above address.

3963 ■ Anil and Neema Thakrar Family Fund *(Undergraduate/Scholarship)*

Purpose: To encourage educational pursuits by providing financial assistance; to assist students for the study of a medical related discipline attending a school in Dauphin, Cumberland or Perry Counties. **Focus:** Mathematics and mathematical science; Science; Engineering. **Qualif.:** Program is open to students intending to study Math, Science and Engineering from the City of Harrisburg School District and Sci-Tech High School, or to high school students in Dauphin, Cumberland and Perry Counties intending to study in a medical-related discipline; must have a minimum of 2.5 GPA on a 4.0 scale. **Criteria:** Selection will be based on leadership/community service; character; and financial need.

Funds Avail.: $3,000. **Number Awarded:** 1. **To Apply:** Applicants must complete and submit the application and other required attachments on or before the deadline. Applicants must provide the following attachments: official transcript of complete high school/college records including GPA; must attach a 300-word essay stating the biggest life

Awards are arranged alphabetically below their administering organizations

challenge and the lesson acquired from the experience; and two personal reference letters from a high school teacher. Letters from family members will not be accepted. Reference should be sealed in an envelope. **Deadline:** April 1. **Contact:** Application form and supporting documents should be submitted to Jennifer Kuntch at the above address or e-mail her at jkuntch@tfec.org.

3964 ■ Jack and Edna May Yost Scholarships
(Undergraduate/Scholarship)

Purpose: To assist students with their college tuition expenses. **Focus:** General studies. **Qualif.:** Applicants must be graduating seniors of a Dauphin or Cumberland County High School who will attend a two or four-year degree program at an accredited college; must have a minimum SAT score of 1,000; must have an overall average between "C+" and "B-"; must be full-time students planning to attend a two or four-year accredited college; must be graduates of any Dauphin or Cumberland County high school; must have minimum GPA of 2.5 on a 4.0 scale; and must be able to demonstrate past or current community service and willingness to work to attain future goals. **Criteria:** Selection will be based on the committee's criteria. Preference will be given to students who demonstrate financial need; children of postal employees; and students who have plan on majoring nursing or have teaching profession.

Funds Avail.: $5,000. **To Apply:** Applicants must complete and submit the following attachments: official transcript of complete high school records with GPA; FAFSA Student Aid Report; two personal reference letters come from a teacher and the other one must come from someone who can attest the applicant's personal characteristics such as motivation, character, ability and potential; and personal essay. Essay should be titled, type-written, 12 point font, double-spaced and maximum of 300 words. **Deadline:** April 1. **Contact:** Dawn Morris, Program Officer at the above address.

3965 ■ Foundation of the Federal Bar Association (FFBA)
1220 N Fillmore St., Ste. 444
Arlington, VA 22201-6501
Ph: (571) 481-9100
Fax: (571) 481-9090
E-mail: fba@fedbar.org
URL: www.fedbar.org/foundation.html

3966 ■ Foundation of the Federal Bar Association Public Service Scholarships
(Undergraduate/Scholarship)

Purpose: To provide financial assistance for high school students continuing higher education. **Focus:** General studies. **Qualif.:** Applicants must be graduating high school seniors planning to attend a four-year college or university; must be students currently enrolled full-time at a four-year college or university; or graduate students enrolled full-time in a graduate or professional degree program. At least one of the applicant's parents or guardians must be a current federal government attorney or federal judge and member of the Federal Bar Association. **Criteria:** Applicants are evaluated based on academic record, leadership recognition, school and community activities and service, and compelling essay response - exhibiting both substance and written communication skills.

Funds Avail.: $5,000. **To Apply:** Applicants must submit

completed application along with most recent transcripts (official copy); letter of acceptance from their college, university or graduate/professional school for new enrollees; and an essay. **Deadline:** March 15.

3967 ■ Foundation Fighting Blindness (FFB)
12th Fl., 890 Yonge St.
Toronto, ON, Canada M4W 3P4
Ph: (416) 360-4200
Fax: (416) 360-0060
Free: 800-461-3331
E-mail: info@ffb.ca
URL: www.ffb.ca

3968 ■ FFB-C Postdoctoral Fellowships
(Postdoctorate/Fellowship)

Purpose: To increase the number of Canadian scientists being trained to investigate the causes, means of detection, prevention and cure of retinitis pigmentosa (RP), macular degeneration and related diseases of the retina. **Focus:** Optometry. **Qualif.:** Applicant must hold an MD, PhD, DDS, DVM, PharmD, or equivalent degree in a field appropriate to retinal degenerative disease research (molecular genetics, molecular biology, physiology, biochemistry, cell biology, or immunology). **Criteria:** Selection is based on the submitted application and materials.

Funds Avail.: No specific amount. **To Apply:** Applicants must complete the application online. **Contact:** research@ffb.ca.

3969 ■ Foundation of the Hospitality Sales and Marketing Association International
1760 Old Meadow Rd., Ste. 500
McLean, VA 22102
Ph: (703) 506-3280
Fax: (703) 506-3266
E-mail: info@hsmai.org
URL: www.hsmai.org

3970 ■ FHSMAI Scholarship Program *(Graduate/Scholarship)*

Purpose: To provide financial assistance to students pursuing associate, baccalaureate and graduate degrees in Hospitality Management or related fields. **Focus:** Hotel, institutional, and restaurant management. **Qualif.:** Applicant must be enrolled as a student in a hospitality management or related curriculum; pursuing a degree; must have hospitality work experience; must demonstrate an interest in a career in hospitality sales and marketing; must be in good academic standing. **Criteria:** Recipients are evaluated based on Grade Point Average, Industry-related work experience, Presentation of application, Involvement in HSMAI, Responses to essay questions, Recommendations, and Extracurricular involvement.

Funds Avail.: No specific amount. **Number Awarded:** 4. **To Apply:** Applicants must submit completed typed application form; transcript from current college or university; two recommendation forms; current resume; and three personal essays. Applicants must send their completed applications to Foundation Scholarship Committee c/o Kathleen Tindell, 1760 Old Meadow Rd., Ste. 500, McLean, VA 22102. **Deadline:** June 15.

3971 ■ Foundation of the International Association of Defense Counsel (IADC)
303 W Madison, Ste. 925
Chicago, IL 60606

Awards are arranged alphabetically below their administering organizations

Ph: (312) 368-1494
Fax: (312) 368-1854
E-mail: info@iadclaw.org
URL: www.iadclaw.org

3972 ■ Gary Walker Memorial Scholarships
(Professional development/Scholarship)

Purpose: To advance the future of the defense and corporate bar by providing tuition reimbursement to deserving IADC Trial Academy students. **Focus:** Law. **Qualif.:** Applicants must be attorneys who have some level of actual trial experience; must have been in trial practice for between 2 and 10 years; and must demonstrate commitment to the advancement of the defense trial bar. **Criteria:** Preference is given to minority and women students as well as those demonstrating financial need.

Funds Avail.: Fund includes the registration fee of $2,850 and the housing and meal package of $1,500 to attend the Trial Academy. **To Apply:** Applicants must submit a completed application form available in the website along with a statement of the applicant's actual trial experience (indicating number of trials, nature of the litigation, nature of role in defense team, etc.); copy of resume; list of any professional, civic or volunteer activities that may demonstrate a commitment to the legal profession and the defense bar; description of additional factors supporting scholarship application; and two letters of recommendation from attorneys who have supervised applicant's work. **Deadline:** May 18. **Contact:** Mary Beth Kurzak, One 303 West Madison, Suite 925, Chicago, IL 60606 USA; phone: 312-368-1494; fax: 312-368-1854; email: mkurzak@iadclaw.org; website: www.iadcfoundation.org.

3973 ■ Foundation for Jewish Culture
PO Box 489
New York, NY 10011
Ph: (212) 629-0500
Fax: (212) 629-0508
E-mail: grants@jewishculture.org
URL: jewishculture.org

3974 ■ Maurice and Marilyn Cohen Fund for Doctoral Dissertation Fellowships in Jewish Studies *(Doctorate/Fellowship)*

Purpose: To promote scholarly research, publication and teaching in the various disciplines of Jewish studies. **Focus:** Jewish studies. **Qualif.:** Applicant must be a citizen or permanent resident of the United States; must have completed all academic requirements for the PhD, except dissertation, by the date of application; demonstrate significant course work in Jewish studies at the graduate level; provide evidence of proficiency in a Jewish language (Hebrew, Yiddish, Ladino, Aramaic, etc.); must be in a reasonable position to complete the work of the thesis during the fellowship year; and have a proposal or prospectus that has been approved by a thesis committee. **Criteria:** Application is reviewed based on academic promise and ability as judged by previous performance and recommendations; potential of project to significantly impact understanding of Jewish life, culture or thought; clarity, originality, breadth, and depth of the thesis proposal; qualifications and academic record of applicant's advisors and references; and likelihood that an applicant will go on to teach Jewish studies in American colleges/universities.

Funds Avail.: $16,000. **Number Awarded:** 4. **To Apply:**

Applicants are required to register and apply online. **Deadline:** December 12. **Contact:** grants@jewishculture.org.

3975 ■ Foundation of the National Student Nurses Association (NSNA)
45 Main St., Ste. 606
Brooklyn, NY 11201
Ph: (718) 210-0705
Fax: (718) 797-1186
E-mail: nsna@nsna.org
URL: www.nsna.org

3976 ■ Breakthrough to Nursing Scholarships
(Undergraduate/Scholarship)

Purpose: To provide financial support to qualified nursing students. **Focus:** Nursing. **Qualif.:** Applicant must be a student committed to providing quality health care services to underserved population; must possess the necessary leadership skills to influence the delivery of quality care; must be a U.S citizen or Alien with U.S permanent resident status/Alien Registration Number; must establish academic achievement; must have an involvement in student nursing organizations and community health activities; must be attending classes and taking no less than six credits per semester. **Criteria:** Selection of applicants will be based on academic achievement, financial need and involvement in student nursing organizations and community health activities. Selection committee of faculty and students from various nursing programs is appointed to select recipients.

Funds Avail.: No specific amount. **To Apply:** Applicants must submit and complete the application form available online; must submit an official transcript of records. Application form and other supporting documents must be sent to Foundation of the National Nurses' Association, 45 Main St., Ste. 606, Brooklyn, NY 11201. **Deadline:** January 11.

3977 ■ Career Mobility Scholarships *(Graduate, Undergraduate, Vocational/Occupational/ Scholarship)*

Purpose: To provide financial support to qualified nursing students. **Focus:** Nursing. **Qualif.:** Applicants must be nursing or pre-nursing students who are registered nurses (RNs) enrolled in RN and BSN and RN to MSN completion programs or a licensed practical/vocational nurses enrolled in programs leading to RN licensure; must be U.S. citizens or Alien with U.S. permanent residents status/Alien Registration Number; must have established academic achievement; must have an involvement in student nursing organizations and community health activities; must be attending classes and taking no less than six credits per semester. **Criteria:** Selection of Scholarships recipients will be based on academic achievement, financial need and involvement in student nursing organizations and community health activities.

Funds Avail.: No specific amount. **To Apply:** Applicants must submit and complete the application form available online; must submit an official transcript of records; application form and other supporting documents must be sent to Foundation of the National Nurses' Association, 45 Main St., Ste. 606, Brooklyn, NY 11201. **Deadline:** January 11.

3978 ■ McKesson Scholarships *(Undergraduate/ Scholarship)*

Purpose: To provide financial support to qualified nursing students. **Focus:** Nursing. **Qualif.:** Applicants must be pre-

Awards are arranged alphabetically below their administering organizations

nursing students taking courses to prepare for matriculation into a nursing program; must be U.S citizens or Alien with U.S permanent residents status/Alien Registration Number; must establish academic achievement; must have an involvement in student nursing organizations and community health activities; must be attending classes and taking no less than six credits per semester. **Criteria:** Selection of applicants will be based on academic achievement, financial need and involvement in student nursing organizations and community health activities. Selection committee of faculty and students from various nursing programs is appointed to select recipients.

Funds Avail.: No specific amount. **To Apply:** Applicants must submit and complete the application form available online; must submit an official transcript of records. Application form and other supporting documents must be sent to Foundation of the National Nurses' Association, 45 Main St., Ste. 606, Brooklyn, NY 11201. **Deadline:** January 11.

3979 ■ Specialty Nursing Scholarships
(Undergraduate/Scholarship)

Purpose: To provide financial support to qualified nursing students. **Focus:** Nursing. **Qualif.:** Applicant must be a student interested in pursuing specialized areas of nursing practice; must be a U.S citizen or Alien with U.S permanent resident status/Alien Registration Number; must establish academic achievement; must have an involvement in student nursing organizations and community health activities; must be attending classes and taking no less than six credits per semester. **Criteria:** Selection of applicants will be based on academic achievement, financial need, and involvement in student nursing organizations and community health activities. Selection committee of faculty and students from various nursing programs is appointed to select recipients.

Funds Avail.: No specific amount. **To Apply:** Applicants must submit and complete the application form available online; must submit an official transcript of records. Application form and other supporting documents must be sent to Foundation of the National Nurses' Association, 45 Main St., Ste. 606, Brooklyn, NY 11201. **Deadline:** January 11.

3980 ■ Foundation for Neonatal Research and Education (FNRE)
E Holly Ave.
Box 56
Pitman, NJ 08071-0056
Ph: (856) 256-2343
Fax: (856) 589-7463
E-mail: fnre@ajj.com
URL: www.inurse.com/fnre

3981 ■ Foundation for Neonatal Research and Education Scholarships *(Doctorate, Graduate, Postgraduate, Undergraduate/Scholarship)*

Purpose: To help students and professionals pursue a higher education. **Focus:** Nursing, Neonatal. **Qualif.:** Applicants must be neonatal nurses admitted to a college or school of higher education on one of the following: a) Bachelor of Science in Nursing (current RN); b) Master in Science in Nursing for Advance Practice in Neonatal Nursing; c) Doctoral degree in Nursing; and d) Master's or Post-Master degree in Nursing Administration or Business Management; must have 3.0 GPA or higher; must be

actively engaged in a service, research, or educational role; active members of a professional association and must demonstrate an ongoing professional education in neonatal nursing; must have not received a FNRE scholarship or grant in the past five years. **Criteria:** Recipients will be selected based on qualifications and submitted materials.

Funds Avail.: Amount not specified. **To Apply:** Applicants must submit a completed application form, current resume or curriculum vitae, an official transcript from each college or school of higher education, a letter of verification of enrollment and acceptance to a college or school. Evaluation forms shall be submitted in the following manner: a) CNS applicants - a separate form from a nurse manager or supervisor and two members of the health team; b) NNP applicants - a separate form from a nurse manager or supervisor, a practicing NNP and a neonatologist or other pediatric physician practicing in neonatal care; c) Nursing Administration or Business Management applicants - a separate form from a nurse manager or supervisor and two members of the health team; d) Doctoral applicants - a separate form from a supervisor and one member of program faculty and one member of the health team; e) BSN applicants - a separate form from a nursing supervisor and two members of the health team. Applicants are also required to submit a (250 words or less) statement addressing the plans of making a significant difference in neonatal nursing practice. **Deadline:** May 1. **Contact:** Anthony J. Jannetti at the above address.

3982 ■ Foundation of the Pennsylvania Medical Society
777 E Park Dr.
Harrisburg, PA 17105-8820
Ph: (717) 558-7750
Fax: (717) 558-7818
Free: 800-228-7823
E-mail: foundation@pamedsoc.org
URL: www.foundationpamedsoc.org

3983 ■ Allegheny County Medical Society Medical Student Scholarships (ACMS)
(Undergraduate/Scholarship)

Purpose: To assist local students with the cost of attending a Pennsylvania medical school. **Focus:** Medicine. **Qualif.:** Applicants must be Pennsylvania residents from one of the following counties: Allegheny, Armstrong, Beaver, Butler, Washington, or Westmoreland; must be enrolled full-time in an accredited Pennsylvania medical school or entering his/her 3rd or 4th year of medical school. **Criteria:** Applicants are evaluated based on financial need.

Funds Avail.: $2,000. **Number Awarded:** 2. **To Apply:** Applicants must submit: completed scholarship application form; two reference letters from persons other than family members, documenting integrity, interpersonal skills and potential as a future physician (one must come from either a medical school professor or a physician); a letter, on school letterhead, from the applicants' medical school verifying that they are enrolled full time as a third or fourth-year medical student at that institution; and a typed, one-page essay addressing the following: Where do you see yourself in 10 years? How do you plan to give back to the community? **Deadline:** September 30. **Contact:** For further information, applicants may call at 717-558-7854; E-mail: studentservices-foundation@pamedsoc.org.

Awards are arranged alphabetically below their administering organizations

3984 ■ Alliance Medical Education Scholarship Fund (AMES) *(Undergraduate/Scholarship)*

Purpose: To financially assist a deserving medical student enrolled in a Pennsylvania medical school. **Focus:** Medicine. **Qualif.:** Applicants must be residents of Pennsylvania who are enrolled in a Pennsylvania medical school as full-time second- or third-year medical students. **Criteria:** Applicants are evaluated based on financial need, merit, leadership and service.

Funds Avail.: $2,500. **To Apply:** Applicants must submit: the completed application form; two reference letters from persons who know them well (other than their families); letter from their medical school verifying that they are enrolled full-time and currently second or third-year medical students; and a typed statement of one page describing their vision for the future of Pennsylvania Medicine. **Deadline:** February 28.

3985 ■ Scott A. Gunder, MD, DCMS Presidential Scholarships *(Undergraduate/Scholarship)*

Purpose: To financially assist deserving second-year medical students at Penn State College of Medicine. **Focus:** Medicine. **Qualif.:** Applicants must have been residents of Pennsylvania for at least 12 months before registering as medical students; must be second-year medical students; must be enrolled full-time at Penn State College of Medicine; and must be members of Pennsylvania Medical Society and their county medical society. **Criteria:** Applicants are evaluated based on financial need.

Funds Avail.: $1,500. **To Apply:** Applicants must submit: completed application form; two reference letters, from persons other than family members, documenting the applicants' integrity, interpersonal skills and potential as future physicians; letter, on school letterhead, from Penn State College of Medicine verifying that they are enrolled full-time and second-year medical students; one-page typed essay describing the person or event that most influenced them to become physicians and how they see themselves leading others into medicine; and completed Pennsylvania Medical Society membership applications if students are not current members. **Deadline:** April 15. **Contact:** For further information, applicants may call at 717-558-7854; E-mail: studentservices-foundation@pamedsoc.org.

3986 ■ Lycoming County Medical Society Scholarships (LCMS) *(Undergraduate/Scholarship)*

Purpose: To provide financial assistance for medical students who are residents of Lycoming County. **Focus:** Medicine. **Qualif.:** Applicants must be residents of Lycoming County in the state of Pennsylvania; must be enrolled full-time in an accredited allopathic or osteopathic medical school within the United States. **Criteria:** Applicants are evaluated based on financial need.

Funds Avail.: $2,000. **Number Awarded:** 2. **To Apply:** Applicants must submit: completed application form; two reference letters, from persons other than family members, documenting the applicants' integrity, interpersonal skills, and potential as future physicians; a letter, on school letterhead, from applicants' medical school verifying that they are enrolled full-time as medical students at their respective institutions; and, one-page, typed essay specifically describing why they chose to become physicians and what contributions they expect to make to the health profession. **Deadline:** September 30. **Contact:** For further information, applicants may call at 717-558-7854; E-mail: studentservices-foundation@pamedsoc.org.

3987 ■ Montgomery County Medical Society Scholarships (MCMS) *(Undergraduate/Scholarship)*

Purpose: To provide financial assistance for medical students who are residents of Montgomery County. **Focus:** Medicine. **Qualif.:** Applicants must be residents of Montgomery County in the state of Pennsylvania; must have been Pennsylvania residents for at least 12 months prior to registering as medical students; must be enrolled full-time in an accredited United States medical school; must be enrolled or entering their first year of medical school. **Criteria:** Applicants are evaluated based on financial need.

Funds Avail.: $1,000. **Number Awarded:** 2. **To Apply:** Applicants must submit a completed application form; two reference letters, from persons other than family members, documenting the applicants' integrity, interpersonal skills and potential as physicians; a letter, on school letterhead, from their medical schools verifying that they are enrolled full time as first-year medical students at that institution; one-page, typed essay addressing the reasons for pursuing medical career, personal goals and plans for future within the profession. **Deadline:** September 30.

3988 ■ Myrtle Siegfried, MD and Michael Vigilante, MD Scholarships *(Undergraduate/Scholarship)*

Purpose: To provide financial assistance to qualified first-year medical students residing in Berks, Lehigh, or Northampton County. **Focus:** Medicine. **Qualif.:** Applicants must be residents of Berks, Lehigh or Northampton County; must be entering first year of medical school; must be enrolled full-time in an accredited United States medical school. **Criteria:** Applicants are evaluated based on financial need.

Funds Avail.: $1,000. **To Apply:** Applicants must submit a completed application form; two reference letters documenting the applicants' integrity, interpersonal skills and potential as future physicians (letters must come from persons who know the applicants well but are not family members); a letter, on school letterhead, from their medical school verifying that they are enrolled full-time at that institution and first-year medical students; one-page, typed essay specifically describing why they chose to become physicians and what contributions they expect to make to the health profession. **Deadline:** September 30. **Contact:** For further information, applicants may call at 717-558-7854; E-mail: studentservices-foundation@pamedsoc.org.

3989 ■ Foundation for the Preservation of Honey Bees

PO Box 1445
Jesup, GA 31598-1445
Ph: (912) 427-4018
Fax: (912) 427-8447
E-mail: info@honeybeepreservation.org
URL: honeybeepreservation.org

3990 ■ Foundation for the Preservation of Honey Bees Graduate Scholarships *(Graduate/Scholarship)*

Purpose: To allow the recipients to attend the annual North American Beekeeping Conference, where they will have an opportunity to meet other researchers and beekeepers and to present their research to the industry. **Focus:** Life science. **Qualif.:** Applicant must be a graduate student in api-

Awards are arranged alphabetically below their administering organizations

culture. **Criteria:** Selection is based on the application.

Funds Avail.: $2,000. **Number Awarded:** 5. **To Apply:** Applicants must submit a cover letter from the advisor outlining the applicant's progress toward graduate degree, tentative graduation date, and any other information about the applicant and the research that would help the committee "get to know" the applicant; a curriculum vitae, or resume, not to exceed 2 pages; and the research proposal (not to exceed 3 pages). **Contact:** Troy H. Fore Jr., Exec. Dir. at troyfore@honeybeepreservation.org.

3991 ■ Foundation for Seacoast Health

100 Campus Dr., Ste. 1
Portsmouth, NH 03801
Ph: (603) 422-8200
E-mail: ffsh@communitycampus.org
URL: www.ffsh.org

3992 ■ Foundation for Seacoast Health Scholarships *(Graduate, Undergraduate/ Scholarship)*

Purpose: To support students pursuing a health-related field of study. **Focus:** Health care services; Health education. **Qualif.:** Applicant must have been and continue to be a resident of New Hampshire (Portsmouth, North Hampton, Greenland, Rye, Newington, New Castle) or Maine (Kittery, Eliot, or York) for a minimum of two years prior to the Scholarship Program and pursuing a health-related field of study as an undergraduate or graduate student in an accredited institution of learning. **Criteria:** Selection is based on academic achievement (class rank, GPA and test scores), course difficulty, work shortage areas of need in Seacoast, job experience, community service, evidence of dedication to chosen field of study and financial need.

Funds Avail.: $1,000-$5,000. **Number Awarded:** 2. **To Apply:** Applicants must submit a completed Scholarship Application form along with three Student Assessment Forms (in sealed envelopes); official school transcripts; test scores; essay; and current resume. **Deadline:** March 1.

3993 ■ Fragile X Research Foundation of Canada (FXRFC)

167 Queen St. W
Brampton, ON, Canada L6Y 1M5
Ph: (905) 453-9366
Fax: (905) 453-0095
E-mail: info@fragilexcanada.ca
URL: www.fragilexcanada.ca

3994 ■ FXRFC Medical Research Postdoctoral Fellowships *(Postdoctorate/Fellowship)*

Purpose: To encourage research aimed at finding a specific treatment for Fragile X syndrome. **Focus:** Medical research. **Qualif.:** Applicant must be nominated by institutions and should have training and experience at least equal to the PhD or MD level. **Criteria:** Selection is based on submitted application materials.

Funds Avail.: $40,000/year. **To Apply:** Application package must include a brief letter of inquiry describing the proposed project; a 6-12 page description of the proposed project (background, objectives, approach, methodological detail, significance, originality, and key references); curriculum vitae for the principal investigator; curriculum vitae

for the postdoctoral fellow to be supported under the grant; three references; financial accounting of how the funds will be spent; a full accounting of any other current and submitted sources of support for the project; and requested start date of the project. Send one complete copy of the application to fxrfc@on.aibn.com in PDF file, and two copies (may be sent on a CD) to Carlo Paribello MSM, MD, President, Fragile X Research Foundation of Canada. **Deadline:** October 1. **Contact:** Dr. Carlo Paribello at the above address.

3995 ■ Joe Francis Haircare Scholarship Foundation

PO Box 50625
Minneapolis, MN 55405
Ph: (651) 769-1757
E-mail: kimlarsonmn@gmail.com
URL: www.joefrancis.com/

3996 ■ Joe Francis Haircare Scholarships *(Undergraduate/Scholarship)*

Purpose: To provide support to deserving students who want to pursue their professional training in hairstyling. **Focus:** Cosmetology. **Qualif.:** Applicant must be actively enrolled in cosmetology school or planning to enroll in cosmetology/barber school. **Criteria:** Recipient will be selected by the independent committee composed of individuals drawn from the professional beauty industry. Selection is based on their potential, financial need, and commitment to a long-term career in cosmetology.

Funds Avail.: $1,000. **To Apply:** Applicant must complete the application form available online; must have a letter of recommendation from an employer, instructor, counselor, or someone qualified to offer testimony of his/her character. Application form and other supporting documents must be sent to Joe Francis Haircare Scholarship Foundation Program, PO Box 50625, Minneapolis, MN 55405. **Deadline:** June 1. **Contact:** Kim Larson, 651-769-1757, kimlarsonmn@gmail.com.

3997 ■ Fraser Stryker

500 Energy Plz., 409 S 17th St.
Omaha, NE 68102-2663
Ph: (402) 341-6000
Fax: (402) 341-8290
Free: 800-544-6041
E-mail: fsinfo@fraserstryker.com
URL: www.fraserstryker.com

3998 ■ Fraser Stryker Diversity Scholarships *(Undergraduate/Scholarship)*

Purpose: To provide financial assistance in the form of college tuition and provide paid internships to students. **Focus:** General studies. **Qualif.:** Applicants must be of African-American, Asian, Latino or Native-American origins who are graduating seniors at any of the public or private high schools in the greater Omaha area; must have been accepted to an accredited college or university located in the United States; must be college students who have received Fraser Diversity Scholarships in prior years. **Criteria:** Recipients are selected based on interest in pursuing a career in law, financial need, top 20% in class rank, SAT scores and academic performance.

Funds Avail.: $2,500. **To Apply:** Applicants must submit a completed application form and evidence of enrollment.

Awards are arranged alphabetically below their administering organizations

Deadline: March 18. **Contact:** Stephen M. Bruckner at sbruckner@fraserstryker.com, or Sherman P. Willis at swillis@fraserstryker.com.

3999 ■ FRAXA Research Foundation

45 Pleasant St.
Newburyport, MA 01950
Ph: (978) 462-1866
Fax: (978) 463-9985
E-mail: info@fraxa.org
URL: www.fraxa.org

4000 ■ FRAXA Postdoctoral Fellowships
(Postdoctorate/Fellowship)

Purpose: To encourage research aimed at finding a specific treatment for fragile X syndrome. **Focus:** General studies. **Qualif.:** Applicants must have training and experience at least equal to the PhD or MD level. **Criteria:** Selection will be based on the committee's criteria.

Funds Avail.: $45,000. **To Apply:** Candidates must be nominated by their institutions. Applicants must provide the following information with their application: description of the proposed project (6-12 pages recommended); curriculum vitae for the principal investigator; curriculum vitae for the postdoctoral fellow to be supported under the grant; names of three references who are willing to be contacted to provide recommendations for candidate postdoctoral fellow; financial accounting of how the funds will be spent, with dollar distribution into major component items; a full accounting of any other current and submitted sources of support for this project and other lab research; requested start date of the project. The earliest possible state date is three months after receipt of the application. Completed application must be submitted via email. Application must be in a PDF format of less than 10 MB. **Deadline:** February 1. **Contact:** Michael Tranfaglia, MD, Medical Dir., mtranfaglia@fraxa.org.

4001 ■ Fredrikson and Byron P.A.

200 S 6th St., Ste. 4000
Minneapolis, MN 55402-1431
Ph: (612) 492-7000
Fax: (612) 492-7077
E-mail: jkoneck@fredlaw.com
URL: www.fredlaw.com

4002 ■ Fredrikson and Byron Foundation Minority Scholarships *(Undergraduate/Scholarship)*

Purpose: To sponsor educational opportunities for minority law students. **Focus:** Law. **Qualif.:** Applicant must be a currently enrolled, first-year minority law student. **Criteria:** Selection is based on the application materials submitted.

Funds Avail.: $10,000. **Number Awarded:** 1. **To Apply:** Applicants must submit a completed application form along with two written recommendations (Applicant Appraisal Form for Law School Professors or Applicant Appraisal Form for Employers of Other Reference); one writing sample from a first year legal writing course; current law school transcripts; undergraduate transcripts from all undergraduate institutions attended; and a resume. Applicants may apply online. All required materials should be directed to: Greta Larson at glarson@fredlaw.com at the above address. **Deadline:** March 31. **Contact:** Greta Larson at glarson@fredlaw.com at the above address.

4003 ■ Freedom Alliance

22570 Market Ct., Ste. 240
Dulles, VA 20166
Ph: (703) 444-7940
Fax: (703) 444-9893
Free: 800-475-6620
URL: www.freedomalliance.org

4004 ■ Freedom Alliance Scholarships
(Undergraduate/Scholarship)

Purpose: To support the children of American heroes. **Focus:** General studies. **Qualif.:** Applicant must be a dependent child of an active service member killed or disabled military as the result of an operational mission/training accident; a senior high school, high school graduate or enrolled in an institution of higher learning; and must be 26 years old and below. **Criteria:** Applicants are selected based on the committee's review of the application materials.

Funds Avail.: No specific amount. **To Apply:** Applicants must complete online application and forward a copy of Government Issued Photo Identification (drivers License, ID Card); must submit a certificate of death or rating letter from the Veterans Administration disability; an essay; scholastic record; and a photo (photo of parents are optional). **Deadline:** June 30. **Remarks:** Freedom of Alliance will mail scholarship check to the school. **Contact:** Adam Morgan, Phone: 800-475-6620; Email: info@fascholarship.com.

4005 ■ Freedom and Justice Foundation

1925 E Beltline Rd., Ste. 475
Carrollton, TX 75006
Ph: (972) 365-8214
Fax: (413) 403-2653
E-mail: info@freeandjust.org
URL: www.freeandjust.org

4006 ■ Texas Muslims Scholarship Fund
(TMSF) *(Graduate, Undergraduate/Scholarship)*

Purpose: To provide funds to students studying in Texas in underrepresented public affairs fields such as journalism and law. **Focus:** Journalism; Law; Political science; International affairs and relations; Communications. **Qualif.:** Applicant must be a U.S. citizen or permanent resident; enrolled in an accredited college/university in Texas; be pursuing a law degree or intending to major in political science, international relations, journalism, communications, or another public affairs related field in which Muslims are underrepresented; have completed one year of community service benefitting the American Muslim community either as a voluntary board member of a Muslim nonprofit organization, volunteering at a civic nonprofit organization benefitting all society, or by starting a nonprofit working to benefit the American Muslim community. **Criteria:** Selection is based on academic merit and student need.

Funds Avail.: No specific amount. **Number Awarded:** Varies. **To Apply:** Applicants must submit a completed scholarship application form together with a proof of U.S. citizenship or permanent residency and two letters of recommendation (outside the family). **Deadline:** June 30. **Contact:** tmsf@freeandjust.org.

Awards are arranged alphabetically below their administering organizations

4007 ■ Freepali

PO Box 638
Milwaukee, WI 53201
E-mail: info@freepali.com
URL: www.freepali.com

4008 ■ Freepali Scholarships *(Graduate, Undergraduate/Scholarship)*

Purpose: To educate the public regarding the Palestinian conflict. **Focus:** General studies. **Qualif.:** Applicant must be an undergraduate or graduate student. **Criteria:** Award is given to the applicant who best displays an effort to end the Palestinian conflict.

Funds Avail.: No specific amount. **Number Awarded:** 1. **To Apply:** Applicants must apply online.

4009 ■ Fried, Frank, Harris, Shriver and Jacobson LLP

One New York Plz.
New York, NY 10004
Ph: (212) 859-8000
Fax: (212) 859-4000
E-mail: maja.hazell@friedfrank.com
URL: www.ffhsj.com

4010 ■ Fried, Frank, Harris, Shriver and Jacobson Fellowships *(Graduate/Fellowship)*

Purpose: To support graduating law students and recent law school graduates. **Focus:** Law. **Qualif.:** Applicant must be a graduating law student or a recent law school graduate (including judicial clerks). **Criteria:** Selection is based on the application materials.

Funds Avail.: No specific amount. **To Apply:** Applicants must submit a resume, two letters of recommendation (one each from a law school faculty member and an employer), a legal writing sample, a 500-word essay, and a law school transcript. **Deadline:** November 1. **Contact:** Maja D. Hazell at 212-859-8345 or fellowship@friedfrank.com.

4011 ■ Friends of Canadian Broadcasting (FCB)

Box 200/238
131 Bloor St. W
Toronto, ON, Canada M5S 1R8
Fax: (416) 968-7406
E-mail: friends@friends.ca
URL: www.friends.ca

4012 ■ Dalton Camp Awards *(All/Prize)*

Purpose: To promote Canadian public affairs. **Focus:** Media arts. **Qualif.:** Applicants must be Canadian citizens or permanent residents of Canada. **Criteria:** Selection will be based on the committee's criteria.

Funds Avail.: $5,000. **To Apply:** Applicants must submit an essay that is written in English and does not exceed 2,000 words. Each entry shall be accompanied by the author's full name and contact information including postal address, email address and a telephone number. Each entry shall also include: a biographical sketch not exceeding 50 words; the word count of the essay; written confirmation that the entry complies with the Rules of The Dalton Camp Award. Essays submitted by email attachment should include, on the first page of the essay, a title followed by

the full name of the author. Subsequent pages should be numbered and contain no information identifying the author. Essays submitted using the online submission form shall contain no information identifying the author in the body of the essay. Applicants may submit their essays through email at submissions@daltoncampaward.ca or may visit the website for the online submission. **Deadline:** March 15.

4013 ■ Friends of the Jose Carreras International Leukemia Foundation

1100 Fairview Ave. N, D5-100
Seattle, WA 98109-1024
Ph: (206) 667-7108
Fax: (206) 667-6498
E-mail: friendsjc@carreras-foundation.org
URL: carreras-foundation.org

4014 ■ E.D. Thomas Post Doctoral Fellowships *(Postdoctorate/Fellowship)*

Purpose: To support research of diagnosis, prevention and cure of leukemia and related hematologic malignancies. **Focus:** Leukemia; Medical research; Oncology. **Qualif.:** Applicants must be M.D. or Ph.D. degree holder and have completed at least three years postdoctoral training but must be less than ten years, of any nationalities but application will be considered from each sponsoring institution, committed to foundation research goals, and able to devote at least 80% of time to the project with the sponsoring institution in academic environment to provide support for the proposed project. **Criteria:** Candidates' applications will be reviewed by the recognized leaders in the field of leukemic research, the Scientific Advisory Committee of the Foundation.

Funds Avail.: $50,000. **Number Awarded:** 1. **To Apply:** Applicants must submit type-written, single-spaced, in English application following the format specified in the application packet. **Deadline:** November 2. **Contact:** Fundacion Internacional Jose Carreras, Muntaner, 383, 08021 Barcelona, Spain Fax: 34 93 201 0588, e-mail: fundacio@fcarreras.es.

4015 ■ Fund for American Studies (TFAS)

1706 New Hampshire Ave. NW
Washington, DC 20009
Ph: (202) 986-0384
Fax: (202) 986-0390
Free: 800-741-6964
E-mail: feedback@tfas.org
URL: www.tfas.org

4016 ■ Congressional Scholarship Awards *(Undergraduate/Scholarship)*

Purpose: To provide financial support for students who wish to attend the Institute on Business and Government Affairs (IBGA) at Georgetown University. **Focus:** Business; Local government. **Qualif.:** Applicant must be an undergraduate student. **Criteria:** Selection will be based on leadership skills, academics, campus and community involvement.

Funds Avail.: No specific amount. **To Apply:** Applicants may contact Jane Mack for the scholarship information and application. **Remarks:** Established in 1990. **Contact:** Jane Mack Tel. No. 202-986-0384.

Awards are arranged alphabetically below their administering organizations

4017 ■ Eben Tisdale Fellowships *(Graduate, Undergraduate/Fellowship)*

Purpose: To make public policy professionals more competent in both policy advocacy and senior management. **Focus:** Technology. **Qualif.:** Applicant must be a junior or senior student interested in public policy and the high-tech industry, or in a graduate program. **Criteria:** The Advisory Committee will evaluate submitted materials.

Funds Avail.: $5,000. **Number Awarded:** 1. **To Apply:** Applicants must submit a completed application form; professional resume; official academic transcripts; evaluation forms from two academic references (in a sealed envelope, author's signature must be across the seal); a 500-word statement on reasons of wanting to be a Tisdale fellow. **Deadline:** February 15. **Remarks:** Established after the death of Eben Tisdale, general manager of government affairs for the Hewlett-Packard Company. **Contact:** Jonathan Tilley, Phone: 202-986-0384 Fax: 202-986-8930, jtilley@tfas.org.

4018 ■ Fund for Theological Education (FTE)
825 Houston Mill Rd., Ste. 100
Atlanta, GA 30329-4211
Ph: (404) 727-1450
Fax: (404) 727-1490
URL: www.fteleaders.org

4019 ■ FTE Congregational Fellowships *(Graduate/Fellowship)*

Purpose: Provides financial support to students entering their first year in a full-time Master of Divinity program. **Focus:** Theology. **Qualif.:** Applicants must hold a bachelor's degree from an accredited college or university; must be in first year full-time Master of Divinity program at a seminary accredited by the Association of Theological Schools; must be U.S. or Canadian citizens; must be 35 years old or younger; must be able to participate in all fellowship activities; must be nominated by their home congregation; congregation must contribute between $1,000 to $5,000. **Criteria:** Selection will be based on evaluation of submitted documents and specific criteria.

Funds Avail.: Up to $5,000. **To Apply:** Applicants must submit a completed application form; official transcript signed and sealed from all schools attended; resume; five collated copies of application form, three-page essay and resume plus originals; academic letter of reference; employer letter of reference; ministry letter of reference; statement of intent to enter ministry; endorsement by seminary or divinity school; nomination and financial commitment by congregation. **Deadline:** April.

4020 ■ FTE Dissertation Fellowships *(Graduate/Fellowship)*

Purpose: To provide assistance for African-American doctoral students who are writing their Ph.D. or Th.D. dissertations. **Focus:** Religion; Theology; Bible Studies. **Qualif.:** Applicants must be U.S. citizens; must be in the final writing stage of dissertation; must be African-American doctoral students in religion, theology and biblical studies. **Criteria:** Selection will be based on evaluation of submitted documents and specific criteria.

Funds Avail.: $20,000. **To Apply:** Applicants must submit a completed application form, dissertation proposal and writing plan approved by the dissertation committee. Applicants may also contact the Organization for other application requirements. **Deadline:** February.

4021 ■ FTE Doctoral Fellowships *(Doctorate, Graduate/Fellowship)*

Purpose: To provide assistance for African-American students pursuing graduate degrees in religious, theological or biblical studies. **Focus:** Religion; Theology; Bible Studies. **Qualif.:** Applicants must be African-American students preparing to enter first year of an accredited Ph.D. or Th.D. program in religion, theology or biblical studies; must be committed to becoming a leader within theological education; must have strong consideration to teaching at a theological school; must be U.S. citizens; must hold bachelor's degree from an accredited college or university. **Criteria:** Selection is based on evaluation of submitted documents and specific criteria.

Funds Avail.: $20,000. **To Apply:** Applicants must submit a completed application form; curriculum vitae; two to three page essay; transcripts of all undergraduate and graduate schools attended; photocopy of GRE school report; two reference letters; completed budget statement form; documentation from school showing amount of financial award to be received; provide six copies of each requirements except for letters of reference and transcripts. **Deadline:** March.

4022 ■ FTE Ministry Fellowships *(Graduate/Fellowship)*

Purpose: To provide assistance to seminary students in the second year of a Master of Divinity program. **Focus:** Theology. **Qualif.:** Applicants must hold a bachelor's degree from an accredited college or university; must be full time first year Master of Divinity students who completed one semester at a seminary accredited by the Association of Theological Schools; must have a seminary GPA of 3.3 or higher; must be U.S. or Canadian citizens; must be 35 years old or younger; must be able to participate in all fellowship activities; must be nominated by the dean or president of their seminary. **Criteria:** Selection will be based on evaluation of submitted documents and specific criteria.

Funds Avail.: $10,000. **To Apply:** Applicants must submit a completed application form; an official transcript signed and sealed from all schools attended; five collated copies of application form, resume and a three-page essay plus originals; academic letter of reference; ministry letter of reference; information on formal candidacy process; letter of nomination from seminary dean or president. **Deadline:** March.

4023 ■ FTE North American Doctoral Fellowships *(Doctorate, Graduate/Fellowship)*

Purpose: To provide financial assistance to talented students from racial and ethnic groups that are traditionally underrepresented in graduate education. **Focus:** Religion; Theology; Bible Studies. **Qualif.:** Applicants must be members of a racial or ethnic group that is traditionally underrepresented in graduate education; enrolled full-time in a Ph.D. or Th.D. program in religion or theology and demonstrate high academic performance; U.S. or Canadian citizens or permanent residents of either countries; demonstrates commitment to teaching and scholarship and capacity for leadership in theological education. **Criteria:** Selection is based on the evaluation of the submitted documents and specific criteria. Preference will be given to students nearing the end of their studies.

Funds Avail.: $5,000 to $10,000. **To Apply:** Applicants must submit a completed application form; curriculum vitae;

Awards are arranged alphabetically below their administering organizations

two-page essay; graduate transcripts; academic form; two reference letters; completed budget statement form; documentation from school showing amount of financial award to be received; provide six copies of each of the requirements except for letters of reference and transcripts. **Deadline:** March.

4024 ■ FTE Undergraduate Fellowships
(Undergraduate/Fellowship)

Purpose: To provide financial help and support to students' junior and senior year of college. **Focus:** Theology. **Qualif.:** Applicants must be current sophomores or juniors in an accredited undergraduate program at a North American college or university; must be nominated by a faculty member, administrator, chaplain, campus minister or current pastor; must have a cumulative GPA of at least 3.0; must be U.S. or Canadian citizens; must possess qualities such as being committed to a life of faith, love of God and church, critical thinking, leadership skills, personal integrity, and dedication to serve the needs of others; **Criteria:** Selection will be based on evaluation of submitted documents and specific criteria.

Funds Avail.: $2,000. **To Apply:** Applicants must submit a completed application form; official transcript signed and sealed from all schools attended; five collated copies of application form, three-page essay and resume plus originals; academic letter of reference; ministry letter of reference. **Deadline:** March.

4025 ■ FTE Volunteers Exploring Vocation Fellowships *(Graduate/Fellowship)*

Purpose: To provide financial help to students' ministry internship in order for them to enrich their preparation for the ministry. **Focus:** Theology. **Qualif.:** Applicants must be U.S. or Canadian citizens; must be 35 years old or younger; must have completed a year of service within the previous four calendar years; must be entering the first year of a full-time Master of Divinity program at an accredited Association of Theological Schools seminary. **Criteria:** Selection will be based on evaluation of submitted documents and specific criteria.

Funds Avail.: $10,000. **To Apply:** Applicants must create an account on the organization's website for an online application and to learn more about the requirements of this fellowship. **Deadline:** April.

4026 ■ Fundacion Educativa Carlos M. Castaneda (FECMC)
1925 Brickell Ave. D-1108
Miami, FL 33129
Ph: (305) 859-9617
E-mail: fundacion_educativa_cmc@yahoo.com
URL: fecmc.tripod.com/
carlosmcastaedaeducationalfoundation

4027 ■ Carlos M. Castaneda Journalism Scholarships *(Graduate/Scholarship)*

Purpose: To promote excellence in journalism and freedom of expression. **Focus:** Journalism. **Qualif.:** Applicant must be a Spanish speaking journalist or journalism student who has completed a four-year undergraduate program with a minimum 3.0 GPA (of 4.0) average or the equivalent to a B average (undergraduate major in journalism is not necessary). Applicant must be pursuing a career in the field of journalism in Spanish and must have mastered the Span-

ish language at the professional level and must be able to translate thoughts into words proficiently. An applicant must also demonstrate knowledge and interest for Hispanic culture and be up-to-date on current events in Latin America. All applicants must have been accepted into a graduate journalism program at an accredited university in the U.S., approved by the FECMC. **Criteria:** Selection is based on the application materials submitted.

Funds Avail.: $7,000. **Number Awarded:** Varies. **To Apply:** Applicants must submit a completed application form together with all transcript(s) of academic work (in sealed envelopes with official school seal or a signature across the flap); proof of acceptance into a graduate journalism program; applicant's (or applicant's parents') most recent 1040 tax form or equivalent tax documents (if from a foreign country); Curriculum Vitae listing educational background, work history, awards, internships, language proficiency and any work done for school/community newspaper; three reference letters in separate sealed envelopes (professors, advisors, employers, etc.); a portfolio with three of the best stories published by professional or school publications in Spanish (photocopied and adapted to fit an 8 1/2" by 11" page); and a 2000-word essay. **Deadline:** April 15.

4028 ■ Funeral Service Foundation (FSF)
13625 Bishop's Dr.
Brookfield, WI 53005-6607
Fax: (262) 789-6977
Free: 877-402-5900
E-mail: info@funeralservicefoundation.org
URL: www.funeralservicefoundation.org

4029 ■ Brenda Renee Horn Memorial Scholarship *(Undergraduate/Scholarship)*

Purpose: To provide financial assistance for top-scoring mortuary science students via the Key Memories scholarship essay contest. **Focus:** Mortuary science. **Qualif.:** Applicants must be students who are enrolled or accepted for enrollment in a mortuary science school accredited by the American Board of Funeral Service Education. **Criteria:** Applicants are judged by members of the Keystone Advisory Board and a Funeral Service Foundation representative.

Funds Avail.: $3,000. **To Apply:** Applicants must submit an essay and must complete application. **Contact:** Mail applications, essay and videotape to Tim Cocke, Keystone Scholarships located at 400 N Ashley Dr., Ste. 1900, Tampa, FL 33602, or e-mail kmscholarship@live.com.

4030 ■ Joseph E. Hagan Memorial Scholarships *(Undergraduate/Scholarship)*

Purpose: To provide financial assistance for mortuary science school students. **Focus:** Mortuary science. **Qualif.:** Applicants must be full-time students who will be enrolled or have been accepted for enrollment in the Fall semester in programs accredited by the American Board of Funeral Service Education. **Criteria:** Applicants are evaluated by the judges from the FSF Board of Trustees based on essay submitted by them.

Funds Avail.: $2,500. **Number Awarded:** 2. **To Apply:** Applicants must submit all the required application information. **Deadline:** June 18.

4031 ■ NFDA Professional Women's Conference Scholarships *(Undergraduate/Scholarship)*
Purpose: To provide financial assistance for tuition and travel stipend for selected individuals who attended the

Awards are arranged alphabetically below their administering organizations

National Funeral Directors Association Professional Women's Conference. **Focus:** Funeral service; Mortuary science. **Qualif.:** Applicants must be verifiably employed in funeral service or a related occupation or mortuary science school students enrolled in school accredited by the American Board of Funeral Service Education. **Criteria:** Applicants are evaluated based on answers to essay.

Funds Avail.: $500. **To Apply:** Applicants must submit all the required application information. **Deadline:** February 1.

4032 ■ Fur Takers of America (FTA)

PO Box 3
Buckley, IL 60918
Ph: (217) 394-2577
E-mail: ckrumwiede@furtakersofamerica.com
URL: www.furtakersofamerica.com

4033 ■ Charles Dobbins FTA Scholarships
(Undergraduate, Vocational/Occupational/ Scholarship)

Purpose: To promote interest in the accumulation and dissemination of knowledge concerning the trapping of fur bearing animals among persons interested therein. **Focus:** Agricultural Science; Biology; Wildlife Conservation and management. **Qualif.:** Applicants must be members of FTA or their immediate relatives; must be majoring in agriculture, biology, wildlife management or related courses in an accredited two-year or four-year college, university, or vocational/technical school. **Criteria:** Recipients are selected based on academic records and quality of the essay submitted.

Funds Avail.: $500. **To Apply:** Applicants must provide a proof of high school graduation or pending graduation; official documents indicating that they have been accepted in an institution as first year students, or registration of classes if applicants are already in school. Applicants must also submit an essay that discusses career goals and how the scholarship would help to achieve these goals. Completed applications should be sent to: Jerry Schilling, 21 Schilling Lane, New Harmony, IN 47631. **Deadline:** May 15. **Contact:** Jerry Schilling, 812-783-1097.

4034 ■ The Gallery Collection

Prudent Publishing
65 Challenger Rd.
Ridgefield Park, NJ 07660
Ph: (201) 641-0070
Free: 800-950-7064
E-mail: service@gallerycollection.com
URL: www.gallerycollection.com

4035 ■ The Gallery Collection's Greeting Card Scholarships *(Undergraduate/Scholarship)*

Purpose: To encourage students to use their talents and pursue their education. **Focus:** Fine arts; Graphic art and design; Photography. **Qualif.:** Applicants must be currently enrolled in high school, college or university; must have a talent in fine arts, graphic design or photography; and must be U.S. citizens. **Criteria:** Winning greeting card will be determined based on overall aesthetic appeal, quality of execution, creativity and originality, successful incorporation of design elements, appropriateness, attractiveness towards customers and suitability as a design in Prudent's Gallery Collection greeting card line.

Funds Avail.: $10,000 for the winner, and $1,000 for the selected school. **Number Awarded:** 2. **To Apply:** Applicants must submit an original photograph - a piece of artwork or graphics file for the front cover. **Contact:** Questions should be addressed to scholarshipadmin@ gallerycollection.com.

4036 ■ Gamewarden of Vietnam Association

80 E Campus Dr.
Belfair, WA 98528
Free: 866-220-7477
E-mail: president@tf116.org
URL: www.tf116.org

4037 ■ Gamewarden Scholarship program *(High School, Undergraduate, Vocational/Occupational/ Scholarship)*

Purpose: To discuss military history, military news and other topics of concern or interest about Vietnam. **Focus:** Vietnamese studies. **Qualif.:** Applicant must be needing the assistance; must be the son, daughter or grandchild of a member of Game wardens; an applicant must be receiving an education from a four-year or two-year college, university, or vocational school. **Criteria:** Committee will consider the application based on the need of the applicant.

Funds Avail.: No specific amount. **Number Awarded:** 4. **To Apply:** Applicant must fill out the application form and send to Game warden of Vietnam Association Office. **Contact:** Glen Fry, normlguy@gmail.com.

4038 ■ Gamma Sigma Alpha (GSA)

3901 W 86th St., Ste. 390
Indianapolis, IN 46268
Ph: (317) 876-4695
URL: gammasigmaalpha.org

4039 ■ Gamma Sigma Alpha Graduate Scholarships *(Graduate/Scholarship)*

Purpose: To assist qualified members pursuing graduate studies at an accredited institution. **Focus:** General studies. **Qualif.:** Applicant must be a member of Gamma Sigma Alpha with a cumulative GPA of 3.5 or better (applicants must have been initiated prior to their application submission). **Criteria:** Selection will be based upon academic record, recommendations submitted, the applicant's statement, and campus and community activities.

Funds Avail.: $1,000. **Number Awarded:** 6. **To Apply:** Applicants must submit a completed application form together with a letter of recommendation; resume; a 250-word essay; and official transcript(s) of all academic work. **Deadline:** April 1.

4040 ■ Garden Club of America (GCA)

14 E 60th St., 3rd Fl.
New York, NY 10022-7147
Ph: (212) 753-8287
Fax: (212) 753-0134
E-mail: hq@gcamerica.org
URL: www2.gcamerica.org

4041 ■ Garden Club of America Awards in Tropical Botany (GCA) *(Doctorate/Award)*

Purpose: To assist doctoral candidates enrolled in a U.S. PhD program to undertake field work in the tropics. **Focus:**

Awards are arranged alphabetically below their administering organizations

Botany. **Qualif.:** Applicants must be PhD enrolled in United States university. **Criteria:** Applicants are selected based on Committee's review of the application materials.

Funds Avail.: $5,500. **Number Awarded:** 2. **To Apply:** Applicants must submit a curriculum vitae; (two-page) statement of proposed research; personal letter describing plans for the future and commitment to tropical conservation; letter of recommendation from student's graduate advisor including an evaluation of the student's progress. **Remarks:** Established in 1983. **Contact:** Andrea Santy, Senior Program Officer, phone: 202-495-4447; e-mail: andrea.santy@wwfus.org.

4042 ■ Katherine M. Grosscup Scholarships
(Graduate, Undergraduate/Scholarship)

Purpose: To provide financial assistance to students who wish to pursue study of horticulture and related field. **Focus:** Horticulture. **Qualif.:** Applicants must be current college sophomores, juniors, seniors or graduate students from Ohio, Pennsylvania, West Virginia, Michigan, Indiana and Kentucky; must have "B" GPA or better. **Criteria:** Applicants will be selected based on Committee's review of the application materials and personal interview.

Funds Avail.: $3,000. **Number Awarded:** varies. **To Apply:** Applicants must submit a completed application form; one letter of recommendation; transcript of college records; and personal statement explaining the career goals and how the chosen area of study will help achieve the objectives. **Deadline:** January 15. **Remarks:** Established in 1981. **Contact:** Cleveland Botanical Garden, 11030 E Blvd., Cleveland, OH 44106. Fax: 216-721-2056.

4043 ■ Garden Conservancy
PO Box 219
Cold Spring, NY 10516
Ph: (845) 424-6500
Fax: (845) 424-6501
E-mail: info@gardenconservancy.org
URL: www.gardenconservancy.org

4044 ■ Marco Polo Stufano Garden Conservancy Fellowships *(Professional development/Fellowship)*

Purpose: To acquire the skills necessary to manage an exceptional garden and develop it for public education and enjoyment. **Focus:** Horticulture. **Qualif.:** Applicants must be gardeners who have demonstrated the potential to distinguish themselves in the field of public horticulture; have the ability to work well with people; should possess strong horticultural skills and aesthetic judgment and a sensitivity to the vision and motives behind the creation of exceptional gardens as well as to the needs of new audiences; must have elevated the level of maintenance and horticultural distinction of these exceptional gardens and each of them has completed a special project such as a management plan, garden documentation or plant inventory. **Criteria:** Applicants will be selected based on their skills and educational background.

Funds Avail.: No specific amount. **To Apply:** For more information about the fellowship, applicants are advised to call the Preservation Projects office at 845-265-9396.

4045 ■ Bill and Melinda Gates Foundation
PO Box 23350
Seattle, WA 98102

Ph: (206) 709-3400
E-mail: media@gatesfoundation.org
URL: www.gatesfoundation.org

4046 ■ William H. Gates Public Service Law Scholarships *(Undergraduate/Scholarship)*

Purpose: To recognize the critical role played by lawyers in establishing and preserving a civil society and their calling in the spirit of public service. **Focus:** Law. **Qualif.:** Applicants must be incoming first year students in the University of Washington Law School. **Criteria:** Recipients are selected based on a competitive review process and a commitment on the part of the recipients to work in public service for five years following graduation.

Funds Avail.: No specific amount. **To Apply:** Applicants must submit a cover letter; an essay, not to exceed 750 words, discussing the factors that have shaped the applicants vision and influenced his/her public service commitment; two recommendations related to commitment to potential contributions to public service; Gates PSL Scholarship recommendation form; resume with details of public service experience; and signed application form. **Deadline:** January 15. **Contact:** PO Box 353020 Seattle, WA 98195; gatespsl@u.washington.edu.

4047 ■ Gay Asian Pacific Alliance (GAPA)
PO Box 421884
San Francisco, CA 94142-1884
E-mail: info@gapa.org
URL: gapa.org

4048 ■ GAPA Scholarships *(Undergraduate/ Scholarship)*

Purpose: To provide financial assistance to lesbian, gay, bisexual and transgender Asian and Pacific Islanders in educational pursuits. **Focus:** Homosexuality. **Qualif.:** Applicant must be an Asian/Pacific Islander; applying or attending school in one of the nine Bay Area counties; and have a minimum GPA of 2.75. **Criteria:** Priority is given to those self-identified as lesbian, gay, bisexual or transgender, or involved in the l/g/b/t community.

Funds Avail.: $1000. **To Apply:** Applicants must submit a completed Horizons Foundation's scholarship application form together with a transcript, a letter of recommendation and a 500-word essay. **Deadline:** July 15. **Remarks:** In memory of George Choy. The scholarship is administered by the Horizons Foundation. **Contact:** Horizons Foundation, 870 Market St., Suite 728, San Francisco, CA 94102; Ty Lim, ty@gapa.org.

4049 ■ Gay and Lesbian Business Association of Santa Barbara (GLBA)
PO Box 90907
Santa Barbara, CA 93190
Ph: (805) 687-5533
E-mail: glba@prideguide.net
URL: www.glbasb.com

4050 ■ Carl Joseph Adelhardt Memorial Scholarships *(Undergraduate/Scholarship)*

Purpose: To provide financial assistance to those students who are in need. **Focus:** General Studies. **Qualif.:** Applicants must be enrolled or planning to enroll at a post-

Awards are arranged alphabetically below their administering organizations

secondary institution in Santa Barbara County. **Criteria:** Recipients will be selected based upon the potential contribution to the Santa Barbara gay and lesbian community; career goals; and financial need.

Funds Avail.: No specific amount. **To Apply:** Applicants must submit the following: completed application including statements of community involvement and financial need; an autobiography/personal statement; a copy of current college and/or high school transcript of records; two letters of recommendation from a community member and the other one must come from a teacher or faculty member of their institution. **Deadline:** July 30. **Contact:** Applications should be sent to: John Chufar at the above address.

4051 ■ Raffin Gathercole Scholarships
(Undergraduate/Scholarship)

Purpose: To provide exceptional and ongoing support to those GLBA students. **Focus:** General Studies. **Qualif.:** Applicants must be enrolled or planning to enroll at a post-secondary institution in Santa Barbara County. **Criteria:** Recipients will be selected based upon the potential contribution to Santa Barbara gay and lesbian community; career goals; and financial need.

Funds Avail.: No specific amount. **To Apply:** Applicants must submit the following: completed application including statements of community involvement and financial need; an autobiography/personal statement; a copy of current college and/or high school transcript of records; two letters of recommendation from a community member and the other one must come from a teacher or faculty member of their institution. **Deadline:** July 30. **Contact:** Applications should be sent to: John Chufar at the above address.

4052 ■ Stephen Logan Memorial Scholarships
(Undergraduate/Scholarship)

Purpose: To provide financial assistance to students who are in need. **Focus:** General studies. **Qualif.:** Applicants must be enrolled or planning to enroll at a post-secondary institution in Santa Barbara County. **Criteria:** Recipients will be selected based upon the potential contribution to the Santa Barbara gay and lesbian community; career goals; and financial need.

Funds Avail.: No specific amount. **To Apply:** Applicants must submit the following: completed application including statements of community involvement and financial need; an autobiography/personal statement; a copy of current college and/or high school transcript of records; two letters of recommendation from a community member and the other one must come from a teacher or a faculty member of their institution. **Deadline:** July 30. **Contact:** If have questions, please write contact Chufar at the above address.

4053 ■ Gemological Institute of America Inc. (GIA)
The Robert Mouawad Campus, 5345 Armada Dr.
Carlsbad, CA 92008
Ph: (760) 603-4000
Fax: (760) 603-4080
Free: 800-421-7250
E-mail: admissions@gia.edu
URL: www.gia.edu

4054 ■ Michael Beaudry Scholarships
(Undergraduate/Scholarship)

Purpose: To promote education in Gemology. **Focus:** Gemology; Art industries and trade. **Qualif.:** Applicant must

be U.S. citizen and permanent resident; at least 18 years old; have a high school diploma or GED equivalency; currently employed or planning to enter in the jewelry industry; applying for On Campus School of Gemology Graduate Gemologist (GG) and the Jewelry Manufacturing Arts Applied Jewelry Arts (AJA) programs; past recipient of GIA scholarship within last five years are not eligible. **Criteria:** Applications will be reviewed by the GIA scholarship committee.

Funds Avail.: $16,585. **Number Awarded:** 1. **To Apply:** Applicant must complete the GIA Scholarship application (available at the website), with a letter of recommendation from a person in the jewelry industry. Send application and supporting documents to: Gemological Institute of America, Office of Student Financial Assistance, MS 7 The Robert Mouawad Campus 5345 Armada Dr. Carlsbad, CA 92008. **Deadline:** October 15. **Contact:** Financial aid representative, 800-421-7250 x-4175, financialaid@gia.edu or scholarship@gia.edu.

4055 ■ ColorMasters Scholarships
(Undergraduate/Scholarship)

Purpose: To promote education in Gemology. **Focus:** Gemology. **Qualif.:** Applicant must be a U.S. citizen and permanent resident; at least 18 years old; have a high school diploma or GED equivalency; currently employed or planning to enter in the jewelry industry (ColorMasters products); applying for Distance Education School of Gemology Accredited Jewelry Professionals (AJP) diploma program; past recipient of GIA scholarship within last five years are not eligible. **Criteria:** Preference will be given to applicants employed by a jewelry store that carries Color-Masters products.

Funds Avail.: $450. **Number Awarded:** 8. **To Apply:** Applicant must complete the GIA Scholarship application (available on the website), with a letter of recommendation from a person in the jewelry industry. Send application and supporting documents to: Gemological Institute of America, Office of Student Financial Assistance, MS 7 The Robert Mouawad Campus 5345 Armada Drive Carlsbad, CA 92008. **Deadline:** October 31. **Contact:** Financial aid representative, 800-421-7250 x-4175, financialaid@gia.edu or scholarship@gia.edu.

4056 ■ GIA Endowment Scholarships - Distance Education *(Graduate/Scholarship)*

Purpose: To promote education in gemology. **Focus:** Gemology. **Qualif.:** Applicant must be U.S. citizen and permanent resident; at least 18 years old; have a high school diploma or GED equivalency; currently employed or planning to enter in the jewelry industry; applying for On Campus School of Gemology Graduate Gemologist (GG) program; past recipient of GIA scholarship within last five years are not eligible. **Criteria:** Applications will be reviewed by the GIA scholarship committee.

Funds Avail.: $1,000. **Number Awarded:** 5. **To Apply:** Applicant must complete the GIA Scholarship application (available at the website), with a letter of recommendation from a person in the jewelry industry. Send application and supporting documents to: Gemological Institute of America, Office of Student Financial Assistance, MS 7 The Robert Mouawad Campus 5345 Armada Drive Carlsbad, CA 92008. **Deadline:** October 15. **Contact:** Financial aid representative, 800-421-7250 x-4175, financialaid@gia.edu or scholarship@gia.edu.

Awards are arranged alphabetically below their administering organizations

4057 ■ GIA Endowment Scholarships - On Campus *(Graduate/Scholarship)*

Purpose: To promote education in gemology. **Focus:** Gemology. **Qualif.:** Applicant must be U.S. citizen and permanent resident; at least 18 years old; have a high school diploma or GED equivalency; currently employed or planning to enter in the jewelry industry; applying for On Campus School of Gemology Graduate Gemologist (GG) program, School of Jewelry Manufacturing Arts Applied Jewelry Arts (AJA) or Graduate Jeweler (GJ) program; past recipient of GIA scholarship within last five years are not eligible. **Criteria:** Applications will be reviewed by the GIA scholarship committee.

Funds Avail.: $18,000. **To Apply:** Applicant must complete the GIA Scholarship application (available at the website), with a letter of recommendation from a person in the jewelry industry. Send application and supporting documents to: Gemological Institute of America, Office of Student Financial Assistance, MS 7 The Robert Mouawad Campus 5345 Armada Drive Carlsbad, CA 92008. **Deadline:** October 31. **Contact:** Financial aid representative, 800-421-7250 x-4175, financialaid@gia.edu or scholarship@gia.edu.

4058 ■ William Goldberg Diamond Corp. Scholarships *(Undergraduate/Scholarship)*

Purpose: To promote education in gemology. **Focus:** Gemology. **Qualif.:** Applicant must be U.S. citizen and permanent resident; at least 18 years old; have a high school diploma or GED equivalency; currently employed or planning to enter in the jewelry industry; applying for any School of Gemology course or program; past recipient of GIA scholarship within last five years are not eligible. **Criteria:** Applications will be reviewed by the GIA scholarship committee.

Funds Avail.: $10,000. **Number Awarded:** 1. **To Apply:** Applicant must complete the GIA Scholarship application (available at the website), with a letter of recommendation from a person in the jewelry industry. Send application and supporting documents to: Gemological Institute of America, Office of Student Financial Assistance, MS 7 The Robert Mouawad Campus 5345 Armada Drive Carlsbad, CA 92008. **Deadline:** October 31. **Contact:** Financial aid representative, 800-421-7250 x-4175, financialaid@gia.edu or scholarship@gia.edu.

4059 ■ Marion H. Halfacre Scholarships *(Graduate/Scholarship)*

Purpose: To promote education in gemology. **Focus:** Gemology. **Qualif.:** Applicant must be a U.S. citizen and permanent resident; at least 18 years old; have a high school diploma or GED equivalency; currently employed or planning to enter in the jewelry industry; applying for On Campus School of Gemology Graduate Gemologist (GG) program; past recipient of GIA scholarship within last five years are not eligible. **Criteria:** Applications will be reviewed by the GIA scholarship committee.

Funds Avail.: $15,000. **Number Awarded:** 1. **To Apply:** Applicant must complete the GIA Scholarship application (available at the website), with a letter of recommendation from a person in the jewelry industry. Send application and supporting documents to: Gemological Institute of America, Office of Student Financial Assistance, MS 7 The Robert Mouawad Campus 5345 Armada Drive Carlsbad, CA 92008. **Deadline:** October 15. **Contact:** Financial aid representative, 800-421-7250 x-4175, financialaid@gia.edu or scholarship@gia.edu.

4060 ■ Morris Hanauer Scholarships *(Undergraduate/Scholarship)*

Purpose: To promote education in gemology. **Focus:** Gemology. **Qualif.:** Applicant must be U.S. citizen and permanent resident; at least 18 years old; have a high school diploma or GED equivalency; currently employed or planning to enter in the jewelry industry; applying for Distance Education School of Gemology course or program; past recipient of GIA scholarship within last five years are not eligible. **Criteria:** Applications will be reviewed by the GIA scholarship committee.

Funds Avail.: $600. **Number Awarded:** 1. **To Apply:** Applicant must complete the GIA Scholarship application (available at the website), with a letter of recommendation from a person in the jewelry industry. Send application and supporting documents to: Gemological Institute of America, Office of Student Financial Assistance, MS 7 The Robert Mouawad Campus 5345 Armada Drive Carlsbad, CA 92008. **Deadline:** October 31. **Contact:** Financial aid representative, 800-421-7250 x-4175, financialaid@gia.edu or scholarship@gia.edu.

4061 ■ Peter Hess Scholarships *(Undergraduate/Scholarship)*

Purpose: To provide educational assistance to students. **Focus:** General studies. **Qualif.:** Applicant must be U.S. citizen and permanent resident; must be a member, related to a member or planning to join California Jewelers Association; have a high school diploma or GED equivalency; currently employed or planning to enter in the jewelry industry; applying for any On Campus or Distance Education course or program; past recipient of GIA scholarship within last five years are not eligible. **Criteria:** Applications will be reviewed by the GIA scholarship committee.

Funds Avail.: $1,000. **Number Awarded:** 1. **To Apply:** Applicant must complete the GIA Scholarship application (available at the website), with a letter of recommendation from a person in the jewelry industry. Send application and supporting documents to: Gemological Institute of America, Office of Student Financial Assistance, MS 7 The Robert Mouawad Campus 5345 Armada Drive Carlsbad, CA 92008. **Deadline:** October 15. **Contact:** Financial aid representative, 800-421-7250 x-4175, financialaid@gia.edu or scholarship@gia.edu.

4062 ■ George W. Juno Memorial Scholarships *(Graduate/Scholarship)*

Purpose: To promote education in gemology. **Focus:** Gemology. **Qualif.:** Applicant must be U.S. citizens and permanent resident; at least 18 years old; have a high school diploma or GED equivalency; currently employed or planning to enter in the jewelry industry; applying for On Campus School of Gemology Graduate Gemologist (GG) courses; past recipient of GIA scholarship within last five years are not eligible. **Criteria:** Applications will be reviewed by the GIA scholarship committee.

Funds Avail.: $1,000. **Number Awarded:** 1. **To Apply:** Applicant must complete the GIA Scholarship application (available at the website), with a letter of recommendation from a person in the jewelry industry. Send application and supporting documents to: Gemological Institute of America, Office of Student Financial Assistance, MS 7 The Robert Mouawad Campus 5345 Armada Drive Carlsbad, CA 92008. **Deadline:** October 31. **Contact:** Financial aid representative, 800-421-7250 x-4175, financialaid@gia.edu or scholarship@gia.edu.

Awards are arranged alphabetically below their administering organizations

4063 ■ Richard T. Liddicoat Scholarships
(Graduate/Scholarship)

Purpose: To promote education in gemology. **Focus:** Gemology. **Qualif.:** Applicant must be U.S. citizen and permanent resident; at least 18 years old; have a high school diploma or GED equivalency; currently employed or planning to enter in the jewelry industry; applying for On Campus and Distance Education School of Gemology Graduate Gemologist (GG) program (includes 3 Lab classes of Diamond Grading, Colored Stone Grading, and Gem Identification); past recipient of GIA scholarship within last five years are not eligible. **Criteria:** Applications will be reviewed by the GIA scholarship committee.

Funds Avail.: $19,000. **Number Awarded:** 2. **To Apply:** Applicant must complete the GIA Scholarship application (available at the website), with a letter of recommendation from a person in the jewelry industry. Send application and supporting documents to: Gemological Institute of America, Office of Student Financial Assistance, MS 7 The Robert Mouawad Campus 5345 Armada Drive Carlsbad, CA 92008. **Deadline:** October 31. **Contact:** Financial aid representative, 800-421-7250 x-4175, financialaid@gia.edu or scholarship@gia.edu.

4064 ■ Lone Star GIA Associate and Alumni Scholarships *(Undergraduate/Scholarship)*

Purpose: To provide educational assistance for students. **Focus:** General studies. **Qualif.:** Applicant must be U.S. citizen and permanent resident; at least 18 years old; have a high school diploma or GED equivalency; currently employed or planning to enter in the jewelry industry; applying for any On Campus, Distance Education, or Lab course or program; past recipient of GIA scholarship within last five years are not eligible. **Criteria:** Applications will be reviewed by the GIA scholarship committee. Preference will be given to applicants residing in Texas, Oklahoma, Louisiana, New Mexico and Arkansas.

Funds Avail.: $500. **Number Awarded:** 1. **To Apply:** Applicant must complete the GIA Scholarship application (available at the website), with a letter of recommendation from a person in the jewelry industry. Send application and supporting documents to: Gemological Institute of America, Office of Student Financial Assistance, MS 7 The Robert Mouawad Campus 5345 Armada Drive Carlsbad, CA 92008. **Deadline:** October 31. **Contact:** Financial aid representative, 800-421-7250 x-4175, financialaid@gia.edu or scholarship@gia.edu.

4065 ■ Mikimoto Scholarships *(Graduate/Scholarship)*

Purpose: To promote education in gemology. **Focus:** Gemology. **Qualif.:** Applicant must be U.S. citizen and permanent resident; at least 18 years old; have a high school diploma or GED equivalency; currently employed or planning to enter in the jewelry industry; applying for Distance Education School of Gemology Graduate Pearls diploma program; past recipient of GIA scholarship within last five years are not eligible. **Criteria:** Applications will be reviewed by the GIA scholarship committee.

Funds Avail.: $750. **Number Awarded:** 8. **To Apply:** Applicant must complete the GIA Scholarship application (available at the website), with a letter of recommendation from a person in the jewelry industry. Send application and supporting documents to: Gemological Institute of America, Office of Student Financial Assistance, MS 7 The Robert Mouawad Campus 5345 Armada Drive Carlsbad, CA 92008. **Deadline:** October 31. **Contact:** Financial aid

representative, 800-421-7250 x-4175, financialaid@gia.edu or scholarship@gia.edu.

4066 ■ Eunice Miles Scholarships
(Undergraduate/Scholarship)

Purpose: To provide educational assistance for students. **Focus:** General studies. **Qualif.:** Applicant must be U.S. citizen and permanent resident; at least 18 years old; have a high school diploma or GED equivalency; currently employed or planning to enter in the jewelry industry; applying for any On Campus School or Distance Education course or program; past recipient of GIA scholarship within last five years are not eligible. **Criteria:** Applications will be reviewed by the GIA scholarship committee.

Funds Avail.: $500. **Number Awarded:** 5. **To Apply:** Applicant must complete the GIA Scholarship application (available at the website), with a letter of recommendation from a person in the jewelry industry. Send application and supporting documents to: Gemological Institute of America, Office of Student Financial Assistance, MS 7 The Robert Mouawad Campus 5345 Armada Drive Carlsbad, CA 92008. **Deadline:** October 31. **Contact:** Financial aid representative, 800-421-7250 x-4175, financialaid@gia.edu or scholarship@gia.edu.

4067 ■ North Texas GIA Alumni Association Scholarships *(Undergraduate/Scholarship)*

Purpose: To provide educational assistance for students. **Focus:** General studies. **Qualif.:** Applicant must be U.S. citizen and a resident of Texas; at least 18 years old; have a high school diploma or GED equivalency; currently employed or planning to enter in the jewelry industry; applying for any On Campus, Distance Education, or Lab course or program; past recipient of GIA scholarship within last five years are not eligible. **Criteria:** Applications will be reviewed by the GIA scholarship committee. Preference will be given to applicants residing in Texas with zip codes ending in 75000-75799, 76000-76999, and 79000-79799.

Funds Avail.: $1,500. **Number Awarded:** 1. **To Apply:** Applicant must complete the GIA Scholarship application (available at the website), with a letter of recommendation from a person in the jewelry industry. Send application and supporting documents to: Gemological Institute of America, Office of Student Financial Assistance, MS 7 The Robert Mouawad Campus 5345 Armada Drive Carlsbad, CA 92008. **Deadline:** October 15. **Contact:** Financial aid representative, 800-421-7250 x-4175, financialaid@gia.edu or scholarship@gia.edu.

4068 ■ Daniel Swarovski and Company Scholarships *(Graduate/Scholarship)*

Purpose: To promote education in gemology. **Focus:** Gemology. **Qualif.:** Applicant must be a U.S. citizen and permanent resident; at least 18 years old; have a high school diploma or GED equivalency; have 2-3 years work experience in jewelry industry; applying for On Campus School of Gemology Graduate Gemologist (GG) courses; past recipient of GIA scholarship within last five years are not eligible. **Criteria:** Applications will be reviewed by the GIA scholarship committee.

Funds Avail.: $1,000. **Number Awarded:** 3. **To Apply:** Applicant must complete the GIA Scholarship application (available on the website), with two letters of recommendation, both of which must be from a person in the jewelry industry. Send application and supporting documents to: Gemological Institute of America, Office of Student Financial Assistance, MS 7 The Robert Mouawad Campus 5345

Awards are arranged alphabetically below their administering organizations

Armada Drive Carlsbad, CA 92008. **Deadline:** October 15. **Contact:** Financial aid representative, 800-421-7250 x-4175, financialaid@gia.edu or scholarship@gia.edu.

4069 ■ Kurt Wayne Scholarships *(Graduate/ Scholarship)*

Purpose: To promote education in gemology. **Focus:** Gemology; Art industries and trade. **Qualif.:** Applicant must be U.S. citizen and permanent resident; at least 18 years old; have a high school diploma or GED equivalency; currently employed or planning to enter in the jewelry industry; applying for On Campus School of Jewelry Manufacturing Arts Graduate Jeweler (GJ) program courses; past recipient of GIA scholarship within last five years are not eligible. **Criteria:** Applications will be reviewed by the GIA scholarship committee.

Funds Avail.: $1,000. **Number Awarded:** 1. **To Apply:** Applicant must complete the GIA Scholarship application (available at the website), with a letter of recommendation from a person in the jewelry industry. Send application and supporting documents to: Gemological Institute of America, Office of Student Financial Assistance, MS 7 The Robert Mouawad Campus 5345 Armada Drive Carlsbad, CA 92008. **Deadline:** October 31. **Contact:** Financial aid representative, 800-421-7250 x-4175, financialaid@gia.edu or scholarship@gia.edu.

4070 ■ Robert B. Westover Scholarships *(Undergraduate/Scholarship)*

Purpose: To provide educational assistance to students. **Focus:** General studies. **Qualif.:** Applicant must be U.S. citizen and permanent resident; must be a member, related to a member or planning to join California Jewelers Association; have a high school diploma or GED equivalency; currently employed or planning to enter in the jewelry industry; applying for any On Campus or Distance Education course or program; past recipient of GIA scholarship within last five years are not eligible. **Criteria:** Applications will be reviewed by the GIA scholarship committee.

Funds Avail.: $1,000. **Number Awarded:** 1. **To Apply:** Applicant must complete the GIA Scholarship application (available at the website), with a letter of recommendation from a person in the jewelry industry. Send application and supporting documents to: Gemological Institute of America, Office of Student Financial Assistance, MS 7 The Robert Mouawad Campus 5345 Armada Drive Carlsbad, CA 92008. **Deadline:** October 15. **Contact:** Financial aid representative, 800-421-7250 x-4175, financialaid@gia.edu or scholarship@gia.edu.

4071 ■ General Aviation Manufacturers Association (GAMA)

1400 K St. NW, Ste. 801
Washington, DC 20005-2485
Ph: (202) 393-1500
Fax: (202) 842-4063
E-mail: bforan@gama.aero
URL: www.gama.aero

4072 ■ Dr. Harold S. Wood Awards for Excellence *(Undergraduate/Award)*

Purpose: To support a college student attending a National Intercollegiate Flying Association member college or university program. **Focus:** Aviation. **Qualif.:** Candidate for the award must: be an enrolled college student; have

completed a semester at a NIFA participating institution with GPA of 3.0 on a 4.0 scale or better; have rendered service to NIFA, aviation clubs or aviation-related activities or non-aviation extra-curricular service and contribution to school and community. **Criteria:** The applicant must be nominated and will be judged on the basis of GPA, community and school activities and aviation-related contributions.

Funds Avail.: $1,000. **Number Awarded:** 1. **To Apply:** Applicants must submit a completed application form together with their transcript and letters of recommendation. **Deadline:** April 1. **Contact:** Katie Pribyl at 202-393-1500 or e-mail at kpribyl@gama.aero.

4073 ■ General Federation of Women's Clubs of Massachusetts

245 Dutton Rd.
Sudbury, MA 01776-0679
Ph: (978) 443-4569
E-mail: gfwcma@live.com
URL: www.gfwcma.org

4074 ■ Boston City Federation "Return to School" Scholarships *(Graduate, Undergraduate/ Scholarship)*

Purpose: To support a woman returning to college after an absence of at least four years. **Focus:** General studies. **Qualif.:** Applicant must be a female maintaining legal residence in Massachusetts and returning to college after an absence of at least four years. **Criteria:** Selection is based on the application materials submitted.

Funds Avail.: $500. **To Apply:** Applicants must submit a completed application form along with a personal statement (maximum of 500 words) addressing professional goals and financial need; letter of reference from recent employer, or mentor in field of study; and official transcript of college grades. Applicants are required to submit the original and three additional copies of the application packet. **Deadline:** February 1. **Contact:** For further information, applicants must contact Jane Howard at the above address; E-mail: jhoward@mountida.edu.

4075 ■ Communication Disorder/Speech Therapy Scholarships *(Graduate/Scholarship)*

Purpose: To support students in their educational pursuit. **Focus:** Speech and language pathology/audiology. **Qualif.:** Applicant must be maintaining legal residence in Massachusetts. **Criteria:** Selection is based on the application materials submitted for review.

Funds Avail.: $800. **To Apply:** Applicants must submit a completed application form along with a personal statement (maximum of 500 words) addressing professional goals and financial need; a letter of reference from the department chair (original on school letterhead); and official transcript of college grades. Applicants are required to submit the original and additional three copies of the application packet. **Deadline:** February 1. **Contact:** For further information, applicants must contact Jane Howard at the above address; E-mail: jhoward@mountida.edu.

4076 ■ Dorchester Woman's Club Scholarships *(Undergraduate/Scholarship)*

Purpose: To support undergraduate voice majors. **Focus:** Music, Vocal. **Qualif.:** Applicant must be a Massachusetts resident and an undergraduate currently enrolled in a four-

Awards are arranged alphabetically below their administering organizations

year accredited college, university or school of music, majoring in voice. **Criteria:** Selection is based on the application materials submitted for review.

Funds Avail.: $500. **To Apply:** Applicants must submit a completed application form along with a personal statement (maximum of 500 words) addressing professional goals, financial need, experience and repertoire; letter of recommendation from college department head, major professor or voice instructor (original on college letterhead); and official transcript of college grades. Send applications to: Joan H. Korslund, Music Chair, 25 Apple Ln., Wrentham, MA 02093. Applicants will be notified at the time of their personal audition which will be held at the Milton Woman's Club, 90 Reedsdale Rd., Milton, MA. **Deadline:** March 1. **Contact:** Questions can be addressed by email to nonnalda@aol.com.

4077 ■ Ann L. Holland Memorial Scholarships
(Graduate, Undergraduate/Scholarship)

Purpose: To support female students majoring in conservation/environmental studies of nursing. **Focus:** Conservation of natural resources; Nursing. **Qualif.:** Applicant must be a female maintaining legal residence in Massachusetts for at least five years, and a college junior, senior or a graduate student majoring in conservation/environmental studies or nursing. **Criteria:** Selection is based on the application materials submitted for review.

Funds Avail.: $500. **To Apply:** Applicants must submit a completed application form together with a personal statement (maximum of 500 words) addressing professional goals and financial need; letter of reference from college department chair or recent employer (original on letterhead); and official transcript(s) of grades from college or graduate school. Send application to: June Alfano, 95 5th St., East Nokomis, Fl 34275. **Deadline:** March 1. **Contact:** June Alfano at jdaheart@comcast.net.

4078 ■ International Study Abroad Scholarships *(Graduate, Undergraduate/Scholarship)*

Purpose: To support undergraduate and graduate students in their educational pursuits. **Focus:** General studies. **Qualif.:** Applicant must be an undergraduate or graduate student maintaining legal residence in Massachusetts. **Criteria:** Selection is based on the application.

Funds Avail.: $500. **To Apply:** Applicants must submit a completed application form together with a personal statement (maximum of 500 words) addressing: "What I hope to gain from this experience"; a letter of reference from the department chair. (original on college letterhead); and official transcript of college grades. **Deadline:** February 1 and June 1. **Contact:** Application form and supporting documents must be submitted to Judith Wilchynski at the above address; Phone: 508-870-1895.

4079 ■ Newtonville Woman's Club Scholarships *(Undergraduate/Scholarship)*

Purpose: To support a student in a teacher-training program. **Focus:** Teaching. **Qualif.:** Applicant must be a senior in a Massachusetts high school who have plan to enroll in a four-year accredited college/university in a teacher-training program that leads to certification to teach. **Criteria:** Selection is based on the application materials submitted for review.

Funds Avail.: $500. **To Apply:** Applicants must submit a completed application form together with a personal statement (maximum of 500 words) addressing professional

goals and financial need; a letter of recommendation from high school principal or counselor (original on school letterhead); and official transcript of high school grades. **Deadline:** February 1. **Contact:** For further information, applicants must contact Judith Wilchynski at the above address or call 508-870-1895.

4080 ■ "Nickels for Notes" Scholarships
(Undergraduate/Scholarship)

Purpose: To support students majoring in Piano, Instrument, Music Education, Music Therapy or Voice. **Focus:** Music, Piano; Music education; Music therapy; Music, Vocal. **Qualif.:** Applicant must be a senior in a Massachusetts High School who will major in Piano, Instrument, Music Education, Music Therapy or Voice. **Criteria:** Selection is based on the application materials submitted for review.

Funds Avail.: $500. **To Apply:** Applicants must submit a completed application form along with a personal statement (maximum of 500 words) addressing professional goals, experience and repertoire (if applicable) and financial need; a letter of recommendation from either High School Principal or Music Instructor (original, on school letterhead); and official transcript of high school grades. Send application to: Joan Korslund, 25 Apple Ln., Wrentham, Ma 02093. Applicants will be notified of a time for the personal audition, which will be held at the Milton Woman's Club, 90 Reedsdale Rd. (Rte. 28), Milton, MA. **Deadline:** March 1. **Contact:** Joan Korslund at nonnalda@aol.com.

4081 ■ Pennies for Art Scholarships
(Undergraduate/Scholarship)

Purpose: To support talented students in their educational pursuits. **Focus:** Art. **Qualif.:** Applicant must be a senior in a Massachusetts High School. **Criteria:** Selection is based on the application.

Funds Avail.: $500. **To Apply:** Applicant must submit a completed application form together with a personal statement (maximum of 500 words) addressing professional goals and financial need; a letter of recommendation from high school art instructor (original on school letterhead); official transcript of grades; and a portfolio of three examples of original artwork, matted, not framed, not larger than 12" X 18" overall dimension (printed name and address on the back of each example and on the portfolio). **Deadline:** February 1.

4082 ■ Catherine E. Philbin Scholarships
(Graduate, Undergraduate/Scholarship)

Purpose: To support graduate or undergraduate students majoring in Public Health. **Focus:** Public health. **Qualif.:** Applicant must be an undergraduate or graduate student maintaining legal residence in Massachusetts and pursuing study in Public Health. **Criteria:** Selection is based on the application materials submitted.

Funds Avail.: $500. **To Apply:** Applicants must submit a completed application form together with a personal statement (maximum of 500 words) addressing professional goals and financial need; a letter of reference from the department chair (original on school letterhead); and official transcript of college grades. Applicants are required to submit the original and three additional copies of the application packet. **Deadline:** February 1. **Contact:** For further information, applicants must contact Jane Howard at the above address; E-mail: jhoward@mountida.edu.

4083 ■ Women's Italian Club of Boston Scholarships *(Undergraduate/Scholarship)*

Purpose: To support students of Italian heritage in their educational pursuits. **Focus:** General studies. **Qualif.:** Ap-

Awards are arranged alphabetically below their administering organizations

plicant must be a senior in a Massachusetts High School. **Criteria:** Selection is based on application materials submitted.

Funds Avail.: $1,000. **To Apply:** Applicant must submit a completed application form together with a personal statement (maximum of 500 words) addressing goals, Italian heritage and work experience; official transcript of high school grades; and two letters of recommendation from counselor or teachers (original on school letterhead). Applicants are required to submit one original and three additional copies of the application packet. **Deadline:** March 1. **Contact:** For further information, applicants must contact Joan Shanahan at cmje@aol.com.

4084 ■ Geological Association of Canada (GAC)

Memorial University of Newfoundland
Dept. of Earth Sciences
Alexander Murray Bldg., Rm. ER4063
St. John's, NL, Canada A1B 3X5
Ph: (709) 864-7660
Fax: (709) 864-2532
E-mail: gac@mun.ca
URL: www.gac.ca

4085 ■ Geological Association of Canada Student Prizes *(Undergraduate/Award)*

Purpose: To promote the study of Earth Science at Canadian universities. **Focus:** Earth sciences. **Qualif.:** Candidates must be students in their penultimate year who are expected to complete their degree in the normal time. **Criteria:** Selection will be based on overall academic standing.

Funds Avail.: No specific amount. **To Apply:** Prospective candidates do not apply for these prizes. Winners are selected on the basis of nomination of a single student in each earth-science department by the respective department head.

4086 ■ Geological Society of America (GSA)

PO Box 9140
Boulder, CO 80301-9140
Ph: (303) 357-1000
Fax: (303) 357-1070
E-mail: gsaservice@geosociety.org
URL: www.geosociety.org

4087 ■ Farouk El-Baz Student Research Grants *(Doctorate, Graduate, Undergraduate/Grant)*

Purpose: To encourage and support desert studies by students in their senior year of undergraduate studies, or at the master's or Ph.D. level. **Focus:** Geology. **Qualif.:** Applicants must be a GSA member; applicants must be in their senior year of their undergraduate studies, or at the master's or Ph.D. level. **Criteria:** Recipients are selected based on the significance of the project proposal.

Funds Avail.: No specified amount. **To Apply:** Applicants must submit a one-page description of proposed research under title; letter of recommendation by university research advisor. **Deadline:** June 1. **Contact:** awards@geosociety.org.

4088 ■ Geological Society of America Graduate Student Research Grants *(Doctorate, Graduate/Grant)*

Purpose: To provide partial support of master's and doctoral thesis research in geological science for graduate students enrolled in universities in the United States, Canada, Mexico, and Central America. **Focus:** Geology. **Qualif.:** Applicants must be GSA members currently enrolled in a U.S., Canadian, or Central American university or college in an earth science degree program with geologic component. **Criteria:** Recipients are selected based on the qualifications of the candidate and their academic standing.

Funds Avail.: No specified amount. **Number Awarded:** 3. **To Apply:** Applicants must fill out the online application form. **Deadline:** February 1. **Contact:** Applicants may e-mail their questions at awards@geosociety.org or call 303-357-1028.

4089 ■ Georgetown Working League

PO Box 262
Georgetown, ME 04548
URL: www.georgetownworkingleague.org

4090 ■ Georgetown Working League Scholarships *(Undergraduate/Scholarship)*

Purpose: To provide financial assistance to students seeking higher education. **Focus:** General studies. **Qualif.:** Applicants must be students seeking higher education who reside in Georgetown, Maine. **Criteria:** Selection will be based on the committee's criteria.

Funds Avail.: $1,000-2,000. **To Apply:** Application form and other eligibility requirements can be downloaded from the website. **Deadline:** April 30.

4091 ■ Riggs Cove Foundation Scholarships *(Undergraduate/Scholarship)*

Purpose: To provide financial assistance to students seeking higher education. **Focus:** General studies. **Qualif.:** Applicants must be students seeking higher education who reside in Georgetown, Maine. **Criteria:** Selection will be based on the committee's criteria.

Funds Avail.: $1,000-2,000. **To Apply:** Application form and other eligibility requirements can be downloaded from the website. **Deadline:** April 30.

4092 ■ Benjamin Riggs Scholarships *(Undergraduate/Scholarship)*

Purpose: To provide financial assistance to students seeking higher education. **Focus:** General studies. **Qualif.:** Applicants must be students seeking higher education who reside in Georgetown, Maine. **Criteria:** Selection will be based on the committee's criteria.

Funds Avail.: $1,000-2,000. **To Apply:** Application form and other eligibility requirements can be downloaded from the website. **Deadline:** April 30.

4093 ■ Robinhood Marine Center Scholarships *(Undergraduate/Scholarship)*

Purpose: To provide financial assistance to students seeking higher education. **Focus:** General studies. **Qualif.:** Applicants must be students seeking higher education who reside in Georgetown, Maine. **Criteria:** Selection will be based on the committee's criteria.

Funds Avail.: $1,000-2,000. **To Apply:** Application form and other eligibility requirements can be downloaded from the website. **Deadline:** April 30.

4094 ■ Josephine Hooker Shain Scholarships *(Undergraduate/Scholarship)*

Purpose: To provide financial assistance to students seeking higher education. **Focus:** General studies. **Qualif.:** Ap-

Awards are arranged alphabetically below their administering organizations

plicants must be students seeking higher education who reside in Georgetown, Maine. **Criteria:** Selection will be based on the committee's criteria.

Funds Avail.: $1,000-2,000. **To Apply:** Application form and other eligibility requirements can be downloaded from the website. **Deadline:** April 30.

4095 ■ Woodex Bearing Company Scholarships
(Undergraduate/Scholarship)

Purpose: To provide financial assistance to students seeking higher education. **Focus:** General studies. **Qualif.:** Applicants must be students seeking higher education who reside in Georgetown, Maine. **Criteria:** Selection will be based on the committee's criteria.

Funds Avail.: $1,000-2,000. **To Apply:** Application form and other eligibility requirements can be downloaded from the website. **Deadline:** April 30.

4096 ■ Georgia Association of Broadcasters (GAB)
8010 Roswell Rd., Ste. 150
Atlanta, GA 30350
Ph: (770) 395-7200
Fax: (770) 395-7235
Free: 877-395-7200
E-mail: piguej@gab.org
URL: www.gab.org

4097 ■ E. Lanier Finch Scholarships
(Undergraduate/Scholarship)

Purpose: To provide financial assistance to deserving students who will carry on the tradition of excellence in Georgia's broadcasting industry. **Focus:** Broadcasting. **Qualif.:** Applicant must be registered as a full time student at a fully accredited college or university; a rising junior or senior studying for a degree in some aspect of the broadcasting industry and a bona fide resident of the state of Georgia. **Criteria:** GAB participating member stations will select the winning candidates.

Funds Avail.: $1,500. **Number Awarded:** Four. **To Apply:** Application form can be downloaded online. Applicants must complete the form, and attach additional sheets as necessary. **Deadline:** April 30.

4098 ■ Georgia Association of Water Professionals (GAWP)
1655 Enterprise Way
Marietta, GA 30067
Ph: (770) 618-8690
Fax: (770) 618-8695
E-mail: jdozier@gawp.org
URL: gawponline.org

4099 ■ GAWP Graduate Scholarships
(Graduate/Fellowship)

Purpose: To provide financial assistance to GAWP members and their children who want to pursue their education. **Focus:** General studies. **Qualif.:** Applicants must hold an active, individual membership in GAWP; must be graduates of an accredited college or university. **Criteria:** Applicants will be selected by the scholarship committee based on their academic achievements.

Funds Avail.: $2,000. **To Apply:** Applicants must complete

the application available in the website and must be mailed to Georgia Association of Water Professionals, Scholarship Committee, 2121 New Market Pkwy, Ste. 144, Marietta, GA 30067. **Deadline:** February 28.

4100 ■ Philip R. Karr, III Scholarship Fund
(Graduate/Fellowship)

Purpose: To provide financial assistance to GAWP members and their children who want to pursue their education. **Focus:** General studies. **Qualif.:** Applicants must be residents of Georgia, or entering or attending a college or university graduate school located in Georgia; must be graduates of an accredited college or university. **Criteria:** Applicants will be selected by the scholarship committee based on their academic achievements.

Funds Avail.: $2,000. **To Apply:** Applicants must complete the application available in the website and must be mailed to Georgia Association of Water Professionals, Scholarship Committee, 2121 New Market Pkwy, Ste. 144, Marietta, GA 30067. **Deadline:** February 28.

4101 ■ Georgia Engineering Foundation
233 Peachtree St., Harris Twr., Ste. 700
Atlanta, GA 30303
Ph: (404) 521-2324
Fax: (404) 521-0283
E-mail: alicia.sosebee@gaengineers.org
URL: www.gefinc.org

4102 ■ Georgia Engineering Foundation Scholarships *(Graduate/Scholarship)*

Purpose: To provide financial assistance to those students who are in need. **Focus:** Engineering. **Qualif.:** Applicants must be Georgia students who are preparing for a career in engineering or engineering technology; must be U.S citizens; must be enrolled in an engineering or engineering technology ABET-accredited program leading to a B.S or graduate degree. **Criteria:** Preference will be given to students who meet the criteria.

Funds Avail.: Ranging from $1,000-$5,000. **To Apply:** Applicants must complete an online application form; must submit official transcript(s) in a sealed envelope; and photograph (no larger than 4"x 6"). **Deadline:** August 31. **Contact:** Supporting documents should be sent to Scholarship Committee at the above address.

4103 ■ Georgia Library Association (GLA)
PO Box 793
Rex, GA 30273
Ph: (678) 466-4339
Fax: (678) 466-4349
E-mail: bob.fox@library.gatech.edu
URL: gla.georgialibraries.org/

4104 ■ Beard Scholarships *(Master's/Scholarship)*

Purpose: To provide financial assistance towards completing a Master's degree in library science. **Focus:** Library and archival sciences. **Qualif.:** Applicants must be completing their senior year at an accredited college or university and have been accepted as students in a Master's degree program at a library school accredited by the American Library Association; must be ready to begin the program of study not later than the fall term of the year in which the

Awards are arranged alphabetically below their administering organizations

scholarship is awarded; must indicate an intention to complete degree requirements within three years; must maintain a passing grade average throughout the program; must agree to work for one year following graduation from a library school. **Criteria:** Selection will be based on the application and supporting documents. Residents of Georgia will be given preference, but not a requirement.

Funds Avail.: $1,000. **To Apply:** Applicants must complete the application form; must submit a proof of admission to an American Library Association-accredited Master's program, two letters of reference, official transcripts of all academic coursework and short essay stating the reasons why choosing to become a librarian and ultimate professional goals. **Deadline:** May 21. **Remarks:** In memory of the late Charles Edward Beard. **Contact:** Documents should be e-mailed to Kimberly Boyd at kimberly.boyd@gpc.edu.

4105 ■ Hubbard Scholarships *(Master's/Scholarship)*

Purpose: To recruit excellent librarians for Georgia and provide financial assistance towards completing a Master's degree in library science. **Focus:** Library and archival sciences. **Qualif.:** Applicants must be completing their senior year at an accredited college or university and have been accepted as students in a Master's degree program at a library school accredited by the American Library Association; must be ready to begin the program of study not later than the fall term of the year in which the scholarship is awarded; must indicate an intention to complete degree requirements within three years; must maintain a passing grade average throughout the program; must agree to work for one year following graduation from a library school. **Criteria:** Selection will be based on the application and supporting documents. Residents of Georgia will be given preference, but not a requirement.

Funds Avail.: $3,000. **To Apply:** Applicants must complete the application form; must submit a proof of admission to an American Library Association-accredited Master's program, two letters of reference, official transcripts of all academic coursework and short essay stating the reasons why choosing to become a librarian and ultimate professional goals. **Deadline:** May 21. **Contact:** Documents should be e-mailed to Kimberly Boyd at kimberly.boyd@gpc.edu.

4106 ■ Georgia Press Educational Foundation (GPEF)

3066 Mercer University Dr., Ste. 200
Atlanta, GA 30341-4137
Ph: (770) 454-6776
Fax: (770) 454-6778
E-mail: mail@gapress.org
URL: www.gapress.org

4107 ■ Durwood McAlister Scholarships *(Undergraduate/Scholarship)*

Purpose: To provide scholarship for outstanding students majoring in print journalism at a Georgia college or university. **Focus:** Journalism. **Qualif.:** Applicants must be enrolled full-time taking up journalism. Parents of applicants must be legal residents of Georgia for two years or applicant must be a resident of the state for three years. **Criteria:** Selection will be based on the committee's criteria.

Funds Avail.: No specific amount. **To Apply:** Scholarship

application can be obtained from the GPEF website. The following documents must be enclosed in the application: most recent grade transcript; anticipated budget; school photograph; copy of SAT scores; parents'/applicant's tax return; and recommendations of high school counselor, principal, college professor, or Georgia Press Association member. **Deadline:** March 1. **Remarks:** The McAlister Scholarship is named in honor of Durwood McAlister, former editor of The Atlanta Journal. **Contact:** Georgia Press Educational Foundation at the above address.

4108 ■ Morris Newspaper Corp. Scholarships *(Undergraduate/Scholarship)*

Purpose: To provide scholarships for outstanding print journalism students. **Focus:** Journalism. **Qualif.:** Applicants must be enrolled full-time taking up journalism. Parents of applicants must be legal residents of Georgia for two years or applicant must be a resident of the state for three years. **Criteria:** Selection will be based on the committee's criteria.

Funds Avail.: No specific amount. **To Apply:** Applications are submitted through newspapers in the Morris Newspaper Corporation chain. **Deadline:** March 1. **Remarks:** Established in 1987 by Charles Morris. **Contact:** Georgia Press Educational Foundation at the above address.

4109 ■ William C. Rogers Scholarships *(Undergraduate/Scholarship)*

Purpose: To award scholarships to Georgia residents attending Georgia colleges and universities. **Focus:** Journalism. **Qualif.:** Applicant must be a junior or senior majoring in the news-editorial sequence at the Grady College of Journalism and Mass Communication at the University of Georgia. Parents of applicants must be legal residents of Georgia for two years or applicant must be a resident of the state for three years. **Criteria:** Recipient is selected from nominations made by the University of Georgia.

Funds Avail.: No specific amount. **To Apply:** Scholarship application can be obtained from the GPEF website. The following documents must be enclosed in your application: most recent grade transcript; anticipated budget; school photograph; copy of SAT scores; parents'/applicant's tax return; and recommendations of high school counselor, principal, college professor, or Georgia Press Association member. **Deadline:** March 1. **Remarks:** The Rogers Scholarship is named in honor of William C. Rogers, Publisher of The Blade, Sawinsboro, and a past president of the Georgia Press Association. **Contact:** Georgia Press Educational Foundation at the above address.

4110 ■ Kirk Sutlive Scholarships *(Undergraduate/Scholarship)*

Purpose: To award scholarships to Georgia residents attending Georgia colleges and universities. **Focus:** Journalism. **Qualif.:** Applicant must be a junior or senior majoring in either the news-editorial or public relations sequence at the Henry W. Grady College of Journalism and Mass Communication at the University of Georgia. Parents of applicants must be legal residents of Georgia for two years or applicant must be a resident of the state for three years. **Criteria:** The recipient is selected from three nominations submitted by the University of Georgia.

Funds Avail.: No specific amount. **To Apply:** Scholarship application can be obtained from the GPEF website. The following documents must be enclosed in your application: most recent grade transcript; anticipated budget; school photograph; copy of SAT scores; parents'/your tax return; and recommendations of high school counselor, principal,

Awards are arranged alphabetically below their administering organizations

college professor, or Georgia Press Association member. **Deadline:** March 1. **Contact:** Georgia Press Educational Foundation at the above address.

4111 ■ Gerber Foundation

4747 W 48th St., Ste. 153
Fremont, MI 49412-8119
Ph: (231) 924-3175
Fax: (231) 924-7906
E-mail: tgf@ncresa.org
URL: www.gerberfoundation.org

4112 ■ Gerber Foundation Merit Scholarships
(Undergraduate/Scholarship)

Purpose: To assist graduating students from one of the five school districts in Newaygo County, Michigan. **Focus:** General studies. **Qualif.:** Students must have a GPA of 3.70 or below. **Criteria:** Selection will be based on merit.

Funds Avail.: $2,300. **To Apply:** Applications may be submitted online or by sending the application forms to the Foundation. Application forms can be obtained from the high school counselor's office or from the Foundation office. Applicants must also submit the following: educational report from Counselor (Form S-1); high school transcript; 1st Recommendation (Form S-2 or letter); 2nd Recommendation (Form S-2 or letter); personal information and financial summary (Form S-3); and a typed, 500-1000 word personal essay. **Deadline:** February 28. **Contact:** Gerber Foundation at the above address.

4113 ■ Daniel Gerber, Sr. Medallion Scholarships *(Undergraduate/Scholarship)*

Purpose: To assist graduating students from one of the five school districts in Newaygo County, Michigan. **Focus:** General studies. **Qualif.:** Students must have a GPA of 3.71 or higher. **Criteria:** Selection will be based on the committee's criteria.

Funds Avail.: $9,200. **To Apply:** Applications may be submitted online or by sending the application forms to the Foundation. Application forms can be obtained from the high school counselor's office or from the Foundation office. Applicants must also submit the following: educational report from Counselor (Form S-1); high school transcript; 1st Recommendation (Form S-2 or letter); 2nd Recommendation (Form S-2 or letter); personal information and financial summary (Form S-3); and a typed, 500-1000 word personal essay. **Deadline:** February 28. **Contact:** Gerber foundation at the above address.

4114 ■ German Academic Exchange Service (DAAD)

871 United Nations Plz.
New York, NY 10017
Ph: (212) 758-3223
Fax: (212) 755-5780
E-mail: daadny@daad.org
URL: www.daad.org

4115 ■ Leo Baeck Institute - DAAD Fellowships
(Doctorate/Fellowship)

Purpose: To provide financial assistance for students doing dissertation research work and to academics writing a scholarly essay or book. **Focus:** German studies. **Qualif.:**

Applicants must be U.S. citizens and PhD candidates or recent PhDs (degree awarded within the last two years). **Criteria:** Selection of applicants will be based on the application and other supporting documents.

Funds Avail.: $2,000. **Number Awarded:** 2. **To Apply:** Applicants must submit the following: completed application form; curriculum vitae; a full description of the research project; for doctoral students, send official transcripts for graduate and undergraduate work, evidence of enrollment in a PhD program, one letter of recommendation by their doctoral advisor and one by another scholar familiar with their work; for PhDs, evidence of their degree (transcripts not required); and two letters of recommendation from two colleagues familiar with their research. **Deadline:** November 1. **Contact:** lbaeck@lbi.cjh.org.

4116 ■ DAAD Study Scholarship Awards
(Graduate/Scholarship)

Purpose: To provide the opportunity to study in Germany, or complete a Master's degree course and obtain a degree from a German higher education institution. **Focus:** Dentistry, Medicine, Pharmacy, Veterinary medicine. **Qualif.:** Applicants must be graduating seniors (fourth or final year of undergraduate studies) or those with undergraduate degree in all academic fields; must be enrolled full-time at any North American University; citizens of US or Canada but foreigners should have studied at any accredited US or Canadian university for two years; requested to have a study project to make a stay in Germany essential. **Criteria:** Preference will be given to applicants who have been invited by a faculty member at a German university to study at a particular university department.

Funds Avail.: 750 Euros. **To Apply:** Applicant must submit the application form with the supplemental form (for music, fine arts, dance only), CV/Resume, study proposal, two letters of recommendation, evidence of contact with German Institution, DAAD Language evaluation form and transcript of records. **Deadline:** November 1 for applicants in the field of music, visual arts and perfomring arts; November 15 for applicants outside the field of music, visual arts and perfomring arts. **Contact:** kim@daad.org.

4117 ■ DAAD Undergraduate Scholarship Program *(Undergraduate/Scholarship)*

Purpose: To support undergraduate US and Canadian students interested in studying, doing research or completing an internship in Germany. **Focus:** General studies. **Qualif.:** Applicants must be currently second or third year students and will be in their third and fourth year during their stay in Germany; must be U.S., Canadian citizens or permanent residents; has interest in contemporary German and European affairs; and full-time students in an undergraduate degree-granting program at an accredited North American college or university. Students with outstanding academic records and personal integrity as evinced by both their grades and letters of recommendation are eligible to apply. **Criteria:** Preference will be given to students whose projects or programs are based at an organized by a German university.

Funds Avail.: 650 Euros. **To Apply:** Applicants must submit the original printout of the application with their signature and three copies of the following supplemental documents: resume; an approximately three pages of project proposal; two recommendation letters from major professors; acceptance into Study Abroad Program, Exchange Program, letter by mentor or invitation from a German university; transcripts; and language evaluation

Awards are arranged alphabetically below their administering organizations

certificate. Application and other supporting documents must be sent to: German Academic Exchange Service/ DAAD New York, 871 United Nations Plaza, New York, NY 10017-USA. **Deadline:** January 31.

4118 ■ Faculty Research Visit Grants
(Doctorate/Grant)

Purpose: To pursue research at universities, libraries, archives, institutes or laboratories in Germany. **Focus:** General studies. **Qualif.:** Applicants must be scholars at United States, Canadian universities or research institutions holding a PhD. (or equivalent); have been working in research or teaching as full time for at least two years after receipt of the doctorate; be U.S. or Canadian citizens (German nationals must have been working in a U.S. or Canadian institution for six consecutive years); should possess adequate knowledge of the German language; applicants may not hold a DAAD grant and a grant from another German or German-American organization concurrently for the same project. Previous grantees can only be qualified after three years. **Criteria:** Scholarship decisions are made by an independent academic selection committee based on an outstanding academic record and potential; validity and feasibility of the proposed project; and the necessity to carry it out in Germany.

Funds Avail.: 2,240 Euros. **To Apply:** Applicants must submit completed DAAD application form entitled "Research Visit for Faculty"; a not to exceed five pages curriculum vitae; complete list of publications; an up to five pages detailed description of the research project which includes a literature review and information on significance, methodology, availability or quality of data and the need for carrying out research in Germany; and letter(s) of invitation from the German institution(s). **Deadline:** October 15.

4119 ■ German Studies Research Grants
(Undergraduate/Grant)

Purpose: To encourage research and promote the study of cultural, political, historical, economic, and social aspects of modern and contemporary German affairs from an inter and multidisciplinary perspective. **Focus:** German studies. **Qualif.:** Applicants must be undergraduate students with at least junior standing pursuing German Studies nominated by their department and/or program chair; must be U.S. citizens who are enrolled full time at the university that nominates them; have completed at least two years of college degree in German; and with a minimum of three courses in German Studies. **Criteria:** Selection of applicants will be based on the application and other supporting documents.

Funds Avail.: $1,500-$2,500. **Number Awarded:** 5. **To Apply:** Applicants must submit a completed DAAD application form; curriculum vitae; detailed description of the research project or the pre-dissertation proposal; budget statement; list of German language and German Studies courses taken; two letters of recommendation wherein, one must come from professor supervising the German Studies curriculum or the research project; DAAD language evaluation form signed by a German Department faculty member; and an official transcript of records. **Deadline:** May 1 for U.S. only; June 1 for Canada only; November 1 for both countries. **Contact:** thomanek@daad.org.

4120 ■ Intensive Language Course Grants
(Doctorate/Grant)

Purpose: To enhance language proficiency in Germany. **Focus:** German studies. **Qualif.:** Applicants must be full-

time students currently enrolled in a graduate program in all fields of study except English, German, or any other modern language or literature; must have completed three semesters of college German or have achieved an equivalent level of language proficiency; foreign nationals other than U.S. and Canada must be full-time graduate students in a U.S. or Canadian university for at least one academic year; must have completed three semesters of college German or equivalent level of language proficiency; not a previous grantee for the past three years; must be no older than 32. **Criteria:** Applicants will be assessed based on academic record and statements of project and professional future.

Funds Avail.: 2,300 Euros plus 300-450 Euros travel subsidy. **To Apply:** Applicants must submit a complete DAAD application form; a detailed statement (in English) of approximately 500 words explaining why the applicant wants to attend the intensive language course; resume; a recommendation letter from a professor in the applicant's major field of study; complete transcript of records; DAAD language evaluation form (Sprachzeugnis); list of German language courses taken. Application must be sent to: DAAD New York office. **Deadline:** December 15.

4121 ■ InternXchange Internships
(Undergraduate/Internship)

Purpose: To place strong emphasis on intercultural exchange and the transmission of cultural values and to provide outstanding young journalism students the opportunity to immerse themselves in the society, culture, values, and political attitudes in Germany. **Focus:** Journalism. **Qualif.:** Applicants should be journalism students or any related field at colleges or universities in United States; undergraduate, graduate and graduating seniors are also eligible to apply; must have German language proficiency at least equal to the advanced intermediate level; have an interest in Germany and Germany affairs; and must have their first experience in practical journalism. **Criteria:** A total of 40 applicants will be invited to a selection interview in New York City. A selection committee of American and German experts will then select up to 20 participants/ scholarship recipients.

Funds Avail.: 650 Euros. **To Apply:** Applicants must complete the online form with signature including: curriculum vitae (English); a two-page, double-spaced statement of motivation written in English; a one-to-two-page journalistic writing sample or broadcast transcript; two letters of recommendation from professor handling the major field; an official academic transcript; and DAAD German Language Evaluation Certificate. All materials must be send triplicate (one original, two photocopies) except the letters of recommendation. Evaluation must be completely signed by the Faculty member of the German Department. **Deadline:** January 31. **Contact:** Uta Gaedeke, gaedeke@ daad.org or call 212-758-3223.

4122 ■ Learn German in Germany Grants
(Doctorate/Grant)

Purpose: To encourage DAAD faculty members to attend intensive language courses at Goethe-Instituts in Germany. **Focus:** German studies. **Qualif.:** Applicants must be faculty members in all academic fields except modern languages and literatures; must have PhD. and have been working in research or teaching full-time at a U.S. university or research institution for at least two years; be U.S. citizens; have no teaching experience in the fields of English, German or any modern languages or literatures accepted. **Criteria:** Preference will be given to applicants in the social

Awards are arranged alphabetically below their administering organizations

sciences, the natural sciences, engineering and professional schools, who are in mid-career and are under 46 years of age; must have a basic knowledge of German; should not have previously studied in a German-speaking country for more than two months and/or received a grant to attend a German language course from DAAD or any other organization within the last three years.

Funds Avail.: 1,700 Euros. **Number Awarded:** 2. **To Apply:** Submit a completed DAAD application form; curriculum vitae not to exceed five pages; a detailed statement explaining why the applicant wants to attend a Goethe Institute language course in Germany; accomplish the language evaluation (self-test form enclosed with application); must have the list of publications and a list of courses taught during the previous academic year. **Deadline:** January 31. **Contact:** E-mail: thomanek@daad.org.

4123 ■ Study Scholarships for Artists or Musicians (Graduate/Scholarship)

Purpose: To provide the opportunity to study in Germany, or complete a postgraduate degree course and obtain a degree from a German higher education institution. **Focus:** Fine arts, Architecture, Music, Dance. **Qualif.:** Applicants in the fields of Fine Arts, Architecture, Music and Dance, other academic fields are welcome to apply for the regular Study Scholarship; graduating seniors must be full-time at an accredited university for two years; U.S. or Canadian citizens. **Criteria:** Preference will be given to applicants who have been invited by a faculty member at a German university to study at a particular university department.

Funds Avail.: 750 Euros. **To Apply:** Applicant must complete the online application form available in the website and must have the following: Supplemental materials, CV/Resume, Study proposal, two letters of recommendation, evidence of contact with German Institution and transcript of records. **Deadline:** November 1. **Contact:** kim@daad.org.

4124 ■ University Summer Course Grants (Undergraduate/Grant)

Purpose: To attend a broad range of summer courses at German universities which focus mainly on literary, cultural, political and economic aspects of modern and contemporary Germany. **Focus:** German studies. **Qualif.:** Applicants must be full-time students at any colleges or universities in U.S. and Canada; must have focus in any field of study; must at least reached their junior standing or third year (10 full-course credits for Canadians) at the time of application. **Criteria:** Applicants will be assessed on the basis of their academic and professional future.

Funds Avail.: 850 Euros. **To Apply:** Applicants must submit a completed DAAD application form; autobiographical essay in German; a detailed, English statement of approximately 500 words explaining why the applicant wants to attend a university summer course; recommendation letter written by a professor in the applicant's major field of study but the recommendation should be different from professor who evaluates the language proficiency; complete, official transcripts of all post-secondary studies; DAAD language evaluation form (Sprachzeugnis) signed by any member of German Department at the applicant's institution or by an official of a Goethe Institute. **Deadline:** December 15. **Contact:** gaedeke@daad.org.

4125 ■ German Historical Institute (GHI)
1607 New Hampshire Ave. NW
Washington, DC 20009-2562

Awards are arranged alphabetically below their administering organizations

Ph: (202) 387-3355
Fax: (202) 483-3430
E-mail: info@ghi-dc.org
URL: www.ghi-dc.org

4126 ■ German Historical Institute Doctoral and Postdoctoral Fellowships (Doctorate, Postgraduate/Fellowship)

Purpose: To provide financial assistance to German and American doctoral students and post-doctoral scholars in the fields of German history, the history of German-American relations, and the history of the role of Germany and the USA in international relations. **Focus:** German studies; History, American. **Qualif.:** Applicants must be German and American doctoral students and post-doctoral scholars in the fields of German history, the history of German-American relations, historical role of Germany and the USA in international relations. **Criteria:** Scholarship recipients will be selected based on the jury's review of the application materials.

Funds Avail.: 1,700 Euro for doctoral students; 2,950 Euro for post-doctoral scholars. **To Apply:** Applicants must submit two copies of: cover letter; curriculum vitae; last diploma; project descriptions (in 3,000 words); research schedule; letter of reference. **Deadline:** April 15.

4127 ■ German Historical Institute Fellowships at the Horner Library (Doctorate/Fellowship)

Purpose: To provide travel subsidy and allowance to PhD and MA students for their research at the Joseph Horner Memorial Library in Philadelphia. **Focus:** General studies. **Qualif.:** Applicants must be PhD or MA students. **Criteria:** Scholarship recipient will be selected based on the Selection Committee's review of the application materials.

Funds Avail.: $1,000-$3,500 and a travel subsidy. **Number Awarded:** 2-4. **To Apply:** Applicants must submit a (two-page) project description; curriculum vitae, copies of transcripts; and the name of the referee. Applications (in English or German) should be made electronically to the GHI. **Deadline:** February 15.

4128 ■ Kade-Heideking Fellowships (Doctorate/Fellowship)

Purpose: To provide financial assistance for German doctoral students. **Focus:** German studies; History, American; European studies. **Qualif.:** Applicants must be German doctoral students working in the areas of: American history and German-American relations; international history; German and European history. **Criteria:** Scholarship recipients will be selected based on the Selection Committee's review of the application materials.

Funds Avail.: No specific amount. **Number Awarded:** 1. **To Apply:** Applicants must submit a cover letter; curriculum vitae; proof of academic degree; 8-10 pages of project description; research schedule; and two confidential reference letters. **Remarks:** The fellowship is funded by the Annette Kade Charitable Trust.

4129 ■ Thyssen-Heideking Fellowships (Postdoctorate/Fellowship)

Purpose: To provide financial assistance for American scholars. **Focus:** German studies; History, American; European studies. **Qualif.:** Applicants must be American scholars working in the areas of: American history and German-American relations; international history; and German and European history. **Criteria:** Scholarship recipients will be selected based on the Selection Committee's review of the application materials.

Funds Avail.: 25,000 Euro. **Number Awarded:** 1. **To Apply:** Applicants must submit a cover letter; curriculum vitae; proof of academic degree; 8-10 pages project description; research schedule; and two confidential reference letters. **Deadline:** October 15. **Contact:** fellowship@ghi-dc.org.

4130 ■ German Marshall Fund of the United States (GMF)
1744 R St. NW
Washington, DC 20009
Ph: (202) 683-2650
Fax: (202) 265-1662
E-mail: info@gmfus.org
URL: www.gmfus.org

4131 ■ APSA Congressional Fellowships
(Professional development/Fellowship)

Purpose: To expand public knowledge and awareness of the U.S. Congress around the world. **Focus:** Political science. **Qualif.:** Applicants must be German citizens, possess superior written and spoken English language skills, and have a minimum of three years work experience. Candidates should demonstrate how their professional path would benefit from the APSA Congressional Fellowship. Potential candidates include political journalists, early-to-mid-career academics with outstanding records, and experts from the fields of foreign policy, economics, migration, environment, science and social issues. Representatives from business, trade organizations and labor unions are invited to apply provided they can demonstrate existing political and public policy ties. **Criteria:** Selection will be based on applicants' commitment to transatlantic relations, quality of their written and oral presentation, preparation for the program, professional excellence and current and future involvement in the public policy in Germany.

Funds Avail.: Monthly stipend of $3,800, plus $2,150 for program-related international travel, $125 for books and additional travel expenses. **To Apply:** Applicants must submit the following: application form (available at the website); a curriculum vitae with accompanying cover letter; two fellowship-specific letters of reference; and an essay addressing the significance of the Congressional Fellowship program for the applicants' future career and what value they would bring to a congressional office or committee. **Deadline:** January 15. **Contact:** Ursula Soyez, Senior Program Officer, Oranienburger Str. 13-14, 10178 Berlin; Phone: 49-30-28881323; Fax: 49-30-28881310; Email: usoyez@gmfus.org.

4132 ■ Marshall Memorial Fellowships *(Professional development/Fellowship)*

Purpose: To provide a unique opportunity for emerging leaders from U.S. and Europe to explore policies, institutions and culture on the other side of the Atlantic. **Focus:** General studies. **Qualif.:** Applicants must be nominated by a recognized leader in their community or professional field. All Marshall Memorial Fellowship alumni are also eligible to nominate for the program. Nominators should be in a senior position and be able to evaluate the candidate's leadership potential. **Criteria:** Selection will be based on the committee's criteria.

Funds Avail.: No specific amount. **To Apply:** Applicants must complete the online application, which currently includes an application form, essays, a resume/CV and two letters of recommendation. Nominators should also submit a letter of recommendation. Upon submitting the applications to the selection partner, candidates will be further informed of the interview and selection process.

4133 ■ Peter R. Weitz Prize *(Professional development/Prize)*

Purpose: To acknowledge excellence and originality in reporting European or transatlantic affairs in the American media. **Focus:** General studies. **Qualif.:** Applicants must be journalists covering European issues for American newspapers, magazines and online media, whether they are correspondents based in Europe or cover Europe from the United States. **Criteria:** Selection will be made by a jury of senior American and European journalists based on work published either in print or online by American news media during the previous calendar year.

Funds Avail.: $10,000. **To Apply:** Applicants may contact the German Marshall Fund office for the application process. **Remarks:** Established in 1999 in memory of Peter R. Weitz, a former GMF director of programs, who took a keen interest in promoting coverage of European topics by American journalists.

4134 ■ Transatlantic Fellows Program *(Professional development/Fellowship)*

Purpose: To develop a range of program and initiatives and build important networks of policymakers and analysts in the Euroatlantic community. **Focus:** General studies. **Qualif.:** Applicants must be policy-practitioners, journalists, business people and academics. **Criteria:** Selection will be based on the committee's criteria.

Funds Avail.: No specific amount. **To Apply:** Applicants may contact GMF office for more information on the application process.

4135 ■ Urban and Regional Policy (Comparative Domestic Policy) Fellowships *(Professional development/Fellowship)*

Purpose: To provide opportunities for practitioners and policy-makers working on economic and social issues at the urban and regional policy levels to meet with their counterparts across the Atlantic and discuss policies and measures that have been implemented. **Focus:** General studies. **Qualif.:** Applicants must be practitioners and policymakers working on local and state policy in the United States and Europe; be mid-career professionals engaged in targeted policy areas with an interest in gaining an understanding of how these issues are approached in a policy context other than their own and ability to translate lessons learned into policy action in their own community. Applicants must be civic leaders, policymakers or practitioners in state/local government, leaders from the private sector or representative of non-profit and policy organizations. **Criteria:** Selection will be based on the committee's criteria.

Funds Avail.: No specific amount. **To Apply:** Interested candidates should see the program summary on the website for further details on the program and application process. **Deadline:** January 15. **Contact:** Casey Kuklick, Program Assistant, ckuklick@gmfus.org.

4136 ■ German Society of Pennsylvania (GSP)
611 Spring Garden St.
Philadelphia, PA 19123-3505

Awards are arranged alphabetically below their administering organizations

Ph: (215) 627-2332
Fax: (215) 627-5297
E-mail: info@germansociety.org
URL: www.germansociety.org

4137 ■ German Society Scholarships
(Undergraduate/Scholarship)

Purpose: To provide financial assistance to undergraduate students majoring in German language and literature. **Focus:** Foreign languages; German studies. **Qualif.:** Applicant must be a resident of the Greater Delaware Valley and a high school senior intending to major in German, or a German major (Double majors are also eligible). **Criteria:** Awards are based on the student's achievement and promise. Financial need may also be considered.

Funds Avail.: $2,500. **To Apply:** Applicant must submit a completed application form; a German writing sample (up to one typewritten page); recent transcript; and two letters of reference. **Deadline:** March 13. **Contact:** scholarships@germansociety.org.

4138 ■ Getty Foundation
1200 Getty Ctr. Dr.
Los Angeles, CA 90049
Ph: (310) 440-7300
E-mail: gettyfoundation@getty.edu
URL: www.getty.edu/foundation

4139 ■ Conservation Guest Scholar Grants
(Professional development/Grant)

Purpose: To provide an opportunity for professionals to pursue scholarly research in an interdisciplinary manner across traditional boundaries in areas of interest to the international conservation community. **Focus:** Conservation of natural resources. **Qualif.:** Applicants must be conservators, scientists or professionals who have attained distinction in conservation and allied fields. Applicants should have at least five years experience in the field of conservation and should have an established record of publications and other contributions to the field. **Criteria:** Grants are awarded on a competitive basis. Applications are reviewed by committee and evaluated by the Conservation Institute based on: an applicant's past achievements; their qualifications to undertake the project; how the project would benefit from the resources at the Getty, including its library and collections; and how the project would contribute to the advancement of practice in the conservation field.

Funds Avail.: $3,500. **To Apply:** Applicants are required to complete and submit the online Getty Conservation Guest Scholar Grant application form, which includes completing an online information sheet, uploading a project proposal, curriculum vitae, selected bibliography and a single optional writing sample. **Deadline:** November 1. **Contact:** Phone: 310-440-7374; Fax: 310-440-7703; Email: researchgrants@getty.edu.

4140 ■ Getty GRI-NEH Postdoctoral Fellowships *(Postdoctorate/Fellowship)*

Purpose: To support emerging scholars who are working on projects related to the Getty Research Institute's annual theme. **Focus:** General studies. **Qualif.:** Applicants must be United States citizens or foreign nationals who can document that they have lived in the US for the three years immediately preceding the fellowship application deadline. **Criteria:** Fellowships are awarded on a competitive basis.

Applications will be evaluated by the Getty Research Institute based on: the overall quality of the application; how the proposed project bears upon the annual research theme; the applicant's past achievements; and how the project would benefit from the resources at the Getty, including its library and collections.

Funds Avail.: $42,000. **To Apply:** Applicants are required to complete and submit the online fellowship application form, which includes completing an online information form and uploading a project proposal, doctoral dissertation plan or abstract, curriculum vitae, writing sample, selected bibliography and confirmation letter of academic status. Applicants are required to have two confidential recommendation letters forwarded by their recommenders via e-mail to the Getty Foundation. **Deadline:** November 1. **Contact:** Phone: 310-440-7374; Fax: 310-440-7703; Email: researchgrants@getty.edu; recletters@getty.edu.

4141 ■ Getty Postdoctoral Fellowships
(Postdoctorate/Fellowship)

Purpose: To support emerging scholars who are working on projects related to the Getty Research Institute's annual theme. **Focus:** General studies. **Qualif.:** Applications are welcome from scholars of all nationalities. Applicants must not have received their degree earlier than 2007. **Criteria:** Fellowships are awarded on a competitive basis. Applications will be evaluated by the Getty Research Institute based on: the overall quality of the application; how the proposed project bears upon the annual research theme; the applicant's past achievements; and how the project would benefit from the resources at the Getty, including its library and collections.

Funds Avail.: $30,000. **To Apply:** Applicants are required to complete and submit the online fellowship application form, which includes completing an online information form and uploading a project proposal, doctoral dissertation plan or abstract, curriculum vitae, writing sample, selected bibliography and confirmation letter of academic status. Applicants are required to have two confidential recommendation letters forwarded by their recommenders via e-mail to the Getty Foundation. **Deadline:** November 1. **Contact:** Phone: 310-440-7374; Fax: 310-440-7703; Email: researchgrants@getty.edu; recletters@getty.edu.

4142 ■ Getty Predoctoral Fellowships
(Doctorate/Fellowship)

Purpose: To support emerging scholars who are working on projects related to the Getty Research Institute's annual theme. **Focus:** General studies. **Qualif.:** Applications are welcome from scholars of all nationalities. Applicants must have advanced to candidacy by the time of the fellowship start date and should expect to complete their dissertations during the fellowship period. **Criteria:** Fellowships are awarded on a competitive basis. Applications will be evaluated by the Getty Research Institute based on: the overall quality of the application; how the proposed project bears upon the annual research theme; the applicant's past achievements; and how the project would benefit from the resources at the Getty, including its library and collections.

Funds Avail.: $25,000. **To Apply:** Applicants are required to complete and submit the online fellowship application form, which includes completing an online information form and uploading a project proposal, doctoral dissertation plan or abstract, curriculum vitae, writing sample, selected bibliography and confirmation letter of academic status. Applicants are required to have two confidential recommendation letters forwarded by their recommenders via e-mail to

Awards are arranged alphabetically below their administering organizations

the Getty Foundation. **Deadline:** November 1. **Contact:** Phone: 310-440-7374; Fax: 310-440-7703; Email: researchgrants@getty.edu; recletters@getty.edu.

4143 ■ Getty Scholar Grants (Professional development/Grant)

Purpose: To provide a unique research experience. **Focus:** Art; Humanities; Social sciences. **Qualif.:** Applicants must be scholars, artists or writers who have attained distinction in their fields. Applications are welcome from researchers of all nationalities who are working in the arts, humanities or social sciences. **Criteria:** Grants are awarded on a competitive basis. Applications will be evaluated by the Getty Research Institute based on: the overall quality of the application; how the proposed project bears upon the annual research theme; the applicant's past achievements; and how the project would benefit from the resources at the Getty, including its library and collections.

Funds Avail.: $65,000. **To Apply:** Applicants are required to complete and submit the online Getty Residential Scholar application form which includes completing an online information sheet and uploading a project proposal, curriculum vitae and optional writing sample. **Deadline:** November 1. **Contact:** Phone: 310-440-7374; Fax: 310-440-7703; Email: researchgrants@getty.edu.

4144 ■ Library Research Grants (All/Grant)

Purpose: To provide partial, short-term support for costs relating to travel and living expenses to scholars whose research requires use of specific collections housed in the Getty Research Institute. **Focus:** General studies. **Qualif.:** Applications are intended for scholars of all nationalities and at any level who demonstrate a compelling need to use materials housed in the Research Library, and whose place of residence is more than eighty miles from the Getty Center. **Criteria:** Selection will be based on the committee's criteria.

Funds Avail.: $500-$2,500. **To Apply:** Applicants will be required to complete and submit the online Getty Library Research Grant application form which includes uploading a project proposal; curriculum vitae; selected bibliography of Getty Research Library Collections you wish to consult; and proposed estimated travel costs. Applicants must have two confidential letters of recommendation forwarded by their recommenders via e-mail to the Getty Foundation. Recommenders should attach a scanned original letter to the e-mail or may provide the recommendation in the body of the email. In all cases, letters of recommendation must come directly from the recommender's e-mail account and must clearly indicate the applicant's name and "Library Research Grant" in the subject line, and include the recommender's name and title. **Deadline:** October 15. **Contact:** Phone: 310-440-7374; Fax: 310-440-7703; Email: researchgrants@getty.edu; recletters@getty.edu.

4145 ■ Postdoctoral Fellowships in Conservation Science (Doctorate/Fellowship)

Purpose: To provide a unique two-year research and learning experience in the field. **Focus:** Chemistry; Physical science. **Qualif.:** Applications are welcome from scientists of all nationalities who are interested in pursuing a career in conservation science and have received a PhD in chemistry/physical science. A background in the humanities is helpful, and strong science working practices are essential. **Criteria:** Selection will be based on the committee's criteria.

Funds Avail.: No specific amount. **To Apply:** Applicants

must complete and submit an online application which includes completing an online information form, and uploading a Statement of Interest in Conservation Science, Doctoral Dissertation Abstract, Curriculum Vitae or Resume, Writing Sample and Degree Confirmation Letter. Applicants are also required to submit two confidential letters of recommendation in support of their application. **Deadline:** November 1. **Contact:** Phone: 310-440-7374; Fax: 310-440-7703; Email: researchgrants@getty.edu; recletters@getty.edu.

4146 ■ Ghana-Canada Association of British Columbia (GCABC)
141-6200 McKay Ave., Ste. 499
Burnaby, BC, Canada V5H 4M9
E-mail: info@ghanaiansinbc.org
URL: www.ghanaiansinbc.org

4147 ■ GCABS Youth Scholarship Awards (High School, Undergraduate/Scholarship)

Purpose: To help Ghanaian-Canadian students pursue their education. **Focus:** General studies. **Qualif.:** Applicants must be Ghanaian-Canadian post-secondary students in B.C. and Ghanaian secondary school students in Ghana; must be 17 to 30 years old; must be of Ghanaian descent; must have plan or currently enrolled in an undergraduate degree in any field of study; and must have minimum of six months voluntary community service prior to the application. **Criteria:** Recipients will be evaluated based on submitted materials.

Funds Avail.: $500-$1,000. **Number Awarded:** 9. **To Apply:** Applicants must complete the application form; must submit three letters of recommendation, a 150-word essay explaining the financial need and reason for competing, and essay explaining the role to make GCABC a better community organization. **Deadline:** January 31.

4148 ■ Gibbons P.C.
1 Gateway Ctr.
Newark, NJ 07102-5310
Ph: (973) 596-4500
Fax: (973) 596-0545
URL: www.gibbonslaw.com

4149 ■ John J. Gibbons Fellowships in Public Interest and Constitutional Law (All/Fellowship)

Purpose: To provide a law school student with practical experience and training in the public sector. **Focus:** Law. **Qualif.:** Applicant must be a person of high academic achievement and professional accomplishment, served as a judicial clerk or have been actively working in the field of public interest law. **Criteria:** Selection is based on the application materials submitted.

Funds Avail.: No specific amount. **Number Awarded:** 1. **To Apply:** Applicants must submit a completed application form together with a law school transcript; two letters of recommendation; resume; and a writing sample. **Deadline:** February 22. **Contact:** Lawrence S. Lustberg at llustberg@gibbonslaw.com.

4150 ■ Gilder Lehrman Institute of American History
19 W 44th St., Ste. 500
New York, NY 10036

Awards are arranged alphabetically below their administering organizations

Ph: (646) 366-9666
Fax: (646) 366-9669
E-mail: info@gilderlehrman.org
URL: www.gilderlehrman.org

4151 ■ Gilder Lehrman Short-Term Fellowships
(Graduate, Postdoctorate/Fellowship)

Purpose: To support historians in their scholarly, pedagogical and professional endeavors. **Focus:** History. **Qualif.:** Applicant may be a post-doctoral scholar at any faculty rank; a doctoral candidate who has completed exams and dissertation reading and writing; or a journalist or independent scholar. **Criteria:** Selection is based on the application materials submitted for review.

Funds Avail.: $3,000. **Number Awarded:** 10. **To Apply:** Applicants must submit a cover sheet on applicant's details (name, mailing address, e-mail address, telephone and fax numbers; current rank, department and institution; title of project; duration and amount of proposed fellowship; and names of recommenders); a curriculum vitae; two-to-three pages project proposal that lists the specific holdings in the collection that the applicant intends to use (specify only one archive); two letters of recommendation; schedule and proposed budget of expenses during the tenure of the fellowship. **Deadline:** December 1 and May 1. **Contact:** Questions can be addressed by email to fellowships@gilderlehrman.org.

4152 ■ Keith Gilmore Foundation
5160 Skyline Way NE
Calgary, AB, Canada T2E 6V1
Ph: (403) 275-2662
E-mail: kgf@keithgilmorefoundation.com
URL: www.keithgilmorefoundation.com

4153 ■ Keith Gilmore Foundation - Diploma Scholarships *(Professional development/ Scholarship)*

Purpose: To provide scholarships for deserving individuals. **Focus:** Agriculture, Economic aspects; Journalism; Communications. **Qualif.:** Applicants must be individuals enrolled in a recognized diploma program in agriculture, journalism and/or communications, leading to a career in the field of agriculture. **Criteria:** Selection of recipients is based on academic merit, contribution to school and/or community and indication of academic promise.

Funds Avail.: $1,500. **Number Awarded:** 4. **To Apply:** Application forms are available online at www.keithgilmorefoundation.com. Completed application must be sent to Keith Gilmore Foundation, 5160 Skyline Way NE, Calgary, AB T2E 6V1. **Deadline:** May 15.

4154 ■ Keith Gilmore Foundation - Postgraduate Scholarships *(Postgraduate/Scholarship)*

Purpose: To provide scholarships for deserving individuals. **Focus:** Agriculture, Economic aspects; Medicine, Veterinary; Journalism; Communications. **Qualif.:** Applicant must be an individual enrolled in a postgraduate degree program in agriculture, veterinary medicine, journalism and/or communications at a recognized university, leading to a career in the field of agriculture. **Criteria:** Selection of recipients is based on academic merit, contribution to school and/or community and indication of academic promise.

Funds Avail.: $2,500. **Number Awarded:** 2. **To Apply:**

Application forms are available online at www.keithgilmorefoundation.com. Completed application must be sent to Keith Gilmore Foundation, 5160 Skyline Way NE, Calgary, AB T2E 6V1. **Deadline:** May 15.

4155 ■ Keith Gilmore Foundation - Undergraduate Scholarships *(Undergraduate/Scholarship)*

Purpose: To provide scholarships for deserving individuals. **Focus:** Agriculture, Economic aspects; Medicine, Veterinary; Journalism; Communications. **Qualif.:** Applicant must be an individual enrolled in an undergraduate degree program in agriculture, veterinary medicine, journalism and/or communications at a recognized university, leading to a career in the field of agriculture. **Criteria:** Selection of recipients is based on academic merit, contribution to school and/or community and indication of academic promise.

Funds Avail.: $2,000. **Number Awarded:** 4. **To Apply:** Application forms are available online at www.keithgilmorefoundation.com. Completed application must be sent to Keith Gilmore Foundation, 5160 Skyline Way NE, Calgary, AB T2E 6V1. **Deadline:** May 15.

4156 ■ Elizabeth Glaser Pediatric AIDS Foundation
1140 Connecticut Ave. NW, Ste. 200
Washington, DC 20036
Ph: (202) 296-9165
Fax: (202) 296-9185
Free: 888-499-4673
E-mail: info@pedaids.org
URL: www.pedaids.org

4157 ■ Elizabeth Glaser Scientist Awards
(Professional development/Award)

Purpose: To allow scientists to focus on their long-term efforts on issues specific to pediatric HIV/AIDS by providing funding support for research. **Focus:** Acquired immune deficiency syndrome. **Qualif.:** Applicants must be scientists who represent the best and brightest investigators from the international medical science community. **Criteria:** Recipients will be selected based on their knowledge, innovation and dedication.

Funds Avail.: No specific amount. **To Apply:** Applicants must submit a completed form designed for the award. **Contact:** For further information, applicants may send an e-mail to research@pedaids.org.

4158 ■ Gleaner Life Insurance Society
5200 W US Hwy. 223
Adrian, MI 49221
Ph: (517) 263-2244
Fax: (517) 265-7745
Free: 800-992-1894
E-mail: gleaner@gleanerlife.org
URL: www.gleanerlife.org

4159 ■ Gleaner Life Insurance Scholarship Foundation *(Undergraduate/Scholarship)*

Purpose: To strengthen the brotherhood; to help Gleaner family members pursuing their post-secondary education. **Focus:** General studies. **Qualif.:** Applicants must be family members who are high school graduates or high school

Awards are arranged alphabetically below their administering organizations

senior students; and have at least 10 or more semester credit hours enrolled. **Criteria:** Recipients will be selected based on completion and quality of application, leadership, quality of activities, letters of recommendation and personal statement.

Funds Avail.: $1,000. **Number Awarded:** 1. **To Apply:** Applicants must fill out the application form and present any information and/or reasons for applying; must attach an official transcript of high school records (applicants already graduated from high school are also required to submit high school transcripts or attach an official transcript of college records if applicable); result of an aptitude test at junior or senior level; evaluation of students (leadership, perseverance, prediction of post-high school success); three letters of personal recommendation that can provide a brief statement on the applicant's behalf. **Contact:** scholarships@gleanerlife.org.

4160 ■ Glendale Latino Association (GLA)
PO Box 806
Verdugo City, CA 91046
URL: www.glendalelatinoassociation.com

4161 ■ Glendale Latino Association Scholarships *(High School, Undergraduate/Scholarship)*

Purpose: To provide encouragement and financial support to Latino students pursuing higher education in colleges and universities. **Focus:** Science; Engineering; Mathematics and mathematical sciences; Photography; Aeronautics; Physics. **Qualif.:** Applicants must be Latino high school or college students who demonstrate potential for successful college careers and who demonstrate financial need. **Criteria:** Recipients will be selected based on demonstrated academic achievement, volunteerism and a future return to their community.

Funds Avail.: Amount not specified. **To Apply:** Applicants must complete the application form; must submit a personal essay, a 50-word personal biography, academic transcripts, recommendation letter and employer/supervisor recommendation letter. Qualified applicants will be considered for a personal interview. **Deadline:** March 23.

4162 ■ Glens Falls Foundation
237 Glen St.
Glens Falls, NY 12801
Ph: (518) 761-7350
Fax: (518) 798-8620
E-mail: administrator@glensfallsfoundation.org
URL: www.glensfallsfoundation.org

4163 ■ Gilberto and Lennetta Pesquera Medical School Scholarships *(Graduate/Scholarship)*

Purpose: To assist qualified students who have graduated from local area schools and have successfully completed the first year of medical school. **Focus:** Medical Education. **Qualif.:** Applicants must be second, third or fourth year medical students. **Criteria:** Selection will be based on submitted documents and specific criteria.

Funds Avail.: $4,000. **Number Awarded:** 4. **To Apply:** Applicants should submit a completed application form; official medical school transcripts; brief personal statement describing applicant's academic and occupational goals, interests and activities; names, phone numbers and e-mail addresses of two personal references. **Deadline:** June 24.

Contact: E-mail at administrator@glensfallsfoundation.org.

4164 ■ Harry B. Pulver Scholarships *(Undergraduate/Scholarship)*

Purpose: To provide financial assistance to area students attending Dartmouth College or Harvard University. **Focus:** General studies. **Qualif.:** Applicants must be in their incoming freshmen college year; must be residents of Warren, Washington, or Saratoga Counties in New York State; must have good moral character; good academic standing and financial need. **Criteria:** Selection will be based on submitted documents and specific criteria.

Funds Avail.: $2,000. **To Apply:** Applicants must submit a completed application form; financial aid letter from Dartmouth College or Harvard University; copy of high school transcript including grades through the first semester of the senior year; complete list of extracurricular activities and volunteer work; at least two letters of recommendation; documentation that the applicant will be attending Dartmouth or Harvard; an essay on how the scholarship will assist the applicant in achieving undergraduate goals. **Deadline:** May.

4165 ■ Global Business Travel Association (GBTA)
110 N Royal St., 4th Fl.
Alexandria, VA 22314
Ph: (703) 684-0836
Fax: (703) 684-0263
E-mail: info@gbta.org
URL: www2.nbta.org/usa/Pages/default.aspx

4166 ■ GLP Program Scholarships *(Professional development/Scholarship)*

Purpose: To provide a high-level education experience to individuals in the process of growth and development within their companies. **Focus:** Travel and Tourism. **Qualif.:** Applicant must be an active member of NBTA and must retain NBTA membership throughout the scholarship period. **Criteria:** Recipient will be selected based on educational background, stature and responsibilities of the individual within his/her company; awards and honors; leadership and participation in NBTA activities; potential growth; number of years of professional experience; supervisor recommendation; and resume.

Funds Avail.: No specific amount. **Number Awarded:** 1. **To Apply:** Applicant must complete an application form. **Contact:** Kerry Gaylor at kgaylor@nbtafoundation.org.

4167 ■ Mike Kabo Global Scholarships *(Professional development/Scholarship)*

Purpose: To provide individuals with the opportunity to attend the two day Global Leadership Program (GLP) session and NBTA's International Convention and Exposition. **Focus:** Travel and tourism. **Qualif.:** Applicant must be: a corporate travel professional from the buyer community; a resident outside of the United States of America; a member of NBTA or one of its Paragon Partner Members. **Criteria:** Recipients will be selected by the NBTA Foundation and the National Business Travel Association based on standard recipient review and selection procedures including: value of experience to corporate enterprise and travel management; educational background; responsibilities within company; potential growth; and industry involvement.

Funds Avail.: No specific amount. **Number Awarded:** 1.

Awards are arranged alphabetically below their administering organizations

To Apply: Applicants must complete the form available at the website and must include an essay (500-1000 words) stating the reasons of being interested in receiving this scholarship and how would help the professional growth or bring value to the company. **Deadline:** June 1.

4168 ■ Godparents for Tanzania

PO Box 20221
Roanoke, VA 24018
E-mail: tellmemore@godparents4tz.org
URL: www.godparents4tz.org

4169 ■ Godparents for Tanzania Scholarships
(Undergraduate/Scholarship)

Purpose: To provide financial assistance for projects that are intended to help educate young people. **Focus:** General studies. **Qualif.:** Applicants must be Tanzanian citizens from the Kilimanjaro or Karatu areas of Tanzania; must demonstrate a satisfactory academic record at current level of education; must be attending school in Tanzania; must be studying on the secondary or first degree university level; and must agree to work in Tanzania for five years following graduation. **Criteria:** Recipients are selected based on multiple criteria including academic ability, family circumstances and financial need.

Funds Avail.: No specific amount. **To Apply:** Applicants must submit completed application along with a letter of reference from a non-related adult, preferably an educator or clergy person.

4170 ■ Goethe Society of North America

Department of German Languages and Literature
1409 Cathedral of Learning
University of Pittsburgh
Pittsburgh, PA 15260
Ph: (412) 624-5840
Fax: (412) 624-6318

4171 ■ Gloria Flaherty Scholarships *(Graduate/Scholarship)*

Purpose: To provide financial aid to worthy graduate students who wish to further their education in areas related to the interests promoted by the society. **Focus:** General studies. **Qualif.:** Applicants must be graduate students working on Goethe and/or the Age of Goethe; must able to complete the research project before receiving a doctoral degree are eligible. **Criteria:** Candidates will be selected based on their research proposal.

Funds Avail.: $500. **To Apply:** Interested students should send their dissertation prospectus as email attachments and a separate attachment of recommendation letter from their dessertation advisers. **Deadline:** September 15. **Contact:** Prof. Clark Muenzer, clark.muenzer@gmail.com.

4172 ■ Golden Belt Community Foundation

1307 Williams St.
Great Bend, KS 67530
Ph: (620) 792-3000
Fax: (620) 792-7900
E-mail: gbcf@goldenbeltcf.org
URL: www.goldenbeltcf.org

4173 ■ John J. Mingenback Memorial Scholarships *(Graduate, Undergraduate/Scholarship)*

Purpose: To provide financial assistance to medical students with personal and professional commitment to the community. **Focus:** Education, Medical. **Qualif.:** Applicants must be from Barton County, Kansas; must be full time undergraduate or graduate students at a university or college with preference given to Kansas schools; must be majoring in a health/medical related field; must have a minimum 3.0 GPA. **Criteria:** Selection will be based on the evaluation of submitted documents and specific criteria.

Funds Avail.: $500. **To Apply:** Applicants should submit a completed application form; recommendation letter; official transcripts; personal essay. **Deadline:** March 31. **Contact:** Susan Miller.

4174 ■ Golden Key International Honour Society (GKIHS)

1040 Crown Pointe Pkwy., Ste. 900
Atlanta, GA 30338
Ph: (678) 689-2200
Fax: (678) 689-2298
Free: 800-377-2401
E-mail: memberservices@goldenkey.org
URL: www.goldenkey.org/gk/gksite/HomePage.aspx

4175 ■ Boeing Business Scholarships
(Undergraduate/Scholarship)

Purpose: To financially assist students studying business. **Focus:** Business. **Qualif.:** Applicant must be a U.S. undergraduate member currently enrolled in classes in a degree-granting program. **Criteria:** Selection is based on academic achievement, and demonstrated leadership qualities.

Funds Avail.: $1000. **Number Awarded:** 1. **To Apply:** Applicants must submit a letter of recommendation from a professor in the discipline; and a current, comprehensive official academic transcript. Submit materials to awards@goldenkey.org. **Remarks:** Applicants may apply for more than one scholarship. **Contact:** awards@goldenkey.org.

4176 ■ Golden Key International Honour Society Study Abroad Scholarships
(Undergraduate/Scholarship)

Purpose: To assist members who participate in a study abroad program. **Focus:** General studies. **Qualif.:** Applicants must be undergraduate members currently enrolled in a study abroad program; or will be enrolled the academic year immediately following the granting of the award. **Criteria:** Selection committee will review applicants based on academic achievement and relevance of study abroad program to major field of study.

Funds Avail.: $1000. **Number Awarded:** 10. **To Apply:** Applicants must register scholarship application online. Print the cover page from the online registration and use it as a cover for the entire application and attach a description of the planned academic program (maximum of 5 pages), a one-page statement signed by a professor, and a current comprehensive official academic transcript. **Deadline:** October 15 and April 1. **Contact:** awards@goldenkey.org.

4177 ■ Golden Key Math Scholarships
(Undergraduate/Scholarship)

Purpose: To financially assist students studying math. **Focus:** Mathematics and mathematical sciences. **Qualif.:** Applicant must be undergraduate member majoring in math and currently enrolled in classes at a degree-granting

Awards are arranged alphabetically below their administering organizations

program. **Criteria:** Selection is based on academic achievement in field and the quality of paper submitted.

Funds Avail.: $1,000. **Number Awarded:** 2. **To Apply:** Applicants must register their scholarship application online. Print the cover page from the online registration and use it as a cover for the entire application and attach a math related paper/report (maximum of 10 pages), an essay (maximum of 500 words), a letter of recommendation, and a current comprehensive official academic transcript. **Deadline:** April 1. **Remarks:** Applicants can apply for more than one scholarship. **Contact:** awards@goldenkey.org.

4178 ■ ProWorld Study Abroad Scholarships
(Undergraduate/Scholarship)

Purpose: To provide opportunities for members to explore some of the most beautiful natural and cultural environments in the world. **Focus:** General studies. **Qualif.:** Applicant must be a member in the Australia, Canada or the United States; currently enrolled in a full-time or part-time undergraduate course of study at an accredited four year college or university; and accepted to a ProWorld semester long program. **Criteria:** Selection is based on the application.

Funds Avail.: $1000. **Number Awarded:** 10. **To Apply:** Applicants must submit a ProWorld Scholarship Application to scholarships@myproworld.org.

4179 ■ Golf Canada
1333 Dorval Dr., Ste. 1
Oakville, ON, Canada L6M 4X7
Ph: (905) 849-9700
Fax: (905) 845-7040
Free: 800-263-0009
E-mail: info@golfcanada.ca
URL: www.rcga.org

4180 ■ Suzanne Beauregard Scholarships
(Undergraduate/Scholarship)

Purpose: To support young golfers who wish to pursue their studies. **Focus:** General studies. **Qualif.:** Applicants must have completed at least one full year in a postsecondary degree program and show a minimum average of 70%; must be full-time students at a university, college or CEGEP; must demonstrate a record of athletic and academic excellence; must be members in good standing of Golf Quebec; must demonstrate regular participation in community and or extracurricular activities. **Criteria:** Candidates will be judged based on the information contained within their applications and support materials.

Funds Avail.: $2,000. **Number Awarded:** 2. **To Apply:** Application forms are available online and must be sent to RCGA, 1333 Dorval Dr., Ste. 1, Oakville, ON L6M 4X7. **Deadline:** June 30.

4181 ■ Canadian Seniors' Golf Association Scholarships *(Undergraduate/Scholarship)*

Purpose: To provide financial assistance to young Canadian men and women. **Focus:** General studies; Athletics. **Qualif.:** Applicants must be Canadian men and women who elect to obtain an education and participate in the golf program at a RCGA Foundation-recognized university in Canada; must have successfully completed at least one full year in a post-secondary degree program and show a minimum average of 70% in each year of the program; must have experience in competitive golf at a regional,

provincial or national level; must have been accepted at and plan to attend an RCGA Foundation recognized college or university; and must have been named or be becoming named to the institution's golf team. **Criteria:** Candidates will be judged based on the information contained in their applications and support materials.

Funds Avail.: $3,000. **Number Awarded:** 4. **To Apply:** Application forms are available online and must be sent to RCGA, 1333 Dorval Dr., Ste. 1, Oakville, ON L6M 4X7. **Deadline:** June 30.

4182 ■ Connor/Spafford Scholarships
(Undergraduate/Scholarship)

Purpose: To assist promising Nova Scotia Atlantic Canada men and women to obtain a degree and participate in the golf program at a university. **Focus:** General studies. **Qualif.:** Applicants must be Canadian citizens or residents in Atlantic Canada; must have successfully completed at least one full year in a postsecondary degree program and have maintained a minimum average of 70%; must have been accepted at a university or college and have been named or will be named to the institution's golf team; must have experience in competitive golf at a regional, provincial or natural level. **Criteria:** Preference will be given to applicants who were born in or are residents in Nova Scotia.

Funds Avail.: $5,000. **Number Awarded:** 2. **To Apply:** Application forms are available online. Applicants must submit official transcripts from last two years of high school/ CEGEP showing 70% average each year; official transcripts from each year of post-secondary degree program showing 70% average each year; proof of acceptance and enrollment in RCGA Foundation recognized school; typed personal letter outlining academic and golf achievements, goals and career objectives; and outlined full details of golf background. Applications and required documents must be sent to RCGA, 1333 Dorval Dr., Ste. 1, Oakville, ON L6M 4X7. **Deadline:** June 30.

4183 ■ Mary Ellen Driscoll Scholarships
(Undergraduate/Scholarship)

Purpose: To provide financial assistance to Canadian women. **Focus:** General studies. **Qualif.:** Applicant must be a female Canadian citizen or a resident in New Brunswick; must have successfully completed at least one full year in a post-secondary degree program at a recognized educational institution; must have been accepted at a university or college and have been named or will be named to the institution's golf team; must have experience in competitive golf at the regional, provincial or national level. **Criteria:** Candidates will be judged based on submitted applications and supporting materials. Preference will be given to applicants who have been accepted to a college or university in Canada with a recognized golf program.

Funds Avail.: $1,000. **To Apply:** Application forms are available online and must be sent to RCGA, 1333 Dorval Dr., Ste. 1, Oakville, ON L6M 4X7. **Deadline:** June 30.

4184 ■ Geordie Hilton Academic Scholarships
(Undergraduate/Scholarship)

Purpose: To assist a promising university student. **Focus:** Sports studies; Business administration. **Qualif.:** Applicants must be university students studying towards a degree in sport/business administration; must show a minimum average of 80% in the last two years of high school or CEGEP and have attained a graduation diploma (minimum Grade 12); must have completed at least one full year of educa-

Awards are arranged alphabetically below their administering organizations

tion in a post-secondary degree program at a recognized institution; must intend to continue in an undergraduate or graduate program in sport/business administration; must have experience in competitive golf at a regional, provincial or national level; must have participated in community and/or extracurricular activities; must be Canadian citizens or landed immigrants. **Criteria:** Candidates will be judged based on the information contained in their applications and support materials.

Funds Avail.: $5,000. **Number Awarded:** 1. **To Apply:** Application forms are available online and must be sent to RCGA, 1333 Dorval Dr., Ste. 1, Oakville, ON L6M 4X7. **Deadline:** June 30.

4185 ■ Marlene Streit Golf Scholarships
(Undergraduate/Scholarship)

Purpose: To support the Canadian female golfers attending Canadian universities and colleges recognized by the RCGA Foundation. **Focus:** General studies. **Qualif.:** Applicants must be Canadian female golfers; must have a minimum of 70% in the last two years of high school/CEGEP and have graduated (minimum grade 12). Applicants must also complete at least one full year in a post-secondary degree program and show a minimum average of 70%; must have experience in competitive golf at a regional, provincial or national level; must have been accepted at an RCGA Foundation recognized college or university; and have been named or will be named to the institution's golf team; must be Canadian citizens or landed immigrants. **Criteria:** Candidates will be judged based on the information contained in their applications and support materials.

Funds Avail.: $3,000. **Number Awarded:** 2. **To Apply:** Application forms are available online and must be sent to RCGA, 1333 Dorval Dr., Ste. 1, Oakville, ON L6M 4X7. **Deadline:** June 30.

4186 ■ Golf Course Superintendents Association of America (GCSAA)
1421 Research Park Dr.
Lawrence, KS 66049-3859
Ph: (785) 841-2240
Fax: (785) 832-3643
Free: 800-472-7878
E-mail: mbrhelp@gcsaa.org
URL: www.gcsaa.org

4187 ■ GCSAA Scholars Competition
(Undergraduate/Scholarship)

Purpose: To recognize and encourage students who wish to pursue a career in golf course management. **Focus:** Turfgrass management. **Qualif.:** Applicants must be undergraduate students who are currently enrolled in two or more years of an accredited program related to golf course management; must have completed the first year (24 credit hours or equivalent); and must be GCSAA members. Graduating seniors prior to the application deadline are ineligible. **Criteria:** Applicants will be evaluated based on academic achievement, potential to become a leading professional, employment history, extracurricular activities, recommendation of a superintendent with whom students have worked with and a current academic advisor.

Funds Avail.: $500 to $6,000. **Number Awarded:** Varies. **To Apply:** Applicants must submit their transcript of records, Advisor's Report and Superintendent's Report.

The essay component must not exceed two double-spaced pages. Additional application forms can be obtained from the Environmental Institute for Golf or may visit the GCSAA website. **Deadline:** June 1.

4188 ■ GCSAA Student Essay Contest *(Graduate, Undergraduate/Prize)*

Purpose: To provide assistance to students pursuing degrees in turfgrass science. **Focus:** Turfgrass management; Agronomy. **Qualif.:** Applicants must be undergraduate and graduate students pursuing degrees in turfgrass science, agronomy, or any related fields to golf course management; and must be GCSAA members. **Criteria:** Selected applicants should have an essay that is original, compelling, well-organized, readable, persuasive and creative. Technical accuracy, composition skills and the student's adherence to the contest rules will be considered.

Funds Avail.: Total amount of $4,500. **Number Awarded:** 3. **To Apply:** Applicant's essay should be 7 to 12 pages in length, double-spaced and must be in type-written format; must include a cover page with the student's name, school and year attended, home and campus addresses, contact numbers and signature. Each page should be numbered including the student's last name. **Deadline:** March 31. **Contact:** Questions can be addressed to Mischia Wright at mwright@gcsaa.org.

4189 ■ Dr. James Watson Fellowship Program
(Doctorate, Graduate/Fellowship)

Purpose: To provide financial assistance for the future educators and researchers of the turfgrass industry. **Focus:** Turfgrass management. **Qualif.:** Applicants must be candidates for masters' or doctoral degrees; be in their second year of a recognized program in turfgrass science or any related fields; must have plans to pursue a career in research, instruction, or extension service in a university setting. **Criteria:** Selection of applicants will be based on academic excellence, peer recommendations, communication skills, commitment to a career as instructors and/or scientists, accomplishment in research and/or education and potential contributions to the industry.

Funds Avail.: $5,000. **Number Awarded:** 4. **To Apply:** Applicants must attach a resume, one-page summaries of any research projects, educational efforts, extension programs, or other relevant activities in which they have been involved; letters of professional recommendation from an adviser or other academic instructors; one letter of recommendation from a superintendent with whom they have had professional contact; and transcript of records. **Deadline:** October 1.

4190 ■ Gonzaga University School of Law
PO Box 3528
Spokane, WA 99220
Ph: (509) 323-3700
E-mail: sharmon@lawschool.gonzaga.edu
URL: www.law.gonzaga.edu

4191 ■ Thomas More Scholarships
(Undergraduate/Scholarship)

Purpose: To help individuals in the pursuit of their educational goals. **Focus:** Law. **Qualif.:** Applicants must be U.S. or Canadian citizens who are entering a law school as first year students; must have a 3.5 GPA or higher and have taken the LSAT. **Criteria:** Recipients are selected based on academic achievement, life, and work experience.

Awards are arranged alphabetically below their administering organizations

Funds Avail.: No specific amount. **Number Awarded:** 5. **To Apply:** Applicants must submit their completed application and two letters of recommendation. **Deadline:** March 1. **Contact:** Pam Pschirrer, 509-323-3742, ppschirrer@lawschool.gonzaga.edu.

4192 ■ Google Inc.
1600 Amphitheatre Pkwy.
Mountain View, CA 94043
Ph: (650) 253-0000
Fax: (650) 253-0001
URL: www.google.com

4193 ■ Dr. Anita Borg Memorial Scholarships - USA *(Graduate, Undergraduate/Scholarship)*

Purpose: To support and encourage women to excel in computing and technology and become active role models and leaders in the field. **Focus:** Computer and information science; Engineering, Computer. **Qualif.:** Applicants must be female students entering their senior year of undergraduate study or be enrolled in a graduate program in the current academic year at a university in the US; must be enrolled in computer science or computer engineering or a closely related technical field as a full-time student for the current year; must maintain a cumulative GPA of at least 3.5 on a 4.0 scale or 4.5 on a 5.0 scale. **Criteria:** Scholarships will be awarded based on the strength of each candidate's academic background and demonstrated leadership.

Funds Avail.: $10,000. **To Apply:** Applicants may apply online. Applicants must submit their electronic resume, essay responses, transcripts and name and email of referrers (PDF format preferred for all requested documents). **Deadline:** February 1. **Contact:** anitaborgscholars@google.com.

4194 ■ Google-American Indian Science and Engineering Society Scholarships *(Graduate, Undergraduate/Scholarship)*

Purpose: To encourage students to excel in their studies and become active role models and leaders. **Focus:** Computer and information science; Engineering, Computer. **Qualif.:** Applicants must be currently pursuing undergraduate and graduate degrees in computer science or computer engineering. **Criteria:** Selection will be based on the committee's criteria.

Funds Avail.: $10,000. **To Apply:** Applicants may contact the society for the application process.

4195 ■ Google Hispanic College Fund Scholarships *(Graduate, Undergraduate/Scholarship)*

Purpose: To encourage students to excel in their studies and become active role models and leaders. **Focus:** Computer and information science; Engineering, Computer. **Qualif.:** Applicants must be of Hispanic background; must be US citizens or permanent residents residing in the US or Puerto Rico; must be studying at an accredited university in the US or Puerto Rico for the upcoming academic year; must be enrolled for the upcoming academic year; must have a minimum GPA of a 3.5 on a 4.0 scale; must be junior or senior undergraduate or graduate students pursuing a degree in computer science or computer engineering for the upcoming academic year. **Criteria:** Selection will be based on demonstrated academic excellence and financial need.

Funds Avail.: $10,000. **To Apply:** Applicants may apply to the Google scholarship program by completing the STEM Majors Application. Applicants must submit their official transcript, proof of family income and proof of citizenship status. Applicant's essay, letter of recommendation, resume and financial aid verification must be submitted online. **Deadline:** February 23.

4196 ■ Government Finance Officers Association of United States and Canada (GFOA)
203 N LaSalle St., Ste. 2700
Chicago, IL 60601-1210
Ph: (312) 977-9700
Fax: (312) 977-4806
E-mail: membership@gfoa.org
URL: www.gfoa.org

4197 ■ Daniel B. Goldberg Scholarships *(Graduate/Scholarship)*

Purpose: To recognize outstanding performance in graduate programs by students preparing for a career in state and local government finance. **Focus:** Finance. **Qualif.:** Applicants must be current, full-time students in a graduate program that prepares students for careers in state and local government finance and are expecting to be enrolled in the spring 2011 semester in a baccalaureate degree or its equivalent; must be citizens or permanent residents of the United States or Canada; and must have not been a winner of scholarship program administered by the GFOA of the US and Canada. **Criteria:** Candidates will be assessed on the basis of plans to pursue a career in state or local government finance; strength of past coursework and present plan of study; letters of recommendation from academic advisor, the dean of the graduate program and others; and undergraduate and graduate grade point averages.

Funds Avail.: $10,000. **To Apply:** Applicants must submit completed application form; statement of proposed career plan in state and local government finance; undergraduate and graduate transcript of grades; resume; academic advisor's or dean's letter of recommendation; and other graduate program faculty letters of recommendation. **Deadline:** February 24.

4198 ■ Frank L. Greathouse Government Accounting Scholarships *(Graduate, Undergraduate/Scholarship)*

Purpose: To recognize outstanding performance in accounting studies by students preparing for a career in state and local government finance. **Focus:** Finance. **Qualif.:** Applicants must be current full-time undergraduate or graduate students in an accounting program preparing for a career in state and local government finance (both advanced undergraduate and graduate students); must be citizens or permanent residents of the United States or Canada; must be recommended by the academic advisor or the accounting program chair; and must have not been past winners of a scholarship program administered by the Government Finance Officers Association of the US and Canada. **Criteria:** Applicants will be selected based on the statement of proposed career plan in state and local government finance or proposed plan of graduate studies in government accounting or public administration; strength of past coursework and present plan of study; letters of recommendation by academic advisor, chair of the accounting program and others; and undergraduate/ graduate grade point averages.

Awards are arranged alphabetically below their administering organizations

Funds Avail.: $5,000. **To Apply:** Applicants must submit completed application form; statement of proposed career plan in state and local government finance; plan of graduate study (if applicable); undergraduate and graduate grade transcripts; resume; academic advisor's or department chair's letter of recommendation; and other letters of recommendation (optional). **Deadline:** February 24.

4199 ■ Minorities in Government Finance Scholarships *(Graduate, Undergraduate/ Scholarship)*

Purpose: To recognize outstanding performance by minority students preparing for careers in state and local government finance. **Focus:** Finance; Public administration; Political science; Economics; Business administration.**Qualif.:** Applicants must be current full- or part-time upper-division undergraduate or graduate students in public administration, accounting, finance, political science, economics or business administration (with a specific focus on government or nonprofit management); must belong to one of the following groups (as defined by the U.S. Census Bureau): Black or African American, American Indian or Alaska Native, Asian, Native Hawaiian or other Pacific islander, Hispanic or Latino; must be citizens or permanent residents of the United States or Canada; must be recommended by academic advisor, the dean of the graduate program (graduate students) or department chair (undergraduate students); must be students who have not received scholarships administered by the Government Finance Officers Association of the United States and Canada. **Criteria:** Recipients will be selected on the basis of plans to pursue a career in state and local government finance; past academic record and work experience; strength of past coursework and present plan of study; and undergraduate and graduate grade point averages.

Funds Avail.: $5,000. **To Apply:** Applicants must submit application form; statement of proposed state and local government finance career plan and if applicable, plan of graduate study; undergraduate and graduate grade transcripts; resume; and academic advisor's, department chair's or dean's letter of recommendation; and other letters of recommendation (optional). **Deadline:** February 24.

4200 ■ George A. Nielsen Public Investor Scholarships *(Graduate, Undergraduate/ Scholarship)*

Purpose: To inspire careers and interest in the efficient and productive investment of public funds. **Focus:** Public administration; Finance; Business administration. **Qualif.:** Program is open to employees of a local government or other public entity who are enrolled or plan to enroll in an undergraduate or graduate program in public administration, finance, business administration, or related field; must be employed at least one year by a state, local government, or special district with significant responsibilities for cash management or treasury activities including a specific focus on the investing of available cash; must be a citizen or permanent resident of the United States or Canada; must have a recommendation by employer; must be enrolled in a graduate or undergraduate program in public administration, finance or business administration before fund is awarded; must be a student who has not been a past winner of a scholarship program administered by the Government Finance Officers Association of the United States and Canada. **Criteria:** Candidate will be selected based on plans to pursue a career with a state, local government or other special purpose government entity; past work experience; present plan of study as it relates to

a career in the public sector; letters of recommendation from employer; and undergraduate and graduate grade point averages.

Funds Avail.: $5,000 (may be two awards of $2,500 each). **To Apply:** Applicants must submit an application form; statement describing experience working for a state, local government or other special purpose government entity, proposed plan of study and how it will help career in the public sector; undergraduate and graduate grade transcripts; resume; employer's letter of recommendation; and other letters of recommendation (optional).

4201 ■ Public Employee Retirement Research and Administration Scholarships *(Graduate/ Scholarship)*

Purpose: To encourage graduate students to pursue research and careers in the area of public-sector retirement benefits. **Focus:** Finance. **Qualif.:** Applicants must be current full or part-time students in a graduate program in public administration, finance, business administration or social sciences; must have a baccalaureate degree or its equivalent; must be citizens or permanent residents of the United States or Canada; must be recommended by academic advisor or dean of the graduate program; must be students who have not become recipients of scholarships administered by the Government Finance Officers Association of the United States and Canada. **Criteria:** Candidates will be evaluated based on the plan to pursue a career in state or local government with a focus on public-sector retirement benefits; past academic records and relevant work experiences, including research in public-sector retirement benefits; strength of past graduate coursework and present plan of study; letters of recommendation from the academic advisor, dean of the graduate program and others; and undergraduate and graduate grade point average.

Funds Avail.: $4,000. **To Apply:** Applicants must submit application form; statement of proposed plan of graduate study and state and local government career plans; undergraduate and graduate grade transcripts; resume; academic advisor's or dean's letter of recommendation; other letters of recommendation (optional); information on pension-related research (optional). **Deadline:** February 29.

4202 ■ Graham and Dunn P.C.
2801 Alaskan Way, Ste. 300
Seattle, WA 98121-1128
Ph: (206) 624-8300
Fax: (206) 340-9599
E-mail: info@grahamdunn.com
URL: www.grahamdunn.com

4203 ■ Graham & Dunn 1L Diversity Fellowships *(Graduate/Fellowship)*

Purpose: To promote diversity in the legal profession. **Focus:** Law. **Qualif.:** Applicant must be a first year law school student in good standing pursuing a Juris Doctor at an ABA-accredited law; must possess a record of academic, employment, community and/or other achievement indicating potential for success in law school and in the legal profession; must contribute to the diversity of the law school student body and the legal community; must demonstrate commitment to fostering diversity in the legal community; must be able to commit to participation in a 12-week summer clerkship program with the firm; and must be ultimately

Awards are arranged alphabetically below their administering organizations

committed to a long-term practicing of law in Seattle. **Criteria:** Selection is based on the submitted application materials.

Funds Avail.: $7,500. **To Apply:** Applicants must submit a resume, complete transcript of undergraduate grades, first semester law school grades, a short personal statement (maximum of 500 words), a legal writing sample (maximum of 5 pages), and a list of two academic or professional references. **Deadline:** January 19. **Contact:** April Upchurch Olsen at the above address.

4204 ■ Grand Canyon Historical Society (GCHS)
c/o Al Richmond
50 Adobe Cir.
Sedona, AZ 86351
Ph: (928) 606-2781
E-mail: alrichmond@npgcable.com
URL: www.grandcanyonhistory.org

4205 ■ Grand Canyon Historical Society Scholarships *(Graduate/Scholarship)*

Purpose: To provide financial assistance to graduate students as support for research. **Focus:** History; Historic Preservation; Environmental Conservation. **Qualif.:** Applicants must be any Arizona university graduate student doing work in history and historic or environmental preservation fields. **Criteria:** Selection will be based on evaluation of submitted documents and specific criteria.

Funds Avail.: $1,000. **To Apply:** Applicants must submit a research project concerning historical individuals and environmental issues in the Grand Canyon region; one-page application letter with a short biography that includes name, address, phone, number, undergraduate or graduate degrees, current degree program, department and advisor; and must submit a short paragraph describing how this award would be applied on the proposed project. **Contact:** Al Richmond at the above address.

4206 ■ Grand Haven Area Community Foundation
One S Harbor Dr.
Grand Haven, MI 49417
Ph: (616) 842-6378
Fax: (616) 842-9518
E-mail: bpost@ghacf.org
URL: www.ghacf.org

4207 ■ Charles A. Bassett Endowed Memorial Scholarship Fund *(Undergraduate/Scholarship)*

Purpose: To improve and enhance the quality of life in the Tri-Cities area by serving as a leader, catalyst and resource for philanthropy; to strive for community improvement through strategic grantmaking in such fields as arts, education, health, environment, youth, social services and other human needs. **Focus:** General studies. **Qualif.:** Applicants must be graduating seniors who have played on the tennis team. **Criteria:** Recipients will be selected based on financial need; academic achievement; leadership ability; community and volunteer service; creativity; and special circumstances.

Funds Avail.: No specific amount. **To Apply:** Applicants must submit: completed application form; current high school or college transcript; Student Aid Report (SAR) from

the Free Application for Federal Student Aid (FAFSA); and letter of recommendation. **Deadline:** March 5. **Contact:** 616-842-6378.

4208 ■ James W. Jr. and Jane T. Brown Scholarship Fund *(Undergraduate/Scholarship)*

Purpose: To assist men and women in the Tri-Cities in returning to school to further their education after a period of working. **Focus:** General studies. **Qualif.:** Applicants must be over the age of 21. **Criteria:** Recipients are selected based on financial need; academic achievement; leadership ability; community and volunteer service; creativity; and special circumstances.

Funds Avail.: No specific amount. **To Apply:** Applicants must submit: completed application form; current high school or college transcript; Student Aid Report (SAR) from the Free Application for Federal Student Aid (FAFSA), unless applying for scholarships that do not consider financial need; and letter of recommendation. **Deadline:** March 5. **Contact:** 616-842-6378.

4209 ■ Geri Coccodrilli Culinary Scholarship Fund *(Undergraduate/Scholarship)*

Purpose: To improve and enhance the quality of life in the Tri-Cities area by serving as a leader, catalyst and resource for philanthropy; to strive for community improvement through strategic grantmaking in such fields as arts, education, health, environment, youth, social services and other human needs. **Focus:** Culinary Arts. **Qualif.:** Applicants must be graduating high school seniors from the Tri-Cities area and Fruitport High School who wish to pursue studies in the Culinary Arts. **Criteria:** Recipients are selected based on leadership ability; community involvement; financial need; creativity; and academic achievement.

Funds Avail.: No specific amount. **To Apply:** Applicants must submit: completed application form; current high school or college transcript; Student Aid Report (SAR) from the Free Application for Federal Student Aid (FAFSA); and letter of recommendation. **Deadline:** March 5. **Contact:** 616-842-6378.

4210 ■ Dake Community Manufacturing Scholarships *(Undergraduate/Scholarship)*

Purpose: To provide encouragement and support to a student who wants to further his/her manufacturing education. **Focus:** Manufacturing. **Qualif.:** Applicants must be from Northwest Ottawa County, Muskegon County or Oceana County; must be high school graduating seniors, current college students or adult students. **Criteria:** Recipients are selected based on financial need; academic achievement; leadership ability; creativity; community and volunteer service; and special circumstances.

Funds Avail.: No specific amount. **To Apply:** Applicants must submit: completed application form; current high school or college transcript; Student Aid Report (SAR) from the Free Application for Federal Student Aid (FAFSA), unless applying for scholarships that do not consider financial need; and letter of recommendation. **Deadline:** March 5. **Contact:** 616-842-6378.

4211 ■ E.V. Erickson Field of Interest Education Scholarship Fund *(Undergraduate/Scholarship)*

Purpose: To improve and enhance the quality of life in the Tri-Cities area by serving as a leader, catalyst and resource for philanthropy; to strive for community improvement through strategic grantmaking in such fields as arts, educa-

Awards are arranged alphabetically below their administering organizations

tion, health, environment, youth, social services and other human needs. **Focus:** Education. **Qualif.:** Applicants must be graduating high school seniors who have excelled not only academically but also demonstrate leadership qualities; must have a 3.8 GPA or better on a 4.0 scale. **Criteria:** Recipients will be selected based on financial need; academic achievement; leadership ability; creativity; community and volunteer service; and special circumstances.

Funds Avail.: No specific amount. **To Apply:** Applicants must submit: completed application form; current high school or college transcript; Student Aid Report (SAR) from the Free Application for Federal Student Aid (FAFSA), unless applying for scholarships that do not consider financial need; and letter of recommendation. **Deadline:** March 5. **Contact:** 616-842-6378.

4212 ■ Kevin Ernst Memorial Scholarship Fund
(Undergraduate/Scholarship)

Purpose: To improve and enhance the quality of life in the Tri-Cities area by serving as a leader, catalyst and resource for philanthropy; to strive for community improvement through strategic grantmaking in such fields as the arts, education, health, environment, youth, social services and other human needs. **Focus:** Mathematics and mathematical sciences. **Qualif.:** Applicants must be students in the Foundation's service area who wish to continue their education in the field of mathematics. **Criteria:** Recipients are selected based on financial need; academic achievement; leadership ability; creativity; community and volunteer service; and special circumstances.

Funds Avail.: No specific amount. **To Apply:** Applicants must submit: completed application form; current high school or college transcript; Student Aid Report (SAR) from the Free Application for Federal Student Aid (FAFSA), unless applying for scholarships that do not consider financial need; and letter of recommendation. **Deadline:** March 5. **Contact:** 616-842-6378.

4213 ■ Bertha M. Fase Memorial Scholarship Fund *(Undergraduate/Scholarship)*

Purpose: To improve and enhance the quality of life in the Tri-Cities area by serving as a leader, catalyst and resource for philanthropy; to strive for community improvement through strategic grantmaking in such fields as arts, education, health, environment, youth, social services and other human needs. **Focus:** Education. **Qualif.:** Applicants must be Grand Haven High School graduating seniors with a 3.5 GPA or better; must plan to pursue studies in the field of Education. **Criteria:** Recipients will be selected based on academic achievement; leadership ability; creativity; community and volunteer service; and special circumstances.

Funds Avail.: No specific amount. **To Apply:** Applicants must submit: completed application form; current high school or college transcript; Student Aid Report (SAR) from the Free Application for Federal Student Aid (FAFSA), unless applying for scholarships that do not consider financial need; and letter of recommendation. **Deadline:** March 5. **Contact:** 616-842-6378.

4214 ■ Scott A. Flahive Memorial Scholarship Fund *(Undergraduate/Scholarship)*

Purpose: To improve and enhance the quality of life in the Tri-Cities area by serving as a leader, catalyst and resource for philanthropy; to strive for community improvement through strategic grantmaking in such fields as arts, education, health, environment, youth, social services and other human needs. **Focus:** Criminal justice. **Qualif.:** Applicants

must be students pursuing career in the field of law enforcement and/or criminal justice. **Criteria:** Recipients are selected based on demonstrated academic excellence; financial need; leadership ability; community and volunteer service; creativity; and special circumstances.

Funds Avail.: No specific amount. **To Apply:** Applicants must submit: completed application form; current high school or college transcript; Student Aid Report (SAR) from the Free Application for Federal Student Aid (FAFSA), unless applying for scholarships that do not consider financial need; and letter of recommendation. **Deadline:** March 5. **Contact:** 616-842-6378.

4215 ■ Floto-Peel Family Scholarship Fund
(Undergraduate, Vocational/Occupational/ Scholarship)

Purpose: To improve and enhance the quality of life in the Tri-Cities area by serving as a leader, catalyst and resource for philanthropy; to strive for community improvement through strategic grantmaking in such fields as arts, education, health, environment, youth, social services and other human needs. **Focus:** Nursing; Business. **Qualif.:** Applicants must be Tri-Cities area residents planning to attend a two-to-four year college, university or vocational school; must plan to study in the field of nursing or business; must have 2.5 GPA. **Criteria:** Recipients are selected based on financial need; academic achievement; leadership ability; community and volunteer service; creativity; and special circumstances.

Funds Avail.: No specific amount. **To Apply:** Applicants must submit: completed application form; current high school or college transcript; Student Aid Report (SAR) from the Free Application for Federal Student Aid (FAFSA), unless applying for scholarships that do not consider financial need; and letter of recommendation. **Deadline:** March 5. **Contact:** 616-842-6378.

4216 ■ John and Victory E. Frantz Scholarship Fund *(Undergraduate/Scholarship)*

Purpose: To improve and enhance the quality of life in the Tri-Cities area by serving as a leader, catalyst and resource for philanthropy; to strive for community improvement through strategic grantmaking in such fields as arts, education, health, environment, youth, social services and other human needs; to assist high school graduating seniors of northwest Ottawa County to pursue a college education. **Focus:** General studies. **Qualif.:** Applicants must be high school graduating seniors of northwest Ottawa County. **Criteria:** Recipients are selected based on demonstrated academic excellence and financial need.

Funds Avail.: No specific amount. **To Apply:** Applicants must submit: completed application form; current high school or college transcript; Student Aid Report (SAR) from the Free Application for Federal Student Aid (FAFSA), unless applying for scholarships that do not consider financial need; and letter of recommendation. **Deadline:** March 5. **Contact:** 616-842-6378.

4217 ■ Gauthier Family Scholarship Fund
(Undergraduate/Scholarship)

Purpose: To improve and enhance the quality of life in the Tri-Cities area by serving as a leader, catalyst and resource for philanthropy; to strive for community improvement through strategic grantmaking in such fields as the arts, education, health, environment, youth, social services and other human needs. **Focus:** Engineering. **Qualif.:** Applicants must be high school students from the Tri-Cities

Awards are arranged alphabetically below their administering organizations

area who wish to pursue studies in mechanical or electrical engineering at Michigan Technical Institute. **Criteria:** Recipients are selected based on demonstrated academic excellence and financial need.

Funds Avail.: No specific amount. **To Apply:** Applicants must submit: completed application form; current high school or college transcript; Student Aid Report (SAR) from the Free Application for Federal Student Aid (FAFSA), unless applying for scholarships that do not consider financial need; and letter of recommendation. **Deadline:** March 5. **Contact:** 616-842-6378.

4218 ■ Tom Gifford Scholarships
(Undergraduate/Scholarship)

Purpose: To improve and enhance the quality of life in the Tri-Cities area by serving as a leader, catalyst and resource for philanthropy; to strive for community improvement through strategic grantmaking in such fields as arts, education, health, environment, youth, social services and other human needs. **Focus:** General studies. **Qualif.:** Applicants must be graduates of Spring Lake High School; must have been SLHS students for three semesters immediately prior to graduation and must have attended for at least three years; must plan to attend Amherst College within 30 months of high school graduation. **Criteria:** Recipients are selected based on demonstrated academic excellence and financial need.

Funds Avail.: No specific amount. **To Apply:** Applicants must submit: completed application form; current high school or college transcript; Student Aid Report (SAR) from the Free Application for Federal Student Aid (FAFSA), unless applying for scholarships that do not consider financial need; and letter of recommendation. **Deadline:** March 5. **Contact:** 616-842-6378.

4219 ■ Grand Haven Offshore Challenge Scholarship Fund *(Undergraduate/Scholarship)*

Purpose: To improve and enhance the quality of life in the Tri-Cities area by serving as a leader, catalyst and resource for philanthropy; to strive for community improvement through strategic grantmaking in such fields as arts, education, health, environment, youth, social services and other human needs. **Focus:** Natural resources. **Qualif.:** Applicants must be graduating high school seniors from the Tri-Cities area who plan to pursue a career in natural resources such as fisheries, wildlife and environmental water quality at any public or private college or university. **Criteria:** Recipients are selected based on demonstrated academic excellence and financial need.

Funds Avail.: No specific amount. **To Apply:** Applicants must submit: completed application form; current high school or college transcript; Student Aid Report (SAR) from the Free Application for Federal Student Aid (FAFSA), unless applying for scholarships that do not consider financial need; and letter of recommendation. **Deadline:** March 5. **Contact:** 616-842-6378.

4220 ■ Barbara and Nicole Heicox Foreign Travel and Study Scholarship Fund
(Undergraduate/Scholarship)

Purpose: To improve and enhance the quality of life in the Tri-Cities area by serving as a leader, catalyst and resource for philanthropy; to strive for community improvement through strategic grantmaking in such fields as arts, education, health, environment, youth, social services and other human needs. **Focus:** General studies. **Qualif.:** Applicants must be juniors, high school and/or college students wish-

ing to pursue their educational opportunities in foreign countries. **Criteria:** Recipients are selected based on financial need; academic achievement; leadership ability; community and volunteer service; creativity; and special circumstances.

Funds Avail.: No specific amount. **To Apply:** Applicants must submit: completed application form; current high school or college transcript; Student Aid Report (SAR) from the Free Application for Federal Student Aid (FAFSA), unless applying for scholarships that do not consider financial need; and letter of recommendation. **Deadline:** March 5. **Contact:** 616-842-6378.

4221 ■ Marjorie M. Hendricks Environmental Education Scholarship Fund *(Undergraduate/ Scholarship)*

Purpose: To assist an upperclassman or graduate student majoring in environmental science field. **Focus:** Environmental science. **Qualif.:** Applicants must be upperclassmen or graduate students majoring in an environmental science field who plan to attend Aquinas College or Grand Valley State University. **Criteria:** Recipients are selected based on financial need.

Funds Avail.: No specific amount. **To Apply:** Applicants must submit: completed application form; current high school or college transcript; Student Aid Report (SAR) from the Free Application for Federal Student Aid (FAFSA), unless applying for scholarships that do not consider financial need; and letter of recommendation. **Deadline:** March 5. **Contact:** 616-842-6378.

4222 ■ Michael Herman Memorial Scholarship Fund *(Undergraduate, Vocational/Occupational/ Scholarship)*

Purpose: To improve and enhance the quality of life in the Tri-Cities area by serving as a leader, catalyst and resource for philanthropy; to strive for community improvement through strategic grantmaking in such fields as arts, education, health, environment, youth, social services and other human needs. **Focus:** General studies. **Qualif.:** Applicants must be soccer players and coaches of younger students who are interested in learning soccer; must be current high school graduates of any Tri-Cities area public or private high school intending to pursue degree or certification at any two-or four-year accredited college, university, vocational or technical school; first consideration shall be given to students who played on a soccer team and wish to continue playing in college on an intramural, club or college team. **Criteria:** Recipients will be selected based on academic achievement; financial need; community and volunteer service; creativity; leadership ability; and special circumstances.

Funds Avail.: No specific amount. **To Apply:** Applicants must submit: completed application form; current high school or college transcript; Student Aid Report (SAR) from the Free Application for Federal Student Aid (FAFSA), unless applying for scholarships that do not consider financial need; and letter of recommendation. **Deadline:** March 5. **Contact:** 616-842-6378.

4223 ■ Hierholzer-Fojtik Scholarship Fund
(Undergraduate/Scholarship)

Purpose: To improve and enhance the quality of life in the Tri-Cities area by serving as a leader, catalyst and resource for philanthropy; to strive for community improvement through strategic grantmaking in such fields as the arts,

Awards are arranged alphabetically below their administering organizations

education, health, environment, youth, social services and other human needs. **Focus:** Law. **Qualif.:** Applicants must be Grand Haven High School graduates planning to pursue law as a career. **Criteria:** Recipients are selected based on financial need; academic achievement; leadership ability; creativity; community and volunteer service; and special circumstances.

Funds Avail.: No specific amount. **To Apply:** Applicants must submit: completed application form; current high school or college transcript; Student Aid Report (SAR) from the Free Application for Federal Student Aid (FAFSA), unless applying for scholarships that do not consider financial need; and letter of recommendation. **Deadline:** March 5. **Contact:** 616-842-6378.

4224 ■ Hoffman Family Scholarship Fund
(Undergraduate/Scholarship)

Purpose: To improve and enhance the quality of life in the Tri-Cities area by serving as a leader, catalyst and resource for philanthropy; to strive for community improvement through strategic grantmaking in such fields as arts, education, health, environment, youth, social services and other human needs. **Focus:** General studies. **Qualif.:** Applicants must be graduating high school seniors at Grand Haven, Spring Lake or Fruitport high schools; must have a 3.0 GPA; special consideration will be given to an individual who is a member of the first generation in their family to attend college. **Criteria:** Recipients are selected based on demonstrated academic excellence and financial need.

Funds Avail.: No specific amount. **To Apply:** Applicants must submit: completed application form; current high school or college transcript; Student Aid Report (SAR) from the Free Application for Federal Student Aid (FAFSA), unless applying for scholarships that do not consider financial need; and letter of recommendation. **Deadline:** March 5. **Contact:** 616-842-6378.

4225 ■ Seth Koehler Central High School Scholarship Fund *(Undergraduate, Vocational/Occupational/Scholarship)*

Purpose: To provide educational financial assistance to a graduating senior from Central High School. **Focus:** General studies. **Qualif.:** Applicants must be graduating seniors from Central High School; must have plan to attend any two-to-four year college, university, vocational or technical school. **Criteria:** Recipients are selected based on financial need; academic achievement; leadership ability; community and volunteer service; creativity; and special circumstances.

Funds Avail.: No specific amount. **To Apply:** Applicants must submit: completed application form; current high school or college transcript; Student Aid Report (SAR) from the Free Application for Federal Student Aid (FAFSA), unless applying for scholarships that do not consider financial need; and letter of recommendation. **Deadline:** March 5. **Contact:** 616-842-6378.

4226 ■ Paul J. Laninga Memorial Scholarship Fund *(Undergraduate/Scholarship)*

Purpose: To improve and enhance the quality of life in the Tri-Cities area by serving as a leader, catalyst and resource for philanthropy; to strive for community improvement through strategic grantmaking in such fields as arts, education, health, environment, youth, social services and other human needs. **Focus:** Business; Accounting. **Qualif.:** Applicants must be graduating seniors of Northwest Ottawa County who plan to attend a public university; must be pursuing education and long-term careers in the areas of

business and/or accounting. **Criteria:** Recipients will be selected based on academic achievement; financial need; leadership ability; community and volunteer service; creativity; and special circumstances.

Funds Avail.: No specific amount. **To Apply:** Applicants must submit: completed application form; current high school or college transcript; Student Aid Report (SAR) from the Free Application for Federal Student Aid (FAFSA), unless applying for scholarships that do not consider financial need; and letter of recommendation. **Deadline:** March 5. **Contact:** 616-842-6378.

4227 ■ Rick and Beverly Lattin Education Scholarship Fund *(Undergraduate/Scholarship)*

Purpose: To provide financial assistance to graduates of Spring Lake or Grand Haven High school who demonstrate financial need. **Focus:** Business. **Qualif.:** Applicants must be graduates of Spring Lake or Grand Haven High School; must have 2.0 to 3.0 GPA and wish to continue their education; must be pursuing skills in the area of business or technical training. **Criteria:** Recipients are selected based on financial need; academic achievement; leadership ability; community and volunteer service; and special circumstances. Strong consideration will be given to students who are pursuing skills in the area of business or technical training.

Funds Avail.: No specific amount. **To Apply:** Applicants must submit completed application form; current high school or college transcript; Student Aid Report (SAR) from the Free Application for Federal Student Aid (FAFSA), unless applying for scholarships that do not consider financial need; and letter of recommendation. **Deadline:** March 5. **Contact:** 616-842-6378.

4228 ■ Jack W. Leatherman Family Scholarship Fund *(Graduate/Scholarship)*

Purpose: To improve and enhance the quality of life in the Tri-Cities area by serving as a leader, catalyst and resource for philanthropy; to strive for community improvement through strategic grantmaking in such fields as arts, education, health, environment, youth, social services and other human needs. **Focus:** General studies. **Qualif.:** Applicants must be Grand Haven area public school graduates. **Criteria:** Recipients are selected based on financial need.

Funds Avail.: No specific amount. **To Apply:** Applicants must submit: completed application form; current high school or college transcript; Student Aid Report (SAR) from the Free Application for Federal Student Aid (FAFSA), unless applying for scholarships that do not consider financial need; and letter of recommendation. **Deadline:** March 5. **Contact:** 616-842-6378.

4229 ■ Pat and John MacTavish Scholarship Fund *(Undergraduate/Scholarship)*

Purpose: To improve and enhance the quality of life in the Tri-Cities area by serving as a leader, catalyst and resource for philanthropy; to strive for community improvement through strategic grantmaking in such fields as arts, education, health, environment, youth, social services and other human needs. **Focus:** Science. **Qualif.:** Applicants must be high school or college students seeking to pursue any of the following areas of study: math, chemistry, geology, technical writing, physics or computer science. **Criteria:** Recipients are selected based on demonstrated academic excellence and financial need.

Funds Avail.: No specific amount. **To Apply:** Applicants

Awards are arranged alphabetically below their administering organizations

must submit: completed application form; current high school or college transcript; Student Aid Report (SAR) from the Free Application for Federal Student Aid (FAFSA), unless applying for scholarships that do not consider financial need; and letter of recommendation. **Deadline:** March 5. **Contact:** 616-842-6378.

4230 ■ Kyle Moreland Memorial Endowment Scholarship Fund *(Undergraduate/Scholarship)*

Purpose: To provide assistance to a Grand Haven High School graduating senior student. **Focus:** General studies. **Qualif.:** Applicants must be Grand Haven High School graduating seniors planning to attend a two or four-year college degree program; must be active in their Christian faith community; must have participated on high school golf or tennis team; must have a 3.0 GPA or above. Scholarship is also open to current graduates of Spring Lake High School and/or Western Christian Michigan High School. **Criteria:** Recipients are selected based on academic performance.

Funds Avail.: No specific amount. **To Apply:** Applicants must submit: completed application form; current high school or college transcript; Student Aid Report (SAR) from the Free Application for Federal Student Aid (FAFSA), unless applying for scholarships that do not consider financial need; and letter of recommendation. **Deadline:** March 5. **Contact:** 616-842-6378.

4231 ■ North Ottawa Hospital Auxiliary Scholarship Fund *(Undergraduate/Scholarship)*

Purpose: To improve and enhance the quality of life in the Tri-Cities area by serving as a leader, catalyst and resource for philanthropy; to strive for community improvement through strategic grantmaking in such fields as arts, education, health, environment, youth, social services and other human needs. **Focus:** Nursing. **Qualif.:** Applicants must be from the Tri-Cities area; currently enrolled as college students who have taken their core requirements and been accepted into their health-care related program of study. **Criteria:** Recipients are selected based on financial need, academic achievement, extracurricular activities, work history, educational goals and personal aspirations.

Funds Avail.: No specific amount. **To Apply:** Applicants must submit: completed application form; current high school or college transcript; Student Aid Report (SAR) from the Free Application for Federal Student Aid (FAFSA), unless applying for scholarships that do not consider financial need; and letter of recommendation. **Deadline:** March 5. **Contact:** 616-842-6378.

4232 ■ Marvin R. and Pearl E. Patterson Family Scholarships Fund *(Undergraduate/Scholarship)*

Purpose: To improve and enhance the quality of life in the Tri-Cities area by serving as a leader, catalyst and resource for philanthropy; to strive for community improvement through strategic grantmaking in such fields as arts, education, health, environment, youth, social services and other human needs. **Focus:** Fine Arts. **Qualif.:** Applicants must be students who will be graduating or graduated from a Tri-Cities area public high school; must have at least 3.0 GPA and plan to attend any two-year or four-year college or university to study graphic arts or fine arts. **Criteria:** Recipients will be selected based on academic achievement; leadership ability; community and volunteer service; creativity; financial need; and special circumstances.

Funds Avail.: No specific amount. **To Apply:** Applicants must submit: completed application form; current high

school or college transcript; Student Aid Report (SAR) from the Free Application for Federal Student Aid (FAFSA), unless applying for scholarships that do not consider financial need; and letter of recommendation. **Deadline:** March 5. **Contact:** 616-842-6378.

4233 ■ P.E.O. Chapter Scholarship Fund *(Undergraduate, Vocational/Occupational/ Scholarship)*

Purpose: To improve and enhance the quality of life in the Tri-Cities area by serving as a leader, catalyst and resource for philanthropy; to strive for community improvement through strategic grantmaking in such fields as arts, education, health, environment, youth, social services and other human needs. **Focus:** General studies. **Qualif.:** Applicants must be graduating female students or non-traditional students who graduated from any Tri-Cities area public or private high school; must plan to pursue a degree or certification at any two or four-year accredited college, university, vocational or technical school. **Criteria:** Recipients are selected based on academic performance.

Funds Avail.: No specific amount. **To Apply:** Applicants must submit: completed application form; current high school or college transcript; Student Aid Report (SAR) from the Free Application for Federal Student Aid (FAFSA), unless applying for scholarships that do not consider financial need; and letter of recommendation. **Deadline:** March 5. **Contact:** 616-842-6378.

4234 ■ Terry Linda Potter Scholarship Fund *(Undergraduate/Scholarship)*

Purpose: To improve and enhance the quality of life in the Tri-Cities area by serving as a leader, catalyst and resource for philanthropy; to strive for community improvement through strategic grantmaking in such fields as arts, education, health, environment, youth, social services and other human needs. **Focus:** Health education. **Qualif.:** Applicants must be graduating high school seniors planning to pursue a health-related field at an accredited two-to-four year college. **Criteria:** Recipients are selected based on financial need; academic achievement; leadership ability; creativity; community and volunteer service; and special circumstances.

Funds Avail.: No specific amount. **To Apply:** Applicants must submit: completed application form; current high school or college transcript; Student Aid Report (SAR) from the Free Application for Federal Student Aid (FAFSA), unless applying for scholarships that do not consider financial need; and letter of recommendation. **Deadline:** March 5. **Contact:** 616-842-6378.

4235 ■ Jacob L. Reinecke Memorial Scholarship Fund *(Undergraduate/Scholarship)*

Purpose: To provide scholarship assistance to a Grand Haven High School student. **Focus:** General studies. **Qualif.:** Applicants must be Grand Haven High School graduating seniors planning to attend a two-to-four year college, university or trade school; consideration will be given to male students who participated in high school athletics, specifically basketball or baseball; must have a 3.0 GPA or above. **Criteria:** Recipients are selected based on hard-working attitude and strong motivation to succeed.

Funds Avail.: No specific amount. **To Apply:** Applicants must submit: completed application form; current high school or college transcript; Student Aid Report (SAR) from the Free Application for Federal Student Aid (FAFSA), unless applying for scholarships that do not consider financial

Awards are arranged alphabetically below their administering organizations

need; and letter of recommendation. **Deadline:** March 5. **Contact:** 616-842-6378.

4236 ■ Daniel L. Reiss Memorial Scholarship Fund *(Undergraduate/Scholarship)*

Purpose: To improve and enhance the quality of life in the Tri-Cities area by serving as a leader, catalyst and resource for philanthropy; to strive for community improvement through strategic grantmaking in such fields as arts, education, health, environment, youth, social services and other human needs. **Focus:** General studies. **Qualif.:** Applicants must be graduating Grand Haven High School students who have at least a 3.8 GPA; must plan to pursue studies at Grand Valley State University or Western Michigan University. **Criteria:** Recipients are selected based on demonstrated academic excellence and financial need.

Funds Avail.: No specific amount. **To Apply:** Applicants must submit: completed application form; current high school or college transcript; Student Aid Report (SAR) from the Free Application for Federal Student Aid (FAFSA), unless applying for scholarships that do not consider financial need; and letter of recommendation. **Deadline:** March 5. **Contact:** 616-842-6378.

4237 ■ Harold and Eleonor Ringelberg Scholarship Fund *(Undergraduate/Scholarship)*

Purpose: To improve and enhance the quality of life in the Tri-Cities area by serving as a leader, catalyst and resource for philanthropy; to strive for community improvement through strategic grantmaking in such fields as arts, education, health, environment, youth, social services and other human needs. **Focus:** General studies. **Qualif.:** Applicants must be Grand Haven High School graduating seniors with a minimum 3.8 GPA; must plan to pursue a college degree at Michigan State University; must have attended Grand Haven Christian School prior to high school. **Criteria:** Recipients are selected based on financial need.

Funds Avail.: No specific amount. **To Apply:** Applicants must submit: completed application form; current high school or college transcript; Student Aid Report (SAR) from the Free Application for Federal Student Aid (FAFSA), unless applying for scholarships that do not consider financial need; and letter of recommendation. **Deadline:** March 5. **Contact:** 616-842-6378.

4238 ■ Charles and Eleonor Rycenga Education Scholarship Fund *(Undergraduate/Scholarship)*

Purpose: To improve and enhance the quality of life in the Tri-Cities area by serving as a leader, catalyst and resource for philanthropy; to strive for community improvement through strategic grantmaking in such fields as arts, education, health, environment, youth, social services and other human needs. **Focus:** General studies. **Qualif.:** Applicants must be graduating seniors of Grand Haven, Spring Lake or Western Christian High School; must have the desire to continue their education at an accredited four-year college, junior college, trade school or apprenticeship, preferably in Michigan. **Criteria:** Recipients are selected based on financial need.

Funds Avail.: No specific amount. **To Apply:** Applicants must submit: completed application form; current high school or college transcript; Student Aid Report (SAR) from the Free Application for Federal Student Aid (FAFSA), unless applying for scholarships that do not consider financial need; and letter of recommendation. **Deadline:** March 5. **Contact:** 616-842-6378.

4239 ■ Millicent M. Schaffner Endowed Memorial Scholarships *(Undergraduate/Scholarship)*

Purpose: To improve and enhance the quality of life in the Tri-Cities area by serving as a leader, catalyst and resource for philanthropy; to strive for community improvement through strategic grantmaking in such fields as the arts, education, health, environment, youth, social services and other human needs. **Focus:** General studies. **Qualif.:** Applicants must be female students who have a strong motivation to continue their education at an accredited four-year college. **Criteria:** Recipients are selected based on financial need.

Funds Avail.: No specific amount. **To Apply:** Applicants must submit: completed application form; current high school or college transcript; Student Aid Report (SAR) from the Free Application for Federal Student Aid (FAFSA), unless applying for scholarships that do not consider financial need; and letter of recommendation. **Deadline:** March 5. **Contact:** 616-842-6378.

4240 ■ David and Ginny Schultz Family Scholarship Fund *(Undergraduate/Scholarship)*

Purpose: To improve and enhance the quality of life in the Tri-Cities area by serving as a leader, catalyst and resource for philanthropy; to strive for community improvement through strategic grantmaking in such fields as arts, education, health, environment, youth, social services and other human needs. **Focus:** General studies. **Qualif.:** Applicants must be graduating seniors who wish to continue their education at a four-year college, junior college, trade school or apprenticeship. **Criteria:** Recipients are selected based on demonstrated academic excellence and financial need.

Funds Avail.: No specific amount. **To Apply:** Applicants must submit: completed application form; current high school or college transcript; Student Aid Report (SAR) from the Free Application for Federal Student Aid (FAFSA), unless applying for scholarships that do not consider financial need; and letter of recommendation. **Deadline:** March 5. **Contact:** 616-842-6378.

4241 ■ David and Sharon Seaver Family Scholarship Fund *(Undergraduate/Scholarship)*

Purpose: To improve and enhance the quality of life in the Tri-Cities area by serving as a leader, catalyst and resource for philanthropy; to strive for community improvement through strategic grantmaking in such fields as arts, education, health, environment, youth, social services and other human needs. **Focus:** Business. **Qualif.:** Applicants must be graduating seniors who plan to pursue a career in Business. **Criteria:** Recipients are selected based on financial need; creativity; community and volunteer service; leadership ability; and special circumstances.

Funds Avail.: No specific amount. **To Apply:** Applicants must submit: completed application form; current high school or college transcript; Student Aid Report (SAR) from the Free Application for Federal Student Aid (FAFSA), unless applying for scholarships that do not consider financial need; and letter of recommendation. **Deadline:** March 5. **Contact:** 616-842-6378.

4242 ■ Ken and Sandy Sharkey Family Scholarship Fund *(Undergraduate/Scholarship)*

Purpose: To improve and enhance the quality of life in the Tri-Cities area by serving as a leader, catalyst and resource for philanthropy; to strive for community improvement through strategic grantmaking in such fields as arts, educa-

Awards are arranged alphabetically below their administering organizations

tion, health, environment, youth, social services and other human needs. **Focus:** General studies. **Qualif.:** Applicants must be graduating seniors from Grand Haven High School who demonstrate civic responsibility and plan to be involved in improving their community in the future. **Criteria:** Recipients are selected based on academic performance; leadership ability; community and volunteer service; financial need; and special circumstances.

Funds Avail.: No specific amount. **To Apply:** Applicants must submit: completed application form; current high school or college transcript; Student Aid Report (SAR) from the Free Application for Federal Student Aid (FAFSA), unless applying for scholarships that do not consider financial need; and letter of recommendation. **Deadline:** March 5. **Contact:** 616-842-6378.

4243 ■ Marion A. and Ruth Sherwood Family Fund Education Scholarships (Undergraduate/Scholarship)

Purpose: To improve and enhance the quality of life in the Tri-Cities area by serving as a leader, catalyst and resource for philanthropy; to strive for community improvement through strategic grantmaking in such fields as arts, education, health, environment, youth, social services and other human needs. **Focus:** Education. **Qualif.:** Applicants must be planning to pursue a career in the field of Education. **Criteria:** Recipients are selected based on academic excellence and financial need.

Funds Avail.: No specific amount. **To Apply:** Applicants must submit: completed application form; current high school or college transcript; Student Aid Report (SAR) from the Free Application for Federal Student Aid (FAFSA), unless applying for scholarships that do not consider financial need; and letter of recommendation. **Deadline:** March 5. **Contact:** 616-842-6378.

4244 ■ Marion A. and Ruth K. Sherwood Family Fund Engineering Scholarships (Undergraduate/Scholarship)

Purpose: To improve and enhance the quality of life in the Tri-Cities area by serving as a leader, catalyst and resource for philanthropy; to strive for community improvement through strategic grantmaking in such fields as the arts, education, health, environment, youth, social services and other human needs. **Focus:** Engineering. **Qualif.:** Applicants must be students planning to pursue a career in the field of engineering. **Criteria:** Recipients are selected based on academic excellence; financial need; leadership ability; creativity; community and volunteer service; and special circumstances.

Funds Avail.: No specific amount. **To Apply:** Applicants must submit: completed application form; current high school or college transcript; Student Aid Report (SAR) from the Free Application for Federal Student Aid (FAFSA), unless applying for scholarships that do not consider financial need; and letter of recommendation. **Deadline:** March 5. **Contact:** 616-842-6378.

4245 ■ Miller G. Sherwood Family Scholarship Fund (Undergraduate/Scholarship)

Purpose: To improve and enhance the quality of life in the Tri-Cities area by serving as a leader, catalyst and resource for philanthropy; to strive for community improvement through strategic grantmaking in such fields as arts, education, health, environment, youth, social services and other human needs. **Focus:** Environmental science. **Qualif.:** Ap-

plicants must be graduating seniors of Grand Haven or Spring Lake High School who plan to pursue an education in the areas of environment or social services. **Criteria:** Recipients are selected based on financial need; academic achievement; leadership ability; community and volunteer service; creativity; and special circumstances.

Funds Avail.: No specific amount. **To Apply:** Applicants must submit: completed application form; current high school or college transcript; Student Aid Report (SAR) from the Free Application for Federal Student Aid (FAFSA), unless applying for scholarships that do not consider financial need; and letter of recommendation. **Deadline:** March 5. **Contact:** 616-842-6378.

4246 ■ Edward P. Suchecki Family Scholarship Fund (Undergraduate/Scholarship)

Purpose: To improve and enhance the quality of life in the Tri-Cities area by serving as a leader, catalyst and resource for philanthropy; to strive for community improvement through strategic grantmaking in such fields as arts, education, health, environment, youth, social services and other human needs. **Focus:** Business. **Qualif.:** Applicants must be high school senior athletes from Grand Haven High School, preferably planning to pursue a career in business. **Criteria:** Recipients are selected based on financial need.

Funds Avail.: No specific amount. **To Apply:** Applicants must submit: completed application form; current high school or college transcript; Student Aid Report (SAR) from the Free Application for Federal Student Aid (FAFSA), unless applying for scholarships that do not consider financial need; and letter of recommendation. **Deadline:** March 5. **Contact:** 616-842-6378.

4247 ■ Henry D. and Ruth G. Swartz Family Scholarship Fund (Undergraduate/Scholarship)

Purpose: To improve and enhance the quality of life in the Tri-Cities area by serving as a leader, catalyst and resource for philanthropy; to strive for community improvement through strategic grantmaking in such fields as arts, education, health, environment, youth, social services and other human needs. **Focus:** Computer and Information Sciences. **Qualif.:** Applicants must be graduating high school seniors from Grand Haven High School, Spring Lake High School, Holland Christian High School or Western Michigan Christian High School in North Ottawa County; must be pursuing a career in engineering, computer science, pre-law or medicine. **Criteria:** Recipients are selected based on leadership ability, community involvement and academic achievement; creativity; financial need; and special circumstances. Preference will be given to those students pursuing a career in engineering, computer science, pre-law and medicine.

Funds Avail.: No specific amount. **To Apply:** Applicants must submit: completed application form; current high school or college transcript; Student Aid Report (SAR) from the Free Application for Federal Student Aid (FAFSA); and letter of recommendation. **Deadline:** March 5. **Contact:** 616-842-6378.

4248 ■ H. Wayne Van Agtmael Cosmetology Scholarship Fund (Undergraduate/Scholarship)

Purpose: To improve and enhance the quality of life in the Tri-Cities area by serving as a leader, catalyst and resource for philanthropy; to strive for community improvement through strategic grantmaking in such fields as arts, education, health, environment, youth, social services and other human needs. **Focus:** Cosmetology. **Qualif.:** Applicants

Awards are arranged alphabetically below their administering organizations

must be students planning to attend a Cosmetology School. **Criteria:** Recipients are selected based on academic excellence and financial need.

Funds Avail.: No specific amount. **To Apply:** Applicants must submit: completed application form; current high school or college transcript; Student Aid Report (SAR) from the Free Application for Federal Student Aid (FAFSA), unless applying for scholarships that do not consider financial need; and letter of recommendation. **Deadline:** March 5. **Contact:** 616-842-6378.

4249 ■ West Michigan Nursery and Landscape Association Scholarship Fund (Undergraduate/Scholarship)

Purpose: To assist graduating high school seniors and currently enrolled college students to pursue a horticulture or green industry career. **Focus:** Horticulture. **Qualif.:** Applicants must be graduating high school seniors or currently enrolled college students planning to pursue a horticulture or green industry career at a two-or-four-year college or university; must be residents of Ottawa, Oceana, Newaygo, Muskegon or Allegan Counties. **Criteria:** Recipients are selected based on demonstrated academic excellence and financial need.

Funds Avail.: No specific amount. **To Apply:** Applicants must submit: completed application form; current high school or college transcript; Student Aid Report (SAR) from the Free Application for Federal Student Aid (FAFSA), unless applying for scholarships that do not consider financial need; and letter of recommendation. **Deadline:** March 5. **Contact:** 616-842-6378.

4250 ■ Louise Wachter Wichman Scholarship Fund (Undergraduate/Scholarship)

Purpose: To assist local graduating high school seniors interested in obtaining a college degree in elementary education. **Focus:** Education. **Qualif.:** Applicants must be graduating high school seniors interested in obtaining a college degree in elementary education; must have a good (but not necessarily perfect) academic record. **Criteria:** Recipients are selected based on academic performance; financial need; leadership ability; creativity; community and volunteer service; and special circumstances.

Funds Avail.: No specific amount. **To Apply:** Applicants must submit: completed application form; current high school or college transcript; Student Aid Report (SAR) from the Free Application for Federal Student Aid (FAFSA), unless applying for scholarships that do not consider financial need; and letter of recommendation. **Deadline:** March 5. **Contact:** 616-842-6378.

4251 ■ Woman's Club of Grand Haven Scholarships Fund (Undergraduate/Scholarship)

Purpose: To improve and enhance the quality of life in the Tri-Cities area by serving as a leader, catalyst and resource for philanthropy; to strive for community improvement through strategic grantmaking in such fields as the arts, education, health, environment, youth, social services and other human needs. **Focus:** General studies. **Qualif.:** Applicants may be traditional and non-traditional students. Traditional students must be graduating from a Tri-Cities area high school with a minimum 2.5 GPA; non-traditional must be female, ages 21 or older. **Criteria:** Recipients are selected based on financial need, academic achievement, community service and college plans.

Funds Avail.: No specific amount. **To Apply:** Applicants

must submit: completed application form; current high school or college transcript; Student Aid Report (SAR) from the Free Application for Federal Student Aid (FAFSA), unless applying for scholarships that do not consider financial need; and letter of recommendation. **Deadline:** March 5. **Contact:** 616-842-6378.

4252 ■ Zenko Family Scholarship Fund (Undergraduate/Scholarship)

Purpose: To provide assistance to students to further their education. **Focus:** General studies. **Qualif.:** Applicants must be graduates of Spring Lake, Grand Haven or Fruitport High School; and have made their own financial contribution through employment to further their education at an accredited four-year college, junior college, trade school or apprenticeship. **Criteria:** Recipients are selected based on financial need.

Funds Avail.: No specific amount. **To Apply:** Applicants must submit: completed application form; current high school or college transcript; Student Aid Report (SAR) from the Free Application for Federal Student Aid (FAFSA), unless applying for scholarships that do not consider financial need; and letter of recommendation. **Deadline:** March 5. **Contact:** 616-842-6378.

4253 ■ Leo Zupin Memorial Scholarship Fund (Undergraduate, Vocational/Occupational/Scholarship)

Purpose: To improve and enhance the quality of life in the Tri-Cities area by serving as a leader, catalyst and resource for philanthropy; to strive for community improvement through strategic grantmaking in such fields as arts, education, health, environment, youth, social services and other human needs. **Focus:** Mathematics and mathematical sciences. **Qualif.:** Applicants must plan to attend any Michigan two-to-four year accredited public college, university, vocational or technology training and/or certification institution; must be students wishing to pursue a degree in mathematics. **Criteria:** Recipients are selected based on financial need, motivation, desire to achieve and academic performance.

Funds Avail.: No specific amount. **To Apply:** Applicants must submit: completed application form; current high school or college transcript; Student Aid Report (SAR) from the Free Application for Federal Student Aid (FAFSA), unless applying for scholarships that do not consider financial need; and letter of recommendation. **Deadline:** March 5. **Contact:** 616-842-6378.

4254 ■ Grand Island Community Foundation
410 W 2nd St., Ste. 2
Grand Island, NE 68801
Ph: (308) 381-7767
E-mail: info@gicf.org
URL: www.gicf.org

4255 ■ Henry and Maria Ahrens Scholarships (Graduate/Scholarship)

Purpose: To provide opportunities and assistance to students who want to further their education. **Focus:** Medicine. **Qualif.:** Applicant must be in medical career schooling including physician, dentist, nurse, technician and LPN; have graduated from a Hall County Nebraska high school. **Criteria:** Selection is based on the requirements; neatness and completeness of the application; quality of personal statement; involvement in community or school activities;

Awards are arranged alphabetically below their administering organizations

accomplishments; employment; and clearly defined goals. Preference will be given to those entering into a graduate field of study.

Funds Avail.: $2,400. **Number Awarded:** 3. **To Apply:** Applicants must submit a completed application form together with a typewritten personal essay, college transcript, applicable graduate school entrance exam and a letter of recommendation from an individual who has supervised the student in medical education or a medical work environment. **Deadline:** June 1. **Contact:** Lisa Katzberg at the above address.

4256 ■ Edgar Barge Memorial Scholarships
(Undergraduate/Scholarship)

Purpose: To provide opportunities and assistance to students who want to further their education. **Focus:** General studies. **Qualif.:** Applicant must be a graduating high school senior registered as parishioner at Blessed Sacrament Church in Grand Island. **Criteria:** Selection is based on the application materials.

Funds Avail.: $100-$2,000. **To Apply:** Applicants must submit a completed application form along with a typewritten personal statement and a letter of recommendation. **Deadline:** March 1. **Remarks:** Established to honor the memory of Edgar Barge. **Contact:** Lisa Katzberg at the above address.

4257 ■ Karen Connick Memorial Scholarships
(Undergraduate/Scholarship)

Purpose: To provide opportunities and assistance to students who want to further their education. **Focus:** General studies. **Qualif.:** Applicant must be a graduating high school senior from the Doniphan, Giltner, or Trumbull area. **Criteria:** Selection is based on the application.

Funds Avail.: $100-$2,000. **To Apply:** Applicants must submit a completed application form along with a typewritten personal statement; and high school transcripts, high school class rank, and ACT scores. Two complete sets of each application must be submitted. **Deadline:** March 1. **Remarks:** Established to honor the memory of Karen Connick. **Contact:** Lisa Katzberg at the above address.

4258 ■ Doniphan Community Foundation Scholarships *(Undergraduate/Scholarship)*

Purpose: To provide opportunities and assistance to students who want to further their education. **Focus:** General studies. **Qualif.:** Applicant must be a Doniphan-Trumbull High School graduate. **Criteria:** Selection is based on the application.

Funds Avail.: $100-$2,000. **To Apply:** Applicants must submit a completed application form along with a typewritten personal statement, high school and college/university transcripts, high school class rank, and ACT scores. **Deadline:** March 1. **Contact:** Lisa Katzberg at the above address.

4259 ■ Howard G. and Gladys A. Eakes Memorial Scholarships *(Undergraduate/Scholarship)*

Purpose: To provide opportunities and assistance to students who want to further their education. **Focus:** General studies. **Qualif.:** Applicant must be a child or stepchild of an Eakes Office Plus employee, and have a cumulative 3.0 GPA or better. **Criteria:** Selection is based on the application.

Funds Avail.: $100-$2,000. **Number Awarded:** 1. Applicants must submit a completed application form along with a typewritten personal statement; and high school transcripts, high school class rank, and ACT scores. Two complete sets of each application must be submitted. **Deadline:** March 1. **Remarks:** Established to honor the memories of Howard and Gladys Eakes. Lisa Katzberg at the above address.

4260 ■ Hall County Medical Society Scholarships *(Graduate/Scholarship)*

Purpose: To provide opportunities and assistance to students who want to further their education. **Focus:** Medicine. **Qualif.:** Applicant must be in medical career schooling including physician, dentist, nurse, technician and LPN; have graduated from a Hall County Nebraska high school. **Criteria:** Selection is based on the requirements; neatness and completeness of the application; quality of personal statement; involvement in community or school activities; accomplishments; employment; and clearly defined goals.

Funds Avail.: $1,000. **Number Awarded:** 1. **To Apply:** Applicants must submit a completed application form together with a typewritten personal essay and a letter of recommendation from an individual who has supervised the student in medical education or a medical work environment. **Deadline:** June 1. **Contact:** Lisa Katzberg at the above address.

4261 ■ Pleasantview Public Schools Fund
(Undergraduate/Scholarship)

Purpose: To provide opportunities and assistance to students who want to further their education. **Focus:** General studies. **Qualif.:** Applicant must be a graduating high school senior who resides or has resided within the geographic area and territory of Pleasantview Public Schools or the former Pleasantview Public Schools, regardless of whether or not he/she attended Pleasantview Public Schools or option enrolled to another school district. **Criteria:** Selection is based on the application.

Funds Avail.: $100-$2,000. **To Apply:** Applicants must submit a completed application form along with a typewritten personal statement; and high school transcripts, high school class rank, and ACT scores. Two complete sets of each application must be submitted. **Deadline:** March 1.

4262 ■ Jim and Dee Price Scholarships
(Undergraduate/Scholarship)

Purpose: To provide opportunities and assistance to students who want to further their education. **Focus:** General studies. **Qualif.:** Applicant must be a child of a Kriz-Davis Co. employee. **Criteria:** Selection is based on the application.

Funds Avail.: $100-$2,000. Applicants must submit a completed application form along with a typewritten personal statement; and high school transcripts, high school class rank, and ACT scores. Two complete sets of each application must be submitted. **Deadline:** March 1.

4263 ■ Carl C. and Abbie Rebman Trust Scholarships *(Undergraduate/Scholarship)*

Purpose: To provide opportunities and assistance to students who want to further their education. **Focus:** Nursing; Automotive technology. **Qualif.:** Applicant must be a Hall County student in nursing or auto mechanics programs. **Criteria:** Selection is based on the application.

Funds Avail.: $100-$1,2000. Applicants must submit a completed application form along with a typewritten personal statement; and high school transcripts, high

Awards are arranged alphabetically below their administering organizations

school class rank, and ACT scores. Two complete sets of each application must be submitted. **Deadline:** March 1. **Contact:** Lisa Katzberg at the above address.

4264 ■ Teammates Mentoring Scholarship
Program (Undergraduate/Scholarship)

Purpose: To provide opportunities and assistance to students who want to further their education. **Focus:** General studies. **Qualif.:** Applicant must have been a part of the Grand Island/Hall County TeamMates mentoring program. **Criteria:** Selection is based on the application.

Funds Avail.: $100-$2,000. **To Apply:** Applicants must submit a completed application form along with a typewritten personal statement; and high school transcripts, high school class rank, and ACT scores. Two complete sets of each application must be submitted. **Deadline:** March 1. **Contact:** Nancy Jones at 308-385-5950.

4265 ■ Woodyard Family Scholarships
(Undergraduate/Scholarship)

Purpose: To provide opportunities and assistance to students who want to further their education. **Focus:** General studies. **Qualif.:** Applicant must be a Hall County high school graduate with a cumulative high school GPA of at least 3.0 and a class rank in the top 25%. **Criteria:** Preference will be given first to students pursuing a degree in education and then to students in a medical related field of study.

Funds Avail.: $100-$2,000. **To Apply:** Applicants must submit a completed application form along with a typewritten personal statement; and high school transcripts, high school class rank, and ACT scores. Two complete sets of each application must be submitted. **Deadline:** March 1.

4266 ■ James and Joy Zana Memorial Scholarships (Undergraduate/Scholarship)

Purpose: To provide opportunities and assistance to students who want to further their education. **Focus:** Fine arts. **Qualif.:** Applicant must be a Grand Island graduating high school senior pursuing a fine arts course of study. **Criteria:** Selection is based on the application.

Funds Avail.: $100-$2,000. **To Apply:** Applicants must submit a completed application form along with a typewritten personal statement; and high school transcripts, high school class rank, and ACT scores. Two complete sets of each application must be submitted. **Deadline:** March 1. **Remarks:** Established in memory of James P. Zana. **Contact:** Lisa Katzberg at the above address.

4267 ■ Grand Lodge of Saskatchewan
1930 Lorne St.
Regina, SK, Canada S4P 2M1
Ph: (306) 522-5686
Fax: (306) 522-5687
Free: 877-661-2231
E-mail: glsask@atssaskmasons.ca
URL: www.saskmasons.ca

4268 ■ Murray Montague Memorial Scholarships (Undergraduate/Scholarship)

Purpose: To provide financial support to students in the higher learning institutions. **Focus:** General studies. **Qualif.:** Applicants must be Saskatchewan High School graduates who proceed to an institution of higher learning anywhere in Canada; must be registered for a full academic load for a full academic year as required by the institution chosen. **Criteria:** Selection will be based on academic achievement, leadership skills, community and school activities and special awards.

Funds Avail.: $1,000. **To Apply:** Applicant must submit the following requirements: completed application form; official final transcript of Grade 12 marks issued by the Saskatchewan Ministry of Education; character reference from a community leader; letter of reference from high school principal or guidance counsellor; letter from the applicant outlining extracurricular activities and educational goals; proof of registration in the chosen institute of higher learning. **Deadline:** August 7. **Contact:** Scholarship Selection Committee, The Grand Lodge of Saskatchewan Ancient Free and Accepted Masons at the above address.

4269 ■ Grand Rapids Community Foundation (GRCF)
185 Oakes St. SW
Grand Rapids, MI 49503
Ph: (616) 454-1751
Fax: (616) 454-6455
E-mail: grfound@grfoundation.org
URL: www.grfoundation.org

4270 ■ Altrusa International of Grand Rapids
Scholarships (Undergraduate/Scholarship)

Purpose: To provide financial support to those students who are in need. **Focus:** General Studies. **Qualif.:** Applicants must be students from Kent, Allegan, Iona, Ottawa, Montcalm or Muskegon counties. Applicants must be entering or returning to college after sitting out of school for two years. Applicants must demonstrate financial need. **Criteria:** Priority will be given to those students with financial need.

Funds Avail.: No specific amount. **To Apply:** Applicants must check the available website for the application process. Applicants must also provide two letters of recommendation. **Deadline:** April 1. **Contact:** Grand Rapids Community Foundation at the above address.

4271 ■ Dr. Noyes L. Avery, Jr. & Ann E. Avery
Scholarships (Undergraduate/Scholarship)

Purpose: To provide financial assistance to those students who are in need. **Focus:** Medicine. **Qualif.:** Applicants must be full-time students from Kent County who are attending the University of Michigan for a medical doctor degree. Applicants must have a minimum of 3.0 GPA. Applicants must have financial need. **Criteria:** Preference will be given to those students who meet the criteria.

Funds Avail.: No specific amount. **To Apply:** Applicants must check the available website for the required materials. **Deadline:** April 1. **Contact:** Grand Rapids Community Foundation at the above address.

4272 ■ Geraldine Geistert Boss Scholarships
(Undergraduate/Scholarship)

Purpose: To provide financial support to those students who are in need. **Focus:** General Studies. **Qualif.:** Applicants must be full-time students with financial need residing in Kent County (5 year minimum) and pursuing an undergraduate degree at an accredited college in Michigan. Applicants must have a minimum of 3.0 GPA. **Criteria:** Preference will be given to those students who meet the criteria.

Awards are arranged alphabetically below their administering organizations

Funds Avail.: No specific amount. **To Apply:** Applicants must check the available website for the required materials. **Deadline:** April 1. **Contact:** Grand Rapids Community Foundation at the above address.

4273 ■ Harry and Lucille Brown Scholarships
(Undergraduate/Scholarship)

Purpose: To provide financial support to those students who are in need. **Focus:** General Studies. **Qualif.:** Applicants must be residents of Kent County; must have financial need; must be pursuing an undergraduate degree at any accredited college in the U.S; must have a minimum of 3.3 GPA. **Criteria:** Preference will be given to those students who meet the criteria.

Funds Avail.: No specific amount. **To Apply:** Applicants must check the available website for the required materials. **Deadline:** April 1. **Contact:** Grand Rapids Community Foundation at the above address.

4274 ■ Orrie & Dorothy Cassada Scholarships
(Undergraduate/Scholarship)

Purpose: To provide financial assistance to those students who are in need. **Focus:** General Studies. **Qualif.:** Applicants must be residents of Kent County who will be attending Aquinas, Calvin, Cornerstone, Davenport, GRCC, GVSU or Kendall. Applicants must have financial need and a 3.0 minimum GPA. **Criteria:** Preference will be given to those students who meet the criteria.

Funds Avail.: No specific amount. **To Apply:** Applicants must check the available website for more information. **Deadline:** April 1. **Contact:** For further information, applicants must contact Ruth Bishop, Education Program Officer at rbishop@grfoundation.org.

4275 ■ Llewellyn L. Cayvan String Instrument Scholarships *(Undergraduate/Scholarship)*

Purpose: To recognize those students with talent in musical instruments by supporting them financially. **Focus:** Music. **Qualif.:** Applicants must be undergraduate or graduate level students studying the violin, viola, violoncello, or the bass violin. No residency or financial need requirements. **Criteria:** Preference will be based on talent.

Funds Avail.: No specific amount. **To Apply:** Applicants must check the available website for the application process and other requirements. **Deadline:** April 1. **Contact:** For further information, applicants must contact Ruth Bishop, Education Program Officer at rbishop@grfoundation.org.

4276 ■ Thomas D. Coffield Scholarships
(Undergraduate/Scholarship)

Purpose: To provide financial assistance to those students who are in need. **Focus:** General Studies. **Qualif.:** Applicants must be senior students at Central High School who will be entering a two or four-year accredited college or university; must have a 2.5 minimum GPA; must have demonstrated financial need. **Criteria:** Preference will be given to those who meet the criteria.

Funds Avail.: No specific amount. **To Apply:** Applicants must check the available website for more information. **Deadline:** April 1. **Contact:** For further information, applicants must contact Ruth Bishop, Education Program Officer at rbishop@grfoundation.org.

4277 ■ Paul Collins Scholarships
(Undergraduate/Scholarship)

Purpose: To provide financial assistance to deserving students. **Focus:** Applied Arts; Fine Arts. **Qualif.:** Ap-

plicants must be undergraduate level students studying Fine or Applied Arts at Aquinas, Calvin, GVSU, GRCC or Kendall. Applicants must be residents of Kent County. Applicants must have a minimum of 2.5 GPA, financial need and demonstrate artistic talent. **Criteria:** Selection will be based on criteria.

Funds Avail.: No specific amount. **To Apply:** Applicants must check the available website for more information. **Contact:** For further information, applicants must contact Ruth Bishop, Education Program Officer at rbishop@grfoundation.org.

4278 ■ Achille & Irene Despres, William & Andre Scholarships *(Undergraduate/Scholarship)*

Purpose: To provide financial assistance to those students who are in need. **Focus:** General Studies. **Qualif.:** Applicants must be of Mexican heritage; must be Kent or Ottawa residents; must be enrolled in an accredited college or university; must have demonstrated financial need; must have a cumulative GPA of at least 2.75. **Criteria:** Priority will be given to those students with financial need.

Funds Avail.: No specific amount. **To Apply:** Applicants must check the available website for the required materials. **Deadline:** April 1. **Contact:** Grand Rapids Community Foundation at the above address.

4279 ■ Virginia Valk Fehsenfeld Scholarships
(Undergraduate/Scholarship)

Purpose: To provide financial support to those students who are in need. **Focus:** General Studies. **Qualif.:** Applicants must be full-time undergraduate students pursuing a degree in Dietetics, Nutrition, Education or General Human Services. Applicants must be residents of Kent County, must have financial need and a 3.4 GPA is required. **Criteria:** Preference will be given to those who meet the criteria.

Funds Avail.: No specific amount. **To Apply:** Applicants must check the available website for the required materials. **Deadline:** April 1. **Contact:** For further information, applicants must contact Ruth Bishop, Education Program Officer at rbishop@grfoundation.org.

4280 ■ Melbourne & Alice E. Frontjes Scholarships *(Undergraduate/Scholarship)*

Purpose: To provide financial assistance to those students who are in need. **Focus:** General Studies. **Qualif.:** Applicants must be Kent County residents who are pursuing an undergraduate degree at Central Michigan University, Western Michigan University, GRCC, University of Michigan or Michigan State University. Applicants must have demonstrated financial need and have a minimum of 2.75 GPA. **Criteria:** Preference will be given to those students who meet the criteria.

Funds Avail.: No specific amount. **To Apply:** Applicants must check the available website for the required materials. **Deadline:** April 1. **Contact:** For further information, applicants must contact Ruth Bishop, Education Program Officer at rbishop@grfoundation.org.

4281 ■ Carolyn Gallmeyer Scholarships
(Undergraduate/Scholarship)

Purpose: To provide financial support to those students who are in need. **Focus:** General Studies. **Qualif.:** Applicants must be Kent County residents who are pursuing an undergraduate degree at any U.S college and must have a minimum of 2.75 GPA. **Criteria:** Recipients will be

Awards are arranged alphabetically below their administering organizations

selected based on financial need.

Funds Avail.: No specific amount. **To Apply:** Applicants must check the available website for the required materials. **Deadline:** April 1. **Contact:** For further information, applicants must contact Ruth Bishop, Education Program Officer at rbishop@grfoundation.org.

4282 ■ Mathilda & Carolyn Gallmeyer Scholarships *(Undergraduate/Scholarship)*

Purpose: To provide financial assistance to those students who are in need. **Focus:** Fine Arts. **Qualif.:** Applicants must be Kent County residents. Applicants must be pursuing Painting or Fine arts. Applicants must demonstrate artistic talent, financial need and a minimum of 2.75 GPA. **Criteria:** Preference will be given to those students who meet the criteria.

Funds Avail.: No specific amount. **To Apply:** Applicants must check the available website for the required materials. **Deadline:** April 1. **Contact:** For further information, applicants must contact Ruth Bishop, Education Program Officer at rbishop@grfoundation.org.

4283 ■ Grand Rapids Scholarship Association *(Undergraduate/Scholarship)*

Purpose: To provide financial assistance to those students who are in need. **Focus:** General Studies. **Qualif.:** Applicants must be Kent County residents who will be attending Aquinas, Calvin, Cornerstone, Davenport, GRCC, GVSU or Kendall. Applicants must have financial need and must have a 3.0 minimum GPA. **Criteria:** Preference will be given to those students who meet the criteria.

Funds Avail.: No specific amount. **To Apply:** Applicants must check the available website for the required materials. **Deadline:** April 1. **Contact:** Grand Rapids Community Foundation at the above address.

4284 ■ Guy D. & Mary Edith Halladay Graduate Scholarships *(Undergraduate/Scholarship)*

Purpose: To provide financial support to those students who are in need. **Focus:** General Studies. **Qualif.:** Applicants must be residents of Kent County and must be graduate level students at a Michigan college. Applicants must have demonstrated financial need and must have a minimum of 3.0 GPA. **Criteria:** Preference will be given to those who meet the criteria.

Funds Avail.: No specific amount. **To Apply:** Applicants must check the available website for more information. **Deadline:** April 1. **Contact:** Grand Rapids Community Foundation at the above address.

4285 ■ Guy D. & Mary Edith Halladay Music Scholarships *(Graduate, Undergraduate/ Scholarship)*

Purpose: To provide financial assistance to deserving students. **Focus:** Music. **Qualif.:** Applicants must be residents of Kent County who are majoring in Music at any college or university in the U.S. Applicants must have financial need. Applicants must have a cumulative GPA of 3.0. **Criteria:** Priority will be given to those students with high financial need.

Funds Avail.: No specific amount. **To Apply:** Applicants must check the available website for the required materials. **Deadline:** April 1. **Contact:** Grand Rapids Community Foundation at the above address.

4286 ■ Donald & Florence Hunting Scholarships *(Undergraduate/Scholarship)*

Purpose: To provide financial assistance to those students who are in need. **Focus:** General Studies. **Qualif.:** Ap-

plicants must be senior students at Rockford High School who will be entering college in the fall. Applicants must have demonstrated financial need. **Criteria:** Priority will be given to those students with financial need.

Funds Avail.: No specific amount. **To Apply:** Applicants must check the available website for more information. **Deadline:** April 1. **Contact:** For further information, applicants must contact Ruth Bishop, Education Program Officer at rbishop@grfoundation.org.

4287 ■ Jack Family Scholarships *(Undergraduate/Scholarship)*

Purpose: To provide financial assistance to those students who are in need. **Focus:** General Studies. **Qualif.:** Applicants must be undergraduate students residing in Kent County who demonstrate financial need. Applicants must have a minimum of 3.3 GPA. **Criteria:** Preference will be given to those students who meet the criteria.

Funds Avail.: No specific amount. **To Apply:** Applicants must check the available website for more information. **Deadline:** April 1. **Contact:** Grand Rapids Community Foundation at the above address.

4288 ■ Camilla C. Johnson Scholarships *(Undergraduate/Scholarship)*

Purpose: To provide financial support to those deserving students. **Focus:** General Studies. **Qualif.:** Applicants must be senior students at Union High School entering college full-time in the fall. Applicants must have financial need. Applicants must have a cumulative of 2.6 GPA. **Criteria:** Preference will be given to those students who meet the criteria.

Funds Avail.: No specific amount. **To Apply:** Applicants must check the available website for the required materials. **Deadline:** April 1. **Contact:** For further information, applicants must contact Ruth Bishop, Education Program Officer at rbishop@grfoundation.org.

4289 ■ Lavina Laible Scholarships *(Undergraduate/Scholarship)*

Purpose: To provide financial assistance to those students who are in need. **Focus:** General Studies. **Qualif.:** Applicants must be female students in their third year or above of undergraduate studies at the University of Michigan. Applicants must be Kent County residents. Applicants must have financial need. Applicants must have a minimum of 3.0 GPA. **Criteria:** Preference will be given to those students who meet the criteria.

Funds Avail.: No specific amount. **To Apply:** Applicants must check the available website for the required materials. **Deadline:** April 1. **Contact:** For further information, applicants must contact Ruth Bishop, Education Program Officer at rbishop@grfoundation.org.

4290 ■ Stephen Lankester Scholarships *(Undergraduate/Scholarship)*

Purpose: To provide financial assistance to those students who are in need. **Focus:** General Studies. **Qualif.:** Applicants must be Kent County residents; must be attending an undergraduate program at a Michigan college; must have financial need; must have a minimum of 3.0 GPA. **Criteria:** Preference will be given to those who meet the criteria.

Funds Avail.: No specific amount. **To Apply:** Applicants must check the available website for more information. **Deadline:** April 1. **Contact:** For further information, ap-

Awards are arranged alphabetically below their administering organizations

plicants must contact Ruth Bishop, Education Program Officer at rbishop@grfoundation.org.

4291 ■ Sherman L. & Mabel C. Lepard Scholarships (Undergraduate/Scholarship)

Purpose: To provide financial assistance to deserving students. **Focus:** General Studies. **Qualif.:** Applicants must be pursuing an undergraduate degree at any accredited college or university in the U.S; must be Kent County residents; must have demonstrated financial need; must have a minimum of 3.3 GPA. **Criteria:** Preference will be given to those students who meet the criteria.

Funds Avail.: No specific amount. **To Apply:** Applicants must check the available website for the required materials. **Deadline:** April 1. **Contact:** For further information, applicants must contact Ruth Bishop, Education Program Officer at rbishop@grfoundation.org.

4292 ■ John T. & Frances Maghielse Scholarships (Undergraduate/Scholarship)

Purpose: To provide financial assistance to students who are in need. **Focus:** General Studies. **Qualif.:** Applicants must be graduates of Grand Rapids Public High School; must be Kent County residents; must be currently pursuing a full-time undergraduate degree in the field of Education at any Michigan public or private college/ university. Applicants must have financial need and must have a minimum of 3.0 GPA. **Criteria:** Preference will be given to those students who meet the criteria.

Funds Avail.: No specific amount. **To Apply:** Applicants must check the available website for the required materials. **Deadline:** April 1. **Contact:** Grand Rapids Community Foundation at the above address.

4293 ■ Joshua Esch Mitchell Aviation Scholarships (Undergraduate/Scholarship)

Purpose: To provide financial support to those students who study flight science. **Focus:** Aviation. **Qualif.:** Applicants must be U.S citizens. Must be enrolled full or part-time at a college or university in the United States providing an accredited flight science curriculum. Applicants must be second year students or above with a minimum of 2.75 GPA; must be pursuing studies in the field of professional piloting with an emphasis in General Aviation, Aviation Management, or Aviation Safety. **Criteria:** Selection will be based on criteria.

Funds Avail.: No specific amount. **To Apply:** Applicants must check the available website for the required materials. **Deadline:** April 1. **Contact:** Grand Rapids Community Foundation at the above address.

4294 ■ Robert L. & Hilda Treasure Mitchell Scholarships (Undergraduate/Scholarship)

Purpose: To provide financial assistance to deserving students. **Focus:** General Studies. **Qualif.:** Applicants must be pursuing an undergraduate degree at any accredited college or university in the United States; must be Kent County residents; must demonstrate financial need; must have a minimum of 3.3 GPA. **Criteria:** Preference will be given to those students who meet the criteria.

Funds Avail.: No specific amount. **To Apply:** Applicants must check the available website for the required materials. **Deadline:** April 1. **Contact:** For further information, applicants must contact Ruth Bishop, Education Program Officer at rbishop@grfoundation.org.

4295 ■ Peggy Kommer Novosad Scholarships (Graduate, Postgraduate/Scholarship)

Purpose: To provide financial support to those students who are in need. **Focus:** Business; Law. **Qualif.:** Applicants must be residents of Kent County who are currently completing or possess an undergraduate degree from GVSU or MSU and will be pursuing a full-time graduate or post-graduate degree in business or law at any accredited university in Michigan. Applicants must have financial need and a minimum of 3.5 GPA. **Criteria:** Preference will be given to those who meet the criteria.

Funds Avail.: No specific amount. **To Apply:** Applicants must check the available website for the required materials. **Deadline:** April 1. **Contact:** For further information, applicants must contact Ruth Bishop, Education Program Officer at rbishop@grfoundation.org.

4296 ■ Patricia & Armen Oumedian Scholarships (Undergraduate/Scholarship)

Purpose: To provide financial support to those students who are in need. **Focus:** Engineering. **Qualif.:** Applicants must be second year or above full-time engineering students at Kettering or transferring from GRCC to Kettering. Applicants must be residents of Kent, Ottawa, or Muskegon County. Applicants must have demonstrated financial need and must have a minimum of 3.0 GPA. **Criteria:** Preference will be given to those students who meet the criteria.

Funds Avail.: No specific amount. **To Apply:** Applicants must check the available website for the required materials. **Deadline:** April 1. **Contact:** For further information, applicants must contact Ruth Bishop, Education Program Officer at rbishop@grfoundation.org.

4297 ■ Josephine Ringold Scholarships (Undergraduate/Scholarship)

Purpose: To provide financial support to those students who are in need. **Focus:** General Studies. **Qualif.:** Applicants must be Kent County residents who will be attending Aquinas, Calvin, Cornerstone, Davenport, GRCC, GVSU or Kendall. Applicants must have financial need and a 3.0 minimum GPA is required. **Criteria:** Preference will be given to those students who meet the criteria.

Funds Avail.: No specific amount. **To Apply:** Applicants must check the available website for more information. **Deadline:** April 1. **Contact:** Grand Rapids Community Foundation at the above address.

4298 ■ Margery J. Seeger Scholarships (Undergraduate/Scholarship)

Purpose: To provide financial assistance to those students who are in need. **Focus:** General Studies. **Qualif.:** Applicants must be Kent County residents who are pursuing an undergraduate degree at any accredited college in the U.S. Applicants must have financial need. Applicants must have a minimum of 3.3 GPA. **Criteria:** Preference will be given to those students who meet the criteria.

Funds Avail.: No specific amount. **To Apply:** Applicants must check the available website for the required materials. **Deadline:** April 1. **Contact:** For further information, applicants must contact Ruth Bishop, Education Program Officer at rbishop@grfoundation.org.

4299 ■ Gladys Snauble Scholarships (Undergraduate/Scholarship)

Purpose: To provide financial support to those students who are in need. **Focus:** General Studies. **Qualif.:** Ap-

Awards are arranged alphabetically below their administering organizations

plicants must be senior students at Cedar Springs High School who will be entering college in the fall. Applicants must have financial need. **Criteria:** Priority will be given to those students with financial need.

Funds Avail.: No specific amount. **To Apply:** Applicants must check the available website for the required materials. **Deadline:** April 1. **Contact:** Grand Rapids Community Foundation at the above address.

4300 ■ Christine Soper Scholarships
(Undergraduate/Scholarship)

Purpose: To provide financial support to those students who are in need. **Focus:** General Studies. **Qualif.:** Applicants must be Kent County residents who will be attending Aquinas, Calvin, Cornerstone, Davenport, GRCC, GVSU or Kendall. Applicants must have financial need. Applicants must have a cumulative of 3.0 GPA. **Criteria:** Priority will be given to those students who meet the criteria.

Funds Avail.: No specific amount. **To Apply:** Applicants must check the available website for the required materials. **Deadline:** April 1. **Contact:** For further information, applicants must contact Ruth Bishop, Education Program Officer at rbishop@grfoundation.org.

4301 ■ Dr. William E. & Norma Sprague Scholarships *(Undergraduate/Scholarship)*

Purpose: To provide financial assistance to those students who are in need. **Focus:** Medicine. **Qualif.:** Applicants must be full-time students and permanent residents in the Michigan counties of Kent, Allegan, Barry, Ionia, Montcalm, Muskegon, Newaygo or Athens County, Ohio, who are pursuing a full-time undergraduate or graduate degree in medicine at Ohio University. Applicants must have financial need. Applicants must have a minimum of 3.0 GPA. **Criteria:** Preference will be given to those students who meet the criteria.

Funds Avail.: No specific amount. **To Apply:** Applicants must check the available website for the required materials. **Deadline:** April 1. **Contact:** Grand Rapids Community Foundation at the above address.

4302 ■ Dorothy B. & Charles E. Thomas Scholarships *(Undergraduate/Scholarship)*

Purpose: To provide financial assistance to those students who are in need. **Focus:** General Studies. **Qualif.:** Applicants must be Kent County residents who will be attending Aquinas, Calvin, Cornerstone, Davenport, GRCC, GVSU or Kendall. Applicants must have a minimum of 3.0 GPA. Applicants must have financial need. **Criteria:** Priority will be given to those students with financial need.

Funds Avail.: No specific amount. **To Apply:** Applicants must check the available website for the application process and for the required materials. **Deadline:** April 1. **Contact:** For further information, applicants must contact Ruth Bishop, Education Program Officer at rbishop@grfoundation.org.

4303 ■ Dorothy J. Thurston Graduate Scholarships *(Undergraduate/Scholarship)*

Purpose: To provide financial assistance to those students who are in need. **Focus:** General Studies. **Qualif.:** Applicants must be Kent County residents who are pursuing full or part-time study at any accredited school in Michigan. Applicants must have financial need. Applicants must have a minimum of 3.0 GPA. **Criteria:** Preference will be given to those students who meet the criteria.

Funds Avail.: No specific amount. **To Apply:** Applicants must check the available website for more information. **Deadline:** April 1. **Contact:** Grand Rapids Community Foundation at the above address.

4304 ■ Mildred E. Troske Music Scholarships
(Undergraduate/Scholarship)

Purpose: To provide financial support to those students who are in need. **Focus:** General Studies. **Qualif.:** Applicants must be residents of Kent County who are studying music at a camp or are undergraduate music majors. Applicants must have demonstrated financial need. Applicants must have a minimum of 3.0 GPA. **Criteria:** Preference will be given to those students who meet the criteria.

Funds Avail.: No specific amount. **To Apply:** Applicants must check the available website for the required materials. **Deadline:** April 1. **Contact:** For further information, applicants must contact Ruth Bishop, Education Program Officer at rbishop@grfoundation.org.

4305 ■ Keith C. Vanderhyde Scholarships
(Undergraduate/Scholarship)

Purpose: To provide financial assistance to those students who are in need. **Focus:** General Studies. **Qualif.:** Applicants must be senior students or graduates of Ottawa Hills High School who are pursuing a full-time undergraduate degree. Applicants must demonstrate financial need. Applicants must have a minimum of 3.0 GPA. **Criteria:** Priority will be given to those students with financial need.

Funds Avail.: No specific amount. **To Apply:** Applicants must check the available website for the required materials. **Deadline:** April 1. **Contact:** For further information, applicants must contact Ruth Bishop, Education Program Officer at rbishop@grfoundation.org.

4306 ■ Jacob R. & Mary M. VanLoo & Lenore K. VanLoo Scholarships *(Undergraduate/ Scholarship)*

Purpose: To provide financial assistance to those students who are in need. **Focus:** General Studies. **Qualif.:** Applicants must be Kent County residents who will be attending Aquinas, Calvin, Cornerstone, Davenport, GRCC, GVSU or Kendall. Applicants must have financial need. Applicants must have a minimum of 3.0 GPA. **Criteria:** Preference will be given to those students who meet the criteria.

Funds Avail.: No specific amount. **To Apply:** Applicants must check the available website for the required materials. **Deadline:** April 1. **Contact:** Grand Rapids Community Foundation at the above address.

4307 ■ Donald M. Wells Scholarships
(Undergraduate/Scholarship)

Purpose: To provide financial assistance to those students who are in need. **Focus:** General Studies. **Qualif.:** Applicants must be senior students or graduates of Central High School who are pursuing undergraduate studies at GRCC, University of Chicago or University of Michigan. Applicants must have financial need and must have a minimum of 2.5 GPA. **Criteria:** Preference will be given to those students who meet the criteria.

Funds Avail.: No specific amount. **To Apply:** Applicants must check the available website for more information regarding this award. **Deadline:** April 1. **Contact:** Grand Rapids Community Foundation at the above address.

4308 ■ Elmo Wierenga Alumni Scholarships
(Undergraduate/Scholarship)

Purpose: To provide financial support to those students who are in need. **Focus:** General Studies. **Qualif.:** Ap-

Awards are arranged alphabetically below their administering organizations

plicants must be senior students at Ottawa Hills High School pursuing full-time undergraduate studies at any 2 or 4-year accredited school in the U.S. Applicants must have financial need and a minimum of 2.5 GPA. **Criteria:** Priority will be given to those students with financial need.

Funds Avail.: No specific amount. **To Apply:** Applicants must check the available website for the required materials. **Deadline:** April 1. **Contact:** Grand Rapids Community Foundation at the above address.

4309 ■ Audrey L. Wright Scholarships
(Undergraduate/Scholarship)

Purpose: To provide financial support to deserving students. **Focus:** Foreign Language; Education. **Qualif.:** Applicants must be residents of Kent County; must be pursuing an undergraduate degree in Foreign Language or Education; must have financial need; must have a minimum of 3.0 GPA. **Criteria:** Preference will be given to those students who meet the criteria.

Funds Avail.: No specific amount. **To Apply:** Applicants must check the available website for the application process and for the required materials. **Deadline:** April 1. **Contact:** For further information, applicants must contact Ruth Bishop, Education Program Officer at rbishop@grfoundation.org.

4310 ■ Grandmothers for Peace International (GPI)
PO Box 1292
Elk Grove, CA 95759-1292
Ph: (916) 730-6476
E-mail: lorraine@grandmothersforpeace.org
URL: www.grandmothersforpeace.org

4311 ■ Barbara Wiedner and Dorothy Vandercook Memorial Peace Scholarships
(Undergraduate/Scholarship)

Purpose: To provide financial assistance to students across the United States, Africa, Kyrgzstan, Canada, Norway and Ukraine. **Focus:** General studies. **Qualif.:** Applicants must be high school seniors or in their first year of college. **Criteria:** Recipients will be evaluated by the Scholarship Selection Committees based on some criteria.

Funds Avail.: $250. **Number Awarded:** 4. **To Apply:** Applicants must submit the completed application form; brief autobiography of activities relating to peace and social justice, nuclear disarmament issues, or conflict resolution; two letters of recommendation; and must describe how they will contribute to a peaceful and just society in the future. **Contact:** Leal Portis, President, 301 Redbud Way, Nevada City, CA 95959, Phone/Fax: 530-265-3887, E-mail: portis.leal@gmail.com.

4312 ■ Granger Business Association (GBA)
PO Box 427
Granger, IN 46530
Ph: (574) 271-7003
Fax: (574) 271-7150
E-mail: info@grangertoday.com
URL: www.grangertoday.com

4313 ■ Granger Business Association College Scholarships *(Undergraduate/Scholarship)*

Purpose: To award scholarships to area students to help defray college expenses. **Focus:** General Studies. **Qualif.:**

Applicants must reside in the 46530 zip code and demonstrate financial need. **Criteria:** Preference will be based on academic standing; extra curricular activities; volunteer work and personal narratives.

Funds Avail.: $1,000. **Number Awarded:** 10-12. **To Apply:** Applicants must check the application process online. **Deadline:** April 1. **Contact:** If have questions, please contact Kathy Smith at the above address, Phone: 574-243-7746, E-mail: kathy.smith@lakecitybank.com.

4314 ■ Grass Foundation
PO Box 241458
Los Angeles, CA 90024
Ph: (424) 832-4188
Fax: (310) 986-2252
E-mail: info@grassfoundation.org
URL: www.grassfoundation.org

4315 ■ Grass Fellowships *(Doctorate, Postdoctorate/Fellowship)*

Purpose: To encourage independent research by investigators early in their careers and to increase research opportunities for persons planning careers in neurobiological investigation. **Focus:** Neurophysiology; Biophysics; Neuroscience; Neurology. **Qualif.:** Applicant may be in the late stages of predoctoral training or be a postdoctoral researcher. Applicants are advised not to combine a Grass Fellowship with writing a PhD thesis. **Criteria:** Priority is given to applicants with a demonstrated commitment to a research career and no prior research experience at the MBL.

Funds Avail.: No specific amount. **Number Awarded:** Varies. **To Apply:** Applicants must complete the application package and must be submitted electronically as a single pdf or MS Word file. **Deadline:** December 5. **Contact:** Ann Wollford, phone: 508-289-7521, fax: 508-289-7934.

4316 ■ Gravure Education Foundation (GEF)
PO Box 25617
Rochester, NY 14625
Ph: (201) 523-6042
Fax: (201) 523-6048
E-mail: bcarlson@gaa.org
URL: www.gaa.org/gravure-education-foundation

4317 ■ ALCOA Foundation Scholarships
(Undergraduate, Graduate/Scholarship)

Purpose: To help undergraduate and graduate students pursue their education through the support of ALCOA employee volunteers. **Focus:** General studies. **Qualif.:** Applicants must be undergraduate or graduate students enrolled in a full-time basis in one of the GEF designated learning resource centers; must have GPA of 3.0 or greater on a 4.0 scale. **Criteria:** Applicants will be chosen based on demonstrated leadership and academic accomplishments.

Funds Avail.: $1,500. **To Apply:** Applicants must submit a completed application form; must contact the Executive Director for further information. **Remarks:** In collaboration with ALCOA Foundation. **Contact:** Bernadette Carlson at bcarlson@gaa.org.

4318 ■ Cerutti Group Scholarships *(Undergraduate, Graduate/Scholarship)*

Purpose: To provide financial assistance to undergraduate and graduate students. **Focus:** General studies. **Qualif.:**

Awards are arranged alphabetically below their administering organizations

Applicants must be undergraduate or graduate students. **Criteria:** Recipients will be chosen based on submitted materials.

Funds Avail.: Amount not specified. **To Apply:** Applicants must contact the Executive Director for further information. **Remarks:** In collaboration with Cerutti Group. **Contact:** Bernadette Carlson at bcarlson@gaa.org.

4319 ■ GEF Scholarship Program *(Undergraduate, Graduate/Scholarship)*

Purpose: To financially assist students interested in graphic communications or any related fields of study. **Focus:** Graphic art and design. **Qualif.:** Applicants must be undergraduate or graduate students enrolled full-time at any of the GEF-funded colleges or universities; must be majoring printing, graphic arts or any fields of study related in graphic communications; must have 3.0 GPA or greater on a 4.0 scale. **Criteria:** Applicants will be selected based on merit.

Funds Avail.: Amount not specified. **To Apply:** Applicants must submit a completed application form. Faxed applications will not be accepted. **Deadline:** April 20.

4320 ■ Gravure Publishing Council Scholarships *(Undergraduate, Graduate/Scholarship)*

Purpose: To encourage students who are in financial need and encourage them to enter the gravure industry. **Focus:** Printmaking. **Qualif.:** Applicants must be undergraduate and graduate students. **Criteria:** Recipients will be selected based on submitted materials.

Funds Avail.: $1,500. **Number Awarded:** 1. **To Apply:** Applicants must contact the Executive Director for further information. **Remarks:** In collaboration with Gravure Publishing Council. **Contact:** Bernadette Carlson at bcarlson@gaa.org.

4321 ■ Harry V. Quadracci Memorial Scholarships *(Undergraduate, Graduate/Scholarship)*

Purpose: To provide financial assistance to students and encourage them to be involved in Gravure industry. **Focus:** Printmaking; Graphic art and design. **Qualif.:** Applicants must be undergraduate and graduate students; must be enrolled full-time at any of the printing management/graphic arts programs at one of the GEF designed learning resource centers; must maintain a GPA of 3.0 or greater. **Criteria:** Applicants will be chosen based on demonstrated academic success, extracurricular/community involvement and financial need.

Funds Avail.: $1,000. **Number Awarded:** 1. **To Apply:** Applicants must contact the Executive Director for further information. **Contact:** Bernadette Carlson at bcarlson@gaa.org.

4322 ■ Grays Harbor Community Foundation
PO Box 615
Hoquiam, WA 98550
Ph: (360) 532-1600
Fax: (360) 532-8111
E-mail: info@gh-cf.org
URL: www.gh-cf.org

4323 ■ Grays Harbor Community Foundation Scholarships *(Graduate, Undergraduate/Scholarship)*

Purpose: To financially support students of Grays Harbor or Pacific County in their educational pursuit. **Focus:** General studies. **Qualif.:** Applicant must be a resident of Grays Harbor or Pacific County; have graduated from a Grays Harbor or Pacific County high school; be in need of financial assistance; an undergraduate student enrolled as a full-time (12 credits minimum) at an accredited college/university and have earned a cumulative GPA of 3.0 (or equivalent B average); or a graduate student accepted into a graduate program at an accredited university and have earned a cumulative GPA of 3.0 (or equivalent B average) both in college and in the first year of graduate school. **Criteria:** Selection is based on applicant's academic performance, financial need, character, ability, industry and service.

Funds Avail.: Varies. **To Apply:** Applicants must submit a completed, printed and signed application form along with a personal essay (1-page, typed); three written letters of recommendation; history of employment; certified transcripts from all schools attended; and a documentation of acceptance by a graduate program at an accredited university (graduate students). **Deadline:** April 1.

4324 ■ Great Lakes Athletic Trainers Association (GLATA)
PO Box 436
Crystal Lake, IL 60039
Ph: (815) 455-8512
E-mail: kevinatc@sbcglobal.net
URL: www.glata.org

4325 ■ GLATA Living Memorial Doctorate Scholarships *(Doctorate, Graduate/Fellowship)*

Purpose: To honor the memory and accomplishments of the deceased members of the GLATA by providing scholarships to students who want to pursue their graduate studies. **Focus:** General studies. **Qualif.:** Applicant must be a member in good standing of the National Athletic Trainers Association; must be a current GLATA Certified member; must have a grade point average of 3.0, its equivalent, or above. **Criteria:** Selection of applicants will be based on the criteria of the Scholarship Committee.

Funds Avail.: $2,000. **To Apply:** Applicants must complete the application form available on the website; must submit an official statement from the registrar of the college or university indicating the applicants current GPA, and that the applicant is enrolled in a PhD, EdD or equivalent terminal degree program and has qualified for dissertation level credits; must have an official transcript through the most recently completed school term; must provide three candidate recommendation forms sent to the District Vice-President (one form must be completed by the applicant's Major Advisor, an Athletic Administrator or another Professor, and a sponsoring Athletic Trainer). **Deadline:** December 1.

4326 ■ GLATA Living Memorial Undergraduate/Graduate Scholarships *(Graduate, Undergraduate/Fellowship, Scholarship)*

Purpose: To honor the memory and accomplishments of the deceased members of the GLATA by providing scholarships to students who want to pursue their graduate studies. **Focus:** General studies. **Qualif.:** Applicant must be a member in good standing of the National Athletic Trainers Association; must be a full time student within GLATA or must be a current GLATA member; must have the intention to pursue certification by the NATA; must have a GPA of B or above. For Graduate applicants: must be a degree-

Awards are arranged alphabetically below their administering organizations

seeking candidate for the upcoming fall academic term; must have worked at least two academic years as an athletic training student on the college level under the supervision of an NATA certified athletic trainer. For Undergraduate applicants: must have a senior standing for the next fall academic term; must have worked at least one academic year as an athletic training student on the college level under the supervision of an NATA certified athletic trainer; must currently be a full time student enrolled in a curriculum leading to a Bachelor's degree at the time of application. **Criteria:** Selection of applicants will be based on the criteria of the Scholarship Committee.

Funds Avail.: No specific amount. **To Apply:** Applicants must complete the application form available on the website; must submit an official statement from the registrar of the college or university indicating the applicant's current GPA, and also indicating that the applicant is a full-time student; must submit an official transcript through the most recently completed school term; must have three candidate recommendation forms sent to the district vice-president (one form must be completed by a professor who is an Athletic Trainer in the applicant's major field, and one form must be completed by a Non-ATC Academic professor in the applicant's major field). **Deadline:** December 1.

4327 ■ Great Lakes Commission

Eisenhower Corporate Pk.
2805 S Industrial Hwy., Ste. 100
Ann Arbor, MI 48104-6791
Ph: (734) 665-9135
Fax: (734) 665-9150
E-mail: glc@great-lakes.net

4328 ■ Great Lakes Commission Sea Grant Fellowships *(Graduate/Scholarship)*

Purpose: To provide fund to work and advance the environmental quality and sustainable economic development goals. **Focus:** Natural resources, Public health. **Qualif.:** Applicants must be graduate or professional students in the field of public policy, public health, natural resources, aquatic sciences or other related field at an accredited institution of higher education in the United States. **Criteria:** Evaluations will be based on academic ability; communication skills; diversity and appropriateness of background; and interests to fellowship experience.

Funds Avail.: $41,000. **To Apply:** Applicants must complete the required documents; personal and academic resume (maximum of two pages); education and career goal statement (1,000 words or less); two letters of recommendation with at least one from the student's major professor; a letter of endorsement from the sponsoring Sea Grant Director; a copy of undergraduates and graduates transcript of records. Must be sent to the Great Lakes Commission. **Deadline:** January 31. **Contact:** E-mail Executive Director, Tim Eder at teder@glc.org.

4329 ■ Carol A. Ratza Memorial Scholarships *(Undergraduate/Scholarship)*

Purpose: To recognize outstanding achievement and vision in electronic communications technology. **Focus:** Electronics; Communications technologies. **Qualif.:** Applicant must be enrolled full-time at a college or university in the Great Lakes states or Canadian provinces; must have a career interest in electronic communication technologies; must have a demonstrated interest in the environmental or economic applications of electronic communications

technology; exhibit academic excellence and have a sincere appreciation for the Great Lakes and their protection. **Criteria:** Selection of applicant will be based on their demonstrated interest in the environmental or economic applications of electronic communications technology; exhibit academic excellence and their sincere appreciation for the Great Lakes and their protection.

Funds Avail.: $1,000. **To Apply:** Application must be submitted along with essay/original web page; resume; letter of intent; grade transcripts and two letters of recommendation.

4330 ■ Great Minds in STEM

3900 Whiteside St.
Los Angeles, CA 90063
Ph: (323) 262-0997
Fax: (323) 262-0946
URL: www.henaac.org

4331 ■ Great Minds in STEM Scholarships *(Graduate, Undergraduate/Scholarship)*

Purpose: To financially support Hispanic students in their educational pursuit. **Focus:** Science; Technology; Engineering; Mathematics and mathematical sciences. **Qualif.:** Applicant must demonstrate leadership through academic achievements and campus/community activities; be a Science, Technology, Engineering or Math related major; have an overall GPA of 3.0 or higher; be enrolled in an undergraduate or graduate program; be of Hispanic origin and/or must significantly participate in and promote organizations and activities in the Hispanic community. **Criteria:** Selection is based on the application materials submitted for review.

Funds Avail.: $500-$5,000. **Number Awarded:** Varies. **To Apply:** Applicant must submit a completed application form together with a 700-word essay on a given topic; a current resume; one letter of recommendation from a peer in a campus or community organization; one letter of recommendation from a college advisor, MEP Director, Dean or faculty member; and official transcript with the official seal of college/high school. **Deadline:** April 30. **Contact:** For further information, applicants must contact Kathy Borunda-Barrera at kathy@greatmindsinstem.org.

4332 ■ Great Seattle Business Association (GSBA)

400 E Pine St., Ste. 322
Seattle, WA 98122
Ph: (206) 363-9188
Fax: (206) 568-3123
E-mail: office@thegsba.org
URL: www.thegsba.org

4333 ■ Greater Seattle Business Association Scholarships *(Undergraduate/Scholarship)*

Purpose: To support undergraduate students by providing financial resources to pursue their educational goals. **Focus:** General studies. **Qualif.:** Applicant must be a current resident of Washington pursuing an undergraduate degree at any college in the US. **Criteria:** Applicants will be evaluated based on leadership potential; academic strength/special skills and talents; and diversity.

Funds Avail.: $3,000 up to $10,000. **To Apply:** Applicants must complete and return scholarship application, letters of

Awards are arranged alphabetically below their administering organizations

reference and transcripts by application deadline. **Deadline:** January 31.

4334 ■ The Greater Tacoma Community Foundation

950 Pacific Ave., Ste. 1100
Tacoma, WA 98402
Ph: (253) 383-5622
Fax: (253) 272-8099
E-mail: info@gtcf.org
URL: www.gtcf.org

4335 ■ Ruth Murphy Evans Scholarships
(Undergraduate/Scholarship)

Purpose: To foster generosity by connecting people who care with causes that matter. **Focus:** Nursing. **Qualif.:** Applicants must be students in a nursing program at Highline Community College, Olympic College, South Puget Sound Community College or Tacoma Community College. **Criteria:** Recipients are selected based on financial need.

Funds Avail.: No specific amount. **To Apply:** Applicants must request an application form at their guidance office.

4336 ■ Dayton E. Finnigan Scholarships
(Undergraduate/Scholarship)

Purpose: To foster generosity by connecting people who care with causes that matter. **Focus:** Metallurgy. **Qualif.:** Applicants must be students enrolled in the sheet metal program at Bates Technical College. **Criteria:** Recipients are selected based on financial need.

Funds Avail.: No specific amount. **To Apply:** Applicants must request an application form at the guidance office of Bates Technical College.

4337 ■ Fuchs-Harden Educational Scholarships Fund *(Undergraduate/Scholarship)*

Purpose: To foster generosity by connecting people who care with causes that matter. **Focus:** Engineering; Business Administration; Social sciences. **Qualif.:** Applicant must be an African American residing in the legal limits of the city of Tacoma, Washington; must be enrolled in and maintain a satisfactory GPA at a college or university in the courses for Business Administration, Engineering, Applied Physics, Dentistry, Medicine, Law, Sociology, Journalism or Home Economics. **Criteria:** Recipients are selected based on financial need.

Funds Avail.: No specific amount. **To Apply:** Applicants must submit a completed application form available through R. Merle Palmer Minority Scholarship Fund. **Contact:** Ms. Becky Gonzales at 253-583-5587 or rgonzal@cloverpark.k12.wa.us.

4338 ■ Clay Huntington Sports Communications Scholarships *(Undergraduate/Scholarship)*

Purpose: To benefit students from Pierce County high schools and help tomorrow's leaders reach their goals and fulfill their dreams. **Focus:** Broadcasting; Media arts. **Qualif.:** Applicants must be graduating seniors at Pierce County High School; must intend to declare a major in radio/television production and/or broadcast editorial journalism or a similar communications-related field. **Criteria:** Recipients are selected based on financial need.

Funds Avail.: No specific amount. **To Apply:** Applicants must request an application form at Tacoma Athletic Com-

mission. **Contact:** PO Box 11304, Tacoma, WA 98411.

4339 ■ The Master Gardeners of Pierce County Scholarships *(Undergraduate/Scholarship)*

Purpose: To foster generosity by connecting people who care with causes that matter; to benefit Washington State University Puyallup Research and Extension Center graduates, undergraduate students or a Pierce County high school student. **Focus:** Horticulture. **Qualif.:** Applicants must plan to study horticulture or the environment. **Criteria:** Recipients are selected based on financial need.

Funds Avail.: No specific amount. **To Apply:** Applicants must contact W.S.U. Puyallup Research and Extension Center Scholarship Committee for application form. **Contact:** 7612 Pioneer Way E Puyallup, WA 98371-4998 or 253-445-4500.

4340 ■ Anna M. Rundquist Memorial Scholarships *(Undergraduate/Scholarship)*

Purpose: To provide assistance for students. **Focus:** General studies. **Qualif.:** Applicants must be graduating students from Highline Community College, Olympic College, South Puget Sound Community College or Tacoma Community College; must be enrolled at a four-year college or university to pursue a nursing career. **Criteria:** Recipients are selected based on academic performance and financial need.

Funds Avail.: No specific amount. **To Apply:** Applicants must submit a completed application form available at the guidance office.

4341 ■ The Tacoma Athletic Commission Scholarships *(Undergraduate, Vocational/Occupational/Scholarship)*

Purpose: To foster generosity by connecting people who care with causes that matter. **Focus:** Athletics. **Qualif.:** Applicants must be current graduating senior students at Pierce County High School; must be enrolled at a vocational school or a two or four-year college. **Criteria:** Recipients are selected based on financial need.

Funds Avail.: No specific amount. **To Apply:** Applicants must request an application form at Tacoma Athletic Commission.

4342 ■ Greater Washington Society of Certified Public Accountants (GWSCPA)

1111 19th St. NW, No. 1200
Washington, DC 20036
Ph: (202) 464-6001
Fax: (202) 238-9604
E-mail: info@gwscpa.org
URL: www.gwscpa.org

4343 ■ GWSCPA Scholarships *(Undergraduate/Scholarship)*

Purpose: To support students aspiring to become a Certified Public Accountant. **Focus:** Accounting. **Qualif.:** Applicant must be a student attending a GWSCPA eligible school/university on a full time basis and must meet all the other criteria. Eligible Schools/Universities: American University, Catholic University, Gallaudet University, George Washington University, Georgetown University, Howard University, Southeastern University, Strayer University, and University of the District of Columbia. **Criteria:** Selection is

Awards are arranged alphabetically below their administering organizations

based on the application materials submitted.

Funds Avail.: No specific amount. **To Apply:** Applicants must contact their respective schools/universities for the application details.

4344 ■ Greek Orthodox Archdiocese of America
8 E 79th St.
New York, NY 10075-0192
Ph: (212) 570-3500
Fax: (212) 570-3569
E-mail: archdiocese@goarch.org
URL: www.goarch.org

4345 ■ Greek Orthodox Archdiocese of America Paleologos Graduate Scholarships
(Graduate/Scholarship)

Purpose: To help defray the cost of students pursuing graduate degrees. **Focus:** General studies. **Qualif.:** Applicants must be Orthodox Christians from a church who belong to SCOBA (Standing Conference of Canonical Orthodox Bishops in the Americas); must be active in church activities; must be college graduates and in the next academic year, must be either commencing their graduate studies or continuing their graduate program studies on a full-time basis at an accredited university in a non-theological field of study leading to a graduate degree; must be U.S. citizens or permanent residents of the United States. **Criteria:** Selection will be based on evaluation of submitted documents and specific criteria.

Funds Avail.: $10,000. **To Apply:** Applicants must submit a completed application form; academic records including undergraduate and graduate transcripts (past and present); statement of financial need; a copy or transcript of baptismal or chrismation certificate; resume or curriculum vitae; scholarship proposal; personal statement (optional); five recommendation letters. **Deadline:** April. **Contact:** Questions should be directed to the Scholarship Office at scholarships@goarch.org.

4346 ■ Green Knight Economic Development Corporation (GKEDC)
PO Box 4
Pen Argyl, PA 18072
E-mail: gkedc@gkedc.com
URL: www.gkedc.com

4347 ■ Green Knight Economic Development Corporation Scholarships (GKEDC)
(Undergraduate/Scholarship)

Purpose: To financially support a student living in the Pen Argyl School District who wishes to continue higher education. **Focus:** General studies. **Qualif.:** Applicant must be a graduating high school senior who lives in the Pen Argyl School District and will be continuing his/her education in a college program; must take at least 24 credits per year and must maintain, at a minimum, a cumulative GPA of 2.5. Student attending a two year college and continuing on to obtain his/her bachelor's degree is also welcome to apply. **Criteria:** Award is given based on the application materials.

Funds Avail.: $4,000 each year. **To Apply:** Applicants must submit a completed scholarship application form together with a one-page essay. Guidance counselor must sign and the date the last page of the application verifying the SAT

scores, class rank and GPA. **Deadline:** May 6. **Remarks:** The first segment of $1,000 will be rewarded upon receipt of a certificate of admission or a letter of acceptance. **Contact:** Application form and supporting documents must be sent to Community Relations Committee at comm@gkedc.com.

4348 ■ Greenlining Institute
1918 University Ave. 2nd Fl.
Berkeley, CA 94704
Ph: (510) 926-4001
Fax: (510) 926-4010
E-mail: info@greenlining.org
URL: greenlining.org

4349 ■ Greenlining Institute Fellowships
(Graduate/Fellowship)

Purpose: To empower communities of color and other disadvantaged groups through multi-ethnic economic and leadership development, civil rights and anti-redlining activities. **Focus:** Leadership, Institutional and community. **Qualif.:** Applicant must be a student of color or from must be from other disadvantaged groups, and must have completed at least an undergraduate degree. **Criteria:** Selection is based on the application materials submitted.

Funds Avail.: $33,800. **To Apply:** Applicants must submit a completed application form along with a personal statement; resume; two letters or recommendation; and copies of all higher education transcripts. **Deadline:** February 10. **Contact:** academy@greenlining.org.

4350 ■ Greenwich Scholarship Association (GSA)
One Lafayette Ct.
Greenwich, CT 06830
Ph: (203) 661-9799
Fax: (203) 542-5188
URL: www.greenwichscholarship.org

4351 ■ Greenwich Scholarship Association Scholarships (GSA) *(Undergraduate/Scholarship)*

Purpose: To support graduating seniors attending a public, private or parochial school. **Focus:** General studies. **Qualif.:** Applicants must be graduating seniors residing in Greenwich, CT; must be currently attending a public, private, or parochial school located in Greenwich; must have demonstrated financial need. **Criteria:** Recipients will be selected based on financial need.

Funds Avail.: Varies. **To Apply:** Applicants must submit a completed application form; attach an activity sheet; financial statement; completed and filed FAFSA. **Deadline:** March 9. **Remarks:** Failure to attend the Scholarship Night may result loss of the award. **Contact:** For more information, applicants may contact Marie Hertzig, GSA President, 22 Baldwin Farms N, Greenwich, CT 06831 or e-mail to: mjhertzig@aol.com.

4352 ■ Griffin Foundation
303 W Prospect Rd.
Fort Collins, CO 80526
Ph: (970) 482-3030
Fax: (970) 484-6648
E-mail: carol.wood@thegriffinfoundation.org

Awards are arranged alphabetically below their administering organizations

URL: www.thegriffinfoundation.org

4353 ■ Griffin Foundation Scholarships
(Undergraduate/Scholarship)

Purpose: To award scholarship to qualified applicants who have an associate degree from a junior or community college. **Focus:** General studies. **Qualif.:** Applicants must have an associate degree or at least 60 hours from a junior or community college and are seeking to complete a baccalaureate degree; must have a cumulative GPA of at least a 3.5 on a 4.0 scale in all college level work; must be admitted as full-time, on-campus students in a baccalaureate degree program at the participating university they have selected. **Criteria:** Scholarships will be awarded on a competitive basis by ranking applicants in the following areas for their activities since graduation from high school: scholarship; leadership and service; personal traits; and financial need.

Funds Avail.: $5,000. **To Apply:** Application form can be downloaded from the Griffin Foundation website. Applicants must type or print their application legibly; applicants must attach three letters of recommendation, at least one of which is from a college faculty member, counselor or administrator who can comment on applicant qualifications (be sure recommendations are signed). Applicants must attach an official copy of grade transcript(s) from each college attended. Scholarship can only be used at Colorado State University (Fort Collins Campus), the University of Northern Colorado, or the University of Wyoming (Larimie Campus). **Deadline:** March 1. **Contact:** Carol Wood, Program Dir. at the above address.

4354 ■ Guelph Caribbean Canadian Association
7 Clair Rd. W
Guelph, ON, Canada N1L 0A0
E-mail: info@guelphcaribbean.ca
URL: guelphcaribbean.ca

4355 ■ Guelph Caribbean Canadian Association Scholarships *(Undergraduate/Scholarship)*

Purpose: To financially assist deserving students who have been admitted to post-secondary institution in Canada. **Focus:** General studies. **Qualif.:** Applicants must be students of Caribbean/West Indian heritage who are Canadian citizens; must be residents of the City of Guelph or Wellington County; must be students either entering first year of post-secondary education with a copy of letter of acceptance at a recognized post-secondary institution or second year with proof of ongoing registration. **Criteria:** Recipients will be selected based on academic achievement and demonstrated leadership skills and involvement in extra-curricular activities.

Funds Avail.: $500. **To Apply:** Applicants must complete the application form; must submit one letter of acceptance from an eligible post-secondary institution or proof of ongoing registration, resume, or short essay describing the reasons why they deserve the award. **Deadline:** October 1.

4356 ■ Harry Frank Guggenheim Foundation (HFG)
25 W 53rd Ste.
New York, NY 10019-5401
Ph: (646) 428-0971
Fax: (646) 428-0981
E-mail: info@hfg.org

URL: www.hfg.org

4357 ■ Harry Frank Guggenheim Fellowships
(Doctorate/Fellowship)

Purpose: To increase of the causes, manifestations, and control of violence, aggression, and dominance in the modern world. **Focus:** Social sciences; Humanities. **Qualif.:** Applicants must be citizens of any country and studying as doctoral candidates in colleges and universities in any country. **Criteria:** Recipients are selected based on the comparison of the candidates' theses.

Funds Avail.: $15,000. **Number Awarded:** 10 or more. **To Apply:** Applicants must submit three copies of typewritten title page; abstract; advisors letter; applicant's background; a research plan; protection of subjects.

4358 ■ Harry Frank Guggenheim Foundation Research Grants *(All/Grant)*

Purpose: To increase understanding of the causes, manifestations, and control violence, aggression, and dominance. **Focus:** Social sciences; Humanities. **Qualif.:** Applicants must have a project proposal in the field of natural sciences and humanities. **Criteria:** Recipients are selected based on the project proposal.

Funds Avail.: $15,000-$30,000. **To Apply:** Applicants must submit three copies of typewritten title page; abstract; personnel; budget; budget justification; research plan; protection of subjects; tax exempt status; referees' comments. **Deadline:** August 1.

4359 ■ John Simon Guggenheim Memorial Foundation
90 Park Ave.
New York, NY 10016
Ph: (212) 687-4470
Fax: (212) 697-3248
URL: www.gf.org

4360 ■ John Simon Guggenheim Memorial Fellowships - U.S. and Canadian Competition
(Advanced Professional/Fellowship)

Purpose: To assist men and women in research and artistic creation. **Focus:** Natural sciences; Social sciences; Humanities; Creative arts. **Qualif.:** Applicant must be an individual who has already demonstrated exceptional capacity for productive scholarship or exceptional creative ability in the arts, and must be a U.S. or Canadian citizen. **Criteria:** Selection is based on the application materials submitted for review.

Funds Avail.: No specific amount. **Number Awarded:** Varies. **To Apply:** Applicants must submit a completed application form together with the three separate supplementary statements. The three supplementary statements are: a brief narrative account of the applicant's career, describing previous accomplishments; a list of: Publications (scholar, scientist, or writer), Exhibitions (artist), Performances (choreographer), Compositions (composer), or Films/Videotapes (film or video maker); and a statement of plans for the period for which the Fellowship is requested. Application form must be submitted in PDF format. **Deadline:** September 15.

4361 ■ Gulf and Caribbean Fisheries Institute (GCFI)
c/o Florida Fish and Wildlife Conservation Commission
Marine Research Institute

Awards are arranged alphabetically below their administering organizations

2796 Overseas Highway, Ste. 119
Marathon, FL 33050
Ph: (305) 289-2330
Fax: (305) 289-2334
E-mail: bob.glazer@gcfi.org
URL: www.gcfi.org

4362 ■ Ronald L. Schmied Scholarships
*(Professional development, Undergraduate/
Scholarship)*

Purpose: To encourage students with interest in marine recreational fisheries. **Focus:** Fisheries sciences/management; Marine biology. **Qualif.:** Applicant must be enrolled at a college/university degree program in the wider Caribbean or in one of Gulf of Mexico states (Mexico and the United States); or a student engaged in a research project in the Gulf of Mexico and wider Caribbean region. **Criteria:** Applicants will be selected based on the following: involvement with recreational fisheries issues, level of achievement, innovation, and financial need.

Funds Avail.: $1,500 (covers airfare, lodging, and research-related expenses). **To Apply:** Applicants must submit electronically an application letter (includes name, address, contact numbers, educational institution department, degree level, description of current marine research, career goals, and reasons for the needing financial assistance); an endorsement letter from a faculty; and a vita. **Deadline:** September 15. **Contact:** Dr. Stephen Holland, Chair, at sholland@ufl.edu.

4363 ■ Hagley Museum and Library
PO Box 3630
Wilmington, DE 19807
Ph: (302) 658-2400
Fax: (302) 658-0568
E-mail: tsnyder@hagley.org
URL: www.hagley.org/library

4364 ■ Henry Belin du Pont Dissertation Fellowships *(Doctorate, Graduate/Fellowship)*

Purpose: To support graduate students conducting research for their dissertation. **Focus:** General studies. **Qualif.:** Applicant must be a graduate student who has completed all course work for the doctoral degree and conducting research for his/her dissertation. **Criteria:** Selection is based on demonstrated superior intellectual quality and presentation of a persuasive methodology for the project. Applicant must show that there are significant research materials at Hagley pertinent to the dissertation.

Funds Avail.: $6,000. **To Apply:** Applicants must submit a completed application form together with the dissertation prospectus; statement concerning the relevance of Hagley's research collections to the project; two letters of recommendation; and writing samples. **Deadline:** November 15. **Contact:** Dr. Roger Horowitz at rhorowitz@hagley.org.

4365 ■ Henry Belin du Pont Fellowships
(Graduate/Fellowship)

Purpose: To support research and study in the library, archival and artifact collections of the Hagley Museum and Library. **Focus:** Library and archival sciences. **Qualif.:** Applicants must be pursuing an advanced research and study in the library, archival and artifact collections of the Hagley

Museum and Library, and must be from out of state. **Criteria:** Preference will be given to those whose travel costs to Hagley will be higher.

Funds Avail.: $1,600/month. **To Apply:** Applicants must submit a completed application form along a cover letter noting the requested period of residency; a copy of curriculum vitae (maximum of four pages); and a 4-5 page description of the proposed research project. **Deadline:** March 31, June 30 and October 29. **Contact:** Dr. Philip Scranton at the above address.

4366 ■ Hamilton Industrial Environmental Association (HIEA)
PO Box 35545
Hamilton, ON, Canada L8H 7S6
Ph: (905) 561-4432
E-mail: info@hiea.org
URL: www.hiea.org

4367 ■ Hamilton Industrial Environmental Association Bursaries-Mohawk College
(Undergraduate/Scholarship)

Purpose: To provide financial assistance to those students who are in need. **Focus:** Engineering; Technology; Environmental Technology. **Qualif.:** Applicants must be 2nd year students in their final semester; must have been raised in Hamilton or graduated from Hamilton High School. **Criteria:** Applications will be considered based on their year's work in an internship for a Hamilton employer and a written essay on area of study and career goals.

Funds Avail.: No specific amount. **To Apply:** Applicants must check the available website for more information. **Contact:** Hamilton Industrial Environmental Association at the above address.

4368 ■ George and Mary Josephine Hamman Foundation
3336 Richmond, Ste. 310
Houston, TX 77098
Ph: (713) 522-9891
Fax: (713) 522-9693
E-mail: hammanfdn@aol.com
URL: hammanfoundation.org

4369 ■ George and Mary Josephine Hamman Foundation Scholarships *(Undergraduate/Scholarship)*

Purpose: To provide undergraduate scholarships for Houston area high school seniors. **Focus:** General studies. **Qualif.:** Applicants must be Houston area high school seniors who attend schools or are homeschooled in the following eight counties: Brazoria, Chambers, Fort Bend, Galveston, Harris, Liberty, Montgomery or Waller; must be US citizens. **Criteria:** Applicants are evaluated based on scholastic ability and financial need.

Funds Avail.: $16,000. **Number Awarded:** 70. **To Apply:** Applicants must write for the one-page scholarship application and the two-page financial qualification statement or it may be downloaded from the website. Completed scholarship applications must be submitted with these documents (in the following order): (1) Financial Qualification Statement, (2) complete, legible, signed copy of parents'/guardians' and student's most recent federal income tax

Awards are arranged alphabetically below their administering organizations

return (including all schedules) plus, if applicable, corporate or partnership returns, (3) proof of ACT and/or SAT results, and (4) high school transcript (unofficial is accepted). Mail to: George and Mary Josephine Hamman Foundation, 3336 Richmond, Ste. 310, Houston, TX 77098. **Deadline:** Third Friday of February.

4370 ■ Hampton Roads Community Foundation

101 W Main St., Ste. 4500
Norfolk, VA 23510
Ph: (757) 622-7951
Fax: (757) 622-1751
E-mail: rforeman@hamptonroadscf.org
URL: www.hamptonroadscf.org

4371 ■ Richard D. and Sheppard R. Cooke Memorial Scholarships *(Graduate/Scholarship)*

Purpose: To provide financial assistance to qualified individuals who want to pursue their educational goals. **Focus:** Religion. **Qualif.:** Applicants must be students at Union Theological Seminary in Richmond who are candidates for the ministry; must be enrolled in a degree program. **Criteria:** Selection of recipients will be based on financial need and the scholarship criteria. Preference will be given to students from the Norfolk churches within the Presbytery of Eastern Virginia.

Funds Avail.: No specific amount. **To Apply:** Applicants must complete the application form available from the website; provide a copy of transcripts, recommendation letter and statement of family income. **Deadline:** March 1.

4372 ■ Palmer Farley Memorial Scholarships *(Undergraduate/Scholarship)*

Purpose: To provide financial assistance to qualified individuals who want to pursue their educational goals. **Focus:** Communications. **Qualif.:** Applicants must be students pursuing the creative brand management track at the Virginia Commonwealth University Brandcenter. **Criteria:** Selection of recipients will be based on financial need and the scholarship criteria.

Funds Avail.: No specific amount. **To Apply:** Applicants must complete the application form available from the website; provide a copy of their transcripts, recommendation letter and statement of family income. **Deadline:** March 1.

4373 ■ Victor and Ruth N. Goodman Memorial Scholarships *(Graduate/Scholarship)*

Purpose: To provide financial assistance to qualified individuals who want to pursue their educational goals. **Focus:** Education, Medical. **Qualif.:** Applicants must be students studying medicine or other health professions. **Criteria:** Selection of recipients will be based on financial need and the scholarship criteria.

Funds Avail.: No specific amount. **To Apply:** Applicants must complete the application form available from the website; provide a copy of their transcripts, recommendation letter and statement of family income. **Deadline:** March 1.

4374 ■ Hampton Roads Association of Social Workers Scholarships *(Graduate/Scholarship)*

Purpose: To provide financial assistance to qualified individuals who want to pursue their educational goals. **Focus:** Social work. **Qualif.:** Applicants must be graduate students in social work; must be from Virginia. **Criteria:**

Selection of recipients will be based on financial need and the scholarship criteria.

Funds Avail.: No specific amount. **To Apply:** Applicants must complete the application form available from the website; provide a copy of their transcripts, recommendation letter and statement of family income. **Deadline:** March 1.

4375 ■ Hampton Roads Sanitation District Environmental Scholarships *(Graduate/ Scholarship)*

Purpose: To provide financial assistance to qualified individuals who want to pursue their educational goals. **Focus:** Environmental technology. **Qualif.:** Applicants must be full-time graduate students from the Hampton Roads Sanitation District service area studying environmental health, environmental chemistry, biology or civil or environmental engineering at a public Virginia university. **Criteria:** Selection of recipients will be based on financial need and the scholarship criteria.

Funds Avail.: No specific amount. **To Apply:** Applicants must complete the application form available from the website; provide a copy of transcripts, recommendation letter and statement of family income. **Deadline:** March 1.

4376 ■ Louis I. Jaffe Memorial Scholarships- NSU Alumni *(Graduate/Scholarship)*

Purpose: To provide financial assistance to qualified individuals who want to pursue their educational goals. **Focus:** General studies. **Qualif.:** Applicants must be graduates of Norfolk State University who are enrolled in a graduate program at any institution; must be from anywhere in Virginia. **Criteria:** Selection of recipients will be based on financial need and the scholarship criteria. Priority will be given to applicants from Hampton Roads.

Funds Avail.: No specific amount. **To Apply:** Applicants must complete the application form available from the website; must provide a copy of transcripts, recommendation letter and statement of family income. **Deadline:** March 1.

4377 ■ Louis I. Jaffe Memorial Scholarships- ODU *(Graduate/Scholarship)*

Purpose: To provide financial assistance to qualified individuals who want to pursue their educational goals. **Focus:** Humanities; Art history. **Qualif.:** Applicants must be students at Old Dominion University studying humanities or must be students at any other University studying art history. **Criteria:** Selection of recipients will be based on financial need and the scholarship criteria.

Funds Avail.: No specific amount. **To Apply:** Applicants must complete the application form available from the website; provide a copy of their transcripts, recommendation letter and statement of family income. **Deadline:** March 1.

4378 ■ Lewis K. Martin II, M.D. and Cheryl Rose Martin Scholarship Fund *(Graduate/Scholarship)*

Purpose: To provide financial assistance to qualified individuals who want to pursue their educational goals. **Focus:** Education, Medical. **Qualif.:** Applicants must be Virginia residents pursuing medical school at the University of Virginia School of Medicine. **Criteria:** Selection of recipients will be based on financial need and the scholarship criteria.

Funds Avail.: No specific amount. **To Apply:** Applicants must complete the application form available from the website; provide a copy of transcripts from their postsecondary

Awards are arranged alphabetically below their administering organizations

education; and attach a statement of financial need. **Deadline:** March 1.

4379 ■ William F. Miles Scholarships
(Undergraduate/Scholarship)

Purpose: To provide financial assistance to qualified individuals who want to pursue their educational goals. **Focus:** Religion. **Qualif.:** Applicants must be students preparing for leadership in the field of religious service. **Criteria:** Selection of recipients will be based on financial need and the scholarship criteria. Recipients are recommended by Westminster Chapter No. 99, Order of the Eastern Star.

Funds Avail.: No specific amount. **To Apply:** Applicants must complete the application form available from the website; provide a copy of their transcripts, recommendation letter and statement of family income. **Deadline:** March 1.

4380 ■ Ellis W. Rowe Scholarships
(Undergraduate/Scholarship)

Purpose: To provide financial assistance to qualified individuals who want to pursue their educational goals. **Focus:** Biology, Marine; Nursing; Humanities; Agriculture, Economic aspects. **Qualif.:** Applicants must be students from Gloucester County; must be studying marine science, nursing, ministry, medicine, humanities, agriculture, biology or any other basic science. **Criteria:** Selection of recipients will be based on financial need and the scholarship criteria. Preference will be given to students from the York District attending Virginia Wesleyan College or another Methodist college.

Funds Avail.: No specific amount. **To Apply:** Applicants must complete the application form available from the website; provide a copy of their transcripts, recommendation letter and statement of family income. **Deadline:** March 1.

4381 ■ Drs. Kirkland Ruffin & Willcox Ruffin Scholarships *(Graduate/Scholarship)*

Purpose: To provide financial assistance to qualified individuals who want to pursue their educational goals. **Focus:** Education, Medical. **Qualif.:** Applicants must be students from Norfolk attending Eastern Virginia Medical School. **Criteria:** Selection of recipients will be based on financial need and the scholarship criteria.

Funds Avail.: No specific amount. **To Apply:** Applicants must complete the application form available from the website; provide a copy of transcripts from their postsecondary education; and attach a statement of financial need. **Deadline:** March 1.

4382 ■ Hy Smith Endowment Fund
(Undergraduate/Scholarship)

Purpose: To provide financial assistance to qualified individuals who want to pursue their educational goals. **Focus:** Religion. **Qualif.:** Applicants must be students at Virginia Theological Seminary in Alexandria who are candidates for the ministry; must be residents of the geographic region served by the Diocese of Southern Virginia. **Criteria:** Selection on applicants will be based on financial need and the scholarship criteria. Recipients are recommended by the Eastern Star Training Awards Committee for Religious Leadership of Westminster Chapter No. 99.

Funds Avail.: No specific amount. **To Apply:** Applicants must complete the application form available from the website; provide a copy of the transcripts, recommendation let-

ter and statement of family income. **Deadline:** March 1.

4383 ■ Florence L. Smith Medical Scholarships
(Graduate/Scholarship)

Purpose: To provide financial assistance to qualified individuals who want to pursue their educational goals. **Focus:** Education, Medical. **Qualif.:** Applicants must be Virginia residents attending Eastern Virginia Medical School, University of Virginia School of Medicine or Virginia Commonwealth University School of Medicine. **Criteria:** Selection of recipients will be based on financial need and the scholarship criteria.

Funds Avail.: No specific amount. **To Apply:** Applicants must complete the application form available from the website; provide a copy of transcripts from their postsecondary education; and attach a statement of financial need. **Deadline:** March 1.

4384 ■ Enid W. and Bernard B. Spigel Architectural Scholarships *(Graduate, Undergraduate/Scholarship)*

Purpose: To provide financial assistance to qualified individuals who want to pursue their educational goals. **Focus:** Landscape architecture and design. **Qualif.:** Applicants must be Virginia residents who are junior, senior or graduate students in architecture, architectural history or architectural preservation. **Criteria:** Selection of recipients will be based on financial need and the scholarship criteria. Preference will be given to students from the York District attending Virginia Wesleyan College or another Methodist college.

Funds Avail.: No specific amount. **To Apply:** Applicants must complete the application form available from the website; provide a copy of their transcripts, recommendation letter and statement of family income. **Deadline:** March 1.

4385 ■ Handweavers Guild of America Inc.
1255 Buford Hwy., Ste. 211
Suwanee, GA 30024
Ph: (678) 730-0010
Fax: (678) 730-0836
E-mail: hga@weavespindye.org
URL: www.weavespindye.org

4386 ■ Convergence Assistantship Grants
(Undergraduate/Grant)

Purpose: To provide students in fiber arts programs the opportunity to assist internationally known instructors and to participate in the Convergence experience. **Focus:** Art. **Qualif.:** Applicant must be currently enrolled in an accredited academic program and available to attend a Training Class Saturday at the Convention Center. **Criteria:** Selection of applicants will be based on their application materials.

Funds Avail.: No specific amount. **To Apply:** Awardee must submit a Letter of Nomination from the Professor; must provide the Convergence complete registration form and personal statement. **Deadline:** April 2.

4387 ■ Mearl K. Gable II Memorial Grants
(Professional development/Grant)

Purpose: To provide funds for HGA members to study in non-accredited programs for any skill level. **Focus:** Art. **Qualif.:** Recipients must be HGA members. **Criteria:** Selec-

Awards are arranged alphabetically below their administering organizations

tion of applicants will be based on their application materials.

Funds Avail.: $100. **To Apply:** Application form must be printed and must have the following: Name of school or provider of instruction, title and short description of course (attach brochure). Applicant must provide a resume of the background, current activities, and future goals of the applicant in the fiber field. **Deadline:** February 1. **Contact:** Gable Grant Administrator, Handweavers Guild of America, Inc. at the above address.

4388 ■ Handweavers Guild of America and Dendel Scholarships *(Graduate, Undergraduate/ Scholarship)*

Purpose: To further the education in the field of fiber arts, including training for research, textile history and conservation. **Focus:** Art. **Qualif.:** Applicants must be enrolled at accredited undergraduate or graduate programs in the United States and Canada. **Criteria:** Recipients will be selected based on artistic and technical merit rather than financial needs.

Funds Avail.: $4,000. **To Apply:** Application forms are available on the website. Applicants must have the following: Transcript (a copy of the transcript must accompany the application); maximum of 16 slides or digital images; and an image description sheet. Applicants must provide a self-addressed, stamped envelope suitable for the return of slides or CD. **Deadline:** March 15. **Contact:** Application and other required materials must be sent to HGA Scholarship Chair at the above address.

4389 ■ Silvio and Eugenio Petrini Grants *(Professional development/Grant)*

Purpose: To provide educational opportunities to HGA members and to increase awareness of and appreciation for the fiber arts. **Focus:** Art. **Qualif.:** Recipients must be HGA members. **Criteria:** Selection of applicants will be based on application materials.

Funds Avail.: $300. **To Apply:** Application forms are available on the website. **Deadline:** February 1. **Contact:** Petrini Grant Administrator Scholarship Committee.

4390 ■ Haraldson Foundation

25025 I-45 N, Ste. 410
The Woodlands, TX 77380
Ph: (281) 362-9909
Fax: (281) 298-6001
E-mail: ndossey@haraldsonfoundation.org
URL: www.haraldsonfoundation.org

4391 ■ Haraldson Foundation Scholarships *(Graduate, Undergraduate/Scholarship)*

Purpose: To financially support the education of students at the University of Texas. **Focus:** General studies. **Qualif.:** Applicant must be a high school senior planning to attend the University of Texas, or currently enrolled in a University of Texas undergraduate or graduate program; have volunteered in community service activities; demonstrated academic excellence, leadership and character; and have financial need. Students must maintain a 3.0 GPA each semester and must complete at least 12 hours of course work each semester. **Criteria:** Selection is based on submitted application materials.

Funds Avail.: $33,600. **Number Awarded:** Varies. **To Apply:** Applicants must submit a completed application form

along with three letters of recommendation (at least one from a Math or English teacher); Official high school transcript; one page essay on chosen career and goals; 500-word essay on "How I Will Personally Contribute to Meeting Society's Future Challenges"; and a completed Financial Information. **Deadline:** December 1. **Contact:** Nancy Dossey at the above address.

4392 ■ Hardanger Fiddle Association of America (HFAA)

PO Box 23046
Minneapolis, MN 55423-0046
Ph: (612) 568-7448
E-mail: info@hfaa.org
URL: www.hfaa.org

4393 ■ Bernt Balchen, Jr. Hardingfele Scholarships *(All, Professional development/Scholarship)*

Purpose: To assist Hardingfele (Hardanger fiddle) players intending to attend the HFAA Annual Workshops. **Focus:** Music. **Qualif.:** Applicants must have an experience in playing a string instrument in either classical or folk tradition. **Criteria:** Scholarship will be given to the applicants who best meet the requirements.

Funds Avail.: No specific amount. **To Apply:** Applicants must submit a completed application form (available at the website www.hfaa.org); a personal statement; a letter of reference from a person not related to the applicant, preferably an instructor or a fellow musician; three copies of a 3-5 minute cassette tape or CD recording of the applicant's string instrument playing ability in classical or folk tradition. Send complete application package to: HFAA Balchen Scholarship Committee, c/o Barbara Overby, 118 W Rollins Rd., Columbia, MO 65203. **Deadline:** April 15. **Contact:** scholarships@hfaa.org.

4394 ■ Bryce Harlow Foundation

1701 Pennsylvania Ave. NW, Ste. 400
Washington, DC 20006
Ph: (202) 654-7812
Fax: (202) 638-5178
E-mail: info@bryceharlow.org
URL: www.bryceharlow.org

4395 ■ Bryce Harlow Fellowship Program *(Graduate/Fellowship)*

Purpose: To provide financial assistance to students who are pursuing a career in professional advocacy through public affairs, government relations or lobbying. **Focus:** Public affairs; Government. **Qualif.:** Applicants must be students who have been accepted for admission to a graduate program at a participating university; planning to enroll in part-time graduate studies for credit at the participating university for at least two semesters of the next academic year; demonstrate an interest and strong ability for a career in public affairs, government relations or lobbying; and U.S. citizens. **Criteria:** Applicants are evaluated based on demonstrated strong interest in public affairs, government relations or lobbying; professional achievement and leadership potential; academic achievement and potential; and financial need.

Funds Avail.: $6,000. **To Apply:** Applicants must download and complete the application and recommendation request form(s). Submit it along with two letters of recommendation

Awards are arranged alphabetically below their administering organizations

from persons familiar with the applicants; brief resume; and official transcripts from all undergraduate universities. **Deadline:** April 6.

4396 ■ Harness Horse Youth Foundation (HHYF)

16575 Carey Rd.
Westfield, IN 46074-8925
Ph: (317) 867-5877
Fax: (317) 867-5896
E-mail: ellen@hhyf.org
URL: www.hhyf.org

4397 ■ Charles Bradley Memorial Scholarships
(Undergraduate/Scholarship)

Purpose: To provide financial assistance to the children or relatives of racing officials who were members of the North American Judges and Stewards and licensed pari-mutuel officials. **Focus:** General studies. **Qualif.:** Applicants must be at least in high school and children or relatives of racing officials who were members of the North American Judges and Stewards Association and/or licensed USTA pari-mutuel officials in the following categories: presiding judges, associate judges, paddock judges and starters. **Criteria:** Candidates will be assessed based on scholastic achievement, grade point average, financial need, completeness of application and quality of essay.

Funds Avail.: No amount mentioned. **To Apply:** Applicants must complete and submit application form; must attach (1,000 words) typewritten statement including background, career goals and experiences; a copy of the latest transcript; two letters of recommendation. **Deadline:** April 30. **Contact:** ellen@hhyf.org.

4398 ■ Gallo Blue Chip Scholarships
(Undergraduate/Scholarship)

Purpose: To provide financial assistance to the eligible children of harness horse trainers or licensed caretakers. **Focus:** General studies. **Qualif.:** Applicant must be at least a senior high school student and a child of harness horse trainer or caretaker licensed in New York and/or New Jersey raised; must reside within the two-state region. **Criteria:** Candidates will be evaluated based on demonstrated scholastic achievement, including but not limited to the applicant's GPA, financial need and quality of essay.

Funds Avail.: No specific amount. **To Apply:** Applicant must submit a completed application form; must attach (1) a copy of transcripts; (2) parent's current racing commission license; (3) resume; and (4) 1,000-word essay explaining the accomplishments, plans or career goals and relationship to New York and New Jersey region. **Contact:** ellen@hhyf.org.

4399 ■ Curt Greene Memorial Scholarships
(Undergraduate/Scholarship)

Purpose: To provide financial support for senior high school students who may or may not be pursuing harness racing but demonstrates passion for the sport. **Focus:** General studies. **Qualif.:** Applicant must be at least a high school senior. **Criteria:** Candidates will be assessed based on scholastic achievement, grade point average, financial need, completeness of application and quality of essay.

Funds Avail.: No amount mentioned. **To Apply:** Applicants must complete and submit application form. **Deadline:** April 30. **Contact:** ellen@hhyf.org.

4400 ■ Harness Tracks of America (HTA)

12025 E Dry Gulch Pl.
Tucson, AZ 85749
Ph: (520) 529-2525
Fax: (520) 529-3235
E-mail: info@harnesstracks.com
URL: www.harnesstracks.com

4401 ■ Harness Tracks of America Scholarship Fund *(Undergraduate/Scholarship)*

Purpose: To provide financial assistance to students for post-secondary education. **Focus:** General studies. **Qualif.:** Applicants must be sons or daughters of licensed drivers, trainers, caretakers, management or young people actively engaged in the harness racing industry. **Criteria:** Recipients will be selected based on his or her academic merit, financial need and active harness racing involvement.

Funds Avail.: $5,000. **Number Awarded:** 5. **To Apply:** Applicants must submit completed application form together with essays; official academic transcripts; federal tax forms; student aid report; fee rates schedule; and any other supporting documents. Letters of recommendation are not required but may be included. **Deadline:** May 15. **Contact:** Jen Foley, 520-529-2525; jen@harnesstracks.com.

4402 ■ Harris Corp. (Melbourne, Florida)

1025 W NASA Blvd.
Melbourne, FL 32919-0001
Ph: (321) 727-9100
Fax: (321) 727-4500
Free: 800-442-7747
E-mail: gcsdweb2@harris.com
URL: www.harris.com

4403 ■ Harris Corporation Merit Scholarships
(Undergraduate/Scholarship)

Purpose: To financially assist high school students. **Focus:** General studies. **Qualif.:** Applicants must be high school students who are children of Harris Corporation current employees; must be U.S. citizens or have applied for permanent residence. Applicants who do not take the PSAT/NMSQT because of illness, emergency or other circumstance but meet all the requirements will be accepted. **Criteria:** Applicants will be judged based on PSAT/NMSQT scores, academic records, activities and contributions to school and community, recommendation letter, and essay about characteristics, plans, and goals.

Funds Avail.: $2,000 per year. **To Apply:** Applicants must obtain a copy of PSAT/NMSQT Official Student Guide and take the qualifying exam. **Contact:** National Merit Corporation Attn: Educational Services, 1560 Sherman Ave., Ste. 200, Evanston, IL 60201-4897; Phone: 847-866-5100.

4404 ■ Hartford Foundation for Public Giving

10 Columbus Blvd., 8th Flr.
Hartford, CT 06106
Ph: (860) 548-1888
Fax: (860) 524-8346
E-mail: hfpg@hfpg.org
URL: www.hfpg.org

4405 ■ Frederick G. Adams Scholarships
(Undergraduate/Scholarship)

Purpose: To provide scholarship for graduating high school seniors of Greater Hartford area. **Focus:** General studies.

Awards are arranged alphabetically below their administering organizations

Qualif.: Applicants must be graduating seniors who live in or are attending school in Greater Hartford; must be entering a four-year college or university (full-time enrollment); must have a financial need; must be on a top third of the class or a good academic record; and must be active volunteer in school, community, or other extracurricular activities. **Criteria:** Selection will be based on the committee's criteria.

Funds Avail.: $3,000. **To Apply:** Applicants must download and fill out the online application and attach the following requirements: letter of recommendation from your guidance counselor or a teacher; official high school transcript, including SAT or ACT scores; copy of the essay you submitted with your college application (if you did not have to submit one, write a brief essay, no more than 2 pages, regarding your future goals); copy of pages 1 and 2 of your parents' or guardians' most recent completed federal tax form 1040; and mail everything to Hartford Foundation College Scholarship Program. **Deadline:** February 2. **Contact:** Hartford Foundation College Scholarship Program, Scholarship Management Services, Scholarship America, One Scholarship Way, PO Box 297, St. Peter, MN 56082. 800-537-4180.

4406 ■ Alliance Francaise of Hartford Harpin/Rohinsky Scholarships (Undergraduate/Scholarship)

Purpose: To provide educational assistance for graduating high school seniors who live in or are attending school in Greater Hartford. **Focus:** French studies. **Qualif.:** Applicants must be entering a four-year college or university (full-time enrollment); must pursue French studies in college; must have a financial need; must rank top third of their class; and must be active volunteers in school, community, or other extracurricular activities. **Criteria:** Selection will be based on the committee's criteria.

Funds Avail.: $3,000. **Number Awarded:** 1. **To Apply:** Applicants must download and fill out the online application and attach the following requirements: letter of recommendation from your guidance counselor or a from your teacher; official high school transcript, including SAT or ACT scores; copy of the essay you submitted with your college application (if you did not have to submit one, write a brief essay (no more than 2 pages) regarding your future goals; copy of pages 1 and 2 of your parents' most recent completed federal tax form 1040; and mail everything to Hartford Foundation College Scholarship Program. **Deadline:** February 2. **Contact:** Hartford Foundation College Scholarship Program, Scholarship Management Services, Scholarship America, One Scholarship Way, PO Box 297, St. Peter, MN 56082. 800-537-4180.

4407 ■ American Fire Sprinkler Association Scholarships (Undergraduate/Scholarship)

Purpose: To award scholarships for graduating high school seniors. **Focus:** General studies. **Qualif.:** Applicants must be Connecticut residents who are entering a four-year college or university. **Criteria:** Selection will be based on the committee's criteria.

Funds Avail.: $1,000. **Number Awarded:** 2. **To Apply:** Applicants must complete and submit an application and essay to the association. Applicants may obtain application materials from the American Fire Sprinkler Association, CT Chapter. **Deadline:** March 21. **Contact:** David K. Thompson, American fire Sprinkler Association, Connecticut Chapter, PO Box 2350, Hartford, CT 06146. 860-246-7711. dave@thesprink.com.

4408 ■ American Marketing Association-Connecticut Chapter, Anna C. Klune Memorial Scholarships (Graduate/Scholarship)

Purpose: To award scholarship to a second-year MBA student at any university. **Focus:** Marketing and distribution. **Qualif.:** Applicants must: be a Connecticut resident, may or may not be studying in Connecticut; be a second-year MBA students; be a Marketing or related major; demonstrated leadership record; have entrepreneurial/innovative spirit. **Criteria:** Selection will be based on the committee's criteria.

Funds Avail.: $1,000-$1,500. **Number Awarded:** 1. **To Apply:** Applicants may obtain application materials from the AMA-CT website at www.amact.org. **Deadline:** January 31. **Contact:** Dr. Subroto Roy, Vice President of Collegiate Relations/Scholarship, 18 Colonial Court Cheshire, CT 06410. 203-271-8051; dr.subrotoroy@gmail.com.

4409 ■ ARTC Glenn Moon Scholarships (Undergraduate/Scholarship)

Purpose: To provide scholarship for graduating seniors from any public or private high school in Connecticut. **Focus:** Education. **Qualif.:** Applicants must be entering a four-year college or university and must demonstrate financial need and academic excellence. **Criteria:** Selection will be based on the committee's criteria.

Funds Avail.: $1,500 - one-time award; $2,000 renewable. **Number Awarded:** 4. **To Apply:** Applicants may obtain application materials from their high school guidance counselor or online at the www.artcinc.org. **Deadline:** March 31. **Contact:** ARTC Inc. 203-639-9628.

4410 ■ Officer Brian A. Aselton Memorial Scholarships (Undergraduate/Scholarship)

Purpose: To provide educational assistance for students entering or enrolled as undergraduate students at Manchester Community College. **Focus:** Criminal Justice. **Qualif.:** Applicants must be Connecticut residents, majoring in Criminal Justice and planning a career in law enforcement. **Criteria:** Selection will be based on the committee's criteria.

Funds Avail.: $500-$1,000. **Number Awarded:** 1. **To Apply:** Applicants may obtain the application materials from the Manchester Community College. **Deadline:** March 1. **Contact:** Donna Nicholson, Coordinator, Criminal Justice Program, Manchester Community College, 60 Bidwell St., Manchester, CT 06040; 860-512-2756; dnicholson@mcc.commnet.edu.

4411 ■ Malcolm Baldridge Scholarships (Undergraduate/Scholarship)

Purpose: To provide educational assistance for undergraduate students enrolled in a college or university in Connecticut. **Focus:** Manufacturing; International trade. **Qualif.:** Applicant must be an International trade and manufacturing related major; must demonstrate academic excellence; must be studying foreign language, if majoring in International Business; and must be a resident of Connecticut. **Criteria:** Selection will be based on the committee's criteria.

Funds Avail.: 4,000. **Number Awarded:** 1-3. **To Apply:** Applicants may obtain the application materials from the website at www.conncf.org. **Deadline:** March 1. **Contact:** Connecticut Community Foundation. Tallitha Richardson-Selby, Program/Scholarship Associate, 43 Field St. Waterbury, CT 06702. info@conncf.org. fax: 203-756-3054.

Awards are arranged alphabetically below their administering organizations

4412 ■ John Bell and Lawrence Thornton Scholarship Fund *(Undergraduate/Scholarship)*

Purpose: To provide educational assistance for students presently enrolled at Hampton University. **Focus:** General studies. **Qualif.:** Applicant must be a Greater Hartford resident; must demonstrate academic excellence, financial need, extracurricular activities and community service; must have a GPA of 3.0 and above; and must be rising sophomore and rising junior status. **Criteria:** Selection will be based on the committee's criteria.

Funds Avail.: No specific amount. **Number Awarded:** Varies. **To Apply:** Applicants may obtain application materials from Connecticut River Valley Chapter National Hampton University Alumni Association, Inc. Scholarship Committee, PO Box 2734 Hartford, CT 06146-2734. **Deadline:** March 23. **Contact:** hamptonalumnict@yahoo.com.

4413 ■ Lebbeus F. Bissell Scholarships *(Undergraduate/Scholarship)*

Purpose: To provide educational assistance for graduating high school seniors from Rockville, Tolland or Ellington High Schools. **Focus:** General studies. **Qualif.:** Applicants must demonstrate academic excellence, financial need, extracurricular activities and community service. **Criteria:** Selection will be based on the committee's criteria.

Funds Avail.: $4,000. **Number Awarded:** 3. **To Apply:** Applicants may obtain application materials from Guidance Departments of Rockville, Tolland or Ellington High Schools or from Lebbeus F. Bissel Scholarship Advisory Committee, 183 Reservoir Rd. Vermon, CT 06066. **Deadline:** April 1. **Contact:** Thomas Mason, Chairman. 860-875-0527 or 860-548-1888.

4414 ■ Maria Gonzales Borrero Scholarships *(Undergraduate/Scholarship)*

Purpose: To provide scholarships for graduating Hispanic students from a public high school in the City of Hartford. **Focus:** Health care services. **Qualif.:** Applicants must be entering a four-year college or university (full-time enrollment) pursuing a health-related field; must demonstrate financial need; must be top third with good academic record; and must be active volunteers in school, community, or other extracurricular activities. **Criteria:** Selection will be based on the committee's criteria.

Funds Avail.: $3,000. **Number Awarded:** 1. **To Apply:** Application form can be downloaded online. Applicants must complete the scholarship application. Applicants must also attach the following requirements: letter of recommendation from your guidance counselor or a teacher; official high school transcript (including SAT or ACT scores); copy of the essay you submitted with your college application (If you did not have to submit one, write a brief (no more than two pages) essay regarding your future goals); and copy of pages 1 and 2 of your parents' or guardians' most recent completed federal tax form 1040. Mail everything to Hartford Foundation College Scholarship Program. **Deadline:** February 2. **Contact:** hartfordfoundation@ scholarshipamerica.org or 800-537-4180.

4415 ■ W. Philip Braender and Nancy Coleman Braender Scholarships *(Undergraduate/ Scholarship)*

Purpose: To provide scholarship for graduating high school senior who lives in or attends school in Greater Hartford. **Focus:** General studies. **Qualif.:** Applicants must be entering a four-year college or university (full-time enrollment);

must demonstrate financial need; must be in the top third with good academic record; and must be active volunteer in school, community, or other extracurricular activities. **Criteria:** Selection will be based on the committee's criteria.

Funds Avail.: $3,000. **Number Awarded:** 1. **To Apply:** Application form can be downloaded on-line. Applicants must complete the scholarship application. Applicants must also attach the following requirements: letter of recommendation from your guidance counselor or a teacher; official high school transcript. Including SAT or ACT scores; copy of the essay you submitted with your college application. If you did not have to submit one, write a brief (no more than two pages) essay regarding your future goals; copy of pages 1 and 2 of your parents' or guardians' most recent completed federal tax form 1040. Mail everything to Hartford Foundation College Scholarship Program. **Deadline:** February 2. **Contact:** Hartford Foundation College Scholarship Program, Scholarship Management Services, Scholarship America, One Scholarship Way, PO Box 297, St. Peter, MN 56082. 800-537-4180.

4416 ■ Gail Burns-Smith "Dare to Dream" Fund *(Undergraduate/Scholarship)*

Purpose: To provide scholarship to the resident of Connecticut or student attending a Connecticut high school or college/university. **Focus:** Aggression and violence. **Qualif.:** Applicants be paid or volunteer work experience in the field women's issues or sexual violence prevention/ advocacy and planned commitment to continuing work in the field of sexual violence prevention/advocacy. **Criteria:** Selection will be based on the committee's criteria.

Funds Avail.: $1,000. **Number Awarded:** 1. **To Apply:** Applicants must complete the application form provided by CONNSACS together with the following requirements: two written essays in response to questions listed on application; two character references, submitted as letters of recommendation on behalf of applicant. Applicants may obtain application from address below and submit to CONNSACS, Inc. **Deadline:** March 1. **Contact:** Tara Martin, Dir. of Resource Development, 96 Pitkin St. E Hartford, CT 06108. Fax: 860-291-9335; Phone: 860-282-9881. tara@connsacs.org.

4417 ■ Rhea Sourifman Caplin Memorial Scholarships *(Undergraduate/Scholarship)*

Purpose: To provide scholarship to the Jewish high school senior or college students. **Focus:** Nursing; Health care services. **Qualif.:** Applicants must: be a Greater Hartford resident; be pursuing nursing or health care profession; have a minimum B average in sciences; have a good citizenship and active involvement in the community. **Criteria:** Selection will be based on the committee's criteria.

Funds Avail.: $1,000-$2,000. **Number Awarded:** 1-2. **To Apply:** Applicants may obtain application materials from Jewish Community Foundation of Greater Hartford, 333 Bloomfield Ave. Ste. D West Hartford, CT 06117. **Deadline:** April 15. **Contact:** Michael Elfenbaum, Phone: 860-523-7460; Fax: 860-231-0576; melfenbaum@jcfhartford.org.

4418 ■ The College Club of Hartford Scholarships *(Undergraduate/Scholarship)*

Purpose: To provide scholarship for graduating high school students. **Focus:** General studies. **Qualif.:** Applicants must be graduating public high school seniors residing in Avon, Bloomfield, Canton, East Hartford, Farmington, Glastonbury, Hartford, Manchester, Newington, Rocky Hill, Simsbury, West Hartford, Wethersfield or Windsor; must be at-

Awards are arranged alphabetically below their administering organizations

tending in an accredited two or four-year school; must demonstrate financial need and community service; must be on a class rank upper 10% (Applicant's grades through 2nd quarter of senior year are required); and must be students who attend Trinity College or St. Joseph College in Connecticut. **Criteria:** Selection will be based on the committee's criteria.

Funds Avail.: $1,000. **To Apply:** Applicants may obtain application materials from their high school guidance office and submit it to Scholarship Committee, Sheila Rome, Chairman, 46 Belknap Rd., West Hartford, CT 06117. Phone: 860-236-1747; sheilarome@mac.com. **Deadline:** March 14.

4419 ■ Connecticut Association of Latinos in Higher Education Scholarships *(Undergraduate/Scholarship)*

Purpose: To award scholarship to the students entering or enrolled as undergraduates in an accredited college or university. **Focus:** General studies. **Qualif.:** Applicants must be residents of Connecticut; must be of Latino background; must have financial need and community service; and must have an academic excellence ("B" average). **Criteria:** Selection will be based on the committee's criteria.

Funds Avail.: $1,000. **Number Awarded:** 10. **To Apply:** Applicants must complete the General Scholarship Application and include the following requirements: a copy of your Student Aid Report; a two-page, typed, double-space essay on "How you feel education is going to impact your ability to continue assisting others to pursue an education". **Contact:** Application form and supporting documents must be submitted to: CALAHE Scholarship Chair c/o Office of Dean of Students, Dr. Wilson Luna, Gateway Community College, 60 Sargent Dr., New Haven, CT 06511; Phone: 203-285-2210; Fax:203-285-2211; E-mail: wilsonluna@aol.com.

4420 ■ Connecticut Building Congress Scholarships *(Undergraduate/Scholarship)*

Purpose: To provide scholarship for graduating high school seniors, undergraduate, or graduate students. **Focus:** Engineering; Architecture. **Qualif.:** Applicants must be attending two or four-year college or university; must demonstrate financial need, academic excellence and community service; must be residents of Connecticut. **Criteria:** Selection will be based on the committee's criteria.

Funds Avail.: $500-$2,000. **Number Awarded:** 3-4. **To Apply:** Applicants may obtain application materials from Connecticut Bldg. Congress Scholarship Fund, Inc. PO Box 743, Enfield, CT 06083. Phone: 860-228-1387; Fax: 860-741-8809; cbc@cbc-ct.org. **Deadline:** March 15. **Contact:** Sharon Roberts, Exec. Dir.

4421 ■ Connecticut Capitol Scholarship Program *(Undergraduate/Scholarship)*

Purpose: To provide scholarship for graduating high school seniors. **Focus:** General studies. **Qualif.:** Applicants must be residents of Connecticut entering in a Connecticut college or a college located in one of the following states: District of Columbia, Maine, Massachusetts, New Hampshire, Pennsylvania, Rhode Island, or Vermont; must demonstrate academic excellence being on a class rank of top 20% or SAT above 1800. **Criteria:** Selection will be based on the committee's criteria.

Funds Avail.: $300-$3,000. **To Apply:** Applicants may

obtain application materials from high school guidance counselor or from Connecticut Department of Higher Education. **Deadline:** February 15. **Contact:** Connecticut Department of Higher Education, 61 Woodland St. Hartford, CT 06105; Phone: 860-947-1855; Fax: 860-947-1313; csp@ctdhe.org.

4422 ■ Connecticut Mortgage Bankers Scholarships-Social Affairs Committee *(Undergraduate/Scholarship)*

Purpose: To provide scholarship for graduating high school seniors who live in or are attending school in Greater Hartford. **Focus:** Business; Real estate. **Qualif.:** Applicants must be entering a four-year college or university (full-time enrollment) pursuing a career in business, mortgage or real estate; must have a financial need; must be on a class rank - top third with good academic record; and must be active volunteers in school, community, or other extracurricular activities. **Criteria:** Selection will be based on the committee's criteria.

Funds Avail.: $3,000. **Number Awarded:** 1. **To Apply:** Application form can be downloaded on-line. Applicants must complete the scholarship application. Applicants must also attach the following requirements: letter of recommendation from your guidance counselor or a teacher; official high school transcript. Including SAT or ACT scores; copy of the essay you submitted with your college application. If you did not have to submit one, write a brief (no more than two pages) essay regarding your future goals; copy of pages 1 and 2 of your parents' most recent completed federal tax form 1040. Mail everything to Hartford Foundation College Scholarship Program. **Deadline:** February 6. **Contact:** Hartford Foundation College Scholarship Program, Scholarship Management Services, Scholarship America, One Scholarship Way, PO Box 297, St. Peter, MN 56082. 800-537-4180.

4423 ■ Connecticut Nurserymen's Foundation Scholarships *(Undergraduate/Scholarship)*

Purpose: To provide scholarship for graduating high school seniors or college students enrolled in a Horticulture degree program. **Focus:** Horticulture. **Qualif.:** Applicants must be Connecticut residents entering a two or four-year college program in Horticulture; must demonstrate financial need and academic excellence; must have a work experience and Future Farmers of American membership helpful, but not necessary. **Criteria:** Selection will be based on the committee's criteria.

Funds Avail.: $5,000. **Number Awarded:** 1. **To Apply:** Applicants may obtain the application materials from their high school guidance counselor or from Connecticut Nurserymen's Foundation. **Deadline:** March 12. **Contact:** Judy Mattson, Scholarship Committee Chairman, 131 Hollister St. Manchester, CT 06042, Phone: 860-643-8363; Fax: 860-643-2778; jmattson.negs@sbcglobal.net.

4424 ■ Brian Cummins Memorial Scholarships *(Undergraduate/Scholarship)*

Purpose: To provide scholarship for college junior or senior or graduate students enrolled in a full-time program to teach blind and visually impaired students in Connecticut. **Focus:** General studies. **Qualif.:** Applicants must demonstrate financial need, community service, and academic excellence. **Criteria:** Selection will be based on the committee's criteria.

Funds Avail.: $5,000. **Number Awarded:** 1. **To Apply:** Applicants may obtain scholarship materials from National

Awards are arranged alphabetically below their administering organizations

Federation of the Blind of Connecticut 477 Connecticut Blvd. Ste. 217 E Hartford, CT 06108. **Deadline:** October 15. **Contact:** National Federation of the Blind of Connecticut, Phone: 860-298-1971; Fax: 860-291-2795; info@nfbct.org.

4425 ■ C. Rodney Demarest Memorial Scholarships *(Undergraduate/Scholarship)*

Purpose: To provide scholarship for students who are legally blind. **Focus:** General studies. **Qualif.:** Applicants must be graduating high school seniors or college students residing or attending school full-time in Connecticut. Applicants must demonstrate financial need, community service and academic excellence. **Criteria:** Selection will be based on the committee's criteria.

Funds Avail.: $3,000. **Number Awarded:** 1. **To Apply:** Applicants may obtain application materials from National Federation of the Blind of CT, 477 Connecticut Blvd., Ste. 217 E, Hartford, CT 06108; Phone: 860-289-1971; E-mail: info@nfbct.org or may log on to www.nfbct.org.

4426 ■ Albert and Jane Dewey Scholarships *(Undergraduate/Scholarship)*

Purpose: To provide scholarship to the graduating senior. **Focus:** General studies. **Qualif.:** Applicants must be residents of Manchester who demonstrate financial need. Preference will be given to minority students. **Criteria:** Selection will be based on the committee's criteria.

Funds Avail.: $1,000-$4,000. **To Apply:** Applicants may obtain application materials from Manchester Scholarship Foundation Inc., 20 Hartford Rd. Manchester, CT 06040 or may log on to www.manchesterscholarship.org. **Contact:** Phone: 860-645-1673; Fax: 860-432-9136.

4427 ■ Harry A. Donn Scholarships *(Undergraduate/Scholarship)*

Purpose: To provide scholarship to a high school senior who lives in or attends school in the Greater Hartford area. **Focus:** General studies. **Qualif.:** Applicants must: be entering a four-year college or university (full-time enrollment); demonstrate financial need; be on a class rank - top third with good academic record; be active volunteer in school, community, or other extracurricular activities. **Criteria:** Selection will be based on the committee's criteria.

Funds Avail.: $3,000. **Number Awarded:** 1. **To Apply:** Application form can be downloaded online. Applicants must complete the scholarship application. Applicants must also attach the following requirements: letter of recommendation from your guidance counselor or a teacher; official high school transcript. Including SAT or ACT scores; copy of the essay you submitted with your college application. If you did not have to submit one, write a brief (no more than two pages) essay regarding your future goals; copy of pages 1 and 2 of your parents' most recent completed federal tax form 1040. Mail everything to Hartford Foundation College Scholarship Program. **Deadline:** February 2. **Contact:** Hartford Foundation College Scholarship Program, Scholarship Management Services, Scholarship America, 1505 Riverview Rd., PO Box 297, St. Peter, MN 56082. 800-537-4180.

4428 ■ Charles Dubose Scholarships *(Undergraduate/Scholarship)*

Purpose: To provide scholarship to the students attending five-year accredited colleges or universities offering Architecture. **Focus:** Architecture. **Qualif.:** Applicants must:

completed a two years of Bachelor in Architecture Program; be a Connecticut connection; demonstrated financial need and academic excellence. **Criteria:** Selection will be based on the committee's criteria.

Funds Avail.: $5,000-$10,000. **Number Awarded:** 1-2. **To Apply:** Applicants may obtain application materials from Connecticut Architecture Foundation, 87 Willow St., New Haven, CT 06511. Phone: 203865-2195; Fax: 203562-5378. www.aiact.org. **Deadline:** April 15.

4429 ■ Priscilla Maxwell Endicott Scholarships *(Undergraduate/Scholarship)*

Purpose: To provide scholarship to the students entering or enrolled in a four-year college or university. **Focus:** General studies. **Qualif.:** Applicants must: be a resident of Connecticut; be a female; be active junior golfer with golf handicap; demonstrate financial need and academic excellence. **Criteria:** Selection will be based on the committee's criteria.

Funds Avail.: $3,000. **Number Awarded:** 4. **To Apply:** Applicants may download an application form from www.cwga.org. **Deadline:** April 20. **Contact:** Deborah Boynton, Scholarship Chairwoman, 52 Mountain Spring Rd., Farmington, CT 06032. 860-826-4008. deb@creedmonarch.com.

4430 ■ Farmington UNICO Scholarships *(Undergraduate/Scholarship)*

Purpose: To provide scholarship to the students who will be attending a four-year college or university. **Focus:** General studies. **Qualif.:** Applicants must: be a Farmington or West Hartford resident; be a graduating high school senior; demonstrated financial need and academic excellence. **Criteria:** Selection will be based on the committee's criteria.

Funds Avail.: $1,500. **Number Awarded:** 4. **To Apply:** Applicants may obtain application materials from their high school guidance office or Farmington Chapter of UNICO National, Scholarship Committee, 11 Parkview Rd. West Hartford, CT 06110. **Deadline:** March 15. **Contact:** Jim Kane. Phone: 860-826-4489; Fax: 860-826-1814; jkane@jkanelwa.com.

4431 ■ Symee Ruth Feinburg Memorial Scholarships *(Undergraduate/Scholarship)*

Purpose: To provide scholarship to the graduating high school senior who lives in or attends school in Greater Hartford. **Focus:** Human relations. **Qualif.:** Applicants must: be entering a four-year college or university; pursuing a career in human services; be in a class rank- top third with good academic record; be an active volunteer in school. community, or other extracurricular activities. **Criteria:** Selection will be based on the committee's criteria.

Funds Avail.: $3,000. **Number Awarded:** 1. **To Apply:** Application form can be downloaded online. Applicants must complete the scholarship application. Applicants must also attach the following requirements: letter of recommendation from your guidance counselor or a teacher; official high school transcript. Including SAT or ACT scores; copy of the essay you submitted with your college application. If you did not have to submit one, write a brief (no more than two pages) essay regarding your future goals; copy of pages 1 and 2 of your parents' or guardians' most recent completed federal tax form 1040. Mail everything to Hartford Foundation College Scholarship Program. **Deadline:** February 2. **Contact:** Hartford Foundation College Scholarship Program, Scholarship Management Services,

Awards are arranged alphabetically below their administering organizations

Scholarship America, 1505 Riverview Rd., PO Box 297, St. Peter, MN 56082. 800-537-4180.

4432 ■ First Church of Christ in Wethersfield - Metcalf Scholarships *(Undergraduate/ Scholarship)*

Purpose: To provide scholarship to the graduating seniors from any public high school in the City of Hartford. **Focus:** General studies. **Qualif.:** Applicants must demonstrate financial need; extracurricular activities; have a potential for completing a four-year undergraduate program; have an interview with selection committee members. **Criteria:** Selection will be based on the committee's criteria.

Funds Avail.: $625. **To Apply:** Applicants may obtain application materials from their high school guidance office or contact First Church of Christ in Wethersfield, Metcalf Scholarship Chairperson 250 Main St., Wethersfield, CT 06109. Phone 860-529-1575 ext. 212; Fax: 860-721-7861. **Deadline:** March 1.

4433 ■ James L. and Genevieve H. Goodwin Scholarships *(Undergraduate/Scholarship)*

Purpose: To award scholarship to the students of Connecticut. **Focus:** Forestry. **Qualif.:** Applicants must be enrolled in an undergraduate or graduate curriculum in silviculture or forest resource management; and must be a Connecticut resident. **Criteria:** Selection will be based on the committee's criteria.

Funds Avail.: $1,000-$5,000. **Number Awarded:** 5-10. **To Apply:** Applicants may complete the General Scholarship Application and include a personal statement indicating why you are interested in Forest Management and submit to Connecticut forest and Park Association, Inc. **Deadline:** March 20. **Contact:** Adam Moore, Executive Dir., 16 Meriden Rd. Rockfall, CT 06481. Phone: 860-346-2372; Fax: 860-347-7463; info@ctwoodlands.org.

4434 ■ William G. and Mayme J. Green Scholarships *(Undergraduate/Scholarship)*

Purpose: To award scholarship to a graduating high school senior from Newington or Hartford Public High School. **Focus:** Nursing. **Qualif.:** Applicants must: be entering a four-year college or university (full-time enrollment) pursuing a degree in Nursing; must demonstrate financial need; be on the class rank - top third with a good academic record; be an active volunteer in school, community, or other extracurricular activities. **Criteria:** Selection will be based on the committee's criteria.

Funds Avail.: $2,500. **Number Awarded:** 1. **To Apply:** Application form can be downloaded online. Applicants must complete the scholarship application. Applicants must also attach the following requirements: letter of recommendation from your guidance counselor or a teacher; official high school transcript. Including SAT or ACT scores; copy of the essay you submitted with your college application. If you did not have to submit one, write a brief (no more than two pages) essay regarding your future goals; copy of pages 1 and 2 of your parents' most recent completed federal tax form 1040. Mail everything to Hartford Foundation College Scholarship Program. **Deadline:** February 13. **Contact:** Hartford Foundation College Scholarship Program, Scholarship Management Services, Scholarship America, One Scholarship Way, PO Box 297, St. Peter, MN 56082. 800-537-4180.

4435 ■ Ida L. Hartenberg Charitable Scholarships *(Undergraduate/Scholarship)*

Purpose: To provide scholarship to the graduating high school senior who lives in or attends school in Greater Hartford. **Focus:** Teaching. **Qualif.:** Applicants must: be entering a four-year college or university (full-time enrollment); be pursuing a career in teaching; demonstrate financial need; be on a class rank - top third with good academic record; be an active volunteer in school, community, or other extracurricular activities. **Criteria:** Selection will be based on the committee's criteria.

Funds Avail.: $3,000. **Number Awarded:** 1. **To Apply:** Application form can be downloaded online. Applicants must complete the scholarship application. Applicants must also attach the following requirements: letter of recommendation from your guidance counselor or a teacher; official high school transcript. Including SAT or ACT scores; copy of the essay you submitted with your college application. If you did not have to submit one, write a brief (no more than two pages) essay regarding your future goals; copy of pages 1 and 2 of your parents' or guardians' most recent completed federal tax form 1040. Mail everything to Hartford Foundation College Scholarship Program. **Deadline:** February 6. **Contact:** Hartford Foundation College Scholarship Program, Scholarship Management Services, Scholarship America, One Scholarship Way, PO Box 297, St. Peter, MN 56082. 800-537-4180.

4436 ■ Hartford County Retired Teachers Association Scholarships *(Undergraduate/ Scholarship)*

Purpose: To provide scholarship to the graduating senior residing and attending high school in Hartford County. **Focus:** Teaching. **Qualif.:** Applicants must: be entering a four-year college or university; be a teaching major; demonstrate financial need, community service, leadership abilities and good character; have work experience and school and community participation. **Criteria:** Selection will be based on the committee's criteria.

Funds Avail.: $1,500. **Number Awarded:** 2. **To Apply:** Applicants may obtain application materials from their high school guidance counselor and submit to Hartford County Retired Teachers Association Scholarship Committee. Applicants must also submit a letter of recommendation and a personal essay about the applicant's subject matter and grade level of interest to be pursued. **Deadline:** March 15. **Contact:** Mrs. Roberta Parlin, Chairperson. 35 Ledgecrest Drive, Newington, CT 06111; 860-666-5709.

4437 ■ Hartford Foundation College Scholarship Program *(Undergraduate/Scholarship)*

Purpose: To provide scholarship to the graduating high school senior who lives in or attends school in Greater Hartford. **Focus:** General studies. **Qualif.:** Applicants must: be entering a four-year college or university (full-time enrollment); demonstrate financial need; be on the class rank - top third with good academic record; be an active volunteer in school, community, or other extracurricular activities. **Criteria:** Selection will be based on the committee's criteria.

Funds Avail.: $3,000. **Number Awarded:** 30-40. **To Apply:** Application form can be downloaded on-line. Applicants must complete the scholarship application. Applicants must also attach the following requirements: letter of recommendation from your guidance counselor or a teacher; official high school transcript. Including SAT or ACT scores; copy of the essay you submitted with your college application. If you did not have to submit one, write a brief (no more than two pages) essay regarding your future goals; copy of pages 1 and 2 of your parents' most recent completed federal tax form 1040. Mail everything to Hartford Foundation College Scholarship Program. **Dead-**

Awards are arranged alphabetically below their administering organizations

line: February 2. **Contact:** Hartford Foundation College Scholarship Program, Scholarship Management Services, Scholarship America, One Scholarship Way, PO Box 297, St. Peter, MN 56082. 800-537-4180.

4438 ■ Hartford Grammar School Scholarships
(Undergraduate/Scholarship)

Purpose: To award scholarship to a graduating high school senior form a public high school in the City of Hartford. **Focus:** General studies. **Qualif.:** Applicants must be entering a four-year college or university (full-time enrollment); demonstrate financial need; be on class rank with good academic record; be an active volunteer in school, community, or other extracurricular activities. **Criteria:** Selection will be based on the committee's criteria.

Funds Avail.: $3,000. **Number Awarded:** 1-3. **To Apply:** Application form can be downloaded on-line. Applicants must complete the scholarship application. Applicants must also attach the following requirements: letter of recommendation from your guidance counselor or a teacher; official high school transcript. Including SAT or ACT scores; copy of the essay you submitted with your college application. If you did not have to submit one, write a brief (no more than two pages) essay regarding your future goals; copy of pages 1 and 2 of your parents' or guardians' most recent completed federal tax form 1040. Mail everything to Hartford Foundation College Scholarship Program. **Deadline:** February 6. **Contact:** Hartford Foundation College Scholarship Program, Scholarship Management Services, Scholarship America, One Scholarship Way, PO Box 297, St. Peter, MN 56082. 800-537-4180.

4439 ■ Hartford Jazz Society Scholarships
(Undergraduate/Scholarship)

Purpose: To provide scholarship to the graduating high school senior. **Focus:** Music, Jazz. **Qualif.:** Applicants must: be a Connecticut Capitol Region resident; be attending a four-year college or university; be a Music major with interest in jazz. **Criteria:** Selection will be based on the panel's criteria.

Funds Avail.: $3,000. **Number Awarded:** 2-3. **To Apply:** Applicants must complete the General Scholarship Application and include the following requirements: a cassette tape of applicant both reading and improvising; two letters of reference, at least one form a music teacher or school music director and submit to Hartford Jazz Society, Inc., Chairperson, Scholarship Committee, 116 Cottage Grove Rd., Bloomfield, CT 06002. Phone: 860242-6688; Fax: 860243-8871. hartjazzsocinc@aol.com. **Deadline:** May 1.

4440 ■ Hartford Whalers Booster Club Scholarships
(Undergraduate/Scholarship)

Purpose: To provide scholarship to the students entering or enrolled in a four-year college or university. **Focus:** General studies. **Qualif.:** Applicants must: intend to play collegiate hockey; have an outstanding hockey abilities; be a Connecticut resident; have an academic excellence. **Criteria:** Selection will be based on the committee's criteria.

Funds Avail.: $1,000. **Number Awarded:** 1. **To Apply:** Applicants must complete the General Scholarship Application and include a letter of recommendation from your hockey coach outlining your hockey performance and submit to Hartford Whalers Booster Club. **Deadline:** March 31. **Contact:** Heather Turner Scholarship Coordinator, PO Box 273 Hartford, CT 06141. Phone: 860-643-0842. hartfordwhalersboosterclub@hotmail.com.

4441 ■ Caroline Holt Nursing Scholarships
(Undergraduate/Scholarship)

Purpose: To award scholarship to the undergraduate student enrolled in a Nursing Program. **Focus:** Nursing. **Qualif.:** Applicants must: be a US citizen; be attending an accredited School of Nursing; demonstrate financial need; have a letter of sponsorship from local DAR chapter. **Criteria:** Selection will be based on the committee's criteria.

Funds Avail.: $1,000. **To Apply:** For Connecticut residents to obtain materials, send a self-addressed stamped envelope to National Society Daughters of the American Revolution, 215 Loomis Rd. North Granby, CT 06060. **Deadline:** February 15. **Contact:** Mrs. Michael L. Stewart, CT State Chairperson. 860-653-4203. L2stew@yahoo.com.

4442 ■ Doc Hurley Scholarships
(Undergraduate/Scholarship)

Purpose: To award scholarship to the graduating senior from eligible Greater Hartford area high school. **Focus:** General studies. **Qualif.:** Student must be entering college in the fall semester after graduation. Eligible school can be found on www.docscholar.org. Students demonstrate financial need, academic excellence and community service. **Criteria:** Selection will be based on the committee's criteria.

Funds Avail.: $2,000-$10,000. **To Apply:** Applicants may obtain application materials from eligible high school guidance office. Applications will not be mailed to students. Valid applications must include: Student Air Report (SAR) from FAFSA showing Estimated Family Contribution (EFC); Three letter of recommendation (teacher, guidance counselor, and non-educational person); typed essay (no more than 1 1/2 pages); High School Transcript; SAT or ACT scores. All materials must be submitted to Doc Hurley Scholarship Foundation, Inc. **Deadline:** March. **Contact:** Muriel Hurley - Carter, Executive Dir. PO Box 4008 Hartford, CT 06147. Phone: 860-549-5012; Fax: 860-549-5955; dhsf@docscholar.org.

4443 ■ Interracial Scholarship Fund of Greater Hartford *(Undergraduate/Scholarship)*

Purpose: To provide scholarships to students entering a four-year college or university. **Focus:** General studies. **Qualif.:** Applicants must: be graduating high school senior who lives in or attends school in Greater Hartford; be on a class rank - top third with good academic record; be active volunteer in school, community, or other extracurricular activities; be involved in community service. **Criteria:** Selection will be based on the committee's criteria.

Funds Avail.: $3,000. **Number Awarded:** 1. **To Apply:** Application form can be downloaded online. Applicants must complete the scholarship application. Applicants must also attach the following requirements: letter of recommendation from your guidance counselor or a teacher; official high school transcript. Including SAT or ACT scores; copy of the essay you submitted with your college application. If you did not have to submit one, write a brief (no more than two pages) essay regarding your future goals; copy of pages 1 and 2 of your parents' most recent completed federal tax form 1040. Mail everything to Hartford Foundation College Scholarship Program. **Deadline:** February 6. **Contact:** Hartford Foundation College Scholarship Program, Scholarship Management Services, Scholarship America, One Scholarship Way, PO Box 297, St. Peter, MN 56082. 800-537-4180.

Awards are arranged alphabetically below their administering organizations

4444 ■ Juvenile Arthritis Scholarships
(Undergraduate/Scholarship)

Purpose: To assist graduating high school students who have arthritis or rheumatic disease. **Focus:** General studies. **Qualif.:** Applicants must; be a graduating Connecticut, Maine, New Hampshire, Rhode Island or Vermont high school senior or college undergraduate; must have arthritis or rheumatic disease; have a school or community volunteer service. **Criteria:** Selection will be based on the committee's criteria.

Funds Avail.: $1,000. **Number Awarded:** 3-4. **To Apply:** Applicants may obtain application materials from Arthritis Foundation, Northern and Southern New England Chapter, 35 Cold Spring Rd., Rocky Hill, CT 06067; Phone: 860563-1177 ext. 102; Fax: 860563-6018; info.sne@arthritis.org. **Deadline:** April 17.

4445 ■ Walter Kapala Scholarships
(Undergraduate/Scholarship)

Purpose: To award scholarship to the graduating high school senior from a public high school of Hartford, West Hartford, or Plainfield. **Focus:** General studies. **Qualif.:** Applicants must be entering a four-year college or university in the fall after high school graduation; demonstrate financial need and have an academic excellence. **Criteria:** Selection will be based on the committee's criteria.

Funds Avail.: No specific amount. **To Apply:** Applicants must complete the General Scholarship Application and mail to Merrill Lynch Trust Company, Walter Kapala Scholarship, Hopewell Charitable Trust Center, 1300 Merrill Lynch Drive, Pennington, NJ 08534. **Deadline:** May 1. **Contact:** Merrill Lynch Trust Company. Phone: 800-513-0742. Fax: 609-681-5886.

4446 ■ Herman P. Kopplemann Scholarships
(Undergraduate/Scholarship)

Purpose: To award scholarship to a graduating high school senior who lives in or attends school in Greater Hartford. **Focus:** General studies. **Qualif.:** Applicants must: be entering a four-year college or university; demonstrate financial need; be on a top third with good academic record; be an active volunteer in school, community, or other extracurricular activities; has been a newspaper carrier in Hartford County. **Criteria:** Selection will be based on the committee's criteria.

Funds Avail.: $3,000. **Number Awarded:** 1-4. **To Apply:** Application form can be downloaded on-line. Applicants must complete the scholarship application. Applicants must also attach the following requirements: letter of recommendation from your guidance counselor or a teacher; official high school transcript. Including SAT or ACT scores; copy of the essay you submitted with your college application. If you did not have to submit one, write a brief (no more than two pages) essay regarding your future goals; copy of pages 1 and 2 of your parents' or guardians' most recent completed federal tax form 1040. Mail everything to Scholarship America, Hartford Foundation College Scholarship Program, Scholarship Management Services, 1505 Riverview Rd, PO Box 297, St. Peter, MN 56082. 800537-4180. **Deadline:** February 2.

4447 ■ H.B. Paul Lowenberg Lions Scholarships
(Undergraduate/Scholarship)

Purpose: To provide scholarship to the graduating senior residing in Hartford, East Hartford, Windsor, Bloomfield, Newington, West Hartford, or Wethersfield. **Focus:** General

studies. **Qualif.:** Applicants must: be entering or enrolled in a two- or four-year college or university; demonstrate financial need and academic excellence. Preference is given to entering college students with an interest in music and the arts. **Criteria:** Selection will be based on the committee's criteria.

Funds Avail.: $500-$750. **Number Awarded:** 3. **To Apply:** Applicants must complete the General Scholarship Application and submit it together with your Student Aid Report (SAR) to Hartford Host Lions Club. **Deadline:** April 30. **Contact:** Atty. Bruce Bergman, Lions Scholarship Chairperson. 63 Imlay St. Hartford, CT 06105. Phone: 860-522-1436; Fax: 860-522-9077.

4448 ■ Irene and Daisy MacGregor Memorial Scholarships *(Graduate/Scholarship)*

Purpose: To provide scholarship to the students enrolled in an accredited School of Medicine. **Focus:** Medicine; Nursing, Psychiatric. **Qualif.:** Applicants must: be a US citizen; be on a graduate level, major in Medicine or Psychiatric Nursing; be enrolled in an accredited School of Medicine; have a letter of sponsorship from local DAR chapter. **Criteria:** Selection will be based on the committee's criteria.

Funds Avail.: $5,000. **To Apply:** For Connecticut residents to obtain materials, send a self-addressed stamped envelope to National Society Daughters of the American Revolution, 215 Loomis Rd. North Granby, CT 06060. **Deadline:** April 15. **Contact:** Mrs. Michael L. Stewart, CT State Chairperson. 860-653-4203. L2stew@yahoo.com.

4449 ■ Mary Main Memorial Scholarships
(Undergraduate/Scholarship)

Purpose: To provide scholarship to the graduating senior or college student residing or attending school full-time in Connecticut. **Focus:** General studies. **Qualif.:** Applicants must be legally blind and demonstrate financial need, community service, and academic excellence. **Criteria:** Selection will be based on the committee's criteria.

Funds Avail.: $3,000. **Number Awarded:** 1. **To Apply:** Applicants may obtain application materials from National Federation of the Blind of Connecticut 477 Connecticut Blvd. Ste. 217, East Hartford, CT 06108, or may log on www.nfbct.org. **Contact:** For further information, applicants may send an e-mail at info@nfbct.org; Fax: 860-291-2795; Phone: 860-289-1971.

4450 ■ Manchester Scholarship Foundation Scholarships *(Undergraduate/Scholarship)*

Purpose: To award scholarship to the graduating senior residing in Manchester. **Focus:** General studies. **Qualif.:** Applicants must: demonstrate financial need; have an academic excellence; be involved in community and school activities. **Criteria:** Selection will be based on the committee's criteria.

Funds Avail.: %1,000-$4,000. **Number Awarded:** Varies. **To Apply:** Students may obtain application materials from their Guidance Office or from Manchester Scholarship Foundation, Inc. 20 Hartford Rd. Manchester, CT 06040. **Deadline:** Mid-April. **Contact:** Manchester Scholarship Foundation, Inc., Phone: 860-645-1673; Fax: 860-432-9136.

4451 ■ Dr. Frank and Florence Marino Scholarships *(Undergraduate/Scholarship)*

Purpose: To provide scholarship to the students entering or enrolled in Medical school. **Focus:** Medicine. **Qualif.:**

Awards are arranged alphabetically below their administering organizations

Applicants must: have attended Connecticut school for at least 8 years (K-12) and graduated from Connecticut public or parochial high school; demonstrate financial need; have academic excellence; must be 2nd, 3rd, or 4th year medical students. **Criteria:** Selection will be based on the committee's criteria.

Funds Avail.: $1,000. **To Apply:** Applicants may obtain an application from the financial aid office of their medical school or may contact Mrs. Rita Fry. **Deadline:** May 13. **Contact:** Scholarship Fund c/o Mrs. Rita Fry, PO Box 75 Brookfield, CT 06804. 203-775-3114; rfry@charter.net.

4452 ■ Michaels Jewelers Foundation Scholarships for Athletes (Undergraduate/Scholarship)

Purpose: To provide scholarship to students entering or enrolled in a four-year program at the University of Connecticut. **Focus:** Business. **Qualif.:** Applicants must: be a graduating high school senior residing in Connecticut; be a Business major; participate in intercollegiate athletics. **Criteria:** Selection will be based on the committee's criteria.

Funds Avail.: $2,000. **Number Awarded:** 8. **To Apply:** Applicants may obtain application materials from University of Connecticut Athletic Department. www.michaelsjewelers.com. **Deadline:** April 15. **Contact:** Michael Jewelers Foundation, 203-597-4905. info@michaelsjewelers.com.

4453 ■ Sylvia Parkinson Scholarships (Undergraduate/Scholarship)

Purpose: To provide scholarship to the students attending the University of Connecticut School of Medicine. **Focus:** Medicine. **Qualif.:** Applicants must: be a Capitol Region resident; demonstrate financial need; have an academic excellence; intend to practice in the Greater Hartford area. **Criteria:** Selection will be based on the committee's criteria.

Funds Avail.: $1,500-$3,000. **To Apply:** Applicants may obtain application materials from University of Connecticut School of Medicine. 263 Farmington Ave. MC 1827 Farmington, CT 06030. **Deadline:** March 21. **Contact:** Andrea Deveraux, Director of Financial Aid, Phone: 860-679-3574; Fax: 860-679-1902; devereux@uchc.edu.

4454 ■ Dorothy E. Hofmann Pembroke Scholarships (Undergraduate/Scholarship)

Purpose: To award scholarship to students accepted at and plan to attend Brown University. **Focus:** General studies. **Qualif.:** Applicants must: be a graduating female senior from Hartford Public, Bulkeley, Weaver high school, or any female graduating senior who is a resident of Hartford; have an academic excellence; have extracurricular activities. **Criteria:** Selection will be based on the committee's criteria.

Funds Avail.: $5,000-$7,000. **To Apply:** Applicants may obtain application materials from Bank of America, 777 Main St. Hartford, CT 06115. **Deadline:** April 15. **Contact:** Carmen Britt, at carmen.britt@bankofamerica.com or 860-952-7392/860-952-7395 (fax).

4455 ■ Nicholas J. Piergrossi Scholarships (Undergraduate/Scholarship)

Purpose: To award scholarship to a first-year student attending the University of Connecticut School of Dental Medicine. **Focus:** Dentistry. **Qualif.:** Applicants must be a resident of Connecticut who demonstrates financial need and academic excellence. **Criteria:** Selection will be based on the committee's criteria.

Funds Avail.: $1,000. **Number Awarded:** 1. **To Apply:**

Applicants may obtain application materials from University of Connecticut School of Dental Medicine. 263 Farmington Ave., MC 1827 Farmington, CT 06030. **Deadline:** March 1. **Contact:** Andrea Deveraux, Director of Financial Aid, Phone: 860-679-3574; Fax: 860-679-1902; devereux@uchc.edu.

4456 ■ Day Pitney LLP Scholarships (Undergraduate/Scholarship)

Purpose: To provide scholarship to the graduating high school senior in the City of Hartford. **Focus:** General studies. **Qualif.:** Applicants must: be entering a four-year college or university (full-time enrollment); demonstrate financial need; be on the class rank - top third with good academic record; be active volunteer in school, community, or other extracurricular activities. **Criteria:** Selection will be based on the committee's criteria.

Funds Avail.: $3,000. **Number Awarded:** 1. **To Apply:** Application form can be downloaded on-line. Applicants must complete the scholarship application. Applicants must also attach the following requirements: letter of recommendation from your guidance counselor or a teacher; official high school transcript. Including SAT or ACT scores; copy of the essay you submitted with your college application. If you did not have to submit one, write a brief (no more than two pages) essay regarding your future goals; copy of pages 1 and 2 of your parents' or guardians' most recent completed federal tax form 1040. Mail everything to Hartford Foundation College Scholarship Program. **Deadline:** February 2. **Contact:** Hartford Foundation College Scholarship Program, Scholarship Management Services, Scholarship America, 1505 Riverview Rd., PO Box 297, St. Peter, MN 56082. 800-537-4180.

4457 ■ Dr. Sidney Rafal Memorial Scholarships (Undergraduate/Scholarship)

Purpose: To award scholarship to students attending the University of Connecticut School of Dental Medicine. **Focus:** Dentistry; Dental hygiene. **Qualif.:** Applicants must demonstrate financial need and academic excellence. **Criteria:** Selection will be based on the committee's criteria.

Funds Avail.: $1,200. **Number Awarded:** 1. **To Apply:** Applicants may obtain application materials from University of Connecticut School of Dental Medicine. 263 Farmington Ave., MC 1827 Farmington, CT 06030. **Deadline:** March 21. **Contact:** Andrea Deveraux, Director of Financial Aid, Phone: 860-679-3574; Fax: 860-679-1902; devereux@uchc.edu.

4458 ■ Mary C. Rawlins Scholarships (Undergraduate/Scholarship)

Purpose: To award financial support to the graduating high school senior. **Focus:** General studies. **Qualif.:** Applicants must: be a resident of Connecticut; graduating high school senior; be entering a two- or four-year college or university; have a GPA of 2.5 or higher at end of Fall semester. **Criteria:** Selection will be based on the committee's criteria.

Funds Avail.: $500. **Number Awarded:** 1. **To Apply:** Applicants may obtain application materials from Division of Criminal Justice, The CTAAAP Scholarship Committee, 300 Corporate Place Rocky Hill, CT 06067. **Deadline:** April 30. **Contact:** Patricia Alston-Tyson, 860-258-5800; patricia.alston-tyson@po.state.ct.us.

4459 ■ Alice W. Rooke Scholarships (Undergraduate/Scholarship)

Purpose: To provide financial assistance to students accepted by an accredited medical school. **Focus:** Medicine.

Awards are arranged alphabetically below their administering organizations

Qualif.: Applicants must be pursuing a course of study in medicine, not pre-med; must be a US citizen; have a letter of sponsorship from local DAR chapter. **Criteria:** Selection will be based on the committee's criteria.

Funds Avail.: $5,000. **To Apply:** For Connecticut residents, to obtain application materials, send a self-addressed stamped envelope to: National Society Daughters of American Revolution, 215 Loomis St., North Granby, CT 06060. **Deadline:** April 15. **Contact:** Mrs. Michael L. Stewart, CT State Chairperson, NSDAR Scholarship Committee. L2stew@yahoo.com; 860-653-4203.

4460 ■ Tadeusz Sendzimir Scholarships
(Undergraduate/Scholarship)

Purpose: To provide financial assistance to students entering or enrolled as undergraduate or graduate at a four-year college or university or summer program in Poland. **Focus:** Polish studies; American history. **Qualif.:** Applicants must be Connecticut residents; studying Polish/Slavic Language, history or culture in the United States or Poland. Preference to students of Polish descent. **Criteria:** Selection will be based on the committee's criteria.

Funds Avail.: $1,000-$5,000. **Number Awarded:** 1-5. **To Apply:** Applicants may obtain application materials from Connecticut Community Foundation, 43 Field St., Waterbury, CT 06702. **Contact:** Tallitha Richardson-Selby, Program/Scholarship Associate; Phone: 203-756-3054; E-mail: info@conncf.org.

4461 ■ Peter T. Steinwedell Scholarships
(Undergraduate/Scholarship)

Purpose: To provide scholarship for students attending graduate education program at Saint Joseph College, or the University of Connecticut, Hartford campus, or the University of Hartford. **Focus:** Education. **Qualif.:** Applicant must be an Education major with strong preference given to applicants pursuing teaching career; must demonstrate financial need and academic excellence. **Criteria:** Selection will be based on the committee's criteria.

Funds Avail.: $1,250. **Number Awarded:** 1. **To Apply:** Applicants may obtain an application by contacting either: Dr. Kathleen Butler, Chair, Department of Education St. Joseph College, 860231-5322, kbutler@sjc.edu; Monica Gat, Dean's Office Teacher Certification Program for College Graduates UConn Greater Hartford Campus, 860570-9283; Dr. H. Frederick Sweitzer, Associate Dean College of Education, Nursing and Health Professions University of Hartford, 860768-4279, sweitzer@hartford.edu. **Deadline:** March 21.

4462 ■ Town and County Club Scholarships
(Undergraduate/Scholarship)

Purpose: To award scholarship to the female adult learner - age 24 or older. **Focus:** General studies. **Qualif.:** Applicant must be a resident of Greater Hartford region; must be enrolled full or part-time in an accredited community undergraduate college or university in the Greater Hartford region; must have a completion of 15 semester hours or the equivalent of academic work with a 2.5 GPA; and must demonstrate financial need. **Criteria:** Selection will be based on the committee's criteria.

Funds Avail.: $2,000. **To Apply:** Students may contact the Town and County Club or access the website www.town-county.com for application form. **Contact:** Town and County Club, Scholarship Committee, 22 Woodland St., Hartford, CT 06105; Phone: 860-522-1109; Fax: 860-728-0758;

E-mail: office@towncounty.com.

4463 ■ Elmer Cooke Young - Taylor Young Scholarships *(Undergraduate/Scholarship)*

Purpose: To award scholarship to students entering a four-year college or university. **Focus:** General studies. **Qualif.:** Students must be graduating seniors from Glastonbury or Windsor High School; must demonstrate financial need; must be on a class rank - top third with good academic record; and must be active volunteers in school, community, or other extracurricular activities. **Criteria:** Selection will be based on the committee's criteria.

Funds Avail.: $3,000. **Number Awarded:** 6. **To Apply:** Application forms can be downloaded on-line. Applicants must complete the scholarship application. Applicants must also attach the following requirements: letter of recommendation from your guidance counselor or a teacher; official high school transcript (including SAT or ACT scores); copy of the essay you submitted with your college application (If you did not have to submit one, write a brief essay of no more than two pages regarding your future goals); copy of pages 1 and 2 of your parents' or guardians' most recent completed federal tax form 1040. Mail everything to Hartford Foundation College Scholarship Program. **Deadline:** February 2. **Contact:** Hartford Foundation College Scholarship Program, Scholarship Management Services, Scholarship America, One Scholarship Way, PO Box 297, St. Peter, MN 56082. 800-537-4180.

4464 ■ Hartford Public Library
500 Main St.
Hartford, CT 06103-3075
Ph: (860) 695-6300
Fax: (860) 722-6897
URL: www.hplct.org

4465 ■ Caroline M. Hewins Scholarships
(Graduate/Scholarship)

Purpose: To support students planning to specialize in library work with children. **Focus:** Library and archival sciences. **Qualif.:** Applicant must have received, or be about to receive a four year undergraduate degree and have applied for admission to a library school accredited by the American Library Association. **Criteria:** Preference will be given to applicants who plan to pursue a career in public library service.

Funds Avail.: $4,000. **To Apply:** Applicants must submit a completed application form along with transcript of credits through the first semester of the senior year and an evidence of application to an accredited school of library service. **Contact:** Debra Perry at the above address.

4466 ■ Harvard Law School
1563 Massachusetts Ave.
Cambridge, MA 02138
Ph: (617) 495-3100
Fax: (617) 495-9393
E-mail: hrp@law.harvard.edu
URL: www.law.harvard.edu

4467 ■ Henigson Human Rights Fellowships
(Graduate/Fellowship)

Purpose: To encourage the HLS students to build human rights work and to expand their interest in working in the

Awards are arranged alphabetically below their administering organizations

field. **Focus:** Human rights. **Qualif.:** Applicants must be current and former J.D. students: 3Ls expecting to receive the J.D. degree, as well as J.D graduates who currently clerk for a judge; must be engaged in full-time public interest work; must be active in human rights or public interest work while students at HLS; must be LL.M. students who expect to receive the LL.M. degree and who come from and will return to a country other than the United States; or HLS students and recent graduates with a demonstrated commitment to international human rights and have an interest working in the field. **Criteria:** Selection of recipients will be based on the application materials.

Funds Avail.: $22,000. **To Apply:** Applicants must submit a curriculum vitae, including information about classes, work and extracurricular activities in public interest and human rights inside and outside of Harvard Law School; a personal statement (500 words maximum) about the applicant's relevant experience, interest, and future aspirations with respect to public interest and human rights work; a project description; a letter and supporting materials from sponsoring organization detailing their purpose, function, and particular interest in the work of the applicant; two or three letters of recommendation including at least one from an HLS professor; and an HLS transcript. **Deadline:** March 12.

4468 ■ HRP Global Human Rights Fellowships
(Graduate/Fellowship)

Purpose: To support the graduating 3Ls, LL.M.s, or recent HLS graduates with a demonstrated commitment to human rights. **Focus:** Human rights. **Qualif.:** Applicants must be Harvard Law School J.D. students: must be 3Ls expecting to receive the J.D. degree, as well as recent J.D. graduates; must be Harvard Law School LL.M. students who expect to receive the LL.M. degree. **Criteria:** Selection of recipients will be based on the application materials.

Funds Avail.: $60,000 plus medical and other benefits. **To Apply:** Applicants must submit a curriculum vitae, including information about classes, work and extracurricular activities in public interest and human rights inside and outside of Harvard Law School; a personal statement (500 words maximum) about the applicant's relevant experience, interest, and future aspirations with respect to public interest and human rights work; a project description; a letter and supporting materials from sponsoring organization detailing their purpose, function, and particular interest in the work of the applicant; two or three letters of recommendation, including at least one from an HLS professor; and an HLS transcript. **Deadline:** March 12. **Contact:** Human Rights Program, Harvard Law School at 617-495-9362 or hrp@law.harvard.edu.

4469 ■ Satter Human Rights Fellowships
(Graduate/Fellowship)

Purpose: To enable students to make a significant contribution to addressing human rights violations involving mass atrocities and similar situations during the year of the fellowship and to help students develop careers in human rights. **Focus:** Human rights. **Qualif.:** Applicants must be Harvard Law School J.D. students: 3Ls expecting to receive the J.D. degree, as well as recent J.D. graduates; must be Harvard Law School LL.M. students who expect to receive the LL.M. degree. **Criteria:** Selection of recipients will be based on the application materials.

Funds Avail.: $22,000. **To Apply:** Applicants must submit a curriculum vitae, including information about classes, work and extracurricular activities in public interest and hu-

man rights inside and outside of Harvard Law School; a personal statement (500 words maximum) about the applicant's relevant experience, interest, and future aspirations with respect to public interest and human rights work; a project description; a letter and supporting materials from sponsoring organization detailing their purpose, function, and particular interest in the work of the applicant; two or three letters of recommendation including at least one from an HLS professor; and an HLS transcript. **Deadline:** March 12.

4470 ■ Harvard-Smithsonian Center for Astrophysics
60 Garden St.
Cambridge, MA 02138
Ph: (617) 495-7463
E-mail: www-admin@cfa.harvard.edu
URL: www.cfa.harvard.edu

4471 ■ CfA Postdoctoral Fellowships
(Postdoctorate/Fellowship)

Purpose: To advance knowledge of the Universe through research in astronomy and astrophysics and in related areas of fundamental physics and geophysics. **Focus:** Physics; Geophysics. **Qualif.:** Applicants must be outstanding researchers displaying significant promise in theory, observation, instrumentation, and/or laboratory experiments; must be first-author refereed journal paper and who already received their PhD at the time of application. **Criteria:** Selection will be based on the committee's criteria.

Funds Avail.: Approximately $64,500 with a research budget of $16,000. **To Apply:** Interested applicants must visit the website for the online application process. Applicants must also upload the following forms in PDF or Text format: curriculum vitae; publication list; summary of previous and current research (up to four pages); research proposal (up to four pages); and three reference letters. **Deadline:** October 31.

4472 ■ Clay Postdoctoral Fellowships
(Postdoctorate/Fellowship)

Purpose: To advance knowledge of the Universe through research in astronomy and astrophysics and in related areas of fundamental physics and geophysics. **Focus:** Physics; Geophysics. **Qualif.:** Applicants must be outstanding researchers displaying significant promise in theory, observation, instrumentation, and/or laboratory experiments. **Criteria:** Selection will be based on the committee's criteria.

Funds Avail.: A stipend of approximately $65,500 plus a research budget of $16,000. **To Apply:** Interested applicants must visit the website for the online application process. The following forms must be uploaded in PDF or Text format: curriculum vitae; publication list; summary of previous and current research (maximum of 4 pages); research proposal (maximum of 4 pages). Applicants must also prepare three letters of reference. **Deadline:** October 31.

4473 ■ Have It Your Way Foundation (HIYWF)
5505 Blue Lagoon Dr.
Miami, FL 33126
Ph: (305) 378-3186
Fax: (305) 378-7017
E-mail: bk_hiywfoundation@whopper.com

Awards are arranged alphabetically below their administering organizations

URL: www.haveityourwayfoundation.org

4474 ■ Burger King Employee Scholars Program *(Undergraduate/Scholarship)*

Purpose: To provide scholarship awards to assist students who excel academically while also working part-time and being actively involved in their community. **Focus:** General studies. **Qualif.:** Applicants must be high school seniors who: are salaried or hourly team members of a Burger King restaurant; active on BK payroll for at least 12 months of the current year's application deadline; maintain at least a 2.0 GPA throughout high school or college; enrolled at an accredited college/vocational school in the fall of the scholarship year; participate in extracurricular activities or community service; receive written recommendation from his or her BK employer. **Criteria:** Selection will be based on financial need, community involvement, employment at a participating restaurant location, academic achievements and records.

Funds Avail.: No specific amount. **To Apply:** Applicants must log on to www.applyists.net to get an application and must follow the onscreen instructions. **Contact:** For additional information, applicants must contact the International Scholarship and Tuition Services, Inc.; Phone: 615-320-3149; Fax: 615-320-3151. Application form and supporting documents can be faxed at 615-627-9685 or 615-627-9673 or can be emailed at bkscholars@applyists.com.

4475 ■ Burger King Scholars Program *(Undergraduate/Scholarship)*

Purpose: To provide scholarship awards to assist students who excel academically while also working part-time and being actively involved in their community. **Focus:** General studies. **Qualif.:** Applicants must be high school seniors who: maintain a cumulative GPA of 2.5 or higher on a 4.0 scale or the equivalent; work part-time an average of 15 hours per week; demonstrate participation in community service activities; demonstrate financial need; plan to enroll in an accredited two-year or four-year college, university or vocational/technical school; graduating high school seniors or graduating from home school education; must be U.S. or Canada residents. Companies and franchise restaurants, corporate and field employees are eligible to apply. **Criteria:** Selection will be based on the submitted application.

Funds Avail.: $1,000. **To Apply:** Applicants may apply online. **Deadline:** January 10.

4476 ■ Hawaii Community Foundation

827 Fort Street Mall
Honolulu, HI 96813
Ph: (808) 537-6333
Fax: (808) 521-6286
Free: 888-731-3863
E-mail: info@hcf-hawaii.org
URL: www.hawaiicommunityfoundation.org

4477 ■ Victoria S. and Bradley L. Geist Scholarships *(Undergraduate/Scholarship)*

Purpose: To provide opportunities to students currently or formerly in the foster care system. **Focus:** General studies. **Qualif.:** Applicants must be residents of Hawaii who are planning to attend a vocational school, two- or four-year college or university. **Criteria:** Recipients will be selected based on demonstrated financial need.

Funds Avail.: No specific amount. **To Apply:** Applicants must complete the application form; must submit a personal statement, most recent official college transcript and letter from a case worker verifying foster care status in Hawaii. **Deadline:** June 1. **Contact:** scholarships@hcf-hawaii.org.

4478 ■ Hawaii Community Foundation Scholarships *(Undergraduate, Graduate/Scholarship)*

Purpose: To financially assist students aiming to further their education. **Focus:** General studies. **Qualif.:** Applicants must be residents of Hawaii; must be full-time undergraduate or graduate students who have plan to attend an accredited two- or four-year college or university; must have a minimum GPA of 2.7 and must exhibit good moral character. **Criteria:** Applicants will be chosen based on demonstrated financial need and academic achievement.

Funds Avail.: Amount not specified. **To Apply:** Applicants must complete the application form and must visit the website for further information.

4479 ■ Hawaii Forest Institute

PO Box 66
Ookala, HI 96774
Ph: (808) 933-9411
Fax: (253) 550-3062
E-mail: info@hawaiiforestinstitute.org
URL: www.hawaiiforestinstitute.org

4480 ■ Tommy Crabb Scholarship Fund *(Undergraduate/Scholarship)*

Purpose: To support educational endeavors related to forestry. **Focus:** Forestry. **Qualif.:** Applicant must be a Hawaii high school graduate to pursue a degree in forestry or a related degree program that includes a forestry certificate or specialization at any accredited two-year or four-year college or university. **Criteria:** Award will be based on merit.

Funds Avail.: No specific amount. **To Apply:** Applicant may contact the Institute for application process.

4481 ■ Hawaii Lodging and Tourism Association (HLTA)

2270 Kalakaua Ave., Ste. 1506
Honolulu, HI 96815
Ph: (808) 923-0407
Fax: (808) 924-3843
E-mail: info@hawaiilodging.org
URL: hawaiilodging.org

4482 ■ R.W. "Bob" Holden Memorial Scholarships *(Undergraduate/Scholarship)*

Purpose: To provide support to students with dedication and leadership potential to work toward the standard of excellence. **Focus:** Hotel, institutional and restaurant management. **Qualif.:** Applicant must be a resident of Hawaii and a U.S citizen; must be a junior or senior attending an accredited university or college and accepted in a hotel management program; must have a minimum of 3.0 grade. **Criteria:** Selection of applicants will be based on citizenship and leadership as demonstrated through activities and college performance.

Funds Avail.: $1,000. **To Apply:** Applicant must submit a

Awards are arranged alphabetically below their administering organizations

current transcript; letter of recommendation from a college professor, counselor or dean; must provide an autobiography, photograph and career goals essay. **Deadline:** July 1. **Contact:** Application form and other supporting documents must be sent to R.W. Bob Holden Scholarship Committee at the above address.

4483 ■ Clem Judd Jr. Memorial Scholarships
(Undergraduate/Scholarship)

Purpose: To provide support to students with dedication and leadership potential to work toward the standard of excellence. **Focus:** Hotel, institutional and restaurant management. **Qualif.:** Applicant must provide a proof of Hawaiian ancestry; must be a resident of Hawaii; must be a junior or senior attending an accredited university or college and accepted in a hotel management program; must maintain a minimum 2.8 grade point average. **Criteria:** Selection of applicants will be based on the citizenship and leadership as demonstrated through activities and college performance.

Funds Avail.: $1,000-$2,000. **To Apply:** Applicant must have a proof of residency, proof of U.S. citizenship and proof of Hawaiian ancestry; must have a current transcript of records; must have an autobiography and photograph; must provide a career goals essay; must have a letter of recommendation from a college professor, counselor or dean. Application forms and other supporting documents must be sent to Clem Judd Jr. **Deadline:** July 1. **Contact:** Clem Judd Jr., Memorial Scholarship Committee, Hawaii Hotel Industry Foundation, 2270 Kalakaua Ave., Ste. 1506, Honolulu, HI 96815.

4484 ■ Hawaii Pacific Gerontological Society (HPGS)
PO Box 3714
Honolulu, HI 96812
Ph: (808) 840-1819
E-mail: hpgs.hawaii@gmail.com
URL: hpgs.org

4485 ■ HPGS/ALOH Graduate Scholarships
(Graduate/Scholarship)

Purpose: To support graduate, law and medical students registered in a program of study focused on gerontology or geriatrics. **Focus:** Gerontology; Geriatric medicine. **Qualif.:** Applicants must be graduate, law or medical students at the University of Hawaii, Hawaii Pacific University and Chaminade University who want to pursue careers related to Gerontology and Geriatrics; must have at least two semesters in any graduate program in medicine, law, nursing, social work, psychology, biology, political science, sociology, physical therapy, occupational therapy, speech therapy, architecture and design at the time of the application; must maintain a 3.0 or higher GPA for the past academic year; and must be residents of Hawaii. Applicants must have demonstrated interest in aging through one or more of the following: (a) currently taking, or having taken, one or more aging-related credit courses or certificate programs; (b) paid professional or para-professional work experience with older adults or in an aging-related setting; (c) attendance at one or more non-credit aging-related courses or seminars; (d) volunteer work or internship in an aging-related community site; (e) work on an aging-related project that the applicants as students initiated; (f) assisting or having assisted by a professor on a research project;(g) playing a leadership role in a class or services learning

project that helps older persons. **Criteria:** Preference will be given to students who meet the scholarship criteria and provide evidence offinancial need.

Funds Avail.: $1,000. **Number Awarded:** 1. **To Apply:** Application forms are available online. Applicants must submit evidence of financial need and proof of residency in the State of Hawaii; must provide a copy of recommendation letter from their academic adviser, former professor, instructor, or supervisor at their internship or volunteer site; must submit an essay that addresses their qualifications for receiving the scholarship, including experience in and dedication to the field of gerontology, their future career plans, and financial need; must have a copy of latest community college or university transcript and a valid ID. **Deadline:** May.

4486 ■ HPGS Undergraduate Scholarships
(Undergraduate/Scholarship)

Purpose: To support professionals pursuing their career related to gerontology or geriatrics. **Focus:** Gerontology; Geriatric medicine. **Qualif.:** Applicants must be Hawaiian residents, undergraduates and community college students in the University of Hawaii System, Hawaii Pacific University and Chaminade University pursuing careers in gerontology and geriatrics; must demonstrate a 3.0 GPA or higher for the past academic year at the community or undergraduate level. **Criteria:** Preference will be given to students who have taken, or are currently taking, at least one aging related community college or university course, or to students who demonstrate an interest in the field of gerontology in an aging-related community site, for example: doing volunteer work or performing an internship at an aging related community site; working on an aging related project that you as a student initiated; assisting or having assisted a professor on an aging related project; having played a leadership role in working on a class or service learning project that helped older persons.

Funds Avail.: $1,000. **Number Awarded:** Varies. **To Apply:** Application forms are available online. Applicants must provide a proof of residency in the State of Hawaii; must submit a letter of recommendation from their academic adviser, former professors, instructors, or supervisors at their internship or volunteer site; must submit an essay that addresses their qualifications for receiving the scholarship, including experience in and dedication to the field of gerontology, their future career plans and expression of financial need; must have a copy of latest community college or university transcript. **Deadline:** May 30.

4487 ■ Health Physics Society (HPS)
1313 Dolley Madison Blvd., Ste. 402
McLean, VA 22101
Ph: (703) 790-1745
Fax: (703) 790-2672
E-mail: hps@burkinc.com
URL: www.hps.org

4488 ■ Richard J. Burk, Jr. Fellowships
(Graduate/Fellowship)

Purpose: To support full-time entering or continuing students enrolled in bona fide U.S. graduate programs in health physics or a closely related field. **Focus:** Health sciences; Radiology. **Qualif.:** Applicant must be full-time entering or continuing student enrolled in U.S. graduate programs in health physics or related field. Previous HPS Fellowship holders are ineligible. **Criteria:** Selection is based on the application.

Awards are arranged alphabetically below their administering organizations

Funds Avail.: $5,000. **To Apply:** Applicants must complete the online application. **Deadline:** March 1.

4489 ■ Robert Gardner Memorial Fellowships
(Graduate/Fellowship)

Purpose: To support full-time entering or continuing students enrolled in bona fide U.S. graduate programs in health physics or a closely related field. **Focus:** Health sciences; Radiology. **Qualif.:** Applicant must be full-time entering or continuing student enrolled in U.S. graduate programs in health physics or related field. Previous HPS Fellowship holders are ineligible. **Criteria:** Selection is based on the application.

Funds Avail.: $5,000. **To Apply:** Applicants must complete the online application. **Deadline:** March 1.

4490 ■ Robert S. Landauer, Sr. Memorial Fellowships *(Graduate/Fellowship)*

Purpose: To support full-time entering or continuing students enrolled in bona fide U.S. graduate programs in health physics or a closely related field. **Focus:** Health sciences; Radiology. **Qualif.:** Applicant must be full-time entering or continuing student enrolled in U.S. graduate programs in health physics or related field. Previous HPS Fellowship holders are ineligible. **Criteria:** Selection is based on the application.

Funds Avail.: $6,000. **To Apply:** Applicants must complete the online application. **Deadline:** March 1.

4491 ■ Burton J. Moyer Memorial Fellowships
(Graduate/Fellowship)

Purpose: To support full-time entering or continuing students enrolled in bona fide U.S. graduate programs in health physics or a closely related field. **Focus:** Health sciences; Radiology. **Qualif.:** Applicant must be full-time entering or continuing student enrolled in U.S. graduate programs in health physics or related field. Previous HPS Fellowship holders are ineligible. **Criteria:** Selection is based on the application.

Funds Avail.: $8,000. **To Apply:** Applicants must complete the online application. **Deadline:** March 1.

4492 ■ J. Newell Stannard Fellowships
(Graduate/Fellowship)

Purpose: To support full-time entering or continuing students enrolled in bona fide U.S. graduate programs in health physics or a closely related field. **Focus:** Health sciences; Radiology. **Qualif.:** Applicant must be full-time entering or continuing student enrolled in U.S. graduate programs in health physics or related field. Previous HPS Fellowship holders are ineligible. **Criteria:** Selection is based on the application.

Funds Avail.: $5,000. **To Apply:** Applicants must complete the online application. **Deadline:** March 1.

4493 ■ Health Resources in Action
95 Berkeley St.
Boston, MA 02116
Ph: (617) 451-0049
Fax: (617) 451-0062
URL: www.hria.org

4494 ■ Davis Foundation Postdoctoral Fellowships *(Postdoctorate/Fellowship)*

Purpose: To advance the development of all areas of the lives of children and young adults with special emphasis on those suffering from eating disorders. **Focus:** Health sciences. **Qualif.:** Applicants must be MD, PhD or equivalent awarded from an accredited domestic or foreign institution; have completed no more than three years of full-time postdoctoral research experience by the time funding begins; conduct the proposed research project at a hospital, university or other non-profit research institution where applicants hold their postdoctoral fellowship appointment. **Criteria:** Selection will be based on the following criteria: applicant's demonstrated competency and potential for a career in research; qualifications of the mentor and the degree of commitment to supervise and train the applicant during the proposed research period; letters of recommendation; research hypothesis is novel and/or builds on current knowledge; proposal reviews the relevant literature; objectives are well conceived, realistic and important; research methodology, data collection and date analysis are feasible and appropriate to the proposal's aims; project that will contribute to the professional training and growth of the applicant; and advancing knowledge that may someday lead to improving the quality of human life.

Funds Avail.: $43,000-$63,000 per year. **Number Awarded:** 5. **To Apply:** Applicants must submit a research project which focuses the relevant aspects of the biological causes of anorexia nervosa and bulimia nervosa as defined by clinical criteria; must upload a signed letter of support from their research project mentor; and supply two confidential letters of recommendation, one of which must be from thesis advisor for applicants holding a PhD. If the thesis advisor is unavailable to write a letter of recommendation, a brief explanation of his/her unavailability must be included in the uploaded document. Complete application process required an online submission as well as a mailed copy of the application materials that are submitted online. **Deadline:** January 13 for the online submission; January 20 for the mail submission. **Contact:** Jeanne Brown, Program Officer; Phone: 617-279-2240, ext. 709; email: jbrown@hria.org.

4495 ■ Charles A. King Trust Postdoctoral Fellowships *(Postdoctorate/Fellowship)*

Purpose: To support clinical or health services research scientists in the early mid stages of their research careers and basic scientists in the later stages of their postdoctoral research training. **Focus:** Clinical sciences; Health sciences. **Qualif.:** Applicants must be working in an academic or medical research institution in the state of Massachusetts and have required minimum/maximum years of experience; must hold a fellowship position under the supervision of a faculty member; mentors must confirm that degrees obtained outside the United States are equivalent to the MD, DMD, PhD or other doctoral degree; only one applicant per mentor may apply per application cycle. **Criteria:** Selection will be based on the following criteria: applicant's demonstrated competency and potential for a career in research; qualifications of the mentor and the degree of commitment to supervise and train the applicant during the proposed research period; letters of recommendation; novelty of research hypothesis is novel and ability to build on current knowledge; proposal reviews the relevant literature; objectives are well conceived, realistic and important; research methodology, data collection and date analysis are feasible and appropriate to the proposal's aims; project that will contribute to the professional training and growth of the applicant; and advancing knowledge that may someday lead to improving the quality of human life.

Funds Avail.: $43,500 to $51,000, inclusive of a $2,000 expense allowance. **To Apply:** Applicants must visit the

---

Awards are arranged alphabetically below their administering organizations

website to obtain an application form. The complete application process requires an online submission as well as mailed package containing the Face Sheet with original signatures, four printed copies of the document uploaded online and three confidential letters of recommendation. **Deadline:** December 15 for the online submission; December 17 for the mail submission. **Contact:** Linda Lam, Program Officer; Phone: 617-279-2240, ext. 710; email: llam@hria.org.

4496 ■ Patterson Trust Postdoctoral Fellowships in Brain Circuitry (Postdoctorate/Fellowship)

Purpose: To support research relating to human diseases, their causes and relief. **Focus:** Health sciences. **Qualif.:** Applicants must have received a PhD, MD or equivalent from an accredited domestic or foreign institution; have completed no more than five years of full-time postdoctoral research experience; must conduct the proposed research project in a hospital, university or other non-profit research institutions located in Connecticut, New Jersey and New York. **Criteria:** Selection will be based on the following criteria: applicant's demonstrated competency and potential for a career in research; qualifications of the Mentor and the degree of commitment to supervise and train the applicant during the proposed research period; letters of reference; research hypothesis is novel and/or builds on current knowledge; proposal reviews the relevant literature; objectives are well conceived, realistic and important; research methodology, data collection and date analysis are feasible and appropriate to the proposal's aims; project that will contribute to the professional training and growth of the applicant; project that will advance knowledge in brain circuitry.

Funds Avail.: $44,500-$89,000. **To Apply:** Application form is available in the website. Complete application process requires an online submission as well as mailed copy of the application materials that are submitted online. **Deadline:** September 15 for the online submission; September 19 for the mail submission. **Contact:** Linda Lam, Program Officer; Phone: 617-279-2240, ext. 710; email: llam@hria.org.

4497 ■ Health Resources and Services Administration - Bureau of Health Professions
5600 Fishers Ln.
Rockville, MD 20857
Free: 888-275-4772
E-mail: ask@hrsa.gov
URL: bhpr.hrsa.gov

4498 ■ Nursing Scholarship Program
(Undergraduate/Scholarship)

Purpose: To award scholarships to individuals for attendance at schools of nursing. **Focus:** Nursing. **Qualif.:** Applicants must be US citizens or nationals (permanent residents are not eligible); must be enrolled or accepted for enrollment as full-time or part-time students in an accredited school of nursing in a professional registered nurse program; must begin classes for the fall term on or after July 1 and no later than September 30; must be free from any federal judgment liens; must be free from existing service commitments; and must not be a delinquent on a federal debt. **Criteria:** Preference is given to qualified applicants with the greatest financial need who are enrolled full-time in an undergraduate nursing program.

Funds Avail.: $1,233. **To Apply:** All applicants (regardless of funding preference) must submit an electronic application. Required supporting documentation is available within the online application and includes: a verification of acceptance/good standing report and data collection for tuition and fees; an authorization to release information; form W-4; standard form 1199A (EG) direct deposit sign up form; and a signed contract. **Deadline:** May 14. **Contact:** callcenter@hrsa.gov.

4499 ■ Scholarships for Disadvantaged Students *(Undergraduate/Scholarship)*

Purpose: To provide scholarships for full-time, financially needy students from disadvantaged backgrounds who are enrolled in health professions and nursing programs. **Focus:** Health sciences. **Qualif.:** Applicant must be an individual from a disadvantaged background as defined by the US Department of Health and Human Services and must come from an environment that has inhibited the individual from obtaining the knowledge, skill and abilities required to enroll in and graduate from a health professions school, or from a program providing education or training in an allied health profession; or must come from a family with an annual income below low income thresholds according to family size published by the US Bureau of Census, adjusted annually for changes in the Consumer Price Index, and adjusted by the Secretary, HHS, for use in health professions and nursing programs; must be a citizen, national, or a lawful permanent resident of the United States. **Criteria:** Schools are responsible for selecting scholarship recipients, making reasonable determinations of need, and providing scholarships that do not exceed the cost of attendance (tuition, reasonable educational expenses and reasonable living expenses).

Funds Avail.: No specific amount. **To Apply:** All applicants must submit an electronic application. Required supporting documentation is available within the online application and includes: a verification of acceptance/good standing report and data collection for tuition and fees; an authorization to release information; form W-4; standard form 1199A (EG) direct deposit sign up form; and a signed contract. **Contact:** HRSA at the above address.

4500 ■ Healthcare Financial Management Association - Connecticut Chapter
c/o Stephen W. Vargo, Pres.
Mercy Community Health
2021 Albany Ave.
West Hartford, CT 06117
Ph: (860) 920-6381
Fax: (860) 714-8023
E-mail: svargo@mchct.org
URL: www.cthfma.org

4501 ■ HFMA Connecticut Chapter Scholarships *(Graduate, Undergraduate/Scholarship)*

Purpose: To support students who wish to further their formal education in healthcare. **Focus:** Health care services. **Qualif.:** Applicant may be an undergraduate or graduate student. **Criteria:** Selection is based on the quality of the written response to the question about a current issue in health care.

Funds Avail.: $4,000 first place, $1,000 second place. **Number Awarded:** Varies. **To Apply:** Applicants must submit a completed scholarship application form along with the required documents. **Deadline:** July 27.

Awards are arranged alphabetically below their administering organizations

4502 ■ Healthcare Information and Management Systems Society

230 East Ohio St., Ste. 500
Chicago, IL 60611-3270
Ph: (312) 664-4467
Fax: (312) 664-6143
E-mail: himss@himss.org
URL: www.himss.org

4503 ■ Dvora Brodie Scholarships *(Graduate, Postgraduate, Undergraduate/Scholarship)*

Purpose: To provide financial support to a HIMSS student member who exhibits excellence and future leadership potential in the healthcare information and management system industry. **Focus:** Healthcare services. **Qualif.:** Applicant must be a member in good standing of HIMSS attending a school in New England, or originally be from the New England area; and the primary occupation of the applicant at the time the scholarship is awarded must be that of a student in an accredited undergraduate, Masters, or PhD program related to the healthcare information management systems field. **Criteria:** Recipient will be selected according to merit, financial need, and other factors.

Funds Avail.: $5,000. **To Apply:** Applicants must submit complete application form. **Contact:** Jessica Bird, jbird@himss.org.

4504 ■ Richard P. Covert, Ph.D./FHIMSS Scholarships for Management Systems *(Graduate, Postgraduate, Undergraduate/Scholarship)*

Purpose: To provide financial assistance to students pursuing a degree in Management Engineering. **Focus:** Engineering. **Qualif.:** Applicant must be a member in good standing of HIMSS and the primary occupation of the applicant at the time the scholarship is awarded must be that of student in an accredited undergraduate, Masters or PhD program related to the healthcare information management systems field. **Criteria:** Recipient will be selected according to merit, financial need, and other factors.

Funds Avail.: $5,000. **To Apply:** Applicants must submit complete application form. **Contact:** Jessica Bird, jbird@himss.org.

4505 ■ Healthcare Information Management Systems Scholarships *(Graduate, Postgraduate, Undergraduate/Scholarship)*

Purpose: To provide financial assistance to students in healthcare and IT-related fields. **Focus:** Healthcare services. **Qualif.:** Applicant must be a member in good standing of HIMSS and a student in an accredited undergraduate, Master's or PhD program related to the healthcare information or management systems field. **Criteria:** Recipient will be selected according to merit, financial need, and other factors.

Funds Avail.: $5,000. **Number Awarded:** 3. **To Apply:** Applicants must submit complete application form. **Contact:** Jessica Bird, jbird@himss.org.

4506 ■ Northern California Chapter of HIMSS Scholarships *(Graduate, Postgraduate, Undergraduate/Scholarship)*

Purpose: To provide financial assistance for a student in healthcare informatics who exhibits academic excellence and future leadership potential in the healthcare information and management systems industry. **Focus:** Healthcare

services. **Qualif.:** Applicant must be a member in good standing of HIMSS or member of National HIMSS and the Northern California Chapter attending a school in the Northern California area and the primary occupation of the applicant at the time the scholarship is awarded must be that of student in an accredited undergraduate, Master's or PhD program related to the healthcare information management systems field. **Criteria:** Recipient will be selected according to merit, financial need and other factors.

Funds Avail.: $5,000. **Number Awarded:** 2. **To Apply:** Applicants must submit complete application form. **Contact:** Jessica Bird, jbird@himss.org.

4507 ■ Helicopter Foundation International (HFI)

1635 Prince St.
Alexandria, VA 22314-2818
Ph: (703) 683-4646
Fax: (703) 341-6454
E-mail: marty.pociask@rotor.com
URL: www.helicopterfoundation.org

4508 ■ Helicopter Foundation International Commercial Helicopter Rating Scholarships *(Professional development/Scholarship)*

Purpose: To assist private helicopter pilot candidates who wish to obtain their commercial helicopter ratings. **Focus:** Aviation. **Qualif.:** Applicants must hold a current private helicopter pilot license. **Criteria:** Recipients will be selected based on skills and abilities to be commercial helicopter pilots and interest in pursuing a career as pilot in the helicopter industry.

Funds Avail.: $5,000. **Number Awarded:** 4. **To Apply:** Applicants must submit a clear copy of any and all FAA or international equivalent certificates; must submit a completed application form; current resume; proof of enrollment in helicopter training program at a qualified school; three current letters of recommendation from individual such as employers, flight instructors, HAI members or members of similar aviation organizations who can attest to candidate's background, training and experiences as it relates to the helicopter industry. International applicants must provide proof of foreign citizenship. **Deadline:** November 30. **Contact:** Applications must be signed and mailed to: Elizabeth Meade at the above address.

4509 ■ Helicopter Foundation International Maintenance Technician Certificate Scholarships *(Professional development/Scholarship)*

Purpose: To assist candidates who wish to obtain an A, P or A and A and P certificate. **Focus:** Aviation. **Qualif.:** Applicants must hold a current private helicopter pilot license; and must be helicopter maintenance technicians. **Criteria:** Recipients are selected based on financial need.

Funds Avail.: $2,500. **Number Awarded:** 6. **To Apply:** Applicants must submit a completed HFI application for a Maintenance Technician Scholarship; current resume; proof of enrollment in helicopter training program at a qualified school; three current letters of recommendation from individual such as employers; flight instructors, HAI members or members of similar aviation organizations who can attest to candidate's background, training and experiences as it relates to the helicopter industry. International applicants must provide proof of foreign citizenship. **Deadline:** November 30. **Contact:** Application and supporting documents to: Elizabeth Meade at the above address.

Awards are arranged alphabetically below their administering organizations

4510 ■ Michelle North Scholarships for Safety
(Professional development/Scholarship)

Purpose: To assist private helicopter pilot candidates who wish to obtain their commercial helicopter ratings. **Focus:** Aviation. **Qualif.:** Applicants must be employed in the helicopter industry either in the Safety or Safety Management field, preparing to enter or if in a position other than the Safety Management field. **Criteria:** Recipients are selected based on the demonstrated interest in the field of aviation.

Funds Avail.: $3,000. **Number Awarded: 1. To Apply:** Applicants must submit a completed application form; must submit a current resume; summary of career plans; two letters of recommendation from employer or other helicopter professional; must submit a clear copy of any and all FAA or international equivalent certificates; and a (350-500-word) summary statement attesting how candidate would benefit from the Safety Management course and how would use the knowledge gained to enhance safety at candidate's organization. **Deadline:** November 30. **Contact:** For more information, contact Elizabeth "Libby" Meade at the above address.

4511 ■ Bill Sanderson Aviation Maintenance Technician Scholarships *(Postgraduate/Scholarship)*

Purpose: To assist private helicopter pilot candidates who wish to obtain their commercial helicopter ratings. **Focus:** Aviation. **Qualif.:** Applicant must be about to graduate from an FAA approved Part 147 AMT school or be a recent recipient within the last two years of an Airframe and Powerplant Certificate. **Criteria:** Recipients are selected based on demonstrated interest in the field of aviation.

Funds Avail.: $1,600 (1st place); $1,150 (2nd place); $850 (3rd place); $750 (4th place); $650 (5th place). **Number Awarded: 7. To Apply:** Applicant must submit a completed application form; current resume; and clear copies of any and all FAA international equivalent certificate. **Deadline:** December 30. **Contact:** Jose Orozco at jose.orozco@rotor.com.

4512 ■ Hellenic University Club of Philadelphia (HUC)
PO Box 42199
Philadelphia, PA 19101-2199
Ph: (215) 483-7440
E-mail: hucphila@yahoo.com
URL: www.hucphila.org

4513 ■ Christopher Demetris Scholarships
(Undergraduate/Scholarship)

Purpose: To provide scholarships for students with outstanding academic qualifications and financial need. **Focus:** General studies. **Qualif.:** Applicant must be a student who is a Greek Orthodox and a U.S. citizen. **Criteria:** Selection will be based on merit and financial need.

Funds Avail.: $1,500. **To Apply:** Application form can be obtained from the HUCPhila website. Applicants must complete the application form and mail to Scholarship Chairman. Applicants must also provide one letter of recommendation and scholastic transcripts. **Deadline:** April 20. **Remarks:** Funded by Jack and Olga Demetris in memory of their infant son. **Contact:** hucscholarship@yahoo.com.

4514 ■ Dr. Michael Dorizas Memorial Scholarships *(Undergraduate/Scholarship)*

Purpose: To provide scholarship for students with outstanding academic qualifications and financial need. **Focus:** General studies. **Qualif.:** Applicants must be enrolled full-time in a degree program at an accredited four-year college or university. High school seniors accepted for enrollment in such a degree program may also apply. **Criteria:** Selection will be based on academic merit and financial need.

Funds Avail.: $3,000. **To Apply:** Application form can be obtained from the HUCPhila website. Applicants must complete the application form and mail to Scholarship Chairman. Applicants must also provide one letter of recommendation and scholastic transcripts. **Deadline:** April 20. **Remarks:** Established in honor of the late Dr. Michael Dorizas, a widely respected Philadelphia educator and athlete. **Contact:** Scholarship Chairman at the above address.

4515 ■ Hellenic University Club of Philadelphia Founders Scholarships *(Undergraduate/Scholarship)*

Purpose: To provide scholarships for students with outstanding academic qualifications and financial need. **Focus:** Greek studies. **Qualif.:** Applicants must be of Greek descent; must be U.S. citizens; and must be undergraduate students who have declared majors in Greek studies. **Criteria:** Award is given based on merit.

Funds Avail.: $3,000. **To Apply:** Application form can be obtained from the HUCPhila website. Applicants must complete the application form and mail to Scholarship Chairman. Applicants must also provide one letter of recommendation and scholastic transcripts. **Deadline:** April 20. **Contact:** hucscholarship@yahoo.com.

4516 ■ Nicholas S. Hetos, DDS, Memorial Graduate Scholarships *(Graduate/Scholarship)*

Purpose: To provide scholarships for students with outstanding academic qualifications and financial need. **Focus:** Dentistry. **Qualif.:** Applicants must be senior undergraduate or graduate students with financial need pursuing studies leading to a Doctoral of Dental Medicine (D.M.D.) or Doctoral of Dental Surgery (D.D.S.) Degree. **Criteria:** Selection will be based on merits and financial need.

Funds Avail.: $2,000. **To Apply:** Application form can be obtained from the HUCPhila website. Applicants must send their name and address to Scholarship Chairman. Applicants must also provide one letter of recommendation and scholastic transcripts. **Deadline:** April 20. **Remarks:** Funded by the Hetos family. **Contact:** hucscholarship@yahoo.com.

4517 ■ Dr. Nicholas Padis Memorial Graduate Scholarships *(Graduate/Scholarship)*

Purpose: To provide scholarship for qualified senior undergraduate or graduate students. **Focus:** General studies. **Qualif.:** Applicant must be a full-time senior undergraduate or a graduate student at an accredited university or professional school; must be a U.S. citizen and Greek descent. **Criteria:** Selection will be based on merits and financial need.

Funds Avail.: $5,000. **To Apply:** Application form can be obtained from the HUCPhila website. Applicants must send their name and address to Scholarship Chairman. Applicants must also provide one letter of recommendation

Awards are arranged alphabetically below their administering organizations

and scholastic transcripts. **Deadline:** April 20. **Remarks:** Established in 1986. **Contact:** Scholarship Chairman.

4518 ■ Peter George Pitsakis Memorial Scholarships (Undergraduate/Scholarship)

Purpose: To provide scholarships for students with outstanding academic qualifications and financial need. **Focus:** General studies. **Qualif.:** Applicants must be of Greek descent; must be U.S. citizens; and must be undergraduate students who have declared majors in Greek studies. **Criteria:** Selection will be based on educational merit and financial need.

Funds Avail.: $2,000. **To Apply:** Application form can be obtained from the HUCPhila website. Applicants must complete the application form and mail to Scholarship Chairman. Applicants must also provide one letter of recommendation and scholastic transcripts. **Deadline:** April 20. **Remarks:** Established in accordance with the request of and in memory of Peter G. Pitsakis, a past president of the Hellenic University Club. **Contact:** hucscholarship@yahoo.com.

4519 ■ Dr. Peter A. Theodos Memorial Graduate Scholarships (Graduate/Scholarship)

Purpose: To provide scholarship for students with outstanding academic qualifications and financial need. **Focus:** Medicine. **Qualif.:** Applicants must be senior undergraduate or graduate students with financial need pursuing studies leading to a Doctor of Medicine (M.D.) Degree. **Criteria:** Selection will be based on academic merit and financial need.

Funds Avail.: $2,500. **To Apply:** Application form can be obtained from the HUCPhila website. Applicants must send their name and address to the Scholarship Chairman and provide one letter of recommendation and scholastic transcripts. **Deadline:** April 20. **Remarks:** Established in 1988. **Contact:** Scholarship Chairman at the above address.

4520 ■ Dimitri J. Ververelli Memorial Scholarships (Undergraduate/Scholarship)

Purpose: To provide financial assistance for qualified students pursuing a degree in the fields of Architecture and/or Engineering. **Focus:** Architecture; Engineering. **Qualif.:** Applicants must be of Greek descent; must be U.S. citizens; and must be pursuing a degree in the fields of Architecture and/or Engineering. **Criteria:** Selection will be based on merits and financial need.

Funds Avail.: $2,000. **To Apply:** Application form can be obtained from the HUCPhila website. Applicants must complete the application form and mail to Scholarship Chairman. Applicants must also provide one letter of recommendation and scholastic transcripts. **Deadline:** April 20. **Contact:** hucscholarship@yahoo.com.

4521 ■ Helsell Fetterman L.L.P.
1001 4th Ave., Ste. 4200
Seattle, WA 98154
Ph: (206) 292-1144
Fax: (206) 340-0902
E-mail: hf@helsell.com
URL: www.helsell.com

4522 ■ Richard S. White Fellowships (Undergraduate/Fellowship)

Purpose: To assist in paying the student's tuition. **Focus:** Law. **Qualif.:** Applicants must be second year law students in good standing pursuing a law degree at an ABA-accredited law school; possess an academic record, leadership abilities and a commitment to personal and professional initiatives that indicate promise for a successful legal career; demonstrate an interest and commitment to both the practice areas represented at Helsell Fetterman and to building a practice in the Seattle area. **Criteria:** Scholarship will be based on the committee's criteria.

Funds Avail.: $7,500. **To Apply:** Applicants must prepare a 1- to 2-page personal statement on a topic of their choice that allows the firm to fully evaluate their candidacy and ability to enrich the diversity of the legal community. Completed application form must be submitted together with the following: current resume; copy of final undergraduate transcript and current law school transcript, unofficial is acceptable; legal writing sample up to 10 pages; three professional and/or academic references with contact information.

4523 ■ Hemingway Foundation and Society
PO Box 2770
Winter Park, FL 32789-4499
Ph: (407) 691-1706
Fax: (407) 622-7486
E-mail: hemingwaysocietymembership@gmail.com
URL: www.hemingwaysociety.org

4524 ■ Ernest Hemingway Research Grants (Professional development/Grant)

Purpose: To provide funds for scholars and students who are doing research in the Ernest Hemingway Collection. **Focus:** General studies. **Qualif.:** Applicant must be a scholar and student interested or doing research in Ernest Hemingway Collection. **Criteria:** Grant applications are evaluated on the basis of expected utilization of the Hemingway Collection. Preference is given to dissertation research by Ph.D candidates working in newly opened or relatively unused portions of the collection, but all proposals are welcome and will receive careful consideration.

Funds Avail.: $200-1,000. **To Apply:** Application forms are available at the website; must be accompanied by a brief proposal (three to four pages) in the form of a letter or more describing the planned research, its significance; must submit two letters of recommendation from academic or other appropriate references; must have a sample of your writing, a project budget, and a vitae. Application forms and other supporting materials must be sent to: Grant and Fellowship Coordinator, John F. Kennedy Presidential Library and Museum, Columbia Point, Boston, MA 02125.

4525 ■ Jim & Nancy Hinkle Travel Grants (Postdoctorate/Grant)

Purpose: To defray travel expenses for graduate students who wants to attend the biennial international conferences. **Focus:** General studies. **Qualif.:** Recipients must be members in good standing of the Hemingway Society; must currently be enrolled in a graduate degree program, and must be planning to present a paper at the conference. **Criteria:** Applications are selected by the Hickle Travel Grant Committee and evaluated by the following criteria: clarity, originality, and value in furthering Hemingway scholarship, criticism, or instruction. Application from previous Hinkle winners are welcome, applications from students who have not won before will be given priority.

Funds Avail.: Travel expenses for the biennial international

Awards are arranged alphabetically below their administering organizations

conference. **To Apply:** Application must include the following information: (1) Full name of applicant, (2) address, phone, email, (3) Social Security Number, (4) Paper title & abstract, (5) Degree program and school, (6) Letter of recommendation. Applications should be sent to Hinkle Selection Committee Chair: Suzanne del Gizzo, 380 Wellington Terrace, Jenkintown, PA 19046. **Deadline:** March 1.

4526 ■ Smith-Reynolds Founder Fellowships
(Graduate/Fellowship)

Purpose: To support the students in their research on Ernest Hemingway. **Focus:** General studies. **Qualif.:** Applicant must be a graduate student, independent scholar, or post-doctoral up through the rank of assistant professor. **Criteria:** Applications are ranked by the committee based on the following criteria: clarity, originality, and feasibility, criticism, or instruction; and the likelihood of its publication.

Funds Avail.: $2,000. **To Apply:** Applicant must submit as a Microsoft word attachment or send by mail the following information and agreements: (1) Full name and Social Security Number, (2) Addresses, phone numbers and email address (including summer and between session), (3) Degree program and school, (4) Verification of graduate enrollment status or awarded degree (if appropriate); must have the description of Hemingway Project (200-word limit). **Deadline:** February 1. **Contact:** Application form and supporting documents must be sent to: Prof. Debra A. Moddelmog, Fellowship Committee Chair, Dept. of English, Ohio State University, 421 Denney Hall, 164 W, 17th Ave., Colombus, OH 43210.

4527 ■ Hemophilia Federation of America (HFA)
210 7th St. SE, Ste. 200 B
Washington, DC 20003
Ph: (202) 675-6984
Fax: (972) 616-6211
Free: 800-230-9797
E-mail: info@hemophiliafed.org
URL: www.hemophiliafed.org

4528 ■ Hemophilia Federation of America Educational Scholarships *(Undergraduate/Scholarship)*

Purpose: To assists and advocates for the bleeding disorders community. **Focus:** Hemophilia. **Qualif.:** Applicants must have hemophilia or von Willebrand (VWD) and must be seeking a post-secondary education from a college, university, or trade school; must be members of the bleeding disorders community. Applicants must be able to demonstrate a commitment in improving quality of life by pursuing his/her goals with determination. **Criteria:** Selection will be based on the scholarship Committee of HFA.

Funds Avail.: $1,500. **Number Awarded:** 10. **To Apply:** Applicants must submit a completed application; essay; proof of academic standing; statement of financial need and parents previous year's tax return (if applicant is a dependent, otherwise the applicant's tax return); proof of enrollment; two letters of reference (one professional reference the other from the HTC or physician) **Deadline:** April 30.

4529 ■ Herb Kohl Educational Foundation
PO Box 877
Sheboygan, WI 53082-0877
Ph: (920) 457-1727

E-mail: marggraf@excel.net
URL: www.kohleducation.org

4530 ■ Herb Kohl Educational Foundation Excellence Scholarships *(Undergraduate/Scholarship)*

Purpose: To help graduating high school students pursue an undergraduate education. **Focus:** General studies. **Qualif.:** Applicants must be graduating high school students who intend to enroll in a post-secondary institution, university, college, or vocational/technical college. **Criteria:** Recipients will be chosen for their demonstrated academic potential, outstanding leadership, citizenship, community service and integrity, future, personal, community/society and career goals.

Funds Avail.: $1,000. **Number Awarded:** 100. **To Apply:** Applicants must submit a completed application form.

4531 ■ Herb Kohl Educational Foundation Fellowships *(Professional development/Fellowship)*

Purpose: To recognize the contribution of Wisconsin classroom teachers. **Focus:** General studies. **Qualif.:** Applicants must be Pre-K through Grade 12 Wisconsin teachers who intend to continue teaching for at least the year following the receipt of the fellowship; must be nominated by a parent, teacher, student, community member or administrator. **Criteria:** Educators will be chosen for their superior ability to inspire a love of learning in their students and ability to motivate others through leadership and service within and outside the classroom.

Funds Avail.: $1,000. **Number Awarded:** 100. **To Apply:** Applicants must contact Hern Kohl Educational Foundation office for further information.

4532 ■ Herb Kohl Educational Foundation Initiative Scholarships *(High School/Scholarship)*

Purpose: To recognize students who have not yet received other academic-based scholarships. **Focus:** General studies. **Qualif.:** Applicants must be graduating high school students. **Criteria:** Recipients will be selected based on demonstrated high level of motivation to achieve, have shown strong promise for achieving success in college and beyond, have overcome significant personal obstacles or adversity.

Funds Avail.: $1,000. **Number Awarded:** 85. **To Apply:** Applicants must contact Herb Kohl Educational Foundation office for further information.

4533 ■ Herb Society of America (HSA)
9019 Kirtland Chardon Rd.
Kirtland, OH 44094
Ph: (440) 256-0514
Fax: (440) 256-0541
E-mail: herbs@herbsociety.org
URL: www.herbsociety.org

4534 ■ Nashville Unit Scholarships *(Undergraduate/Scholarship)*

Purpose: To educate its members and the public on the cultivation of herbs and the study of their history and uses. **Focus:** Horticulture. **Qualif.:** Applicants must be permanent residents of Tennessee; must be current college freshman, sophomore or junior students who are American citizens. **Criteria:** Recipients are selected based on financial need and academic performance.

Awards are arranged alphabetically below their administering organizations

Funds Avail.: $2,500. **To Apply:** Applicants must submit a completed application form and two letters of reference. **Deadline:** April 1. **Contact:** Application form and other supporting documents should be sent to: PO Box 150711 Nashville, TN 37215.

4535 ■ Pennsylvania Heartland Unit Scholarships (Undergraduate/Scholarship)

Purpose: To educate its members and the public on the cultivation of herbs and the study of their history and uses. **Focus:** Horticulture. **Qualif.:** Applicants must be third or fourth year students of an associate degree program within the study of horticulture; must be residents of Berks, Montgomery, York, Lancaster or Schuylkill county. **Criteria:** Recipients are selected based on financial need and academic performance.

Funds Avail.: $1,500. **To Apply:** Applicants must submit: a completed application form; two letters of reference from which one must come from an advisor or professor and one from a reference of the student's choice; must submit an official school transcript; and an essay stating their reasons for choosing the field of horticulture and future plans. **Deadline:** April 1. **Contact:** Jeannette Lanshe, jetlan1@aol.com.

4536 ■ South Texas Unit Scholarships (Undergraduate/Scholarship)

Purpose: To educate its members and the public on the cultivation of herbs and the study of their history and uses. **Focus:** Horticulture. **Qualif.:** Applicants must be students who are studying agronomy, horticulture, botany or a closely-related discipline at an accredited four-year college or university; must be either permanent residents of Texas or attending an accredited college or university in Texas; must have completed two full years of college and be entering their junior or senior year of studies. **Criteria:** Recipients are selected based on academic performance and financial need.

Funds Avail.: $1,000. **To Apply:** Applicants must submit a completed application form and recommendation from professor or guidance counselor. **Deadline:** April 1. **Contact:** Application form and other supporting documents should be sent to PO Box 6515 Houston, TX 77265-6515.

4537 ■ Western Reserve Herb Society Scholarships (Undergraduate/Scholarship)

Purpose: To educate its members and the public on the cultivation of herbs and the study of their history and uses. **Focus:** Horticulture. **Qualif.:** Applicants must be: undergraduate students; Ohio residents; studying horticulture or a related field such as landscape architecture or horticultural therapy; planning a career involving teaching/research or work in the public sector; entering their second to fifth year of an undergraduate program at an accredited college or university. **Criteria:** Recipients are selected based on academic performance and financial need.

Funds Avail.: $2,500. **To Apply:** Applicants must submit a completed application form.

4538 ■ Francis Sylvia Zverina Scholarships (Undergraduate/Scholarship)

Purpose: To educate its members and the public on the cultivation of herbs and the study of their history and uses. **Focus:** Horticulture. **Qualif.:** Applicants must be students in good scholastic standing who are studying horticulture or related fields such as landscape architecture or horticultural therapy; must have horticultural career goals involving teaching/research or work in the public sector; must be U.S. citizens; must have completed their second or third year of undergraduate school at an accredited college or university anywhere in United States. **Criteria:** Recipients are selected based on academic records and financial need.

Funds Avail.: $3,000. **Number Awarded:** 2. **To Apply:** Applicants must submit a completed application form.

4539 ■ Hereditary Disease Foundation (HDF)

3960 Broadway, 6th Fl.
New York, NY 10032
Ph: (212) 928-2121
Fax: (212) 928-2172
E-mail: cures@hdfoundation.org
URL: www.hdfoundation.org

4540 ■ Hereditary Disease Foundation Research Grants (Postdoctorate/Grant)

Purpose: To provide support for research focusing on Huntington's disease. **Focus:** Huntington's disease. **Qualif.:** Applicants must be in their post-graduate level. **Criteria:** Applications will be reviewed by the Scientific Advisory Board. Consideration is relevance to treatments and cures for Huntington's disease. Selected applicants will receive a written notification of the funding decision.

Funds Avail.: $50,000. **To Apply:** Applicants must complete a one-page letter of intent (available at the website) consisting of contact information and summary of the proposed research (maximum of 500 words). Application requires an administrative contact, (not to exceed 200 words) project summary, budgets, other current and pending support, biographical sketch, protection of human subjects, protection of animal subjects and study proposal. Send application thru email in PDF and five hard copies to Carl D. Johnson, PhD. **Deadline:** October 15. **Contact:** Hereditary Disease Foundation, Attn: Carl D. Johnson, PhD 3960 Broadway, 6th Fl. New York, NY 10032 USA. carljohnson@hdfoundation.org.

4541 ■ John J. Wasmuth Postdoctoral Fellowships (Postdoctorate/Fellowship)

Purpose: To support research focusing on Huntington's disease. **Focus:** Huntington's disease. **Qualif.:** Applicants must be in their post-graduate level. **Criteria:** Recipients are selected based on merit.

Funds Avail.: $40,500-$56,000. **To Apply:** Applicants must complete the following: completed application form; curriculum vitae of the applicant and the applicant's research sponsor; a letter of support from the sponsor; and two letters of recommendation from two others familiar with the applicant, one of whom is normally the applicant's PhD sponsor. Completed applications should be submitted by email and five hard copies to Carl D. Johnson, PhD. **Deadline:** October 15. **Remarks:** Established in honor of John J. Wasmuth, a member of the Huntington's Disease Collaborative Research. **Contact:** Hereditary Disease Foundation, Attn: Carl D. Johnson, PhD 3960 Broadway, 6th Fl. New York, NY 10032 USA; carljohnson@hdfoundation.org.

4542 ■ Hill Country Master Gardeners

3655 Hwy. 27 E
Kerrville, TX 78028
Ph: (830) 257-6568

Awards are arranged alphabetically below their administering organizations

Fax: (830) 257-6573
E-mail: kerr@ag.tamu.edu
URL: www.hillcountrymastergardeners.org

4543 ■ Hill Country Master Gardeners Horticulture Scholarships *(Graduate, Undergraduate/Scholarship)*

Purpose: To provide financial support to two undergraduate or graduate students at Texas A&M, Texas Tech, Tarleton State or Stephen F. Austin State University. **Focus:** Horticulture. **Qualif.:** Applicants must be pursuing a horticultural sciences degree; must be full-time students (12 hours for undergraduate and nine hours for graduate students) in one of the four universities mentioned; must be in junior level with a GPA of 3.0; must be Texas residents; preference will be given to students residing at Kerr, Kendal, Gillespie and Bandera Counties. **Criteria:** Selection will be based on the evaluation of submitted documents and specific criteria.

Funds Avail.: Total amount of $2,000. **Number Awarded:** 2. **To Apply:** Applicants must submit a completed application form; two letters of recommendation from an instructor and other qualified persons; college transcripts, including the most recent semester, sealed in an envelope. **Deadline:** May.

4544 ■ Hispanic Association of Colleges and Universities (HACU)

8415 Datapoint Dr., Ste. 400
San Antonio, TX 78229
Ph: (210) 692-3805
Fax: (210) 692-0823
E-mail: hacu@hacu.net
URL: www.hacu.net

4545 ■ Bridging the GAP for Hispanic Success Awards *(Undergraduate/Scholarship)*

Purpose: To promote the development of member colleges and universities; to improve access to and the quality of post-secondary educational opportunities for Hispanic students; and to meet the needs of business, industry and government through the development and sharing of resources, information and expertise. **Focus:** Management; Fashion Design. **Qualif.:** Applicants must be full-time or part-time, undergraduate students attending two or four year HACU-member institutions; must possess a minimum cumulative GPA of 3.0. **Criteria:** Recipients are selected based on the demonstrated financial need and ability to meet the specified criteria for the scholarship to which they are applying.

Funds Avail.: $1,000. **To Apply:** Applicants must fill out the application form and must provide documents showing that they are currently enrolled or accepted by a college, university, or institution. **Deadline:** June 5.

4546 ■ Chrysler Foundation Scholarship Awards *(Undergraduate/Scholarship)*

Purpose: To promote the development of member colleges and universities; to improve access to and the quality of post-secondary educational opportunities for Hispanic students; and to meet the needs of business, industry and government through the development and sharing of resources, information and expertise. **Focus:** Electrical engineering; Mechanical engineering; Automotive technology; Marketing and distribution; Accounting; Finance;

Information science and technology; Science. **Qualif.:** Applicants must be full-time undergraduate students attending 2-to-4 year institutions; must possess a minimum cumulative GPA of 3.0. **Criteria:** Recipients are selected based on the demonstrated financial need and ability to meet the specified criteria for the scholarship to which they are applying.

Funds Avail.: $1,980. **To Apply:** Applicants must fill out the application form and must provide documents showing that they are currently enrolled or accepted by a college, university, or institution. **Deadline:** June 5.

4547 ■ HACU/Wal-Mart Achievers Scholarships *(Undergraduate/Scholarship)*

Purpose: To promote the development of member colleges and universities; to improve access to and the quality of post-secondary educational opportunities for Hispanic students; and to meet the needs of business, industry and government through the development and sharing of resources, information and expertise. **Focus:** Business Administration; Management. **Qualif.:** Applicants must be full-time undergraduate students attending two or four year institutions and must possess a minimum cumulative GPA of 3.0. **Criteria:** Recipients are selected based on the demonstrated financial need and ability to meet the specified criteria for the scholarship to which they are applying.

Funds Avail.: $1,000. **To Apply:** Applicants must fill out the application form and must provide any documents showing that they are currently enrolled or accepted by a college, university, or institution.

4548 ■ Hispanic Association of Colleges and Universities Scholarships *(Undergraduate/Scholarship)*

Purpose: To promote the development of member colleges and universities; to improve access to and the quality of post-secondary educational opportunities for Hispanic students; and to meet the needs of business, industry and government through the development and sharing of resources, information and expertise. **Focus:** General studies. **Qualif.:** Applicants must be Hispanic Association of Colleges and Universities member institutions; must be attending a HACU-member institution at the time applications are completed and scholarships are made. **Criteria:** Recipients are selected based on the demonstrated financial need and ability to meet the specified criteria for the scholarship to which they are applying.

Funds Avail.: Varies. **To Apply:** Applicants must fill out the application form and must provide documents showing that they are currently enrolled or accepted by a college, university, or institution. **Deadline:** June 10.

4549 ■ Office Depot Scholarships *(Undergraduate/Scholarship)*

Purpose: To promote the development of member colleges and universities; to improve access to and the quality of post-secondary educational opportunities for Hispanic students; and to meet the needs of business, industry and government through the development and sharing of resources, information and expertise. **Focus:** Business; Marketing and Distribution; Information Science and Technology. **Qualif.:** Applicants must be undergraduate students attending four year institutions and must possess a minimum cumulative GPA of 3.0. **Criteria:** Recipients are selected based on demonstrated financial need and ability to meet the specified criteria for the scholarship which they are applying.

Awards are arranged alphabetically below their administering organizations

Funds Avail.: $1,120. **To Apply:** Applicants must fill out the application form and must provide any documents showing that they are currently enrolled or accepted by a college, university, or institution. **Deadline:** May 28.

4550 ■ NASCAR/Wendell Scott Awards (Graduate, Undergraduate/Scholarship)

Purpose: To promote the development of member colleges and universities; to improve access to and the quality of post-secondary educational opportunities for Hispanic students; and to meet the needs of business, industry and government through the development and sharing of resources, information and expertise. **Focus:** Business; Engineering; Public Relation; Technology; Management. **Qualif.:** Applicants must be full-time or part-time, undergraduate and graduate students attending four year institutions; must possess a minimum cumulative GPA of 3.0. Applying graduate students must be attending school at least on a part-time basis and must possess a minimum cumulative GPA of 3.0. **Criteria:** Recipients are selected based on the demonstrated financial need and ability to meet the specified criteria for the scholarship to which they are applying.

Funds Avail.: $12,500. **To Apply:** Applicants must fill out the application form and must provide any documents showing that they are currently enrolled or accepted by a college, university, or institution. **Deadline:** June 5.

4551 ■ Wachovia Scholars Program
(Undergraduate/Scholarship)

Purpose: To promote the development of member colleges and universities; to improve access to and the quality of post-secondary educational opportunities for Hispanic students; and to meet the needs of business, industry and government through the development and sharing of resources, information and expertise. **Focus:** Finance; Accounting; Business Administration. **Qualif.:** Applicants must be full-time undergraduate students attending two or four year institutions and must have a minimum cumulative GPA of 3.0. **Criteria:** Recipients are selected based on the demonstrated financial need and ability to meet the specified criteria for the scholarship to which they are applying.

Funds Avail.: $1,000. **To Apply:** Applicants must fill out the application form and must provide any documents showing that they are currently enrolled or accepted by a college, university, or institution. **Deadline:** June 5.

4552 ■ Hispanic Association on Corporate Responsibility (HACR)
1444 I St. NW, Ste. 850
Washington, DC 20005
Ph: (202) 835-9672
Fax: (202) 682-0086
E-mail: hacr@hacr.org
URL: www.hacr.org

4553 ■ Hispanic Association on Corporate Responsibility Scholarship Program
(Undergraduate/Scholarship)

Purpose: To provide financial educational assistance to help the next generation of youth reach their full potential. **Focus:** General studies. **Qualif.:** Applicants must be member students of Hispanic Association of Colleges and Universities; must be full-time undergraduate students with minimum of 3.0 GPA at four-year HACU member higher

education institutions who have completed at least 12 undergraduate units of any major with an interest in the entertainment, news, media, and telecommunications industries. **Criteria:** Recipients are evaluated based on academic performance and financial need.

Funds Avail.: $300,000. **To Apply:** Applicants must submit all the required application information.

4554 ■ Hispanic Dental Association (HDA)
3085 Stevenson Dr., Ste. 200
Springfield, IL 62703
Ph: (217) 529-6517
Fax: (217) 529-9120
Free: 800-852-7921
E-mail: hispanicdental@hdassoc.org
URL: www.hdassoc.org

4555 ■ Colgate-Palmolive/HDA Foundation Scholarships (Master's, Postgraduate/ Scholarship)

Purpose: To support students who seek to advance their scientific and applied clinical knowledge in the area of dentistry to further their commitment to aiding and supporting the Hispanic community. **Focus:** Dentistry; Dental hygiene. **Qualif.:** Applicant must be a member of the Hispanic Dental Association who has been accepted into or is currently enrolled in an accredited Masters or above program in a Dentistry Related Field; must have an undergraduate or graduate degree in an oral health related field (dental hygienist, dentistry etc.) from the U.S. or abroad; and must have permanent resident status in the U.S. **Criteria:** Selection is based on students' commitment and dedication to improving the oral health of the Hispanic community; community service (volunteer efforts in school, medical facilities, church, etc.); leadership skills; and scholastic achievement.

Funds Avail.: $10,000. **To Apply:** Applicants must submit a complete application. **Deadline:** July 1. **Contact:** rbrummett@hdassoc.org.

4556 ■ Procter & Gamble Professional Oral Health/HDA Foundation Scholarships
(Undergraduate/Scholarship)

Purpose: To support promising students as they enter into their academic training. **Focus:** Dentistry; Dental hygiene; Dental laboratory technology. **Qualif.:** Applicant must be a student member of the Hispanic Dental Association who has been accepted into an accredited dental, dental hygiene, dental assisting or dental technician program; and must have permanent resident status in the U.S. **Criteria:** Selection is based on students' commitment and dedication to improving the oral health of the Hispanic community; community service (volunteer efforts in school, medical facilities, church, etc.); leadership skills; and scholastic achievement.

Funds Avail.: $1,000. **To Apply:** Applicants must submit a complete application. **Deadline:** July 1. **Contact:** rbrummett@hdassoc.org.

4557 ■ Dr. Juan D. Villarreal/HDA Foundation Scholarships (Undergraduate/Scholarship)

Purpose: To support promising students in their academic training. **Focus:** Dentistry; Dental hygiene. **Qualif.:** Applicant must be a student member of the Hispanic Dental

Awards are arranged alphabetically below their administering organizations

Association who has been accepted into or is currently enrolled in an accredited dental school or dental hygiene program in the state of Texas (student may be at any stage of the undergraduate program, first through fourth year); and must have permanent resident status in the U.S. **Criteria:** Selection is based on students' commitment and dedication to improving the oral health of the Hispanic community; community service (volunteer efforts in school, medical facilities, church, etc.); leadership skills; and scholastic achievement.

Funds Avail.: $500-$1,000. **To Apply:** Applicants must submit a complete application. **Deadline:** July 1. **Contact:** rbrummett@hdassoc.org.

4558 ■ Hispanic Faculty Staff Association (HFSA)

1 University Station, L800
Austin, TX 78712
Ph: (512) 475-7348
URL: www.utexas.edu/staff/hfsa

4559 ■ Jamail/Long Challenge Grant Scholarships *(Graduate, Undergraduate/Scholarship)*

Purpose: To promote communication and to support networking; to serve as a voice for university, educational, professional and cultural Hispanic issues; to promote career growth, development and initial employment; and to provide opportunities for social and cultural interaction for Hispanic professionals. **Focus:** General studies. **Qualif.:** Applicants must be Hispanic students enrolled as full-time undergraduate, graduate or transfer students at the University of Texas, Austin; must maintain satisfactory progress toward completion of their degree requirements as determined by the regular procedures of the Texas Exes. **Criteria:** Recipients are selected based on academic performance.

Funds Avail.: $1,000. **To Apply:** Applicants must complete the online Continuing & Transfer Scholarship Application provided by the Office of Student Financial Services. Applicants must select "Texas Exes Scholarships" on the "Scholarship Choices" page of the application and then enter the correct scholarship code, ESA-HISPANIC, in the space provided. **Deadline:** March 1. **Remarks:** Established by HFSA to recognize the accomplishments of deserving Hispanic students at The University of Texas at Austin.

4560 ■ Hispanic Lawyers Association of Illinois

321 S Plymouth Ct., Ste. 600
Chicago, IL 60604
Ph: (312) 554-2045
E-mail: membership@hlai.org
URL: www.hlai.org

4561 ■ Barbri Scholarships for Bar Preparation *(Undergraduate/Scholarship)*

Purpose: To help increase excellence among individuals pursuing careers in the legal field. **Focus:** Law. **Qualif.:** Program is open to post-graduation law students that secure legal or related employment with a government agency, a non-profit organization, or public interest agency intending to apply in a BARBRI preparation course. **Criteria:** Scholarship is given based on merit.

Funds Avail.: $500-$1,000. **To Apply:** Applicants may download application form at HLAI website. Complete and submit the application form (including the two short essays about the applicant's commitment to public interest law and

to serving the legal and social needs of the Hispanic community). Applicants must also provide a copy of law school transcript. **Deadline:** April 7. **Contact:** Christina Lopez-Nutzman; Wessels and Pautsch, P.C. 35 West Monroe, Suite 1120 Chicago, IL 60603; 312-629-9300 chlopez@chgo.w-p.com.

4562 ■ Kaplan Scholarships *(Undergraduate/Scholarship)*

Purpose: To help increase excellence among individuals pursuing careers in the legal field. **Focus:** Law. **Qualif.:** Program is open to law students that demonstrate a genuine interest in pursuing a legal career. **Criteria:** Scholarship is given based on merit.

Funds Avail.: No specific amount. **To Apply:** Applicants must submit completed application (available at the website) and submit along with two short essays about your commitment to public interest law and to serving the legal and social needs of the Hispanic community. Applicants must also provide a copy of law school transcript. **Deadline:** April 7. **Contact:** Christina Lopez-Nutzman; Wessels and Pautsch, P.C. 35 West Monroe, Suite 1120 Chicago, IL 60603; 312-629-9300 chlopez@chgo.w-p.com.

4563 ■ Hispanic Metropolitan Chamber

PO Box 1837
Portland, OR 97207
Ph: (503) 222-0280
Fax: (503) 243-5597
E-mail: info@hmccoregon.com
URL: www.hmccoregon.com

4564 ■ Hispanic Metropolitan Chamber Scholarships *(Graduate, Undergraduate/Scholarship)*

Purpose: To provide support and encourage Hispanics to pursue higher education. **Focus:** General studies. **Qualif.:** Applicant must be of Hispanic ancestry; residing in Oregon or Clark County Washington; have at least a 2.75 GPA as evidenced by a certified high school or college transcript; and enrolled in an accredited Community College, 4 year University or an accredited Graduate Degree Program. **Criteria:** Selection is based on academic achievements, extracurricular activities in the community and a written essay.

Funds Avail.: No specific amount. **To Apply:** Applicants must submit a completed application form together with the required materials. **Deadline:** January 30.

4565 ■ Hispanic National Bar Association (HNBA)

1900 L St. NW, Ste. 700
Washington, DC 20036
Ph: (202) 223-4777
Fax: (202) 223-2324
URL: www.hnba.com

4566 ■ ABA Legal Opportunity Scholarship Funds *(Undergraduate/Scholarship)*

Purpose: To promote diversity in the legal profession by providing financial assistance to law students attending an ABA-accredited law school. **Focus:** Law. **Qualif.:** Applicants must be students entering their first year in law school; must have achieved a minimum cumulative grade

Awards are arranged alphabetically below their administering organizations

point average of 2.5 on a 4.0 grading scale at their undergraduate degree at the time the application is submitted; must be citizens or permanent residents of the United States. **Criteria:** Committee of ABA members will select the recipients based on their application and financial need.

Funds Avail.: $5,000 renewable up to $15,000. **To Apply:** Applicants must complete the attached application form and must have the following documents: personal statement, recommendation, transcript, and personal, family and educational background. **Deadline:** March 2.

4567 ■ Hispanic Scholarship Fund (HSF)

55 Second St., Ste. 1500
San Francisco, CA 94105
Fax: (415) 808-2302
Free: 877-473-4636
E-mail: info@hsf.net
URL: www.hsf.net

4568 ■ Ford Motor Company Scholarship
Program *(Undergraduate/Scholarship)*

Purpose: To assist graduating high school seniors of Hispanic heritage in obtaining a bachelor's degree. **Focus:** General studies. **Qualif.:** Applicant must be of Hispanic heritage; U.S. citizen or legal permanent resident with a valid permanent resident card or passport stamped I-551; graduating from high school in 2011; have a minimum GPA of 3.0 on a 4.0 scale or equivalent; enrolling full-time in a degree-seeking program at a four-year U.S. accredited institution in the U.S., Puerto Rico, U.S. Virgin Islands or Guam; must apply for federal financing aid using the Free Application for Federal Student Aid (FAFSA) at www.fafsa.ed.gov. **Criteria:** Applicants who participated in the Ford PAS program will be given preference.

Funds Avail.: $2,500. **To Apply:** Applications must be submitted using the HSF online application system; Student Aid Report (SAR); and school or HSF enrollment verification form. Submit all required documents in one envelope. **Remarks:** In partnership with Ford Motor Company Fund.

4569 ■ The Gates Millennium Scholars
(Undergraduate/Scholarship)

Purpose: To promote academic excellence and to provide an opportunity for outstanding students with significant financial need to reach their fullest potential. **Focus:** Mathematics and mathematical sciences; Science; Engineering; Education; Public health; Library and archival sciences. **Qualif.:** Applicant must be a graduating high school senior student; be an African American, American Indian/Alaska Native, Asian Pacific Islander American and Hispanic American heritage; a U.S. citizen or legal permanent resident; have a minimum 3.3 GPA on a 4.0 scale; must demonstrate leadership skills; must demonstrate financial need. **Criteria:** Recipients will be selected based on the merits of the application.

Funds Avail.: No specific amount. **To Apply:** Applicant must complete all three required forms available at the award site www.gmsp.org. American Indian/Alaska Native must submit proof of tribal enrollment or a certificate of descent if selected as finalist. **Deadline:** January 11 (paper applications) January 10 (on-line applications). **Remarks:** Established in 1999 and funded by a grant from the Bill and Melinda Gates Foundation. **Contact:** E-mail all questions to: gmsinfo@hsf.net.

4570 ■ Hispanic Scholarship Fund College
Scholarship Program (HSF) *(Graduate, Undergraduate/Scholarship)*

Purpose: To assist students of Hispanic heritage in obtaining a college degree. **Focus:** General studies. **Qualif.:** Applicant must be of Hispanic heritage; U.S. citizen or legal permanent resident with a valid permanent resident card or passport stamped I-551; have a minimum 3.0 GPA on a 4.0 scale or the equivalent; must apply for federal financing aid using the Free Application for Federal Student Aid (FAFSA) at www.fafsa.ed.gov; must be pursuing his/her first undergraduate of graduate degree; must have plans to enroll full-time in a degree seeking program at a two-year or four-year U.S. accredited institution in the U.S., Puerto Rico, U.S. Virgin Islands or Guam. **Criteria:** Recipients will be selected based on the merits of the application.

Funds Avail.: $1,000 to $5,000. **To Apply:** Applications must be submitted using the HSF online application system; Student Aid Report (SAR); and school or HSF enrollment verification form. Submit all required documents in one envelope. **Deadline:** December 15.

4571 ■ HSBC-North America Scholarship
Program *(Undergraduate/Scholarship)*

Purpose: To provide educational assistance for sophomore students who will be transferring to a four-year college. **Focus:** Accounting; Actuarial science; Advertising; Public relations; Business; Engineering, Computer; Computer and information sciences; Economics; Finance; International trade; Marketing and distribution; Management. **Qualif.:** Applicant must be of Hispanic heritage; U.S. citizen or legal permanent resident with a valid permanent resident card or passport stamped I-551; be a current sophomore or community college student transferring to a four-year college/university and will be a junior status for the upcoming academic year; be enrolled full-time in a degree-seeking program at an accredited institution in the U.S., Puerto Rico, U.S. Virgin Islands or Guam; have a minimum 3.0 GPA on a 4.0 scale or 4.00 on a 5.00 scale; must be majoring in one of the following: Accounting, Business Administration, Economics, Finance and Management; must reside in one of the following states: California, Florida, Illinois, New York, Nevada, Washington, D.C., Virginia and Texas. Applicants must also submit a resume; must have applied for federal financial aid and must be pursuing his/her first undergraduate degree. **Criteria:** Recipients will be selected based on academic achievement, financial need, personal strengths and leadership.

Funds Avail.: No specific amount. **To Apply:** Applicant must use the HSF online application system; Student Aid Report (SAR); and school or HSF enrollment verification form. Submit all required documents in one envelope. **Deadline:** December 15. **Remarks:** In partnership with HSBC.

4572 ■ HSF/Atrisco Heritage Foundation
Scholarship Program *(Graduate, Undergraduate/ Scholarship)*

Purpose: To assist outstanding Latinos who are heirs of the Atrisco Land Grant of New Mexico. **Focus:** General studies. **Qualif.:** Applicant must be of Hispanic heritage; U.S. citizen or legal permanent resident with a valid permanent resident card or passport stamped I-551; have a minimum 2.0 GPA on a 4.0 scale or the equivalent; must apply for federal financing aid using the Free Application for Federal Student Aid (FAFSA) at www.fafsa.ed.gov; must be pursuing his/her first undergraduate of graduate degree;

Awards are arranged alphabetically below their administering organizations

have plans to enroll full-time in a degree seeking program at a two or four year U.S. accredited institution in the U.S., Puerto Rico, U.S. Virgin Islands or Guam. **Criteria:** Recipients will be selected based on the merits of the application. **Funds Avail.:** $2,000. **To Apply:** Applications must be submitted using the HSF online application system. **Deadline:** February 28. **Contact:** Anita Lucero at 505-836-0306.

4573 ■ HSF/Citi Fellows Program
(Undergraduate/Scholarship)

Purpose: To provide financial assistance for Hispanic junior and senior students. **Focus:** Business administration; Economics; Finance. **Qualif.:** Applicant must be of Hispanic heritage; U.S. citizen or legal permanent resident with a valid permanent resident card or passport stamped I-551; a sophomore enrolled full-time at a four-year accredited college/university in the U.S. (must be enrolled as junior in the following academic year); be pursuing a Business Administration, Economics or Finance degree; have a minimum 3.0 GPA on a 4.0 scale or the equivalent; must be a resident or attending college in: New York City metropolitan area; Miami/Fort Lauderdale area; Tampa, Florida; Dallas, Texas; Austin, Texas; Los Angeles, California; San Francisco Bay Area, California. Or must attend college at: Columbia University, Cornell University, Dartmouth College, Duke University, Georgetown University, Harvard University, New York University, Northwestern University, Princeton University, Rutgers University, Stanford University, University of California - Los Angeles, University of Chicago, University of Pennsylvania, University of Virginia, University of Texas at Austin, or Yale University. **Criteria:** Recipients will be selected based on the merits of the

Funds Avail.: $10,000. **To Apply:** Applicants must use the HSF online application system. **Deadline:** January 31. **Remarks:** Fellows will be paired with a Citi employee as a professional mentor and offer career guidance.

4574 ■ HSF/General Motors Scholarship Program *(Undergraduate/Scholarship)*

Purpose: To provide financial resources for outstanding Latinos pursuing degrees in engineering and business. **Focus:** Electrical engineering; Engineering, Industrial; Manufacturing; Mechanical engineering; Accounting; Business administration; Economics; Finance; Personnel administration/human resources. **Qualif.:** Applicants must be graduating high school seniors or current undergraduate students; must be of Hispanic heritage; U.S. citizens or legal permanent residents with a valid permanent resident card or passport stamped I-551; enrolled full-time in a degree-seeking program at any four-year accredited institution in the U.S., Puerto Rico, U.S. Virgin Islands or Guam; have a minimum 3.0 GPA on a 4.0 scale or the equivalent; pursue degrees in Engineering, Business or Human Resources; must apply for federal financing aid using the Free Application for Federal Student Aid (FAFSA) at www-.fafsa.ed.gov. For semi-finalists, applicants must complete the GM Online Assessment. **Criteria:** Applicants who best meet the requirements will be given preference.

Funds Avail.: $2,500. **To Apply:** Applicants must use the HSF online application system. **Deadline:** July 15. **Remarks:** Given in partnership with General Motors (GM).

4575 ■ HSF/IDT Hope High School Scholarship Program *(Undergraduate/Scholarship)*

Purpose: To assist graduating Hispanic high school seniors in obtaining a bachelor's degree. **Focus:** General studies.

Qualif.: Applicant must be of Hispanic heritage; must reside in the areas: Maryland, Virginia, Washington D. C., metropolitan areas of New York City or Newark, or any legal resident of U.S. with a valid card or passport stamped I-551; have a minimum GPA of 3.0 on a 4.0 scale; enrolling full-time in a degree-seeking program at a four-year U.S. accredited institution such as: Puerto Rico, U.S. Virgin Islands or Guam; must apply for federal financing aid using the Free Application for Federal Student Aid (FAFSA) at www.fafsa.ed.gov; or either be a dependent of an IDT employee. **Criteria:** Recipients will be selected based on academic achievement, financial need, personal strengths and leadership.

Funds Avail.: $10,600. **To Apply:** Applicant must submit an application using the HSF online application system; Student Aid Report (SAR); and school or HSF enrollment verification form. Submit all required documents in one envelope.

4576 ■ HSF/Nissan Community College Transfer Scholarship Program *(Undergraduate/ Scholarship)*

Purpose: To support outstanding Community College Transfer Students. **Focus:** Business; Engineering; Communications; Media arts. **Qualif.:** Applicants must be of Hispanic heritage; U.S. citizen or legal permanent resident with a valid permanent resident card or passport stamped I-551; currently enrolled part-time or full-time at a community college; planning to transfer and enroll full-time in a degree-seeking program at a four-year U.S. accredited institution; must reside or transfer to a four-year institution in Atlanta, Georgia; Chicago Illinois; Greater Dallas/Forth Worth, Texas; Jackson/Canton, Mississippi; Los Angeles, California; Nashville, Tennessee; Northern California; New York City/New Jersey; be pursuing a degree in Business, Engineering, Communications or Media Arts; have a minimum GPA of 3.0 on a 4.0 scale; must apply for federal financing aid using the Free Application for Federal Student Aid (FAFSA) at www.fafsa.ed.gov. **Criteria:** Preference will be given to applicants who will best meet the requirements.

Funds Avail.: $5,000. **To Apply:** Applications must be submitted using the HSF online application system. **Deadline:** March 31. **Remarks:** In partnership with Nissan North America, Inc. **Contact:** Scholarship Office, 318 N 6th St., Terre Haute, IN 47809; Phone: 812-237-2121; Email: scholarships@indstate.edu.

4577 ■ HSF/Wal-Mart Stores Inc. Scholarship Program *(Graduate, Undergraduate/Scholarship)*

Purpose: To provide financial assistance for students of Hispanic heritage. **Focus:** Marketing and distribution; Accounting; Business; Finance; Management; Computer and information sciences; Information science and technology; Civil engineering; Construction; Electrical engineering; Geology; Engineering, Industrial; Fashion design; Law; **Qualif.:** Applicant must be of Hispanic heritage; U.S. citizen or legal permanent resident with a valid permanent resident card or passport stamped I-551; enrolled as sophomore, junior, senior undergraduate or First or Second year Master student in a full-time degree-seeking program at an accredited U.S. institution, Puerto Rico, U.S. Virgin Islands or Guam; have a minimum 3.0 GPA on a 4.0 scale; must apply for Federal Financing Aid; pursuing his/her first undergraduate or graduate degree. Undergraduate students must be majoring in: Marketing, Accounting, Business, Finance, Management, Computer Science, Computer Programming, Information Technology (IT), Civil Engineering, Construction, Electrical Engineering, Environmental/

Awards are arranged alphabetically below their administering organizations

Geological Engineering, Industrial Engineering and Fashion. Master's students must be majoring in: Business, Finance, Marketing, Civil Engineering, Construction, Electrical Engineering, Environmental/Geological Engineering and Law. **Criteria:** Applicants who best meet the requirements will be given preference.

Funds Avail.: $2,500. **To Apply:** Applications must be submitted using the HSF online application system. **Remarks:** In partnership with Wal-Mart Stores, Inc.

4578 ■ Marathon Oil Corporation College Scholarship Program *(Graduate, Undergraduate/ Scholarship)*

Purpose: To provide financial assistance for those who are studying engineering. **Focus:** Chemical engineering; Civil engineering; Electrical engineering; Mechanical engineering; Petroleum engineering; Geology; Geophysics; Accounting; Marketing and distribution; Land management; Transportation; Logistics; Engineering, Petroleum **Qualif.:** Applicants must be of Hispanic American, African American, Asian Pacific Islander American or American Indian/Alaskan Native heritage; U.S. citizens or legal permanent residents with a valid Social Security Number and a permanent resident card or passport stamped I-551; have a minimum 3.0 GPA on a 4.0 scale; a sophomore majoring in chemical engineering, civil engineering, electrical engineering, mechanical engineering, petroleum engineering, geology, geophysics, accounting, marketing, global procurement or supply chain management, environmental health & safety, energy management or petroleum land management, transportation & logistics or geotechnical engineering; or a senior pursuing a Masters degree in geology or geophysics; must participate in a possible paid summer internship opportunity in Marathon Oil Corporation; must apply for federal financing aid using the Free Application for Federal Student Aid (FAFSA) at www.fafsa.ed.gov. **Criteria:** Preference will be given to the applicants who best meet the requirements.

Funds Avail.: $30,000. **To Apply:** Applications must be submitted using the HSF online application system. **Deadline:** November 15. **Remarks:** Scholars will be paired with a Marathon Oil Corporation employee as a professional mentor.

4579 ■ McNamara Family Creative Arts Project Grants *(Graduate, Undergraduate/Grant)*

Purpose: To provide financial assistance for creative arts-related undergraduate and graduate students beginning or completing an art project. **Focus:** Art; Media arts; Broadcasting; Filmmaking; Performing arts; Communications; Writing. **Qualif.:** Applicant must be of Hispanic heritage; U.S. citizen or legal permanent resident with a valid permanent resident card or passport stamped I-551; enrolled full-time undergraduate or graduate student in a degree-seeking program at a U.S. accredited institution in the U.S., Puerto Rico or U.S. Virgin Islands in the upcoming academic year; pursuing a major in Arts, including but not limited to media, film, performing arts, communications or writing; have a minimum 3.0 GPA on a 4.0 scale; must apply for federal financing aid using the Free Application for Federal Student Aid (FAFSA) at www.fafsa.ed.gov. **Criteria:** Grants will be given to applicants who best meet the requirements.

Funds Avail.: $15,000. **To Apply:** Applicants must submit (600 words or less) project summary; (three-page) project description; (one-page) budget sheet; resume; portfolio cover sheet; (two copies) portfolio/work samples; two cop-

ies of an audio or video recording for performance-based art; maximum of five slides, compact disc or photographs for visual art category; and samples of work for the category of writing. **Deadline:** December 15. **Remarks:** In partnership with the McNamara Family Foundation.

4580 ■ Peierls Rising Star Scholarship Program *(Undergraduate/Scholarship)*

Purpose: To provide financial assistance for current high school seniors from Colorado and Texas. **Focus:** General studies. **Qualif.:** Applicant must be of Hispanic heritage; U.S. citizen or legal permanent resident with a valid permanent resident card or passport stamped I-551; have a minimum GPA of 2.50 and maximum of 2.99 on a 4.0 scale; enrolling full-time in a degree-seeking program at a four-year U.S. accredited institution in the U.S., Puerto Rico, U.S. Virgin Islands or Guam; must apply for federal financing aid using the Free Application for Federal Student Aid (FAFSA) at www.fafsa.ed.gov; reside in Colorado or Texas. Applicants must have participated in of the pre-collegiate programs: Colorado UpLift; CU-Denver Pre-Collegiate Program; College Summit Peer Leaders; Colorado "I Have A Dream"; Denver Scholarship Foundation; Big Brothers/Big Sisters of South Texas; CAMP; Communities in Schools; HSF Peer Counseling Program; UTSA Early Outreach Program; UTSA G-Force Student Mentorship; UTSA Talent Search; UTSA Upward Bound. **Criteria:** Scholarships will be given to applicants who will best meet the requirements.

Funds Avail.: No specific amount. **To Apply:** Applicants must apply online. Download and mail the HSF Recommender Form to Hispanic Scholarship Fund: Peierls Rising Star Scholarship Program 55 Second St., Ste. 1500 San Francisco, CA 94105.

4581 ■ Toyota High School Scholarship Program *(Undergraduate/Scholarship)*

Purpose: To provide financial resources to assist outstanding Latino high school graduates. **Focus:** Accounting; Actuarial science; Advertising; Architecture; Automotive technology; Bioengineering; Business; Chemical engineering; Civil engineering; Engineering, Computer; Electronics; Computer and information sciences; Construction; Drafting; Economics; Education; Education, Bilingual and cross-cultural; Education, Early childhood; Education, Special; Counseling/Guidance; Electrical engineering; Engineering; Environmental design; Environmental science; Geology; Educational administration; Education-Curricula; Personnel administration/ human resources; Industrial design; Engineering, Industrial; Information science and technology; Management; Marketing and distribution; International trade; Manufacturing; Mechanical engineering; Engineering, Nuclear; Public administration; Public relations; Transportation. **Qualif.:** Applicant must be of Hispanic heritage; U.S. citizen or legal permanent resident with a valid permanent resident card or passport stamped I-551; have a minimum GPA of 3.0 on a 4.0 scale or equivalent; must apply for federal financing aid using the Free Application for Federal Student Aid (FAFSA) at www.fafsa.ed.gov; enrolling as full-time freshman at: Arizona State University; Central Missouri University; Colorado State University, Pueblo; Cornell University; Ferris State; Florida International University; Harvard University; Indiana University; Massachusetts Institute of Technology; New York University; Northwestern University; Pennsylvania Tech College; Pittsburg State University; Southern Illinois University; Stanford University; Texas A&M University; University of Arizona; University of California, Berkeley; University of California,

Awards are arranged alphabetically below their administering organizations

Davis; University of California, Los Angeles; University of California, San Diego; University of Florida; University of Houston; University of Illinois at Chicago; University of Illinois at Urbana-Champaign; University of Michigan; University of New Mexico; University of Pennsylvania; University of Southern California; University of Texas at Austin; University of Texas at El Paso; University of Texas at San Antonio; University of Texas, Pan American; or Weber State University. Applicants must pursue a degree in: Accounting; Actuarial Science; Advertising; Architecture; Automotive Technology; Bio-Engineering; Business; Chemical Engineering; Civil Engineering; Computer Electronics; Computer Engineering; Computer Information Systems (CIS); Computer Programming; Computer Science; Construction; Drafting/CAD; Economics; Education Admin./Leadership; Education/Teaching; Education: Bilingual; Education: Early Childhood/ Elementary; Education: Special; Educational Counseling; Electrical Engineering; Engineering; Environmental Design/Landscaping; Environmental Management/Science; Environmental/Geological Engineering; Human Resource Management; Industrial Design; Industrial Engineering; Information Technology (IT); International Business; Management; Management Information Systems (MIS); Manufacturing Engineering; Marketing; Materials/ Manufacturing; Mechanical Engineering; Network Administration; Non-Profit Management; Nuclear Engineering; Office Administration; Public Administration; Public Relations; Supply Chain Management; or Transportation. **Criteria:** Preference will be given to the applicants who best meet the requirements.

Funds Avail.: $5,000. **To Apply:** Applications must be submitted using the HSF online application system. **Remarks:** In partnership with Toyota Motor Sales, USA.

4582 ■ TU@UT HSF College Scholarship Program *(Undergraduate/Scholarship)*

Purpose: To provide financial assistance for high school seniors entering the University of Texas at Austin. **Focus:** General studies. **Qualif.:** Applicant must be of Hispanic heritage; U.S. citizen or legal permanent resident with a valid permanent resident card or passport stamped I-551; must apply by March 1 for federal financing aid using the Free Application for Federal Student Aid (FAFSA) at www.fafsa.ed.gov; have demonstrated financial need; plan to enroll full-time at the University of Texas at Austin; be a graduate of one of the following high schools: Harlingen, Harlingen South, Rio Hondo, San Benito, Los Fresnos, Gladys Porter, Simon Rivera, James Pace, Homer Hanna, Lopez, John H. Reagan, Sidney Lanier, William B. Travis **Criteria:** Applicants who are Pell grant eligible and those who have unmet needs are given priority.

Funds Avail.: $2,500. **To Apply:** Applications must be submitted using the HSF online application system. **Contact:** scholar1@hsf.net.

4583 ■ University Alliance HSF/UGA College Scholarship Program *(Undergraduate/ Scholarship)*

Purpose: To provide financial assistance for students who are classified as Georgia residents. **Focus:** General studies. **Qualif.:** Applicant must be of Hispanic heritage; U.S. citizen or legal permanent resident with a valid permanent resident card or passport stamped I-551; must apply by March 1 for federal financing aid using the Free Application for Federal Student Aid (FAFSA) at www.fafsa.ed.gov; must demonstrate financial need; have a minimum 3.0 GPA on a 4.0 scale; plan to enroll full-time at the University of Georgia. **Criteria:** Applicants who are Pell grant eligible

and have demonstrated financial need are given priority.

Funds Avail.: $2,500. **To Apply:** Applicants must use the HSF online application system in applying for the scholarship. **Deadline:** January 31. **Remarks:** Students planning to enroll at University of Georgia must be continuing graduates or transfer students.

4584 ■ Valley Alliance of Mentors for Opportunities and Scholarship Program (VAMOS) *(Undergraduate/Scholarship)*

Purpose: To help high school seniors of Hispanic heritage from Hidalgo County in Texas obtain a bachelor's degree. **Focus:** General studies. **Qualif.:** Applicants must be of Hispanic heritage; U.S. citizen or legal permanent resident with a valid permanent resident card or passport stamped I-551; graduating high school from Hidalgo County, Texas; belonging to the top 25% of high school graduating class; have a minimum GPA of 3.0 on a 4.0 scale or equivalent; plan to enroll full-time in a degree-seeking program at a four-year U.S. accredited institution in the U.S., Puerto Rico, U.S. Virgin Islands or Guam; apply for federal financing aid using the Free Application for Federal Student Aid (FAFSA) at www.fafsa.ed.gov. **Criteria:** Applicants who best meet the requirements will be given preference.

Funds Avail.: $5,000 per year. **To Apply:** Applications must be submitted using the HSF online application system. **Deadline:** January 31.

4585 ■ Wells Fargo Scholarship Program *(Graduate, Undergraduate/Scholarship)*

Purpose: To assist college students who are interested in financial and banking based careers. **Focus:** Banking; Finance. **Qualif.:** Applicants must be of Hispanic heritage; U.S. citizens or permanent residents with a valid card or passport stamped I-551; sophomores enrolled full-time at a four-year accredited college/university in the U.S. (must be enrolled as juniors in the following academic year); pursuing a degree in Business, Economics, Finance, Accounting or IT, including CIS, MIS and Computer Engineering; have a minimum 3.0 GPA on a 4.0 scale or the equivalent; must apply for Federal Financing Aid. **Criteria:** Priority will be given to students from the following universities: Arizona State University, California State University - Fresno, California State University - Fullerton, California State University - San Francisco, Columbia University, Iowa State University, San Jose State University, Santa Clara University, Stanford University, Texas A&M University, University of Arizona, University of California - Berkeley, University of California - Davis, University of California - Los Angeles, University of California - San Diego, University of Minnesota, University of Southern California, University of Texas at Austin, University of Washington. Priority will also be given to residents of: Alaska, Arizona, California, Colorado, Iowa, Idaho, Illinois, Indiana, Michigan, Minnesota, Montana, Nebraska, Nevada, New Mexico, North Dakota, Ohio, Oregon, South Dakota, Texas, Utah, Washington, Wisconsin, Wyoming.

Funds Avail.: $2,000. **To Apply:** Applicants must use the HSF online application system; Student Aid Report (SAR); and school or HSF enrollment verification form. Submit all required documents in one envelope. **Deadline:** December 15. **Remarks:** In partnership with Wells Fargo.

4586 ■ Western Governors University Scholarship Program *(Undergraduate/Scholarship)*

Purpose: To provide financial assistance for new students of Western Governors University. **Focus:** General studies.

Awards are arranged alphabetically below their administering organizations

Qualif.: Applicants must be of Hispanic heritage; U.S. citizens or legal residents with a valid resident card or passport stamped I-551; have a minimum 3.0 GPA on a 4.0 scale or the equivalent; must apply for federal financing aid using the Free Application for Federal Student Aid (FAFSA) at www.fafsa.ed.gov; be enrolled at Western Governors University. **Criteria:** Priority will be given to those who attend the Town Hall Meeting.

Funds Avail.: $2,500. **To Apply:** Applicants must use the HSF online application system.

4587 ■ Historians of Islamic Art Association (HIAA)

UNC-Chapel Hill
115 S Columbia St.
Chapel Hill, NC 27514
Fax: (919) 962-0722
E-mail: historiansofislamicart@gmail.com
URL: www.historiansofislamicart.org

4588 ■ HIAA Graduate Student Travel Grants
(Graduate/Grant)

Purpose: To defray the travel costs of students who are presenting papers at the Annual Meeting. **Focus:** General studies. **Qualif.:** Applicants must be graduate students. **Criteria:** Preference will be given to applicants whose papers will be presented at HIAA-sponsored panels.

Funds Avail.: $500. **To Apply:** Applicants must submit a curriculum vitae, an outline of the projected travel expenses and an abstract paper. Applicants must also forward a proof of acceptance of the paper. **Deadline:** December 12 or July 1. **Contact:** Materials must be submitted to Dr. Nancy Micklewright.

4589 ■ Margaret B. Sevcenko Prize in Islamic Art and Culture *(Doctorate/Prize)*

Purpose: To support unpublished articles written by young scholars on any aspect of Islamic visual culture. **Focus:** Culture; Art history. **Qualif.:** Applicants must be scholars (pre-dissertation to three years after the PhD degree) on any aspect of Islamic visual culture. **Criteria:** Selection will be based on submitted articles.

Funds Avail.: $500. **To Apply:** An attachment of the paper must be in DOC., .DOCX, or .PDF format with the author's contact information. A letter of recommendation should be sent separately by an advisor or referee through e-mail. **Contact:** Submissions must be directed to Bernard O'Kane or e-mail bokane@aucegypt.edu.

4590 ■ Ho-Chunk Nation

Tribal Office Bldg.
W9814 Airport Rd.
Black River Falls, WI 54615
Ph: (715) 284-9343
Fax: (715) 284-2632
Free: 800-294-9343
URL: www.ho-chunknation.com

4591 ■ Josephine P. White Eagle Graduate Fellowships *(Graduate, Master's, Doctorate/ Fellowship)*

Purpose: To provide funding to Ho-Chunk student members to complete their Master's and/or Doctoral degree at a

non-profit Title IV institution. **Focus:** Education; Business; Health sciences; Law. **Qualif.:** Applicants must be enrolled members of the Ho-Chunk Nation; must be accepted into a non-profit Title IV institution offering graduate level degrees within the borders or jurisdiction of the United States. Applicants must be interested in the fields of Education, Business, Health Sciences and Law; must be enrolled in a full-time basis; must have GPA of 3.0 on a 4.0 scale. Applicants who are accepted in an approved Title IV law school must be accredited by the American Bar Association. **Criteria:** Applicants will be evaluated based on submitted materials.

Funds Avail.: No specific amount. **To Apply:** Applicants must complete the application form; must submit a letter of acceptance, an official transcript from all prior post-secondary instutions attended, a 500-1000-word personal essay, three letters of recommendation from non-related persons, graduate outline and the Higher Education Division's academic plan, official class schedule, Ho-Chunk Nation background check and written verification of application for funding from minimum of two other sources.

4592 ■ Joseph A. Holmes Safety Association (JAHSA)

PO Box 9375
Arlington, VA 22219
Ph: (703) 235-0249
Fax: (202) 693-9571
E-mail: mail@holmessafety.org
URL: www.holmessafety.org

4593 ■ Joseph A. Holmes Safety Association Scholarships *(Graduate, Undergraduate/ Scholarship)*

Purpose: To provide financial aid to students in the pursuit of education related to mine safety to result in safer mines and healthier environments within the mining industry. **Focus:** Mining. **Qualif.:** Applicant must be a U.S. citizen or permanent resident (green-card holder); pursuing a career in the mining industry, safety and health-related field; a high school graduate enrolled in a college/university degree program; or an undergraduate student currently enrolled in a college/university degree program; or a graduate of a college/university pursuing a graduate degree. **Criteria:** Selection is based on demonstrated outstanding academic achievement, financial need, GPA, leadership and future career interest in a mine related field.

Funds Avail.: No specific amount. **To Apply:** Applicants must submit a completed application form together with transcript of grades for the last three years of completed education; completed Financial Disclosure Information; essay on "Why I am pursuing a degree in mining or in a mine safety/health-related field"; and a list of extracurricular activities and/or a list of other academic achievements. Mail Completed Application to: Sylvia Ortiz, Committee Chairperson, University of Texas at Austin, c/o Joseph A. Holmes Scholarship Program, PO Box 7518 Austin, TX 78713-7518. **Deadline:** May 1. **Contact:** Sylvia Ortiz at s.ortiz@mail.utexas.edu.

4594 ■ Holocaust and Human Rights Center of Maine (HHRC)

University of Maine at Augusta
46 University Dr.
Augusta, ME 04330-1644
Ph: (207) 621-3530

Awards are arranged alphabetically below their administering organizations

E-mail: infohhrc@maine.edu
URL: www.hhrc.uma.edu

4595 ■ Lawrence Alan Spiegel Remembrance Scholarships *(Undergraduate/Scholarship)*

Purpose: To provide financial assistance for high school students residing in Maine. **Focus:** General studies. **Qualif.:** Applicants must be high school seniors or home-schoolers who are residents of Maine and who have been accepted at any accredited and Title IV eligible college, university or technical school. **Criteria:** Applicants are evaluated by a panel of judges based on submitted essay.

Funds Avail.: $1,000. **To Apply:** Applicants must write an essay on "Why is it important that the remembrance, history and lessons of the Holocaust be passed to a new generation?" The essay must not exceed four pages, must be double-spaced and be accompanied by a self-addressed, stamped envelope and a completed application. **Deadline:** March 31.

4596 ■ Herbert Hoover Presidential Library Association (HHPLA)

PO Box 696
West Branch, IA 52358
Ph: (319) 643-5327
Fax: (319) 643-2391
Free: 800-828-0475
E-mail: info@hooverassociation.org
URL: www.hooverassociation.org

4597 ■ Herbert Hoover Uncommon Student Awards *(Undergraduate/Scholarship)*

Purpose: To encourage academic excellence and innovativeness among young students of Iowa by providing educational assistance. **Focus:** General Studies. **Qualif.:** Applicant must be a junior in an Iowa high school or a home schooled program in the fall of 2010; program is not open to the child or grandchild of a staff member or trustee of the Hoover Library Association, Library-Museum or National Historic Site. **Criteria:** Evaluations will be based on the project proposal and letters of recommendation of selected 15 students from Iowa High School. (Grades, test score, essays and financial need are not evaluated).

Funds Avail.: $5,000. **Number Awarded:** 3. **To Apply:** Applicants must submit a completed application form, project proposal and two letters of recommendation. Forms are available at the website and must be sent to Hoover Library Association. **Deadline:** March 31. **Contact:** Delene McConnaha at 800-828-0475, E-mail: scholarship@hooverassociation.org.

4598 ■ Hope for the Warriors

1335 Western Blvd., Ste. E
PMB 48
Jacksonville, NC 28546
Ph: (910) 938-1817
Fax: (910) 938-1805
Free: 877-246-7349
E-mail: info@hopeforthewarriors.org
URL: www.hopeforthewarriors.org

4599 ■ Hope for the Warriors Spouses Scholarships *(Graduate, Master's, Undergraduate, Vocational/Occupational/Scholarship)*

Purpose: To identify, recognize and reward exceptional spouses to aid in their continued education at a reputable, accredited college or trade school as they assume critical roles in the financial well being of their families. **Focus:** General studies. **Qualif.:** Applicant must possess a valid military ID card and be the legal spouse of a U.S. military member who was wounded/injured or killed in the line of duty between 2001 and the present; currently reside in the United States; intend to make application to or be currently enrolled in an accredited college or trade school, in pursuit of a bachelors/masters degree or vocational program pursuing certification; and must show proof of satisfactory academic progress (score of at least 650 on the GED, a high school diploma with a 2.6 overall GPA based on a 4.0 scale or similar rating of current studies if within the last five years). **Criteria:** Selection is based on eligibility, commitment to succeed as indicated by academic achievement, personal goals, letters of recommendation, resume and an original essay response.

Funds Avail.: $5,000. **Number Awarded:** 5. **To Apply:** Applicants must submit a completed application form along with the proof of service, proof of injury/death, original essay, two-page questionnaire and two letters of recommendation. **Contact:** Questions can be addressed to Kathi Delay or email at kathi@hopeforthewarriors.org.

4600 ■ Hormel Foods Corp.

1 Hormel Pl.
Austin, MN 55912-3673
Ph: (507) 437-5611
Fax: (302) 655-5049
E-mail: media@hormel.com
URL: www.hormel.com

4601 ■ Hormel Foods Charitable Trust Scholarships *(Undergraduate/Scholarship)*

Purpose: To help academically-talented students to obtain college scholarships. **Focus:** General studies. **Qualif.:** Applicants must be high school senior students who will enter an accredited college. **Criteria:** Recipients are selected based on financial need, scholastic abilities, involvement in school or community activities and leadership qualities.

Funds Avail.: No specific amount. **To Apply:** Applicants must submit a completed application form to Julie H. Craven, Administrator, Hormel Foods Charitable Trust. **Deadline:** January 10. **Contact:** Julie H. Craven at the above address.

4602 ■ Hospitality Association of South Carolina

1122 Lady St., Ste. 1210
Columbia, SC 29201
Ph: (803) 765-9000
Fax: (803) 252-7136
Free: 800-803-4272
E-mail: info@schospitality.org
URL: www.schospitality.org

4603 ■ South Carolina Tourism and Hospitality Educational Foundation Scholarships *(Undergraduate/Scholarship)*

Purpose: To provide educational assistance for students who demonstrate an interest in and commitment to the hospitality (restaurant, lodging tourism) industry. **Focus:** Travel and tourism. **Qualif.:** Applicants must be currently employed in the hospitality industry and/or enrolled in an industry-related educational program at an accredited

Awards are arranged alphabetically below their administering organizations

institution. **Criteria:** Recipients are selected based on presentation of application; strength of letters of recommendation; a well-written and within word count essay; industry-related work experience and GPA. Preference will be given to applicants who will be classified as full-time students.

Funds Avail.: No specific amount. **To Apply:** Applicants must submit a completed application form; three letters of reference; three completed Character Reference Forms; current official transcript; and a double-spaced essay (minimum of 500 words and maximum of 1,000 words). **Contact:** To have an application form, applicants must contact Xavier Meier at the above address; E-mail xavier@schospitality.org.

4604 ■ South Carolina Undergraduate Scholarships (Undergraduate/Scholarship)

Purpose: To encourage educational pursuits by providing financial assistance. **Focus:** Culinary arts. **Qualif.:** Applicants must be enrolled in a post-secondary restaurant/hospitality program and must be attending an accredited post college or university in South Carolina. **Criteria:** Recipients are selected based on financial need and academic performance.

Funds Avail.: No specific amount. **To Apply:** Applicants must submit a completed application form; three letters of reference; three completed character reference forms; current official transcript; and (minimum of 500 words and maximum of 1,000 words, double-spaced) essay. **Deadline:** June 1. **Contact:** Application form and supporting documents should be sent to Xavier Meier at the above address; E-mail: xavier@schospitality.org.

4605 ■ Houghton Mifflin Co.
222 Berkeley St.
Boston, MA 02116-3748
Ph: (617) 351-5000
Fax: (617) 351-1105
E-mail: investor_relations@hmco.com
URL: www.hmco.com

4606 ■ Gerda and Kurt Klein Scholarships
(High School/Scholarship)

Purpose: To provide financial assistance to high school student working to affect change in the community. **Focus:** General studies. **Qualif.:** Applicant must be a high school student who works to affect change in the community by fostering ethnic and religious tolerance and acting against bigotry and hatred. **Criteria:** Award is given based on the submitted application materials.

Funds Avail.: $10,000. **Number Awarded:** 1. **To Apply:** Applicant must submit a completed scholarship application form; 500-word essay; letter of recommendation and official high school transcript in one envelope to Gerda and Kurt Klein Scholarships. **Deadline:** August 31. **Contact:** Houghton Mifflin Harcourt Scholarships 6277 Sea Harbor Drive Orlando, FL 32887.

4607 ■ House of Puerto Rico San Diego
PO Box 81982
San Diego, CA 92138
Ph: (619) 234-3445
E-mail: hprsd@houseofpuertorico.com
URL: www.houseofpuertorico.com

4608 ■ Casilda Pagan Educational/Vocational Scholarships (Graduate, Undergraduate/Scholarship)

Purpose: To assist individuals attain their educational and professional goals. **Focus:** General studies. **Qualif.:** Applicants must be high school seniors, graduates, or college/post-graduate students; must be current active members of House of Puerto Rico San Diego or San Diego County residents of Puerto Rican descent who have contributed at least 10 hours of community service through HPRSD. **Criteria:** Evaluations will be based on need, goal, motivation, application and contribution.

Funds Avail.: No specific amount. **To Apply:** Applicants must submit a personal essay (minimum of 250 words) including educational goals, financial needs, contribution to community service through the house of Puerto Rico, prior history of community service; proof of current enrollment in an educational or vocational institution; transcripts reflecting most recent academic achievement; three recommendation letters from teachers, counselors, employers or community leaders; completed application form; any additional materials that could enhance application. **Deadline:** July 31. **Contact:** Joe Carballo at jcarballo@san.rr.com.

4609 ■ Houston Geological Society (HGS)
14811 St. Marys Ln., Ste. 250
Houston, TX 77079
Ph: (713) 463-9476
Fax: (281) 679-5504
E-mail: office@hgs.org
URL: www.hgs.org

4610 ■ W.L. Calvert Memorial Scholarships (Graduate/Scholarship)

Purpose: To financially assist graduate students to pursue a career in some area of economic geology. **Focus:** Earth sciences. **Qualif.:** Applicants must be graduate students who are admitted to a graduate degree program leading to an M.S. or PhD at any accredited U.S. college or university; must be U.S. citizens who are interested in earth sciences or any related field of study. **Criteria:** Applicants will be chosen based on academic record, demonstrated potential to complete graduate degree requirements as attested by professional earth scientists in academia, government and industry. Financial need will be a secondary consideration.

Funds Avail.: $3,000. **To Apply:** Applicants must complete the application form and must provide an evidence of their acceptance for a graduate study. **Deadline:** June 1. **Contact:** Dr. Alison Henning, Rice University, Department of Earth Science, 6100 Main St., Houston, TX 77005.

4611 ■ HGS Foundation Scholarships (Undergraduate/Scholarship)

Purpose: To provide scholarships to deserving undergraduate students majoring in geosciences. **Focus:** Geosciences. **Qualif.:** Applicants must be juniors and seniors in the current academic year; must be enrolled full-time carrying a normal academic load in geosciences; and must be U.S. citizens. **Criteria:** Recipients will be selected based on academic achievement.

Funds Avail.: $1,500. **To Apply:** Nominated candidates must contact the head of geosciences department for further information.

Awards are arranged alphabetically below their administering organizations

4612 ■ Houston Intellectual Property Law Association (HIPLA)

c/o Norma Bennett, Sec.
1250 Four Houston Ctr.
1331 Lamar St.
Houston, TX 77010
Ph: (713) 590-9333
Fax: (713) 590-9399
E-mail: nbennett@mcfall-law.com
URL: www.hipla.org

4613 ■ HIPLA Judicial Fellowships
(Undergraduate/Fellowship)

Purpose: To promote development and understanding of the Intellectual Property Law to law students. **Focus:** Law. **Qualif.:** Applicant must be a full-time student at the University of Law Center, the Thurgood Marshall School of Law or the South Texas College of Law who is not receiving law school credit for his/her internship and intends to practice intellectual property law. The applicant must be a U.S. citizen have completed at least 30 hours of course work at the time the internship begins and have a GPA average that ranks in the top half of the applicant's law school class. **Criteria:** Selection is based on student's qualifications and on submitted application materials.

Funds Avail.: $3,000. **To Apply:** Applicants must submit a resume, a letter describing interest in intellectual property law, a letter from the court or USPTO stating that student has been accepted for an internship and a description of any circumstances to be considered. **Contact:** Application form and supporting documents must be submitted to Bryan Adams at the above address.

4614 ■ HIPLA Scholarships for University of Houston Law Center Students *(Graduate, Undergraduate/Scholarship)*

Purpose: To support students interested in intellectual property. **Focus:** Law. **Qualif.:** Applicant must be a University of Houston Law Center student who has demonstrated interest in intellectual property law, has completed at least 30 hours of law study and has not previously received a HIPLA scholarship or fellowship. **Criteria:** Consideration will be given to students who have interned for a Houston Federal Judge, the U.S. Court of Appeals for the Federal Circuit, or the USPTO.

Funds Avail.: $3,000. **Number Awarded:** Up to 3. **To Apply:** Application materials, including transcript and a copy of financial aid award, should be returned to the Office of Student Services or sent via electronic mail to Associate Dean Sondra Tennessee at stennessee@uh.edu. **Deadline:** October 15. **Contact:** Sondra Tennessee at stennessee@uh.edu.

4615 ■ Houtan Scholarship Foundation

300 Central Ave.
Egg Harbor Township, NJ 08234
Ph: (609) 601-2332
Fax: (609) 601-2331
E-mail: info@houtan.org
URL: www.houtan.org

4616 ■ Houtan Scholarships *(Graduate/ Scholarship)*

Purpose: To promote Iranian studies. **Focus:** Area and ethnic studies. **Qualif.:** Applicants should have a working knowledge of Farsi and should demonstrate an active interest in Iranian culture, heritage and literature; must be attending or anticipating to attend an accredited graduate school; must have superior academic performance or a significant increase of academic performance over the course of the academic career; and may have financial need. **Criteria:** Recipient is selected based on submitted documents, financial need, and the interview.

Funds Avail.: $2,500. **Number Awarded:** 1. **To Apply:** Applicants must submit a completed application form along with two letters of recommendation, college transcript, and goals and aspirations essay. **Deadline:** June 1 and October 1. **Contact:** at the above address.

4617 ■ Hudson River Foundation (HRF)

17 Battery Pl., Ste. 915
New York, NY 10004
Ph: (212) 483-7667
Fax: (212) 924-8325
E-mail: info@hudsonriver.org
URL: www.hudsonriver.org

4618 ■ Hudson River Graduate Fellowships
(Doctorate, Master's/Fellowship)

Purpose: To gather important information on all aspects of the River. **Focus:** General studies. **Qualif.:** Applicant must be enrolled in an accredited doctoral or master's program, must have a thesis advisor and advisory committee (if appropriate to the institution), and must have a thesis research plan approved by the student's institution or department. **Criteria:** Selection is based on the submitted application and materials.

Funds Avail.: $15,000 for doctoral students; $11,000 for Master's level students. **Number Awarded:** 3. **To Apply:** Applicants must submit a proposal cover page; a description of the thesis project (maximum of 10 pages); a timetable for the completion of the research; an estimated cost of supplies, travel, etc.; applicant's curriculum vitae; a letter from the University stating that the applicant will receive a tuition waiver or reimbursement for the period of the fellowship; and two letters of recommendation (one from an advisor, mailed directly to the Foundation). Electronic copy of the application should be sent in PDF format with the subject heading Graduate Fellowship Submittal. **Deadline:** March 21.

4619 ■ Tibor T. Polgar Fellowships *(Graduate, Undergraduate/Fellowship)*

Purpose: To gather important information on all aspects of the River and to train students in conducting estuarine studies and public policy research. **Focus:** General studies. **Qualif.:** Applicant must be an undergraduate or graduate student who will conduct research on the Hudson River. **Criteria:** Selection is based on submitted application materials.

Funds Avail.: $3,800. **Number Awarded:** 8. **To Apply:** Applications should include a letter of interest in the program, a short description (4-6 pages) of the research project, a timetable of the research, an estimated cost of supplies and travel expenses, a letter of support from student's advisor and curriculum vitae. Electronic copy of the application should be sent in PDF format indicating Polgar Proposal Submittal in the subject line. **Deadline:** February 20. **Contact:** Questions can be addressed to Helena Andreyko at the above address.

Awards are arranged alphabetically below their administering organizations

4620 ■ Howard Hughes Medical Institute (HHMI)

4000 Jones Bridge Rd.
Chevy Chase, MD 20815-6789
Ph: (301) 215-8500
E-mail: commpub@hhmi.org
URL: www.hhmi.org

4621 ■ Gilliam Fellowships for Advanced Study
(Doctorate/Fellowship)

Purpose: To offer an extraordinary opportunity to pursue graduate studies in the life sciences. **Focus:** Biomedical research. **Qualif.:** Applicants must be past participants in the HHMI Exceptional Research Opportunities Program must be graduating seniors or must be enrolled or planning to enroll in a PhD program in the biomedical or related sciences. In addition, applicants must not have completed more than one year in a PhD program by the application date. **Criteria:** Fellowships are awarded on the basis of the candidate's promise as a scientific investigator and potential for leadership in the scientific community, as reflected by academic records, relevant educational and personal experiences, previous accomplishment and goals, research experience, proposed research plan, references and scores attained on the Graduate Record Examination general test or the Medical College Admission Test.

Funds Avail.: $46,500. **To Apply:** Applicants are expected to complete an application, which will be made available electronically to all eligible Exceptional Research Opportunities Program (EXROP) students. The application will be submitted via HHMI's web-based competition system at www.hhmi.org/competitions. A complete application consists of the following items: applicant information including name, current and permanent addresses, email address and other pertinent information; educational history including names of all colleges and universities attended, dates of attendance and degrees obtained; all undergraduate transcripts (to be sent to HHMI directly by institutions attended); list of relevant honors, awards and professional activities; educational and personal experiences relevant to applicant's career goals and objectives; research experiences, including dates, project summary and the applicant's role in the project; list of publications, presentations and posters, if applicable; proposed research plan with literature cited; leadership statement demonstrating leadership potential and/or how receipt of the Gilliam Fellowship will help advance scientific careers of underrepresented students; three letters of reference sent directly to HHMI. Letters should be from those who can speak best to potential as a scientist, and one from HHMI program director; recent score on the Graduate Record Examination General Test or Medical College Admission Test. **Deadline:** October 13. **Contact:** Maryrose Franko at 301-215-8880 or 800-448-4882 ext. 8880; gilliam@hhmi.org.

4622 ■ HHMI International Student Research Fellowships *(Doctorate/Fellowship)*

Purpose: To support outstanding international predoctoral students studying in the United States who are ineligible for fellowships or training grants through U.S. federal agencies. **Focus:** Biomedical research. **Qualif.:** Applicants must be in their 3rd or 4th year of a PhD program in the biomedical or related sciences at a designated nominating institution; have demonstrated exceptional talent for research; have entered laboratory in which they will conduct their dissertation research; must not be U.S. citizens, non-citizens or permanent residents of the United States. **Criteria:** Fellows will be chosen based on their promise as scientific investigators.

Funds Avail.: $30,000 plus an educational allowance. **To Apply:** Application will be submitted online using HHMI's web-based competition system at www.hhmi.org/competitions. A complete application will consist of the following: applicant information, including name, contact information and email address; graduate degree information, including name of department/program, date of entry into the graduate program and name and email address of the dissertation advisor(s); description of intended dissertation research with a limited bibliography of key references; brief discussion of the significance and innovation of the intended research project; research experiences, including dates, project summary and the applicant's role in the project; list of publications, presentations and posters, if applicable; list of relevant honors, awards and professional activities; letters of reference. One letter must be from the applicant's dissertation advisor. Other letters should be from those who can speak best to the applicant's potential as a researcher. These letters must be uploaded in the competition system by the reference writer; educational history, including names of all colleges and universities attended, dates of attendance and degrees obtained; graduate transcripts (to be uploaded by the applicant); scores on the GRE or MCAT and TOEFL. **Deadline:** February. **Contact:** Correspondence should be directed to Maryrose Franko at 301-215-8880 or e-mail predoc@hhmi.org.

4623 ■ HHMI Medical Research Fellowships
(Undergraduate/Fellowship)

Purpose: To support full-time biomedical research training for medical, dental and veterinary students. **Focus:** Biomedical research. **Qualif.:** Applicants must be enrolled in a medical, dental or veterinary school located in the United States. The fellowship research may be conducted at any academic or nonprofit institution in the United States, except the National Institutes of Health. **Criteria:** Fellowships are awarded on the basis of the applicant's ability and promise for a research career as a physician-scientist or medically trained researcher and the quality of the training that will be provided.

Funds Avail.: $28,000. **To Apply:** Applicants may visit the Institute's website for the web-based submission process and other application requirements. **Deadline:** January 11. **Contact:** 800-424-9924; medfellows@hhmi.org.

4624 ■ Hughes Memorial Foundation

PO Box 5371
Danville, VA 24540
Ph: (434) 836-2577
Fax: (434) 792-1825
E-mail: info@hughesmemorialfoundation.org
URL: www.hughesmemorialfoundation.org

4625 ■ Hughes Memorial Foundation Scholarships *(Graduate/Scholarship)*

Purpose: To provide financial assistance to needy students and be able to further their career. **Focus:** General studies. **Qualif.:** Applicants must be needy and/or at-risk children living in the Virginia counties of Pittsylvania, Halifax, Mecklenburg, Charlotte, Campbell, Bedford, Franklin, Henry and Patrick; the North Carolina counties of Stokes, Rockingham, Caswell and Person; and the cities of Virginia and North Carolina that are located geographically within those counties; must have a minimum of 2.5 GPA. **Criteria:** Recipients will be selected based on the degree of need, demonstrated ability to succeed in educational endeavor,

Awards are arranged alphabetically below their administering organizations

impact towards beneficiary, accuracy, completeness and reasonableness of application.

Funds Avail.: No specific amount. **To Apply:** Applicants must submit a completed application form for Federal Student Aid; Student aid report; parents' federal Income Tax Return; description of all motor vehicles owned by the family with year, make and model; description of all real estate owned by the family with the tax-appraised value; description of any other significant debts by the family; official transcripts from high schools and colleges attended; official SAT, ACT or graduate/professional exam scores.

4626 ■ Huguenot Society of South Carolina
138 Logan St.
Charleston, SC 29401-1941
Ph: (843) 723-3235
Fax: (843) 853-8475
E-mail: director@huguenotsociety.org
URL: www.huguenotsociety.org

4627 ■ Mary Mouzon Darby Undergraduate Scholarships *(Undergraduate/Scholarship)*

Purpose: To financially support undergraduate students. **Focus:** General studies. **Qualif.:** Applicants must be of Huguenot descent and either members of the Huguenot Society of South Carolina or the child or grandchild of a current member of the Society. **Criteria:** Preference will be given to those qualified applicants entering first year of college and/or those with demonstrated financial need.

Funds Avail.: $1,000. **Number Awarded:** 1. **To Apply:** Applicants must submit: the cover sheet with contact information; the lineage sheet listing the applicant's lineage to the Huguenot ancestor; a brief (three pages, double-spaced) paper that includes a biographical sketch of the applicant's Huguenot ancestor and what this Huguenot heritage means to the applicants. **Deadline:** December 31.

4628 ■ Huguenot Society of South Carolina Graduate Scholarships *(Graduate/Scholarship)*

Purpose: To support students working toward a graduate degree in history. **Focus:** History. **Qualif.:** Applicants must be students working toward a graduate degree in history. **Criteria:** Selection will be based on submitted essay.

Funds Avail.: $1,000. **To Apply:** Applicants must submit two hard copies of the essay, as well as a cover letter giving full name, address, telephone number, details of the undergraduate degree and also the graduate degree currently in progress, and the thesis and significance of the paper. The text should not exceed 25 typed and double-spaced pages, excluding footnotes, illustrations and bibliography (one-inch margins for the top, bottom, left, and right). All submissions must include footnotes and any other necessary documentation. Titles of the works cited in the essay and notes should be typed in italics and indexed if possible, using the standards set forth in the Chicago Manual of Style, 15th Edition. The essay must be a work of scholarship on a Huguenot topic; may examine any aspect of the religious, political, economic, social, or intellectual history of the French or Walloon Protestants from the sixteenth century to the present; may deal with any appropriate geographical area. Submissions must be original, not previously published and not under consideration by another publication. The author of the winning essay will be asked to submit a copy of his/her paper on a MS Word-Compatible CD. **Deadline:** December 31.

4629 ■ Human Race Theatre Company
126 N Main St., Ste. 300
Dayton, OH 45402-1710
Ph: (937) 461-3823
Fax: (937) 461-7223
E-mail: contact@humanracetheatre.org
URL: www.humanracetheatre.org

4630 ■ Stephen Schwartz Musical Theatre Scholarships *(Undergraduate/Scholarship)*

Purpose: To support singers/actors in the greater Dayton area who are training for a career in musical theatre. **Focus:** Theater arts. **Qualif.:** Applicants must have a permanent address in Montgomery County or one of seven contiguous counties (Preble, Darke, Miami, Clark, Greene, Warren or Butler); must be currently enrolled at a college in one of the eight counties previously listed. High school senior applicants must be currently applying or accepted into a college program and have plans to train in musical theatre. College student must be currently training for a career in musical theatre. **Criteria:** Awards are given based on the auditions and applications.

Funds Avail.: $1,500 for high school senior; $3,500 for a college student. **Number Awarded:** 2. **To Apply:** Applicants must submit a completed application; two letters of recommendation: one from a faculty including a private lessons instructor; and one from a Director or Music Director from a show where applicants appeared in the past two years; current photograph; resume; and must prepare two contrasting songs that best show the vocal and acting ability. **Deadline:** November 20. **Remarks:** Established in honor of musical theatre legend Stephen Schwartz. **Contact:** Kevin Moore, Executive Director, at 937-461-3823 x 3115, or email kevin@humanracetheatre.org.

4631 ■ Human Resources Research Organization (HumRRO)
66 Canal Center Plz., Ste. 700
Alexandria, VA 22314-1591
Ph: (703) 549-3611
Fax: (703) 548-5574
URL: www.humrro.org

4632 ■ Meredith P. Crawford Fellowships in I/O Psychology *(Doctorate/Fellowship)*

Purpose: To provide financial support while the student completes his/her dissertation in the field of Industrial-Organizational (I-O) Psychology, or in a field congruent with the objectives of the Society for Industrial Psychology, Inc. (SIOP). **Focus:** Psychology. **Qualif.:** Applicants must be doctoral candidates whose dissertation topic has been proposed and approved by his/her graduate faculty in Industrial-Organizational (I-O) Psychology, Inc. **Criteria:** Applicants will be evaluated on the basis of merit, research promise, academic achievement and professional productivity.

Funds Avail.: $12,000. **Number Awarded:** 1. **To Apply:** Applicants must provide a completed application form, a personal statement, three completed recommendation forms and an official transcript from each institution attended for graduate academic work. **Deadline:** July 2. **Contact:** For questions, just call Jessica Terner at 703-706-5687.

4633 ■ Human Rights Campaign (HRC)
1640 Rhode Island Ave. NW
Washington, DC 20036-3278

Awards are arranged alphabetically below their administering organizations

Ph: (202) 628-4160
Fax: (202) 347-5323
Free: 800-777-4723
E-mail: hrc@hrc.org
URL: www.hrc.org

4634 ■ McCleary Law Fellows Program *(Graduate, Undergraduate/Fellowship)*

Purpose: To provide training opportunities for law students. **Focus:** Law. **Qualif.:** Applicant must possess a strong academic record at an accredited American law school, excellent interpersonal, legal research and writing skills and an interest in civil rights, policy and/or nonprofit lawyering. 1Ls, 2Ls, 3Ls and LL.M. candidates are eligible. **Criteria:** Selection is based on the submitted application materials.

Funds Avail.: No specific amount. **Number Awarded:** Up to 4. **To Apply:** Applicants must submit, via e-mail, a cover letter; resume; brief legal writing sample (five pages or less); names of two references and; a law school transcript to lawfellowship@hrc.org. **Deadline:** Fall Law Fellowships: First Tuesday in July; Spring Law Fellowships: First Tuesday in November; Summer Law Fellowships: 2L-First Tuesday in January; 1L-First Tuesday in February. **Contact:** Sarah Warbelow at lawfellowship@hrc.org.

4635 ■ Humane Society of the United States

2100 L St. NW
Washington, DC 20037
Ph: (202) 452-1100
URL: www.humanesociety.org

4636 ■ Shaw-Worth Memorial Scholarships *(Undergraduate/Scholarship)*

Purpose: To help students achieve their dreams of working in the service of animals, the environment and humankind. **Focus:** Animal rights. **Qualif.:** Applicants must be high school seniors who have made contributions to animal protection; must be from New England public, private and vocational schools. **Criteria:** Recipients will be selected based on submitted application materials. Scholastic standing and financial need are not the basis for the award.

Funds Avail.: $2,500. **To Apply:** Application should be written in letter form which includes a narrative statement of the applicant's achievements and attitude towards animal protection. Applicants must submit a documentation of activities such as recommendations from at least three persons and description of future plans for humane work. Supporting letters from teachers, mentors, supervisors, peers and other observers are not required but may help. Applications should include the student's home address and phone numbers. **Deadline:** March 25. **Remarks:** The Shaw-Worth Scholarship honors the memories of the members of Shaw and Worth families. **Contact:** Applications and all supporting documents must be sent to Humane Society Youth, 67 Norwich Essex Turnpike, East Haddam, CT 06423.

4637 ■ Hungarian American Coalition (HAC)

1120 Connecticut Ave. NW, Ste. 280
Washington, DC 20036
Ph: (202) 296-9505
Fax: (202) 775-5175
E-mail: hac@hacusa.org

URL: www.hacusa.org

4638 ■ Dr. Elemer and Eva Kiss Scholarship Fund *(Undergraduate/Scholarship)*

Purpose: To provide partial annual scholarships for Hungarian students who will be admitted at any U.S. college or university. **Focus:** General studies. **Qualif.:** Applicant must be a citizen of Hungary or a member of an ethnic Hungarian community in Slovakia, Romania, Voivodina, Serbia, or Ukraine; must have gained admission as a full-time student to a U.S. college or university. **Criteria:** Preference will be given to deserving students.

Funds Avail.: $1,000. **Number Awarded:** 2-4. **To Apply:** Applicants must provide proof of scholarship and other sources of financial support; record of excellent academic standing; and two letters of recommendation regarding the applicant's personal and academic achievements. **Remarks:** Scholarship recipients are asked to provide a copy of their registration form and are expected to keep the Coalition informed of their academic progress. **Contact:** Application form and supporting documents can be submitted electronically to scholarship@hacusa.org.

4639 ■ Hungarian-American Enterprise Scholarship Fund (HAESF)

300 Fore St.
Portland, ME 04101
Ph: (207) 553-4130
Fax: (207) 553-5130
E-mail: aarvizu@ciee.org
URL: www.haesf.org

4640 ■ HAESF Graduate Scholarships *(Graduate/Scholarship)*

Purpose: To provide opportunities for Hungarian Society leaders to receive an international education that leads to professional occupations. **Focus:** General studies. **Qualif.:** Applicants must be recent graduate students who have obtained their five-year program in any Hungarian university. Applicants who have obtained their three years of education under the old curriculum and continued their remaining two years under the new higher education system are eligible to apply; must maintain a minimum of 3.0 GPA; must hold a Hungarian passport; and must be accepted to an American university/college, or certificate-granting institution. **Criteria:** Applicants will be judged based on, but not limited to: 1) potential future contributions to Hungarian Society; 2) professional objectives to the values and mission of HAESF; 3) articulated professional goals; 4) personality; 5) strength of recommendations; 6) ability to serve as ambassadors of Hungary; 7) communication skills; 8) diversity of majors and professional interests; 9) financial need.

Funds Avail.: $25,000 per year. **To Apply:** Applicants must fill out the HAESF Graduate Scholarship Application form; must submit an acceptance letter from the receiving academic institution, detailed budget proposal, personal statement, current curriculum vitae, a copy of transcript of records, a letter signed in English which includes the average of all subjects taken and any related to the major field of study, a copy of diploma, copies of relevant certificates of completion and three letters of reference discussing the following: 1) relationship with the applicants; 2) program's relevance for applicant's future and career goals; 3) assessment of applicant's character, abilities, strength and weaknesses; 4) English language communication skill; 5)

Awards are arranged alphabetically below their administering organizations

detailed contact information of the referee. Supporting documents should be in translated in English. **Contact:** Application form and supporting documents must be submitted to HAESF Hungary Office. Questions can be addressed to Kati Szalay, Program Officer; Phone: 361-413-0018; Fax: 361-413-0019.

4641 ■ HAESF Professional Internship Program
(Doctorate/Internship)

Purpose: To provide opportunities for Hungarian society leaders to have an international training experience. **Focus:** Business; Public administration; Social sciences; Public health; Medicine; Agricultural economics; Art; Media arts; Communications. **Qualif.:** Program is open to PhD students who have started their studies within six months of completing their university degree program; full-time students who have completed their four years out of a five-year university degree program under the old curriculum; students who have completed their three years plus two-year program in the same or related discipline under the new higher education system; graduated a five-year university program or three years plus two-year program no more than six months before the application deadline. Applicants must pursue studies at an accredited Hungarian university; must hold a Hungarian passport; and level of English must be sufficient to perform in a native English-speaking environment. **Criteria:** Applicants will be judged based on, but not limited to: 1) potential future contributions to Hungarian Society; 2) professional objectives to the values and mission of HAESF; 3) articulated professional goals; 4) personality; 5) strength of recommendations; 6) ability to serve as ambassadors of Hungary; 7) communication skills; 8) diversity of majors and professional interests; 9) clear understanding on what the program can offer.

Funds Avail.: $30,000 for one year. **To Apply:** Applicants must fill out the HAESF Professional Internship Program Application form; must submit a personal statement, current curriculum vitae, a copy of transcript of records (translated in English), a letter signed in English which includes the average of all subjects taken and any related to the major field of study, a copy of diploma, copies of relevant certificates of completion and three letters of reference discussing the following: 1) Relationship with applicants; 2) Internship's relevance for applicant's future and career goals; 3) Assessment of applicant's character, abilities, strength and weaknesses; 4) English language communication skill. **Deadline:** April and October. **Contact:** Application form and supporting documents must be submitted to HAESF Hungary Office. Questions can be addressed to Kati Szalay, Program Officer; Phone: 361-413-0018; Fax: 361-413-0019.

4642 ■ HAESF Senior Leaders and Scholars Fellowships *(Professional development/ Fellowship)*

Purpose: To help mid-level and senior-level Hungarian professionals to pursue their projects in the United States. **Focus:** Business; Public administration. **Qualif.:** Program is open to mid-level and senior-level Hungarian professionals in Business, Public Administration, non-profit organizations and academia. Candidates should hold a PhD degree or at least five years of professional or relevant experience; must hold a Hungarian passport; must not have been physically present in the United States as non-immigrants on a J-1 visa within the 12-month period unless their presence in the United States was less than six months duration or short-term scholar exchange activity; level of English must be sufficient to perform in a native English-speaking work

environment. **Criteria:** Applicants will be judged based on, but not limited to: 1) potential future contributions to Hungarian Society; 2) professional objectives to the values and mission of HAESF; 3) articulated professional goals; 4) professionalism; 5) strength of recommendations; 6) ability to serve as ambassadors of Hungary; 7) communication skills; 8) diversity of majors and professional interests; 9) project proposal.

Funds Avail.: $60,000. **To Apply:** Applicants must fill out the HAESF Senior Leaders and Scholars Fellowship Application form; must submit a detailed budget proposal, personal statement, current curriculum vitae, letter(s) of invitation from the host organization(s) in the United States, project proposal and two letters of reference discussing the following: 1) Relationship with applicants; 2) Relevance of the proposed project to applicant's future and career goals; 3) Assessment of applicant's character, abilities, strength and weaknesses; 4) English language communication skill; 5) Detailed contact information of the referee. Supporting documents should be in translated in English. **Deadline:** April and October. **Contact:** Application form and supporting documents must be submitted to HAESF Hungary Office. Questions can be addressed to Kati Szalay, Program Officer; Phone: 361-413-0018; Fax: 361-413-0019.

4643 ■ Huntington's Disease Society of America (HDSA)
505 8th Ave., Ste. 902
New York, NY 10018
Ph: (212) 242-1968
Fax: (212) 239-3430
Free: 800-345-4372
E-mail: hdsainfo@hdsa.org
URL: www.hdsa.org

4644 ■ HDSA Research Grants *(Professional development/Grant)*

Purpose: To provide seed funding for new or innovative research projects. **Focus:** Huntington's disease. **Qualif.:** Applicants must be principal investigators. **Criteria:** Recipients are selected based on the potential of their research.

Funds Avail.: $50,000. **Number Awarded:** 1.

4645 ■ Huntington's Disease Society of America Research Fellowships *(Postdoctorate/ Fellowship)*

Purpose: To help promising postdoctoral investigators in the early stages of their careers. **Focus:** Huntington's disease. **Qualif.:** Applicants must be investigators who want to enter the field of HD research. **Criteria:** Recipients are selected according to the potential of their research.

Funds Avail.: $40,000.

4646 ■ Don King Student Fellowships
(Undergraduate/Fellowship)

Purpose: To sponsor HD investigations that can be conducted over a 10-week period. **Focus:** Huntington's disease. **Qualif.:** Applicants must be matriculated undergraduate life sciences students, pre-medical students, and first-year medical students who are currently attending accredited institutions in the United States where HDSA sponsors ongoing HD research. **Criteria:** Recipient will be selected based on the academic credentials, scientific merit of the proposed project and the relevance of the proposal to HD.

Awards are arranged alphabetically below their administering organizations

Funds Avail.: $3,000. **Deadline:** May 1.

4647 ■ Hydro Research Foundation (HRF)

25 Massachusetts Ave. NW, Ste. 450
Washington, DC 20001
Ph: (303) 674-5254
E-mail: info@hydrofoundation.org
URL: www.hydrofoundation.org

4648 ■ Hydro Research Foundation Fellowships *(Master's/Fellowship)*

Purpose: To provide opportunities and benefits to outstanding early career graduate students. **Focus:** Hydrology. **Qualif.:** Applicants must be Master's or Post-Master's graduate students enrolled full-time at a U.S. university. **Criteria:** Fellows will be selected based on research vision, innovation, academic performance, potential for leadership and overall strength of the research proposal.

Funds Avail.: $26,000 for living expenses, $16,000 annual tuition and $900 for university-provided health insurance. **Number Awarded:** 33. **To Apply:** Applicants must complete an application form; must submit a research proposal, release form, copy of transcript(s), copy of GRE scores, resume, two references, letter of support from university department, supporting documents (optional). **Deadline:** March 1.

4649 ■ Hydrocephalus Association

4340 E West Hwy., Ste. 905
Bethesda, MD 20814
Ph: (301) 202-3811
Fax: (301) 202-3813
Free: 888-598-3789
URL: www.hydroassoc.org

4650 ■ Anthony Abbene Scholarships *(Undergraduate/Scholarship)*

Purpose: To offer scholarships to young adults with hydrocephalus. **Focus:** General studies. **Qualif.:** Applicants must be between 17 and 30 years old and have hydrocephalus. **Criteria:** Priority will be given to those students who meet the criteria.

Funds Avail.: $1,000. **To Apply:** Applicants must email their contact information to the association to obtain an application form. **Deadline:** April 1. **Remarks:** This fund was established in 2002 by Anthony Abbene's extended family. Anthony is a teenager with hydrocephalus. This fund awards two scholarships in honor of Anthony and to help others with hydrocephalus with their education.

4651 ■ Justin Scot Alston Memorial Scholarships *(Undergraduate/Scholarship)*

Purpose: To offer scholarships to young adults with hydrocephalus. **Focus:** General studies. **Qualif.:** Applicants must be between 17 and 30 years old and have hydrocephalus. **Criteria:** Priority will be given to those students who meet the criteria.

Funds Avail.: $1,000. **To Apply:** Applicants must email their contact information to the association to obtain an application form. **Deadline:** April 1. **Remarks:** Gloria M. Alston established this scholarship in loving memory of her son, Justin Scot Alston, who died in 2004. Justin received a Hydrocephalus Association scholarship in 2002 and will be remembered for his tremendous upbeat attitude and for all that he accomplished during his short life.

4652 ■ Laura Beckley Barsotti Memorial Scholarships *(Undergraduate/Scholarship)*

Purpose: To offer scholarships to young adults with hydrocephalus. **Focus:** General studies. **Qualif.:** Applicants must be between 17 and 30 years old with hydrocephalus; and must express an interest in education or social work. **Criteria:** Priority will be given to those students who meet the criteria.

Funds Avail.: No stated amount. **To Apply:** Applicants must check the available website for details. **Remarks:** The Beckley-Clark family established this scholarship in 2008 in loving memory of Laura Beckley Barsotti. **Contact:** Hydrocephalus Association at the above address.

4653 ■ Gerard Swartz Fudge Memorial Scholarships *(Undergraduate/Scholarship)*

Purpose: To offer scholarships to young adults with hydrocephalus. **Focus:** General studies. **Qualif.:** Applicants must be between 17 and 30 years old and have hydrocephalus. **Criteria:** Priority will be given to those students who meet the criteria.

Funds Avail.: $1,000. **Number Awarded:** 2. **To Apply:** Applicants may visit the website or contact the Assocation for more information on the application process. **Deadline:** April 1. **Remarks:** This fund was established in 1994 by the Fudge family. Their son, Gerard, had hydrocephalus and died in 1992 at the age of 22 in the midst of his college experience. **Contact:** Hydrocephalus Association at the above address.

4654 ■ Mario J. Tocco Hydrocephalus Foundation Scholarships *(Undergraduate/Scholarship)*

Purpose: To offer scholarships to young adults with hydrocephalus. **Focus:** General studies. **Qualif.:** Applicants must be between 17 and 30 years old and have hydrocephalus. **Criteria:** Priority will be given to those students who meet the criteria.

Funds Avail.: $1,000. **To Apply:** Applicants must email their contact information to the association to obtain an application form. **Deadline:** April 1. **Remarks:** Greg and Georgana Tocco and their families established this scholarship in 2007 in loving memory of Greg's grandfather, Mario, and in honor of the Hydrocephalus Foundation, Inc of Saugus, MA.

4655 ■ Morris L. and Rebecca Ziskind Memorial Scholarships *(Undergraduate/Scholarship)*

Purpose: To offer scholarships to young adults with hydrocephalus. **Focus:** General studies. **Qualif.:** Applicants must be between 17 and 30 years old and have hydrocephalus. **Criteria:** Priority will be given to those students who meet the criteria.

Funds Avail.: $1,000. **To Apply:** Applicants must email their contact information to the association to obtain an application form. **Deadline:** April 1. **Remarks:** This fund was established in 2001 by Rebecca Ziskind and her family in memory of her husband, Dr. Morris Ziskind, who had NPH. After Rebecca Ziskind's death in 2005, their three surviving children and their spouses-Carrie and Dee Norton, Jerome and Rosemary Ziskind, and Janet and Charles Tarino-graciously funded one more scholarship in loving memory of their parents, so that two scholarships are now awarded from this fund.

Awards are arranged alphabetically below their administering organizations